SELECTED PAPERS

by

Chia-Shun Yih

SELECTED PAPERS

by

Chia-Shun Yih

S. P. Timoshenko Dist. University Professor Emeritus
The University of Michigan

Editors
W. M. Lai
Columbia University

S.-P. Lin
Clarkson University

Volume II

Advanced Series on Fluid Mechanics

Published by

World Scientific Publishing Co. Pte. Ltd.

P O Box 128, Farrer Road, Singapore 9128

USA office: 687 Hartwell Street, Teaneck, NJ 07666

UK office: 73 Lynton Mead, Totteridge, London N20 8DH

SELECTED PAPERS BY CHIA-SHUN YIH, Vol. II

All rights reserved. This book, or parts thereof, may not be reproduced in any form or by any means, electronic or mechanical, including photocopying, recording or any information storage and retrieval system now known or to be invented, without written permission from the Publisher.

ISBN 981-02-0309-8
       981-02-0543-0 (Set)

Printed in Singapore by JBW Printers and Binders Pte. Ltd.

Contents

Volume I

Part A. Stratified Flows and Internal Waves

Part B. Theory of Hydrodynamic Stability

Volume II

Part C. Gravity Waves

Corrigenda for Parts C, D, and E

C3. In line 5 of p. 392, ϕ should be p at two places. In second and third lines below equation (6.5), delete the words "of the smaller basin".

C10. In (13), dy should be dy/dk. In (14), dx should be dx/dk.

C12. 1. In the last term of line 6 from the bottom of p. 170, a plus sign should be added between ϕ_x^2 and ϕ_y^2.

    2. In the last term of (25), g^2 should be c_g^2.

    3. In (37), the factor a should be added after the first two equality signs, and $\varepsilon^3 a^3$ should be $\varepsilon^2 a^3$ at two places.

    4. In (63), ε should be ε^2.

    5. In (59), 48 should be 24. In (60), 56 should be 32. All the numbers in (64) to (68), and in (77) and the equation following (77), which are divisible by 7 should be multiplied by 4/7. Furthermore, in (78) 17 should be 11.

All these corrections in Paper C12 are mentioned in Paper C13.

D1. The diffusivity α was defined as $k/\rho c_v$. It should be defined as $k/\rho c_p$, even if the fluid is a liquid. The reason is rather subtle. The dynamic compressibility of liquid can usually be neglected, but the thermal expansivity cannot. Since for jets the pressure is constant over the entire field of flow, the specific heat at constant pressure (c_p) should be used instead of the specific heat at constant volume (c_v).

E4. Professor Landweber had provided the following correction:

Mr. K. Eggers of the Hamburg Institüt für Schiffbau has pointed out that the term $\frac{16}{3}\pi^2 \rho\sigma\mu_i$ in the expression for the force in Eq. (61) of the paper by Yih and myself (Journal of Fluid Mechanics, Sept. 1967, p. 332) cannot of itself contribute to the force. If it did then a closed body, generated by a source-sink distribution of zero total strength in which a doublet was embedded, in steady motion in an infinite, unbounded fluid, would be subject to a force.

It is stated in the text following Eq. (61) that, in computing v_i' and $\partial v_i'/\partial x_i$ in (60) and (61), the contributions from all the internal singularities may be omitted. This statement should have been amplified to state that all the mutual contributions to the force (and moment) from internal singularities annul each other and may be omitted. In the case of a doublet of vector strength μ_i embedded in a source distribution σ, the term $\frac{16}{3}\pi^2 \rho\sigma\mu_i$ appears as an internal interaction term between the doublet and the source distribution which we might expect would be cancelled when all the internal interactions are considered. It will now be shown how this occurs.

In the expression for the force F_i we need consider only the terms

$$-4\pi\rho\left[\int \sigma v_i d\tau - \Sigma \frac{4}{3}\pi\sigma\mu_i + \Sigma\mu_j \frac{\partial v_i'}{\partial x_j}\right] .$$

Let the doublet μ_i be situated at the point $P(x_1, x_2, x_3)$ and let (ξ_1, ξ_2, ξ_3) denote the coordinates of a point when referring to the source distribution. Then the velocity v_i at a source element due to the doublet is

$$v_i = \frac{3\mu_j(x_i - \xi_i)(x_j - \xi_j)}{r^5} - \frac{\mu_j}{r^3} , \quad r^2 = (x_i - \xi_i)(x_i - \xi_i) ,$$

and the contribution of the doublet to the force on the source distribution is

$$-4\pi\rho \int_R \sigma \left[\frac{3\mu_j(x_i - \xi_i)(x_j - \xi_j)}{r^5} - \frac{\mu_i}{r^3}\right] d\tau \ , \quad d\tau = d\xi_1 d\xi_2 d\xi_3 \ ,$$

where the region R is bounded internally by a small sphere about the point P. Next, the velocity at P due to the source distribution is

$$v_i = \int_{R+S'} \sigma(\xi_1, \xi_2, \xi_3)\frac{x_i - \xi_i}{r} d\tau \ ,$$

where S' denotes the volume of the same sphere about P, and

$$\frac{\partial v_i}{\partial x_j} = \int_{R+S'} \sigma \left[\frac{\delta_{ij}}{r^3} - \frac{3(x_i - \xi_i)(x_j - \xi_j)}{r^5}\right] d\tau \ .$$

Hence the contribution of the source distribution to the force on the doublet is

$$-4\pi\rho \int_{R+S'} \sigma \left[\frac{\mu_i}{r^3} - \frac{3\mu_j(x_i - \xi_i)(x_j - \xi_j)}{r^5}\right] d\tau \ .$$

It is now seen that the integrands in the above two cases are equal and opposite and hence the integrals over the region R annul each other. The last integral over the small sphere S' is indeterminate, so that it will be evaluated by an alternative means.

For a sufficiently small sphere σ may be considered constant. Applying Gauss' theorem for the flux of fluid out of a sphere of radius r about P, we have

$$v_i = \frac{4}{3}\pi\sigma x_i$$

and

$$\mu_j \frac{\partial v_i}{\partial x_j} = \frac{4}{3}\pi\sigma\mu_i \ .$$

Hence the contribution of the source distribution in the neighborhood of the doublet to the force on the doublet is $-\frac{16}{3}\pi^2\rho\sigma\mu_i$. But this is equal and opposite to the remaining doublet – source distribution term, so that the total contribution from their interactions is zero, as was stated.

Thus it is seen that, when the internal interactions are omitted from the expression for the force (or moment), the term $\frac{16}{3}\pi^2\rho\sigma\mu_i$ (and the corresponding one for the moment) will vanish.

E14. Peristaltic motion involves the interpretation of the results in the Lagrangian way of describing fluid motion, and it is here we committed some errors. Corrections prepared by Professor Y. C. Fung were published in a later issue of the J. Appl. Mech.

Part C
Gravity Waves

Transactions, American Geophysical Union   Volume 34, Number 3   June 1953

ON TIDES IN ESTUARIES AND AROUND SMALL ISLANDS

Chia-Shun Yih

Abstract--Tides in estuaries and around small islands are studied in this paper. Under the assumption that the width and the mean depth of the estuary can be adequately expressed as power functions of the longitudinal distance from a certain point upstream, and that the depth of the ocean varies as a power function of the radial distance from the island, analytical solutions can be found by very simple transformations.

Tides in estuaries--The problem of determining the variation of the amplitude of tide in a gradually widening and deepening estuary while a periodic motion is maintained at sea is of some interest. With sufficient latitude one can assume that the width b and the average depth h of the estuary vary as certain arbitrary powers of x, which is measured along the estuary downstream from a certain point. Denoting by s, b_s, and h_s respectively the values of x, b, and h at the mouth of the estuary, one can write

$$b/b_s = (x/s)^m = \xi^m \quad\quad\quad\quad\quad\quad (1)$$

$$h/h_s = (x/s)^n = \xi^n \quad\quad\quad\quad\quad\quad (2)$$

where

$$\xi = x/s \quad\quad\quad\quad\quad\quad\quad\quad (3)$$

The periodic motion maintained at the mouth of the estuary can be described by

$$\eta_s = C \cos (\sigma t + \epsilon) \quad\quad\quad\quad\quad\quad (4)$$

where η is the deviation of the water surface from its equilibrium position and η_s is its value at $x = s$, t is the time, and C, σ, and ϵ are respectively the amplitude, frequency, and phase angle of the periodic motion. The differential equation for η at any point in the estuary is [LAMB, 1945, p. 274]

$$\partial^2 \eta / \partial t^2 = (g/b) (\partial/\partial x) (h\, b\, \partial \eta / \partial x) \quad\quad\quad\quad (5)$$

where g is the gravitational acceleration. In virtue of (1), (2), and (3), (5) can be written as

$$(s^2/g\, h_s) \partial^2 \eta / \partial t^2 = \xi^{-m} (\partial/\partial \xi) (\xi^{m+n} \partial \eta / \partial \xi) \quad\quad\quad (6)$$

If one takes

$$\eta = C \cos (\sigma t + \epsilon)\, X\, (\xi) \quad\quad\quad\quad\quad (7)$$

then (6) becomes

$$\xi^{-m} (d/d\xi) (\xi^{m+n}\, d\, X/d\xi) + (s^2 \sigma^2/g\, h_s)\, X = 0 \quad\quad\quad (8)$$

For convenience one writes

$$\lambda^{2-n} = s^2 \sigma^2/g\, h_s \quad\quad \xi_1 = \lambda \xi \quad\quad\quad\quad (9)$$

Then (8) becomes

$$(d/d\xi_1) (\xi_1^{m+n}\, d\, X/d\xi_1) + \xi_1^m\, X = 0 \quad\quad\quad\quad (10)$$

To seek a solution of (10) in terms of familiar functions, one tries the transformations

$$X = \xi_1^p\, f\, (\zeta) \quad\quad \zeta = \xi_1^q \quad\quad\quad\quad\quad (11)$$

Then

$$d\,X/d\,\xi_1 = p\,\xi_1^{p-1}\,f\,(\zeta) + q\,\xi_1^{p+q-1}\,f'\,(\zeta) \quad\ldots\ldots\ldots\ldots \quad (12)$$

$$d^2\,X/d\,\xi_1^2 = p\,(p-1)\,\xi_1^{p-2}\,f\,(\zeta) + q\,(2p+q-1)\,\xi_1^{p+q-2}\,f'\,(\zeta) + q^2\,\xi_1^{p+2q-2}\,f''\,(\zeta) \quad\ldots \quad (13)$$

where the primes denote differentiation with respect to ζ. Substituting (11) to (13) into (10), one obtains

$$f'' + [(2p+m+n+q-1)/q\,\zeta]\,f' + \left[(\zeta^{\frac{-n-2q+2}{q}}/q^2) + p\,(p+m+n-1)/q^2\,\zeta^2\right]\,f = 0 \quad\ldots \quad (14)$$

Demanding

$$p = (1-m-n)/2 \qquad q = (2-n)/2 \quad\ldots\ldots\ldots\ldots \quad (15)$$

one obtains Bessel's differential equation

$$f'' + f'/\zeta + (1/q^2 - p^2/q^2\,\zeta^2)\,f = 0 \quad\ldots\ldots\ldots\ldots \quad (16)$$

the solutions of which are $J_\nu\,(\zeta/q)$ and $J_{-\nu}\,(\zeta/q)$ where $\nu = |p/q|$. Of these two solutions, only one will give an $X\,(\xi_1)$ which is finite at $\xi_1 = 0$ together with $d\,X/d\,\xi_1$, unless ν is an integer, when they will coincide. One will assume $n \leq 1$, so that q is positive. Remembering $\zeta = \xi_1^q$, and that [WHITTAKER and WATSON, 1945, p. 359]

$$J_\nu\,(\zeta/q) = \zeta^\nu (a_0 + a_2\,\zeta^2 + \ldots)$$

$$J_{-\nu}\,(\zeta/q) = \zeta^{-\nu}\,(b_0 + b_2\,\zeta^2 + \ldots)$$

where a_0, a_2, b_0, b_2, etc., are numerical constants depending on ν, one easily sees that with p negative (so that $\nu q = -p$),

$$\xi_1^p\,J_\nu\,(\zeta/q) = \xi_1^{p+\nu q}\,(a_0 + a_2\,\zeta^2 + \ldots) = a_0 + a_2\,\zeta^2 + \ldots$$

$$\xi_1^p\,J_{-\nu}\,(\zeta/q) = \xi_1^{2p}\,(b_0 + b_2\,\zeta^2 + \ldots)$$

$$(d/d\,\xi_1)\,[\xi_1^p\,J_\nu\,(\zeta/q)] = \xi_1^{q-1}\,(2\,a_2\,\zeta + 4\,a_4\,\zeta^3 + \ldots) = \xi_1^{1-n}\,(2\,a_2 + 4\,a_4\,\zeta^2 + \ldots)$$

$$(d/d\,\xi_1)\,[\xi_1^p\,J_{-\nu}\,(\zeta/q)] = 2\,p\,\xi_1^{2p-1}\,(b_0 + b_2\,\zeta^2 + \ldots) + \xi_1^{2p+q-1}\,(2\,b_2\,\zeta + 4\,b_4\,\zeta^3 + \ldots)$$

Thus when p is negative, $\xi_1^p\,J_\nu\,(\zeta/q)$ and its derivative with respect to ξ_1 are finite at $\xi_1 = 0$ (recalling $n \leq 1$), whereas, with $2p-1 = -(m+n)$, the quantity

$$(d/d\,\xi_1)\,[\xi_1^p\,J_{-\nu}\,(\zeta/q)]$$

is definitely infinite at $\xi_1 = 0$. Thus $A\,\xi_1^p\,J_\nu\,(\zeta/q)$ should be chosen to be the solution. Similarly, when p is positive, $B\,\xi_1^p\,J_{-\nu}\,(\zeta/q)$ should be used.

    The constants A and B are determined from (4) (the boundary condition at x = s where $\xi = 1$, $\xi_1 = \lambda$, $\zeta = \lambda^q$) to be

$$A = 1/\lambda^p\,J_\nu\,(\lambda^q/q) \qquad B = 1/\lambda^p\,J_{-\nu}\,(\lambda^q/q) \quad\ldots\ldots\ldots\ldots \quad (17)$$

Thus one concludes that, for negative p

$$\eta = C\,A\,(\lambda\,\xi)^p\,J_\nu\,(\zeta/q)\cos(\sigma t + \epsilon) \quad\ldots\ldots\ldots\ldots \quad (18)$$

and for positive p

$$\eta = C\,B\,(\lambda\,\xi)^p\,J_{-\nu}\,(\zeta/q)\cos(\sigma t + \epsilon) \quad\ldots\ldots\ldots\ldots \quad (19)$$

where A and B are given by (17) and ζ is given by (9) and (11) to be $(\lambda\,\xi)^q$. When ν is an integer, the solutions given by (18) and (19) are identical.

    As an example one takes the case $m + n - 1$, $p = 0$. The solution is

$$\eta = C\,A\,J_0\,(\zeta/q)\cos(\sigma t + \epsilon)$$

In order to visualize the variation of the function $J_0 (\zeta/q)$, it is plotted in Figure 1 against ζ/q. It is seen that at certain points of the estuary the function is a maximum in absolute value, and these maximum values increase in the upstream direction, so that the tide is augmented in the

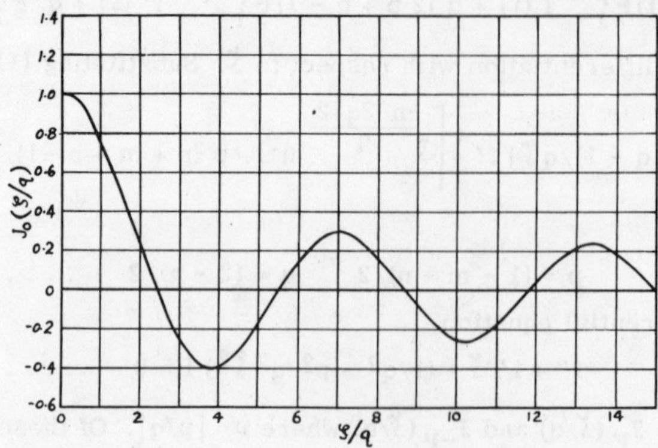

neighborhood of these points. It is also seen that at certain other points of the estuary the function $J_0 (\zeta/q)$ is zero. These are the nodal points where the elevation of the water surface is not affected by the tide. Similar conclusions can be drawn for the cases in which p is not equal to zero.

The points at which the amplitude is a maximum are determined by

$$d\, J_0 (\zeta/q)/d\zeta = 0$$

or [WHITTAKER and WATSON, 1945, p. 360, formula (B)]

$$J_1 (\zeta/q) = 0$$

the roots of which are [JAHNKE and EMDE, 1945, p. 168]

$$\zeta_1/q = 0 \qquad \zeta_2/q = 3.832 \qquad \zeta_3/q = 7.016 \qquad \zeta_4/q = 10.173 \ \ldots \quad \ldots \ldots \ (20)$$

the spacing of subsequent roots being approximately π. For cases in which $p \neq 0$, the points at which the amplitude is a maximum can be similarly located.

The points of zero amplitude (the nodes) are determined by

$$J_0 (\zeta/q) = 0$$

the roots of which are [JAHNKE and EMDE, p. 168]

$$\zeta_1/q = 2.405 \qquad \zeta_2/q = 5.520 \qquad \zeta_3/q = 8.624 \ \ldots \quad \ldots \ldots \ldots \ (21)$$

the spacing of subsequent roots being approximately π. For cases in which $p \neq 0$, the nodes can be similarly located. Of course, the actual number of nodes as well as that of maximum amplitudes is limited by the length of the estuary for a certain frequency and a certain h_s. If the value of λ calculated from (9) is too small, it may happen that there are no nodes at all, and that the only maximum amplitude occurs at $\zeta = 0$ (or $x = 0$). This happens if the estuary is not extremely long. Thus for an ordinary estuary there is an augmentation of the amplitude of tide over its entire length.

Another point of interest is the phenomenon of resonance. There are many values of λ for which $J_0 (\lambda^q/q)$ is zero. In fact, they are given by (21) on changing ζ to λ^q. For a given estuary there are many values of σ corresponding to these values of λ according to (9). These special values of σ will cause A to become infinite and can be called the natural or characteristic frequencies of the given channel. When the frequency at the sea comes near the natural frequencies of the channel, a state of resonance is approached. In such cases the given solution fails, and one is compelled to take friction into consideration. For an estuary of moderate length, σ is usually so small that even the first of these natural frequencies is not reached.

392   **CHIA-SHUN YIH**   [Trans. AGU, V. 34 - 3]

<u>Tides around small islands</u>--Supposing that r is measured radially from an island which is small compared with the wave length of the tide, and that the depth h of the sea is a power function of r

$$h/h_s = (r/s)^n \qquad \dots\dots\dots\dots\dots\dots\dots\dots (22)$$

where s is the value of r at which a periodic motion is maintained (at the open sea) and h_s is the value of h at r = s, one proposes to study the amplitude of tides around the island. Let the periodic motion at the open sea be represented by

$$\eta_s = C \cos(\sigma t + \epsilon)\, e^{i\mu\theta} \qquad \dots\dots\dots\dots\dots\dots\dots (23)$$

where θ is the coordinate angle and the other quantities have the same meanings as before. The differential equation for η is [LAMB, 1945, p. 291]

$$\partial^2 \eta/\partial t^2 = g\,(h\nabla^2 \eta + (d\,h/d\,r)\,\partial\eta/\partial r) \qquad \dots\dots\dots\dots\dots (24)$$

where

$$\nabla^2 \equiv \partial^2/\partial r^2 + (1/r)\partial/\partial r + (1/r^2)\partial^2/\partial\theta^2$$

and g is again the gravitational acceleration.

With $\rho = r/s$ one can write (24) as

$$(s^2/g\,h_s)\,\partial^2 \eta/\partial t^2 = (\rho^n \nabla_\rho^2 \eta + n\rho^{n-1}\,\partial\eta/\partial\rho) \qquad \dots\dots\dots\dots\dots (25)$$

where

$$\nabla_\rho^2 \equiv \partial^2/\partial\rho^2 + (1/\rho)\,\partial/\partial\rho + (1/\rho^2)\partial^2/\partial\theta^2$$

Taking

$$\eta = C\cos(\sigma t + \epsilon)\,R\,(\rho)\,e^{i\mu\theta}$$

one has

$$\rho^n\,[R'' + (1/\rho)\,R' - (\mu^2/\rho^2)\,R] + n\rho^{n-1}\,R' + \lambda^{2-n}\,R = 0$$

where

$$\lambda^{2-n} = s^2\sigma^2/g\,h_s \qquad \dots\dots\dots\dots\dots\dots\dots\dots (26)$$

Writing ρ_1 for $\lambda\rho$, one has

$$d^2R/d\rho_1^2 + (2/\rho_1)\,d\,R/d\rho_1 - (\mu^2/\rho_1^2)\,R + (1/\rho_1^n)\,R = 0 \qquad \dots\dots\dots\dots (27)$$

To seek a solution in terms of familiar functions, one tries the transformations

$$R = \rho_1^q\,f\,(\zeta) \qquad \zeta = \rho_1^q$$

substitution of which into (27) yields, in a way similar to that of deriving (14)

$$d^2 f/d\zeta^2 + [(2p+q+n)/q\,\zeta]\,d\,f/d\zeta + \left\{[\zeta^{(-n+2-2q)/q}/q^2] - [\mu^2 - p\,(p+n)]/q^2\,\zeta^2\right\}f = 0$$

Demanding

$$p = -n/2 \qquad q = (2-n)/2 \qquad \dots\dots\dots\dots\dots\dots\dots (28)$$

one obtains the Bessel equation

$$d^2f/d\zeta^2 + (1/\zeta)\,d\,f/d\zeta + [1/q^2 - (\mu^2 + n^2/4)/q^2\,\zeta^2]\,f = 0 \qquad \dots\dots\dots (29)$$

the solutions of which are $J_\nu\,(\zeta/q)$ and $J_{-\nu}\,(\zeta/q)$ where

$$\nu = \sqrt{(\mu^2/q^2) + (n^2/4\,q^2)} \qquad \dots\dots\dots\dots\dots\dots (30)$$

It may be noted that since values of n greater than two are unlikely, q will be considered as positive. Since p = - n/2 is always negative, J_ν should always be chosen so that R will not have a pole at $\zeta = 0$. It is interesting to note that since $J_\nu (\zeta/q)$ varies as

$$\zeta^\nu = \rho_1^{(\mu^2 + n^2/4)^{1/2}}$$

near the origin,

$$R = \rho_1^p \, J_\nu \, (\zeta/q) = \rho_1^{-n/2} \, J_\nu (\zeta/q)$$

varies there as

$$\rho_1^{(\mu^2 + n^2/4)^{1/2} - n/2}$$

which vanishes at $\eta = 0$ for $\mu \neq 0$. Consequently, only the effect of the gravest mode corresponding to $\mu = 0$ is felt at the island.

In view of (23) (since $\rho_1 = \lambda\rho$ and $\rho = 1$ at $r = s$) the solution is thus

$$\eta = [C/J_\nu \, (\lambda^q/q)] \, \rho^{-n/2} \, J_\nu \, (\zeta/q) \, \cos \, (\sigma t + \epsilon) \, e^{i\mu\theta} \qquad \ldots\ldots\ldots\ldots \quad (31)$$

This solution can be discussed in a way similar to that for the case of the estuary. It is topographically unlikely that any nodal circle exists for the low frequency of the ordinary tide. For the gravest mode ($\mu = 0$) usually there will be only one point of maximum amplitude, which is at the origin. Thus for this mode (which is the most likely to occur), the amplitude of tide increases with decreasing distance from the island.

For higher modes ($\mu = 1, 2, 3, \ldots$), there are nodal lines radiating from the island dividing the whole angle into equal segments.

It is obvious that (31) can be generalized to satisfy the following boundary condition at $r = s$

$$\eta_s = C \, \cos \, (\sigma t + \epsilon) \, F \, (\theta)$$

where $F \, (\theta)$ has a period 2π. All that is necessary is to expand $F \, (\theta)$ in a Fourier series, and to use as the solution the corresponding series consisting of terms like the one on the right side of (31).

Concluding remarks--Under the assumptions on which the calculations of this paper are based, it can be concluded from the foregoing that there is an augmentation of the amplitude of tide over certain portions of the estuary if it is extremely long, that this augmentation is over the entire length of the estuary if it is of ordinary length, that at the island only the effect of the gravest mode of the tide (which is the most likely to occur) is felt, and that for this mode the amplitude of tide generally increases with decreasing distance from the island.

It is worth noticing that if the periodic motion at the mouth of the estuary or in the open sea for the case of the island is described by a general periodic function of time, the corresponding problems can be solved by superposition and applying the Fourier series, utilizing the results obtained in the foregoing.

Acknowledgment--The writer wishes to acknowledge support of this project by the Office of Naval Research and the Civil Engineering Department of the Colorado Agricultural and Mechanical College, and the assistance rendered by the staff of the Iowa Institute of Hydraulic Research in preparing the manuscript.

References

JAHNKE, E., and F. EMDE, Table of functions, Dover Publications, 1945.
LAMB, H., Hydrodynamics, Dover, 1945.
WHITTAKER, E. I., and G. N. WATSON, Modern analysis, MacMillan, 1945.

Iowa Institute of Hydraulic Research
　　　State University of Iowa
　　　　　Iowa City, Iowa

(Communicated manuscript received April 2, 1952, and as revised, January 28, 1953; open for formal discussion until November 1, 1953.)

J. Fluid Mech. (1972), *vol.* 51, *part* 2, *pp.* 209–220

© *Cambridge University Press*, 1972

Surface waves in flowing water

By CHIA-SHUN YIH

Department of Engineering Mechanics,
The University of Michigan

(Received 24 July 1970 and in revised form 13 September 1971)

Surface waves in flowing water and their stability are studied. With $U(y)$ denoting the mean velocity and d the depth of water, the following results are obtained: (i) in the plane of the complex wave velocity, $c = c_r + ic_i$, all eigenvalues c with a positive c_i lie within a semicircle which has as its diameter the range of the velocity $U(y)$ of the primary flow, y being the vertical co-ordinate. (ii) If $U''(y)$ does not change sign and U is monotonic in the field of flow, singular neutral modes (for which $c = U$ somewhere in the field of flow) are impossible and the flow is stable. (iii) If U is analytic and U'' vanishes at the point or points where U is equal to the same constant U_c and where U' is not zero then at least one neutral mode exists with $c = U_c$, provided $U(d) \neq U_c$. (iv) If U is monotonic and $U''/(U - c)$ is finite and non-zero at the critical point (c real), where U'' vanishes, then the neutral mode mentioned in (iii) above is contiguous with unstable modes. (v) If $U'' < 0$ and $U' \geqslant 0$ there are waves with $c \leqslant U(0)$, with a finite maximum wavenumber k_c corresponding to $c = U(0)$ and with c decreasing monotonically to a finite c_0 for $k = 0$. (vi) If $U'' < 0$ and $U' \geqslant 0$ waves of all wavenumbers can travel with $c > U(d)$. The eigenvalue c for any k is bounded.

---

1. Introduction

The question of surface waves in flowing water is inseparable from the question of their stability. In previous studies of this question, by Burns (1953), Hunt (1955) and Benjamin (1962), the question of stability has not been posed. With $U(y)$ denoting the velocity of the primary flow at elevation y, Burns found that if $U''(y)$ is non-positive and $U(y)$ increases monotonically with y then two real values of the wave velocity exist for *long* waves, one of which is greater than the surface velocity $U(d)$, d being the depth of water, and the other less than $U(0)$. Benjamin (1962) questioned the existence of the smaller $c < U(0)$ claimed by Burns. In his criticism Benjamin seems to believe that for $U''(y) < 0$ a singular neutral mode with $U(0) < c < U(d)$ exists when $U(d)$ is very much greater than the speed of very long waves in quiet water. However, Burns's conclusion is supported by the present work. Hunt was not concerned with whether a neutral mode may be singular in his calculation of (real) eigenvalues of c for a seventh-power law for U ($U = Cy^{\frac{1}{7}}$). It will be seen in this paper that unless $U''(y)$ vanishes somewhere in the field of flow there cannot be singular neutral modes with $c = U(y)$ for $0 < y < d$.

210   *C.-S. Yih*

The present work is concerned not only with surface waves but their stability. Where it deals with neutral waves the approach is different from those of previous writers.

2. Governing equations

If p denotes the pressure perturbation, that is, the *deviation* of the pressure from the hydrostatic pressure, ρ denotes the (constant) density, t denotes the time, and x and y are Cartesian co-ordinates, with y measured in the vertical direction, then the linearized equations of motion of a liquid, with viscous effects neglected, are

$$\rho(u_t + Uu_x + U'v) = -p_x, \tag{1}$$

$$\rho(v_t + Uv_x) = -p_y, \tag{2}$$

where u and v are the components of the velocity perturbation in the directions of increasing x and y, respectively, U is the mean velocity, which is in the direction of x and is a function of y only, subscripts denote partial differentiation and primes on U denote differentiation with respect to y. The equation of continuity

$$u_x + v_y = 0$$

allows one to use the stream function ψ in terms of which

$$u = \psi_y, \quad v = -\psi_x. \tag{3}$$

We shall assume

$$\psi = f(y)\, e^{ik(x-ct)}, \tag{4}$$

where

$$c = c_r + ic_i \tag{5}$$

is the wave velocity. Eliminating p between (1) and (2) and using (3) and (4) we arrive at the well-known equation

$$f'' + [U''/(c-U) - k^2]f = 0. \tag{6}$$

It is sometimes more convenient to use the function $F(y)$ defined by

$$f(y) = (c-U)F(y).$$

In terms of $F(y)$, (6) becomes, as can be readily verified,

$$[(U-c)^2 F']' - k^2(U-c)^2 F = 0. \tag{7}$$

The boundary condition for f at the bottom, where $y = 0$, is

$$f(0) = 0. \tag{8}$$

At the free surface the condition is

$$p(d) - \rho g \eta = 0, \tag{9}$$

where η is the displacement of the free surface from its mean position. Since the kinematic condition at the free surface is

$$\eta_t + U\eta_x = v = -\psi_x, \tag{10}$$

from (1), (9) and (10) we obtain, remembering that p also has the factor $\exp ik(x-ct)$,

$$f'(d) = \left[\frac{g}{(U-c)^2} + \frac{U'}{U-c}\right] f(d), \tag{11}$$

In terms of $F(y)$, (8) and (11) become respectively

$$F(0) = 0 \tag{12}$$

and

$$(U-c)^2 F'(d) = gF(d). \tag{13}$$

3. The semicircle theorem

By a slight extension Howard's semicircle theorm (1961) can be generalized to apply to flows with a free surface. With $W = U - c$ we can write (7) as

$$(W^2 F')' - k^2 W^2 F = 0. \tag{14}$$

Multiplying this equation by F^*, integrating from zero to d and using (12) and (13) whenever necessary, we have

$$\int W^2(|F'|^2 + k^2|F|^2)\,dy - g|F(d)|^2 = 0, \tag{15}$$

where the limits of integration are understood. The real and imaginary parts of (15) are

$$\int [(U-c_r)^2 - c_i^2]\,Q\,dy - g|F(d)|^2 = 0 \tag{15a}$$

and

$$2c_i \int (U-c_r)\,Q\,dy = 0, \tag{15b}$$

where

$$Q = |F'|^2 + k^2|F|^2. \tag{16}$$

If c_1 is not zero then

$$\int UQ\,dy = \int c_r Q\,dy \tag{17}$$

and (15a) can be written as

$$\int U^2 Q\,dy = (c_r^2 + c_i^2)\int Q\,dy + g|F(d)|^2. \tag{18}$$

If a and b are the minimum and maximum of U respectively, so that $a \leqslant U \leqslant b$, it is obvious that

$$0 \geqslant \int (U-a)(U-b)\,Q\,dy = \int U^2 Q\,dy - (a+b)\int UQ\,dy + ab\int Q\,dy.$$

Using (17) and (18) we then have

$$0 \geqslant [c_r^2 + c_i^2 - (a+b)\,c_r + ab]\int Q\,dy + g|F(d)|^2,$$

from which it follows that

$$[c_r - \tfrac{1}{2}(a+b)]^2 + c_i^2 \leqslant [\tfrac{1}{2}(a+b)]^2 - ab = [\tfrac{1}{2}(b-a)]^2. \tag{19}$$

Hence the semicircle theorem:

212   *C.-S. Yih*

THEOREM 1. The complex wave velocity c for any unstable mode must lie inside the semicircle in the upper half of the complex c plane which has the range of U for diameter.

4. The Reynolds stress

We have just seen that if c_r is outside of the range of U then c_i must be zero. Such wave modes, if they exist, are called non-singular modes. On the other hand, if c_r falls within the range of U then c_i may or may not be zero. Such modes, if $c_i = 0$, are called singular neutral modes. In order to study singular neutral modes and the unstable modes contiguous to them (as we shall see later) we consider the Reynolds stress in the fluid defined by

$$\tau = -\rho\overline{uv}, \tag{20}$$

the bar indicating a time average. Remembering that u and v are the real parts of $f'(y)\,e^{ik(x-ct)}$ and $-ikf(y)\,e^{ik(x-ct)}$ respectively we easily obtain

$$\tau = \tfrac{1}{2}\rho k\,\mathrm{Im}\,(f^*f')\,e^{2kc_it} = (\rho k/4i)\,(f^*f' - ff^{*\prime})\,e^{2kc_it}, \tag{21}$$

where f^* is the complex conjugate of f. If we differentiate (21) and use (6) we obtain the expression of Foote & Lin (1950):

$$\frac{d\tau}{dy} = \frac{1}{k}\rho\overline{v^2}\,c_i\,\frac{U''}{|U-c|^2}. \tag{22}$$

If now we let c_i approach zero we see that $d\tau/dy$ approaches zero everywhere except at the critical point, where $U = c_r$. Integration of (22) across the critical point yields the jump† in τ as c_i approaches zero:

$$[\tau] = \tau(y_c^+) - \tau(y_c^-) = (\pi/k)\,\overline{v^2}U_c''/|U_c'|, \tag{23}$$

which is given by Lin (1955, p. 54), the subscript c meaning 'critical'. Thus for a singular neutral mode τ is constant between critical points, but suffers a jump as given by (23) across a critical point.

Now consider the Reynolds stress at the free surface. From (11) and (21) it follows that at the free surface

$$\tau = \tfrac{1}{2}\rho k\,c_i\left[\frac{g(U-c_r)}{|U-c|^4} + \frac{U'}{|U-c|^2}\right]|f|^2, \tag{24}$$

where all variables depending on y are to be evaluated at $y = d$. It is evident that $\tau = 0$ if $c_i = 0$. Hence for a neutral mode the Reynolds stress is zero at the free surface. At the bottom, where f is zero, the Reynolds stress is zero for any mode, neutral or unstable.

The jump in τ at the critical point is zero if U_c' is not zero but either U_c'' or v is zero there. If U is monotonic there can be only one critical point. If at that point

---

† One referee of this paper thinks the validity of (23) depends on the existence of unstable modes with complex values of c in the neighbourhood of the real c under discussion. The author of this paper does not share this view but chooses to record the disagreement here.

Surface waves in flowing water 213

U'' is not zero and v cannot be zero then singular neutral mode for that c (real) is not possible, since there is a jump in τ which is, however, prohibited by the boundary conditions.

5. Sufficient conditions for stability

Multiplying (6) by f^* and integrating in the fluid domain, we have, upon using (8) and (11),

$$-\int (|f'|^2 + k^2|f|^2)\,dy - \int \frac{U''}{U-c}|f|^2\,dy + \left(\frac{g}{(U-c)^2} + \frac{U'}{U-c}\right)_d |f(d)|^2 = 0, \quad (25)$$

in which the subscript d indicates that the bracket is to be evaluated at $y = d$. After multiplication by -1, the imaginary part of (25) is

$$c_i\left\{\int \frac{U''}{|U-c|^2}|f|^2 - \left(\frac{2g(U-c_r)}{|U-c|^4} + \frac{U'}{|U-c|^2}\right)_d |f(d)|^2\right\} = 0. \quad (26)$$

If
$$U'' < 0 \quad \text{and} \quad U'(d) \geqslant 0, \quad (27)$$

and we suppose $c_i \neq 0$, then (26) demands

$$U(d) = \max U < c_r. \quad (28)$$

But, by theorem 1, if (28) is satisfied c_i must vanish, leading to a contradiction of the supposition $c_i \neq 0$. Hence c_i must be zero if (27) is satisfied and we have

THEOREM 2(a). If $U'' < 0$ throughout the fluid domain and $U'(d) \geqslant 0$, the free-surface flow is stable.

By almost identical arguments we also have

THEOREM 2(b). If $U'' > 0$ throughout the fluid domain and $U'(d) \leqslant 0$, the free-surface flow is stable.

Actually theorem 2(b) is an obvious consequence of theorem 2(a) since upon reversing the positive direction of flow theorem 2(b) becomes theorem 2(a).

6. Singular neutral modes

If (27) is satisfied we can show that singular neutral modes are impossible. Let c be real and $U = c$ at $y = y_c > 0$. First, we note that $v \neq 0$ (i.e. $f \neq 0$) at this point. For if $f(y_c)$ were zero, then multiplying (6) by f^* and integrating between zero and y_c we would have

$$\int_0^{y_c} (|f'|^2 + k^2|f|^2)\,dy + \int_0^{y_c} \frac{U''}{U-c}|f|^2\,dy = 0, \quad (29)$$

which is evidently absurd since $U \leqslant c$ and $U'' < 0$ in the domain of integration. Hence $f(y_c) \neq 0$. Note that if $f(y_c) = 0$, f contains only the solution f_1 which is analytic at y_c and contains the factor $(y - y_c)$. Hence all the integrals are convergent. The other solution of (6) is of the form

$$f_2 = 1 + \ldots + \frac{U_c''}{U_c'} f_1 (y - y_c) \ln (y - y_c),$$

as is well known. Then if (27) is satisfied the jump in τ across the critical point (if any) given by (23) cannot be zero. Since τ is zero both at $y = 0$ and at $y = d$, this jump cannot happen. Hence there cannot be a critical point, i.e. there cannot be a singular neutral mode if (27) is satisfied. The same is true if $U'' > 0$ and $U' \leqslant 0$. Hence we have

THEOREM 3. *If U is monotonic and the U–y curve has no point of inflexion, singular neutral modes are impossible.*

Note that since $f(0) = 0$, if $y_c = 0$ the solution must be the non-singular one f_1.

We shall now show that a singular neutral mode exists if U is analytic and monotonically increasing and $U''(y)$ vanishes at some point in the fluid domain. In fact, the c will be the U at the point where U'' vanishes. For then

$$K(y) = U''/(c - U) \tag{30}$$

is analytic everywhere, including the critical point y_c. We can then apply the Sturm–Liouville theory to (6) and its boundary conditions. With

$$U(y_c) = c \quad \text{and} \quad U''(y_c) = 0, \tag{31}$$

a solution satisfying (8) can always be found for any k. But we have to show that (11) can be satisfied for that c and some real value of k, with (8) satisfied. To do so we multiply (6) by $U - c$ and integrate from zero to d, obtaining

$$[U(d) - c]f'(d) - [U(0) - c]f'(0) - f(d)\,U'(d) - k^2 \int (U - c)f\,dy = 0. \tag{32}$$

We may assign the value 1 to $f'(0)$, since the eigenfunction can be multiplied by an arbitrary constant, and for convenience denote the positive number $c - U(0)$ by the symbol c'. Then (32) can be written as

$$\frac{f'}{f} = \frac{U'}{U - c} - \frac{c'}{(U - c)f} + \frac{k^2}{(U - c)f} \int_0^d (U - c)f\,dy, \tag{33}$$

in which all functions of y, except those inside the integration sign, are evaluated at $y = d$, where, one recalls, $U - c$ is positive. We know from the Sturm theory that if k^2 increases $f'(d)/f(d)$ will increase. For $k = 0$,

$$\frac{f'}{f} = \frac{U'}{U - c} - \frac{c'}{(U - c)f}, \tag{33a}$$

with all functions of y evaluated at d. Very near y_c, just above it, $U'/(U - c)$ is positive and as large as we please, and hence is greater than† f'/f evaluated at

---

† This is so because $f(y_c)$ cannot be zero, as can be seen from an equation similar to (32), with y_c replacing d.

$$[U(y_c) - c]f'(y_c) - [U(0) - c]f'(0) - f(y_c)\,U'(y_c) - k^2 \int_0^{y_c} (U - c)f\,dy = 0.$$

The dominant term in $f'(y)$ near y_c comes from $f_2'(y)$ and is equal or proportional to

$$U_c'' \ln(y - y_c)/U_c',$$

since the expansion of $f_1(y)$ near y_c starts with the term $(y - y_c)$. The term $U(y) - c$ behaves like $U'(y_c)\,(y - y_c)$ near y_c since $U(y)$ is analytic. Hence the first term in the equation vanishes. If we set k equal to zero then $f(y_c)$ cannot be zero, since the second term in the equation is not zero. Hence f'/f can only be logarithmically large, whereas $U'/(U - c)$ can be large like $(y - y_c)^{-1}$.

the same place. Sturm's second comparison theorem then says that at $y = d$
$U'/(U - c)$ must be greater than f'/f, since for $k = 0$ we have

$$f'' - \frac{U''}{U - c} f = 0 \tag{34}$$

and

$$(U - c)'' - \frac{U''}{U - c}(U - c) = 0, \tag{35}$$

so that f and $U - c$ satisfy the same differential equation. According to this conclusion, since $c'/(c - U)$ is negative $f(d)$ must be positive as can be seen from $(33a)$. In fact $f(y)$ cannot vanish for $y > y_c$, for otherwise we would have a $f'(y)/f(y)$ as large as we pleased above or below the zero of $f(y)$. Hence $f(d) \neq 0$ for $k = 0$, even if $f(y)$ is not the eigenfunction. If $f(y)$ is the eigenfunction then the free-surface condition forbids $f(d)$ to vanish. (From Sturm's first comparison theorem we also see that f cannot vanish below y_c except once, at $y = 0$. Thus for $k = 0$, $f(y)$ vanishes only at $y = 0$.) Hence for a very small k the two last terms in (33) definitely have a negative sum. The question then is whether $f'(d)/f(d)$ will increase to the value specified by (11) for the c under consideration as k^2 increases from zero, that is, whether the sum of the last two terms in (33) will reach $g/(U - c)^2$ evaluated at d. To answer this question, let us see how those terms behave at large k^2. Recalling that the $K(y)$ given by (30) is analytic let us denote its maximum value by M and its minimum value by m. Since f is made to vanish at $y = 0$, and $f'(0) = 1$, it can be readily shown that for $k^2 > M$,

$$\sinh(k''y)/k'' \leqslant f(y) \leqslant \sinh(k'y)/k', \tag{36}$$

where $$k'' = (k^2 - M)^{\frac{1}{2}} \quad \text{and} \quad k' = (k^2 - m)^{\frac{1}{2}}.$$

In fact (36) is a consequence of Sturm's second comparison theorem, stating that

$$k'' \coth k''y \leqslant f'(y)/f(y) \leqslant k' \coth k'y. \tag{37}$$

Integration of (37) gives (36). The integral in (33), denoted by I, can be written as

$$I = I_1 + I_2,$$

where $$I_1 = \int_0^{y_c} (U - c)f\,dy, \quad I_2 = \int_{y_c}^d (U - c)f\,dy. \tag{38}$$

Since f is positive for $k^2 > M$, on inspection of (6), with $f'(0) = 1$, we see that I_1 is negative and I_2 positive for $k^2 > M$. Let us define two numbers α and β such that

$$\alpha(y_c - y) > c - U \quad \text{for} \quad y \leqslant y_c, \tag{39}$$

$$\beta(y - y_c) < U - c \quad \text{for} \quad y_c \leqslant y. \tag{40}$$

Then

$$I > \int_0^{y_c} \alpha(y - y_c)\frac{\sinh k'y}{k'} + \int_{y_c}^d \beta(y - y_c)\frac{\sinh k''y}{k''}$$

$$= \frac{\beta}{k''^2}(d - y_c)\cosh k''d - \frac{\beta}{k''^3}(\sinh k''d - \sinh k''y_c) - \frac{\alpha y_c}{k'^2} - \frac{\alpha}{k'^3}\sinh k'y_c. \tag{41}$$

216   *C.-S. Yih*

For large k^2, then, the integral I behaves like

$$\frac{\beta(d-y_c)}{k^2}\cosh kd,$$

provided $d \neq y_c$, and the last term in (33) behaves like

$$\frac{k\beta}{U(d)-c}(d-y_c)\coth kd. \tag{42}$$

The term in (33) containing c' behaves like

$$-\frac{c'}{U(d)-c}\frac{k}{\sinh kd}$$

for large k and is negligible compared with (42). As k increases, (42) increases without bound. Hence, being deficient at $k = 0$, as compared with (11), $f'(d)/f(d)$ must finally reach the value specified in (11) as k increases. Hence a singular neutral mode exists under the conditions stated and with c given by (31).

We have, for convenience of exposition, assumed U to be monotonically increasing. The same conclusion is reached if it is monotonically decreasing. In fact, the conclusion still holds even if U is not monotonic, provided that U'' vanishes at all points where $U = c$. We shall sketch the essence of the proof as follows.

(i)   If there is more than one point at which $U = c$, $U - c$ vanishes more than once in $0 \leqslant y < d$. Hence using (34) and (35) for comparison we know that for $k = 0$ f vanishes at least once in the same interval (not including $y = 0$, where f is always zero). Hence on increasing k we can always make $f(d) = 0$ and $f'(d) < 0$. On increasing k a little more, it is evident that $f'(d)/f(d)$ can be made as near minus infinity as we please. Therefore the 'deficiency' of $f'(d)/f(d)$ as compared with its value demanded by (11) is established for some $k^2 = k_0^2 > 0$.

(ii)   As k^2 increases beyond k_0^2, f is always positive for $y > 0$. Then, by a procedure similar to the one we have used above to discover the behaviour of I for large k^2 we can *always* show that the last term in (33) increases without bound as k^2 increases indefinitely, provided $U(d) \neq c$, whether $U(d) - c$ is positive or negative. It can in fact be shown that the integral I is dominated by that part of it which is between the largest y_c and d, and that the last term in (33) is positive and increases without bound as k^2 increases indefinitely. Hence the 'deficiency' mentioned in (i) can always be exactly eliminated, arriving at a neutral mode with c equal to U at one or more points of the flow. This mode really should not be called 'singular' any more.

Hence we have

THEOREM 4. If U is analytic and U'' vanishes at the point or points where U is equal to the same constant U_c and where U' does not vanish, then at least one neutral mode exists with $c = U_c$, provided $U(d) \neq U_c$.

The reason for using the words 'at least' is that if there is more than one point at which $U = U_c$ and $U'' = 0$, (11) may well be satisfied for more than one positive value of k^2. We have only shown that at least one such value exists. It can also be shown that for any k the eigenvalue c cannot be $U(d)$, whether $y = d$ is a critical point or not.

7. Unstable modes contiguous to singular neutral modes

If we vary k^2 slightly from its eigenvalue for the singular neutral modes mentioned in theorem 4 we obtain unstable modes. The demonstration is entirely similar to that of Lin (1955, pp. 122–123), the difference in the upper boundary condition causing no trouble whatever. We shall not reproduce Lin's analysis but shall only quote the results that can be obtained by his approach:

$$-dk^2/dc = A+iB, \tag{43}$$

where A and B are real and

$$B\int_0^d f_s^2\,dy = \pi\sum_i [K(y_c)f_s^2(y_c)]_i, \tag{44}$$

the summation being over all the critical points (where U'' vanishes and $U = c$). f_s is the eigenfunction for the 'singular' neutral mode. The free-surface boundary condition affects A but not B, except through f. If there is only one y_c and $K(y_c)$ is not zero, B is not zero and a slight change in k^2, be it positive or negative, will produce a positive c_i. Otherwise B may be zero, in which case a change in k^2 produces only a change in c_r. Hence we have

THEOREM 5. *If U is monotonic and $K(y_c)$ is not zero the neutral mode mentioned in theorem 4 is contiguous to unstable modes.*

8. Non-singular neutral modes

We shall restrict our attention to flows with the following properties:

$$U''(y) < 0 \quad \text{and} \quad U' \geqslant 0. \tag{45}$$

There are two classes of waves: class 1, with $c \leqslant U(0)$ and class 2, with $c > U(d)$.

Class 1

Consider first the limiting case of $c = U(0)$. For this case the c' in (33) is zero, and comparison of (33) with (11) produces

$$\frac{g}{U(d)-U(0)} = \frac{k^2}{f(d)}\int_0^d [U(d)-U(0)]f(y)\,dy, \tag{46}$$

for $y = d$. Since f cannot vanish† in the domain of flow it is positive throughout, except at $y = 0$. The discussion in §6 shows that the right-hand side of (46) increases without bound with k. Hence for some $k = k_c$ (depending on the flow), (46) and hence (11) are satisfied.

For $k < k_c$ we have $c < U(0)$ and c decreasing algebraically as k decreases. This can be seen by using Sturm's second comparison theorem on (6). For if k decreases and c does not decrease, the coefficient of f in (6) increases and hence $f'(d)/f(d)$ decreases according to Sturm's second comparison theorem. On the other hand if c does not decrease [and $c < U(0)$] the same quantity, $f'(d)/f(d)$, does

---

† Compare the f in (b) with the $U-c$ in (35). Both vanish at $y = 0$ if $c = U(0)$ and $U-c$ has no other zero. Since $k^2 \geqslant 0$, f cannot have a second zero.

not decrease, according to (11), leading to a contradiction. Hence c decreases as k decreases. It is also easy to see that c is bounded for $k = 0$. For otherwise, from the differential equation and $f(0) = 0$, we have $f(y) = y$, so that $f'(d)/f(d) = 1/d$, whereas (11) gives $f'(d)/f(d) = 0$. Hence

THEOREM 6. Under conditions (45) there are waves with $c \leqslant U(0)$, with a finite maximum wavenumber $k = k_c$ corresponding to $c = U(0)$, and with c decreasing monotonically to a finite value c_0 for $k = 0$.

Class 2

We now consider wave propagating downstream for which $c > U(d)$. Since the expression in parenthesis in (6) is positive, f is non-oscillatory and is in fact monotonically increasing from zero, as y increases. Therefore it is easy to see that $f(d) > d$. Since f is only zero at $y = 0$ and is positive elsewhere, and since c' is positive, the equation

$$c' + k^2 \int_0^d (c - U) f \, dy = \frac{g}{c - U(d)} f(d),$$

obtained by comparison of (33) with (11), can always be satisfied, whatever the value of k. Again it can be shown that the c corresponding to any k is bounded. Hence we have

THEOREM 7. Under conditions (45) waves of all wavenumbers can travel downstream with $c > U(d)$. The eigenvalue c for any k is bounded.

The present results support those of Burns (1953) which are for long waves only. Benjamin doubted the existence of waves with $c < U(0)$ when the surface velocity is a long way supercritical and brought the amplitude of the waves and the possibility of separation into his arguments against the existence of such waves. I do not follow Benjamin's arguments. However his statement that "in fact the wave will be convected downstream at an absolute velocity not much different from $\overline{U} - C_0$" ($\overline{U}$ = mean U, C_0 = wave speed in quiet water) is contradicted by our theorem 3, since Benjamin's statements apply explicitly to $U'' < 0$.

For an intuitive understanding of the propagation of long waves against the stream it is helpful to consider the density of the kinetic energy of very long waves, $[f'(y)]^2$, with the factor $\frac{1}{2}\rho$ omitted. If U'' is negative throughout and U increases monotonically with y, then for $k = 0$ and $c < U(0)$ integration of (6) subject to the conditions $f(0) = 0$, $f'(0) = 1$ shows that $f'(y)$ decreases with y, initially at least. Hence the kinetic energy at the bottom is at least a relative maximum and one is not surprised that a long wave can propagate its energy against the current near the bottom, where the situation is advantageous. This is, of course, merely an attempt to understand what goes on in an intuitive imprecise way. Its imprecision should not be allowed to cast doubt on the theory, which is entirely independent of such an intuitive argument.

In an open channel the waves with $c < U(0)$ can only be observed if a wave maker oscillates in the flowing water without blocking the flow. A stationary obstacle placed in the stream cannot be expected to produce upstream propagating waves, since even for a subcritical stream with uniform U, for which upstream propagating waves are known to exist, no such waves can be seen upstream from the obstacle. This phenomenon is related to the fact that the phase velocity is greater than the group velocity and is an altogether different matter. It should not be used as a basis for doubting the validity of the present results.

We note that for the special case of simple shear $U'' = 0$, and the differential equation (6) becomes identical to that for potential flow. The flow is always stable and no mode is singular, but it is now possible to have any c between $U(0)$ and $U(d)$. The only difference from wave motion in quiet water arises through (11).

We note also that if viscosity is taken into account, waves propagating against the stream may well be damped out and unstable modes with c_r in the range of U, permitted by the present theory, may be damped by viscosity to become neutral. These possibilities were pointed out by Velthuizen & Wijngaarden (1969), who considered a horizontal flow of a viscous fluid with a free surface. Strictly speaking, such a flow cannot be maintained, since there is no energy source, and not only waves, but the flow itself, must in time be damped out. Their calculation, however, is not without significance over a (relatively) short time. With this in mind we recall the results of Benjamin (1957) and Yih (1963), who found that for a viscous liquid layer flowing down an inclined plane: (a) No long waves can propagate upstream. (b) Undamped long waves propagate downstream with a speed equal to twice the surface (maximum) velocity of the mean flow, giving no indication of the existence of a singular neutral mode in the inviscid limit.

This work has been supported by the National Science Foundation and the Office of Naval Research.

Appendix

A referee has pointed out an interesting physical explanation for the upstream propagation of long waves even if the surface velocity is high. In what follows the original idea and the conclusion are his and the derivation is mine.

In a co-ordinate system moving with the waves the flow is steady. Choosing x and the stream function ψ in that system as independent variables, the total horizontal velocity component along a streamline in that system is

$$\hat{U}(\psi) + \hat{u}(\psi, x),$$

in which (the notation used in the paper being used for the other quantities)

$$\hat{U}(\psi) = U(y) - c, \quad \hat{u} = u + \eta U'(y) = f'(y)\, e^{ikx} + \eta U'. \tag{A 1}$$

We note that
$$v = \hat{U}\eta_x$$

which, in view of (3) and (4), means that

$$\eta = -\frac{f(y)}{U - c}\, e^{ikx}, \tag{A 2}$$

that is to say that the $F(y)$ in (7) is the amplitude of η. Then from (A 1) and (A 2) we have

$$\hat{U}\hat{u} = (f'\hat{U} - fU')\, e^{ikx}. \tag{A 3}$$

220   *C.-S. Yih*

Now for long waves the governing equation is (34), integration of which gives

$$(U-c)f' - U'f = C.$$

Thus

$$\hat{U}\hat{u} = C\,e^{ikx},$$

which is independent of ψ.

Since $\hat{u}^2$ is proportional to the kinetic energy (along a streamline) of perturbation for long waves, this kinetic energy is a maximum where $|\hat{U}|$ is a minimum. For a monotonically increasing $U(y)\,(>0)$ and for $c<0$ (propagation upstream), $\hat{U} = |\hat{U}|$ is a minimum at $y=0$. Thus the kinetic energy is large at and near $y=0$ if $U(0)=0$, $c<0$, and $|c| \ll 1$, and it is understandable why it can propagate against the weak current $U(y)$ near $y=0$.

REFERENCES

BENJAMIN, T. B. 1957 Wave formation in the laminar flow down an inclined plane. *J. Fluid Mech.* **2**, 554–574.

BENJAMIN, T. B. 1962 The solitary wave on a stream with an arbitrary distribution of vorticity. *J. Fluid Mech.* **12**, 97–116.

BURNS, J. C. 1953 Long waves in running water. *Proc. Camb. Phil. Soc.* **49**, 695.

FOOTE, J. R. & LIN, C. C. 1950 Some recent investigations in the theory of hydrodynamic stability. *Quart. Appl. Math.* **8**, 265–280.

HOWARD, L. N. 1961 Note on a paper by John W. Miles. *J. Fluid Mech.* **10**, 509–512.

HUNT, J. N. 1955 Gravity waves in flowing water. *Proc. Roy. Soc.* A **231**, 496–504.

LIN, C. C. 1955 *The Theory of Hydrodynamic Stability*. Cambridge University Press.

VELTHUIZEN, H. G. M. & VAN WIJNGAARDEN, L. 1969 Gravity waves over a non-uniform flow. *J. Fluid Mech.* **39**, 817–829.

YIH, C.-S. 1963 Stability of liquid flow down an inclined plane. *Phys. Fluids*, **6**, 321–334.

QUARTERLY OF APPLIED MATHEMATICS
JANUARY, 1976

COMPARISON THEOREMS FOR GRAVITY WAVES
IN BASINS OF VARIABLE DEPTH*

BY

CHIA-SHUN YIH

University of Michigan

Abstract. Surface waves of a homogeneous liquid and internal waves of a stratified liquid in basins of variable depth are considered. Inequalities involving the frequencies of oscillation are obtained when a container with one size or geometry is compared with another with a different size or geometry, when waves with one wavelength are compared with waves with another wavelength, or when one stratification is compared with another. Since exact solutions for gravity waves in basins of variable depth are so rare, one hopes the comparison theorems presented herein will be useful.

1. Introduction. The number of explicit analytical solutions for water waves in channels of variable depth is extremely small. The few solutions in Lamb's book [1] (pp. 442–450) remain to this day the only ones in existence. The situation with internal waves is quite similar; the only explicit analytical solutions extant are for linearly or exponentially stratified fluid in ellipsoids and elliptic channels, when the Boussinesq approximation is used. For this reason it is desirable to have some comparison theorems that enable one to estimate the frequency of oscillation reliably and quickly, for all modes of wave motion.

In this paper a few such theorems will be given, when one size or geometry is compared with another, one wavelength with another, or one stratification with another. Some of the theorems are fairly obvious, but in combination with the less obvious ones give a powerful means of locating the range in which the frequency must lie.

2. System governing surface waves. Consider first surface waves in a homogeneous liquid contained in a basin of arbitrary shape. The fluid can be treated as incompressible, and we can neglect the effect of viscosity for the main body of the fluid. We shall assume the flow to be irrotational, so that a velocity potential ϕ exists, the gradient of which gives the velocity vector. In Cartesian coordinates x, y, and z, with y measured in the direction of the vertical, the equation satisfied by ϕ is, as is well known,

$$\phi_{xx} + \phi_{yy} + \phi_{zz} = 0, \tag{2.1}$$

where the subscripts indicate partial differentiation. The condition at any stationary solid boundary is

$$\phi_n = 0, \tag{2.2}$$

* Received July 21, 1974. This work has been sponsored jointly by the National Science Foundation and the Office of Naval Research.

CHIA-SHUN YIH

where n is measured in the direction of the normal to the boundary.

At the free surface there are a kinematic condition and a dynamic condition of constant pressure, which can be combined into ([1], p. 364)

$$\phi_{tt} + g\phi_y = 0. \tag{2.3}$$

We shall assume ϕ to have the time factor $\exp(-i\sigma t)$. Then (2.3) can be written as

$$\sigma^2\phi = g\phi_y . \tag{2.4}$$

3. Comparison theorems for surface waves. The most obvious theorem presents itself when we compare one container with another one similar in shape but different in size. Let the first basin be B and the second one be B', and let all linear dimensions of B' (including the depth of the liquid in it) be m times that of B. If $\phi(x, y, z)$ is the solution for wave motion of any mode in B, then $\phi(m^{-1}x, m^{-1}y, m^{-1}z)$ is the solution for wave motion of the same mode in B', provided

$$\sigma^2 = m\sigma'^2, \tag{3.1}$$

σ being the frequency for B and σ' the frequency for B'. Thus we have

THEOREM 1.   If the size and liquid depth in a basin is multiplied by a factor m, the frequency of wave motion for any given mode is multiplied by a factor $(1/m)^{1/2}$.

This result is fairly obvious, for on inspection of (2.1) to (2.4), we see that for any given geometry, σ depends only on g and the linear dimension L, so that $\sigma^2 L/g$ must be constant. Indeed, we see also that σ^2 varies directly with g for any given mode. But in conjunction with another, less obvious theorem it is very useful.

Moiseev [2] has given the following theorem:

THEOREM 2.   The frequency of water waves for any given mode in a basin of variable depth is always greater than that in another basin provided the free surface is exactly the same for both basins, the water-occupied domain in the former basin contains that in the latter basin, and no infinite velocity occurs in either basin.

We shall, for the sake of completeness, give the essential arguments of the proof. Let the first basin be denoted by B' and its water-occupied domain be denoted by D', and the second basin be denoted by B and its water-occupied domain be denoted by D. It can be shown that an interior angle less than π on the boundary of B will in general give rise to a distributed singularity outside of B, but that that singularity distribution does not affect the conclusion. If there is an interior angle less than π on the boundary of B', the result also remains, since the boundary of B' can be approached by a succession of smooth curves. Therefore we need only consider smooth boundaries for B and B' here. Then there is no singularity of ϕ on the boundary of B or of the continuation of ϕ infinitely close to it, since the velocity field along that boundary is finite and free from singularities, and we can take B' sufficiently close to B so that $D' - D$ is free from singularities. Since the solution ϕ' for B' differs very little from the solution ϕ for B and for the same mode, the projection of the gradient of ϕ' on the gradient of ϕ must be everywhere positive in $D' - D$, i.e.,

$$P \equiv \phi_x'\phi_x + \phi_y'\phi_y + \phi_z'\phi_z > 0, \tag{3.2}$$

and, furthermore, over the free surface S

COMPARISON THEOREMS 389

$$Q \equiv \int_S \phi\phi' \, dS > 0. \tag{3.3}$$

Now ϕ' must also satisfy (2.1), (2.2), and (2.4). We shall denote the three equations satisfied by ϕ' by (2.1'), (2.2'), and (2.4'), without explicitly displaying them. Multiplying (2.1') by ϕ, integrating over D', and using (2.2') and (2.4'), we have

$$\lambda'Q = \int_{D'} P \, dV, \tag{3.4}$$

where $\lambda' = \sigma'^2/g$. Similarly, multiplying (2.1) by ϕ' and integrating over D, we have

$$\lambda Q = \int_D P \, dV, \tag{3.5}$$

where $\lambda = \sigma^2/g$. The difference between (3.4) and (3.5) is

$$(\lambda' - \lambda)Q = \int_{D'-D} P \, dV. \tag{3.6}$$

Since P and Q are positive, $\lambda' > \lambda$. The process can be continued, and Theorem 2 follows.

A good many results follow from the two theorems above. For instance, we have

THEOREM 3. If the horizontal dimensions of a basin is magnified (shrunk) by a constant factor, while the vertical dimension is unchanged, the frequency of any specified mode of water waves in it is reduced (increased).

We shall consider the case of horizontal magnification, since the case of horizontal shrinkage is entirely similar. Let the horizontally magnified basin be denoted by B' and the original basin by B. We introduce a third basin B'' obtained by shrinking B' in all directions uniformly, so that B'' is similar to B' but smaller, and in addition B'' and B have exactly the same free surface. Then by Theorem 1,

$$\sigma'^2 < \sigma''^2,$$

and since D obviously contains D'' (water-occupied domain in basin B''), by Theorem 2

$$\sigma''^2 < \sigma^2,$$

and Theorem 3 follows.

Since trapezoidal channels occur in practice very often, we shall indicate how to obtain upper and lower bounds for the frequency of the first sloshing mode of water waves in such a channel. For an upper bound, we can use a rectangular channel with the same width at the free surface as the trapezoidal channel and a depth equal to the maximum depth of the trapezoidal channel. For a sharp lower bound, we select a streamline in a rectangular channel of width b and depth d which is tangent to the trapezoidal boundary (of the crosssection of the channel under consideration) at the free surface and at the horizontal bottom (see Figure 1). The b and d have to be calculated to achieve this. By Theorem 2, the frequency of waves in this curvilinear channel, which is exactly the same as that in the rectangular channel for the same mode, provides the lower bound needed. Since the curvilinear channel deviates from the trapezoidal channel mostly near its corners, where the velocity is small, the lower bound is likely to be near the actual frequency for waves in the trapezoidal channel.

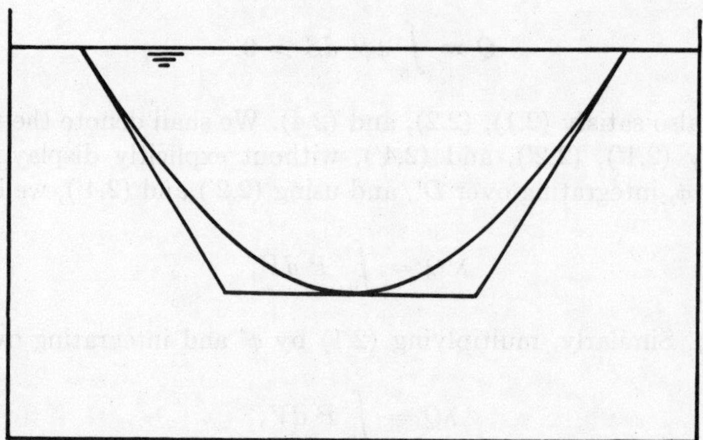

Fig. 1.   The curve is a streamline in sloshing motion of the first mode in the rectangular channel. The frequency of that motion provides a sharp lower bound for the first sloshing mode in the trapezoidal channel. The curve is tangent to the trapezoid at three points: two at the level of the free surface, one at the middle of the horizontal bottom of the trapezoid.

4. Gravity waves in superposed layers of homogeneous fluids. For superposed homogeneous layers of different densities, within each layer (2.1) and (2.2) still are to be satisfied, and (2.4) is still the free-surface condition. At an interface the conditions are

$$\sigma^2(\rho_l\phi_l - \rho_u\phi_u) = g(\rho_l - \rho_u)\phi_y , \qquad (\phi_l)_y = (\phi_u)_y = \phi_y . \tag{4.1}$$

where l means "lower" and u means "upper". One can easily verify that Theorem 1 is still true, and that Theorem 2 is still true if we require that the interfaces as well as the free surface must remain identical for the two basins under comparison. Under this requirement, we can compare two neighboring states as the vertical scale is slightly changed, and by continuation reach Theorem 3. In this comparison, analytic continuations of ϕ_l or ϕ_u beyond an interface are needed if it is raised or lowered.

5. Differential system governing internal waves. Let the density in the absence of wave motion be $\rho_0(y)$, and the pressure be p_0 . Then

$$dp_0/dy = -g\rho_0 . \tag{5.1}$$

Let the velocity components in the directions of increasing x, y, and z be denoted by u, v, and w, and let p and ρ be the perturbations in pressure and in density, respectively. The linearized equations of motion are, after (5.1) has been used,

$$\rho_0 u_t = -p_x , \tag{5.2}$$

$$\rho_0 v_t = -p_y - g\rho, \tag{5.3}$$

$$\rho_0 w_t = -p_z . \tag{5.4}$$

The linearized equation of incompressibility is

$$\rho_t + v\rho_0' = 0, \tag{5.5}$$

where the prime indicates differentiation with respect to y. The equation of continuity is then, since the fluid is incompressible,

COMPARISON THEOREMS

391

$$u_x + v_y + w_z = 0. \tag{5.6}$$

Again, the time factor $\exp(-i\sigma t)$ will be assumed for all perturbation quantities. Then

$$i\sigma\rho_0 u = p_x , \qquad i\sigma\rho_0 w = p_z , \tag{5.7}$$

and combination of (5.3) and (5.5) gives

$$v = -\frac{i\sigma p_y}{\sigma^2 \rho_0 + g\rho_0'}. \tag{5.8}$$

Substituting (5.7) and (5.8) into (5.6), we have

$$p_{xx} + p_{zz} + \sigma^2 \rho_0 \frac{\partial}{\partial y} \frac{p_y}{\sigma^2 \rho_0 + g\rho_0'} = 0. \tag{5.9}$$

If the direction numbers of the normal to a stationary rigid boundary are (l, m, n), the boundary condition there is

$$lu + mv + nw = 0. \tag{5.10}$$

At a free surface the pressure is constant. But the pressure variation has two parts: the perturbation pressure p and the variation of the mean pressure due to the free-surface displacement (denoted by η). Hence the condition on pressure at the free surface is

$$p - g\rho_0\eta = 0. \tag{5.11}$$

The kinematic condition at the free surface is

$$v = \eta_t . \tag{5.12}$$

Combination of (5.8), (5.11), and (5.12) gives

$$p = \frac{g\rho_0 p_y}{\sigma^2 \rho_0 + g\rho_0'}. \tag{5.13}$$

It is well known, and it can be easily shown, that if ρ_0' is never positive σ^2 is positive (i.e., σ is real), and that, for truly internal waves,

$$\sigma^2 < -\max(g\rho_0'/\rho_0). \tag{5.14}$$

6. Comparison theorems for internal waves.   For the case of a horizontal channel with depth varying with z but not with x (measured along the axis of the channel), the variation of σ^2 with k^2, with k denoting the wave number in the x-direction, has been discussed by Yih [3], who found that for the same mode

$$\frac{d\sigma^2}{d(k^2)} > 0, \qquad \frac{dc^2}{d(k^2)} < 0, \tag{6.1}$$

where $kc = \sigma$. We shall not repeat the discussion.

We shall now show

THEOREM 4. σ^2 increases if ρ_0 is reduced by a constant or if both ρ_0 and ρ_0' (henceforth assumed negative) are everywhere decreased, that is, if ρ_0 is everywhere decreased in such a way that $-\rho_0'$ is everywhere increased.

To prove this theorem let us compare two wave motions, one with

$$\rho_0 = \rho_1 , \qquad p = p_1 , \qquad \sigma = \sigma_1 .$$

and the other with

$$\rho_0 = \rho_2 \leq \rho_1 , \qquad p = p_2 , \qquad \sigma = \sigma_2 , \qquad \rho_2' \leq \rho_1' < 0.$$

The two motions are near each other in the sense that ρ_2 is only slightly less than ρ_1 for all values of y, so that ϕ_1 is nearly the same as ϕ_2, and σ_1 nearly the same as σ_2.

We shall first treat the case in which no free surface or other density discontinuities exist. Consider the integral (with V denoting the fluid volume, as before)

$$\int_V \left[\left(\frac{1}{\rho_1} p_2 p_{1x} \right)_x + \left(\frac{1}{\rho_1} p_2 p_{1z} \right)_z + \sigma_1^2 \left(\frac{p_2 p_{1y}}{\sigma_1^2 \rho_1 + g \rho_1'} \right)_y \right] dV, \tag{6.2}$$

and another in which the subscripts 1 and 2 are exchanged. Since p_1 satisfies (5.9) with σ replaced by σ_1 and ρ_0 by ρ_1, and p_2 satisfies (5.9) with σ replaced by σ_2 and ρ_0 by ρ_2, (6.2) gives, upon use of the Gauss-Green theorem,

$$i\sigma_1 \int_S p_2 (lu_1 + mv_1 + nw_1) \, dS$$

$$= \int_V \left[\frac{1}{\rho_1} (p_{1x} p_{2x} + p_{1z} p_{2z}) + \frac{\sigma_1^2}{\sigma_1^2 \rho_1 + g \rho_1'} p_{1y} p_{2y} \right] dV, \tag{6.3}$$

where S is the surface of V. From the integral which is (6.2) with subscripts 1 and 2 exchanged, we obtain the result

$$i\sigma_2 \int_S p_1 (lu_2 + mv_2 + nw_2) \, dS$$

$$= \int_V \left[\frac{1}{\rho_2} (p_{1x} p_{2x} + p_{1z} p_{2z}) + \frac{\sigma_2^2}{\sigma_2^2 \rho_2 + g \rho_2'} p_{1y} p_{2y} \right] dV. \tag{6.4}$$

The left-hand sides of (6.3) and (6.4) are zero because of (5.10), the condition at the rigid boundary. The difference between (6.3) and (6.4) is

$$\int_V \left(\frac{1}{\rho_2} - \frac{1}{\rho_1} \right) (p_{1x} p_{2x} + p_{1z} p_{2z}) \, dV$$

$$+ \int_V \frac{\sigma_1^2 \sigma_2^2 (\rho_1 - \rho_2) + g(\sigma_2^2 \rho_1' - \sigma_1^2 \rho_2')}{(\sigma_2^2 \rho_2 + g \rho_2')(\sigma_1^2 \rho_1 + g \rho_1')} p_{1y} p_{2y} \, dV = 0. \tag{6.5}$$

Upon making ρ_2 close to ρ_1, p_1 is close to p_2, σ_1 is close to σ_2, etc. Then quantities like $p_{1x} p_{2x}$ and so on are positive everywhere except possibly near the stagnation points of the smaller basin, where their absolute values are small. Hence they are positive on the average. Then, since

$$0 < \rho_2 \leq \rho_1 \quad \text{and} \quad \rho_2' \leq \rho_1' < 0, \tag{6.6}$$

(6.5) shows that σ_2^2 must be greater than σ_1^2.

If there is a free surface, the left-hand sides of (6.3) and (6.4) are, upon the use of the free-surface boundary condition (5.13), with ρ_0 identified with ρ_1 or ρ_2, σ identified with σ_1 or σ_2,

$$\int_{S'} \frac{g \rho_2 \sigma_1^2 v_1 v_2}{\sigma_1 \sigma_2} \, dS', \qquad \int_{S'} \frac{g \rho_1 \sigma_2^2 v_1 v_2}{\sigma_1 \sigma_2} \, dS' \tag{6.7}$$

respectively, and the term

$$\int_{S'} \frac{g(\sigma_1^2 \rho_2 - \sigma_2^2 \rho_1)v_1 v_2}{\sigma_1 \sigma_2}\, dS' \tag{6.8}$$

must be added to the right-hand side of (6.5), with S' denoting that part of S that is the free surface. The conclusion that

$$\sigma_2^2 > \sigma_1^2 \tag{6.9}$$

therefore remains valid.

If there are internal density discontinuities terms like (6.8) but somewhat more complicated must be added to the right-hand side of (6.5), and the conclusion (6.9) remains valid.

Note that since the conclusion (6.9) is reached when (6.6) holds, by a comparison of neighboring states, it is automatically guaranteed that wave motions of the same mode are being compared. Furthermore, the restriction of neighboring states can be removed by continuation *through neighboring states*, so that the same mode is maintained while the two motions finally compared are no longer in neighboring states, that is, ρ_1 is no longer near ρ_2. (Mathematically speaking, ρ_1 being near ρ_2 means $(\rho_1 - \rho_2)\rho_1^{-1} \ll 1$.)

Since for truly internal waves (5.14) holds, for small ρ_0' the vertical velocity at the free surface is very small, as can be seen from (5.13) and (5.8). Therefore when studying truly internal waves (i.e., with free-surface waves excluded) we can treat the free surface as rigid, and replace (5.13) by

$$p_\nu = 0. \tag{6.10}$$

We shall now assume ρ_0 to be continuous, and attempt to see what effect a change of shape or size of the fluid-occupied domain of a basin has on the frequency of internal waves. For this purpose we need to use the Boussinesq approximation, which amounts to ignoring the variation of ρ_0 except for the term $g\rho_0'$ in (5.8) and (5.9). Whether we consider an exponentially stratified fluid with

$$\rho_0 = C \exp(-\beta y) \tag{6.11}$$

or a linearly stratified fluid with

$$\rho_0 = C(1 - \beta y), \tag{6.12}$$

after the Boussinesq approximation is made we can write (5.9) as

$$p_{xx} + p_{zz} - \lambda^2 p_{yy} = 0, \tag{6.13}$$

where

$$\lambda^2 = \frac{\sigma^2}{g\beta - \sigma^2}. \tag{6.14}$$

Let the boundary of the basin be given by

$$F(x, y, z) = 0. \tag{6.15}$$

For an open basin of the simplest shapes, z is a single-valued function of x and y. But it can be multi-valued. For a closed basin flowing full, it is at least double-valued. The condition at the boundary, (5.10), can now be written as

                                CHIA-SHUN YIH

$$F_x p_x + F_z p_z - \lambda^2 F_y p_y = 0. \tag{6.16}$$

Since we treat a free surface as a rigid surface and therefore a part of (6.15), we can absorb (6.10) into (6.16).

Inspection of (6.13) and (6.16) gives

THEOREM 5.   With the actual ρ_0 given by (6.11) or (6.12) maintained unchanged (i.e., with βy equal to $\beta' y'$ after a scale magnification or reduction), if any horizontal dimension of the basin is multiplied by M and the vertical dimension by N, i.e., if x, y, and z in $F(x, y, z)$ are replaced by

$$x/M, \qquad y/N, \qquad z/M,$$

then λ^2 is multiplied by N^2/M^2.

Hence if the widening exceeds the deepening, λ^2 (hence σ^2) is reduced, if the deepening exceeds the widening, σ^2 is increased, and if the magnification (or reduction) of scale is uniform in all directions, $M = N$, and σ^2 remains unchanged.

REFERENCES

[1] H. Lamb, *Hydrodynamics*, Cambridge Univ. Press, 6th Ed., 1932
[2] N. N. Moiseev, Adv. Appl. Mech. 8, 241 (1964)
[3] C. -S. Yih, *Internal waves in channels of variable depth*, presented to 9th Symposium of Naval Hydro-dynamics, 1972, Paris

Proc. 14th Symposium of Naval Hydrodynamics, 1982

Binnie Waves

by
Chia-Shun Yih
The University of Michigan

Abstract

Surface waves created by water flowing in an open channel with
vertical side-walls and variable width are considered and analytical
solutions given. It is shown that there are infinitely many Froude
numbers, depending on the wavenumber of the channel-width variation
and on the transverse wavenumber, at which the amplitude of one of the
wave components becomes infinite. These critical Froude numbers are
interpreted physically. The waves created generally have a diamond
pattern.

The case of channels of varibale depth as well as variable width
is then investigated and the solutions given. Finally, internal waves
are treated briefly and some results presented.

I. INTRODUCTION

More than two decades ago Binnie (1960) observed self-induced surface waves in a channel with vertical corrugated side-walls. The longitudinal wavelengths of these waves were observed to be an integral multiple of the basic wavelength of the wall corrugation, and there were transverse wavenumbers as well, so that the waves observed have a diamond pattern in general. I believe that although there are papers in the literature dealing with corrugated walls Binnie's paper is the only one that deals with dispersive waves, which are much more interesting and richer in substance than the nondispersive sound waves.

In his brief analysis Binnie treated the side-walls as straight. In doing so he necessarily did not reveal the mechanism by which his waves are created and the amplitudes of the many wave components, each with a different transverse wavenumber, are determined. His corrugated walls serve merely to provide the basic longitudinal wavelength.

In this paper Binnie's waves will be given a more complete analysis and the analytical solutions presented. The waviness of the side-walls will be taken fully into account. It is found that resonance occurs at an infinite number of critical Froude numbers (or internal Froude numbers for the case of internal waves), at which the amplitude of one of the wave components becomes infinite. The critical Froude numbers are given a physical interpretation which illuminates their significance. For a given Froude number, there is in general one wave component with the maximum amplitude, and this component must be what Binnie observed. The analysis given here is capable of predicting which component will be dominant at a given Froude number.

The case of variable depth (as well as variable width) will then be considered, and similar analytical results given. Finally, internal waves in a channel with vertical side-walls and variable width will be briefly treated, and the results for the special case of two fluid layers of equal depth presented.

II. FORMULATION OF THE PROBLEM

The theory will be constructed on the assumption of irrotational flow. Let x, y, and z denote Cartesian coordinates measured in units of L, which is the half-width of the channel at some section, and let U be the mean velocity in the x-direction. Then the velocity components u, v, and w, for the directions of increasing x, y, and z, respectively, will be measured in units of U and the velocity potential ϕ will be measured in units of UL. We shall then treat the Cartesian coordinates, the velocity components, and ϕ as dimensionless.

91

We have

$$(u, v, w) = (\phi_x, \phi_y, \phi_z), \tag{1}$$

where the subscripts denote partial differentiation. Since the fluid is assumed incompressible, ϕ satisfies the Laplace equation

$$\phi_{xx} + \phi_{yy} + \phi_{zz} = 0. \tag{2}$$

Let the displacement of the free surface above its mean position (or the plane of the free surface if there were no flow) be denoted by ζ, measured in units of L. Then the kinematic condition of the free surface is

$$u\zeta_x + v\zeta_y = w, \tag{3}$$

and the Bernoulli equation written for the free surface is

$$u^2 + v^2 + w^2 + 2F^{-2}\zeta = \text{constant}, \quad F^2 = U^2/gL. \tag{4}$$

Combining (3) and (4), and using (1), we have the free-surface condition

$$\left(\phi_x \frac{\partial}{\partial x} + \phi_y \frac{\partial}{\partial y}\right)(\phi_x^2 + \phi_y^2 + \phi_z^2) + 2F^{-2}\phi_z = 0. \tag{5}$$

If the dimensional mean water depth is h, and

$$d = \frac{h}{L}, \tag{6}$$

then the condition at the bottom is

$$\phi_z = 0 \quad \text{at} \quad z = -d \tag{7}$$

The condition at the side-walls is

92

$$\phi_n = 0 \tag{8}$$

where n is measured in a direction normal to the side-walls. Equation (2), (5), (7), and (8) govern the fluid motion in the channel.

III.   A TRANSFORMATION FOR THE CHANNEL SHAPE

So far we have not accounted for the variation of the channel width. This variation is represented by the transformation

$$x + iy = \alpha + i\beta + a \sin k(\alpha + i\beta)$$

or

$$x = \alpha + a \sin k\alpha \cosh k\beta,$$

$$y = \beta + a \cos k\alpha \sinh k\beta, \tag{9}$$

where k is the wavenumber of the channel-width variation, and a its amplitude. The Jacobin of the transformation is

$$J = \frac{\partial(x,y)}{\partial(\alpha,\beta)} = 1 + 2ak \cos k\alpha \cosh k\beta + a^2 k^2 (\cos^2 k\alpha + \sinh^2 k\beta). \tag{10}$$

The boundary of the channel is given by $\beta = \pm 1$.
In terms of α, β, and z, (2) and (5) become

$$\frac{1}{J}(\phi_{\alpha\alpha} + \phi_{\beta\beta}) + \phi_{zz} = 0, \tag{11}$$

and

$$\frac{1}{J}(\phi_\alpha \frac{\partial}{\partial\alpha} + \phi_\beta \frac{\partial}{\partial\beta})[\frac{1}{J}(\phi_\alpha^2 + \phi_\beta^2) + \phi_z^2] + 2F^{-2}\phi_z = 0 \tag{12}$$

The condition (7) remains the same, but (8) is now replaced by

$$\phi_\beta = 0 \text{ at } \beta = \pm 1. \tag{13}$$

93

The governing system now consists of (11), (12), (13), and (7).

VI. SOLUTION OF THE PROBLEM

It is evident that the amplitude of the waves produced by the channel-width variation is proportional to the amplitude of that variation. Hence we assume

$$\phi = \phi_0 + a\phi_1 + a^2\phi_2 + \ldots \tag{14}$$

Since in the absence of any width variation the flow is just a uniform flow in the x or α direction, it is evident that

$$\phi_0 = \alpha. \tag{15}$$

Substituting (14) and (15) into (11) and (12), and sorting out the terms of first order in a (Remember that J contains a, α, and β.), we have

$$\phi_{1\alpha\alpha} + \phi_{1\beta\beta} + \phi_{1zz} = 0 \tag{16}$$

$$\phi_{1\alpha\alpha} + F^{-2}\phi_{1z} = -k^2 \sin k\alpha \cosh k\beta. \tag{17}$$

The solution satisfying (16), (7), and (13) is, since $\cosh k\beta$ is even in β,

$$\phi_1 = \sum_{n=0}^{\infty} B_n \sin k\alpha \cos n\pi\beta \cosh \gamma_n (z + d) , \tag{18}$$

where

$$\gamma_n = (k^2 + n^2\pi^2)^{1/2} \tag{19}$$

and B_n is determined by (17). The result is

94

$$B_n C_n = -k^2 \int_{-1}^{1} \cos n\pi\beta \, \cosh k\beta \, d\beta = \frac{2(-1)^{n+1} k^3 \sinh k}{\gamma_n^2} , \quad (20)$$

where

$$C_n = -k^2 \cosh \gamma_n d + F^{-2} \gamma_n \sinh \gamma_n d. \quad (21)$$

To the order a, then, ζ is determined from (4) to be

$$\zeta = -ak^{-1} \cos k\alpha \sum_{n=0}^{\infty} B_n \gamma_n \sinh \gamma_n d \cos n\pi\beta \quad (22)$$

which gives a diamond pattern for the free-surface displacement. In obtaining (22), we have made use of the result

$$\phi_x^2 + \phi_y^2 = \frac{1}{J}(\phi_\alpha^2 + \phi_\beta^2) ,$$

as well as (20), which gives the Fourier coefficients for $\cosh k\beta$. The free-surface displacement is shown in Figure 1 for one half wavelength of the channel-width variation.

Note that as $C_n \to 0$, $B_n \to \infty$. The infinite number of values of F given by $C_n = 0$ then are critical values, at which resonance occurs. For $C_n = 0$,

$$F^2 = \frac{\gamma_n^2}{k^2} \frac{\tanh \gamma_n d}{\gamma_n} ,$$

or

$$\frac{k}{\gamma_n} U = \left(\frac{g \, h \, \tanh \gamma_n d}{\gamma_n d} \right)^{1/2} . \quad (23)$$

In (23), k/γ_n is the cosine of the angle between the α-direction and the direction normal to the wave fronts of the slanted waves with wavenumber $\gamma_n d$ (which is the wavenumber non-dimensionalized with the length h instead of the length L), and the right-hand side is precisely the wave speed of these waves. Thus, the n-th critical value of U is such that its component normal to the fronts of the waves with wave-

95

number $\gamma_n d$ is equal to their wave speed. When U has such a value, the amplitude of the γ_n-waves (with wavenumber γ_n or $\gamma_n d$, depending on the length scale used to non-dimensionalize the wavenumber) becomes infinite, and resonance occurs. This is reminiscent of the resonance that occurs when a layer of water flows over a wavy bottom with a speed equal to the speed of waves with the same wavenumber as the bottom. But now there are infinitely many critical values of U, and slanted waves are involved, so that the resonance is somewhat more subtle.

Higher approximations can be carried out systematically. For the sake of brevity we shall refrain from doing so, but shall mention that at the second approximation two new longitudinal wavenumbers will be produced: zero and 2k. The former give no finite critical values for V, whereas the latter does -- in much the same way that the basic longitudinal wavenumber k gives rise to such critical values, as shown in the foregoing. At the third approximation the new wavenumber 3k is brought forth, which gives rise to another set of critical values for V. Thus there are infinitely many sequences of critical values of U, each sequence consisting of an infinite number of such critical values.

V. CHANNELS WITH VARIABLE WIDTH AND DEPTH

Since natural streams have variable depth, often with a maximum depth much smaller than their width, we shall use the shallow-water theory to deal with the case of variable depth. We shall retain the meanings of the symbols used so far, but d now is given by

$$d = 1 - \beta^2. \tag{24}$$

The total (dimensionless) depth is

$$D = d + \zeta, \tag{25}$$

and the equation of continuity is

$$\frac{\partial}{\partial x}(D\phi_x) + \frac{\partial}{\partial y}(D\phi_y) = 0, \tag{26}$$

and the Bernoulli equation for the free surface is

$$\phi_x^2 + \phi_y^2 + 2F^{-2}\zeta = \text{constant}, \tag{27}$$

where ϕ_z^2 is neglected, in consistency with the shallow-water theory.
Converting (26) and (27) to the α-β coordinates, we have

$$(d\phi_\beta)_\beta + d\phi_{\alpha\alpha} + \phi_\alpha \zeta_\alpha = 0, \tag{28}$$

and

$$\frac{1}{J}(\phi_\alpha^2 + \phi_\beta^2) + 2F^{-2}\zeta = \text{constant}, \tag{29}$$

where J is given by (10).

Using (10), (14), (15), and (29), we have

$$\zeta_\alpha = -aF^2\phi_{1\alpha\alpha} - aF^2 k^2 \sin k\alpha \cosh k\beta + 0(a^2). \tag{30}$$

Substituting (14), (15), (24), and (30) into (28), extracting terms of
order a, and writing

$$\phi_1 = \sin k\alpha \, f(\beta), \tag{31}$$

we obtain

$$[(1 - \beta^2)f']' + [k^2 F^2 - k^2(1 - \beta^2)]f = F^2 k^2 \cosh k\beta, \tag{32}$$

where the primes indicate differentiation with respect to β. Equation
(32) is singular at $\beta = \pm 1$. What is needed is a nonsingular solution
of (32). This solution can always be found, but if k^2 is not small
compared with 1 much computation is needed. Fortunately for most
natural streams k^2 is small, permitting a simple calculation.

Consider the equation

$$[(1 - \beta^2)G']' + [\lambda - k^2(1 - \beta^2)]G = 0, \tag{33}$$

and seek nonsingular solutions of this equation. Let

$$\lambda = \mu_0 + k^2\mu_1 + k^4\mu_2 + \ldots, \tag{34}$$

97

$$G = g_0 + k^2 g_1 + k^4 g_2 + \ldots . \tag{35}$$

Substituting (34) and (35) into (33), and collecting terms not containing k, we obtain the Legendre equation for g_0. For a nonsingular solution, then,

$$\mu_0 = n(n + 1), \quad g_0 = P_n(\beta) , \tag{36}$$

where $P_n(\beta)$ is the n-th Legendre polynomial in β. Collecting terms of order k^2, we obtain

$$Lg_1 \equiv [(1 - \beta^2)g_1']' + n(n + 1)g_1 = (1 - \beta^2)g_0 - \mu_1 g_0 . \tag{37}$$

first, the requirement that g_1 be nonsingular demands that the right-hand side of (37) be orthogonal to g_0. (To prove this statement, one needs only to multiply (37) by g_0 and integrate, by parts if necessary, between -1 and 1.) This determines μ_1 and g_1 in principle. In practice it is easier to use the formulas on page 115 of Jahnke and Emde (1945), for instance, and obtain

$$L \left\{ \frac{1}{6+4n} \left(\beta^2 P_n - \frac{2n}{2n-1} \beta P_{n-1} \right) \right\} = - \beta^2 P_n + \frac{2n^2+2n-1}{(2n+3)(2n-1)} P_n ,$$

so that

$$g_1 = \frac{1}{6+4n} \left(\beta^2 P_n - \frac{2n}{2n-1} \beta P_{n-1} \right) , \tag{38}$$

$$\mu_1 = 1 - \frac{2n^2+2n-1}{(2n+3)(2n-1)} . \tag{39}$$

For a given n, we shall denote the corresponding λ and G by λ_n and G_n, respectively. Since the right-hand side of (32) is even, we have $n = 2m$, where m is an integer, including zero, and

$$f(\beta) = \sum_{m=0}^{\infty} B_{2m} G_{2m} . \tag{40}$$

98

Substituting this into (32), and using the orthogonality of the eigen-functions G_{2m}, we obtain

$$B_{2m} (k^2 F^2 - \lambda_{2m}) \int_{-1}^{1} G_{2m}^2 \, d\beta = F^2 k^2 \int_{-1}^{1} \cosh k\beta \, G_{2m} \, d\beta, \qquad (41)$$

which determine B_{2m}. Then (40), (31), and

$$\phi = \alpha + a\phi_1$$

give the solution up to $O(a)$. We note that stopping at terms of $O(k^2)$ involves an error of $O(k^4)$, which for $k = 1/4$ is negligible, and for $k = 1/2$ is of the order of 0.06.

Let the two integrals in (41) be denoted by I_1 and I_2 (I_1 for the left-hand side), we obtain the following table, for n up to 4.

TABLE 1. Values of Integrals

k	n	0	2	4
1/4	I_1	2.014	0.399	0.222
	I_2	2.028	0.006	0.000
1/2	I_1	2.056	0.395	0.222
	I_2	2.114	0.022	0.000

For $k^2 F^2 = \lambda_{2m}$, $m = 0, 1, 2, \ldots$, there is again resonance. The physical interpretation for these critical values is analogous to that for the case of vertical side-walls, but the arguments lose some sharpness due to the fact that the Legendre polynomials cannot be easily combined with $\sin k\alpha$ or $\cos k\alpha$ to form a sine or cosine function which is easily seen to represent waves.

VI. INTERNAL WAVES

Since it is easier to create internal waves of large amplitudes, internal waves created in channels of variable width by flowing water will be briefly discussed. The solution for internal waves so created can be obtained by the same approach as described in Sections 2-4. The results for the case of two layers of fluid of the same depth h and with density ρ' for the upper layer and density ρ for the lower layer will be given here, because they are obtainable from (18) - (22) upon simple modifications of coefficients. If in the C_n the F^{-2} is replaced by $F_i^{-2} = \frac{\rho - \rho'}{\rho + \rho'} F^{-2}$, and then the B_n determined by (20) is multiplied by $\frac{\rho - \rho'}{\rho + \rho'}$, (18) and (22) will give the solutions for ϕ (of the lower layer) and ζ. As for ϕ', the velocity potential for the upper layer, it is

$$\phi' = - \sum_{n=0}^{\infty} B_n \sin k\alpha \cos n\pi\beta \cosh \gamma_n (z - d), \tag{42}$$

where B_n is the modified B_n obtained by the process mentioned in the fore-going.

Finally, we note that the theory is not merely for supercritical flows, and that when k is large waves of large amplitude can occur even at subcritical speeds. The figure given in this paper is for supercritical speeds, for the F would be larger than 1 if it were based on the mean depth, and the pattern agree qualitatively with that obtained from the classical shallow-water theory at supercritical speed and for vertical side walls. But this should not obscure the fact that the present theory is for all Froude numbers, however large or small.

We note also that Binnie (1960) observed time-periodic oscillations in his waves. These are freely propagating waves with longitudinal wavelengths which are integral multiples of the wave length of the corrugation and transverse wave numbers (denoted by n here). They are not bound to the corrigations studied in this paper, and their production is presumably due to some mechanism of instability not discussed here.

ACKNOWLEDGMENT

This work has been supported by the Office of Naval Research. Marc Ingber assisted the author by producing the figures in the table.

REFERENCES

1. Binnie, A.M. (1960). Self-induced waves in a conduit with corrugated walls. I. Experiments with water in an open horizontal channel with vertically corrugated sides. Proc. Roy. Soc. A, <u>259</u>, 18-27.

2. Jahnke, E. and F. Emde, <u>Table of Functions</u>, Dover, New York, 1945.

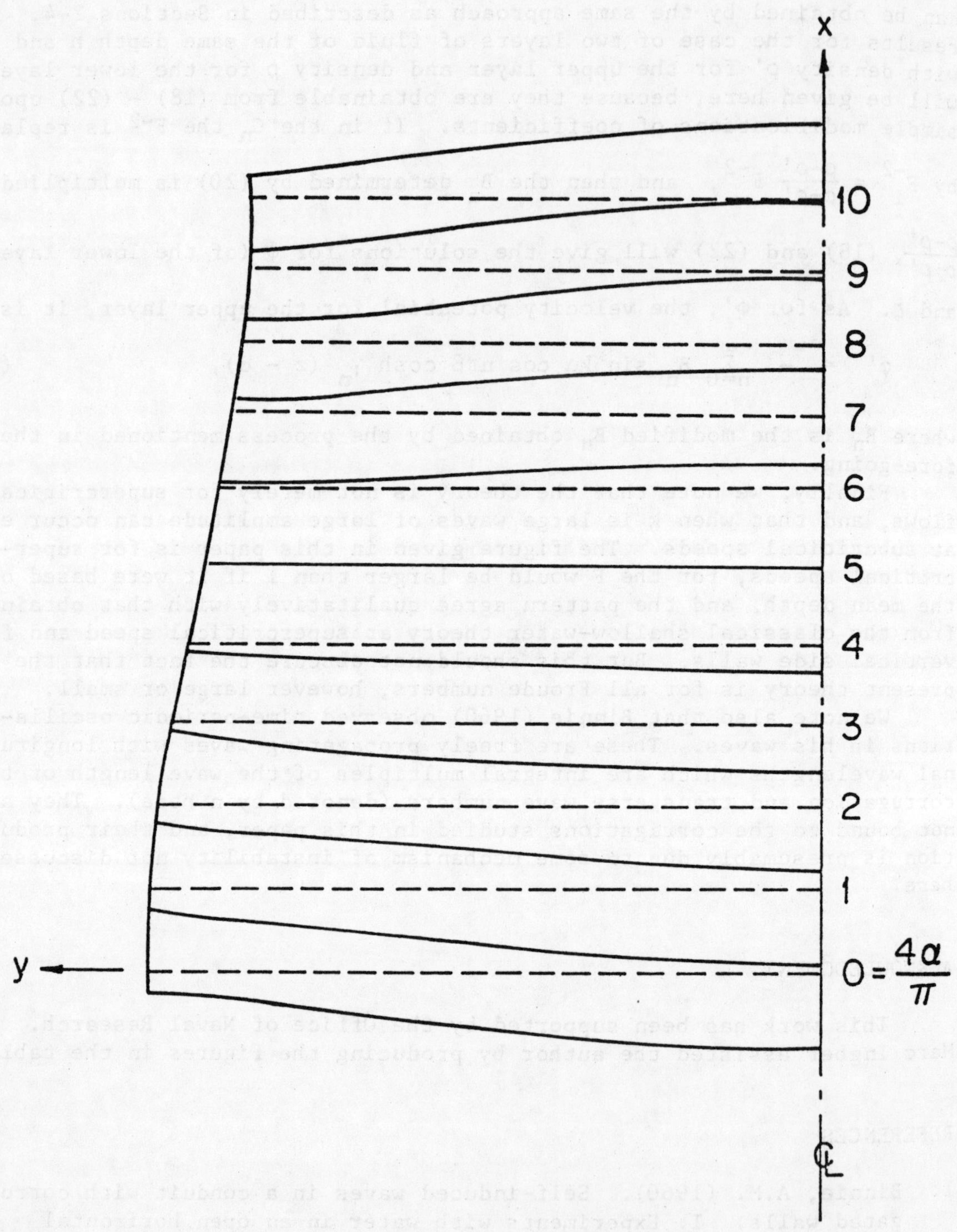

Figure 1. Graphs showing the free surface, at F = 2, k = 0.4, d = 0.2. The maximum dimensionless ζ/a is 0.242, at $k\alpha = \pi$ (or $4\alpha/\pi = 10$) and $\beta = 0$. On $k\alpha = 0.5\pi$, $\zeta = 0$. The dimensionless ζ/a is plotted above or below the dotted lines. The figure can be reflected across the planes $\alpha = 0$ and $\beta = 0$ sequentially to produce the free surface for a whole wavelength and for the whole channel.

101

Discussion

A.T. Chwang (University of Iowa)

Regarding the question of resonance, I would imagine that for a simply divergent or convergent channel with straight side walls, there would be a continuous spectrum of resonant frequencies. Would you please comment on it and tell me if I am wrong.

L.J. Doctors (University of New South Wales)

Professor Yih takes into account the effect of the wavy channel walls by means of the transformation given by Equation (9).

Since the amplitude of the waviness in the wall is considered to be small, it would also seem possible to represent this effect by means of a source distribution on the walls. To first order, this source distribution would be constant with respect to depth below the free surface but vary along the channel.

Could Professor Yih comment on this approach and compare it with his own? It should be added that an infinite set of image source distributions would be required—as is usual with tank problems.

E. Palm (University of Oslo)

Since the driving mechanism for the waves is revealed mathematically in the form of a forcing term in the free-surface boundary conditions, should not these waves formally be closely related to waves due to pressure applied on the free surface?

Author's Reply

C.-S. Yih (University of Michigan)

To T. Chwang

For a divergent or convergent channel one can use a different conformal mapping from Equation (9) in my paper, and then the solution would involve Fourier integrals with a continuous spectrum in k, with the Fourier coefficients to be determined. The very interesting thing is that the value of k that, if discrete, would cause resonance, will now give the lee-wave (which, in general, has diamond patterns) components after the contraction or expansion.

102

To L.J. Doctors

Professor Doctors is right in saying that the effect of the wavy wall can be represented by sources and sinks. The strengths of these sources and sinks are independent of depth to the zeroth order, i.e., if the effect of surface waves is ignored, but will vary with depth already in a first-order calculation. For large composite wave number γ_n, this variation is confined to a thin layer near the free surface. For n = 0 and k (the longitudinal wave number) very small, the variation will be weak.

If the variation of the channel width is periodic but otherwise arbitrary, one can use a Fourier series in my approach, and if it is not periodic, under certain restrictions a Fourier integral can be used. I prefer this approach to using sources and sinks, because it is simpler and more elegant, if I may say so. While the method of sources and sinks can always be applied, it is cumbersome. Among other things, one has to calculate for and trace out the boundary shape from the source-sink distribution, which is a nuisance.

To E. Palm

Professor Palm rightly perceives the analogy of the driving mechanism given in my paper with a pressure distribution applied at the free surface of water flowing in a straight channel. Indeed, Equation (17) indicates this analogy, with the right-hand side, which arises in a roundabout way from the variation in channel width, standing for the fictitious pressure distribution.

WAVES IN OPEN CHANNELS

By Jinsung Shi[1] and Chia-Shun Yih[2]

ABSTRACT: Gravity waves in trapezoidal channels and channels with curved bottoms, including sloshing, longitudinal, and combined modes, are treated. Analytical-numerical solutions are given for the wave frequency and the velocity potential for waves in trapezoidal channels, and analytical solutions based on the shallow-water theory are obtained for waves in curved channels.

INTRODUCTION

Although the subject of gravity waves is an old one in civil engineering, the frequency, wave velocity, and the velocity distribution of wave motion in open channels other than rectangular have seldom been accurately determined. The chief reason for this state of affairs is no doubt that when the channel is of variable depth the method of separation of variables cannot be applied, and immediately great difficulties are encountered in any attempt to determine these things, except in a few cases where exact solutions are available. Four decades ago, when Sir Richard V. Southwell was advocating his relaxation method, the possibility of solving thitherto unsolved problems of fluid flow caused some excitement. But the tedium of using the relaxation method seriously limited the usefulness of that method. It was after modern computers became widely available that numerical solutions of difficult problems in science and engineering became practical, and various numerical methods were rapidly developed for solving a wide variety of problems.

In this paper gravity waves in trapezoidal channels and curved channels will be studied, and rather extensive results will be given for the frequency, wave velocity, and the velocity distribution. Wave motion in a channel may be from one side of the channel to the other, in a to-and-fro fashion. If so, we call it a sloshing mode. Or the wavelength is along the longitudinal axis of the channel. Then we shall call the wave motion a longitudinal mode.

Both sloshing and longitudinal modes will be studied here. For sloshing modes the motion is two-dimensional, and the method of conformal mapping can be used to advantage in the case of trapezoidal channels. We shall, by successful transformations, transform the cross section of the channel from a trapezoid into a rectangle. Then the method of separation of variable can be applied to satisfy the Laplace equation and the conditions on the solid boundaries (i.e., bottom and side walls). That leaves only the free-surface condition to be satisfied. This satisfaction is brought about by numerical computation, thereby giving the frequency and the velocity distribution in the entire channel. For longitudinal modes

[1]Asst. Prof., Math. Dept., Tech. Univ. of Water Resources, Nanking, China.

[2]Stephen P. Timoshenko Univ. Prof. of Fluid Mech., Univ. of Michigan, Ann Arbor, Mich. 48109.

Note.—Discussion open until November 1, 1984. To extend the closing date one month, a written request must be filed with the ASCE Manager of Technical and Professional Publications. The manuscript for this paper was submitted for review and possible publication on June 7, 1983. This paper is part of the *Journal of Engineering Mechanics*, Vol. 110, No. 6, June, 1984. ©ASCE

the flow is three-dimensional, and the use of conformal mapping then gives no great advantage. We shall use a Bessel-function expansion to solve the problem. We arrange to have the boundary conditions on the side walls (as well as the Laplace equation) satisfied by this expansion, and endeavor to determine the coefficients of the terms to satisfy the condition at the bottom and the free-surface condition, giving, in the process, the frequency (and therefore the wave velocity) and the velocity distribution.

For curved channels we adopt the shallow-water theory, which is applicable in most practical cases of interest. The solutions for sloshing and longitudinal modes are entirely analytical, and will be given in terms of Legendre polynomials. We shall treat shallow curved channels only, which can always be approximated by a parabolic channel.

We emphasize that for trapezoidal channels numerical computation is not carried over the two-dimensional space occupied by water, only on the free surface for the sloshing modes, and only on the free surface and at the bottom for the longitudinal modes. Thus the use of classical-analytical methods had reduced an otherwise two-dimensional numerical computation to a one-dimensional one. For curved channels, if the shallow-water theory is not applied, a similar procedure can be devised, and if the shallow-water theory is used, a completely classical analysis will solve the problem. Of course, the method of integral equation has the same merit as the methods used here for trapezoidal channels, and a wider application as well.

FORMULATION OF PROBLEM OF WAVE MOTION

We shall assume irrotational motion for the fluid (water), which will be considered incompressible. Then a velocity potential ϕ exists, which satisfies the Laplace equation

$$\left(\frac{\partial^2}{\partial x^2} + \frac{\partial^2}{\partial y^2} + \frac{\partial^2}{\partial z^2}\right)\phi = 0 \dots\dots\dots\dots\dots\dots\dots\dots\dots (1)$$

in which x, y, and z are Cartesian coordinates, with x measured along the width of the channel, y measured vertically upward, and z measured along the longitudinal axis of the channel. At solid boundaries,

$$\frac{\partial \phi}{\partial n} = 0 \dots\dots\dots\dots\dots\dots\dots\dots\dots\dots\dots\dots\dots\dots\dots (2)$$

in which n is the distance along the normal to the solid boundary. The gravitational acceleration, acting in the direction of decreasing y, will be denoted by g, and the frequency of the wave motion will be denoted by $\sigma/2\pi$. On the free surface

$$\frac{\partial^2 \phi}{\partial t^2} + g \frac{\partial \phi}{\partial y} = 0 \dots\dots\dots\dots\dots\dots\dots\dots\dots\dots\dots\dots\dots (3)$$

In the next two sections dealing with wave motion in a channel of trapezoidal cross section, we shall use the maximum depth D of the trapezoid as the length scale. Then all distances will be measured in units of D, and the free-surface condition is, as is well known,

$$\lambda\phi = \frac{\partial\phi}{\partial y}, \quad \left(\lambda = \frac{\sigma^2 D}{g}\right) \dots\dots\dots\dots\dots\dots\dots\dots\dots\dots\dots\dots (4)$$

in which y is now dimensionless. Since Eqs. 1, 2, and 3 are linear in ϕ, whatever scale is chosen for ϕ will not affect the results. Indeed, the amplitude of wave motion, supposed to be small, is otherwise arbitrary, since the governing differential system, consisting of Eqs. 1, 2, and 3, is linear.

SLOSHING MODES IN TRAPEZOIDAL CHANNELS

Consider a symmetric trapezoidal channel shown in Fig. 1, in which D is the maximum depth, L is the minimum width, and α is the angle of inclination of the sides. We shall choose D as the length scale. Then the cross section of the channel is shown in Fig. 2(a), in dimensionless terms. We wish to transform the trapezoidal cross section to a rectangular one, as shown in Fig. 2(b), in which the (dimensionless) width is chosen to be 1, for convenience. The plane of the trapezoid will be called the z-plane and that of the rectangle the z'-plane, z and z' being the complex variables

$$z = x + iy; \quad z' = x' + iy' \dots\dots\dots\dots\dots\dots\dots\dots\dots\dots\dots\dots (5)$$

x and y being Cartesian coordinates in the z-plane; and x' and y' being those in the z'-plane. The origins of the coordinates are shown in Fig. 2. The use of z as a complex variable should not introduce confusion since the flow for sloshing modes is two-dimensional. The desired transformation is achieved through an intermediate complex variable t, and both the trapezoid and the rectangle will be transformed to the upper half of the t-plane.

The transformation between z and t is the well-known Schwartz-Christoffel transformation

$$z = M \int_0^t \frac{dt}{(t^2 - e^2)^\beta (t^2 - a^2)^{1-\beta}} = Mf(t) \dots\dots\dots\dots\dots\dots\dots\dots\dots (6)$$

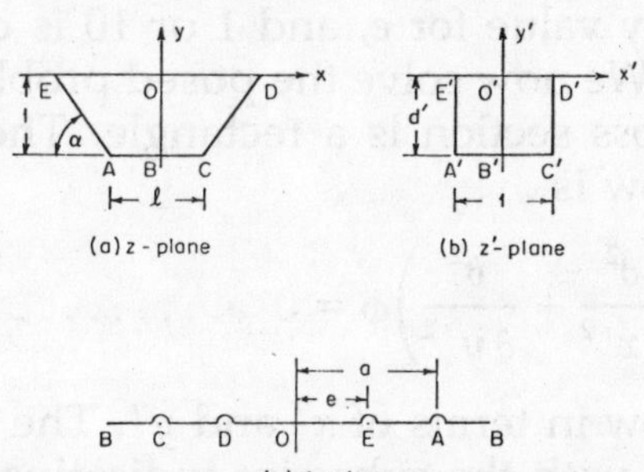

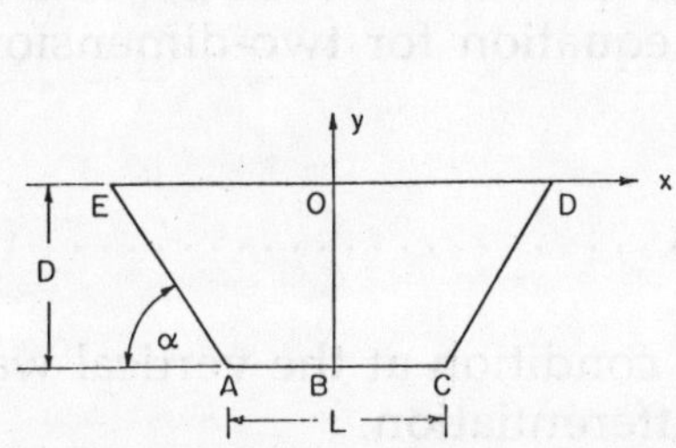

FIG. 1.—Definition Sketch for Trapezoidal Cross-Section of Channel

FIG. 2.—Definition Sketch in Dimensionless Terms: (a) z-Plane, Cross Section of Trapezoidal Channel; (b) z'-Plane, Transformed Cross Section of Channel; and (c) t-Plane

in which $\quad \beta = \dfrac{\pi - \alpha}{\pi}$ . . . . (7)

In Eq. 3, $e =$ the value of t at the point E in the t-plane, Fig. 2(c), and a = that of point A. The value of t is $-e$ at point D, and $-a$ at point C. We have used A, B, C, D, and E to denote corresponding points in the three complex-variable planes, without danger of ambiguity. Even though D has been used previously to denote the maximum depth of the (dimensional) trapezoid, the new use of D to indicate a point should not cause any confusion. Note that the lower limit in Eq. 3 means that when $t = 0$ we have $z = 0$, as desired.

We shall assume $e = 1$ or 10, as convenience dictates, and assign a real positive value for a. Then from Eq. 6 we have, by considering the position of point A in the z-plane,

$$-\frac{\ell}{2} - i = Mf(a) \dots \dots \dots \dots \dots \dots \dots \dots \dots \dots \dots \dots \dots \dots (8)$$

We determine M by demanding that the imaginary part of $Mf(a)$ be $-i$. Then if the real part of $Mf(a)$ is not equal to $-\ell/2$ we change the value of a until it is. The transformation between the z-plane and the t-plane is then complete. (And now a is determined for each value of L/D.)

To map the rectangle in Fig. 2(b) onto the upper half of the t-plane, we have

$$z' = M' \int_0^t \frac{dt}{(t^2 - e^2)^{1/2}(t^2 - a^2)^{1/2}} = M'g(t) \dots \dots \dots \dots \dots (9)$$

Choosing $\ell' = 1$, we have

$$-\frac{1}{2} - id' = M'g(a) \dots \dots \dots \dots \dots \dots \dots \dots \dots \dots \dots \dots \dots \dots (10)$$

Using the real part of Eq. 10, we determine M'. Then demanding the equality of the imaginary parts of Eq. 10, we have d', without trial. The mapping between the z' and t planes is now determined. The values of a, M, M', and d' for given values of α, L/D, and assumed values (1 or 10) of e are given in Table 1. Note that we have the freedom to choose any value for e, and 1 or 10 is chosen for convenience.

We now solve the posed problem in the z' plane, in which the channel cross section is a rectangle. The Laplace equation for two-dimensional flow is

$$\left(\frac{\partial^2}{\partial x'^2} + \frac{\partial^2}{\partial y'^2} \right) \phi = 0 \dots \dots \dots \dots \dots \dots \dots \dots \dots \dots \dots \dots (11)$$

now in terms of x' and y'. The boundary condition at the vertical walls is, with the subscript indicating partial differentiation,

$$\phi_{x'} = 0 \quad \text{at} \quad x' = \pm \frac{1}{2} \dots \dots \dots \dots \dots \dots \dots \dots \dots \dots \dots \dots (12)$$

and the boundary condition at the bottom is

$$\phi_{y'} = 0 \quad \text{at} \quad y' = -d' \dots \dots \dots \dots \dots \dots \dots \dots \dots \dots \dots \dots (13)$$

TABLE 1.—Parameters of Schwarz-Christoffel Transformation

α	L/D	e	a	M	M'	d'
(1)	(2)	(3)	(4)	(5)	(6)	(7)
60.00	0.50	1.00	8.5408	1.6606	2.7135	1.1226
60.00	0.75	1.00	3.8615	1.1156	1.2111	0.8657
60.00	1.00	1.00	2.4210	0.9019	0.7370	0.7081
60.00	1.25	1.00	1.7985	0.7985	0.5244	0.5998
60.00	1.50	1.00	1.4803	0.7403	0.4081	0.5206
60.00	1.50	10.00	14.8100	7.4045	4.0841	0.5208
60.00	1.75	10.00	13.0030	7.0551	3.3612	0.4598
60.00	2.00	10.00	11.9300	6.8300	2.8751	0.4120
60.00	2.25	10.00	11.2465	6.6996	2.5242	0.3726
60.00	2.50	10.00	10.8180	6.6102	2.2607	0.3404
45.00	0.50	1.00	5.3950	1.1441	1.7050	0.9748
45.00	0.75	1.00	2.8795	0.9078	0.8901	0.7678
45.00	1.00	1.00	1.9900	0.8005	0.5907	0.6378
45.00	1.25	1.00	1.5758	0.7467	0.4440	0.5471
45.00	1.50	1.00	1.3525	0.7143	0.3578	0.4793
45.00	1.50	10.00	13.5210	7.1430	3.5765	0.4792
45.00	1.75	10.00	12.2190	6.9447	3.0152	0.4263
45.00	2.00	10.00	11.4300	6.8061	2.6215	0.3841
45.00	2.25	10.00	10.9190	6.7384	2.3274	0.3488
45.00	2.50	10.00	10.5971	6.6859	2.0999	0.3195
30.00	0.50	1.00	4.2230	0.9832	1.3271	0.8951
30.00	0.75	1.00	2.3795	0.8522	0.7238	0.7020
30.00	1.00	1.00	1.7320	0.7903	0.5003	0.5851
30.00	1.25	1.00	1.4300	0.7616	0.3887	0.5052
30.00	1.50	1.00	1.2629	0.7431	0.3199	0.4446
30.00	1.50	10.00	12.6290	7.4315	3.1998	0.4446
30.00	1.75	10.00	11.6405	7.3169	2.7353	0.3966
30.00	2.00	10.00	11.0400	7.2236	2.3994	0.3579
30.00	2.25	10.00	10.6584	7.1989	2.1471	0.3257
30.00	2.50	10.00	10.4170	7.1692	1.9448	0.2985

Only the free-surface condition introduces any complications. This condition, given for the z-plane by Eq. 3, now has the form

$$\lambda\phi - \phi_y'\frac{\partial y'}{\partial y} = 0 \quad \text{at} \quad y' = 0 \dots\dots\dots\dots\dots\dots\dots\dots\dots\dots\dots (14)$$

since $\dfrac{\partial x'}{\partial y} = 0$ on $y' = 0$,

the transformation between z and z' being conformal. By virtue of Eqs. 6 and 9,

$$\frac{\partial y'}{\partial y} = \frac{M'}{M}\left(\frac{t^2 - e^2}{t^2 - a^2}\right)^{\beta - 0.5} = h(x') \dots\dots\dots\dots\dots\dots\dots\dots\dots\dots (15)$$

For a given t we obtain a given x' from Eq. 9. But this is done numerically, so that $h(x')$ is given numerically only.

We now take, for an n-term approximation and for antisymmetric

α	60°						
(1)	(2)	(3)	(4)	(5)	(6)	(7)	(8)
L/D	0.5	1	1.5	2	2.5	0.5	1
λ_1	1.538	1.162	0.910	0.717	0.580	0.882	0.721
λ_2	5.369	4.120	3.349	2.795	2.407	3.426	2.844
λ_3	8.832	6.783	5.529	4.626	4.001	5.816	4.831

sloshing modes.

$$\phi(x', y') = e^{-i\sigma t} \sum_{j=1}^{n} A_j \sin (2j - 1) \pi x' \cosh (2j - 1) \pi (y' + d') \dots (16)$$

which satisfies Eqs. 12 and 13. We substitute Eq. 16 into Eq. 14, and demand its satisfaction, thereby determining λ and A_n. The satisfaction of Eq. 14 can be accomplished by multiplying it by $\sin (2j - 1) \pi x'$ and integrating between $-1/2$ and $1/2$. But it turns out that the Gauss method of integration is much more accurate. This wonderful method (Lanczos (3), pp. 396–407) has the great advantage of having the accuracy of using $2n$ points for numerical integration when actually only n points are used. If the interval of integration of a function $Y = F(\zeta)$ is (b, c), and if n points are chosen at

$$\zeta_m = \frac{c + b}{2} + \frac{c - b}{2} \xi_m; \quad (m = 1, 2, \dots, n) \dots (17)$$

in which $\xi_m = $ the mth zero (or root) of the Legendre polynomial $P_n(\xi)$, we have

$$\int_b^c F(\zeta) d\zeta = \frac{c - b}{2} \sum_{j=1}^{n} w_j F(\zeta_j) \dots (18a)$$

In Eq. 18a, $w_m = $ the weight defined by

$$w_m = \int_{-1}^{1} \frac{1}{P'_n(\xi_j)} \frac{P_n(\xi)}{\xi - \xi_j} d\xi \dots (18b)$$

In our case here, ζ is x',

$$c = \frac{1}{2}; \quad b = -\frac{1}{2} \dots (18c)$$

and the function $F(\zeta)$ or $F(x')$ is the left-hand side of Eq. 14. Thus $F(x')$ contains λ to the first power. Since that is equal to zero, the condition given by Eq. 14, written over the free surface in the z'-plane as (as an approximation to Eq. 14)

$$\int_{-1/2}^{1/2} F(x') dx' = 0 \dots (18d)$$

amounts to $F(x'_j) = 0, j = 1, 2 \dots, n \dots (19)$

Antisymmetric Sloshing Modes

45°			30°				
(9)	(10)	(11)	(12)	(13)	(14)	(15)	(16)
1.5	2	2.5	0.5	1	1.5	2	2.5
0.600	0.490	0.409	0.477	0.413	0.364	0.303	0.258
2.444	2.094	1.852	2.116	1.861	1.674	1.456	1.290
4.145	3.572	3.154	3.887	3.411	3.034	2.667	2.376

and the weights w_m become immaterial in this case. These n equations have the unknowns A_j, with j ranging from $1-n$. Since these equations are linear and homogenous, the determinant of the coefficients of the unknowns (A_j) must be zero for a non-trivial solution to exist. This gives the eigenvalues for λ, which we shall denote by λ_1, λ_2, ..., λ_n. When any of these eigenvalues are substituted for λ in Eqs. 19, and any $n-1$ equations are taken, we can solve, upon putting $A_1 = 1$, for A_2, A_3,

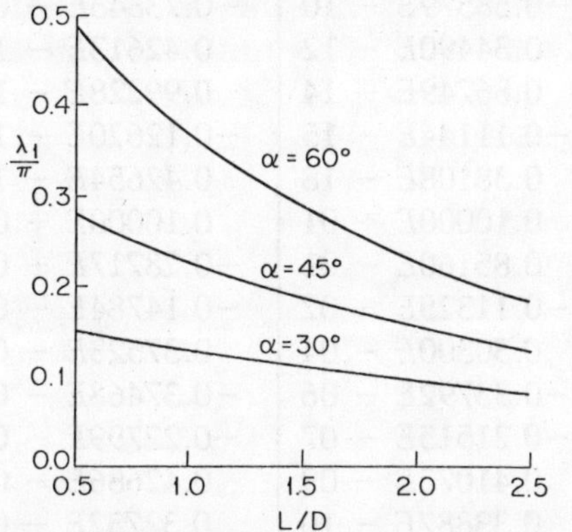

FIG. 3.—Eigenvalue λ_1 of $\lambda(= \sigma^2 D/g)$ for First Sloshing Mode in Trapezoidal Channels. α = Angle of Inclination of Sides

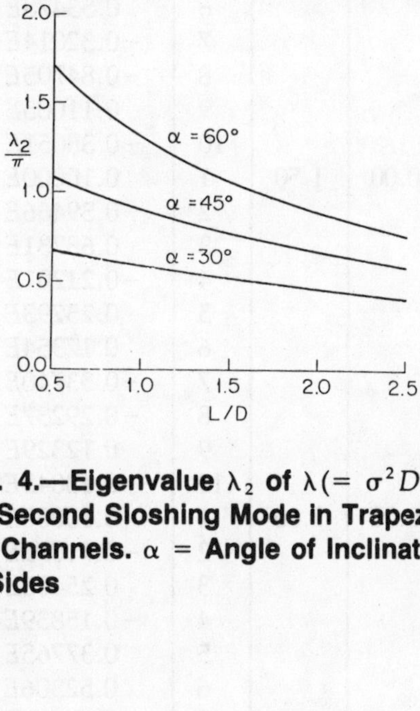

FIG. 4.—Eigenvalue λ_2 of $\lambda(= \sigma^2 D/g)$ for Second Sloshing Mode in Trapezoidal Channels. α = Angle of Inclination of Sides

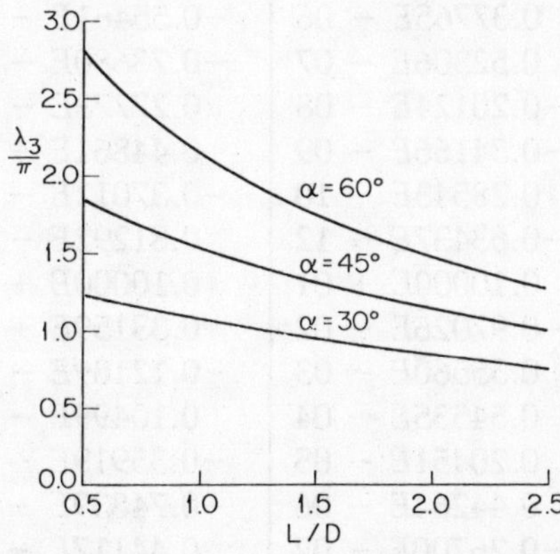

FIG. 5.—Eigenvalue λ_3 of $\lambda(= \sigma^2 D/g)$ for Third Sloshing Mode in Trapezoidal Channels. α = Angle of Inclination of Sides

TABLE 3.—Values of A_j for Antisymmetric Sloshing Modes

α (1)	L/D (2)	j (3)	$n = 1$ (4)	$n = 2$ (5)	$n = 3$ (6)
60.00	0.50	1	$0.10000E + 01$	$0.10000E + 01$	$0.10000E + 01$
		2	$-0.10111E - 03$	$0.16914E - 02$	$-0.80868E - 02$
		3	$0.39745E - 07$	$-0.55453E - 06$	$-0.85526E - 05$
		4	$-0.28081E - 10$	$0.33920E - 09$	$0.53316E - 08$
		5	$0.77063E - 14$	$-0.85419E - 13$	$-0.12069E - 11$
		6	$0.12100E - 16$	$-0.12682E - 15$	$-0.17247E - 14$
		7	$-0.53566E - 20$	$0.55254E - 19$	$0.73916E - 18$
		8	$-0.10476E - 22$	$0.10271E - 21$	$0.12706E - 20$
		9	$0.10065E - 25$	$-0.97593E - 25$	$-0.11956E - 23$
		10	$-0.25734E - 29$	$0.24681E - 28$	$0.29890E - 27$
60.00	1.00	1	$0.10000E + 01$	$0.10000E + 01$	$0.10000E + 01$
		2	$-0.13258E - 02$	$0.23646E - 01$	$-0.10251E + 00$
		3	$0.70873E - 05$	$-0.10303E - 03$	$-0.15005E - 02$
		4	$-0.67809E - 07$	$0.85485E - 06$	$0.12440E - 04$
		5	$0.25179E - 09$	$-0.29111E - 08$	$-0.38015E - 07$
		6	$0.53478E - 11$	$-0.58579E - 10$	$-0.73645E - 09$
		7	$-0.32014E - 13$	$0.34490E - 12$	$0.42613E - 11$
		8	$-0.84705E - 15$	$0.86749E - 14$	$0.99228E - 13$
		9	$0.11005E - 16$	$-0.11144E - 15$	$-0.12620E - 14$
		10	$-0.38051E - 19$	$0.38108E - 18$	$0.42654E - 17$
60.00	1.50	1	$0.10000E + 01$	$0.10000E + 01$	$0.10000E + 01$
		2	$-0.39466E - 02$	$0.85160E - 01$	$-0.28717E + 00$
		3	$0.68731E - 04$	$-0.11325E - 02$	$-0.14784E - 01$
		4	$-0.21201E - 05$	$0.30300E - 04$	$0.37523E - 03$
		5	$0.25793E - 07$	$-0.33792E - 06$	$-0.37468E - 05$
		6	$0.17354E - 08$	$-0.21515E - 07$	$-0.22799E - 06$
		7	$-0.33740E - 10$	$0.41075E - 09$	$0.42686E - 08$
		8	$-0.29237E - 11$	$0.33887E - 10$	$0.32732E - 09$
		9	$0.12329E - 12$	$-0.14118E - 11$	$-0.13484E - 10$
		10	$-0.13845E - 14$	$0.15674E - 13$	$0.14790E - 12$
60.00	2.00	1	$0.10000E + 01$	$0.10000E + 01$	$0.10000E + 01$
		2	$-0.71072E - 02$	$0.18296E + 00$	$-0.49538E + 00$
		3	$0.25408E - 03$	$-0.46615E - 02$	$-0.52893E - 01$
		4	$-0.15839E - 04$	$0.25452E - 03$	$0.25824E - 02$
		5	$0.37765E - 06$	$-0.55461E - 05$	$-0.49981E - 04$
		6	$0.52306E - 07$	$-0.73680E - 06$	$-0.64204E - 05$
		7	$-0.20124E - 08$	$0.27773E - 07$	$0.23661E - 06$
		8	$-0.34166E - 09$	$0.44861E - 08$	$0.35604E - 07$
		9	$0.28543E - 10$	$-0.37011E - 09$	$-0.29026E - 08$
		10	$-0.63437E - 12$	$0.81292E - 11$	$0.62967E - 10$
60.00	2.50	1	$0.10000E + 01$	$0.10000E + 01$	$0.10000E + 01$
		2	$-0.97026E - 02$	$0.33159E + 00$	$-0.66737E + 00$
		3	$0.55560E - 03$	$-0.12189E - 01$	$-0.12452E + 00$
		4	$-0.54535E - 04$	$0.10499E - 02$	$0.88681E - 02$
		5	$0.20451E - 05$	$-0.35919E - 04$	$-0.26780E - 03$
		6	$0.44264E - 06$	$-0.74839E - 05$	$-0.53825E - 04$
		7	$-0.26700E - 07$	$0.44117E - 06$	$0.30907E - 05$
		8	$-0.71259E - 08$	$0.11217E - 06$	$0.73558E - 06$
		9	$0.93333E - 09$	$-0.14495E - 07$	$-0.93787E - 07$

TABLE 3.—Continued

(1)	(2)	(3)	(4)	(5)	(6)
		10	$-0.32528E - 10$	$0.49896E - 09$	$0.31865E - 08$
45.00	0.50	1	$0.10000E + 01$	$0.10000E + 01$	$0.10000E + 01$
		2	$-0.36709E - 03$	$0.21298E - 02$	$0.43722E - 01$
		3	$0.43184E - 06$	$-0.30832E - 05$	$0.54982E - 04$
		4	$-0.85992E - 09$	$0.62037E - 08$	$-0.14957E - 06$
		5	$0.57132E - 12$	$-0.36401E - 11$	$0.68632E - 10$
		6	$0.27107E - 14$	$-0.19525E - 13$	$0.51622E - 12$
		7	$-0.30460E - 17$	$0.21745E - 16$	$-0.57035E - 15$
		8	$-0.14438E - 19$	$0.94277E - 19$	$-0.21367E - 17$
		9	$0.35341E - 22$	$-0.23017E - 21$	$0.52394E - 20$
		10	$-0.22911E - 25$	$0.14807E - 24$	$-0.33462E - 23$
45.00	1.00	1	$0.10000E + 01$	$0.10000E + 01$	$0.10000E + 01$
		2	$-0.29326E - 02$	$0.18665E - 01$	$0.54539E + 00$
		3	$0.28761E - 04$	$-0.21740E - 03$	$0.59641E - 02$
		4	$-0.47636E - 06$	$0.36297E - 05$	$-0.13023E - 03$
		5	$0.26323E - 08$	$-0.17719E - 07$	$0.49995E - 06$
		6	$0.10373E - 09$	$-0.78828E - 09$	$0.30723E - 07$
		7	$-0.96856E - 12$	$0.72883E - 11$	$-0.28147E - 09$
		8	$-0.38184E - 13$	$0.26320E - 12$	$-0.88205E - 11$
		9	$0.77670E - 15$	$-0.53374E - 14$	$0.17949E - 12$
		10	$-0.41847E - 17$	$0.28530E - 16$	$-0.95221E - 15$
45.00	1.50	1	$0.10000E + 01$	$0.10000E + 01$	$0.10000E + 01$
		2	$-0.72491E - 02$	$0.57894E - 01$	$-0.31036E + 02$
		3	$0.19124E - 03$	$-0.16742E - 02$	$-0.10319E + 01$
		4	$-0.84858E - 05$	$0.74249E - 04$	$0.55974E - 01$
		5	$0.12823E - 06$	$-0.99482E - 06$	$-0.60119E - 03$
		6	$0.13303E - 07$	$-0.11536E - 06$	$-0.92508E - 04$
		7	$-0.33608E - 09$	$0.28802E - 08$	$0.22830E - 05$
		8	$-0.36159E - 10$	$0.28474E - 09$	$0.19752E - 06$
		9	$0.19890E - 11$	$-0.15597E - 10$	$-0.10834E - 07$
		10	$-0.29004E - 13$	$0.22552E - 12$	$0.15538E - 09$
45.00	2.00	1	$0.10000E + 01$	$0.10000E + 01$	$0.10000E + 01$
		2	$-0.12078E - 01$	$0.11358E + 00$	$-0.28041E + 01$
		3	$0.59868E - 03$	$-0.57599E - 02$	$-0.18003E + 00$
		4	$-0.49439E - 04$	$0.47552E - 03$	$0.17003E - 01$
		5	$0.13402E - 05$	$-0.11382E - 04$	$-0.32494E - 03$
		6	$0.26467E - 06$	$-0.25287E - 05$	$-0.94559E - 04$
		7	$-0.12165E - 07$	$0.11461E - 06$	$0.42240E - 05$
		8	$-0.23564E - 08$	$0.20467E - 07$	$0.66653E - 06$
		9	$0.23610E - 09$	$-0.20405E - 08$	$-0.66418E - 07$
		10	$-0.62644E - 11$	$0.53665E - 10$	$0.17315E - 08$
45.00	2.50	1	$0.10000E + 01$	$0.10000E + 01$	$0.10000E + 01$
		2	$-0.15948E - 01$	$0.19775E + 00$	$-0.18759E + 01$
		3	$0.12039E - 02$	$-0.13782E - 01$	$-0.20456E + 00$
		4	$-0.15018E - 03$	$0.17029E - 02$	$0.26652E - 01$
		5	$0.60988E - 05$	$-0.61102E - 04$	$-0.77184E - 03$
		6	$0.18217E - 05$	$-0.20399E - 04$	$-0.32539E - 03$
		7	$-0.12560E - 06$	$0.13832E - 05$	$0.21667E - 04$
		8	$-0.36478E - 07$	$0.37201E - 06$	$0.52080E - 05$
		9	$0.54848E - 08$	$-0.55580E - 07$	$-0.77575E - 06$
		10	$-0.21836E - 09$	$0.21919E - 08$	$0.30301E - 07$

TABLE 3.—Continued

(1)	(2)	(3)	(4)	(5)	(6)
30.00	0.50	1	$0.10000E + 01$	$0.10000E + 01$	$0.10000E + 01$
		2	$-0.75263E - 03$	$0.17596E - 02$	$0.16711E - 01$
		3	$0.16838E - 05$	$-0.71112E - 05$	$0.17413E - 04$
		4	$-0.60792E - 08$	$0.29714E - 07$	$-0.13806E - 06$
		5	$0.63498E - 11$	$-0.24990E - 10$	$0.45498E - 10$
		6	$0.58315E - 13$	$-0.32347E - 12$	$0.20388E - 11$
		7	$-0.10841E - 15$	$0.59997E - 15$	$-0.37907E - 14$
		8	$-0.81915E - 18$	$0.40071E - 17$	$-0.20266E - 16$
		9	$0.33271E - 20$	$-0.16367E - 19$	$0.84480E - 19$
		10	$-0.35651E - 23$	$0.17455E - 22$	$-0.89780E - 22$
30.00	1.00	1	$0.10000E + 01$	$0.10000E + 01$	$0.10000E + 01$
		2	$-0.50429E - 02$	$0.13521E - 01$	$0.13635E + 00$
		3	$0.79163E - 04$	$-0.35864E - 03$	$0.10824E - 02$
		4	$-0.20042E - 05$	$0.10417E - 04$	$-0.55751E - 04$
		5	$0.14698E - 07$	$-0.61865E - 07$	$0.14490E - 06$
		6	$0.94484E - 09$	$-0.55375E - 08$	$0.39268E - 07$
		7	$-0.12316E - 10$	$0.71926E - 10$	$-0.51027E - 09$
		8	$-0.65331E - 12$	$0.33847E - 11$	$-0.19435E - 10$
		9	$0.18607E - 13$	$-0.96857E - 13$	$0.56629E - 12$
		10	$-0.13983E - 15$	$0.72421E - 15$	$-0.42168E - 14$
30.00	1.50	1	$0.10000E + 01$	$0.10000E + 01$	$0.10000E + 01$
		2	$-0.11141E - 01$	$0.39630E - 01$	$0.46459E + 00$
		3	$0.41753E - 03$	$-0.22231E - 02$	$0.10574E - 01$
		4	$-0.25250E - 04$	$0.15150E - 03$	$-0.11378E - 02$
		5	$0.45296E - 06$	$-0.22332E - 05$	$0.87888E - 05$
		6	$0.68373E - 07$	$-0.45671E - 06$	$0.43654E - 05$
		7	$-0.21537E - 08$	$0.14303E - 07$	$-0.13631E - 06$
		8	$-0.27837E - 09$	$0.16488E - 08$	$-0.12944E - 07$
		9	$0.19151E - 10$	$-0.11379E - 09$	$0.90600E - 09$
		10	$-0.34794E - 12$	$0.20555E - 11$	$-0.16284E - 10$
30.00	2.00	1	$0.10000E + 01$	$0.10000E + 01$	$0.10000E + 01$
		2	$-0.17716E - 01$	$0.73681E - 01$	$0.11861E + 01$
		3	$0.11840E - 02$	$-0.67510E - 02$	$0.50408E - 01$
		4	$-0.12673E - 03$	$0.80570E - 03$	$-0.86668E - 02$
		5	$0.38421E - 05$	$-0.20090E - 04$	$0.11957E - 03$
		6	$0.10562E - 05$	$-0.73964E - 05$	$0.97459E - 04$
		7	$-0.57378E - 07$	$0.39860E - 06$	$-0.52173E - 05$
		8	$-0.12640E - 07$	$0.79018E - 07$	$-0.86831E - 06$
		9	$0.15018E - 08$	$-0.94036E - 08$	$0.10441E - 06$
		10	$-0.47058E - 10$	$0.29286E - 09$	$-0.32321E - 08$
30.00	2.50	1	$0.10000E + 01$	$0.10000E + 01$	$0.10000E + 01$
		2	$-0.23102E - 01$	$0.12202E + 00$	$0.41346E + 01$
		3	$0.22969E - 02$	$-0.14835E - 01$	$0.29035E + 00$
		4	$-0.36381E - 03$	$0.25698E - 02$	$-0.65014E - 01$
		5	$0.15795E - 04$	$-0.92462E - 04$	$0.14142E - 02$
		6	$0.65460E - 05$	$-0.50088E - 04$	$0.14809E - 02$
		7	$-0.51641E - 06$	$0.39102E - 05$	$-0.11434E - 03$
		8	$-0.16403E - 06$	$0.11282E - 05$	$-0.28286E - 04$
		9	$0.28329E - 07$	$-0.19483E - 06$	$0.49142E - 05$
		10	$-0.12894E - 08$	$0.88081E - 08$	$-0.22058E - 06$

..., A_n, and the problem is solved. The λ values for the first three antisymmetric sloshing modes are given in Table 2 and represented graphically in Figs. 3, 4, and 5. The corresponding A_j values are given in Table 3, in which the n stands for mode number for antisymmetric modes.

With the ϕ given by Eq. 16, the stream function ψ can be easily found by the Cauchy-Riemann equations to be

$$\psi(x',y') = e^{-i\sigma t} \sum_{j=1}^{n} A_j \cos (2j - 1)\, \pi x' \sinh (2j - 1)\, \pi (y' + d') \dots\dots (20)$$

Since the transformations given by Eqs. 6 and 9 allow one to obtain the values of x and y corresponding to any pair of values (x',y'), the solution for the z-plane is found once that for the z'-plane is known. The equipotential lines (ϕ-lines) and streamlines (ψ-lines) are shown in Figs. 6 and 7 for the first two antisymmetric modes, respectively.

The results just presented are for antisymmetric sloshing modes. For symmetric (with respect to the y-axis) modes, Eqs. 16 and 20 are replaced respectively by

$$\phi(x',y') = e^{-i\sigma t} \sum_{j=1}^{n} A_j \cos 2j\pi x' \cosh 2j\pi (y' + d') \dots\dots\dots\dots (21)$$

$$\psi(x',y') = -e^{-i\sigma t} \sum_{j=1}^{n} A_j \sin 2j\pi x' \sinh 2j\pi (y' + d') \dots\dots\dots\dots (22)$$

All else remains the same. We shall not pursue the matter further, since for sloshing modes the antisymmetric ones (the first one, at any rate) are more important.

According to a comparison theorem of Yih (5), the frequency σ, or the λ value, for the trapezoidal channel is less than that for a rectangular channel of the same free-surface width, provided the maximum depth of the trapezoid is the same as the depth of the rectangle, and provided

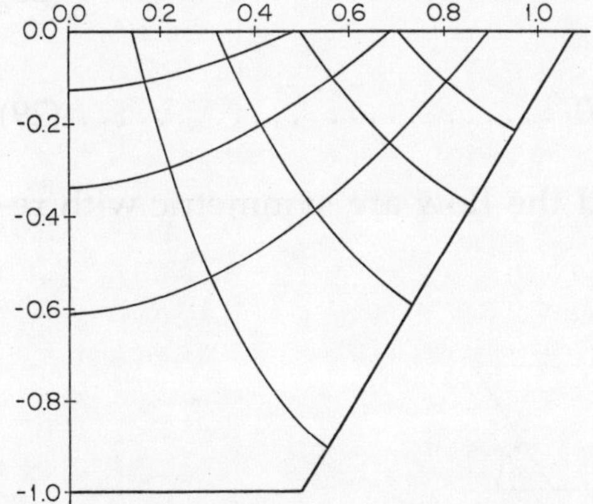

FIG. 6.—Flow Pattern for First Antisymmetric Sloshing Mode in Trapezoidal Channel, $\alpha = 60°$, $L/D = 1$. Intervals $\Delta\phi$ and $\Delta\psi$ are 0.2

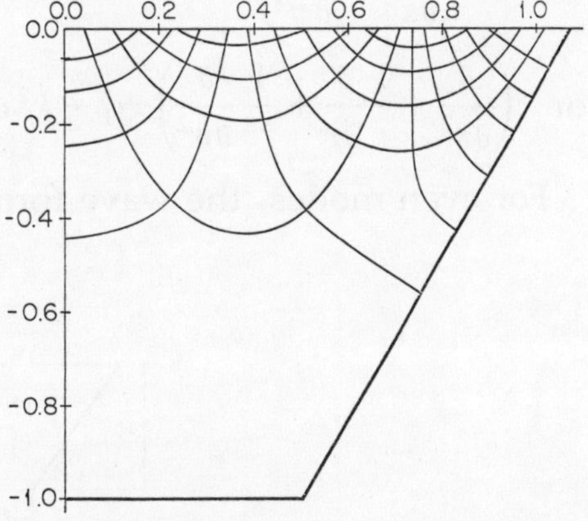

FIG. 7.—Flow Pattern for Second Antisymmetric Sloshing Mode in Trapezoidal Channel, $\alpha = 60°$, $L/D = 1$. Intervals $\Delta\phi$ and $\Delta\psi$ are 0.2

the same modes are being compared. We have found that our results are in agreement with this comparison theorem.

WAVES PROPAGATING LONGITUDINALLY IN TRAPEZOIDAL CHANNELS

For waves propagating longitudinally in trapezoidal channels, we take the longitudinal axis passing through the origin as the z-axis, with z now indicating the third of the Cartesian, and indeed also of the cylindrical, coordinates. In the plane $z = 0$, the origin is now taken to be the intersection of the slanting sides of the trapezoid. Again, the maximum depth D is chosen to be the length scale, so that on the free surface the dimensionless y is now

$$y = 1 + \frac{\ell}{2} \tan \alpha \dotfill (23)$$

and on the sides, if (r, θ, z) are cylindrical coordinates, as shown in Fig. 8,

$$\theta = \pm\left(\frac{\pi}{2} - \alpha\right) = \pm\beta \dotfill (24)$$

Note that in Fig. 8 the coordinate θ is measured clockwise from the y-axis, so that

$$x = r \sin \theta; \quad y = r \cos \theta \dotfill (25)$$

We take the velocity potential to be

$$\phi = \phi_1(x, y)\, e^{i(kz - \sigma t)} \dotfill (26)$$

in which k = longitudinal wave number, defined by

$$k = \frac{2\pi D}{L'}, \quad L' = \text{longitudinal wavelength} \dotfill (27)$$

$$\text{Then} \quad \left(\frac{\partial^2}{\partial x^2} + \frac{\partial^2}{\partial y^2}\right)\phi_1 - k^2\phi_1 = 0 \dotfill (28)$$

$$\text{or} \quad \left(\frac{\partial}{\partial r^2} + \frac{1}{r}\frac{\partial}{\partial r} + \frac{1}{r^2}\frac{\partial}{\partial \theta^2}\right)\phi_1 - k^2\phi_1 = 0 \dotfill (29)$$

For even modes, the wave form and the flow are symmetric with re-

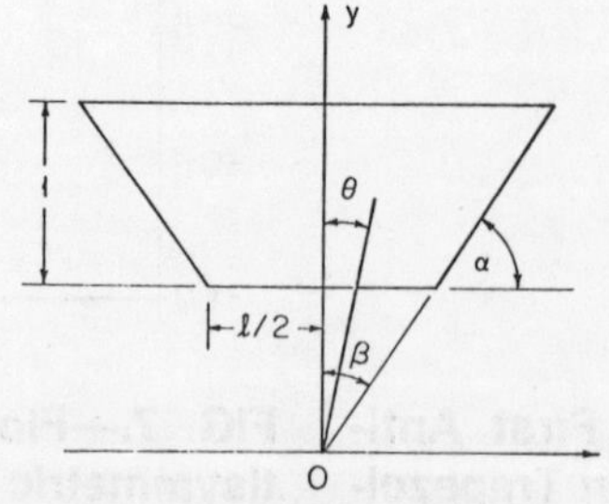

FIG. 8.—Definition Sketch for Trapezoidal Cross Section, in Dimensionless Terms

spect to the y-axis. These are more important than the odd modes, for which the flow is antisymmetric. We shall therefore treat the even modes only. For these modes,

$$\phi_1 = f(r) \cos \frac{n\pi}{\beta} \theta \quad\text{.......................................} \quad (30)$$

which satisfies the boundary conditions on the side walls (Fig. 8):

$$\frac{\partial \phi_1}{\partial \theta} = 0 \quad \text{at} \quad \theta = \pm \beta \quad\text{..} \quad (31)$$

Substituting Eq. 30 into Eq. 29, we obtain

$$f'' + \frac{1}{r} f' - \left[\left(\frac{n\pi}{\beta} \right)^2 \frac{1}{r^2} + k^2 \right] f = 0 \quad\text{............................} \quad (32)$$

The boundary condition at the horizontal bottom of the channel is

$$\frac{\partial \phi_1}{\partial y} = 0 \quad \text{at} \quad y = \frac{\ell}{2} \tan \alpha \quad\text{...............................} \quad (33)$$

in which $\quad \dfrac{\partial}{\partial y} = \cos \theta \dfrac{\partial}{\partial r} - \dfrac{\sin \theta}{r} \dfrac{\partial}{\partial \theta} \quad\text{.................}\quad (34)$

The free-surface condition is

$$\lambda \phi_1 = \frac{\partial}{\partial y} \phi_1 \quad \text{at} \quad y = 1 + \frac{\ell}{2} \tan \alpha \quad\text{.............................}\quad (35)$$

in which the operator $\partial / \partial y$ is given by Eq. 34.

Using the customary notation I and K for the modified Bessel functions and writing, for simplicity,

$$g_n(r) = I_{n\pi/\beta}(kr); \quad h_n(r) = K_{n\pi/\beta}(kr) \quad\text{...........................}\quad (36)$$

the N-term solution for ϕ_1 is

$$\phi_1 = \sum_{n=1}^{N} [A_n g_n(r) + B_n h_n(r)] \cos \frac{n\pi}{\beta} \theta \quad\text{...........................}\quad (37)$$

The functions I and K are defined in pages 77 and 78 of Watson's book (4) on Bessel functions.

Let $\xi_0, \xi_1, \ldots, \xi_{N-1}$ be the N non-negative roots of the equation $P_{2N-1}(\xi) = 0$, in which P_{2N-1} = Legendre polynomial of the $(2N - 1)$th order. The first root ξ_0 is zero, since the order of $P_{2N-1}(\xi)$ is odd. The interval for x is $-\ell/2 \leq x \leq \ell/2$ so that the b and c in Eq. 17 are given by $b = -\ell/2; c = \ell/2;$ and

$$x_j = \frac{\ell}{2} \xi_j; \quad j = 0, 1, \ldots, N - 1 \quad\text{.................................}\quad (38)$$

We require the satisfaction of Eq. 33 at these values of x_j. (Since the function ϕ, is even in θ or x, the satisfaction of Eq. 33 at $x_{-j} = -\ell/2\xi_j$; $j = 1, 2, \ldots, N - 1$ is automatically guaranteed.) This requirement provides N equations for the $2N$ unknown A's and B's in Eq. 37. The other

TABLE 4.—Coefficients A_n and B_n for Symmetric Waves Propagating Longitudinally

α (1)	L/D (2)	K (3)	Value (4)	Vector A				Vector B			
				(5)	(6)	(7)	(8)	(9)	(10)	(11)	(12)
60.00	0.50	1	0.53661	$0.100000E + 01$	$-0.119740E + 02$	$0.214145E + 07$	$-0.132283E + 14$	$0.136555E + 00$	$0.294794E - 08$	$0.182041E - 17$	$-0.248150E - 28$
			3.42708	$0.100000E + 01$	$0.222307E + 05$	$0.407476E + 10$	$-0.123627E + 17$	$0.115348E + 00$	$-0.288245E - 08$	$-0.148367E - 17$	$0.203695E - 28$
			7.18842	$0.100000E + 01$	$-0.768117E + 05$	$-0.478550E + 12$	$-0.490601E + 19$	$0.209330E + 00$	$0.227740E - 07$	$0.131638E - 16$	$-0.179877E - 27$
			11.18739	$0.100000E + 01$	$-0.295277E + 05$	$0.416843E + 12$	$0.388786E + 20$	$0.165101E + 00$	$0.109616E - 07$	$0.626382E - 17$	$-0.856376E - 28$
60.00	0.50	2	1.51026	$0.100000E + 01$	$-0.554309E + 01$	$0.688208E + 04$	$-0.787719E + 09$	$0.797608E + 00$	$0.104247E - 05$	$0.408349E - 13$	$-0.354895E - 22$
			7.38172	$0.100000E + 01$	$-0.256984E + 04$	$-0.276341E + 09$	$-0.472094E + 14$	$0.101462E + 01$	$0.395215E - 05$	$0.146358E - 12$	$-0.127460E - 21$
			11.31220	$0.100000E + 01$	$-0.990660E + 03$	$0.246998E + 09$	$0.374359E + 15$	$0.882868E + 00$	$0.222363E - 05$	$0.822385E - 13$	$-0.716284E - 22$
			3.79619	$0.100000E + 01$	$0.631400E + 03$	$0.222338E + 07$	$-0.104636E + 12$	$0.743349E + 00$	$0.307805E - 06$	$0.144612E - 13$	$-0.124930E - 22$
60.00	0.50	3	2.46828	$0.100000E + 01$	$-0.325994E + 01$	$0.281732E + 03$	$-0.314545E + 07$	$0.289186E + 01$	$0.393862E - 04$	$0.173167E - 10$	$-0.170342E - 18$
			4.33617	$0.100000E + 01$	$0.108281E + 03$	$0.447098E + 05$	$-0.185681E + 09$	$0.272944E + 01$	$0.207345E - 04$	$0.982231E - 11$	$-0.963702E - 19$
			7.69059	$0.100000E + 01$	$-0.550088E + 03$	$-0.602176E + 07$	$-0.999321E + 11$	$0.368233E + 01$	$0.129177E - 03$	$0.538020E - 10$	$-0.530293E - 18$
			11.51531	$0.100000E + 01$	$-0.204284E + 03$	$0.537030E + 07$	$0.760160E + 12$	$0.319004E + 01$	$0.745452E - 04$	$0.310629E - 10$	$-0.306186E - 18$
60.00	1.00	1	0.58105	$0.100000E + 01$	$-0.135960E + 00$	$0.342207E + 06$	$-0.305480E + 12$	$0.797149E + 00$	$0.103629E - 05$	$0.406118E - 13$	$-0.352950E - 22$
			5.55449	$0.100000E + 01$	$-0.228403E + 05$	$-0.297792E + 11$	$-0.635164E + 17$	$0.258404E + 01$	$0.220653E - 04$	$0.913726E - 12$	$-0.792192E - 21$
			8.61355	$0.100000E + 01$	$-0.819085E + 04$	$0.243320E + 11$	$0.469747E + 18$	$0.162115E + 01$	$0.146990E - 04$	$0.437863E - 12$	$-0.384886E - 21$
			2.69977	$0.100000E + 01$	$0.542677E + 04$	$0.214376E + 09$	$-0.133568E + 15$	$0.335897E + 00$	$-0.518813E - 05$	$-0.183619E - 12$	$0.160193E - 21$
60.00	1.00	2	1.58103	$0.100000E + 01$	$-0.305193E + 01$	$0.118834E + 04$	$-0.231849E + 08$	$0.891054E + 01$	$0.610034E - 03$	$0.147543E - 08$	$-0.808306E - 16$
			3.14671	$0.100000E + 01$	$0.197122E + 03$	$0.167612E + 06$	$-0.162907E + 10$	$0.633297E + 01$	$-0.607918E - 03$	$-0.121850E - 08$	$0.672545E - 16$
			5.80164	$0.100000E + 01$	$-0.943288E + 03$	$-0.225796E + 08$	$-0.837273E + 12$	$0.199935E + 02$	$0.513222E - 02$	$0.130922E - 07$	$-0.715546E - 15$
			8.77500	$0.100000E + 01$	$-0.349774E + 03$	$0.197826E + 08$	$0.637025E + 13$	$0.142885E + 02$	$0.378566E - 02$	$0.707178E - 08$	$-0.391613E - 15$
60.00	1.00	3	9.03305	$0.100000E + 01$	$0.902798E + 02$	$0.599106E + 06$	$0.187166E + 11$	$0.115003E + 03$	$0.206522E + 00$	$0.410725E - 05$	$-0.252839E - 11$
			6.18932	$0.100000E + 01$	$-0.263203E + 03$	$-0.697861E + 06$	$-0.267520E + 10$	$0.167315E + 03$	$0.279228E + 00$	$0.765639E - 05$	$-0.464808E - 11$
			2.53063	$0.100000E + 01$	$-0.241357E + 01$	$0.501080E + 02$	$-0.105334E + 06$	$0.705652E + 02$	$0.413225E - 01$	$0.107304E - 05$	$-0.653074E - 12$
			3.78890	$0.100000E + 01$	$0.405993E + 02$	$0.467899E + 04$	$-0.402907E + 07$	$0.530013E + 02$	$-0.948230E - 02$	$-0.123046E - 06$	$0.776544E - 13$
60.00	1.50	1	0.60540	$0.100000E + 01$	$0.311380E + 01$	$0.925801E + 05$	$-0.998293E + 10$	$0.288267E + 01$	$0.383460E - 04$	$0.168924E - 10$	$-0.166157E - 18$
			2.26345	$0.100000E + 01$	$0.182610E + 04$	$0.217894E + 08$	$-0.403417E + 13$	$0.249175E + 00$	$-0.260505E - 03$	$-0.104666E - 09$	$0.103303E - 17$
			4.54292	$0.100000E + 01$	$-0.106127E + 05$	$-0.404108E + 10$	$-0.250884E + 16$	$0.143445E + 02$	$0.681854E - 03$	$0.554113E - 09$	$-0.535250E - 17$
			7.01360	$0.100000E + 01$	$-0.365305E + 04$	$0.317171E + 10$	$0.177097E + 17$	$0.110292E + 02$	$0.144119E - 02$	$0.389549E - 09$	$-0.390124E - 17$
60.00	1.50	2	1.61935	$0.100000E + 01$	$-0.195164E + 01$	$0.381496E + 03$	$-0.128982E + 07$	$0.703807E + 02$	$0.408067E - 01$	$0.106048E - 05$	$-0.645412E - 12$
			4.84161	$0.100000E + 01$	$-0.500860E + 03$	$-0.377181E + 07$	$-0.428366E + 11$	$0.220531E + 03$	$0.244730E + 00$	$0.112508E - 04$	$-0.672621E - 11$
			7.20955	$0.100000E + 01$	$-0.176567E + 03$	$0.320819E + 07$	$0.308144E + 12$	$0.183336E + 03$	$0.543295E + 00$	$0.883681E - 05$	$-0.547389E - 11$
			2.77591	$0.100000E + 01$	$0.850437E + 02$	$0.248606E + 05$	$-0.710259E + 08$	$0.350790E + 02$	$-0.603482E - 01$	$-0.134344E - 05$	$0.822593E - 12$
60.00	1.50	3	2.56073	$0.100000E + 01$	$-0.205354E + 01$	$0.173337E + 02$	$-0.646778E + 04$	$0.136650E + 04$	$0.543233E + 01$	$0.141280E - 02$	$-0.926931E - 08$
			3.49903	$0.100000E + 01$	$0.206138E + 02$	$0.952041E + 03$	$-0.235814E + 06$	$0.768804E + 03$	$-0.252323E + 01$	$-0.454765E - 03$	$0.303373E - 08$

60.00	2.00	1	5.29997	$0.100000E + 01$	$-0.178842E + 03$	$-0.163833E + 06$	$-0.206582E + 09$	$0.460394E + 04$	$0.260855E + 02$	$0.118545E - 01$	$-0.763455E - 07$
			7.52055	$0.100000E + 01$	$-0.539871E + 02$	$0.130187E + 06$	$0.126850E + 10$	$0.366062E + 04$	$0.544894E + 02$	$0.886209E - 02$	$-0.592382E - 07$
			0.61996	$0.100000E + 01$	$0.415653E + 01$	$0.360812E + 05$	$0.104356E + 10$	$0.881907E + 01$	$0.567764E - 03$	$0.137979E - 08$	$-0.755786E - 16$
			1.98011	$0.100000E + 01$	$0.764617E + 03$	$0.337511E + 07$	$-0.263366E + 12$	$-0.844007E + 00$	$-0.390796E - 02$	$-0.872410E - 08$	$0.479327E - 15$
			3.85730	$0.100000E + 01$	$-0.558785E + 04$	$-0.778379E + 09$	$-0.175233E + 15$	$0.452413E + 02$	$-0.697834E - 02$	$0.404675E - 07$	$-0.209768E - 14$
			5.92418	$0.100000E + 01$	$-0.259929E + 04$	$0.805295E + 09$	$0.162145E + 16$	$0.716786E + 02$	$0.501218E - 01$	$0.678797E - 07$	$-0.375954E - 14$
60.00	2.00	2	1.64204	$0.100000E + 01$	$-0.131559E + 01$	$0.189094E + 03$	$0.319442E + 04$	$0.507213E + 03$	$0.115541E + 01$	$0.155891E - 03$	$-0.514984E - 09$
			4.20479	$0.100000E + 01$	$-0.329238E + 03$	$-0.982294E + 06$	$-0.428909E + 10$	$0.173859E + 04$	$-0.280656E + 01$	$0.140934E - 02$	$-0.441878E - 08$
			6.15430	$0.100000E + 01$	$-0.115179E + 03$	$0.838104E + 06$	$0.300744E + 11$	$0.208758E + 04$	$0.248912E + 02$	$0.193481E - 02$	$-0.646501E - 08$
			2.54749	$0.100000E + 01$	$0.449899E + 02$	$0.566993E + 04$	$-0.630259E + 07$	$0.180454E + 03$	$-0.168102E + 01$	$-0.194512E - 03$	$0.646422E - 09$
60.00	2.00	3	2.57584	$0.100000E + 01$	$-0.184110E + 01$	$0.101731E + 02$	$0.210987E + 03$	$0.251844E + 05$	$0.321318E + 03$	$0.396687E + 00$	$-0.135715E - 04$
			4.72623	$0.100000E + 01$	$-0.151795E + 03$	$-0.606937E + 05$	$-0.318038E + 08$	$0.108632E + 06$	$-0.373628E + 03$	$0.305579E + 01$	$-0.992736E - 04$
			6.51412	$0.100000E - 01$	$-0.381362E + 02$	$0.424153E + 05$	$0.161979E + 09$	$0.100414E + 06$	$0.464095E + 04$	$0.337236E + 01$	$-0.116853E - 03$
			3.33305	$0.100000E + 01$	$0.126030E + 02$	$0.294392E + 03$	$-0.258968E + 05$	$0.107889E + 05$	$-0.145013E + 03$	$-0.122660E + 00$	$0.427139E - 05$
60.00	2.50	1	0.62926	$0.100000E + 01$	$0.453551E + 01$	$0.175776E + 05$	$0.681333E + 09$	$0.249682E + 02$	$0.511371E - 02$	$0.462498E + 07$	$-0.955460E - 14$
			3.36077	$0.100000E + 01$	$-0.257172E + 04$	$-0.155438E + 09$	$-0.148434E + 14$	$0.766724E + 02$	$-0.230050E + 00$	$0.615327E - 06$	$-0.106737E - 12$
			1.78597	$0.100000E + 01$	$0.376376E + 03$	$0.687475E + 06$	$-0.323897E + 11$	$-0.439398E + 01$	$-0.324467E - 01$	$-0.271059E - 06$	$0.561505E - 13$
			5.13528	$0.100000E + 01$	$-0.390852E + 04$	$0.490048E + 09$	$0.417044E + 15$	$0.672710E + 03$	$0.145637E + 01$	$0.733979E - 05$	$-0.150159E - 11$
60.00	2.50	2	1.65630	$0.100000E + 01$	$-0.855516E + 00$	$0.122801E + 03$	$0.699920E + 05$	$0.352410E + 04$	$0.207606E + 02$	$0.968517E - 02$	$-0.116856E - 06$
			3.75593	$0.100000E + 01$	$-0.240263E + 03$	$-0.335912E + 06$	$-0.663428E + 09$	$0.109757E + 05$	$-0.265095E + 03$	$0.561275E - 01$	$-0.590540E - 06$
			5.39858	$0.100000E + 01$	$-0.921515E + 02$	$0.311397E + 06$	$0.490532E + 10$	$0.213713E + 05$	$0.601673E + 03$	$0.163749E + 00$	$-0.196188E - 05$
			2.39929	$0.100000E + 01$	$0.273610E + 02$	$0.172925E + 04$	$-0.967642E + 06$	$0.956095E + 03$	$-0.264465E + 02$	$-0.104964E - 01$	$0.127436E - 06$
60.00	2.50	3	5.80350	$0.100000E + 01$	$-0.175920E + 02$	$0.106569E + 05$	$0.187600E + 08$	$0.139361E + 07$	$0.122285E + 06$	$0.287482E + 03$	$-0.340971E - 01$
			4.33379	$0.100000E + 01$	$-0.929988E + 02$	$-0.191173E + 05$	$-0.491326E + 07$	$0.140832E + 07$	$-0.702849E + 05$	$0.193386E + 03$	$-0.205172E - 01$
			2.58311	$0.100000E + 01$	$-0.146414E + 01$	$0.726018E + 01$	$0.610557E + 03$	$0.404531E + 06$	$0.111982E + 05$	$0.432661E + 02$	$-0.514943E - 02$
			3.23194	$0.100000E + 01$	$0.835600E + 01$	$0.115524E + 03$	$-0.418320E + 04$	$0.147919E + 06$	$-0.459052E + 04$	$-0.114558E + 02$	$0.139331E - 02$
45.00	0.50	1	0.48038	$0.100000E + 01$	$-0.114652E + 01$	$0.361428E + 03$	$0.919824E + 06$	$0.862127E - 01$	$0.145705E - 05$	$0.356449E - 13$	$-0.807706E - 20$
			2.06791	$0.100000E + 01$	$0.239563E + 03$	$0.571521E + 05$	$0.137867E + 08$	$0.160905E - 01$	$-0.111492E - 05$	$-0.909990E - 14$	$0.510653E - 20$
			4.48337	$0.100000E + 01$	$0.427807E + 04$	$0.264950E + 08$	$0.152588E + 12$	$-0.115136E + 01$	$-0.438769E - 04$	$-0.759090E - 12$	$0.224623E - 18$
			6.84732	$0.100000E + 01$	$-0.734979E + 04$	$-0.488370E + 09$	$-0.128596E + 14$	$0.205509E + 01$	$0.725594E - 04$	$0.138782E - 11$	$-0.378712E - 18$
45.00	0.50	2	1.32305	$0.100000E + 01$	$-0.179124E + 01$	$0.868225E + 01$	$0.114960E + 04$	$0.465770E + 00$	$0.123946E - 03$	$0.479742E - 10$	$-0.174474E - 15$
			2.62075	$0.100000E + 01$	$0.227858E + 02$	$0.515101E + 03$	$0.128018E + 05$	$0.317645E + 00$	$0.481901E - 04$	$0.262557E - 10$	$-0.750082E - 16$
			4.77726	$0.100000E + 01$	$0.411484E + 03$	$0.179808E + 06$	$0.724851E + 08$	$-0.200525E + 01$	$-0.113815E - 02$	$-0.316586E - 09$	$0.148497E - 14$
			7.02241	$0.100000E + 01$	$-0.491303E + 03$	$-0.203459E + 07$	$-0.349918E + 10$	$0.318286E + 01$	$0.149401E - 02$	$0.472872E - 09$	$-0.200081E - 14$
45.00	0.50	3	2.09839	$0.100000E + 01$	$-0.195306E + 01$	$0.244377E + 01$	$0.181839E + 02$	$0.154536E + 01$	$0.200717E - 02$	$0.388252E - 08$	$-0.715511E - 13$
			3.39805	$0.100000E + 01$	$0.795250E + 01$	$0.613237E + 02$	$0.498693E + 03$	$0.112968E + 01$	$0.108962E - 02$	$0.251042E - 08$	$-0.407590E - 13$
			5.23618	$0.100000E + 01$	$0.103153E + 03$	$0.106772E + 05$	$0.100954E + 07$	$-0.282543E + 01$	$-0.762745E - 02$	$-0.106339E - 07$	$0.252248E - 12$
			7.30283	$0.100000E + 01$	$-0.153374E + 03$	$-0.125568E + 06$	$-0.456699E + 08$	$0.740587E + 01$	$0.147793E - 01$	$0.243258E - 07$	$-0.505970E - 12$
45.00	1.00	1	0.49506	$0.100000E + 01$	$0.115316E + 00$	$0.499432E + 03$	$0.810359E + 06$	$0.454331E + 00$	$0.118100E - 03$	$0.462911E - 10$	$-0.166793E - 15$

TABLE 4.—Continued

(1)	(2)	(3)	(4)	(5)	(6)	(7)	(8)	(9)	(10)	(11)	(12)
			3.77864	0.100000E + 01	0.788237E + 03	0.231768E + 07	0.653085E + 10	−0.403112E + 01	−0.215374E − 02	−0.641406E − 09	0.284724E − 14
			1.81961	0.100000E + 01	0.116673E + 03	0.138257E + 05	−0.300341E + 05	−0.246894E + 00	−0.240422E − 03	−0.566684E − 10	0.304090E − 15
			5.72781	0.100000E + 01	−0.592995E + 05	−0.187883E + 10	−0.240136E + 14	0.145607E + 03	0.566443E − 01	0.450788E − 07	−0.992534E − 13
45.00	1.00	2	1.34670	0.100000E + 01	−0.136065E + 01	0.150143E + 02	0.152991E + 04	0.419464E + 01	0.159587E − 01	0.972687E − 07	−0.561031E − 11
			4.12333	0.100000E + 01	0.151491E + 03	0.334785E + 05	0.691498E + 07	−0.231184E + 02	−0.143498E + 00	−0.714600E − 06	0.480004E − 10
			5.93560	0.100000E + 01	−0.360128E + 03	−0.713271E + 06	−0.606292E + 09	0.341817E + 02	0.161706E + 00	0.158068E − 05	−0.647481E − 10
			2.41767	0.100000E + 01	0.137195E + 02	0.185532E + 03	0.290984E + 04	0.132843E + 01	−0.922554E − 03	0.150942E − 07	0.141077E − 13
45.00	1.00	3	2.10984	0.100000E + 01	−0.182555E + 01	0.319610E + 01	0.384064E + 02	0.269817E + 02	0.437081E + 00	0.131646E − 04	−0.378296E − 08
			3.25705	0.100000E + 01	0.558507E + 01	0.294449E + 02	0.178911E + 03	0.107805E + 02	0.949261E − 01	0.434199E − 05	−0.932424E − 09
			4.64956	0.100000E + 01	0.524186E + 02	0.295742E + 04	0.152422E + 06	−0.835850E + 02	−0.187873E + 01	−0.488611E − 04	0.156665E − 07
			6.26313	0.100000E + 01	−0.114908E + 03	−0.453529E + 05	−0.836011E + 07	0.145850E + 03	0.264088E + 01	0.106504E − 03	−0.246281E − 07
45.00	1.50	1	0.49242	0.100000E + 01	0.133421E + 01	0.531523E + 03	0.614382E + 06	0.140942E + 01	0.170776E − 02	0.342936E − 08	−0.614796E − 13
			3.29741	0.100000E + 01	0.234019E + 03	0.352751E + 06	0.541126E + 09	−0.697935E + 01	−0.163532E − 01	−0.272958E − 07	0.560732E − 12
			4.93092	0.100000E + 01	−0.327939E + 03	−0.610481E + 07	−0.425148E + 11	−0.759837E + 01	−0.256568E − 01	0.219718E − 07	0.593418E − 12
			1.69063	0.100000E + 01	0.614991E + 02	0.338599E + 04	−0.179884E + 07	−0.110534E + 01	−0.383986E − 02	−0.489405E − 08	0.124812E − 12
45.00	1.50	2	1.35029	0.100000E + 01	−0.674838E + 00	0.224185E + 02	0.178637E + 04	0.245097E + 02	0.384978E + 00	0.118086E − 04	−0.334803E − 08
			3.68681	0.100000E + 01	0.602018E + 02	0.737530E + 04	0.874425E + 06	−0.880301E + 02	−0.194256E + 01	−0.540906E − 04	0.164418E − 07
			5.17042	0.100000E + 01	−0.115745E + 03	−0.128260E + 06	−0.606012E + 08	−0.750790E + 02	−0.254877E + 01	0.330926E − 04	0.143774E − 07
			2.30067	0.100000E + 01	0.932130E + 01	0.829478E + 02	0.533744E + 03	0.272994E + 01	−0.748102E − 01	−0.687810E − 07	0.483963E − 09
45.00	1.50	3	5.54118	0.100000E + 01	−0.816497E + 02	−0.176532E + 05	−0.185586E + 07	−0.193959E + 03	−0.373074E + 02	0.666927E − 02	0.348350E − 05
			2.11239	0.100000E + 01	−0.151112E + 01	0.476301E + 01	0.693613E + 02	0.336183E + 03	0.189962E + 02	0.263391E − 02	−0.389053E − 05
			4.26699	0.100000E + 01	0.281290E + 02	0.962906E + 03	0.304757E + 05	−0.771010E + 03	−0.514054E + 02	−0.736362E − 02	0.103929E − 04
			3.17207	0.100000E + 01	0.438983E + 01	0.176682E + 02	0.903345E + 02	0.718527E + 02	0.190349E + 01	0.512712E − 03	−0.473904E − 06
45.00	2.00	1	0.48286	0.100000E + 01	0.240685E + 01	0.512090E + 03	0.415267E + 06	0.350302E + 01	0.119050E − 01	0.770412E − 07	−0.425293E − 11
			2.96966	0.100000E + 01	0.101371E + 03	0.826225E + 05	0.737578E + 08	−0.109501E + 02	−0.697009E − 01	−0.408370E − 06	0.241420E − 10
			1.63962	0.100000E + 01	0.355373E + 02	0.334584E + 03	−0.155783E + 07	−0.282148E + 01	−0.253667E − 01	−0.103864E − 06	0.815757E − 11
			4.33255	0.100000E + 01	−0.194067E + 02	−0.451177E + 06	−0.188332E + 10	−0.144968E + 02	−0.111588E + 00	−0.108314E − 06	0.309361E − 10
45.00	2.00	2	1.34486	0.100000E + 01	0.273076E + 00	0.299526E + 02	0.178467E + 04	0.116491E + 03	0.445956E + 01	0.431372E − 03	−0.369702E − 06
			3.39706	0.100000E + 01	0.288226E + 02	0.206930E + 04	0.151603E + 06	−0.251940E + 03	−0.125238E + 02	−0.118410E − 02	0.102772E − 05
			4.60325	0.100000E + 01	−0.170191E + 02	−0.150016E + 05	−0.433632E + 07	−0.445828E + 03	−0.259820E + 02	−0.908318E − 03	0.179626E − 05
			2.23643	0.100000E + 01	0.690397E + 01	0.411161E + 02	−0.194268E + 03	0.189808E + 01	−0.993229E + 00	−0.263682E − 04	0.661256E − 07
45.00	2.00	3	2.11207	0.100000E + 01	−0.851507E + 00	0.741071E + 01	0.103273E + 03	0.344561E + 04	0.408568E + 03	0.186685E + 00	−0.750794E − 03
			4.01655	0.100000E + 01	0.160646E + 02	0.355354E + 03	0.748203E + 04	−0.473529E + 04	−0.616183E + 03	−0.286771E + 00	0.113441E − 02
			5.01423	0.100000E + 01	−0.299601E + 02	−0.420610E + 04	−0.276456E + 06	−0.116020E + 05	−0.177767E + 04	−0.392659E + 00	0.282531E − 02
			3.11562	0.100000E + 01	0.371483E + 01	0.123405E + 02	0.572584E + 02	0.446375E + 03	0.244992E + 02	0.216482E − 01	−0.566945E − 04
45.00	2.50	1	0.47257	0.100000E + 01	0.326819E + 01	0.459006E + 03	0.260121 + 06	0.766684E + 01	0.550387E − 01	0.887797E − 06	−0.116125E − 09

			1.63788	0.100000E + 01	0.221554E + 02	−0.727285E + 03	−0.112205E + 07	−0.592404E + 01	−0.110286E + 00	−0.107676E − 05	0.207152E − 09
			2.75620	0.100000E + 01	0.551299E + 02	0.253493E + 05	0.135816E + 08	−0.169881E + 02	−0.226611E + 00	−0.353132E − 05	0.470363E − 09
			3.85857	0.100000E + 01	0.126205E + 02	−0.613147E + 05	−0.170643E + 09	−0.226453E + 02	−0.346229E + 00	−0.215222E − 05	0.605510E − 09
45.00	2.50	2	1.33692	0.100000E + 01	0.131506E + 01	0.350033E + 02	0.154391E + 04	0.469336E + 03	0.330149E + 02	0.774399E − 02	−0.153746E − 04
			3.21556	0.100000E + 01	0.164798E + 02	0.720511E + 03	0.339480E + 05	−0.672434E + 03	−0.593169E + 02	−0.141787E − 01	0.276170E − 04
			2.20361	0.100000E + 01	0.543465E + 01	0.204878E + 02	−0.395832E + 03	−0.121477E + 02	−0.753185E + 01	−0.601657E − 03	0.286034E − 05
			4.16085	0.100000E + 01	0.131413E + 01	−0.222883E + 04	−0.438258E + 06	−0.120130E + 04	−0.117314E + 03	−0.164443E − 01	0.485688E − 04
45.00	2.50	3	2.11130	0.100000E + 01	0.163894E + 00	0.104254E + 02	0.123967E + 03	0.282576E + 05	0.545665E + 04	0.580179E + 01	−0.523149E − 01
			3.85901	0.100000E + 01	0.101233E + 02	0.150302E + 03	0.221483E + 04	−0.244119E + 05	−0.501332E + 04	−0.558627E + 01	0.485238E − 01
			4.61161	0.100000E + 01	−0.543287E + 01	−0.773861E + 03	−0.348198E + 05	−0.637369E + 05	−0.144444E + 05	−0.110886E + 02	0.127836E + 00
			3.07381	0.100000E + 01	0.330517E + 01	0.963356E + 01	0.426348E + 02	0.272894E + 04	0.258987E + 03	0.527896E + 00	−0.313900E − 02
30.00	0.50	1	0.41830	0.100000E + 01	−0.921470E + 00	0.107280E + 02	0.111808E + 04	0.546615E − 01	0.780883E − 05	−0.177458E − 10	−0.175914E − 16
			2.54657	0.100000E + 01	0.913851E + 02	0.128517E + 05	0.106159E + 07	−0.134532E + 00	−0.393869E − 04	0.109550E − 09	0.568187E − 16
			3.82173	0.100000E + 01	0.456413E + 03	0.190114E + 06	0.616184E + 08	−0.870943E + 00	−0.222473E − 03	0.601123E − 09	0.348283E − 15
			1.17029	0.100000E + 01	0.172218E + 02	0.708874E + 01	0.610400E + 03	0.172390E − 01	−0.153885E − 05	0.751167E − 11	−0.290984E − 17
30.00	0.50	2	0.99276	0.100000E + 01	−0.178816E + 01	0.250046E + 01	0.792263E + 01	0.294716E + 00	0.347538E − 03	−0.643342E − 08	−0.485673E − 13
			2.00210	0.100000E + 01	0.375857E + 01	0.273373E + 01	0.169035E + 02	0.183211E + 00	0.143649E − 03	−0.210066E − 08	−0.271656E − 13
			3.01224	0.100000E + 01	0.161946E + 02	0.334492E + 03	0.464556E + 04	−0.644131E − 01	−0.308295E − 03	0.747889E − 08	0.205194E − 13
			4.07171	0.100000E + 01	0.682397E + 02	0.379882E + 04	0.159955E + 06	−0.108589E + 01	−0.216731E − 02	0.467285E − 07	0.218216E − 12
30.00	0.50	3	1.49964	0.100000E + 01	−0.196594E + 01	0.205343E + 01	−0.160252E + 01	0.928582E + 00	0.363982E − 02	−0.227690E − 06	−0.576578E − 11
			4.43704	0.100000E + 01	0.194519E + 02	0.338439E + 03	0.439057E + 04	−0.905721E + 00	−0.649815E − 02	0.480633E − 06	0.709085E − 11
			3.70593	0.100000E + 01	0.729347E + 01	0.579830E + 02	0.351499E + 03	0.126398E + 00	−0.802919E − 03	0.836190E − 07	−0.162272E − 12
			2.99692	0.100000E + 01	0.243846E + 01	0.211604E + 01	0.323424E + 01	0.544283E + 00	0.150876E − 02	−0.780987E − 07	−0.308692E − 11
30.00	1.00	1	0.42474	0.100000E + 01	−0.419750E + 00	0.238017E + 02	0.205116E + 04	0.267358E + 00	0.297568E − 03	−0.537309E − 08	−0.433065E − 13
			2.32950	0.100000E + 01	0.532158E + 02	0.509381E + 04	0.294644E + 06	−0.774618E + 00	−0.159488E − 02	0.344691E − 07	0.159084E − 12
			3.41916	0.100000E + 01	0.149021E + 03	0.416426E + 05	0.940091E + 07	−0.244200E + 01	−0.455255E − 02	0.946750E − 07	0.496128E − 12
			1.11493	0.100000E + 01	0.124556E + 02	0.145670E + 01	−0.108931E + 03	0.836310E − 02	−0.176067E − 03	0.469361E − 08	0.639301E − 14
30.00	1.00	2	0.99463	0.100000E + 01	−0.156018E + 01	0.365299E + 01	0.232164E + 02	0.226021E + 01	0.197443E − 01	−0.288356E − 05	−0.179510E − 09
			1.97704	0.100000E + 01	0.325882E + 01	0.367522E + 01	0.261098E + 02	0.928155E + 00	0.415528E − 02	−0.352646E − 06	−0.635408E − 10
			2.82554	0.100000E + 01	0.119194E + 02	0.179029E + 03	0.188677E + 04	−0.133505E + 01	−0.220860E − 01	0.385105E − 05	0.136245E − 09
			3.69349	0.100000E + 01	0.373043E + 02	0.143669E + 04	0.425633E + 05	−0.742324E + 01	−0.916006E − 01	0.147370E − 04	0.685722E − 09
30.00	1.00	3	1.49955	0.100000E + 01	−0.190194E + 01	0.215446E + 01	−0.100111E + 01	0.117091E + 02	0.304132E + 00	−0.146395E − 03	−0.322956E − 07
			3.56948	0.100000E + 01	0.608448E + 01	0.384593E + 02	0.192151E + 03	−0.206716E + 01	−0.121355E + 00	0.728847E − 04	0.784505E − 08
			4.07567	0.100000E + 01	0.126229E + 02	0.151831E + 03	0.137861E + 04	−0.121086E + 02	−0.426262E + 00	0.226043E − 03	0.377058E − 07
			2.98926	0.100000E + 01	0.229604E + 01	0.228183E + 01	0.389296E + 01	0.418438E + 01	0.705265E − 01	−0.250863E − 04	−0.105096E − 07
30.00	1.50	1	0.42329	0.100000E + 01	0.286218E + 00	0.355743E + 02	0.243766E + 04	0.735471E + 00	0.257227E − 02	−0.153077E − 06	−0.441278E − 11
			2.19685	0.100000E + 01	0.308016E + 02	0.198628E + 04	0.772338E + 05	−0.172797E + 01	−0.108933E − 01	0.773043E − 06	0.131633E − 10
			3.10802	0.100000E + 01	0.639192E + 02	0.119457E + 05	0.193121E + 07	−0.362945E + 01	−0.204786E − 01	0.135275E − 05	0.283930E − 10
			1.08742	0.100000E + 01	0.931875E + 01	−0.949327E + 01	−0.919994E + 03	−0.572331E − 01	−0.182799E − 02	0.156240E − 06	0.110372E − 11

TABLE 4.—Continued

(1)	(2)	(3)	(4)	(5)	(6)	(7)	(8)	(9)	(10)	(11)	(12)
30.00	1.50	2	0.99371	$0.100000E + 01$	$-0.107370E + 01$	$0.532351E + 01$	$0.391300E + 02$	$0.102710E + 02$	$0.259675E + 00$	$-0.123452E - 03$	$-0.281113E - 07$
			2.70440	$0.100000E + 01$	$0.876166E + 01$	$0.968290E + 02$	$0.784724E + 03$	$-0.600101E + 01$	$-0.239962E + 00$	$0.131808E - 03$	$0.196406E - 07$
			1.95334	$0.100000E + 01$	$0.297239E + 01$	$0.451466E + 01$	$0.302475E + 02$	$0.300479E + 01$	$0.340393E - 01$	$-0.623983E - 05$	$-0.707881E - 08$
			3.40342	$0.100000E + 01$	$0.203320E + 02$	$0.542371E + 03$	$0.116208E + 05$	$-0.202741E + 02$	$-0.656940E + 00$	$0.328655E - 03$	$0.639620E - 07$
30.00	1.50	3	1.49750	$0.100000E + 01$	$-0.191365E + 01$	$0.173216E + 01$	$-0.324210E + 01$	$0.843334E + 02$	$0.570541E + 01$	$-0.888637E - 02$	$-0.709771E - 05$
			2.98048	$0.100000E + 01$	$0.218738E + 01$	$0.215093E + 01$	$0.290837E + 01$	$0.203367E + 02$	$0.884504E + 00$	$-0.942759E - 03$	$-0.159788E - 05$
			3.48060	$0.100000E + 01$	$0.538442E + 01$	$0.290780E + 02$	$0.127733E + 03$	$-0.200091E + 02$	$-0.207126E + 01$	$0.373232E - 02$	$0.195741E - 05$
			3.77630	$0.100000E + 01$	$0.851640E + 01$	$0.715774E + 02$	$0.463762E + 03$	$-0.539899E + 02$	$-0.450147E + 01$	$0.743515E - 02$	$0.501365E - 05$
30.00	2.00	1	0.41878	$0.100000E + 01$	$0.104300E + 01$	$0.440675E + 02$	$0.241981E + 04$	$0.157012E + 01$	$0.117230E - 01$	$-0.159388E - 05$	$-0.118818E - 09$
			2.86827	$0.100000E + 01$	$0.352052E + 02$	$0.440600E + 04$	$0.519804E + 06$	$-0.477756E + 01$	$-0.568513E - 01$	$0.823957E - 05$	$0.497234E - 09$
			2.13861	$0.100000E + 01$	$0.192017E + 02$	$0.802131E + 03$	$0.156645E + 05$	$-0.288575E + 01$	$-0.393689E - 01$	$0.645736E - 05$	$0.280948E - 09$
			1.07647	$0.100000E + 01$	$0.718541E + 01$	$-0.201419E + 02$	$-0.136856E + 04$	$-0.174618E + 00$	$-0.878283E - 02$	$0.175532E - 05$	$0.321054E - 10$
30.00	2.00	2	0.98926	$0.100000E + 01$	$-0.440893E + 00$	$0.663193E + 01$	$0.461751E + 02$	$0.351271E + 02$	$0.174801E + 01$	$-0.189293E - 02$	$-0.110436E - 05$
			2.62090	$0.100000E + 01$	$0.663310E + 01$	$0.542743E + 02$	$0.335945E + 03$	$-0.164347E + 02$	$-0.122406E + 01$	$0.151731E - 02$	$0.605616E - 06$
			1.93050	$0.100000E + 01$	$0.280597E + 01$	$0.510569E + 01$	$0.304649E + 02$	$0.811687E + 01$	$0.165650E + 00$	$-0.331344E - 04$	$-0.222953E - 06$
			3.17795	$0.100000E + 01$	$0.125685E + 02$	$0.234680E + 03$	$0.371753E + 04$	$-0.407192E + 02$	$-0.248185E + 01$	$0.271802E - 02$	$0.148997E - 05$
30.00	2.00	3	1.49261	$0.100000E + 01$	$-0.278580E + 01$	$-0.905927E + 00$	$-0.149034E + 02$	$0.321638E + 03$	$0.436078E + 02$	$-0.171287E + 00$	$-0.257199E - 03$
			3.45151	$0.100000E + 01$	$0.584695E + 01$	$0.324986E + 02$	$0.141684E + 03$	$-0.781697E + 02$	$-0.148294E + 02$	$0.619980E - 01$	$0.735206E - 04$
			3.45151	$0.100000E + 01$	$0.906609E + 01$	$0.674642E + 02$	$0.355551E + 03$	$-0.181083E + 03$	$-0.280991E + 02$	$0.107145E + 00$	$0.166344E - 03$
			2.98183	$0.100000E + 01$	$0.199550E + 01$	$0.110515E + 01$	$-0.179603E + 01$	$0.655153E + 02$	$0.482614E + 01$	$-0.104888E - 01$	$-0.512123E - 04$
30.00	2.50	1	0.41399	$0.100000E + 01$	$0.173148E + 01$	$0.484734E + 02$	$0.215390E + 04$	$0.289363E + 01$	$0.372060E - 01$	$-0.944379E - 05$	$-0.152253E - 08$
			2.68884	$0.100000E + 01$	$0.226364E + 02$	$0.190935E + 04$	$0.166338E + 06$	$-0.611836E + 01$	$-0.126834E + 00$	$0.330860E - 04$	$0.467620E - 08$
			2.14348	$0.100000E + 01$	$0.127879E + 02$	$0.290391E + 03$	$-0.538906E + 04$	$-0.437122E + 01$	$-0.107261E + 00$	$0.339130E - 04$	$-0.298590E - 08$
			1.07193	$0.100000E + 01$	$0.568519E + 01$	$-0.278488E + 02$	$-0.147225E + 04$	$-0.316619E + 00$	$-0.286632E - 01$	$0.112507E - 04$	$0.386623E - 09$
30.00	2.50	2	0.97923	$0.100000E + 01$	$-0.111322E + 00$	$0.583941E + 01$	$0.337173E + 02$	$0.946926E + 02$	$0.773250E + 01$	$-0.161174E - 01$	$-0.184464E - 04$
			1.91158	$0.100000E + 01$	$0.268937E + 01$	$0.522740E + 01$	$0.268841E + 02$	$0.193055E + 02$	$0.565306E + 00$	$0.920497E - 04$	$-0.335875E - 05$
			2.52210	$0.100000E + 01$	$0.545355E + 01$	$0.350693E + 02$	$0.177795E + 03$	$-0.318095E + 02$	$-0.401588E + 01$	$0.961139E - 02$	$0.737435E - 05$
			2.98648	$0.100000E + 01$	$0.960345E + 01$	$0.135346E + 03$	$0.165104E + 04$	$-0.707953E + 02$	$-0.687503E + 01$	$0.135648E - 01$	$0.166816E - 04$
30.00	2.50	3	1.48930	$0.100000E + 01$	$-0.575333E + 01$	$-0.704992E + 01$	$-0.382052E + 02$	$0.439601E + 03$	$0.198291E + 03$	$-0.212361E + 01$	$-0.707431E - 03$
			2.99927	$0.100000E + 01$	$0.176472E + 01$	$-0.249665E + 00$	$-0.690279E + 01$	$0.148169E + 03$	$0.132952E + 02$	$-0.366299E - 01$	$-0.593655E - 03$
			3.29905	$0.100000E + 01$	$0.533075E + 01$	$0.231464E + 02$	$0.715308E + 02$	$-0.881421E + 01$	$-0.364482E + 02$	$0.394386E + 00$	$0.169309E - 04$
			3.29905	$0.100000E + 01$	$0.203451E + 02$	$0.156405E + 03$	$0.714174E + 03$	$-0.691786E + 03$	$-0.188005E + 03$	$0.137465E + 01$	$0.337601E - 02$

N equations are provided by the requirement that the free-surface condition, or Eq. 35, be satisfied at the points

$$x_j = \frac{\ell_u}{2}\, \xi_j; \quad j = 0, 1, \ldots, N - 1 \dots\dots\dots\dots\dots\dots\dots (39)$$

in which ℓ_u is the width of the free surface when it is undisturbed, and is given by

$$\ell_u = \ell + 2 \cot \alpha \dots\dots\dots\dots\dots\dots\dots\dots\dots\dots\dots\dots\dots (40)$$

When x_j is given by Eq. 38, the corresponding values for θ and r are given by

$$\tan \theta_j = \frac{x_j}{y}; \quad \text{with} \quad y = \frac{\ell}{2} \tan \alpha; \quad \text{and} \quad r_j = x_j \csc \theta_j \dots\dots\dots\dots (41)$$

When x_j is given by Eq. 39, the corresponding θ and r are given by

$$\tan \theta_j = \frac{x_j}{y}; \quad r_j = x_j \csc \theta_j \dots\dots\dots\dots\dots\dots\dots\dots\dots\dots (42)$$

with y given by Eq. 35.

With the $2N$ equations, linear in the A's and B's, which are provided by requiring Eqs. 33 and 35 to be satisfied at N points, we demand, for a nontrivial solution, that the determinant of the coefficients of the A's and B's be zero, thereby obtaining an equation in λ. We obtain in this way, in principle, $2N$ eigenvalues for λ, and for each eigenvalue of λ we obtain a set of values for the $2N$ coefficients $A_1, \ldots, A_n$, and $B_1, \ldots, B_n$. If we order the eigenvalues for λ in an ascending order, as $\lambda_1, \lambda_2, \ldots, \lambda_{2N}$, then the smaller j is, the more accurate λ_j is. In general, the value λ_j is not very accurate for $j > N$. It is wise to take only the first few λ's so obtained as sufficiently accurate. Note that the first eigen-

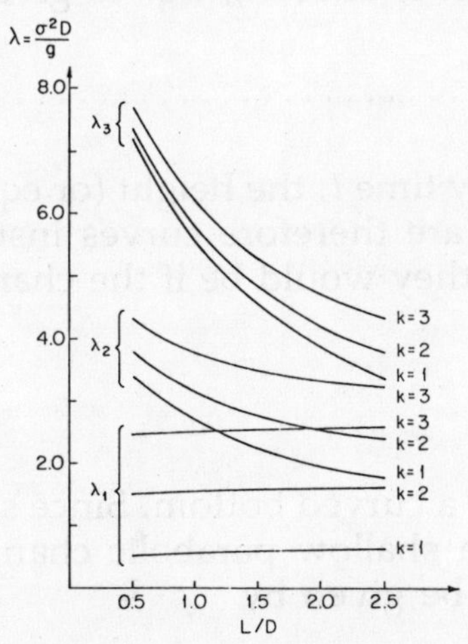

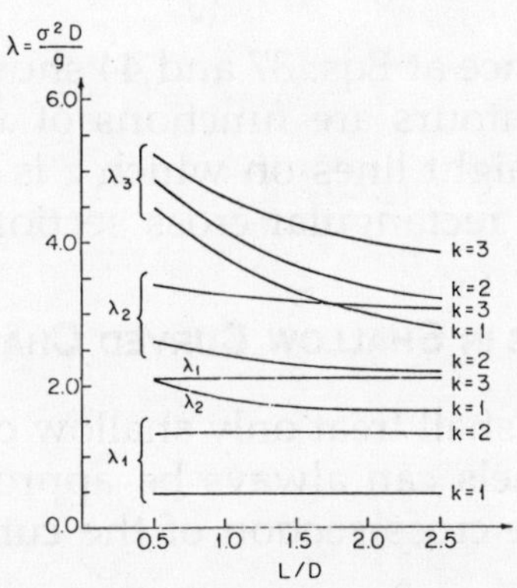

FIG. 9.—First Three Eigenvalues of $\lambda (= \sigma^2 D/g)$ for Symmetric Modes of Waves Propagating Longitudinally in Trapezoidal Channels. $\alpha = 60°$; $k = 2\pi D/L'$ = Wave Number

FIG. 10.—First Three Eigenvalues of $\lambda (= \sigma^2 D/g)$ for Symmetric Modes of Waves Propagating Longitudinally in Trapezoidal Channels. $\alpha = 45°$; $k = 2\pi D/L'$ = Wave Number

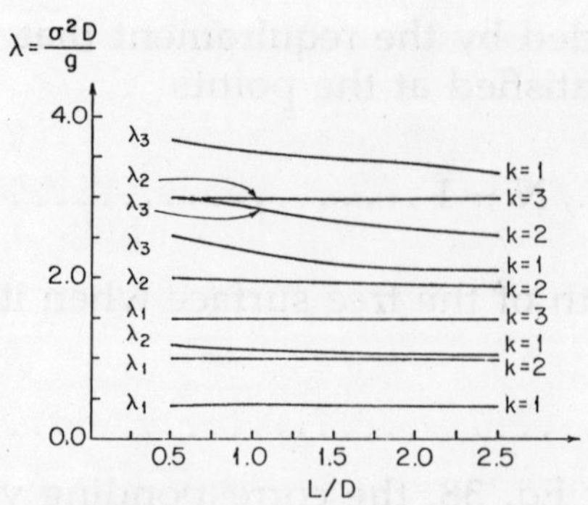

FIG. 11.—First Three Eigenvalues of $\lambda\,(=\sigma^2 D/g)$ for Symmetric Modes of Waves Propagating Longitudinally in Trapezoidal Channels. $\alpha = 30°$; $k = 2\pi D/L' =$ **Wave Number**

values λ_1, corresponds to a purely longitudinal mode, and all higher eigenvalues correspond to combined (sloshing and longitudinal) modes.

The eigenvalues λ_n, indicated by the word "value," are given in Table 4 for various channel shapes and three different values of the wave number k. The first three λ's are given graphically in Figs. 9, 10, and 11, for various values of α and k. The coefficients A_n and B_n are also given as components of the vectors A and B in Table 4, for each of the eigenvalues λ_n.

Note that the contour lines (of equal height) are lines of constant η, η being the free-surface displacement related to ϕ by

$$\frac{\partial \eta}{\partial t} = \frac{\partial \phi}{\partial y} \dots\dots\dots\dots\dots\dots\dots\dots\dots\dots\dots\dots\dots\dots\dots\dots\dots\dots (43)$$

on the free surface. If the real part of Eq. 26 is chosen (it being immaterial whether the real of the imaginary part is chosen), Eq. 43 gives

$$\eta = -\frac{\sin(kz - \sigma t)}{\sigma}\frac{\partial \phi_1}{\partial y} \quad \text{at} \quad y = 1 + \frac{\ell}{2}\tan\alpha \dots\dots\dots\dots\dots\dots\dots (44)$$

A glance at Eqs. 37 and 44 shows that, at any time t, the height (or equal-η) contours are functions of x and z, and are therefore curves instead of straight lines on which z is constant, as they would be if the channel had a rectangular cross section.

WAVES IN SHALLOW CURVED CHANNELS

We shall treat only shallow channels with a curved bottom. Since such channels can always be approximated by a shallow parabolic channel, let the cross section of the curved channel be given by

$$d = D(1 - \xi^2), \quad \text{with} \quad \xi = \frac{x}{b} \dots\dots\dots\dots\dots\dots\dots\dots\dots\dots\dots\dots\dots (45)$$

in which $d =$ depth; $D =$ maximum depth; the Cartesian coordinate x is measured along the width of the channel from the midpoint of the free surface, and $b =$ half-width of the free surface. The shape given by

Eq. 45 is parabolic, and any symmetric shallow curved channel can be represented by this parabolic shape.

We shall consider sloshing modes first. For $b >> D$, we shall use the shallow-water theory based on the assumption that the velocity is uniform throughout the depth (i.e., is independent of y) and that the vertical component of the velocity is small enough for the pressure to be hydrostatic in the vertical direction. (As a matter of fact, the second part of the assumption will not be used here.) The equation of continuity for two-dimensional flow (independent of the longitudinal Cartesian coordinate z) is then $\partial\eta/\partial t + \partial/\partial x\,[(d + \eta)\partial\phi/\partial x] = 0$, in which η is the displacement of the free surface from its mean position and ϕ is the velocity potential. Since small-amplitude motion is being considered, this equation can be written as

$$\frac{\partial\eta}{\partial t} + \frac{\partial}{\partial x}\left(d\,\frac{\partial\phi}{\partial x}\right) = 0 \dots\dots\dots\dots\dots (46)$$

with the d given by Eq. 45. The Bernoulli equation, applied at the free surface, gives

$$\frac{\partial\phi}{\partial t} + g\eta = 0 \quad\text{at}\quad y = 0 \dots\dots\dots\dots\dots (47)$$

With $\quad \phi = f(\xi)\,e^{-i\sigma t}; \quad \lambda = \dfrac{\sigma^2 b^2}{gD} \dots\dots\dots\dots\dots (48)$

elimination of η between Eqs. 46 and 47 gives, with primes indicating differentiation with respect to ξ,

$$[(1 - \xi^2)f']' + \lambda f = 0 \dots\dots\dots\dots\dots (49)$$

which is Legendre's differential equation. For the solution to be nonsingular at $\xi = \pm 1$ (the edges of water when undisturbed),

$$\lambda = n(n + 1) \dots\dots\dots\dots\dots (50)$$

$$\text{and}\quad f = P_n(\xi) \dots\dots\dots\dots\dots (51)$$

in which P_n denotes the Legendre polynomial of nth order. With λ and f known, ϕ is known and η can be found from Eq. 47. The antisymmetric modes (with respect to x) correspond to odd integral values of n, and the symmetric modes correspond to even integral values of n. The results contained in Eqs. 50 and 51 have been known for some time. See, for instance, p. 277 of Lamb's book (2).

Next we consider waves propagating in the z direction. The equation of continuity is now

$$\frac{\partial\eta}{\partial t} + \frac{\partial}{\partial x}\left(d\,\frac{\partial\phi}{\partial x}\right) + \frac{\partial}{\partial z}\left(d\,\frac{\partial\phi}{\partial z}\right) = 0 \dots\dots\dots\dots\dots (52)$$

in which $\quad \phi = f(\xi)e^{i(kz - \sigma t)} \dots\dots\dots\dots\dots (53)$

The Bernoulli equation is still given by Eq. 47. Elimination of η between it and Eq. 52, using Eqs. 45 and 53, gives

$$[(1 - \xi^2)f']' + [\lambda - k^2(1 - \xi^2)]f = 0 \dots\dots\dots\dots\dots (54)$$

The wave number k is now given by

$$k = \frac{2\pi b}{L'} \dots\dots\dots\dots\dots\dots\dots\dots\dots\dots\dots\dots\dots\dots\dots\dots \tag{55}$$

L' being the longitudinal wavelength. We shall consider long waves and assume $k^2 \ll 1$, and solve Eq. 54 by expansion of f and λ in power-series of k^2.

$$f = g_0 + k^2 g_1 + k^4 g_2 + \dots\dots\dots\dots\dots\dots\dots\dots\dots\dots\dots\dots \tag{56}$$

$$\lambda = \mu_0 + k^2 \mu_1 + k^4 \mu_2 + \dots \dots\dots\dots\dots\dots\dots\dots\dots\dots \tag{57}$$

Substituting Eqs. 56 and 57 into Eq. 54 and sorting out the various powers of k, we see immediately that

$$\mu_0 = n(n + 1); \quad g_0 = P_n(\xi) \dots\dots\dots\dots\dots\dots\dots\dots\dots\dots \tag{58}$$

To determine μ_1 and g_1, we treat the equation obtained from the terms containing k^2, which is

$$[(1 - \xi^2) g_1']' + n(n + 1) g_1 = (1 - \xi^2) g_0 - \mu_1 g_0 \dots\dots\dots\dots\dots \tag{59}$$

If g_1 is to be nonsingular at $\xi = \pm 1$, as we want it to be, the right-hand side of Eq. 59 must be orthogonal to g_0. For we can multiply Eq. 59 by g_0 and integrate between -1 and 1, by parts when dealing with the first term in Eq. 59, and obtain zero for the left-hand side, giving

$$\int_{-1}^{1} (1 - \mu_1 - \xi^2) g_0^2 d\beta = 0 \dots\dots\dots\dots\dots\dots\dots\dots\dots\dots\dots\dots \tag{60}$$

which determines μ_1. Then we can obtain g_1 by solving Eq. 59. In practice, it is more convenient to use the familiar identities involving Legendre polynomials, such as given on p. 115 of Jahnke and Emde's book (1). Doing so, and denoting the left-hand side of Eq. 59 by $\mathscr{L} g_1$ in order to define $\mathscr{L}$, we find

$$\mathscr{L}\left[\frac{1}{6 + 4n} \left(\xi^2 P_n - \frac{2n}{2n - 1} \xi P_{n-1} \right) \right] = -\xi^2 P_n + \frac{2n^2 + 2n - 1}{(2n + 3)(2n - 1)} P_n$$

so that $\quad g_1 = \frac{1}{6 + 4n} \left(\xi^2 P_n - \frac{2n}{2n - 1} \xi P_{n-1} \right) \dots\dots\dots\dots\dots\dots \tag{61}$

$$\mu_1 = 1 - \frac{2n^2 + 2n - 1}{(2n + 3)(2n - 1)} \dots\dots\dots\dots\dots\dots\dots\dots\dots\dots\dots\dots \tag{62}$$

We can go on like this to determine g_2 and μ_2, and so on. For each integral value of n, i.e., for the nth mode, we have then an eigenvalue λ_n and an eigenfunction f_n, and the problem for long waves, previously unsolved, is now solved.

It is understood that either the real or imaginary part of Eq. 48 can be taken to be the solution for sloshing modes, and either the real or imaginary part of Eq. 53 can be used as the solution for waves propagating longitudinally. With this understanding, it is evident that for waves propagating longitudinally and for any mode (i.e., for any n), the contours of equal height (or the equal-η lines) of the free surface are, unlike those for a rectangular channel, not straight, as can be seen from Eq. 53. However, these contours are not to be confused with the crest (or trough) lines, which are lines joining the points of maximum (or minimum) heights at various values of x. These crest lines and trough lines are indeed straight, as in rectangular channels.

CONCLUSIONS

From the foregoing we draw the following conclusions.

1. Methods for solving problems of gravity-wave motion in trapezoidal channels have been given.
2. The frequencies and velocity potentials for sloshing antisymmetric wave motion in trapezoidal channels of various cross-sectional shapes, and the flow patterns for two modes, are given.
3. The frequencies and velocity potentials for various modes of symmetric waves propagating along the longitudinal axis of trapezoidal channels of various cross-sectional shapes are given.
4. Analytical solutions for all modes of gravity-wave motion in shallow curved channels have been found on the basis of the shallow-water theory.

ACKNOWLEDGMENT

The work of the senior writer (C.-S. Yih) has been partially supported by the Office of Naval Research.

APPENDIX I.—REFERENCES

1. Jahnke, E., and Emde, F., *Table of Functions*, Dover Publications, New York, N.Y., 1945.
2. Lamb, H., *Hydrodynamics*, Dover Publications, New York, N.Y., 1945.
3. Lanczos, C., *Applied Analysis*, Prentice Hall, Englewood Cliffs, N.J., 1956.
4. Watson, G. N., *Theory of Bessel Functions*, 2nd ed., Cambridge Univ. Press, Cambridge, England, 1944.
5. Yih, C.-S., "Comparison Theorems for Water Waves in Basins of Variable Depth," Quarterly of Applied Mathematics, Vol. 33, 1976, pp. 387–394.

APPENDIX II.—NOTATION

The following symbols are used in this paper:

$$
\begin{aligned}
A, B, C, D, E &= \text{points;} \\
a &= \text{distance of point A from origin in } t\text{-plane;} \\
b &= \text{half width of curved channel at free surface;} \\
b, c &= \text{limits of integration;} \\
D &= \text{maximum depth in the channel, when not used as point;} \\
d &= \text{variable depth of curved channel;} \\
d' &= \text{dimensionless depth of rectangular cross section in the } z'\text{-plane;}
\end{aligned}
$$

$$
\begin{aligned}
e \;&=\; \text{distance of point } E \text{ from origin in } t\text{-plane;}\\
F(\zeta) \;&=\; \text{function of } \zeta;\\
f(r) \;&=\; \text{function of } r;\\
f(t) \;&=\; \text{function of } t,\ \text{not same as function represented by } f(r);\\
f(\xi) \;&=\; \text{function of } \xi,\ \text{not same as functions represented by } f(r) \text{ and } f(t);\\
g \;&=\; \text{gravitational acceleration;}\\
g(t) \;&=\; \text{function of } t;\\
g_0(\xi),\ g_1(\xi),\ \ldots \;&=\; \text{functions of } \xi;\\
g_n(r); \;&=\; \text{functions of } r,\ \text{different from } g_n(\xi);\\
h(x') \;&=\; \text{function of } x';\\
h_n(r) \;&=\; \text{functions of } r;\\
j,m,n \;&=\; \text{integers;}\\
k \;&=\; 2\pi D/L' \text{ for trapezoidal channels, or } 2\pi b/L' \text{ for curved channels;}\\
L \;&=\; \text{minimum width of trapezoid;}\\
L' \;&=\; \text{longitudinal wavelength;}\\
\mathscr{L} \;&=\; \text{differential operator;}\\
\ell \;&=\; L/D;\\
M,M' \;&=\; \text{coefficients in the Schwarz-Cristoffel transformation;}\\
N \;&=\; \text{number of terms taken;}\\
O \;&=\; \text{origin;}\\
P_n \;&=\; \text{Legendre polynomial of order } n;\\
r,\theta,z \;&=\; \text{cylindrical coordinates;}\\
t \;&=\; \text{time, or complex variable;}\\
x,y,z \;&=\; \text{Cartesian coordinates;}\\
x',y' \;&=\; \text{Cartesian coordinates in the } z'\text{-plane;}\\
z \;&=\; \text{complex variable } x + iy,\ \text{when not used as co-ordinate;}\\
z' \;&=\; x' + iy';\\
\alpha \;&=\; \text{angle of inclination of sloping sides of trapezoid;}\\
\beta \;&=\; 1 - \alpha/\pi \text{ for sloshing modes; } \pi/2 - \alpha \text{ for longitudinal modes;}\\
\zeta \;&=\; \text{variable;}\\
\zeta_m \;&=\; \text{coordinate related to } \xi_m;\\
\eta \;&=\; \text{surface displacement;}\\
\lambda \;&=\; \sigma^2 D/g \text{ for trapezoidal channels, or } \sigma^2 b^2/gD \text{ for curved channels;}\\
\lambda_1,\ \lambda_2,\ \lambda_3 \ldots \;&=\; \text{eigenvalues of } \lambda \text{ for various modes;}\\
\mu_0,\ \mu_1,\ \ldots \;&=\; \text{coefficients in expansion of } \lambda \text{ in powers of } k^2;\\
\xi \;&=\; x/b \text{ for curved channels, or variable for Legendre polynomial } P_n(\xi);\\
\xi_m \;&=\; \text{the } m\text{th zero of the Legendre polynomial } P_n(\xi);\\
\sigma \;&=\; \text{circular frequency;}\\
\phi \;&=\; \text{velocity potential; and}\\
\psi \;&=\; \text{stream function.}
\end{aligned}
$$

J. Fluid Mech. (1983), *vol.* 130, *pp.* 109–121

Waves in meandering streams

By CHIA-SHUN YIH

The University of Michigan, Ann Arbor, Michigan 48109

(Received 25 June 1982)

Free-surface and internal stationary waves in a meandering stream are treated, and analytical solutions given. It is shown that for each category there is an infinite number of Froude numbers, depending on the wavenumber of the meander, at which resonance occurs, and the amplitude of one of the wave components becomes infinite, according to the linear theory. These critical Froude numbers are interpreted physically. Furthermore, variable depth is treated for the case of free-surface waves, and in this treatment it is shown, incidentally, how the eigenvalues of a singular differential equation can be found under the requirement that the eigenfunction be non-singular.

Finally, an attempt is made to explain the self-induced, non-stationary waves in water flowing between corrugated vertical walls, found by Binnie (1960), by an instability mechanism proposed by Yih (1976). There is strong evidence that this mechanism is at work, at least when a sloshing mode is involved in the wave-triad interaction.

1. Introduction

When there is need to transport water in open channels from one location to another in a mountainous region, these channels often wind their way more or less along the contour lines of the terrain, and it has been observed that at a certain speed of flow waves of large amplitude form, endangering the unpaved part of the sidewalls. In another practice of hydraulic engineering, water is allowed to shoot at high speed down spillways on the side of a dam. At the entrance of the spillway there is necessarily a contraction, creating violent waves of a diamond pattern, which are obviously undesirable. Hence waves in meandering streams or in channels of variable width are of practical importance. Yet, while the general topic of waves has of late received much attention from research workers, especially that part of it which has to do so with solitons and the inverse-scattering theory, waves in meandering or bulging and contracting streams have seldom been treated. One possible reason for this is perhaps that the problem is not very tractable at first sight.

One of the few papers on the aforementioned problem extant in the literature is that of Binnie (1960), who observed self-induced waves in a conduit with corrugated walls, with longitudinal wavelengths which are an integral multiple of the wavelength of the wall corrugation, and with transverse wavenumbers as well. Binnie gave a brief analysis of slanted waves in otherwise *quiet* water in a rectangular channel with straight sidewalls, which serves to organize his experimental results. His analysis confirmed the existence of the waves propagating upstream, which he observed. But it did not explain how these waves arose. It will be shown at the end of this paper that these progressive waves are induced by an instability mechanism proposed by Yih (1976), originally for the instability of gravity waves in water flowing over a wavy bottom, but adaptable to apply to the stationary waves treated here.

In this paper stationary waves in a meandering stream will be analysed and a complete solution given. The waviness of the sidewalls and its consequences will be fully taken into account, and the solution will give the amplitudes of the various components of the slant waves produced by the flow through the wavy channel at any given value of the Froude number, and in particular will give the transverse wavenumber of the dominant wave at that Froude number. As the Froude number approaches any of an infinite number of critical values resonance occurs, and the amplitude of one of the infinite number of wave components approaches infinity. This result will be given a physical interpretation.

In addition, surface waves created by water flowing in a meandering stream of variable depth, as well as internal waves in a meandering channel with vertical sidewalls, are treated in turn, and similar results are obtained. The results on waves in symmetric channels of variable depth can be treated in the same way (Yih 1982).

2. Formulation of the problem

We neglect the effects of viscosity and assume the flow to be irrotational. The velocity components therefore possess a potential ϕ:

$$(u, v, w) = (\phi_x, \phi_y, \phi_z), \tag{1}$$

where the subscripts denote partial differentiation, x, y, and z are Cartesian coordinates, and u, v, and w are measured in the directions of increasing x, y, and z respectively. The fluid being assumed incompressible, the equation of continuity is

$$u_x + v_y + w_z = 0,$$

which, by virtue of (1), gives the Laplace equation

$$\phi_{xx} + \phi_{yy} + \phi_{zz} = 0, \tag{2}$$

which is the differential equation governing the flow. The coordinate z is measured vertically upward from the free surface when there is no flow, and x and y are measured down and across the channel respectively.

Let the displacement of the free surface above its mean position (which is the position it would have if there were no flow) be denoted by ζ, which is a function of x and y only, since the flow under consideration here is steady. Then the kinematic condition for the free surface is

$$u\zeta_x + v\zeta_y = w, \tag{3}$$

and the dynamic condition there is the Bernoulli equation

$$u^2 + v^2 + w^2 + 2g\zeta = \text{constant}. \tag{4}$$

Combining (3) and (4), we have

$$\left(u\frac{\partial}{\partial x} + v\frac{\partial}{\partial y}\right)(u^2 + v^2 + w^2) + 2gw = 0. \tag{5}$$

Let h be the depth of water in the meandering channel when there is no flow, L be the half-width of the channel at some cross-section, and U be the mean velocity at that cross-section. We shall use L as the lengthscale and U as the velocity scale, and define the following dimensionless variables:

$$\begin{aligned} (\hat{x}, \hat{y}, \hat{z}) &= \left(\frac{x}{L}, \frac{y}{L}, \frac{z}{L}\right), \quad (\hat{u}, \hat{v}, \hat{w}) = \left(\frac{u}{U}, \frac{v}{U}, \frac{w}{U}\right), \\ \phi &= \frac{\phi}{UL}, \quad d = \frac{h}{L}, \quad F^2 = \frac{U^2}{gL}. \end{aligned} \tag{6}$$

Then, after the carets are dropped, (2) retains its form:

$$\phi_{xx}+\phi_{yy}+\phi_{zz}=0, \tag{7}$$

which we repeat here because it is dimensionless and will be understood to be so when we later refer to (7). Equation (5), after (1) and (6) are used and the carets in (6) are dropped, now has the *dimensionless* form

$$\left(\phi_x\frac{\partial}{\partial x}+\phi_y\frac{\partial}{\partial y}\right)(\phi_x^2+\phi_y^2+\phi_z^2)+2F^{-2}\phi_z=0. \tag{8}$$

The boundary condition at the bottom of the channel is

$$\phi_z=0 \quad (z=-d), \tag{9}$$

and the condition at the vertical walls is

$$\phi_n=0, \tag{10}$$

where n is measured in a direction normal to the vertical walls bounding the stream. Equations (7)–(10) constitute the differential system governing the problem.

3. A transformation for the meandering

So far we have not taken into account the meander of the stream. This will be represented by the conformal mapping

$$x+iy=\alpha+i\beta+ia\cos k(\alpha+i\beta),$$

or

$$\left.\begin{array}{l} x=\alpha+a\sin k\alpha\sinh k\beta, \\[4pt] y=\beta+a\cos k\alpha\cosh k\beta, \end{array}\right\} \tag{11}$$

where a is an amplitude, and k is a wavenumber of the meander. From (11) we obtain the Jacobian

$$J\equiv\frac{\partial(x,y)}{\partial(\alpha,\beta)}=1+2ak\cos k\alpha\sinh k\beta+a^2k^2(\sinh^2 k\beta+\sin^2 k\alpha). \tag{12}$$

The transformation (11) gives the meander of the stream: the boundaries of the stream given by $\beta=\pm 1$ are sinuous. Of course other representations are possible, but (11), being conformal, makes subsequent calculations much simpler, and, among the conformal mappings that can possibly represent the meander, it is the simplest.

In terms of α and β (instead of x and y), (7) and (8) become

$$\frac{1}{J}(\phi_{\alpha\alpha}+\phi_{\beta\beta})+\phi_{zz}=0, \tag{13}$$

$$\frac{1}{J}\left(\phi_\alpha\frac{\partial}{\partial\alpha}+\phi_\beta\frac{\partial}{\partial\beta}\right)\left[\frac{1}{J}(\phi_\alpha^2+\phi_\beta^2)+\phi_z^2\right]+2F^{-2}\phi_z=0. \tag{14}$$

Equation (9) remains unchanged, but (10) now has the form

$$\phi_\beta=0 \quad (\beta=\pm 1). \tag{15}$$

The governing system now consists of (13), (14), (9) and (15).

4. Solution of the problem

Recalling that a in (11) is the amplitude of the meander and therefore the amplitude of the waves produced by it, we expand ϕ in a power series in a:

$$\phi = \phi_0 + a\phi_1 + a^2\phi_2 + \dots. \tag{16}$$

It is evident that

$$\phi_0 = \alpha, \tag{17}$$

which says in effect that in the absence of meander the flow is just unidirectional and uniform flow in a straight channel. Substituting (16) and (17) into (13) and (14), and carefully sorting out the terms of first order in a, we obtain

$$\phi_{1\alpha\alpha} + \phi_{1\beta\beta} + \phi_{1zz} = 0, \tag{18}$$

$$\phi_{1\alpha\alpha} + F^{-2}\phi_{1z} = -k^2 \sin k\alpha \sinh k\beta. \tag{19}$$

The solution for ϕ_1 satisfying (9) and (15) as well as (18) and (19) is, since $\sinh k\beta$ is odd in β,

$$\phi_1 = \sum_{n=1}^{\infty} B_n \sin k\alpha \sin \tfrac{1}{2}(2n-1)\pi\beta \cosh \gamma_n(z+d), \tag{20}$$

where

$$\gamma_n = [k^2 + \tfrac{1}{4}(2n-1)^2 \pi^2]^{\frac{1}{2}}, \tag{21}$$

and B_n is given by

$$B_n C_n = -k^2 \int_{-1}^{1} \sinh k\beta \sin \tfrac{1}{2}(2n-1)\pi\beta \, d\beta = \frac{(-1)^n 2k^3 \cosh k}{\gamma_n^2}, \tag{22}$$

where

$$C_n = -k^2 \cosh \gamma_n d + F^{-2}\gamma_n \sinh \gamma_n d. \tag{23}$$

To order a, then, the *dimensionless* ζ is obtained from (4) (which is in dimensional form) as

$$\zeta = -ak^{-1} \cos k\alpha \sum_{n=1}^{\infty} B_n \gamma_n \sinh \gamma_n d \sin \tfrac{1}{2}(2n-1)\pi\beta. \tag{24}$$

In obtaining (24), we have made use of the result

$$u^2 + v^2 = \frac{1}{J}(\phi_\alpha^2 + \phi_\beta^2)$$

as well as (22), which gives the Fourier coefficients for $\sinh k\beta$. The free-surface displacement given by (24) is shown for one half-wavelength of the meander in figure 1. A perspective view of the free surface is shown in figure 2.

Equations (16), (20), and (23) give the results of the linear theory. Before going on to discuss the next approximation, which takes terms $O(a^2)$ into account, we shall discuss the outstanding features of the results of the linear theory and interpret them in physical terms. First, we see from (22) and (23) that $B_n \to \infty$ when $C_n \to 0$. But for $C_n = 0$

$$F^2 = \frac{\gamma_n^2}{k^2} \frac{\tanh \gamma_n d}{\gamma_n}$$

or

$$\frac{k}{\gamma_n} U = \left(\frac{gh \tanh \gamma_n d}{\gamma_n d} \right)^{\frac{1}{2}}. \tag{25}$$

In (25), k/γ_n is the cosine of the angle between the direction of increasing α and the direction normal to the wave fronts of the slanted waves with wavenumber $\gamma_n d$ (which is the wavenumber non-dimensionalized with the length h instead of the length L), and the right-hand side is the wave speed of waves with the wavenumber $\gamma_n d$. Thus

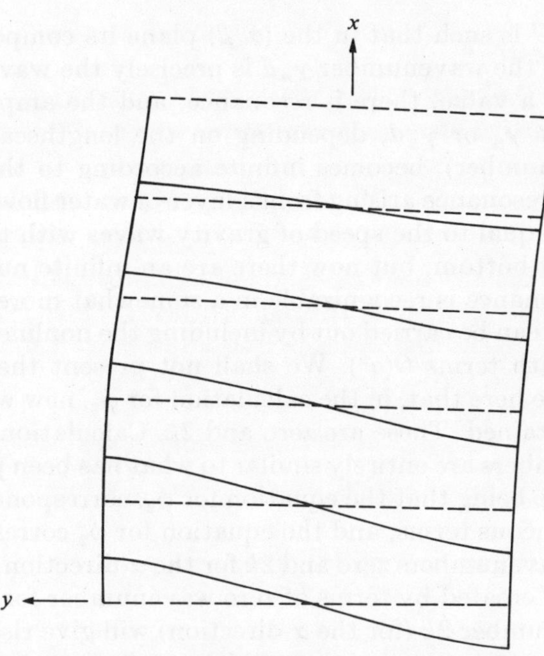

FIGURE 1. Graphs showing the free surface, at $F = 1$, $k = 0.4$, $d = 0.2$. The scale of x is $\frac{1}{4}\pi$ times that of y. The dotted lines are constant-α lines on the undisturbed free surface, for $10k\alpha/\pi = 0$, 1, 2, 3, 4, 5. On the highest one ($4\alpha/\pi = 5$), $\zeta = 0$. The dimensionless ζ/a is plotted above or below the dotted lines. The maximum ζ/a is 0.217, at $\alpha = 0$ and $\beta = 1$. The figure can be extended to $4\alpha/\pi = 10$ by antisymmetry, and then the whole figure can be reflected across the plane $\alpha = 0$ to get the free surface for a whole wavelength.

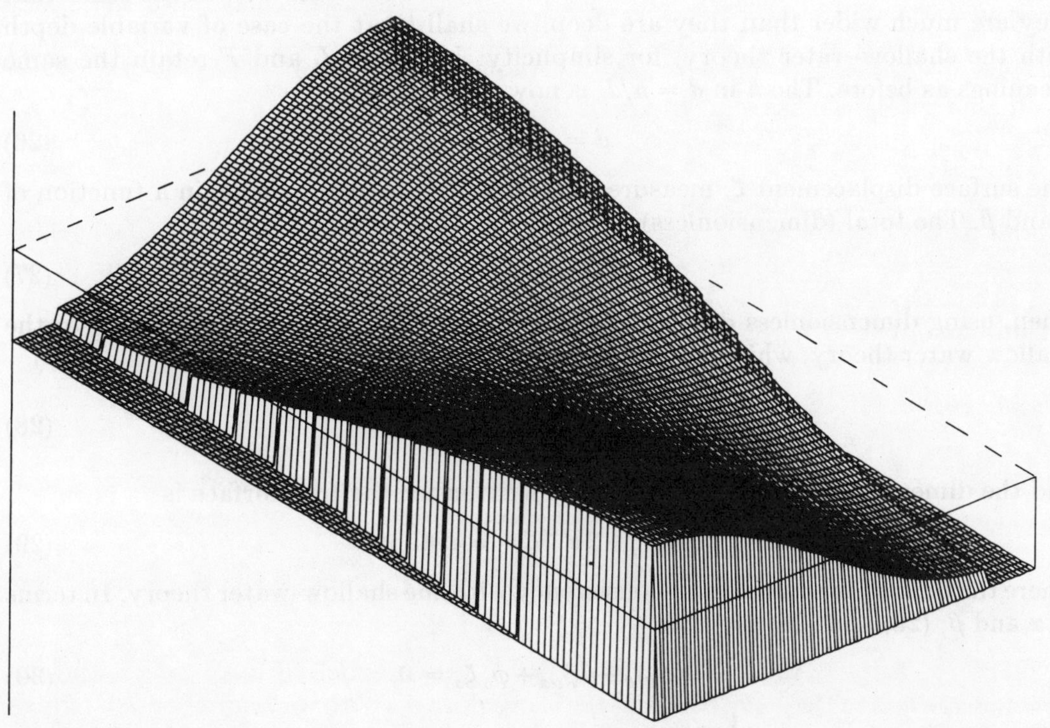

FIGURE 2. Free surface in perspective for half a wavelength, for $F^2 = 0.8$, $k = 0.75$, $d = 0.23$.

114   *C.-S. Yih*

the nth critical value of U is such that in the (α, β)-plane its component normal to the fronts of the waves of the wavenumber $\gamma_n d$ is precisely the wave speed of those waves. When U has such a value, there is resonance, and the amplitude of the γ_n waves (with wavenumber γ_n or $\gamma_n d$, depending on the lengthscale used to non-dimensionalize the wavenumber), becomes infinite according to the linear theory. This is reminiscent of the resonance arising from a layer of water flowing over a wavy surface when its speed is equal to the speed of gravity waves with the wavenumber equal to that of the wavy bottom, but now there are an infinite number of critical values for U, and the resonance is recognizable in a somewhat more subtle way.

Higher approximations can be carried out by including the nonlinear terms in (12), (13) and (14), starting with terms $O(a^2)$. We shall not present the rather lengthy calculations, but shall note here that, in the calculation for ϕ_2, new wavenumbers for the α-direction will be obtained. These are zero and $2k$. Calculations to account for terms with these wavenumbers are entirely similar to what has been presented in this section, the only difference being that the equation for ϕ_2, corresponding to (18), will now contain non-homogeneous terms, and the equation for ϕ_2 corresponding to (19) will contain terms with wavenumbers zero and $2k$ for the α-direction. No new critical values for F (or U) will be created by terms of zero wavenumber for the α-direction, but the terms with wavenumber $2k$ (for the α-direction) will give rise to new critical values for F, corresponding to new resonances, which can be interpreted in much the same way as the resonances presented in detail for the basic wavenumber k in this section.

5. Meandering channels of variable depth

Since natural streams have variable depth and are often shallow in the sense that they are much wider than they are deep, we shall treat the case of variable depth with the shallow-water theory, for simplicity. Let α, β, L and F retain the same meanings as before. The h in $d = h/L$ is now variable. Let

$$d = 1 - \beta^2. \tag{26}$$

The surface displacement ζ, measured in units of L as before, is again a function of α and β. The total (dimensionless) depth is

$$D = d + \zeta. \tag{27}$$

Then, using dimensionless $\phi, x,$ and y, the equation of continuity, according to the shallow-water theory, which will be used here, is

$$\frac{\partial}{\partial x}(D\phi_x) + \frac{\partial}{\partial y}(D\phi_y) = 0, \tag{28}$$

and the dimensionless Bernoulli equation written for the free surface is

$$\phi_x^2 + \phi_y^2 + 2F^{-2}\zeta = \text{constant}, \tag{29}$$

where the term ϕ_z^2 is neglected, in consistency with the shallow-water theory. In terms of α and β, (28) and (29) are

$$(d\phi_\beta)_\beta + d\phi_{\alpha\alpha} + \phi_\alpha \zeta_\alpha = 0, \tag{30}$$

$$\frac{1}{J}(\phi_\alpha^2 + \phi_\beta^2) + 2F^{-2}\zeta = \text{constant}. \tag{31}$$

Using (12), (16) and (17), we obtain from (31)

$$\zeta_\alpha = -aF^2\phi_{1\alpha\alpha} - ak^2F^2 \sin k\alpha \sinh k\beta + O(a^2). \tag{32}$$

Substituting (16), (17), (26) and (32) into (30), extracting terms of first order in a, and writing

$$\phi_1 = \sin k\alpha f(\beta), \tag{33}$$

we have

$$[(1-\beta^2)f']' + [k^2F^2 - k^2(1-\beta^2)]f = F^2k^2 \sinh k\beta, \tag{34}$$

where primes indicate differentiation with respect to β. Since k is based on the *horizontal* lengthscale L, it does not have to be small for the shallow-water theory to apply. However, in most applications (to rivers especially) k is fairly small compared with 1.

We shall now consider the *non-singular* solutions (which will serve as the eigenfunctions) of the equation

$$[(1-\beta^2)G']' + [\lambda - k^2(1-\beta^2)]G = 0, \tag{35}$$

which is singular at $\beta^2 = 1$. Let

$$\begin{aligned}
\lambda &= \mu_0 + k^2\mu_1 + k^4\mu_2 + \dots, \\
G &= g_0 + k^2g_1 + k^4g_2 + \dots.
\end{aligned} \tag{36}$$

Then it is clear that

$$\mu_0 = n(n+1), \quad g_0 = P_n(\beta), \tag{37}$$

where n is an integer and P_n is the nth Legendre polynomial. To find μ_1 and g_1, we obtain from (35) and (36), upon collecting terms of order k^2,

$$\mathrm{L}g_1 \equiv [(1-\beta^2)g_1']' + n(n+1)g_1 = (1-\beta^2)g_0 - \mu_1 g_0. \tag{38}$$

If g_1 is to be non-singular at $\beta^2 = 1$, the right-hand side of (38) must be orthogonal to g_0. This can be seen by multiplying (38) by g_0 and integrating between -1 and 1 with respect to β:

$$\int_{-1}^{1} g_0 \mathrm{L}g_1 \, \mathrm{d}\beta = \int_{-1}^{1} g_1 L g_0 \, \mathrm{d}\beta = 0 = \int_{-1}^{1} (1-\mu_1-\beta^2)g_0^2 \, d\beta. \tag{39}$$

This determines μ_1, and g_1 is then found from (38). In practice, we use the well-known identities involving Legendre polynomials, such as those on p. 115 of Jahnke & Emde (1945), and find that

$$\mathrm{L}\left\{\frac{1}{6+4n}\left(\beta^2 P_n - \frac{2n}{2n-1}\beta P_{n-1}\right)\right\} = -\beta^2 P_n + \frac{2n^2+2n-1}{(2n+3)(2n-1)}P_n,$$

so that

$$g_1 = \frac{1}{6+4n}\left(\beta^2 P_n - \frac{2n}{2n-1}\beta P_{n-1}\right), \tag{40}$$

$$\mu_1 = 1 - \frac{2n^2+2n-1}{(2n+3)(2n-1)}. \tag{41}$$

We shall now, for clarity, denote the eigenvalue λ and the eigenfunction G for any particular n by λ_n and G_n, which is the nth (non-singular) eigenfunction of (35). Then, realizing that the right-hand side of (34) is odd in β, we write

$$f(\beta) = \sum_{m=1}^{\infty} B_{2m-1} G_{sm-1}. \tag{42}$$

Substituting this into (34), multiplying the result by G_{2p-1}, and integrating, we have, writing n for $2p-1$,

$$B_n(k^2F^2 - \lambda_n) \int_{-1}^{1} G_n^2 \, \mathrm{d}\beta = F^2 k^2 \int_{-1}^{1} \sinh k\beta \, G_n \, \mathrm{d}\beta, \tag{43}$$

which determines B_n (for $n = 2p-1$). Equations (43), (36), (37), and (40)–(42) then give the $f(\beta)$ in (33), and

$$\phi = \alpha + a\phi_1$$

gives the solution for a linear theory, which is all one can attempt in the shallow-water theory. In the foregoing we have determined g_n only to $O(k^2)$. It can be determined up to any power of k^2 with a little patience. For $k = \frac{1}{4}$, it is unnecessary to go beyond what has been done here. For $k = \frac{1}{2}$, the error committed in stopping at terms $O(k^2)$ in g_n is at most 6%.

For $k = \frac{1}{4}$, the integrals in (43), without their coefficients, have been evaluated. If the first integral is denoted by I_1 and the second integral by I_2, then, for $p = 1, 2, 3$ respectively,

$$I_1 = 0.6551, \quad 0.2870, \quad 0.1917;$$

$$I_2 = 0.1662, \quad 0.0005525, \quad 0.003846.$$

For $k = \frac{1}{2}$,

$$I_1 = 0.6208, \quad 0.2955, \quad 0.1993;$$

$$I_2 = 0.3298, \quad 0.0009392, \quad 0.03908;$$

again for $p = 1, 2, 3$ respectively.

The B_n determined by (43) is infinite for k^2F^2 equal to any of the infinitely many eigenvalues λ_n. There is therefore again resonance at these critical values for k^2F^2, and the physical interpretation for these critical values is analogous to that given in the case of vertical sidewalls in §4, but the mathematical arguments supporting this physical interpretation are now not so transparent, though their vestiges are still evident.

6. Internal waves in a meandering stream

If a stream is laden with sediment, or when water with stratified salinity flows during high tide backward from the sea, internal waves will be created if the stream meanders. These waves generally have a larger amplitude than surface waves and, in the case of the sediment-laden stream, may give rise to turbidity spots where the crests of the internal waves come near the free surface (where water is in contact with air).

For simplicity we shall only give the solution for the case of two layers of liquid of equal and constant depth h. The case of unequal constant depths can be treated similarly, with somewhat more complicated results but no additional difficulty whatever.

Let ρ be the density of the lower fluid and ρ' the density of the upper fluid, and let the corresponding velocity potentials be denoted by ϕ and ϕ' respectively. These both satisfy the Laplace equations.

The displacement of the interface of the two fluids will be denoted by ζ. Then (3) holds for the lower fluid, and a similar one holds for the upper fluid:

$$u'\zeta_x + v'\zeta_y = w', \tag{44}$$

where the primes indicate the upper fluid. We shall describe these in dimensional terms until a later time. Denoting the pressure by p, the Bernoulli equations for the two fluids are

$$\tfrac{1}{2}\rho q^2 + \rho g\zeta + p = C,$$

$$\tfrac{1}{2}\rho' q'^2 + \rho' g\zeta + p = C',$$

$$\tfrac{1}{2}(\rho q^2 - \rho' q'^2) + \Delta\rho g\zeta = C - C', \tag{45}$$

where

$$q^2 = u^2 + v^2 + w^2 = |\operatorname{grad}\phi|^2, \tag{46}$$

$$q'^2 = u'^2 + v'^2 + w'^2 = |\operatorname{grad}\phi'|^2, \tag{47}$$

$$\Delta\rho = \rho - \rho'. \tag{48}$$

Combining (3) with (45), we have the interfacial conditions

$$\left(\phi_x\frac{\partial}{\partial x} + \phi_y\frac{\partial}{\partial y}\right)(\rho q^2 - \rho' q'^2) + 2g\,\Delta\rho\,\phi_z = 0, \tag{49}$$

$$\left(\phi'_x\frac{\partial}{\partial x} + \phi'_y\frac{\partial}{\partial y}\right)(\rho q^2 - \rho' q'^2) + 2g\,\Delta\rho\,\phi'_z = 0. \tag{50}$$

The other boundary conditions are

$$\phi_n = 0 = \phi'_n \quad \text{at the vertical sidewalls}, \tag{51}$$

$$\phi_z = 0 \quad (z = -h), \quad \phi'_z = 0 \quad (z = h), \tag{52}$$

where n again denotes the distance along the normal to the sidewalls. The last condition in (52) is obtained by treating the free surface as if it were rigid, as one can do if $\Delta\rho$ is small compared with ρ or ρ'.

We now use the dimensionless variables defined by (6) and similar ones for the upper fluid, removing the carets afterwards, and consider a meander described by (11). The differential equation satisfied by ϕ, in dimensionless terms, remains (13), and the corresponding one for ϕ' is

$$\frac{1}{J}(\phi'_{\alpha\alpha} + \phi'_{\beta\beta}) + \phi'_{zz} = 0. \tag{53}$$

The dimensionless forms for (49) and (50) are

$$\frac{1}{J}\left(\phi_\alpha\frac{\partial}{\partial\alpha} + \phi_\beta\frac{\partial}{\partial\beta}\right)K + 2F_{\mathrm{i}}^{-2}\phi_z = 0, \tag{54}$$

$$\frac{1}{J}\left(\phi'_\alpha + \phi'_\beta\frac{\partial}{\partial\beta}\right)K + 2F_{\mathrm{i}}^{-2}\phi'_z = 0, \tag{55}$$

where

$$K = \frac{1}{J(\rho+\rho')}[\rho(\phi_\alpha^2 + \phi_\beta^2) - \rho'(\phi_\alpha'^2 + \phi_\beta'^2)] + \rho\phi_z^2 - \rho'\phi_z'^2, \tag{56}$$

and F_{i} is the interfacial Froude number defined by

$$F_{\mathrm{i}}^2 = \frac{U^2(\rho+\rho')}{\Delta\rho g L}. \tag{57}$$

Assuming

$$\phi = \alpha + a\phi_1 + a^2\phi_2 + \dots, \quad \phi' = \alpha + a\phi'_1 + a^2\phi'_2 + \dots,$$

substituting these into (13) and (53)–(55), and sorting out the terms of order a, we have

$$\phi_{1\alpha\alpha} + \phi_{1\beta\beta} + \phi_{1zz} = 0, \tag{58}$$

$$\phi'_{1\alpha\alpha} + \phi_{1\beta\beta} + \phi_{1zz} = 0, \tag{59}$$

$$\frac{1}{\rho+\rho'}(\rho\phi_{1\alpha\alpha} - \rho'\phi'_{1\alpha\alpha}) + F_{\mathrm{i}}^{-2}\phi_{1z} = -\frac{\Delta\rho}{\rho+\rho'}k^2\sin k\alpha \sinh k\beta \quad (z=0), \tag{60}$$

$$\frac{1}{\rho+\rho'}(\rho\phi_{1\alpha\alpha} - \rho'\phi'_{1\alpha\alpha}) + F_{\mathrm{i}}^{-2}\phi'_{1z} = -\frac{\Delta\rho}{\rho+\rho'}k^2\sin k\alpha \sinh k\beta \quad (z=0). \tag{61}$$

Equations (60) and (61) immediately give

$$\phi_{1z} = \phi'_{1z}, \tag{62}$$

which can be used to replace (61).

The boundary conditions are now

$$\phi_\beta = 0 = \phi'_\beta \quad (b = \pm 1), \tag{63}$$

$$\phi_z = 0 \quad (z = -d), \quad \phi'_z = 0 \quad \left(z = d \equiv \frac{h}{L}\right). \tag{64}$$

These boundary conditions are satisfied by

$$\phi_1 = \sum_{n=1}^{\infty} B_n \sin k\alpha \sin \tfrac{1}{2}(2n-1)\pi\beta \cosh \gamma_n(z+d), \tag{65}$$

$$\phi'_1 = \sum_{n=1}^{\infty} B'_n \sin k\alpha \sin \tfrac{1}{2}(2n-1)\pi\beta \cosh \gamma_n(z-d), \tag{66}$$

where γ_n is still given by (21).

Now it is evident that condition (62) is satisfied by

$$B'_n = -B_n, \tag{67}$$

and it remains only to determine the B_n in (60), which now has the form

$$\phi_{1\alpha\alpha} + F_{\mathrm{i}}^{-2}\phi_{1z} = -\frac{\Delta\rho}{\rho+\rho'}k^2\sin k\alpha \sinh k\beta. \tag{68}$$

Comparing (68) with (19), we see that the present B_n is equal to $\Delta\rho(\rho+\rho')^{-1}$ times the B_n given by (22), if the F in (23) is replaced by F_{i}. The surface displacement ζ is given by (45) in dimensional terms. For the linear theory we can assume

$$C - C' = \tfrac{1}{2}\Delta\rho\, U^2.$$

The critical Fronde numbers are given by

$$F_{\mathrm{i}}^2 = \frac{\gamma_n}{k^2}\tanh \gamma_n d,$$

and this can be interpreted physically as in §4. The discussion for higher approximations is also similar to that for the surface waves treated in §4.

Finally, we note that the theory presented in the foregoing sections is not merely for supercritical flows, and that when k is large waves of large amplitude can occur even at subcritical speeds. The figures given in this paper are for supercritical speeds, for the F would be larger than 1 if it were based on the mean depth, and the pattern agrees qualitatively with that obtained from the classical shallow-water theory at supercritical speed and for vertical sidewalls. But this should not obscure the fact that the present theory is for all Froude numbers, however large or small.

For supercritical flows in curved channels or channel contractions and expansions (all of rectangular cross-sections), the method of characteristics under the assumption of shallow-water theory can be applied. See, for instance, the four excellent papers in an ASCE Symposium (Ippen *et al.* 1951). For corrugated vertical walls of small amplitude, the shallow-water approximation gives a partial differential equation of constant coefficients and of the hyperbolic type, solvable immediately by the method of separation of variables. For subcritical flows the problem is more interesting and the solutions are richer, as this work shows.

7. Explanation for the self-induced waves observed by Binnie

When one makes water flow between two vertical wavy walls, as Binnie (1960) did, stationary waves bound to the wall corrugation are necessarily created, as shown here in §§2–4. These I have called Binnie waves (Yih 1982†). But Binnie also observed self-induced waves propagating upstream. These, and sloshing two-dimensional waves which I think must have also existed in his experiments, are also Binnie waves. It now remains to explain how these unsteady waves, which are either progressive or standing waves, are produced.

Benjamin (1967), in an important paper dealing with the interesting Benjamin–Feir instability of dispersive waves (Benjamin & Feir 1967), said of Binnie's progressive waves: 'I am strongly inclined to believe this is an instance of the type of instability under discussion.' He did not, however, use Binnie's data to support or disprove his claim. It turns out that the mechanism I proposed (Yih 1976) for the instability of gravity waves created by a stream of water flowing over a wavy bottom can be applied to the stationary waves treated in §2–4. This seems quite natural. I shall now study some of Binnie's statements and examine his data in some detail, to show that there is considerable evidence that my instability mechanism may be the cause for Binnie's non-stationary (unsteady) waves.

The wavenumbers γ_n defined by (21) are for a meandering channel. Those for a symmetric channel with wavy walls (or for half of one), which was what Binnie used, are given by (Yih 1982)

$$\gamma_n = (k^2 + n^2\pi^2)^{\frac{1}{2}}, \quad n \text{ an integer.} \tag{69}$$

The wavy sides have the basic wavenumber k, and to $O(a)$ the symmetric channel is described by

$$y = \beta + a \cos kh \sinh k\beta, \quad \beta = \pm 1. \tag{70}$$

If we allow a modulation for (70), and replace it by (with a corresponding equation for x)

$$y = \beta + a(\cos kh \sinh k\beta + \epsilon_1 \cos \tfrac{1}{2}k_x \sinh \tfrac{1}{2}k\beta + \epsilon_2 \cos \tfrac{1}{3}k \sinh \tfrac{1}{3}k\beta + \dots). \tag{71}$$

Then there are stationary waves with wavenumbers

$$(\tfrac{1}{4}k^2 + n^2\pi^2)^{\frac{1}{2}}, \quad (\tfrac{1}{9}k^2 + n^2\pi^2)^{\frac{1}{2}}, \quad \text{etc.}$$

When $n = 0$, these are

$$\tfrac{1}{2}k, \quad \tfrac{1}{3}k, \quad \tfrac{1}{4}k, \quad \text{etc.}$$

Allowing these, and letting i and j denote the unit vectors in the directions of increasing x and y respectively, we ask the critical question: is there a progressive wavetrain with wavenumbers. (The n below is not the n in (69).)

$$\frac{k}{m}i \pm n\pi j, \quad m, n \text{ integers,} \tag{72}$$

† The B_0 given in that paper is twice as large is it should be.

and a frequency σ (not Binnie's notation), and a transverse oscillation (which is a standing wave) with the wavenumbers

$$\pm n\pi \boldsymbol{j} \tag{73}$$

and the *same* frequency σ? If so, taking either the $+$ or $-$ sign in (72) and (73), and labelling the wavenumbers $\boldsymbol{k}_1$ and $\boldsymbol{k}_2$ and their frequencies σ_2 and σ_1 $(=\sigma_2)$ respectively, we have the satisfaction of the resonance conditions specified by Yih (1976), whose analysis can be extended to the two-dimensional wavenumber space under discussion here. These conditions are

$$\boldsymbol{k}_1 - \boldsymbol{k}_2 = \frac{k}{m}\boldsymbol{i}, \tag{74}$$

$$\sigma_1 - \sigma_2 = 0. \tag{75}$$

The conditions are the same as found by Phillips (1960, 1961) for interaction of wave triads, but, in the case when one wavetrain is created by fluid flow over a wavy boundary, provide the conditions of instability of that wavetrain.

Examining Binnie's tables 1 and 2, one sees that wavenumbers (72) exist. Indeed the agreements between the calculated and observed wave velocity relative to the flowing water in these tables confirms the progressive waves as free (i.e. not bound to wall corrugations) waves progressing upstream, with $m = 2$, 3 and 4, and $n = 0$, 1 and 2 in (72), in the cases observed by Binnie. Binnie did not observe standing waves with wavenumbers $\pm n\pi \boldsymbol{j}$, but it did occur to him to calculate the period of the sloshing modes. (Incidentally he assumed the water to be 'deep', which was true for most cases. When the exact formula for the transverse period is used, I find that the figures for the calculated transverse period are somewhat larger in the cases of the smaller water depths, but in general not affecting – and sometimes even improving – the agreement between the transverse period and the observed period in Binnie's tables.) Assuming that such sloshing modes did exist,† there is general agreement between the periods Binnie observed for his progressive waves and the calculated periods for the sloshing modes with waves $\pm n\pi \boldsymbol{j}$. That is to say, (75) is satisfied – nearly if not precisely, and very consistently, for all cases in which $n = 1$ or 2.

For $n = 0$ the instability is more closely of the kind described by Yih (1976) for wavetrains with wavenumbers all in the longitudinal direction, and (74) is replaced by

$$\boldsymbol{k}_1 - \boldsymbol{k}_2 = \frac{k}{m}. \tag{76}$$

k_1 is the wavenumber of waves progressing upstream that Binnie observed, and k_2 is a smaller wavenumber of waves travelling downstream (even relative to the flowing water). I have checked to see whether (75) and (76) are satisfied by the data Binnie furnished for the cases $n = 0$, and found that the satisfaction is not good, though the magnitudes of the quantities checked are not far off. But even Binnie's observed and calculated values for wave velocity relative to water do not show good agreement for $n = 0$ in his table 1. Thus one must consider the cases of zero n not yet satisfactorily studied. For $n = 1$ and 2, I think there is strong but incomplete evidence that the instability mechanism proposed by me was at work in Binnie's experiments.

---

† Binnie did say '... these measurements (of wavelengths) were difficult, particularly when large, because over an interval of minutes the amplitudes were unsteady, rising and dying away like beats and the lengths but not the periods are variable.' Could the beats be caused by the standing waves of the sloshing modes?

The smaller m is, the more cycles for the instability mechanism to work, and therefore the more manifest the waves observed by Binnie. This seems to be in general true, except that he never observed any case with $m = 1$. I have checked to see how large the water velocity has to be for (75) and (76) to be satisfied (i.e. for cases $n = 0$) when $m = 1$, and have found that the water velocity has to be less than those used by Binnie. I venture to suggest that travelling waves with $n = 0$ and with $m = 1$ in (76) are possible and can be observed under the right circumstances.

Finally, I note that the mechanism of instability mentioned above does exist theoretically, even though it has been only incompletely demonstrated that it was indeed at work in Binnie's experiments.

This work has been supported by the Office of Naval Research. One referee's query led to the addition of §7, and I am grateful to him. This piece of work was inspired by the work of Binnie (1960). I should be much gratified if this work brings some pleasure to an old friend.

REFERENCES

BENJAMIN, T. B. 1967 Instability of periodic wave trains in nonlinear dispersive systems. *Proc. R. Soc. Lond.* **A299**, 59–75.

BENJAMIN, T. B. & FEIR, J. E. 1967 The disintegration of wave trains on deep water. *J. Fluid Mech.* **27**, 417–430.

BINNIE, A. M. 1960 Self-induced waves in a conduit with corregated walls. I. Experiments with water in an open horizontal channel with vertically corrugated sides. *Proc. R. Soc. Lond.* **A259**, 18–27.

IPEN, A. T. *et al.* 1951 High velocity flow in open channels. (A Symposium.) Paper no. 2434. *Trans. ASCE* **116**, 265–400.

JAHKE, E. & EMDE, F. 1945 *Tables of Functions*, Dover.

PHILLIPS, O. M. 1960 On the dynamics of unsteady gravity waves of finite amplitude. Part 1. The elementary interactions. *J. Fluid Mech.* **9**, 193–217.

PHILLIPS, O. M. 1961 On the dynamics of unsteady gravity waves of finite amplitude. Part 2. Local properties of a random wave field. *J. Fluid Mech.* **11**, 143–155.

YIH, C.-S. 1976 Instability of surface and internal waves. *Adv. Appl. Mech.* **16**, 369–419.

YIH, C.-S. 1982 Binnie waves. Paper presented to the 14th Symp. on Naval Hydrodynamics, Ann Arbor, Michigan, August 1982.

Proc. 15th Symposium of Naval Hydrodynamics, 1984

EDGE WAVES CREATED BY A LONGSHORE CURRENT
AND A RIDGE IN THE SEA-BED

CHIA-SHUN YIH

ABSTRACT

A mechanism for creation of edge waves is proposed. It is shown that a longshore current flowing over a ridge in a sloping sea-bed with an angle of inclination γ not greater than $\pi/4$ produces edge waves in the lee of the ridge. These edge waves have a wave number equal to $gU^{-2}\sin\gamma$, where g is the gravitational acceleration, U the velocity of the longshore current, and γ the angle of inclination of the sea-bed. The amplitude of the edge waves produced depends on the amplitude and geometry of the ridge as well as on the three variables mentioned above.

1. INTRODUCTION

Edge waves, discovered theoretically by Stokes (1846), are waves with amplitude decreasing exponentially toward sea, and exist if the sea-bed is an inclined plane. The question of creation of edge waves in nature, however, has never been studied. Creation by wind is, of course, a possibility, but any creation of edge waves by wind would seem to require that the wind be along the shore, and that its velocity decrease toward sea - a condition not often satisfied.

In this paper a mechanism of creation of edge waves is proposed: by a longshore current flowing over a ridge in a sloping sea-bed. The ridge assumed is either two- or three- dimensional, depending on γ.

It will be shown that the wave number of the edge waves produced is $gU^{-2}\sin\gamma$, where g is the gravitational acceleration, U the general velocity of the longshore current, apart from perturbations due to the ridge, and γ is the angle of inclination of the sea-bed to the undisturbed sea surface. The amplitude of the edge waves created depends on the amplitude of ridge as well as on g, U, and γ. The attenuation of the amplitude of the ridge toward sea depends, however, on γ, if edge waves are to be produced.

2. FORMULATION

Let x, y, and z be Cartesian coordinates,

*University of Michigan, Ann Arbor, Michigan 48109-2125, U.S.A.

with the shoreline as the x-axis when the sea is at rest, with y measured horizontally <u>away</u> from the sea, and with z measured vertically upward (Figure 1). We neglect the effects of viscosity, and consequently can, as usual,

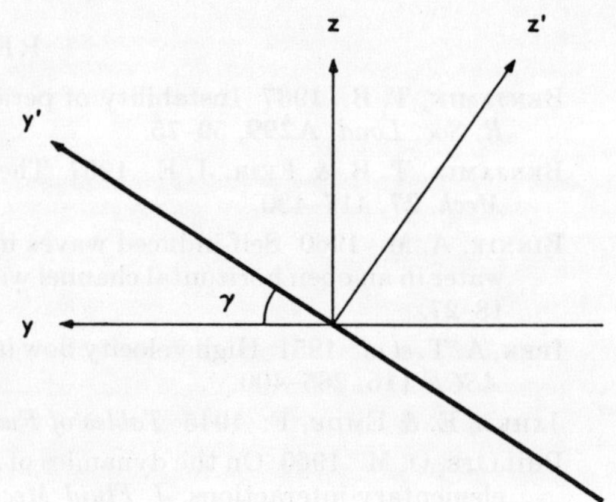

Figure 1. Definition of Coordinates.

assume the motion to be irrotational, so that a velocity potential ϕ exists, in terms of which the velocity components u, v, and w, in the direction of increasing x, y, and z, can be expressed:

$$u = \phi_x, \quad v = \phi_y, \quad w = \phi_z,$$

where the subscripts indicate partial differentiation. The equation of continuity then gives

$$\phi_{xx} + \phi_{yy} + \phi_{zz} = 0 \tag{1}$$

which is the equation governing the motion.

At the free surface, where $z = \zeta$. the kinematic condition is

$$\left(\phi_x \frac{\partial}{\partial x} + \phi_y \frac{\partial}{\partial y}\right)\zeta = \phi_z, \tag{2}$$

and, since the flow is supposed to be steady,

the Bernoulli equation is

$$q^2 + 2g\zeta = \text{constant}, \qquad (3)$$

in which

$$q^2 = u^2 + v^2 + w^2 = \phi_x^2 + \phi_y^2 + \phi_z^2. \qquad (4)$$

Combining (3) and (4), we have the free-surface condition

$$(\phi_x \frac{\partial}{\partial x} + \phi_y \frac{\partial}{\partial y}) q^2 + 2 g \phi_z = 0. \qquad (5)$$

At the sea-bed the boundary condition is

$$\frac{\partial \phi}{\partial n} = 0, \qquad (6)$$

where n is measured along the normal to the sea-bed. Very far from the shore the condition is

$$\phi = Ux \qquad \text{at} \qquad y = -\infty. \qquad (7)$$

Equations (1), (5), (6), and (7) constitute the differential system to be solved. The exact shape of the ridge will be specified later.

3. ANALYSIS

To solve the problem posed, we introduce another set of Cartesian coordinates (x', y', z'). The axes of y' and z' are shown in Figure 1. The y'-axis, inclined at angle γ with the y-axis, is along the line of steepest ascent of the sea bed in the absence of the ridge. Thus

$$y' = y \cos\gamma + z \sin\gamma, \quad z' = -y \sin\gamma + z \cos\gamma. \qquad (8)$$

Both sets of Cartesian coordinates are right-handed. In the absence of the ridge, the sea-bed would be given by $z' = 0$. Since the amplitude of the ridge is supposed to be small (compared with its width or with the wave length of the edge waves produced), the kinematic condition for the velocity at the sea-bed can be imposed at $z' = 0$.

Before considering a ridge, we shall consider a corrugated sea-bed given by $z' = \zeta'$, with

$$\zeta' = a \cos kx \exp(ky'\cos2\gamma), \qquad (9)$$

where k is the wave number in the x-direction. If $\gamma = \pi/4$, the ridge is cylindrical. If $\gamma < \pi/4$, the amplitude of the ridge decreases exponentially toward sea. We shall therefore restrict ourselves to values of γ in the range

$$\gamma \leq \pi/4.$$

The explanation for the form of the ridge assumed by (9) will become clear later. In terms of the new coordinates (x, y', z'), the equations for ϕ is still the Laplace equation

$$\phi_{xx} + \phi_{y'y'} + \phi_{z'z'} = 0. \qquad (10)$$

It can be readily verified that, to the first order in a, the velocity potential that will produce the bottom corrugation specified by (9) is

$$\phi = Ux + \frac{U}{\sin2\gamma} \sin kx[b \exp ky' +$$

$$a \exp (ky'\cos2\gamma - kz'\sin2\gamma)]. \qquad (11)$$

It is evident that (10) is satisfied, and that the term with amplitude b does not contribute a velocity in the z'-direction. At $z' = 0$,

$$U \frac{\partial}{\partial x} \zeta' = \phi_{z'}$$

is satisfied by (9) and (11), as a brief calculation will show. Thus the satisfaction of (6) is guaranteed.

On the free surface, the condition (5) reduces to the form

$$(g \sin\gamma - U^2 k)b - (g \sin\gamma + U^2 k)a = 0, \qquad (12)$$

or

$$b = \frac{k_e + k}{k_e - k} a = -(1 + \frac{2k_e}{k - k_e})a, \qquad (13)$$

in which

$$k_e = \frac{g \sin \gamma}{U^2}. \qquad (14)$$

Equations (11) and (13) give the solution sought.

As to the free-surface displacement ζ, it is to be found from

$$U \frac{\partial}{\partial x} \zeta = \phi_z. \qquad (15)$$

Noting that (8) gives

$$y' \cos2\gamma - z'\sin2\gamma = y \cos\gamma - z \sin\gamma, \qquad (16)$$

we obtain from (11), (13), and (15) that

$$\zeta = \frac{a}{\cos\gamma} (1 + \frac{k_e}{k - k_e})\cos kx \exp(ky\cos\gamma). \qquad (17)$$

Thus edge waves are obtained. These are bound waves, however, with the wavelength exactly equal to the wavelength of the sea-bed corrugation. For $k = k_e$, the solution fails, however small a is, and there is resonance. It will be seen that, when the bottom protrusion is a single ridge, the edge waves produced have exactly the wave number k_e.

It is appropriate here to note that Stokes' edge waves attenuate seaward as $\exp (ky\cos\gamma)$. This attenuation is provided by the term with amplitude b in (11), and further demands the factor

$$\exp k(y'\cos2\gamma - z'\sin2\gamma)$$

in (11), which, as can be seen from (16), gives the required attenuation at $z = 0$. Thus the assumption (9) is not arbitrary, but is forced upon us if we want the bottom corrugation to produce pure edge waves. As a consequence, the form of any sea-bed geometry cannot be arbitrary either, if pure edge waves are to be produced.

The results just obtained for a sea-bed corrugation periodic in x can be generalized by Fourier integration. Consider, for instance, a bottom protrusion given by

$$z' \equiv \zeta' = \frac{A(B - y'\cos2\gamma)}{(B - y'\cos2\gamma)^2 + x^2}, \qquad (18)$$

which can be expressed as

$$\zeta' = A \int_0^\infty e^{-Bk}\cos kx \exp(ky'\cos2\gamma)dk, \qquad (19)$$

where A has the dimension of length squared. We shall now, for economy, write (11) as

$$\phi = Ux + Ua\phi_1, \qquad (20)$$

where

$$\phi_1 = \frac{\sin kx}{\sin2\gamma}\left[\frac{k_e + k}{k_e - k}\exp ky' + \right.$$

$$\exp(ky'\cos2\gamma - kz'\sin2\gamma)]. \qquad (21)$$

Then on inspection of (9) and (19), the solution for ϕ for the protrusion (18) or (19) is

$$\phi + Ux + UA\int_0^\infty e^{-Bk}\phi_1(k)dk, \qquad (22)$$

and the free-surface displacement is given by, on inspection of (9), (19), and (17),

$$\zeta = \frac{A}{\cos\gamma}\int_0^\infty \left(1 + \frac{k_e}{k - k_e}\right)e^{-Bk}\cos kx$$

$$\cdot\exp(ky\cos\gamma)dk. \qquad (23)$$

Equations (22) and (23) give the solution to the problem. But the integrals therein need to be evaluated to exhibit the edge waves created in the lee of the protrusion on the one hand, and the local disturbances, on the other.

4. <u>EVALUATION OF THE INTEGRALS</u>

Let us define the integrals I and J by

$$I = \int_0^\infty \frac{1}{k - k_e}\sin kx \exp k(y'-B)dk =$$

$$Im\int_0^\infty \frac{1}{k - k_e}\exp k(y'-B + ix)dk, \qquad (24)$$

$$J = \int_0^\infty \frac{1}{k - k_e}\cos kx \exp k(y\cos\gamma - B)dk =$$

$$Re\int_o^\infty \frac{1}{k - k_e}\exp k(y\cos\gamma - B + i\chi)dk \qquad (25)$$

We shall, in calculating I and J, which are the two most significant integrals in (22) and (23), first replace k_e by $k_e + i\mu$, with μ positive, and then let μ approach zero. This is the well-known and often used device of Rayleigh, to make the gravity waves appear only in the lee of the obstacle. Furthermore, we shall replace the variable k by the complex variable $\chi = k+im$, and use the Cauchy integral theorem in the plane of the complex variable χ.

For $x > 0$, we shall use the contour shown in Figure 2. Upon letting R tend to infinity,

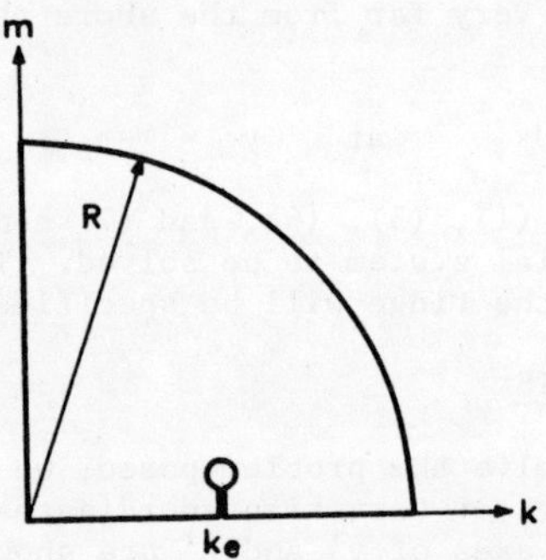

Figure 2. Contour in the -plane for $x > 0$.

we have,

$$I = 2\pi\cos k_e x \exp k_e(y' - B) +$$

$$Im\int_\infty^0 \frac{i}{im - k_e}\exp[-mx + im(y' - B)]dm = 0, \qquad (26)$$

or

$$I = 2\pi\cos k_e x \exp k(y' - B) + I_1, \qquad (27)$$

where

$$I_1 = \int_0^\infty \frac{1}{m^2 + k_e^2}e^{-mx}[m \sin m(y' - B) -$$

$$k_e\cos m(y' - B)]dm.$$

For $x < 0$, we use the contour shown in Figure 3, and obtain

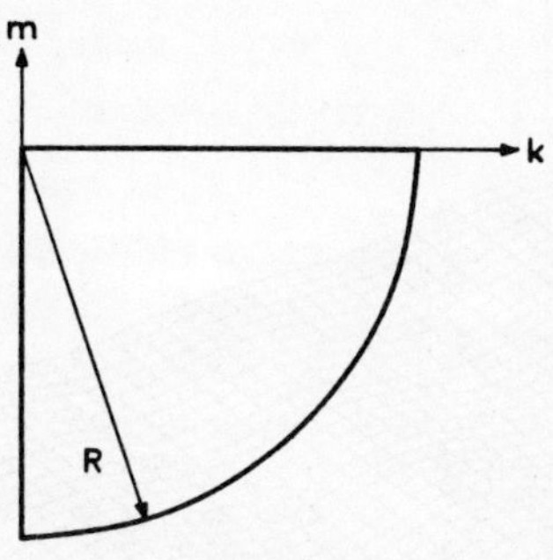

Figure 3. Contour in the -plane for x < 0.

$$I = -\int_0^\infty \frac{1}{m^2 + k_e^2} e^{mx} [m \sin m(y' - B) -$$

$$k_e \cos m(y' - B)] dm. \qquad (28)$$

It can be shown that (27) and (28) give the same value for I at x = 0. All we need to do is to evaluate the integral

$$\int \frac{1}{\chi - k_e} \exp \chi(y' - B + ix) d\chi$$

along a contour consisting of a section of length 2R of the m-axis and a large semi-circle to the right of it, with that section as its diameter, use the Cauchy residue theorem, and let R approach infinity. The center of the semi-circle is the origin.

As to J, a similar approach gives, for x > 0,

$$J = -2\pi \sin k_e x \exp k_e(y\cos\gamma - B) + J_1, \qquad (29)$$

where

$$J_1 = \int_0^\infty \frac{1}{m^2 + k_e^2} e^{-mx} [m \cos m(y\cos\gamma - B) +$$

$$k_e \sin m(y\cos\gamma - B)] dm. \qquad (30)$$

For x < 0, the contour in Figure 3 is used, and we obtain

$$J = \int_0^\infty \frac{1}{m^2 + k_e^2} e^{mx} [m \cos m(y\cos\gamma - B) +$$

$$k_e \sin m(y\cos\gamma - B) dm. \qquad (31)$$

The other integrals in (22) and (23) are

easy to evaluate. The final results are

$$\phi = Ux + \frac{UA}{\sin 2\gamma} [-2k_e I - \frac{x}{(y' - B)^2 + x^2} +$$

$$\frac{x}{(y\cos\gamma - z\sin\gamma)^2 + x^2}], \qquad (32)$$

where I is given by (26) if x > 0 and by (28) if x < 0, and

$$\zeta = \frac{A}{\cos\gamma} [k_e J + \frac{B - y\cos\gamma}{(B - y\cos\gamma)^2 + x^2}], \qquad (33)$$

where J is given by (29) if x > 0, and by (31) if x < 0. It is evident from (32) and (26), and from (33) and (29), that there is a wave component for ϕ and one for ζ for x > 0, but no wave component at all for ϕ and ζ, if x < 0. The other terms in ϕ and ζ represent local disturbances. Fig. 4 shows a perspective of ζ.

5. DISCUSSION

We note first of all that the J_1 given by (30) for x > 0 is exactly equal to the J given by (31) for x < 0, for the same absolute value of x. Thus the J_1 given by (30) and the J given by (31) represent local disturbances of the free surface due to the bottom protrusion. Furthermore, the last term in (33), which is symmetric with respect to x, also represents such a disturbance.

The edge waves created are given by the first term on the right-hand side of (29), after it has been multiplied by the factor $Ak_e \sec\gamma$, as shown in (33). It is interesting that the amplitude of these waves decreases exponentially as $\exp(-k_e B)$, as B increases. That is, the wider (in the x-direction) the protrusion is, the smaller the amplitude. It should be noted that, for a fixed x, (18) gives a ζ' which decreases asymptotically with y' as $A(B-y'\cos 2\gamma)^{-1}$.

Inspection of (9) and (19) shows that the solution fails if $\gamma > \pi/4$, for then ζ' would be so large that the linear theory fails. This seems to indicate that pure edge waves cannot be created by a long-shore current if $\gamma > \pi/4$. To reasure oneself that this is so one may consider the case $\gamma = \pi/2$. The sea-bed is then a vertical sea wall. If there is any seaward protrusion of it, the waves created by it are certainly more like ship waves than edge waves.

The question naturally arises: For $\gamma \leq \pi/4$, if the bottom protrusion does not have exactly the y'-dependence required, what waves will be created? In that case, it seems that, in addition to the edge waves there will be other waves created, which account for the deviation of the y'-dependence of ζ' from the required one. What we have presented in this paper is the solution of pure edge waves created by a longshore current flowing over a sloping sea-bed inclined generally at an angle $\gamma \leq \pi/4$, with a protrusion that decreases in some way as y' decreases toward negative infinity.

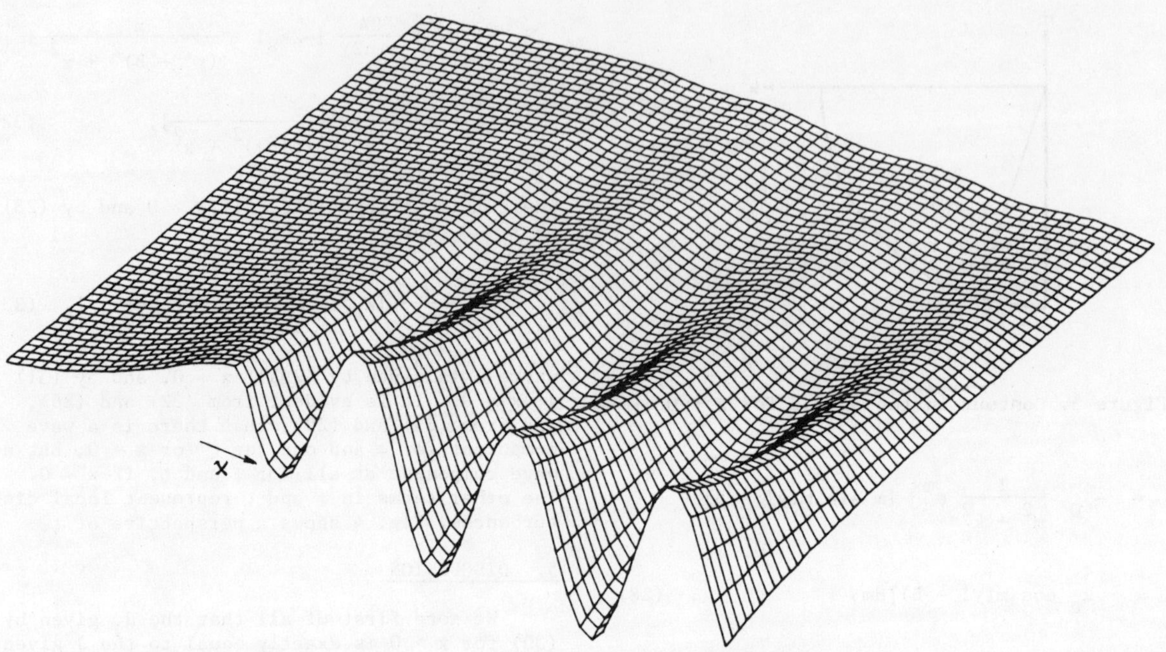

Figure 4. A perspective of the free surface for a bottom protrusion given by (18). With $\gamma = \pi/4$, $k_e = 5$, and with B as the length scale.

ACKNOWLEDGEMENT

This work has been sponsored by the Office of Naval Research. Drafting and computation assistance has been rendered by Mr. Marc Ingber. The sponsorship and the assistance are much appreciated.

REFERENCE

Stokes, G.G., (1846): Report on recent researches in hydrodynamics, Brit. Assoc. Rept.

QUARTERLY OF APPLIED MATHEMATICS
VOLUME XLV, NUMBER 1
APRIL 1987, PAGES 177–183

A SOLITARY GROUP OF TWO-DIMENSIONAL DEEP-WATER WAVES*

BY

CHIA-SHUN YIH

University of Michigan

Summary. If the magnitude of a line of concentrated force moving with a constant velocity on the surface of deep water oscillates with a constant frequency, a single group of two-dimensional gravity waves is created. The group moves with the velocity of the concentrated force, and the waves in it have a wave number and phase velocity which are determined by the velocity of the concentrated force and the frequency of oscillation of its magnitude. If these latter quantities are such that the velocity of the force is near the group velocity, in the classical sense, of the waves created, the length of the group will be very long, but in general it can take on any value. The phase velocity of the waves created is larger than that of classical deep-water waves of the same wave number, whereas the velocity of the group is less than the group velocity of these classical waves. The respective differences, as well as the magnitude of the concentrated force, tend to zero as the length of the group increases indefinitely. The solution given provides the elemental solution from which gravity wave groups caused by any travelling oscillating pressure distribution can be found.

1. Introduction. It is well known that when a time-independent two-dimensional pressure distribution, applied to the surface of a body of water, travels with a constant velocity, gravity waves are created behind and travel with it. It is easily seen that if a stationary but oscillating two-dimensional pressure distribution is applied to the water surface, gravity waves will be created on both sides of it, travelling toward infinity in opposite directions. It is then to be expected that if the oscillatory pressure distribution travels with a constant velocity on the water surface there will be gravity waves fore and aft. The solution for the ensuing flow could in principle be obtained by superposition from the solution given by Poisson (1816) and Cauchy (1827), as quoted by Lamb [1, p. 384], for instantaneous force applied to the water surface. But the calculation for the asymptotic state (for large values of time t) will be not only very involved and tedious but also unnecessary.

---

* Received January 2, 1986.

©1987 Brown University

In this paper a simple solution for gravity waves created by a concentrated oscillatory force travelling with a constant velocity on the surface of deep water is given. A single group of gravity waves is found, which moves with the same velocity as the surface force. Within it, individual waves have a wave number k and a phase velocity c, which are determined by the velocity c_g and the frequency ω of the surface force. As c_g approaches the classical group velocity for waves with frequency ω, the envelope of the group will be very long (the length of the group can be defined). In the limit it will be infinite and the magnitude of the force will be zero, in agreement with the classical concept of group velocity. But in general, the group can have any length; the phase velocity of the individual waves created is larger, whereas the velocity of the group is smaller, than their respective classical counterparts for the same frequency ω.

2. Surface gravity waves. Surface gravity waves represent the archetype of dispersive waves, and the simplest among these are two-dimensional deep-water waves, which will therefore be treated first.

We will assume the wave motion to be irrotational, so that the velocity has a potential ϕ which satisfies the Laplace equation

$$\phi_{xx} + \phi_{yy} = 0, \tag{1}$$

in which x and y are Cartesian coordinates, with x measured in a horizontal direction and y measured in the direction opposite to the gravitational acceleration. One boundary condition is

$$\phi \to 0 \qquad \text{as } y \to -\infty. \tag{2}$$

At the free surface, the kinematic condition is, in its linear form,

$$\eta_t = \phi_y, \tag{3}$$

in which η is the displacement of the free surface from its equilibrium position and t denotes the time. The Bernoulli equation at the free surface is

$$p = -\rho(\phi_t + g\eta), \tag{4}$$

where p denotes pressure, ρ denotes the density, and g is the gravitational acceleration. An arbitrary function of time has been omitted from (4), because it can be absorbed in the term ϕ_t, and p is assumed zero whenever the right-hand side of (4) is zero. Conditions (3) and (4) are imposed at $y = 0$. On differentiation of (4) with respect to t and use of (3), one has

$$p_t = -\rho(\phi_{tt} + g\phi_y). \tag{5}$$

One seeks to find a solution for a single wave group, with the feature that the envelope of the group propagates with a velocity c_g and the individual waves propagate with velocity c within the envelope, the amplitude of which approaches zero as x approaches $\pm\infty$.

As will become clear, the solution contains infinitely many terms. The motivation for this series solution is obscure unless one presents the solution in the way of its discovery. One tries, at first, the single-term solution

$$\phi = a \operatorname{sech} \varepsilon(z - c_g t) \exp[-ik(z - ct)], \qquad z = x + iy, \tag{6}$$

or, to save writing,

$$\phi = a \operatorname{sech} \varepsilon\xi\, e^{-ik\zeta},$$

(7)

where

$$\xi = z - c_g t, \qquad \zeta = z - ct.$$

(8)

We pointed out immediately that the term $\operatorname{sech} \varepsilon\xi$ has singularities in the fluid domain. Since these can be removed without affecting the course of the calculation, we shall ignore them for the time being and discuss the matter of singularity removal in a later section. It is to be understood that the real part of (7) is meant for ϕ. Obviously, (7) and hence its real and imaginary parts satisfy (1) and (2). Substitution of (7) into (5) gives

$$-p_t/\rho = a\Big\{ \varepsilon^2 c_g^2 \operatorname{sech} \varepsilon\xi \big(1 - 2\operatorname{sech}^2 \varepsilon\xi\big) - k^2 c^2 \operatorname{sech} \varepsilon\xi$$
$$+ 2ik\varepsilon c c_g \operatorname{sech} \varepsilon\xi \tanh \varepsilon\xi + kg \operatorname{sech} \varepsilon\xi$$
$$- i\varepsilon g \operatorname{sech} \varepsilon\xi \tanh \varepsilon\xi \Big\} e^{-i\zeta},$$

(9)

which shows that if we take

$$-k^2 c^2 + \varepsilon^2 c_g^2 + gk = 0$$

(10)

and

$$2kcc_g = g,$$

(11)

we have

$$p_t/\rho = 2a\varepsilon^2 c_g^2 \operatorname{sech}^3 \varepsilon\xi\, e^{-i\zeta}$$

(12)

on the free surface. Again, the real part of the right-hand side is meant. When the pressure distribution is given by (12), we do have a single wave group travelling with velocity c_g, with the individual waves travelling with velocity c. These wave velocities are given by (10) and (11), or

$$c^2 = \frac{g}{k} \frac{1 + \sqrt{1 + (\varepsilon/k)^2}}{2},$$

(13)

$$c_g = \frac{g}{2kc}.$$

(14)

It is interesting that for $\varepsilon^2 \ll k^2$ the c given by (13) is very close to the wave velocity of classical deep-water waves with wave number k, and c_g is very close to their group velocity in the classical sense. But in general c is greater, whereas c_g is smaller, than its counterpart in classical theory.

The only artificiality of the solution is the pressure required, given by (12), to maintain the wave group. Let us try to eliminate the right-hand side of (12) by taking

$$\phi = ae^{-ik\zeta}\big(1 + b_1 \operatorname{sech}^2 \varepsilon\xi\big) \operatorname{sech} \varepsilon\xi.$$

(15)

Then we find that for $b_1 = \tfrac{1}{4}$ we still have (10) and (11), but (12) is replaced by

$$p_t/\rho = 3a\varepsilon^2 c_g^2 \operatorname{sech}^5 \varepsilon\xi\, e^{-ik\zeta}.$$

(16)

Thus the pressure distribution is more concentrated around $\xi = 0$. We can go on adding terms, and the $(n + 1)$-term solution is

$$\phi = ae^{-ik\xi} \operatorname{sech} \varepsilon\xi \sum_{m=0}^{n} b_m \operatorname{sech}^{2m} \varepsilon\xi, \tag{17}$$

where

$$b_0 = 1, \qquad b_m = \frac{2m - 1}{2m + 2} b_{m-1}.$$

For the $(n + 1)$-term solution given by (17), the pressure distribution at the free surface is given by

$$p_t/\rho = (2n + 1)(2n + 2) ab_n \varepsilon^2 c_g^2 \operatorname{sech}^{2n+3} \varepsilon\xi e^{-ik\xi}, \tag{19}$$

which is more and more concentrated near $\xi = 0$ as n increases. We will now write the real part of (19) explicitly for $y = 0$:

$$p_t/\rho = (2n + 1)(2n + 2) ab_n \varepsilon^2 c_g^2 \operatorname{sech}^{2n+3} \varepsilon(x - c_g t) \cos k(x - ct), \tag{20}$$

where

$$b_n = \frac{1}{4} \frac{3}{6} \frac{5}{8} \frac{7}{10} \frac{9}{12} \frac{11}{14} \cdots \frac{2n - 1}{2n + 2}. \tag{21}$$

Let

$$x' = x - c_g t, \qquad x - ct = x' - (c - c_g)t. \tag{22}$$

Then (20) becomes, for $y = 0$,

$$p_t/\phi = (2n + 1)(2n + 2) ab_n \varepsilon^2 c_g^2 \operatorname{sech}^{2n+3} \varepsilon x' \cos k\left[x' - (c - c_g)t\right]. \tag{23}$$

For large n (so that p_t is concentrated near $x' = 0$) integration gives

$$p/\rho = -\frac{(2n + 1)(2n + 2)}{k(c - c_q)} ab_n \varepsilon^2 c_g^2 \operatorname{sech}^{2n+3} \varepsilon x' \sin k\left[x' - (c - c_g)t\right]. \tag{24}$$

It is interesting to see what the distribution of p is for very large n. We note, first, that the pressure distribution becomes more and more concentrated near $x' = 0$ as n increases and, second,

$$\varepsilon \int_0^{\infty} \operatorname{sech}^{2n+3} \varepsilon x' \, dx' = \int_0^{\pi/2} \cos^{2(n+1)}\theta \, d\theta = \frac{2n + 1}{2(n + 1)} \frac{\pi}{2} c_n, \tag{25}$$

where

$$c_n = \frac{2n - 1}{2n} \frac{2n - 3}{2(n - 1)} \cdots \frac{1}{2} = \frac{1}{2} \frac{3}{4} \frac{5}{6} \cdots \frac{2n - 1}{2n}, \tag{26}$$

and θ is defined by

$$\sin \theta = \tanh \varepsilon x'. \tag{27}$$

As n becomes very large, p is very concentrated near $x' = 0$, and (24) gives

$$\int_{-\infty}^{\infty} p \, dx' = \frac{\pi a \rho \epsilon c_g^2 \sin k(c - c_g)t}{k(c - c_g)}(2n + 1)^2 b_n c_n.$$

We need to evaluate b_n and c_n for very large n. Note first that

$$\frac{1}{4}\frac{2}{5}\frac{3}{6}\frac{4}{7} \cdots \frac{2n - 3}{2n} = \frac{6}{2n(2n - 1)(2n - 2)}, \tag{29}$$

since, apart from the first three numerators of the left-hand side and the last three denominators, the rest, upon one-to-one cancelling, is equal to 1. Furthermore, it is clear that

$$\frac{\dfrac{1}{4}\dfrac{3}{6}\dfrac{5}{8} \cdots \dfrac{2n - 3}{2n}}{\dfrac{2}{5}\dfrac{4}{7}\dfrac{6}{9} \cdots \dfrac{2n - 4}{2n - 1}} = \frac{5}{2}\frac{7}{16}\frac{27}{36}\frac{55}{64} \cdots \frac{2n - 3}{2n}$$

$$= \frac{5}{2}\left(1 - \frac{9}{16}\right)\left(1 - \frac{9}{36}\right)\left(1 - \frac{9}{64}\right) \cdots \frac{2n - 3}{2n}, \tag{30}$$

which, as n approaches infinity, approaches $5Q/2$, where

$$Q = \left(1 - \frac{9}{16}\right)\left(1 - \frac{9}{36}\right)\left(1 - \frac{9}{64}\right) \cdots \tag{31}$$

is a convergent infinite product [3, p. 32] of value less than 1 and different from zero, since $\frac{1}{16} + \frac{1}{36} + \frac{1}{64} + \cdots$ is a convergent series. Noting that the upper product on the left-hand side of (30) is exactly b_{n-1}, we obtain from (29) and (30) that, for very large n,

$$\frac{2}{5Q}b_n^2 = \frac{3}{4n^3}. \tag{32}$$

The value of Q given by (31) can be determined from the well-known formula [2, p. 30]

$$x\left(1 - \frac{x^2}{\pi^2}\right)\left(1 - \frac{x^2}{4\pi^2}\right)\left(1 - \frac{x^2}{9\pi^2}\right) \cdots = \sin x,$$

or on replacing x by $3x/2$,

$$\frac{3x}{2}\left(1 - \frac{9x^2}{4\pi^2}\right)\left(1 - \frac{9x^2}{16\pi^2}\right)\left(1 - \frac{9x^2}{36\pi^2}\right) \cdots = \sin\frac{3x}{2}.$$

If we put $x = \pi$ in this last formula, we obtain

$$Q = \frac{8}{15\pi} \quad \text{or} \quad \frac{5Q}{2} = \frac{4}{3\pi}. \tag{33}$$

Thus (32) becomes, for very large n,

$$b_n^2 = \frac{1}{\pi n^3} \quad \text{or} \quad b_n = (\pi n^3)^{-1/2}. \tag{34}$$

For the calculation of c_n we start from the obvious formula

$$\frac{1}{2}\frac{2}{3}\frac{3}{4} \cdots \frac{2n - 1}{2n} = \frac{1}{2n}, \tag{35}$$

from which we obtain

$$c_n d_n = \frac{1}{2n},$$ (36)

where

$$d_n = \frac{2}{3} \frac{4}{5} \frac{6}{7} \cdots \frac{2n-2}{2n-1}.$$ (37)

From (26) and (37) we have

$$\frac{d_n}{c_n} = 2 \frac{8}{9} \frac{24}{25} \frac{48}{49} \cdots \frac{2n(2n-2)}{(2n-1)^2} = 2\left(1 - \frac{1}{9}\right)\left(1 - \frac{1}{25}\right) \cdots \left(1 - \frac{1}{(2n-1)^2}\right).$$ (38)

But [2, p. 31]

$$\cos x = \left(1 - \frac{4x^2}{\pi^2}\right)\left(1 - \frac{4x^2}{9\pi^2}\right)\left(1 - \frac{4x^2}{25\pi^2}\right) \cdots,$$ (39)

and moving the first factor on the right-hand side of (39) to the other side, putting $x = \pi/2$, and applying l'Hôpital's rule, we obtain

$$(1 - \tfrac{1}{9})(1 - \tfrac{1}{25}) \cdots = \pi/4.$$ (40)

Thus, for very large n, (38) and (40) give

$$d_n/c_n = \pi/2$$ (41)

and from (36) we obtain, for very large n,

$$\pi c_n^2 = \frac{1}{n} \quad \text{or} \quad c_n = \left(\frac{1}{n\pi}\right)^{1/2}.$$ (42)

Putting (34) and (42) into (28), we have, for very large n,

$$F = \int_{-\infty}^{\infty} p \, dx' = \frac{4a\rho c_g^2 \sin k(c - c_g)t}{k(c - c_g)}.$$ (43)

Given c_g and

$$\omega = k(c - c_g),$$ (44)

we can calculate k and c from (14) and (44) and then ε from (13). The conclusion, then, is that if a finite force F given by $4a\rho\varepsilon c_g^2 \sin \omega t/\omega$ moves with speed c_g on the free surface, a single group of waves of wave number k advances with speed c_g, whereas the individual waves advance with speed c. The velocity potential is given by (17). The surface displacement η is given by (3), by integration with respect to t—which is not an easy task at first sight. However, at any finite distance from $x' = 0$ the pressure p is zero and η is then given by (4) to be

$$\eta = (1/g)\phi_t,$$

with ϕ given by (17). At $x' = 0$, it is understandable that η is not finite. However, for a distribution of p given as a function of x, c_g, and ω, ϕ can be obtained by integration, and η is then everywhere finite.

3. Removal of singularities in the solution. It can be readily verified that the solution (6) has singularities (doublets) at

$$z = x + iy = c_g t - \frac{2N - 1}{2\varepsilon}\pi i = \alpha_N, \tag{45}$$

for any integral value of N from 1 onward. The singularities can be removed by adding to (6) or (7) the terms

$$-a e^{ik(c - c_g)t} \sum_{N=1}^{\infty} \frac{i(-1)^N}{\varepsilon(z - \alpha_N)} \exp\left(-\frac{2N - 1}{2\varepsilon}k\pi\right). \tag{46}$$

Note that on the free surface

$$\varepsilon|z - \alpha_N| \geqslant \frac{2N - 1}{2}\pi. \tag{47}$$

If

$$\frac{k}{\varepsilon} \gg 1, \tag{48}$$

the magnitude of (46) is obviously extremely small at the free surface. Thus the added terms can be neglected in subsequent development up to (14).

But (15) again contains singularities. Those for the sech $\varepsilon\xi$ term have already been removed by adding (46). Those for the remaining term can be similarly dealt with.

The argument can be repeated. The singularities to be removed successively involve poles of various orders. At the n-th approximation the terms to be added to remove the highest singularities are of the form

$$-a e^{ik(c - c_g)t} \sum_{N=1}^{\infty} \frac{(-1)^N (i)^n}{[\varepsilon(z - \alpha_N)]^n} \exp\left(-\frac{2N - 1}{2\varepsilon}k\pi\right), \tag{49}$$

and there are other terms representing poles of the first to the $(n - 1)$th orders. Again all the terms added for singularity removal have negligible effects on the calculation at the free surface, provided (48) is satisfied. Thus, with this provision, singularities can be removed from (17) for any n to produce a nonsingular solution that leaves intact (13), (14), and (43), which constitute the main conclusions of this paper.

Acknowledgment. This work has been sponsored by the Fluid Mechanics Program of the Office of Naval Research.

REFERENCES

[1] H. Lamb, *Hydrodynamics*, Dover, New York, 1945
[2] G. Polya, *Induction and analogy in mathematics*, Princeton Univ. Press, Princeton, N. J., 1954
[3] E. T. Whittaker and G. N. Watson, *Modern analysis*, Macmillan, New York, 1945

QUARTERLY OF APPLIED MATHEMATICS
VOLUME XLVI, NUMBER 4
DECEMBER 1988, PAGES 737–750

FINITE GROUPS OF GRAVITY WAVES*

By

CHIA-SHUN YIH

Dept. of Aerospace Engineering, Mechanics, and Engineering Science
The University of Florida, Gainesville, Florida

Summary. Groups of gravity waves of finite length created in deep, originally quiescent water by an oscillating or moving surface pressure are constructed by superposition of the Cauchy–Poisson solution. This construction gives substance and reassurance to the concept of "wave packets" progressing with group velocity associated with the individual waves in the packets, a concept so important to water-wave research. The effects of viscosity are taken into account, thereby not only justifying the extensively used but completely artificial damping factor initiated by Lamb (1916, see Lamb 1945, p. 413), but also showing the hitherto largely unexplored spatial damping of waves.

1. Introduction. The phenomenon of an isolated water-wave group and its velocity of advance were observed by Russel (1844, see Lamb 1945, p. 380). The first derivation of the group velocity of dispersive waves seems to have been given by Stokes (1876, see Lamb 1945, p. 381), although the significance of the group velocity as the velocity of propagation of the wave number was already at least implicit in the solution of Cauchy (1815, see Lamb 1945, p. 384, and p. 17 for reference to original work) and Poisson (1816, see Lamb 1945, p. 384) for waves created by an initial concentrated disturbance, long before Russel's observations and Stokes' work.

In Stokes' derivation, two wave trains of slightly different wave numbers and correspondingly slightly different frequencies are superposed, and the result is a train of waves of the mean wave number and the mean frequency bounded by an envelope with an amplitude sinusoidally and slowly varying with time and distance. The velocity of the envelope is the group velocity, which for gravity waves is less than the phase velocity of the individual waves contained in the envelope.

Stokes' derivation has the great merit of simplicity. Although the requirement of two wave trains of slightly different wave numbers and frequencies seems artificial at first sight, waves of neighboring wave numbers and frequencies do arise naturally in many problems to which the Fourier analysis can be applied, and these are essential for the formation of wave groups. Wave trains with two discrete wave numbers are merely an extreme idealization. However, these wave trains necessarily entail

---

*Received July 6, 1987.

©1988 Brown University

infinitely many wave groups, and this fact renders Stokes' construction inadequate for explaining Russel's observations or for supporting the many and frequent statements or implications in contemporary literature concerning isolated wave groups. It is thus very desirable to construct some examples of dispersive-wave groups of finite length.

As already mentioned in the foregoing, an interpretation of the Cauchy–Poisson solution, as given in pp. 384–398 of Lamb's book (1945), shows the significance of the group velocity as the velocity with which the wave number propagates—or a packet of waves of that wave number propagates. This strongly suggests that if the forcing at the free surface has a certain frequency, or moves with a certain velocity, a group of waves with that frequency, or moving with a phase velocity equal to that velocity, will be created. The present paper is the outcome of acting on that suggestion.

The deep mystery that when a wave maker oscillates $n(\gg 1)$ times in deep water (for instance) only $n/2$ waves are created can be dispelled satisfactorily only by considering the cancellation of waves, perhaps principally near the front of the group. The mechanics of that cancellation is already contained in the solution given in this paper, but has not been pursued in detail. However, the construction herein of wave groups of finite length, in showing the existence of such groups that propagate with their appropriate group velocities, and in being the *result* of that cancellation, provides an important step toward dispelling that mystery, and gives one reassurance when one talks about isolated wave packets.

In making the solutions determinate, the simple damping factor employed by Lamb (1916, see Lamb 1945, p. 413) will first be used, but will be justified later in this paper on the basis of the Navier–Stokes equations governing the dynamics of viscous fluids. This justification is a second purpose of this paper.

Stokes' construction of infinitely many wave groups and Lamb's artifice of the exponential damping factor have the merit of simplicity, and since they both contain a measure of what is needed, have been successful in explaining things and thus very useful to workers on water waves. The simplicity and the success have long been a blessing, but the very simplicity and success have in time become a curse, since they discourage the expenditure of arduous work to put something better in their place. The time for replacing them has arrived, and this work, motivated by the demand of reason, is a tribute to Professor C. C. Lin on the occasion of his retirement.

2. The Cauchy–Poisson solution. Let x and y be Cartesian coordinates, with x measured in a horizontal direction and y measured vertically upward from the free surface when the fluid (water) is at rest, and let t be the time. Consider irrotational gravity waves created in deep water by a distribution of the velocity potential ϕ applied instantaneously at the free surface at $t = 0$, and let this initial ϕ be denoted by ϕ_0 and given by

$$\phi_0 = aF(x), \tag{1}$$

where $F(x)$ is dimensionless and a has the dimension L^2/T, i.e., the dimension of the velocity potential.

The velocity potential ϕ has to satisfy the Laplace equation

$$\phi_{xx} + \phi_{yy} = 0. \tag{2}$$

At the free surface, where

$$y = \eta(x, t), \tag{3}$$

the kinematic condition is

$$\eta_t = \phi_y, \tag{4}$$

with ϕ_y evaluated at $y = 0$, and the dynamic condition requiring constant pressure is

$$\phi_t + g\eta = 0, \tag{5}$$

where g is the gravitational acceleration. The ϕ_y and ϕ_t in (4) and (5) are evaluated at $y = 0$ in a linear theory. Another boundary condition is

$$\phi \to 0 \quad \text{as} \quad y \to -\infty. \tag{6}$$

Let k denote the wave number and σ the corresponding frequency (defined as 2π divided by the period). Then the solution for ϕ satisfying (1), (2), (4), (5), and (6) is

$$\phi = \frac{a}{\pi} \int_0^\infty \cos \sigma t e^{ky} \, dk \int_{-\infty}^\infty F(\alpha) \cos k(x - \alpha) \, d\alpha, \tag{7}$$

and the corresponding solution for η is

$$\eta = \frac{a}{\pi g} \int_0^\infty \sigma \sin \sigma t \, dk \int_{-\infty}^\infty F(\alpha) \cos k(x - \alpha) \, d\alpha, \tag{8}$$

provided

$$\sigma^2 = gk. \tag{9}$$

Equation (9) is the dispersion equation, which has a different form if surface-tension effects are included, or if the water depth is finite.

The famous Cauchy–Poisson solution is obtained if one lets $F(\alpha)$ in (7) and (8) be a Dirac distribution, i.e., if $F(\alpha)$ is zero everywhere except at $\alpha = 0$, in such a way that

$$\frac{1}{L} \int_{-\varepsilon}^\varepsilon F(\alpha) \, d\alpha = 1$$

for any ε however small, if L is the length scale. We can work with (7) and (8) without using the Cauchy–Poisson solution. But we note in passing that the Cauchy–Poisson solution demonstrates beautifully how wave packets of various wave numbers disperse, each packet of a given wave number propagating with the group velocity for that wave number. So this kinematic significance of the group velocity was already implied in the work of Cauchy in 1815 and Poisson in 1816 (see Lamb 1945, p. 17 and p. 384 for dates of the references) long before this significance was reaffirmed and emphasized by others in the second half of the twentieth century.

Before we go on to use (7) and (8) to construct single wave groups, we note that (9) gives two values for σ for each real positive value of k, one positive and one negative. Taking the positive root gives the same ϕ and η as taking the negative root, as can be seen from (7) and (8). If we take both the positive and the negative roots of σ and add the results in each of (7) and (8), we merely get double the values of ϕ_0, ϕ, and η, with no other effects. Consequently we need not consider the negative root, and henceforth consider σ to be positive. Remembering this will remove a lot of ambiguities later.

The physical meaning of (1) has seldom been made clear. Lamb referred to it as an impulse. But since the pressure on the free surface is given by (for $y = 0$)

$$p = -\rho(\phi_t + g\eta), \tag{10}$$

and the right-hand side is zero by virtue of (7) and (8), provided the integrals are convergent, the pressure on the free surface is always zero (or constant if we did not drop the constant in the Bernoulli equation above). So the use of the term impulse is rather confusing. The correct way of thinking is to regard (7) and (8) as valid only for $t \geq 0$, and to assume both ϕ and η to be zero for $t \leq 0$. Then ϕ_t is infinite at $t = 0$, and integration of ϕ_t between $t = -\varepsilon$ and $t = 0$ gives ϕ at $t = 0$ equal to

$$\phi = \frac{a}{\pi} \int_0^\infty e^{ky}\, dk \int_{-\infty}^\infty F(\alpha) \cos k(x - \alpha)\, d\alpha,$$

while integrating η in the same interval gives nothing. Hence the integration of p in the same interval at $y = 0$ gives $-\rho\phi_0$. This is what has been considered the impulse.

3. Wave groups produced by an oscillating pressure distribution. Using (7) and (8) as building blocks, one can obtain by time-wise superposition a more general solution as follows:

$$\phi = \frac{a}{\pi} \int_0^\infty \left[\int_0^t \omega \cos \sigma(t - \tau) \sin \omega\tau e^{-\mu(t-\tau)}\, d\tau \int_{-\infty}^\infty F(\alpha) \cos k(x - \alpha)\, d\alpha \right] e^{ky}\, dk, \tag{11}$$

$$\eta = \frac{a}{\pi g} \int_0^\infty \left[\int_0^t \omega\sigma \sin \sigma(t - \tau) \sin \omega\tau e^{-\mu(t-\tau)}\, d\tau \int_{-\infty}^\infty F(\alpha) \cos k(x - \alpha)\, d\alpha \right] dk. \tag{12}$$

In (11) and (12), we have added the exponential damping factor $\exp[-\mu(t-\tau)]$, where μ is a damping coefficient much smaller than ω, and not the dynamic viscosity, to make the results determinate. This device may be called the device of fading memory, and was used by Lamb (1916, see Lamb 1945, p. 413). The only difference in its usage here is that we consider the damping to start from $t = \tau$, at which an element of ϕ_0 acts. Later in this paper, we shall provide a rational foundation for the use of some damping factor, though not exactly the same as the one above, by invoking the solution for water waves in a viscous fluid.

The solution for ϕ given by (11) certainly satisfies the Laplace equation and (6). Equations (11) and (12) also satisfy (4) at the free surface, provided (9) is satisfied.

A look at the remaining condition, the dynamic condition at the free surface, is most revealing. The linearized Bernoulli equation at the free surface is

$$p = -\rho(\phi_t + g\eta). \tag{13}$$

A calculation with (11) and (12) gives

$$p = -\frac{\rho a}{\pi} \int_0^\infty \left[\omega \sin \omega t \int_{-\infty}^\infty F(\alpha) \cos k(x - \alpha) \, d\alpha \right] dk, \tag{14}$$

after y is equated to zero after the calculation. Note that differentiation of (11) with respect to t within the integral signs (for τ) contributes a term that exactly cancels $g\eta$ on the right-hand side of (13), on account of (9). Since

$$\frac{1}{\pi} \int_0^\infty \left[\int_{-\infty}^\infty F(\alpha) \cos k(x - \alpha) \, d\alpha \right] dk = F(x),$$

equation (14) is

$$p = -\rho a\omega \sin \omega t F(x). \tag{15}$$

Hence (11) and (12) are solutions for wave motion created by the pressure distribution (15), from $t = 0$ up to time t, at the free surface, in water otherwise at rest.

It is important to note that (14) results from the variable upper limit of the τ-integral in (11). This explains why, in spite of (9), which is derived from the condition of constant or zero pressure at the free surface, an x-dependent pressure distribution is nonetheless obtained. This fact is related to the interpretation of (7) as giving an impulse at $t = 0$. But interpreting (11) as corresponding to a pressure distribution (15) makes things much easier to grasp, since pressure is far more familiar a quantity than impulse. Without (11) and (12), the formulation of the problem of wave generation by a pressure distribution is cumbersome at best.

Now let

$$F(x) = 1 \quad \text{in} \; -b \le x \le b, \tag{16}$$

and zero elsewhere. The visible quantity η then can be calculated from (12), and is

$$\eta = \frac{a\omega}{\pi g} \int_0^\infty \sigma I_1 I_2 \, dk, \tag{17}$$

where

$$\begin{aligned} I_1 &= \int_0^t \sin \sigma(t - \tau) \sin \omega\tau e^{-\mu(t-\tau)} \, d\tau \\ &= \frac{1}{2} e^{-\mu t} \int_0^t \{\cos[\sigma t - (\sigma + \omega)\tau] - \cos[\sigma t - (\sigma - \omega)\tau]\} e^{\mu\tau} \, d\tau, \end{aligned} \tag{18}$$

and

$$I_2 = \int_{-b}^b \cos k(x - \alpha) \, d\alpha = -\frac{1}{k}[\sin k(x - b) - \sin k(x + b)]. \tag{19}$$

Multiplying I_1 to I_2, expressing the product in terms of sine functions, and treating these as the imaginary parts of exponential functions, one can carry out the integration with respect to τ, and obtain

$$\eta = -\frac{a\omega e^{-\mu t}}{4\pi g} \int_0^\infty \frac{\sigma I}{k} \, dk, \tag{20}$$

where

$$I = f(x_1) - f(x_2). \tag{21}$$

CHIA-SHUN YIH

$$f(x_1) = \mathrm{Im}\left[\frac{1}{i(\sigma + \omega) + \mu}\{\exp i(kx_1 + \omega t - i\mu t) - \exp i(kx_1 - \sigma t)\}\right.$$

$$+ \frac{1}{-i(\sigma + \omega) + \mu}\{\exp i(kx_1 - \omega t - i\mu t) - \exp i(kx_1 + \sigma t)\}$$

$$- \frac{1}{i(\sigma - \omega) + \mu}\{\exp i(kx_1 - \omega t - i\mu t) - \exp i(kx_1 - \sigma t)\}$$

$$\left. - \frac{1}{-i(\sigma - \omega) + \mu}\{\exp i(kx_1 + \omega t - i\mu t) - \exp i(kx_1 + \sigma t)\}\right], \quad (22)$$

and

$$x_1 = x - b, \qquad x_2 = x + b. \tag{23}$$

In (22), Im means "the coefficient of i" in the expression that follows it.

Recalling that we need only consider positive values of σ, we see that the first two members within the brackets of (22) will make no contributions to waves in the flow, that the third member will give waves propagating to the right, and the fourth member will give waves propagating to the left. Similarly the term containing x_2 in (20) will contain a term giving waves going to the left and one going to the right. Obviously the solution for η will be symmetric with respect to $x = 0$. We need therefore consider only waves propagating to the right. Doing that, and writing

$$dk = 2\sigma \, d\sigma/g,$$

we see from (18) and (19) that the part of η corresponding to waves propagating to the right is contained in

$$-\frac{a\omega}{2\pi g} \, \mathrm{Im}(J_1 + J_2), \tag{24}$$

where

$$J_1 = \int_0^\infty \frac{1}{\sigma - (\omega + i\mu)} [\exp i(kx_1 - \omega t) - \exp i(kx_2 - \omega t)] \, d\sigma \tag{25}$$

and

$$J_2 = -\int_0^\infty \frac{e^{-\mu t}}{\sigma - (\omega + i\mu)} [\exp i(kx_1 - \sigma t) - \exp i(kx_2 - \sigma t)] \, d\sigma. \tag{26}$$

The integral J_1 is obtained upon taking the contour in Figure 1, for positive x_1 or x_2, and the contour in Figure 2, for negative x_1 or x_2. In Figures 1 and 2, $\sigma = \sigma_r + i\sigma_i$, and the radius of the circular portion is very large.

The angle of inclination of the slanted portion of the contour in these figures can have any value between zero and $\pi/2$. It has been chosen to be $\pi/8$ because when viscous effects are taken into account later, it will be seen that the angle must not exceed $\pi/6$. The contribution to J_1 from the circular part is zero. The contribution from the slanted lines can be shown not to contain any discrete wave component in the following way. Let J_{1s} be the integral J_1, but with lower and upper limits changed to

$$\sigma_\infty = \lim_{|\sigma| \to \infty} |\sigma| e^{i\pi/8} \text{ and zero,}$$

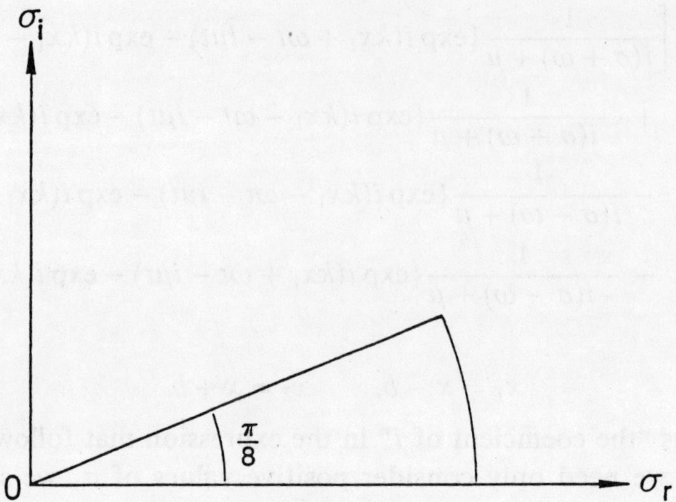

FIG. 1. Contour for evaluating the integral in (25), for positive x_1 or x_2. $\sigma = \sigma_r + i\sigma_i$.

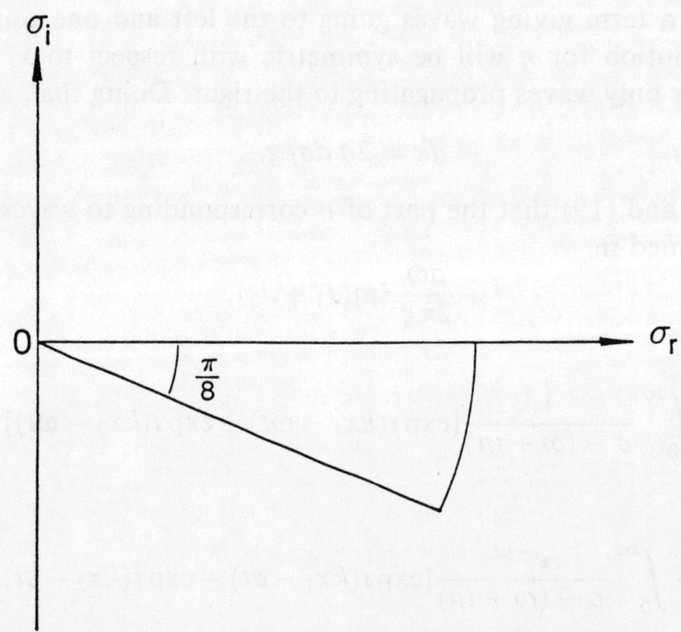

FIG. 2. Contour for evaluating the integral in (25), for negative x_1 or x_2. $\sigma = \sigma_r + i\sigma_i$.

respectively, for Figure 1. Multiply J_{1s} by

$$\exp i(k'x - \sigma't), \quad \text{with } k'g = \sigma'^2,$$

and integrate with respect to x over the entire x-axis, from minus to plus infinity. The integrals with respect to x and σ are both convergent along the slanted line in Figure 1, and the result is not singular in any way. If J_{1s} contained a discrete Fourier component, the result would be infinite for some value of k'. A similar argument applies to the slanted line in Figure 2. Thus, the wavy part of J_1 is, with $k_e = \omega^2/g$,

$$2\pi i[\exp\{i(k_e x_1 - \omega t) - 2\mu\omega g^{-1} x_1\} - \exp\{i(k_e x_2 - \omega t) - 2\mu\omega g^{-1} x_2\}] \qquad (27)$$

for positive x_1, zero for negative x_2, and

$$-2\pi i \exp\{i(k_e x_2 - \omega t) - 2\mu\omega g^{-1} x_2\} \qquad (28)$$

for

$$-b < x < b.$$

The integral J_2 requires more care. Since $k = \sigma^2/g$,

$$\exp i(k x_1 - \sigma t) = \exp[i(\sigma_r^2 - \sigma_i^2)g^{-1}x_1 - i\sigma_r t - \sigma_i(2\sigma_r g^{-1}x_1 - t)], \qquad (29)$$

and similarly when x_2 replaces x_1. For a given x_1 and a given t, and for the first term in J_2, if

$$x_1 - \frac{gt}{2\sigma_r} \qquad (30)$$

is positive we use a circular contour above the σ_r-axis, followed by a slanted line, as shown in Figure 3. At the value of σ_r, denoted by $\hat{\sigma}_r$, that makes (30) vanish, the contour follows a vertical path from P to its image point Q below the σ_r-axis. Then the lower slanted line is followed all the way to the origin, whereby the circuit is completed. Use Figure 4 if $\hat{\sigma}_r$ is reached before $\pi/8$.

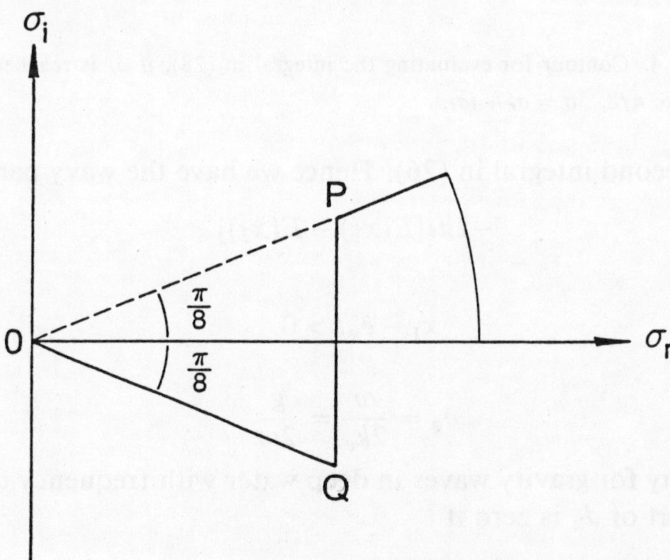

FIG. 3. Contour for evaluating the integral in (28), if $\pi/8$ is reached before $\hat{\sigma}_r$. $\sigma = \sigma_r + i\sigma_i$.

Hence, if $\hat{\sigma}_r > \omega$, the pole $\omega + i\mu$ is not within the circuit, and the residue of the contour integral of the first term in the integral of (26) is zero. Otherwise it is

$$2\pi i E(x_1), \qquad (31)$$

where

$$E(x) = \exp[i(k_e x - \omega t) - 2\mu\omega g^{-1}x]; \qquad (32)$$

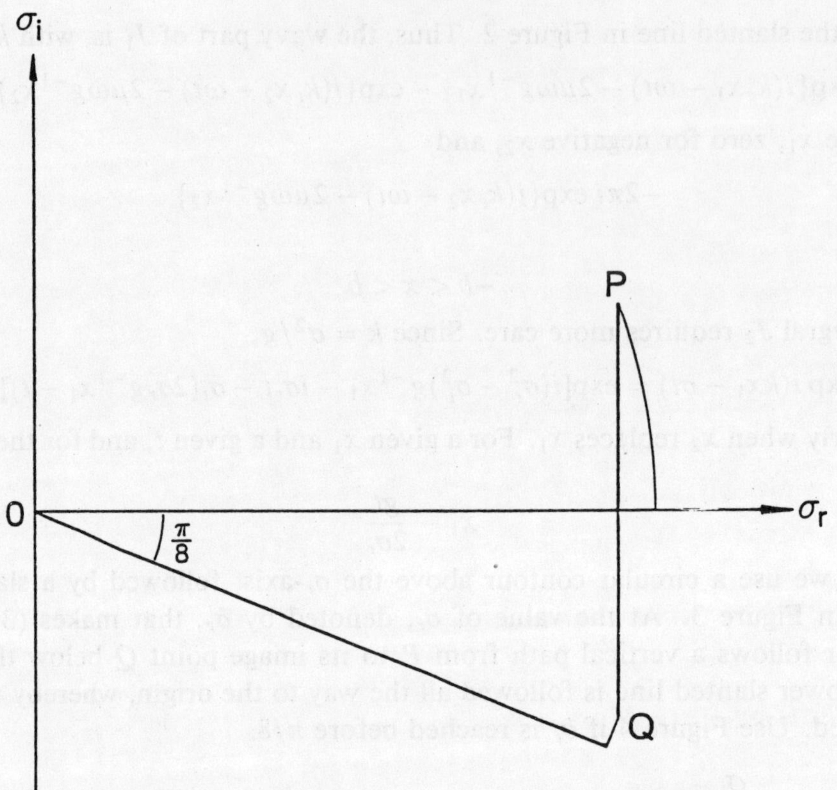

FIG. 4. Contour for evaluating the integral in (28), if $\hat{\sigma}_r$ is reached before $\pi/8$. $\sigma = \sigma_r + i\sigma_i$.

similarly for the second integral in (26). Hence we have the wavy part of J_2 equal to

$$-2\pi i[E(x_1) - E(x_2)] \tag{33}$$

if

$$x_1 - \tilde{c}_g t > 0, \tag{34}$$

where

$$\tilde{c}_g = \frac{\omega}{2k_e} = \frac{g}{2\omega} \tag{35}$$

is the group velocity for gravity waves in deep water with frequency ω. On the other hand, the wavy part of J_2 is zero if

$$x_2 - \tilde{c}_g t < 0, \tag{36}$$

and is

$$2\pi i E(x_2) \tag{37}$$

if

$$-b + \tilde{c}_g t < x < b + \tilde{c}_g t. \tag{38}$$

In the evaluation of J_2 by using the contour in Figure 3, the integral over the slanted lines again contributes nothing to the wavy part of J_2. The contribution from the vertical leg in Figure 3 to the wavy part of J_2 is also zero. This can be seen by taking the part involving x_1, since the development involving x_2 follows the same arguments. That part is, in view of (29) and the definition of $\hat{\sigma}_r$,

$$J_3 = -\exp(i\hat{\sigma}_r t/2 - \mu t)\int_{\sigma_{iP}}^{\sigma_{iQ}} \frac{i}{\sigma - (\omega + i\mu)}\exp(-i\sigma_i^2 g^{-1}x_1)\,d\sigma_i, \tag{39}$$

where $\hat{\sigma}_r \neq \omega$. For a fixed x_1 and large t, it can be shown from (40) that $J_3 \sim t^{-1}$, since $\hat{\sigma}_r$ is proportional to t for fixed x_1, and $\sigma = \hat{\sigma}_r + i\sigma_i$. The same conclusion holds for the part of J_2 containing x_2. Hence the contribution of the vertical leg in the contour in Figure 3 to J_2 is only transient for any x_1.

Let the part of η that corresponds to right-going waves be denoted by η_{wr}. Going back to (24), and using the results obtained for the wavy parts of J_1 and J_2, we can evaluate η_{wr}. Let

$$G(x) = \sin(k_e x - \omega t)\exp(-2\mu\omega g^{-1}x).$$

then the final results are:

(i)   if $x < -b$, $\eta_{wr} = 0$;

(ii)   if $x_2 - \tilde{c}_g t < 0$ and $x_1 < 0 < x_2$, $\eta_{wr} = -\dfrac{a\omega}{g}G(x_2)$;   (40)

(iii)   if $x_2 - \tilde{c}_g t < 0$ and $x_1 > 0$, $\eta_{wr} = \dfrac{a\omega}{g}[G(x_1) - G(x_2)]$;   (41)

(iv)   if $b < -b + \tilde{c}_g t < x < b + \tilde{c}_g t$, $\eta_{wr} = \dfrac{a\omega}{g}G(x_1)$;   (42)

(v)   if $x_1 > \tilde{c}_g t$, $\eta_{wr} = 0$.

There is a slight reduction of k_e, of $O(\mu^2)$, which has been neglected.

These results may seem complicated. They become immediately easy to grasp if one restates them as follows.

Two wave trains both with wave number k_e and frequency ω, one starting from $x = -b$ and the other starting from $x = b$, progress to the right with group velocity $\tilde{c}_g$ into otherwise quiet water.

Since the flow is symmetric with respect to $x = 0$, there is a set of results for left-going waves which can be obtained by symmetry arguments from results (i) to (v). These can be restated as follows.

Two other wave trains, both with wave number k_e and frequency ω, one starting from $x = b$ and the other starting from $x = -b$, progress to the left with group velocity $\tilde{c}_g$ into otherwise quiet water.

Note that where the two wave trains both exist [see (iii)], they reinforce each other if $k_e b = \pi/2$ or $(2n + 1)\pi/2$, but tend to cancel each other if $k_e b = n\pi$. (The reinforcement or cancellation would be complete if $\mu = 0$.)

The investigation for Section 3 is now finished, and we call attention to the fact that the radiation condition of Sommerfeld has not been applied because it is not at all needed, that the wave trains are exponentially damped with respect to x_1 and x_2, that they may reinforce or cancel each other where they both exist, and that they progress into wave-free water. The artificial factor $\exp[-\mu(t - \tau)]$ will be discussed in terms of the true viscosity of the fluid in a later section.

4. Wave trains of finite length. If, in the problem treated in Section 3, the oscillating pressure is removed at $t = T$, the integral I_1 given by (18) is now replaced by

$$I_1 = \int_0^T \sin \sigma(t - \tau) \sin \omega\tau e^{-\mu(t-\tau)} \, d\tau$$

$$= \frac{1}{2} e^{-\mu t} \int_0^T \{\cos[\sigma t - (\sigma + \omega)\tau] - \cos[\sigma t - (\sigma - \omega)\tau]\} e^{\mu\tau} \, d\tau.$$

The development in Section 3 can be repeated, and one obtains the result that two wave trains with wave number k_e, frequency ω, and length $\tilde{c}_g T$, progress to the right. One of these terminates at a point which is at a distance $\tilde{c}_g(t - T)$ from $x = b$, and the other terminates at the same distance from $x = -b$. Similarly there are two left-going wave trains. The flow is symmetric with respect to $x = 0$. Again where the right-going wave trains co-exist, they may reinforce or (partially) cancel each other, similarly for the left-going wave trains.

Thus we have constructed single wave groups of finite length. Each would progress into wave-free water and leave the water behind wave-free, except for the waves of the other trains.

For inviscid fluids, the μ in the exponential factors in the final results can be put to zero, since it has served the purpose of making the flow determinate. The factors can then be dropped. The same holds true for (40)–(42).

5. Wave groups produced by a moving pressure distribution. Consider the waves created by a pressure distribution moving to the left with speed c:

$$p = \beta\rho c^2 \quad \text{in } -b < x + ct < b. \tag{43}$$

Then (11) and (12) are replaced by

$$\phi = \frac{\beta c^2}{\pi} \int_0^\infty \left[\int_0^t \cos \sigma(t - \tau) e^{-\mu(t-\tau)} \, d\tau \int_{-b-ct}^{b-ct} \cos k(x - \alpha) \, d\alpha \right] e^{ky} \, dk, \tag{44}$$

$$\eta = \frac{\beta c^2}{\pi g} \int_0^\infty \left[\sigma \int_0^t \sin \sigma(t - \tau) e^{-\mu(t-\tau)} \, d\tau \int_{-b-ct}^{b-ct} \cos k(x - \alpha) \, d\alpha \right] dk. \tag{45}$$

Proceeding as in Section 3, we have

$$\eta = -\frac{\beta c^2}{\pi} \int_0^\infty \frac{\sigma}{k} I \, dk, \tag{46}$$

where

$$I = \int_0^t \sin \sigma(t - \tau)[\sin k(x_1 + ct) - \sin k(x_2 + ct)] e^{-\mu(t-\tau)} \, d\tau$$

$$= \frac{1}{2} RP[H(x_1) - H(x_2)], \tag{47}$$

$$H(x_1) = \frac{1}{i(kc + \sigma) + \mu} [e^{ik(x_1+ct)} - e^{i(kx_1+\sigma t)-\mu t}]$$

$$- \frac{1}{i(kc - \sigma) + \mu} [e^{ik(x_1+ct)} - e^{i(kx_1+\sigma t)-\mu t}], \tag{48}$$

where x_1 and x_2 are given by (23).

The roots of

$$kc - \sigma - i\mu = 0 \qquad (49)$$

are, since $kg = \sigma^2$,

$$\sigma = \frac{g}{2c} \pm \left(\frac{g^2}{4c^2} + \frac{ig\mu}{c} \right)^{1/2}. \qquad (50)$$

One of them is in the first quadrant in the complex σ-plane, and the other in the fourth. For small μ the roots can be approximated by

$$\sigma = -i\mu - \frac{c}{g}\mu^2, \qquad \sigma = \frac{g}{c}(1 + \mu^2) + i\mu. \qquad (51)$$

The roots of

$$kc + \sigma - i\mu = 0 \qquad (52)$$

are obviously the negatives of those of (49). So the roots of (49) and (52) are in the first or fourth quadrant only. Furthermore, the root of (52) in the first quadrant is outside of the contour in Figure 1, since μ is assumed much smaller than g/c. This can be seen from the first root given by (50) after the signs have been changed. Thus, in evaluating I in (47) by using the contours shown in the figures, as the situation demands, it is only the root given by (50) with the positive sign that is significant in determining the wavy part of η.

The terms in (48) corresponding to waves are, after the relevant part is extracted from the second bracket,

$$\frac{ig}{(g + i2\mu c)(\sigma - gc^{-1} - i\mu)}[\exp ik(x_1 + ct) - \exp\{i(kx_1 + \sigma t) - \mu t\}],$$

if terms of $O(\mu^2)$ are neglected. Similar results hold for the terms in $H(x_2)$ corresponding to waves. The rest of the development follows closely the steps described in Section 3, and is omitted here. The final results are as follows.

(i) There are no waves ahead of the moving disturbance.

(ii) Behind the disturbance there are two overlapping wave trains, both of wave velocity c and wave number $k_e = g/c^2$, and both of length $(c_g)_e t$, where $(c_g)_e$ is the group velocity of the waves, and is equal to $c/2$. One of the trains starts at $x_2 = 0$ and the other at $x_1 = 0$. Depending on the length over which the disturbance acts, the two trains may reinforce or partially cancel each other where they overlap.

(iii) The damping factor for the train starting at $x_1 = 0$ is

$$\exp[-2\mu(x_1 + ct)/c],$$

and the damping factor for the other train is the same factor with x_2 replacing x_1.

(iv) There is a slight increase of k_e of $O(\mu^2)$ over g/c^2, as a result of the second equation in (51). This is neglected.

If the moving disturbance is a moving body, floating or submerged, the development and the results are similar. The creation of an ever-lengthening gravity-wave group (which is the sum of the two trains, with the parts outside of their common interval neglected) behind the body allows one to calculate the wave drag from the rate of increase of the wave energy behind the body, upon letting μ be zero. This is a much more direct way of seeing things than calculating the wave drag from an infinite wave train behind the body. In that case, as is well known, one has to calculate the energy flux (or rate of work done) at a section behind the body.

6. Gravity-wave trains of finite length created by a moving disturbance in deep water. If a surface pressure is applied at $t = 0$ and moves to the left with speed c, and is then removed at time T, a group of waves of length $cT/2$ will be formed, and will move to the left with the group velocity $c/2$ (if the effect of the spread of the disturbance is neglected). Only gravity waves have been considered here. Had surface-tension effects been included, one would expect two wave groups, one of the gravity type and the other of the capillary type. When the disturbance is removed, the two groups will separate, since the train of the capillary type has a greater group velocity, even though the individual waves in either group still move with the same phase velocity c.

7. Effects of viscosity. When viscous effects are taken into account, but the Reynolds number ($g^2/(\omega^3\nu)$ or $c^3/(g\nu)$, as the case may be, ν being the kinematic viscosity) is large, Lamb's solution (1945, pp. 625–627) applies, and in the solution for ϕ or η instead of the factor $\exp i(kx - \sigma t)$ one now has, with σ^2 still equal to gk,

$$\exp[i(kx - \sigma t) - 2\nu k^2 t].$$

Thus one may consider the factor $\exp(-\mu t)$ as a useful but empirical representation of the true factor $\exp(-2\nu k^2 t)$. Replacing the former by the latter, one can carry out the calculation in Section 3 or 5 as before, and the results are the same. Of course, since the new factor involves k, one has to go through the calculation to see that it will cause no new difficulties. But the contours in the figures have been chosen with the factor $\exp(-2\nu k^2 t)$ in mind, and in the following we shall show that indeed no new difficulties arise.

The factor in Section 3,

$$(\sigma - \omega - i\mu)^{-1},$$

is now replaced by

$$(\sigma - \omega - i2\nu k^2)^{-1}, \tag{53}$$

and the factors in Section 5,

$$(kc - \sigma - i\mu)^{-1} \quad \text{and} \quad (kc + \sigma - i\mu)^{-1},$$

are now replaced by

$$(kc - \sigma - i2\nu k^2)^{-1} \quad \text{and} \quad (kc + \sigma - i2\nu k^2)^{-1}. \tag{54}$$

We have to determine the poles of (53) and (54). Aside from the important one which is, for small ν, at

$$\sigma = \omega + i2\nu\omega^4 g^{-2} \tag{55}$$

approximately, the other three of (53) are at large values of $|\sigma|$, given approximately for small ν by

$$1 - i2\nu g^{-1}\sigma^3 = 0. \tag{56}$$

If we write

$$\sigma = |\sigma|e^{i\theta},$$

then (56) gives

$$\theta = -\frac{\pi}{6}, \quad \frac{\pi}{2}, \quad \frac{7\pi}{6}. \tag{57}$$

The contours in the figures avoid all three poles with these values of θ. Indeed, they were chosen with this avoidance in mind in the first place.

As to the poles of (54), one is at $\sigma = 0$. Examination of (47) and (48) with μ replaced by $2\nu k^2$ reveals that this is not really a pole, since the numerators of (48) also vanish at $\sigma = 0$. Thus $H(x_1)$ and $H(x_2)$ do not become infinite at $\sigma = 0$.

The important pole of the first factor in (54) is at

$$\sigma = \frac{g}{c} + \frac{i2\nu g^2}{c^4} \tag{58}$$

approximately, for small ν. The other two poles of that factor are at

$$\sigma = \left(\frac{gc}{2\nu}\right)^{1/2} \left[\exp\left(-\frac{i\pi}{4}\right), \exp\left(\frac{i3\pi}{4}\right)\right] \tag{59}$$

approximately, for small ν. The poles of the second factor in (54) are at values of σ which are the negatives of those given by (58) and (59). All the poles except the one given by (58) are outside of the contours chosen in the figures. Thus for Section 5 new difficulties do not arise either when the new damping factor $\exp(-2\nu k^2 t)$ is used.

Note that in Lamb's solution the stress layer at the free surface has been ignored, since the Reynolds number is assumed high, and therefore the normal stress at the free surface is simply represented by $-p$.

When μ is replaced by $2\nu k^2$ to begin with in the development in Sections 3 and 5, all the results remain valid after μ in the results is replaced by $2\nu k_e^2$, as the mathematics requires. Thus the damping factor has been replaced by one involving the wave number, as required by the Navier–Stokes equations, and the artificiality of a frequently invoked device in wave dynamics has been removed. This and the construction of gravity-wave groups of finite length constitute the dual purpose of this paper.

Acknowledgment. This work has been supported by the Fluid-dynamics Division of the Office of Naval Research through the grant N00014-87-C-0194, for which the author wishes to express his appreciation.

REFERENCE

[1] H. Lamb, *Hydrodynamics*, Dover, New York, 1945

QUARTERLY OF APPLIED MATHEMATICS
VOLUME XLVII, NUMBER 1
MARCH 1989, PAGES 17–33

PATTERNS OF SHIP WAVES*

BY

CHIA-SHUN YIH AND SONGPING ZHU

The University of Michigan, Ann Arbor, Michigan

Abstract. Patterns of water waves created by a moving disturbance representing a moving body, floating or submerged, can be found by applying (1) the principle of stationary phase, (2) the principle that the phase lines are normal to the wave-number vector, and (3) the perception that the local phase velocity of the waves must be equal to the component of the velocity of the disturbance normal to the phase line. The three equations thus obtained are solved, and formulas for the phase lines are derived, which depend explicitly on the dispersion equation, and on that equation only. These formulas are applied to deep-water surface waves, surface waves in water of finite depth, internal waves, and capillary waves in thin sheets to obtain the wave patterns sufficiently far from the moving disturbance.

Finally, the patterns of the surface waves in deep water created by a moving body are determined, with the nonuniformity of the mean velocity of the fluid in the wake taken into account. The vorticity in the direction along the phase lines is shown to be small, so that the wave motion can still be assumed irrotational in a first approximation. The wave patterns differ from the Kelvin-wave pattern, as a result of the nonuniformity of fluid velocity in the wake.

1. Introduction. The pattern of gravity waves created by a moving disturbance in deep water was determined by Lord Kelvin (Sir W. Thomson, 1887) fully a century ago, by applying his principle of stationary phase to the well-known Cauchy–Poisson solution (see Lamb, 1945, pp. 429–434) for an instantaneous concentrated force (a concentrated impulse). But Kelvin's application of his own principle of stationary phase did not result in explicit formulas giving the wave pattern created by a moving disturbance, once the dispersion equation expressing the wave velocity in terms of the wave number is known, whatever the kind of wave—gravity wave in deep water or water of finite waves, internal waves, or capillary-gravity waves. These explicit formulas were given by Yih (1985). In this paper Yih's formulas will be presented and applied to gravity waves created by a moving disturbance, which can be regarded as representing a ship, floating or submerged. Results for gravity waves in deep water or water of finite depth and for internal waves will be presented graphically. Finally, the effects of nonuniformity of fluid velocity in the wake of the ship will be

---

*Received July 6, 1987.

©1989 Brown University

considered, and gravity-wave patterns will be shown, with the principal effect of this nonuniformity taken into account.

2. Formulas for phase lines in a ship-wave pattern. For simplicity, we can regard the moving disturbance to be a moving pressure distribution on the free surface, although this particularity does not affect the establishment of the formulas for determining the phase lines. This fact indicates that whatever the details of the disturbance may be, the wave pattern obtained will be the same, if the region under consideration is sufficiently far from the disturbance.

Let U be the speed of the disturbance, moving horizontally to the left. The direction opposite to the velocity of the disturbance is taken to be the direction of increasing x. The y-axis is normal to this direction but is also horizontal. The z-axis is directed vertically upward. The wave-number components in the directions of increasing x and y will be denoted by ξ and η respectively, and

$$k^2 = \xi^2 + \eta^2. \tag{1}$$

For our purpose it is not necessary to give the formulas for the velocity distribution in the wave motion (or the velocity potential when it exists), or for the displacement of the free surface or interface. Such formulas are given for Kelvin's waves in Whitham (1972, p. 448, Eq. 13.56), for surface waves in water of finite depth and for gravity-capillary waves in Havelock (1908), and for internal waves in two superposed fluid layers by Hudimac (1961), Carrier and Baski (1963), and Yih (1985, Eqs. 30 and 31), among others. What is important for our purpose is that in these formulas there is always the exponential factor

$$\exp i(\xi x + \eta y) \tag{2}$$

in a double integral with respect to ξ and η.

The application of Kelvin's principle of stationary phase at any point (x, y) requires,[1] because of the factor (2),

$$\frac{y}{x} = -\frac{d\xi}{d\eta}. \tag{3}$$

The normal to any curve of constant phase has the slope η/ξ. The slope of the tangent to any curve of constant phase must then have the value $-\xi/\eta$, so that for that curve

$$\frac{dy}{dx} = -\frac{\xi}{\eta}. \tag{4}$$

The requirement that the wave velocity at any point must be equal to the component of the velocity of the disturbance normal to the wave front (or the phase line) is expressed by

$$\frac{U\xi}{k} = c(k), \tag{5}$$

---

[1] The Fourier integration is in the (ξ, η)-plane. The main contribution to the integral comes from the neighborhood of a ξ-η curve where a factor in the denominator vanishes. This vanishing is represented by (5). The integration in this neighborhood involves essentially an integration across this curve (giving what amounts to residues) and an integration along that curve subsequently. It is to this latter integration that the method of stationary phase applies. After this application ξ, η, and k are considered (slowly varying) functions of x and y. This understanding should be kept in mind from (3) onward.

where $c(k)$ denotes the wave velocity, dependent on k, the geometry (for instance, depth of water), and the physical parameters relevant to the problem, such as the gravitational acceleration g and the surface tension T. We are concerned in this paper with gravity waves mainly. We shall use U as the velocity scale, and a finite depth d as the length scale. If such a depth is not available we shall use U^2/g as the length scale. Then ξ, η, k, x, and y are dimensionless. The dimensionless form of (5) is now

$$\xi = F(k), \tag{6}$$

where $F(k) = kc(k)$, and the function $F(k)$ may depend on other parameters, such as the Froude number, as well as k, because $c(k)$ does.

Since (6) is an equation between ξ and k, it is convenient to write (3) and (4) in terms of ξ and k explicitly. A brief calculation gives, upon use of (1),

$$\frac{y}{x} = -\frac{1}{d\eta/d\xi} = \frac{(k^2 - \xi^2)^{1/2}}{k(dk/d\xi) - \xi}, \tag{7}$$

$$\frac{dy}{dx} = -\frac{\xi}{(k^2 - \xi^2)^{1/2}}. \tag{8}$$

Finally, upon using (6), we have

$$\frac{y}{x} = -\frac{F'(k^2 - F^2)^{1/2}}{k - FF'}, \tag{9}$$

$$\frac{dy}{dx} = -\frac{F}{(k^2 - F^2)^{1/2}}. \tag{10}$$

We can write

$$y = -f(k)F'(k^2 - F^2)^{1/2}, \tag{11}$$

$$x = f(k)(k - FF'), \tag{12}$$

which satisfy (9), and endeavor to determine $f(k)$. From (11) and (12) we obtain

$$dy = -\frac{1}{(k^2 - F^2)^{1/2}}[fF'(k - FF') + (fF')'(k^2 - F^2)], \tag{13}$$

$$dx = f(k - FF')' + f'(k - FF'). \tag{14}$$

These, together with (10), give

$$fF(k - FF')' + f'F(k - FF') = fF'(k - FF') + (fF')'(k^2 - F^2). \tag{15}$$

It is satisfying that this equation can always be explicitly integrated, for it can be rewritten as

$$fF(k - FF')' + (fF)'(k - FF') = 2fF'(k - FF') + (fF')'(k^2 - F^2), \tag{16}$$

and this can be immediately integrated to (a = constant of integration)

$$fF(k - FF') = fF'(k^2 - F^2) + a, \tag{17}$$

or

$$f = \frac{a}{k(F - kF')}. \tag{18}$$

Thus,

$$y = -\frac{aF'}{k(F - kF')}(k^2 - F^2)^{1/2}, \tag{19}$$

$$x = \frac{a(k - FF')}{k(F - kF')}. \tag{20}$$

These are the parametric equations for the curves of constant phase, when the eikonal equation is in the form of (6), *and it is remarkable that they can be explicitly given in terms of $F(k)$*. The function $F(k)$ can easily be obtained for any kind of waves and any geometry in a two-dimensional wave motion (or one-dimensional propagation). Once it is given, (19) and (20) can be applied to find the wave pattern directly. Thus they are very useful and convenient.

2.1. *Determination of the critical angle ϕ_c.* The critical angle ϕ_c is determined by

$$\frac{d^2\eta}{d\xi^2} = 0, \qquad \text{or} \quad \frac{d}{d\xi}\frac{k\,dk/d\xi - \xi}{(k^2 - \xi^2)^{1/2}} = 0. \tag{21}$$

When (6) is the eikonal equation, this becomes

$$\frac{d}{dk}\left[\frac{k - FF'}{F'(k^2 - F^2)^{1/2}}\right] = 0. \tag{22}$$

Given F, this can be solved for k. With k known and equal to k_c (say), ξ is known from (6), η is known, and x and y are known, so that

$$\phi_c = \tan^{-1}\left.\frac{y}{x}\right|_{k_c}. \tag{23}$$

If there is more than one root of (22), take the greatest of the values of ϕ corresponding to these roots to be ϕ_c. This determines the vertex angle ($2\phi_c$) of the wedge in which waves can be found. Equation (22), too, is an important result. One expects to find waves only in some wedge where

$$-\phi_c < \phi < \phi_c.$$

3. Applications.

3.1. *Gravity waves in deep water, or Kelvin waves.* For Kelvin waves the dimensionless eikonal equation is (the length scale for this case is U^2/g)

$$\xi^2 = k. \tag{24}$$

Then

$$F(k) = k^{1/2} \quad \text{and} \quad F'(k) = \frac{1}{2}k^{-1/2}, \tag{25}$$

$$y = -\frac{a}{k^2}(k^2 - k)^{1/2}, \tag{26}$$

$$x = \frac{a(2k - 1)}{k^{3/2}}. \tag{27}$$

Following Lamb (1945, p. 433), we define θ as the angle of inclination of the normal to any curve of constant phase, so that, along any curve of constant phase

$$\frac{dy}{dx} = -\frac{\xi}{\eta} = -\cot\theta. \tag{28}$$

Because of (24),

$$k^2 - k = k^2 - \xi^2 = \eta^2,$$

so that

$$y = -\frac{a\eta}{k^2} = -\frac{a}{\xi^3}\frac{\eta}{\xi}. \tag{29}$$

Now (28) can be written as

$$\pm \cot\theta = \frac{\xi}{(k^2 - \xi^2)^{1/2}} = \frac{\xi}{(\xi^4 - \xi^2)^{1/2}} = \frac{1}{(\xi^2 - 1)^{1/2}} \tag{30}$$

so that

$$\xi = \sec\theta, \tag{31}$$

and (29) becomes

$$y = -a\cos^3\theta\tan\theta = -a\sin\theta\cos^2\theta. \tag{32}$$

Similarly, (27) becomes

$$x = \frac{a(2k-1)}{k^{3/2}} = \frac{a(2\xi^2 - 1)}{\xi^3} = a\cos\theta(2 - \cos^2\theta),$$

or

$$x = a\cos\theta(1 + \sin^2\theta). \tag{33}$$

Equations (32) and (33) are exactly the equations (Lamb, 1945, p. 434) for the Kelvin curves of constant phase for surface waves. The wave pattern is shown in Fig. 1, upon taking a equal to 1, 2, 3, etc. Since on the centerline $k = 1$, because the length scale is U^2/g and on the centerline $U = c$, the increment in a, indicating a wavelength on the centerline, corresponds to $2\pi U^2/g$ when converted to dimensional length. (Recall wave number $= 2\pi/$wavelength.) The cusps occur at $\xi = (3/2)^{1/2}$, giving a ϕ_c of $19°28'$. The flow near the cusps requires better resolution. This was provided by Ursell (1960).

3.2. *Gravity waves in water of finite depth.* Let the depth of the water be d. Then, as is well known, in *dimensional* terms the phase velocity $c(k)$ is given by

$$c^2 = \frac{g}{k}\tanh kd.$$

In dimensionless terms, with d as the length scale and U the velocity scale, this becomes

$$c^2 = N_F^{-2}k^{-1}\tanh k, \tag{34}$$

where N_F is the Froude number defined by

$$N_F^2 = \frac{U^2}{gd}. \tag{35}$$

Then (6) takes the form

$$\xi = N_F^{-1}(k\tanh k)^{1/2}, \tag{36}$$

the right-hand side of which is $F(k)$. Using this $F(k)$ in (19) and (20), we obtain the wave patterns shown in Figs. 2 for

$$N_F = 0.2, \ 0.4, \ 0.6, \ 0.8, \ 1.0, \ 1.5, \ 2.0, \ \text{and} \ 5.0,$$

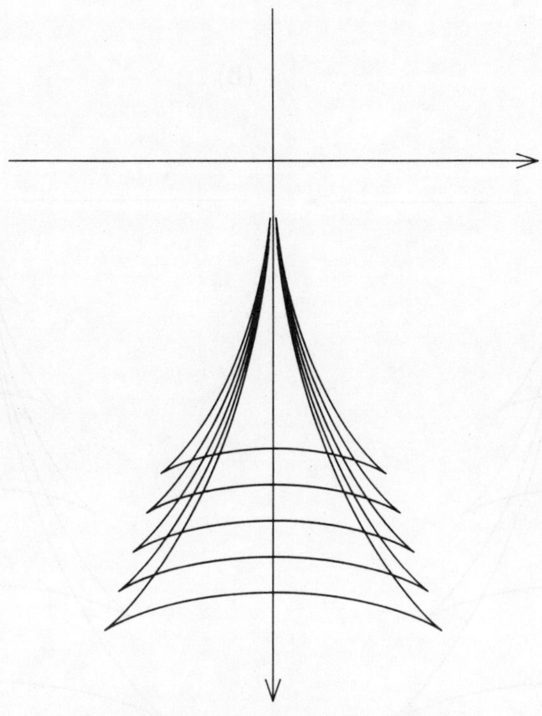

Fig. 1. Kelvin-wave pattern.

respectively. On the centerline, $\xi = k = k_0$, and (36) gives

$$N_F^2 = \frac{1}{k_0} \tanh k_0. \tag{37}$$

The wavelength of transverse waves is $2\pi d/k_0$ on the centerline. Given the Froude number N_F and the depth d, k_0 is determined from (37) and the wavelength on the centerline is known. The patterns in the figures should be read with this in mind. The fact that the patterns have been obtained by assigning integral values to a in (19) and (20) is of little importance since the scale used in plotting the figures is arbitrary.

The most important feature of Fig. 2 is that only when the Froude number N_F is less than 1 are there transverse waves. This is because the wave velocity c is bounded by $(gd)^{1/2}$, so that when N_F exceeds 1 no waves, however long, can be stationary at the centerline, so that no transverse waves can exist. When N_F exceeds 1, the phase lines at large distances from the disturbance appear to approach asymptotes.

The k_c (k at the cusps), defined by (23) when $N_F < 1$, and the ϕ_c giving the half angle of the wedge in which waves exist, depend on the value of N_F. We note that when transverse waves exist, k increases from k_0 on the centerline to k_c at the cusp, and then increases monotonically along the phase line of a divergent wave. When transverse waves do not exist, k increases along such a line as $|y|$ decreases; i.e., as the centerline is approached. The same is true for internal waves.

3.3. *Internal waves.* Let us consider gravity waves in two superposed fluids. The upper fluid has density ρ and depth h, and the lower fluid has density $\rho'(> \rho)$ and infinite depth. Let the velocity potential perturbations (from the mean flow of

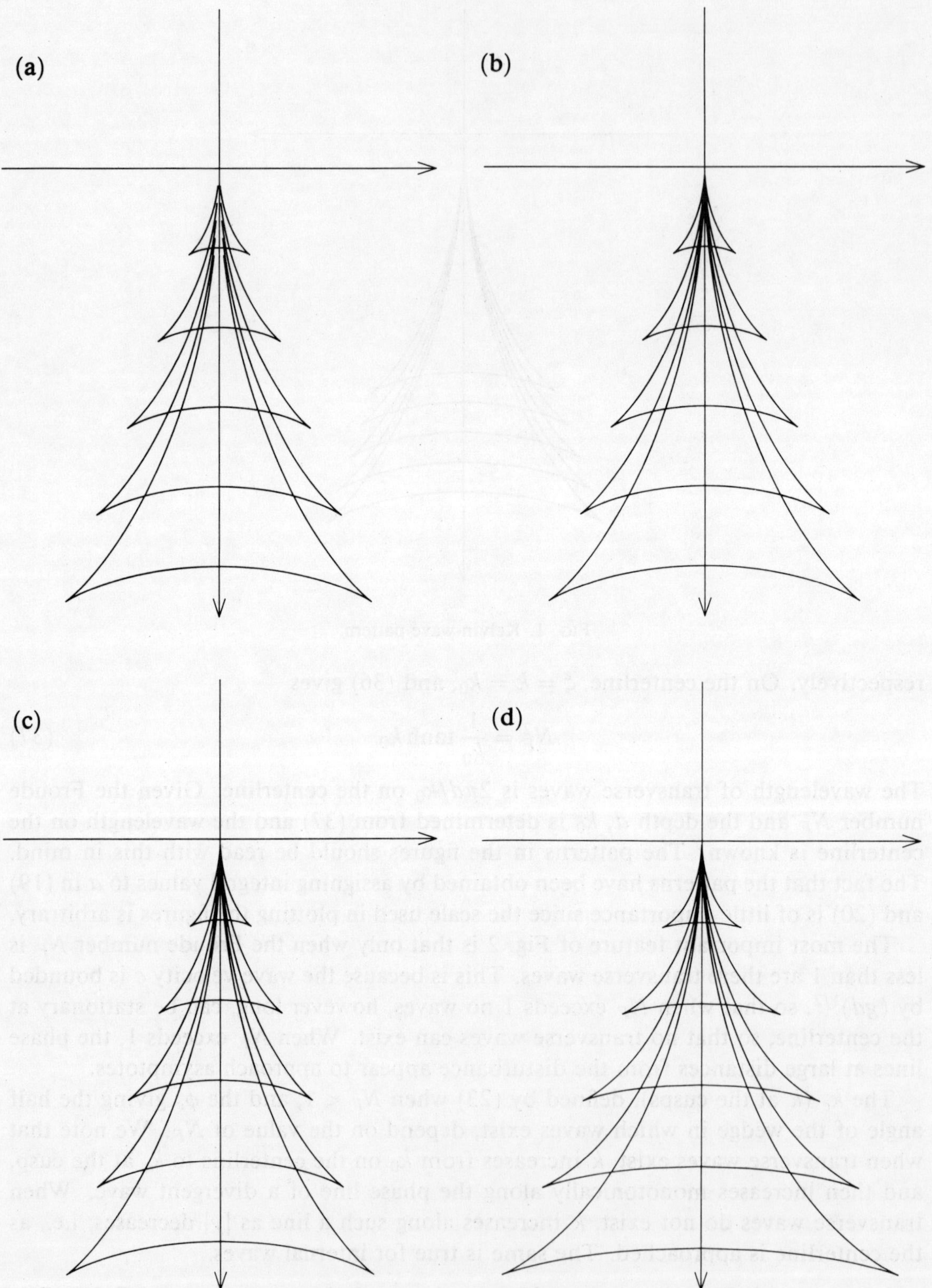

Fig. 2. (a)–(d). Pattern of ship waves in water of finite depth.
(a) $N_F = 0.2$, (b) $N_F = 0.4$, (c) $N_F = 0.6$, (d) $N_F = 0.8$.

24   CHIA-SHUN YIH AND SONGPING ZHU

velocity c) for the two layers be ϕ and ϕ', respectively. The displacement of the free surface is denoted by ζ and that of the interface by ζ'. All quantities will be dimensional until otherwise stated. The phase velocity c will be determined from a calculation for stationary waves, that is, for a coordinate system moving with the waves to the left. Then the kinematic condition at the free surface is (the origin of z being at the interface)

$$c\zeta_x = \phi_z \quad \text{at } z = h, \tag{38}$$

and the dynamic condition there is the Bernoulli equation

$$g\zeta + c\phi_x = 0 \quad \text{at } z = h. \tag{39}$$

Combination of (38) and (39) gives

$$s\phi_{xx} = -\phi_z \quad \text{at } z = h \tag{40}$$

for the free surface, where

$$s = \frac{c^2}{g}. \tag{41}$$

At the interface, the kinematic conditions are

$$c\zeta'_x = \phi_z \quad \text{and} \quad c\zeta'_x = \phi'_z \quad \text{at } z = 0, \tag{42}$$

and the dynamic condition is

$$\rho g\zeta' + \rho c\phi_x = \rho' g\zeta' + \rho' c\phi'_x \quad \text{at } z = 0. \tag{43}$$

Defining

$$\beta = \frac{\rho' - \rho}{\rho} \tag{44}$$

and substituting (42) into (43), we obtain

$$\frac{\beta}{s}\phi_z = -(\beta + 1)\phi'_{xx} + \phi_{xx} \quad \text{at } z = 0. \tag{45}$$

Equations (42) can be combined into

$$\phi_z = \phi'_z \quad \text{at } z = 0. \tag{46}$$

One last condition is

$$\phi' = 0 \quad \text{at } z = -\infty. \tag{47}$$

Taking

$$\phi = (Ae^{kz} + Be^{-kz})\cos kx, \qquad \phi' = Ce^{kz}\cos kx, \tag{48}$$

which satisfies (47), since k is assumed positive, we use (40), (45), and (46) to eliminate the constants $A, B,$ and C, and obtain from a straightforward calculation

$$(ks - 1)[ks(2 + \beta + \beta e^{-2kh}) - \beta(1 - e^{-2kh})] = 0. \tag{49}$$

The root

$$s = \frac{c^2}{g} = \frac{1}{k} \tag{50}$$

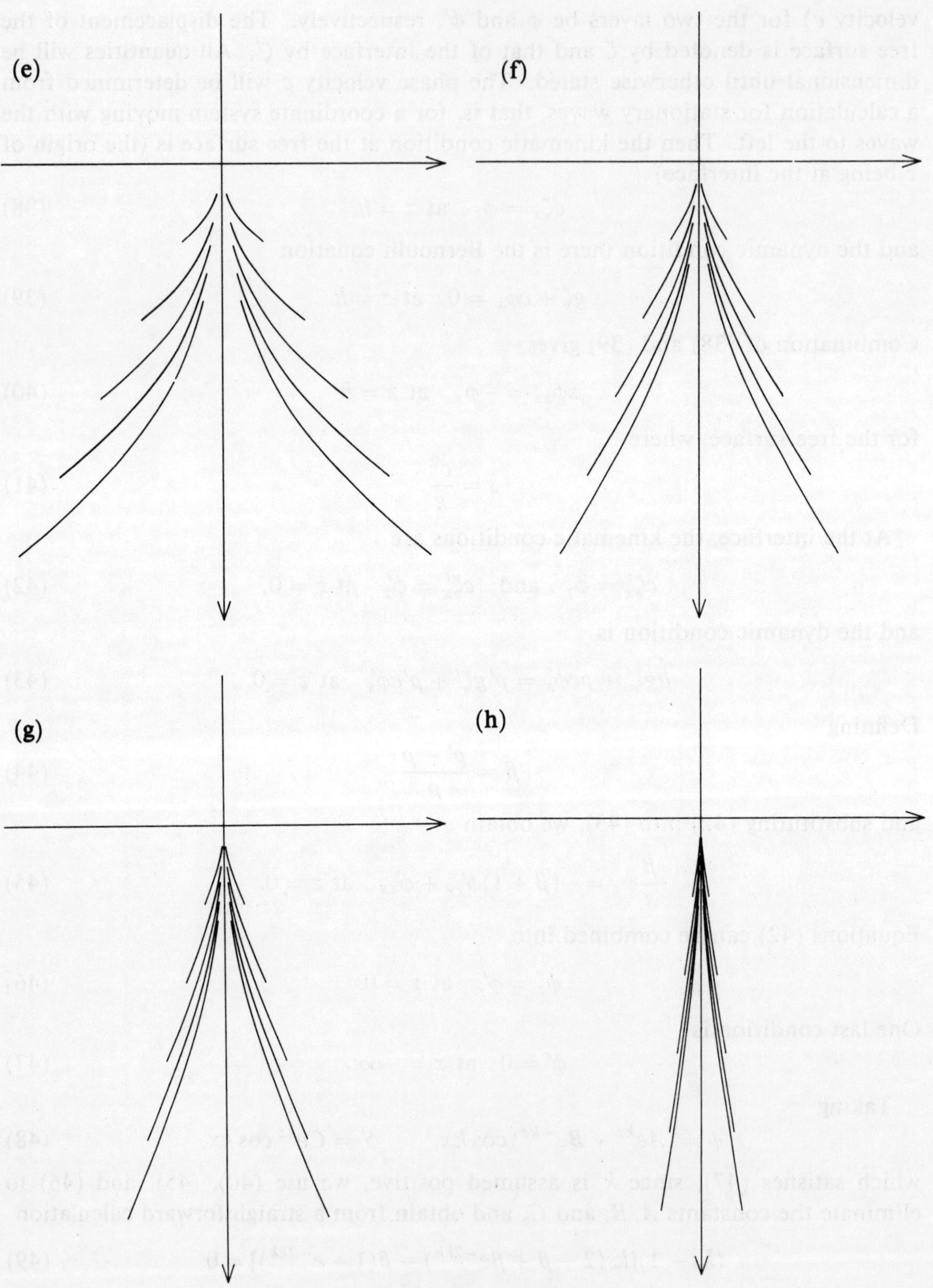

FIG. 2. (e)–(h). Pattern of ship waves in water of finite depth.
(e) $N_F = 1$, (f) $N_F = 1.5$, (g) $N_F = 2$, (h) $N_F = 5$.

corresponds to irrotational wave motion of the entire fluid, with no vortex sheet even at the interface, as is well known (Yih 1960, and 1980, pp. 60–62). This wave motion has the Kelvin-wave pattern presented in subsection 3.2. The other root of (49) is

$$c^2 = \frac{\beta g}{k} \frac{e^{2kh} - 1}{(2 + \beta)e^{2kh} + \beta},$$

(51)

and corresponds to predominantly internal waves. Substituting (51) into (5), using h as the length scale, we obtain the dimensionless equation

$$\xi = N_F^{-1} \left(\frac{\beta \gamma k}{\alpha} \right)^{1/2},$$

(52)

$$\alpha(k) = (2 + \beta)e^{2k} + \beta,$$

(53)

$$\gamma(k) = e^{2k} - 1,$$

(54)

and N_F is the Froude number now defined by

$$N_F^2 = \frac{U^2}{gh}.$$

We have done the calculations for the internal-wave patterns for $\beta = 0.04$. The patterns are shown in Fig. 3 for

$$N_F = 0.01, \ 0.05, \ 0.1, \ 0.15, \ 0.2, \ 0.5, \ 1, \ \text{and} \ 2,$$

respectively. Again transverse waves exist only if N_F is sufficiently small. The critical N_F can be calculated from (52) upon putting ξ equal to k, letting k approach zero (to get the longest wavelength possible), and taking the limit. Doing so, we obtain the critical Froude number

$$(N_F)_c = \frac{\beta}{1 + \beta}.$$

(55)

When $N_F > (N_F)_c$, no transverse waves are possible. For $\beta = 0.04$, $(N_F)_c$ is approximately 0.2. That is why in Fig. 3(e) no transverse waves appear.

As for surface waves in water of finite depth, the angle ϕ_c which the line of cusps makes with the centerline, defined by (23), depends on N_F. This dependence is evident upon examination of Figs. 3(c) and 3(d). From Fig. 3(e) onward to Fig. 3(h), the wave region narrows as the phase lines, which appear to approach asymptotes, make smaller and smaller angles with the centerline.

3.4. *Capillary waves on a thin sheet.* For a fluid sheet of thickness $2h$, there are two modes of capillary waves. For the one mode, the sheet deforms as a whole antisymmetrically, with hardly any change in thickness. In this mode the waves are nondispersive. For the other mode, the sheet deforms symmetrically, and the dimensional dispersive equation is, upon neglect of gravity effects and on the assumption that the wavelength anywhere is much greater than h,

$$c^2 = \frac{Th}{\rho} k^2,$$

where T is the surface tension, ρ is density of the fluid, and c and k are the dimensional phase velocity and wave number, respectively. (See Whitham, 1972, p.

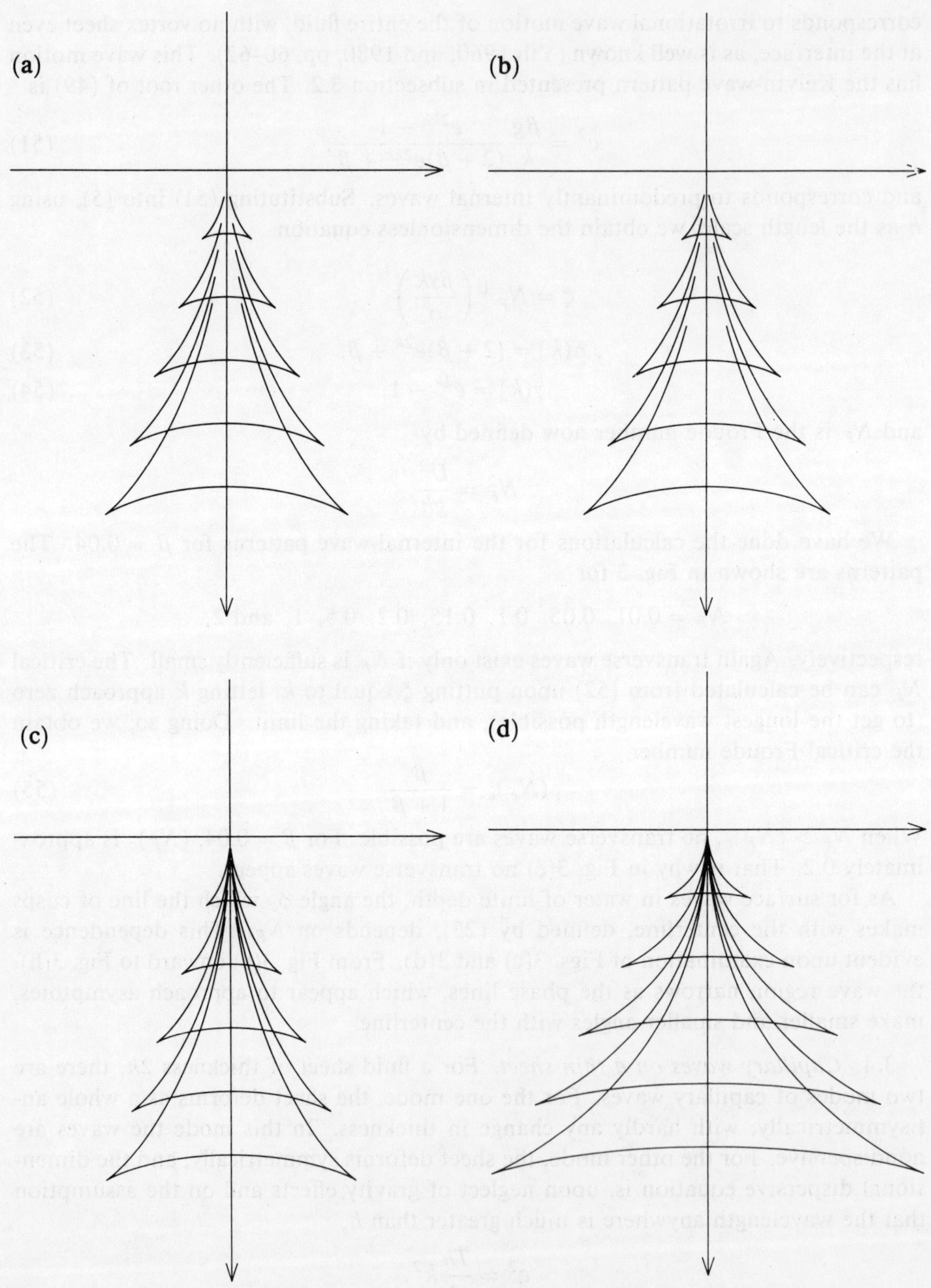

FIG. 3. (a)–(d). Pattern of internal waves created by a moving body.
(a) $N_F = 0.01$, (b) $N_F = 0.05$, (c) $N_F = 0.1$, (d) $N_F = 0.15$.

405.) We shall use h as the length scale and $(\rho h^3/T)^{1/2}$ as the time scale. Then the dimensionless dispersion equation becomes

$$c = k, \qquad \text{or} \quad F(k) = ck = k^2.$$

Putting this into (11) and (12), we have

$$y = -\frac{2a}{k}(1 - k^2)^{1/2},$$

$$x = -\frac{a(1 - 2k^2)}{k^2},$$

in which the square root may be positive or negative, while k is restricted to values less than 1.

It is a very simple matter to show that the x and y given above satisfy a parabolic relation

$$\frac{x}{a} = 1 - \left(\frac{y}{a}\right)^2. \tag{56}$$

The source of the disturbance is at $x = 0 = y$, at which a must be taken to be zero. Along the centerline ($y = 0$) *in front* of the disturbance, the dimensionless k is 1. That is to say, the dimensionless wavelength λ (in units of h) is 2π. Hence to show the wave pattern one must take successively

$$a = 2\pi, \ 4\pi, \ 6\pi, \ \text{etc.}$$

Whitham (1972, pp. 415–416) gave a more indirect derivation of the pattern of capillary waves in thin sheets, and obtained "roughly parabolic crests" in his Fig. 12.7. From our derivation here it is clear that the crests are not merely roughly parabolic, but exactly parabolic.

We note that Whitham's Fig. 12.7 (Whitham 1972, p. 416) is for the disturbance moving to the left. Our formula (56) is for the disturbance moving to the right. Otherwise our pattern for capillary waves is the same as his.

4. Gravity waves in the wake of a moving body. The wake behind a moving body is an important effect of viscosity, for it is ultimately related to the boundary layer on the body. Again let U^2/g be the length scale and use x and r as dimensionless coordinates, r being the radial distance from the x-axis. The velocity distribution in the wake can take a variety of forms, depending on the shape of the body and the Reynolds number, as is well known. Using U again as the velocity scale, the dimensionless velocity can be represented, without serious error, by a class of profiles as follows (α and β are not the same as in subsection 3.3):

$$u = 1 - \alpha x^{-2/3}\exp(-\beta r^2 x^{-2/3}). \tag{57}$$

The momentum flux across any section of constant x below the free surface is, for the mean flow given by (57),

$$\frac{\pi\alpha}{2\beta}\rho U^6 g^{-2}, \tag{58}$$

and this is equal to the viscous drag force $C_D A\rho U^2$, if A is a cross section of the body and C_D the coefficient of drag. This equality is based on the neglect of the

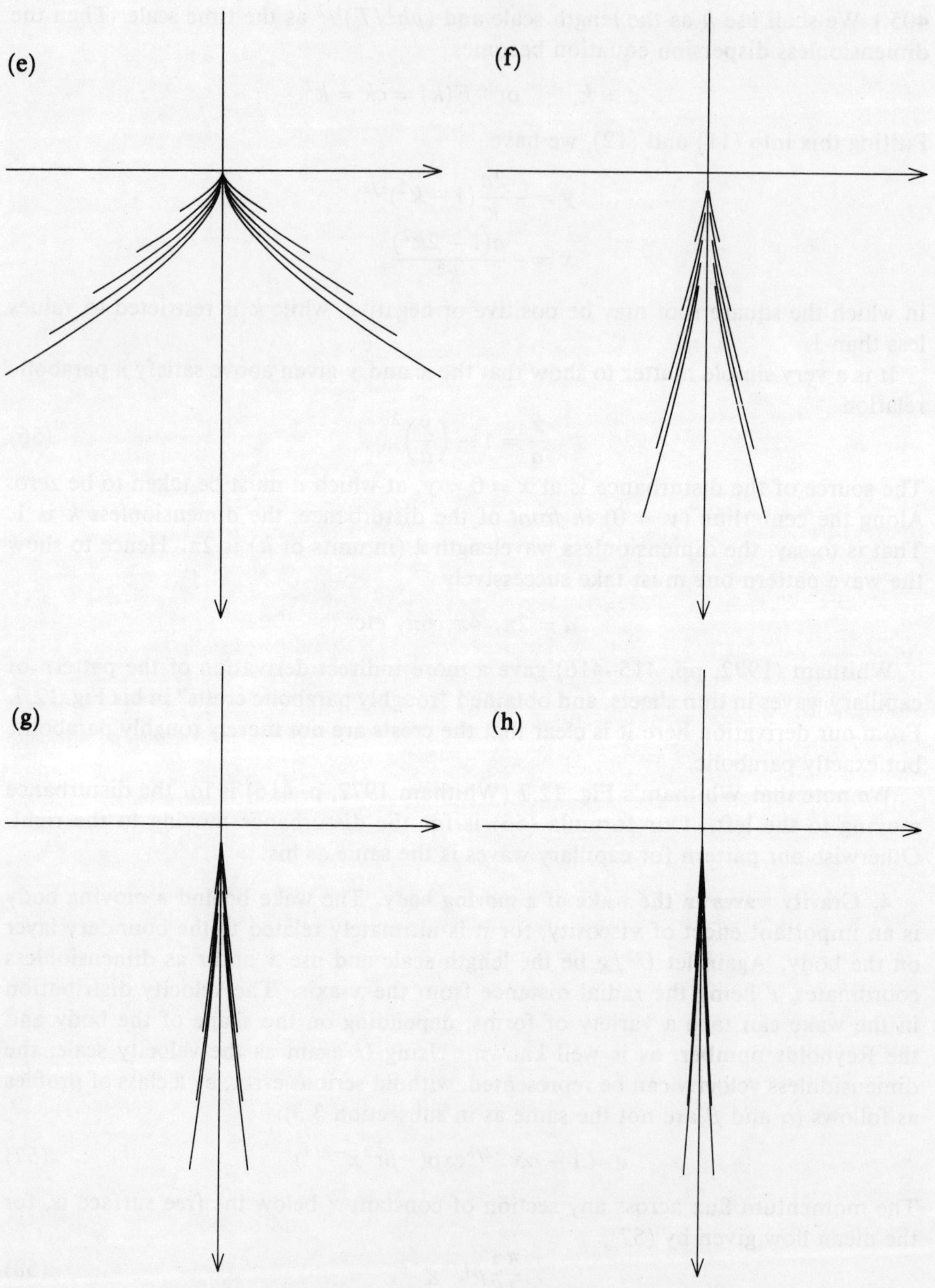

FIG. 3. (e)–(h). Pattern of internal waves created by a moving body.
(e) $N_F = 0.2$, (f) $N_F = 0.5$, (g) $N_F = 1$, (h) $N_F = 2$.

longitudinal stress across any section of constant x, and gives

$$\frac{\alpha}{\beta} = \frac{2}{\pi} C_D F_A^{-4},\tag{59}$$

where F_A is a Froude number based on a linear dimension $A^{1/2}$, defined by

$$F_A^4 = \frac{U^4}{g^2 A}.\tag{60}$$

In our calculation we have taken

$$C_D = 0.05,\tag{61}$$

$$\frac{\alpha}{\beta} = \frac{1}{20}.\tag{62}$$

This corresponds to

$$F_A = \left(\frac{2}{\pi}\right)^{1/4} = 0.89,\tag{63}$$

not an unreasonable number. Other values of C_D and F_A can be taken, resulting in other values of α/β.

On the free surface (57) becomes

$$u = 1 - \alpha x^{-2/3}\exp(-\beta y^2 x^{-2/3}).\tag{64}$$

We shall assume this velocity to be prevailing in the fluid, and furthermore shall assume the wave motion to be irrotational. This requires some justification and explanation. Assuming (64) throughout the fluid amounts to assuming that the wave motion does not penetrate the fluid significantly to distances below the free surface where u is very different from that given by (64). This is true only if x is large. As to the irrotationality of the wave motion, one justifies it on two grounds.

(i) The length scale of the variation of u for large values of x is large, and therefore much greater than the wavelengths in the wave region.

(ii) All the vorticity lines for the flow (57) are circles in planes normal to the x-axis. Near the free surface they are nearly vertical, whereas the local wave motion, assumed irrotational in the plane containing the wave-number vector and a vertical line, can become rotational only if the local wave motion bends the vertical vorticity lines of the mean flow in the direction of the phase lines. But any bending of the vorticity lines by the local wave motion would be in the direction normal to the phase lines. Thus the irrotationality of the local wave motion is hardly affected.

We can use equations (3) and (4) again, but must modify (6) to

$$u\xi = F(k).\tag{65}$$

The calculation is one of step-by-step computation, as k is increased from k_0 (now not constant) on the centerline toward k_c (at the cusp) and beyond. The k_0 for the transverse waves on the centerline is determined from (64).

We have performed the calculations for

$$\alpha = 1/8, 1/4, 1/2, 3/4,$$

$$\beta = 2.5, 5, 10, 15.$$

The results are shown in Fig. 4, in which (a) is for $(\alpha, \beta) = (1/8, 2.5)$, etc. In starting the lines of the same phase, we start with $x = 8$ on the centerline, calculate the wavelength of the transverse wave there, and mark off the next point on the centerline of the same phase, and use that point to start the calculation for the next line of the same phase, and so on. From Fig. 4 it can be seen that near the centerline the transverse waves bent back toward positive x more pronouncedly than in the Kelvin-wave pattern, but become straight sooner. The curvature of the transverse waves at the centerline is larger when there is a wake.

For the Kelvin-wave pattern,

$$\xi = \xi_c = (3/2)^{1/2}$$

at the cusp, and $\phi_c = 19°28'$. In our case, since u in (65) is variable, it is not obvious that ϕ_c has the same value. However, our calculations seem to give the same value. An explanation of this on analytical grounds goes as follows. It can easily be verified that for *any fixed* value of u the maximum value of $d\eta/d\xi$ occurs at $\xi = (3/2)^{1/2}$, and gives $\phi_c = 19°28'$. Now fix the x and y in u, and perform the calculation for the phase lines as if u were constant. A cusp is encountered at some point (x_c, y_c). If these are not the same as the fixed x and y, the cusp has no real significance. But if they happen to be the same, then, since the calculation in a neighborhood of that point is now valid, it must be a cusp in the wave pattern. This can be seen in the following way. Start from any cusp point (x_c, y_c), calculate $u(x_c, y_c)$, fix u at this value, then use the equations of Section 2 to trace out the two branches of the phase line originating from the cusp. Let us call this line A. Then starting from the same cusp, use the actual u in the step-by-step numerical computation in this section to trace out the two branches of the phase line originating from the cusp. Let us call this line B. Lines A and B are not the same, of course, but they have the same cusp and are nearly coincident near the cusp.

5. Range of k values for the figures. For the benefit of those who wish to reproduce the wave patterns given in the figures of this paper, we supply the ranges of the values of the dimensionless k for each of the figures, except Figures 4(a)–4(d), in Table 1.

TABLE 1

Values for $k_{\min}$ and k at cusp for the figures.

Figure	1	2a	2b	2c	2d	2e-2h
$k_{\min}$	1	25	6.24995	2.7554	1.37458	1.5
k at cusp	$(3/2)^{1/2}$	37.432	9.39995	4.0574	1.74508	

Figure	3a	3b	3c	3d	3e-3h
$k_{\min}$	196.0784	7.84313	1.91763	0.6113	0.3
k at cusp	294.3604	11.74913	2.72963	0.7933	

For Figures 4, the minimum k for each of the phase lines is for the transverse wave at the centerline, and this minimum k is determined by the equality of the local wave velocity of the transverse waves at the centerline and the local speed of the fluid in the wake. Because of the nonhomogeneity of fluid velocity in the wake (even apart from wave effects), the spacing of crests at the centerline cannot be determined simply, and can only be approximated by computing the locations of many intermediate phase lines. For this reason only phase lines, which are not necessarily crests, are shown in Figure 4, to give a general idea of the wave pattern. The maximum λ, for all the figures, including Figure 4, is infinity. We have simply stopped at a large enough value; the precision of the difference has caused the limit of these phase lines distinctly. We believe this description will be sufficient to guide anyone willing to reproduce our data.

Acknowledgement. This work has been supported by the Ship Hydrodynamics Project at the University of Michigan, funded by the David Taylor Research, in lieu of the Office of Naval Research, under Contract No. N00014-86-K-0684. It has also been supported by the Office of Naval Research under Contract No. N00014-87-C-0194.

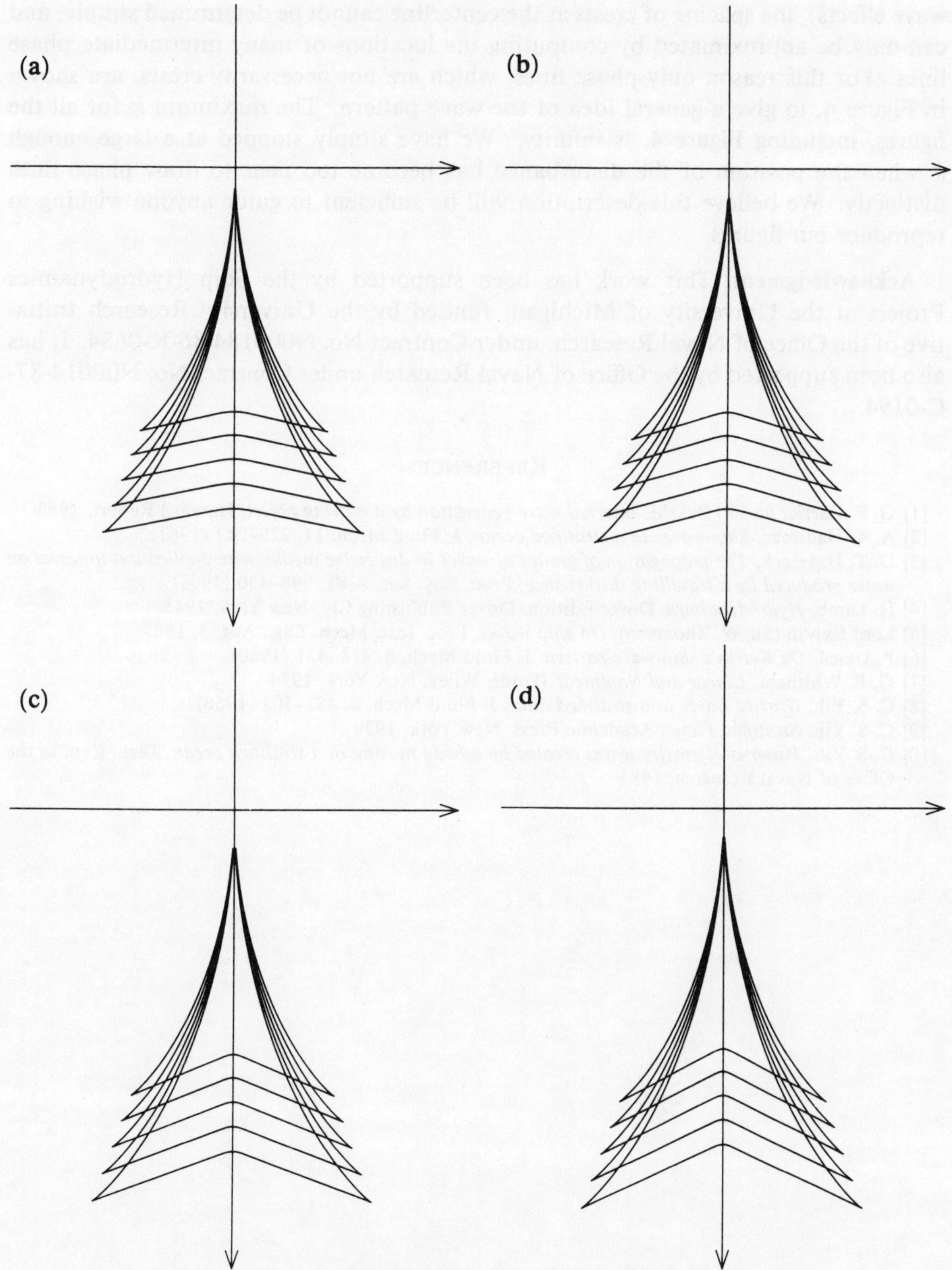

FIG. 4. (a)–(d). Pattern of gravity waves in the wake of a ship. (a) $\alpha = 1/8, \beta = 2.5$, (b) $\alpha = 1/4, \beta = 5$, (c) $\alpha = 1/2, \beta = 10$, (d) $\alpha = 3/4, \beta = 15$. The phase difference between consecutive phase lines is approximately 1 radian.

wave effects), the spacing of crests at the centerline cannot be determined simply, and can only be approximated by computing the locations of many intermediate phase lines. For this reason only phase lines, which are not necessarily crests, are shown in Figure 4, to give a general idea of the wave pattern. The maximum k for all the figures, including Figure 4, is infinity. We have simply stopped at a large enough k when the position of the disturbance has become too near to draw phase lines distinctly. We believe this description will be sufficient to guide anyone wishing to reproduce our figures.

Acknowledgment. This work has been supported by the Ship Hydrodynamics Project at the University of Michigan, funded by the University Research Initiative of the Office of Naval Research, under Contract No. N000184-86-K-0684. It has also been supported by the Office of Naval Research under Contract No. N00014-87-C-0194.

REFERENCES

[1] G. F. Carrier and P. Bakshi, *Internal wave generation by a moving object*, Harvard Report, 1963

[2] A. A. Hadimac, *Ship waves in a stratified ocean*, J. Fluid Mech. **11**, 229–243 (1961)

[3] D. T. Havelock, *The propagation of groups of waves in dispersive media, with application to waves on water produced by a travelling disturbance*, Proc. Roy. Soc. A **81**, 398–430 (1908)

[4] H. Lamb, *Hydrodynamics*, Dover Edition, Dover Publishing Co., New York, 1945

[5] Lord Kelvin (Sir W. Thomson), *On ship waves*, Proc. Inst. Mech. Eng., Aug. 3, 1887

[6] F. Ursell, *On Kelvin's ship-wave pattern*, J. Fluid Mech. **8**, 418–431 (1960)

[7] G. B. Whitham, *Linear and Nonlinear Waves*, Wiley, New York, 1974

[8] C.-S. Yih, *Gravity waves in a stratified fluid*, J. Fluid Mech. **8**, 481–508 (1960)

[9] C.-S. Yih, *Stratified Flows*, Academic Press, New York, 1980

[10] C.-S. Yih, *Patterns of gravity waves created by a body moving in a stratified ocean*, Tech. Rep. to the Office of Naval Research, 1985

QUARTERLY OF APPLIED MATHEMATICS
VOLUME XLVII, NUMBER 1
MARCH 1989, PAGES 35–44

PATTERNS OF SHIP WAVES II.
GRAVITY-CAPILLARY WAVES*

By

CHIA-SHUN YIH (*University of Florida, Gainesville, Florida*)

AND

SONGPING ZHU (*University of Michigan, Ann Arbor, Michigan*)

In a previous paper [4], Yih's formulas [3] were used to obtain patterns of gravity waves, or of capillary waves in a thin fluid sheet, created by a moving disturbance. In this paper the effects of surface tension are taken into account in finding the patterns of capillary-gravity waves in deep water with a free surface created by a moving disturbance, and much more extensive results than those of Rayleigh [2] have been obtained. The most important feature of the waves is that there are capillary waves *behind* the disturbance, which have very short wavelengths at high values of the speed U of the disturbance and which are confined to a wedge of an angle that decreases as U increases. Of interest too is the existence of two cusps in the phase lines on either side of the centerline at high values of U (relative to a minimum wave velocity defined in the paper) for those waves which are entirely behind the disturbance.

1. Introduction. Explicit formulas for phase lines of any kind of dispersive waves created by a point disturbance moving in a fluid with a free surface were given by Yih [3]. These formulas are in terms of the parameter k, which is the local wavenumber. The point disturbance is an idealized representation of a ship, for instance, so that the formulas are useful for determining the pattern of waves far enough away from the ship. Yih's formulas were used by Yih and Zhu [4] to obtain patterns of ship waves in deep water (Kelvin waves), in water of finite depth, in a stratified ocean, and in the wake of a ship, as well as patterns of waves in a thin sheet caused by a moving point disturbance. But capillary-gravity waves were not treated in [4]. It will be treated in this paper, and many patterns of capillary-gravity waves caused by a moving disturbance will be presented.

The main reason for giving capillary-gravity waves a closer examination is that the treatment by Rayleigh [2], as quoted in Lamb ([1], pp. 469–471), is very sketchy and calls for a new calculation after more than a century, especially in view of the relevance of the problem to remote sensing. As will be seen, one important feature of capillary-gravity waves caused by a moving disturbance is that there are (predominantly) capillary waves *behind* the disturbance. This point has not been stressed in

---

*Received June 23, 1988.

©1989 Brown University

Lamb's book, but explains the presence of short waves within a narrow wedge which are often found in photographs obtained by remote sensing in the wake of a ship.

2. Analysis. Let the point disturbance move with speed U in the horizontal direction of decreasing x. The y-axis is also horizontal, and is normal to the x-axis. As in [4], ρ denotes the density of the fluid, g denotes the gravitational acceleration, T denotes surface tension, and we shall continue to use U^2/g as the length scale, so that the local wavenumber k will continue to be measured in units of g/U^2. The x and y components of the wavenumber vector k will again be denoted by ξ and η, so that

$$\xi^2 + \eta^2 = k^2. \tag{1}$$

With this in mind, the requirement that the local wave velocity must be equal to the component of the velocity of the disturbance normal to the wave front (or the phase line) is

$$\xi = F(k) = k(1/k + \sigma k)^{1/2}, \tag{2}$$

which is Eq. (6) in [4] for the present problem. The σ in (2) is

$$\sigma = \frac{Tg}{\rho U^4} = \frac{1}{4}\left(\frac{c_{\min}}{U}\right)^4, \tag{3}$$

where $c_{\min} = 2(Tg/\rho)^{1/2}$ is the minimum value of the wave velocity c calculated from the dimensional dispersion equation, given by

$$c^2 = \frac{g}{\hat{k}} + \frac{T}{\rho}\hat{k}, \tag{4}$$

in which $\hat{k}$ denotes the dimensional local wavenumber. The $\hat{k}$ for $c_{\min}$ is

$$\hat{k}_{cr} = \{\rho g/T\}^{1/2}. \tag{5}$$

If $\hat{k} > \hat{k}_{cr}$, or

$$k > (1/\sigma)^{1/2},$$

the waves are predominantly capillary waves. If

$$k < (1/\sigma)^{1/2},$$

the waves are predominantly gravity waves. The word "predominantly" may from time to time be omitted in the rest of this paper for brevity.

Yih's formulas for phase lines are (see Eqs. (19) and (20) in [1])

$$y = -\frac{aF'}{k(F - kF')}(k^2 - F^2)^{1/2}, \tag{6}$$

$$x = \frac{a(k - FF')}{k(F - kF')}, \tag{7}$$

where a is a constant of integration. The k in (1) will be treated as positive. Since y is real, (6) demands that

$$k^2 - F^2 \geq 0, \tag{8}$$

or

$$\sigma k^2 - k + 1 \leq 0. \tag{9}$$

That means

$$k_{\min} \leq k \leq k_{\max}, \tag{10}$$

where

$$k_{\min} = \frac{1 - (1 - 4\sigma)^{1/2}}{2\sigma}, \tag{11}$$

$$k_{\max} = \frac{1 + (1 - 4\sigma)^{1/2}}{2\sigma}. \tag{12}$$

Equations (11) and (12) show that there are no waves if $\sigma \geq \frac{1}{4}$. This condition can be written as $U/c_{\min} \leq 1$, by virtue of (3).

Equation (7) contains the factor

$$h(k) = k - FF' = -\tfrac{3}{2}\sigma k^2 - k - \tfrac{1}{2}. \tag{13}$$

This can be written as

$$h(k) = -\tfrac{3}{2}\sigma(k - k_1)(k - k_2), \tag{14}$$

where

$$k_1 = \frac{1}{3\sigma}[1 - (1 - 3\sigma)^{1/2}], \tag{15}$$

$$k_2 = \frac{1}{3\sigma}[1 + (1 - 3\sigma)^{1/2}]. \tag{16}$$

Thus

$$h(k) > 0 \quad \text{if} \quad k_1 < k < k_2,$$
$$h(k) < 0 \quad \text{if} \quad k \leq k_1 \text{ or } k \geq k_2.$$

The sign of $h(k)$ affects the sign of x through (7).

Another quantity of which the sign is important is

$$q(k) = F - kF' = \frac{1}{2(k + \sigma k^3)^{1/2}}(1 - \sigma k^2). \tag{17}$$

It is evident that

$$q(k) \geq 0 \quad \text{if} \quad k < k_3 = \sigma^{-1/2},$$
$$q(k) < 0 \quad \text{if} \quad k > k_3 = \sigma^{-1/2}.$$

The sign of $q(k)$ affects the sign of y through (6), and the sign of x through (7).

It can be shown (the demonstration is omitted here), that

$$k_1 \leq k_{\min} \leq k_3 \leq k_2 \leq k_{\max}. \tag{18}$$

Hence k_1 has no significance, since a k less than $k_{\min}$ results in no waves.

Finally, the k-values for the cusps, denoted by k_{c1} and k_{c2}, are determined from

$$\frac{d^2\eta}{d\xi^2} = 0, \tag{19}$$

or

$$\frac{d}{d\xi} \frac{k \, dk/d\xi - \xi}{(k^2 - \xi^2)^{1/2}} = 0.$$

With (1), this becomes, after a brief calculation,

$$\frac{d}{d\xi} \frac{2h(k)\xi}{(1 + 3\sigma k^2)(k^2 - \xi^2)^{1/2}} = 0. \tag{20}$$

This can only be solved numerically once σ is given, and we shall list the values of k_{c1} and k_{c2} in Table 1 for various values of σ.

$\textsc{Table}$ 1. Important values of k and values of γ and ϕ.

$\dfrac{U}{c_{min}}$	k	Waves of Sets 2 and 3				
		$a = 1$	$a = 2$	$a = 3$	$a = 4$	$a = 5$
10	k_{st}			1.000025		
	k_{c1}			1.500253		
	k_{c2}			78.41496		
	k_{en}	196.3524	192.7049	189.6653	186.0177	182.3702
6	k_{st}			1.000193		
	k_{c1}			1.501962		
	k_{c2}			28.06051		
	k_{en}	70.02272	67.82574	65.84847	63.65150	61.23482
4	k_{st}			1.000978		
	k_{c1}			1.510122		
	k_{c2}			12.30653		
	k_{en}	30.71992	29.34138	27.96284	26.38736	24.71341
2	k_{st}			1.016133		
	k_{c1}			1.808496		
	k_{c2}			2.535961		
	k_{en}	7.590197	7.180394	6.715951	6.224187	5.623143
1.8	k_{st}			1.025022		
	k_{en}	6.152701	5.798128	5.416279	4.979881	4.461658
1.5	k_{st}			1.054960		
	k_{en}	4.276073	4.304920	3.759316	3.466488	3.087534
1.1	k_{st}			1.279578		
	k_{en}	2.248937	2.089277	1.941023	1.809875	1.695823

| $\frac{U}{c_{\min}}$ | k | \multicolumn{5}{c}{Waves of Set 1} | γ | ϕ |

$\frac{U}{c_{\min}}$	k	$a=1$	$a=2$	$a=3$	$a=4$	$a=5$	γ	ϕ
10	k_{st}			39999			6000	5.71°
	k_{c1}							
	k_{c2}							
	k_{en}	4816.684	7045.430	8716.984	10070.15	11104.93		
6	k_{st}			5183			750	9.59°
	k_{c1}							
	k_{c2}							
	k_{en}	613.7659	899.9819	1114.644	1278.196	1421.304		
4	k_{st}			1023			150	14.47°
	k_{c1}							
	k_{c2}							
	k_{en}	127.1359	182.6319	224.2538	255.9658	283.7139		
2	k_{st}			62.98387			10	29.98°
	k_{c1}							
	k_{c2}							
	k_{en}	11.07910	13.27845	15.37935	16.57748	17.89709		
1.8	k_{st}			40.96538			10	
	k_{en}	8.962947	10.68722	11.99766	13.10193	14.06678		
1.5	k_{st}			19.19504			10	
	k_{en}	6.057674	7.027547	7.732909	8.291320	8.732171		
1.1	k_{st}			4.576822			1	
	k_{en}	2.588232	2.752151	2.907442	3.054106	3.187829		

3. Procedure of Computation. There are three sets of waves created by the moving disturbance:

1. Set 1. Capillary waves *ahead* of the disturbance.
2. Set 2. Largely gravity waves behind the disturbance.
3. Set 3. Capillary waves *behind* (!) the disturbance.

The first set is the well-known fish-line waves. The starting k-value for this set, denoted by k_{st} in Table 1, is just $k_{\max}$. There are no cusps in the phase lines for this set, and for each phase line the k-values decrease from $k_{\max}$, at which $y = 0$ and x is negative, to k_2, at which $x = 0$, and then to k_3 at which x is positive and both x and y are infinite. In plotting the phase lines, one cannot reach k_3, of course, and we have stopped at an ending k, denoted by k_{en}, and given numerically for all values of $c_{\min}/U$ and for Sets 1 and 3.

Set 2 corresponds to Kelvin waves, except the effect of surface tension has been taken into account. For this set one starts with a k_{st} equal to $k_{\min}$, at the centerline $y = 0$ and a value of x given by (7), once a is given. One then proceeds along a transverse phase line to the first cusp on either side of the centerline, where k is k_{c1}. Then one increases k toward k_{c2}, in the process tracing out the phase line corresponding to the divergent part of the Kelvin waves, except that one does not

40 CHIA-SHUN YIH AND SONGPING ZHU

reach the origin (where the disturbance is) but reaches the second cusp instead, at which k is k_{c2}.

Then one traces another divergent wave, of Set 3, as one increases k from k_{c2} to k_3, in the process tracing out the phase line that is almost straight, and diverges from the second cusp toward infinity (with positive x), asymptotically making an angle ϕ with the centerline. The angle ϕ is recorded in Table 1 for all cases, and is, incidentally, the same for Set 1 and Set 3. That is, the asymptotes of phase lines for Set 1 at infinity also make the same angle ϕ with the centerline. The angle ϕ is determined analytically by putting $k = k_3 = \sigma^{-1/2}$ in

$$\frac{dy}{dx} = \tan\phi = -\frac{F}{(k^2 - F^2)^{1/2}}, \tag{21}$$

with F defined by (2). Equation (21) is equation (6) of [4]. It is immediately clear that, as σ decreases to zero, k_3 approaches infinity and ϕ approaches zero—a result of great significance to remote sensing.

It is clear from the foregoing description that

$$k_3 < k \leq k_{max}$$

for Set 1,

$$k_{min} \leq k \leq k_{c2}$$

for Set 2, and

$$k_{c2} \leq k < k_3$$

for Set 3. For Set 2 (Kelvin waves with surface tension taken into account)

$$k_{min} \leq k \leq k_{c1}$$

for transverse waves, and

$$k_{c1} \leq k \leq k_{c2}$$

for divergent waves.

4. Results. The results for various values of σ, represented by U/c_{min}, are given in Table 1 and the figures. In Table 1, the results for Sets 2 and 3 are presented together, and those for Set 1 are presented separately. For U/c_{min} equal to or less than 1, there are no waves, as mentioned in Sec. 2.

The various k-values given and the angle ϕ in Table 1 have been explained in Sec. 3. Since the wavelength for Set 2 at the centerline is enormously greater than the wavelength for Set 1 at the centerline, it is inconvenient to present the entire wave pattern in a single figure with the same length scale. For this reason, for all cases except $U/c_{min} = 1.1$ (see Figure 1), the phase lines for Set 1 are presented separately from those for Sets 2 and 3. The ratio of the length scale for Sets 2 and 3 to that for Set 1 is denoted by γ, and given in Table 1. In reading the figures, then, one must, for all cases except $U/c_{min} = 1.1$, imagine the parts b to be magnified γ times in one's mind. It is also helpful to keep in mind that along the centerline ($y = 0$) consecutive phase lines for Set 1 and Set 2 are spaced at one wavelength apart, and

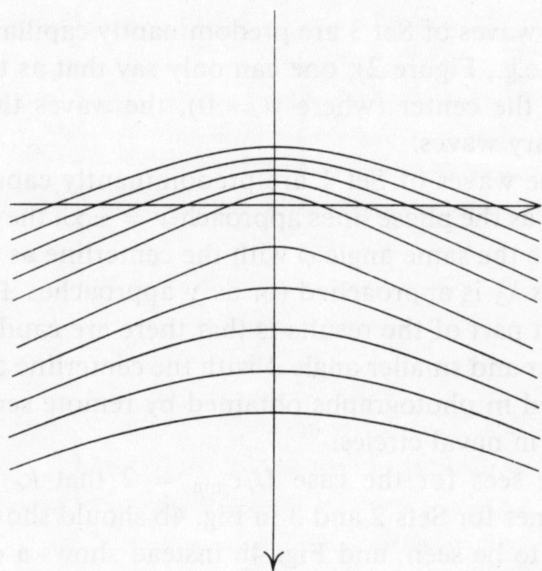

FIG. 1. Pattern of gravity-capillary waves at $U/c_{\min} = 1.1$.

that the wavelength for Set 1 (predominantly capillary waves) is very much smaller than that for Set 2 (predominantly gravity waves).

From Table 1, one sees that for transverse waves of Set 2 the k-values are of order 1. These are predominantly gravity waves. For divergent waves of Set 2, k increases from k_{c1} to k_{c2}, and k_{c2} may be considerably greater than k_{c1} if $U/c_{\min}$ is greater than 4. Hence the divergent waves of Set 2, which have their counterpart in Kelvin waves (for which only gravity is taken into account), become more and more capillary waves as k_{c2} is approached for $U/c_{\min}$ greater than 4 (which is not a sharp boundary, and is cited here only because it is one value of $U/c_{\min}$ chosen in Table 1 which seems to divide large values of k_{c2}/k_{c1} from modest ones of order 1).

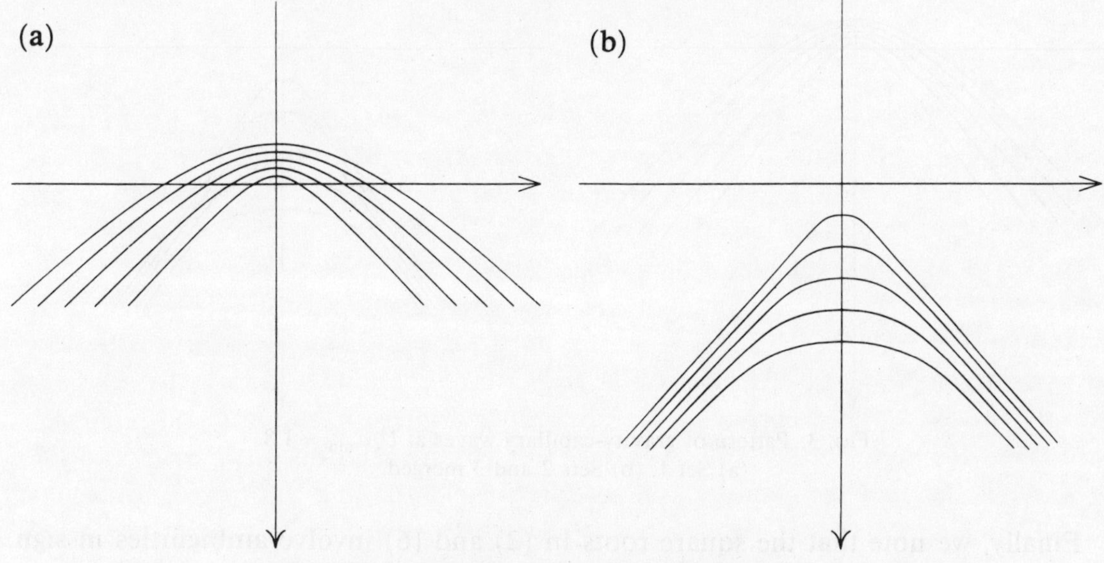

FIG. 2. Pattern of gravity-capillary waves at $U/c_{\min} = 1.5$.
(a) Set 1, (b) Sets 2 and 3 merged.

For $U/c_{\min} \geq 4$, the waves of Set 3 are predominantly capillary waves. For smaller values of $U/c_{\min}$ (see, e.g., Figure 2), one can only say that as the phase lines depart more and more from the center (where $y = 0$), the waves they represent become more and more capillary waves.

As noted before, the waves of Set 1 are predominantly capillary waves, and it is emphasized again that as the phase lines approach $y = \pm\infty$, they become increasingly straight lines that make the same angle ϕ with the centerline as the asymptotes of the phase lines of Set 3, as k_3 is approached (or as y approaches $\pm\infty$).

The most important part of the results is that there are capillary waves with wave fronts making a smaller and smaller angle ϕ with the centerline as $U/c_{\min}$ is increased. This has been observed in photographs obtained by remote sensing, and has been a point of keen interest in naval circles.

From Table 1, one sees for the case $U/c_{\min} = 2$ that k_{c2} is not equal to k_{c1}. Therefore the phase lines for Sets 2 and 3 in Fig. 4b should show a loop as in Fig. 5b. The loop is too small to be seen, and Fig. 4b instead shows a discontinuity in slope at a point near where the loop should be. This loop disappears when $U/c_{\min} = 1.8$ (which may be taken as the limiting value of $U/c_{\min}$ below which there is no loop), which may be compared with the tentative value 2 of Lamb ([1], p. 471, footnote 1). When the loop disappears, the slope at the juncture of the transverse waves of Set 2 and the divergent waves of Set 3 should be continuous. Figure 3b (for $U/c_{\min} = 1.8$) shows a slight but detectable discontinuity at that juncture. That discontinuity should not be there, and is a consequence of the finite-difference calculation when Δk, the increment of k, is not small enough for the neighborhood of the juncture.

(a)   (b)

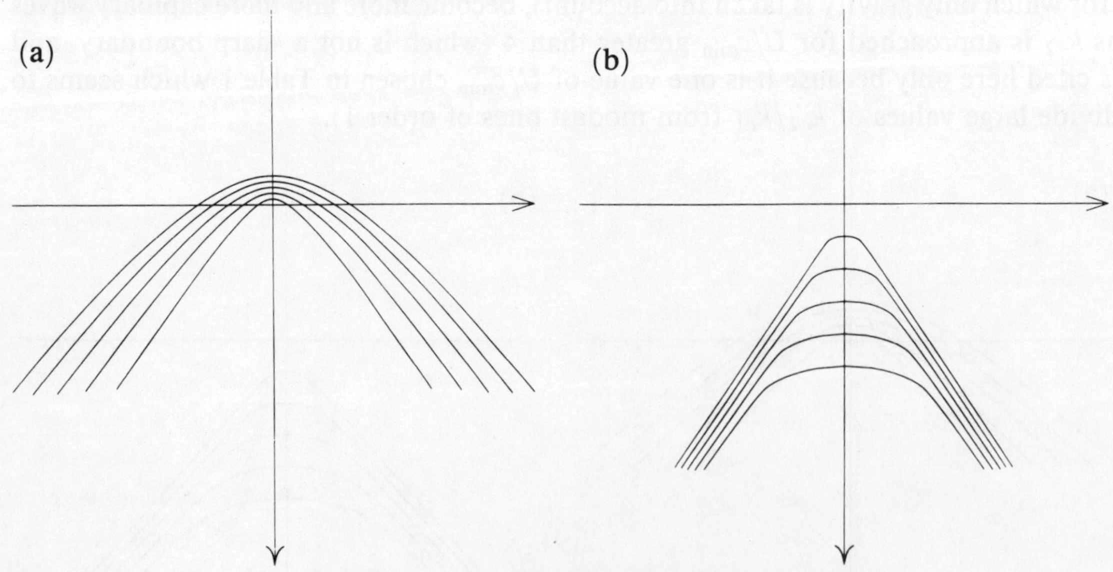

FIG. 3. Pattern of gravity-capillary waves at $U/c_{\min} = 1.8$.
(a) Set 1, (b) Sets 2 and 3 merged.

Finally, we note that the square roots in (2) and (6) involve ambiguities in sign. The square root in (6) can be positive or negative, so that both positive and negative y-values are allowable. The sign of the square root in (2), which has a consequence on the sign of x given by (7), is chosen so that waves of Set 1 start in front of the disturbance before they wrap around it to positive values of x, and that waves of Sets 2 and 3 are *behind* the disturbance, so that x is always positive for waves of these sets.

Acknowledgment. This work has been supported by the Fluid-Dynamics Program of the Office of Naval Research, under Contract N00014-87-C-0194.

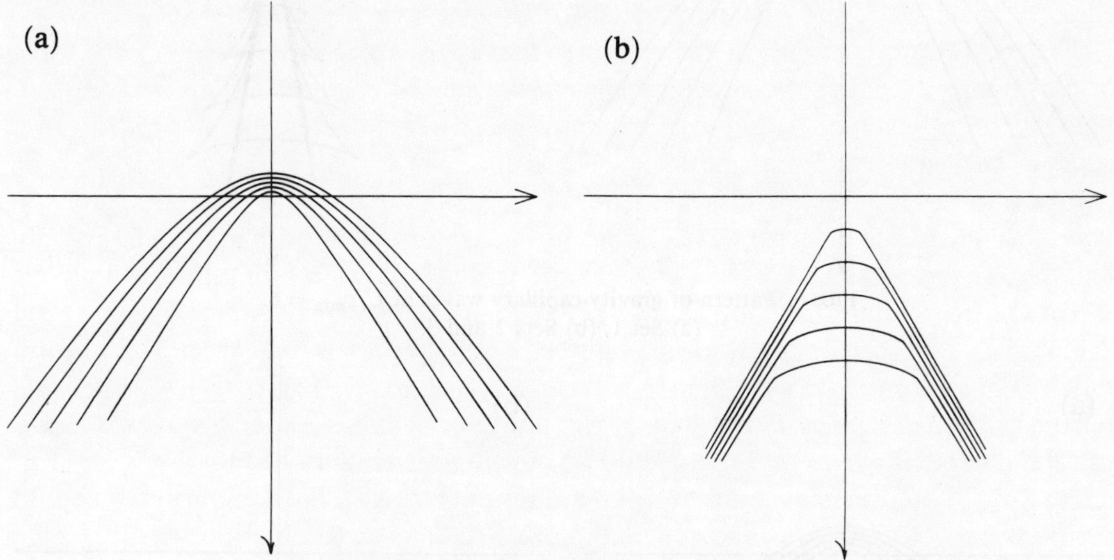

FIG. 4. Pattern of gravity-capillary waves at $U/c_{\min} = 2$.
(a) Set 1, (b) Sets 2 and 3 (loop with cusps invisible).

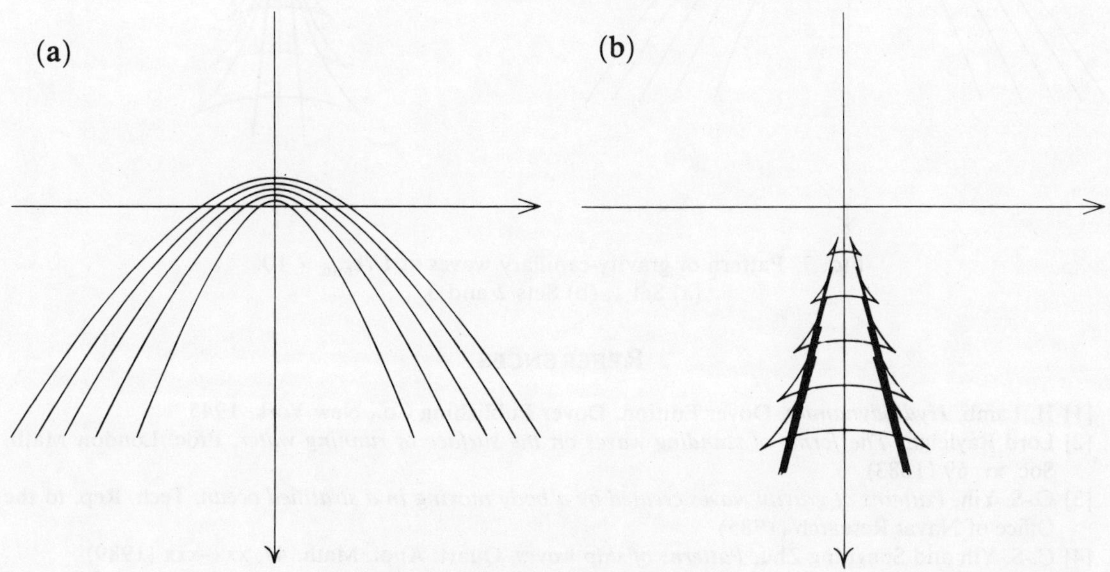

FIG. 5. Pattern of gravity-capillary waves at $U/c_{\min} = 4$.
(a) Set 1, (b) Sets 2 and 3.

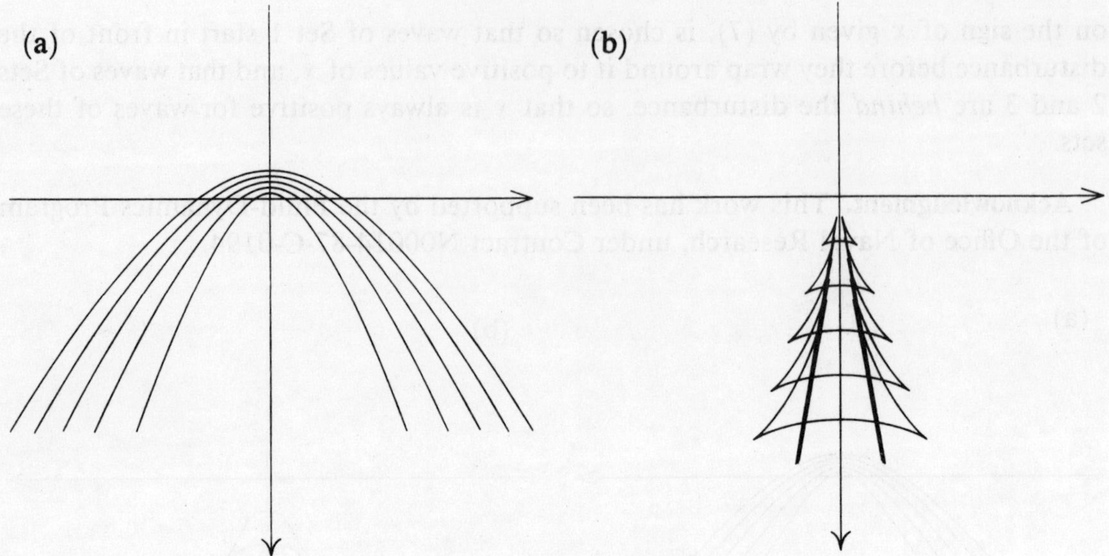

FIG. 6. Pattern of gravity-capillary waves at $U/c_{\min} = 6$.
(a) Set 1, (b) Sets 2 and 3.

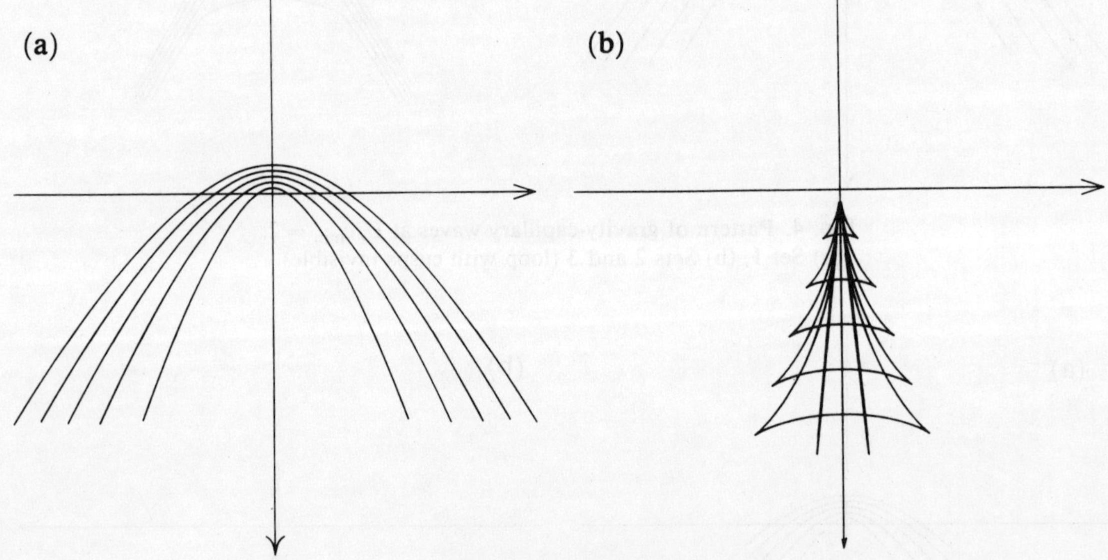

FIG. 7. Pattern of gravity-capillary waves at $U/c_{\min} = 10$.
(a) Set 1, (b) Sets 2 and 3.

REFERENCES

[1] H. Lamb, *Hydrodynamics*, Dover Edition, Dover Publishing Co., New York, 1945
[2] Lord Rayleigh, *The forms of standing waves on the surface of running water*, Proc. London Math. Soc. **xv**, 69 (1883)
[3] C.-S. Yih, *Patterns of gravity waves created by a body moving in a stratified ocean*, Tech. Rep. to the Office of Naval Research (1985)
[4] C.-S. Yih and Songping Zhu, *Patterns of ship waves*, Quart. Appl. Math. **47**, xxx–xxx (1989)

QUARTERLY OF APPLIED MATHEMATICS
VOLUME XLVII, NUMBER 1
MARCH 1989, PAGES 167–184

NONLINEAR GRAVITY-WAVE GROUPS*

By

CHIA-SHUN YIH

University of Florida, Gainesville, Florida

Abstract. Groups of gravity waves of permanent form in deep water are investigated. The analysis provides a systematic procedure for determining the form of the group to any order of approximation, and a calculation is carried to the third order of the amplitude at least and, where it matters, to the fourth order. Closed formulas for the phase velocity c of the basic waves and the group velocity c_g are obtained. Inspection of the analytic procedure reveals that these formulas remain intact for all subsequent calculations to any order of approximation. These formulas are in terms of the group wavenumber ε which, to the attained order of approximation, is found to be proportional to the amplitude a and the square of the basic wavenumber k, but is, for any assigned k, a power series in a. It is found that c increases and c_g decreases with ε, in such a way that $2cc_g = g/k$, where g is the gravitational acceleration. The results are compared with the corresponding ones obtained by the cubic-Schrödinger-equation (CBE) approach, and wherever comparison is possible there is agreement. The CBE approach, however, does not give the variation of c_g with the amplitude.

The collision of wave groups with different group velocities is also investigated, and it is found that after the faster group has overtaken the slower one, both groups retain their original forms, without any phase shift for either group. The interaction terms eventually die down everywhere. When a group is reflected by a vertical boundary normal to its velocity, then the reflected group is, in time, just the continuation of its mirror image across the boundary, without any phase shift.

1. Introduction. The famous works of Cauchy (1815, cited in Lamb [9], pp. 17, 384) and Poisson (1816, cited in Lamb [9], p. 384) showed already early in the last century that gravity waves created by a concentrated impulse travel in groups with velocities dependent on their wavelengths, although in these works the wave groups are not separate, especially at the beginning. Later, isolated gravity-wave groups were observed by Russell (1844, cited in Lamb [9], p. 380). The first derivation of the group velocity of dispersive waves was given by Stokes (1876, cited in Lamb [9], p. 381), although Stokes' treatment necessarily involves infinitely many wave groups one after another.

---

*Received May 12, 1988.

©1989 Brown University

In an effort to construct a single wave group by a linear theory, Yih [11] obtained such a group of gravity waves in deep water, but as the free-surface pressure was eliminated by successive approximations, it was found that some residue of pressure always remained, and that residue finally becomes a concentrated force of oscillatory magnitude. It was then thought that perhaps nonlinearity could provide the elimination of free-surface pressure present in the linear theory, and the present work was begun.

As the work progressed, I became aware of the seminal papers of Benney and Newell [3], Zakharov [12], and Benney and Roskes [4] on the evolution of wave packets, and of the substantial papers treating water waves by Hasimoto and Ono [8], Djordjević and Redekopp [6, 7], and Ablowitz and Segur [1, 2]. When the superficial differences of the results of these latter authors are reconciled, and my results are compared with theirs, there is general agreement wherever comparison is possible. Since all these authors use the cubic Schrödinger equation, and that equation is based on a third-order approximation only, they have not produced a determination of the group velocity c_g as a function of the amplitude. Comparison of results for c_g is therefore impossible.

As will be shown in this paper, two closed formulas give the phase velocity c and group velocity c_g as functions of the group wavenumber ε, which in turn depends on the amplitude of the waves, though not in closed form. The two closed formulas remain intact at any higher order of approximation, as an inspection of the analytical procedure reveals. These formulas show that c increases and c_g decreases with ε (which in turn increases with the amplitude), and are the main contributions of this paper. Detailed comparison of the present work with previous results based on the cubic-Schrödinger-equation (CBE) approach will be made later.

One restriction of the CBE is that it applies only to a specific basic wavenumber. A single equation for studying the interaction of wave groups of different basic wavenumbers is not available. The approach used in this paper allows conclusions to be drawn on the persistence of nonlinear wave groups of different basic wavenumbers after interaction. This is another contribution of the present work that is of some significance.

2. Formation of the differential system. Consider two-dimensional gravity waves in deep water with an envelope that approaches the undisturbed free surface at infinity, which is at $y = 0$. The line $y = 0$ is the x-axis, and the waves and their envelope are supposed to propagate in the positive x-direction.

Irrotationality is assumed, so that a potential ϕ exists, which satisfies the Laplace equation

$$\phi_{xx} + \phi_{yy} = 0, \tag{1}$$

where subscripts x and y indicate partial differentiation. At the free surface,

$$y = \eta(x, t), \tag{2}$$

with η approaching zero as x approaches infinity. The kinematic condition at the free surface is

$$\eta_t + \phi_x \eta_x = \phi_y, \tag{3}$$

and the dynamic condition there is

$$\phi_t + g\eta + \frac{\phi_x^2 + \phi_y^2}{2} = 0, \tag{4}$$

where g is the magnitude of the gravitational acceleration, acting in the direction of decreasing y. All the derivatives of ϕ in (3) and (4) are evaluated at $y = \eta$, and the zero on the right-hand side of (4) is a consequence of the fact that $\eta = 0 = \phi$ at $x = \infty$. The last boundary condition is

$$\phi \to 0 \quad \text{as} \quad y \to -\infty. \tag{5}$$

The differential system consists of (1), (3), (4), and (5), and is exact.

But since all the derivatives of ϕ in (3) and (4) are evaluated at $y = \eta$, further development of these conditions is necessary before a systematic calculation can begin. One needs a combined free-surface condition in terms of ϕ alone, in which all quantities are evaluated at $y = 0$ instead of $y = \eta$.

3. The combined free-surface condition. Let (4) be written as

$$-g\eta = L\phi = \phi_t + \tfrac{1}{2}(\phi_x^2 + \phi_y^2). \tag{6}$$

This can be written as

$$-g\eta = L\phi + (L\phi)_y\,\eta + (L\phi)_{yy}\,\eta^2/2 + \cdots, \tag{7}$$

in which, and *henceforth*, the derivatives of ϕ are evaluated at $y = 0$. Iteration of (7) gives

$$-g\eta = L\phi + (L\phi)_y\left[-\frac{1}{g}\left\{L\phi + (L\phi)_y\left(-\frac{1}{g}L\phi\right)\right\}\right]$$
$$+ \frac{1}{2}(L\phi)_{yy}\left[-\frac{1}{g}\left\{L\phi + (L\phi)_y\left(-\frac{1}{g}L\phi\right)\right\}\right]^2 + \cdots, \tag{8}$$

where the quantity in the brackets is η carried to the second iteration only. To the third order in ϕ, (8) becomes

$$-g\eta = L\phi - \frac{1}{g}L\phi(L\phi)_y + \frac{1}{2g^2}(\phi_t^2\phi_{ty})_y$$
$$= L\phi - \frac{1}{2g}[(L\phi)^2]_y + \frac{1}{2g^2}(\phi_t^2\phi_{ty})_y. \tag{9}$$

One now multiplies (3) by g and writes the result in terms of derivatives of ϕ evaluated at $y = 0$, by expansions about that point. When this is done to the third order in the magnitude of ϕ, one has, with all derivatives evaluated at $y = 0$,

$$g\left[\phi_y + \phi_{yy}\left(-\frac{1}{g}L\phi + \frac{1}{g^2}\phi_t\phi_{ty}\right) + \frac{1}{2g^2}\phi_t^2\phi_{yyy}\right]$$

$$= -(L\phi)_t + \frac{1}{g}\left\{\phi_t(L\phi)_y + \frac{\phi_x^2 + \phi_y^2}{2}\phi_{ty}\right\}_t - \frac{1}{2g^2}(\phi_t^2\phi_{ty})_{yt}$$

$$+ (\phi_x + \phi_{xy}\eta)\left\{-(L\phi)_x + \frac{1}{2g}(\phi_t^2)_{yx}\right\}$$

$$= -(L\phi)_t + \frac{1}{g}\left\{\phi_t(L\phi)_y + \frac{\phi_x^2 + \phi_y^2}{2}\phi_{ty}\right\}_t - \frac{1}{2g^2}(\phi_t^2\phi_{ty})_{yt}$$

$$+ \phi_x\left\{-(L\phi)_x + \frac{1}{2g}(\phi_t^2)_{yx}\right\} + \frac{\phi_t}{g}\phi_{xy}\phi_{xt}, \tag{10}$$

in which one appearance of η is allowed in an intermediate step to show the route of calculation. The first three terms on the right-hand side of (10), up to and including the term containing the factor $1/(2g^2)$, is η_t, and the terms that follow it represent $\phi_x\eta_x$ evaluated at $y = \eta$.

Equation (10) will be written in the form

$$I_1 + I_2 + I_3 = 0, \tag{11}$$

where

$$I_1 = g\phi_y + \phi_{tt}, \tag{12}$$

$$I_2 = -\phi_t\phi_{yy} + \left(\frac{\phi_x^2 + \phi_y^2}{2}\right)_t - \frac{1}{g}(\phi_t\phi_{ty})_t + \phi_x\phi_{tx}$$

$$= (\phi_t\phi_x)_x + \left(\frac{\phi_x^2 + \phi_y^2}{2}\right)_t - \frac{1}{g}(\phi_t\phi_{ty})_t, \tag{13}$$

$$I_3 = -\frac{1}{2}\phi_{yy}(\phi_x^2 + \phi_y^2) + \frac{1}{g}\phi_t\phi_{ty}\phi_{yy} + \frac{1}{2g}\phi_t^2\phi_{yyy}$$

$$- \frac{1}{2g}\left\{\phi_t(\phi_x^2 + \phi_y^2)\right\}_{yt} + \frac{1}{2g^2}(\phi_t^2\phi_{ty})_{yt} + \frac{1}{2}\phi_x(\phi_x^2\phi_y^2)_x$$

$$- \frac{1}{2g}\phi_x(\phi_t^2)_{yx} - \frac{1}{g}\phi_t\phi_{xy}\phi_{xt}$$

$$= \frac{1}{2}\left\{\phi_x(\phi_x^2 + \phi_y^2)\right\}_x + \frac{1}{2g}(\phi_t^2\phi_{yy})_y - \frac{1}{2g}\left\{\phi_t(\phi_x^2 + \phi_y^2)\right\}_{yt}$$

$$+ \frac{1}{2g^2}(\phi_t^2\phi_{ty})_{yt} - \frac{1}{2g}\left\{\phi_x(\phi_t^2)_x\right\}_y$$

$$= \frac{1}{2}\left\{\phi_x(\phi_x^2 + \phi_y^2)\right\}_x - \frac{1}{2g}\left[(\phi_t^2\phi_x)_x + \left\{\phi_t(\phi_x^2 + \phi_y^2)\right\}_t\right]_y$$

$$+ \frac{1}{2g^2}(\phi_t^2\phi_{ty})_{yt}. \tag{14}$$

In (13) and (14), (1) has been used whenever it is advantageous to replace ϕ_{yy} by $-\phi_{xx}$. With the I's so defined, (11) is the free-surface condition on ϕ. It is emphasized here once again that all the derivatives of ϕ appearing in (11) are evaluated at $y = 0$.

4. The solution of the differential system. Since ϕ must satisfy the Laplace equation, it will be assumed to be the real part of an analytic function of the complex variable

$$z = x + iy,$$

and it is convenient to use the $\hat{X}$ and $\hat{Y}$ defined as

$$\hat{X} = \varepsilon(z - c_g t), \qquad \hat{Y} = k(z - ct), \tag{15}$$

in which k and c are the wavenumber and phase velocity of the basic waves and ε and c_g are those of their envelope, or of the group. The value of c in the linear theory is

$$c_0 = (g/k)^{1/2}. \tag{16}$$

Given k, the task is to determine c, c_g, and ε for an isolated wave group as functions of the amplitude of the waves, which can be represented by the amplitude of the potential function ϕ, which will be denoted by $2a$ for convenience. Let

$$\varepsilon^2 = a^2(\alpha_1 + \alpha_2 a^2 + \alpha_3 a^4 + \cdots), \tag{17}$$

$$c^2 = c_0^2(1 + \beta_1 \varepsilon^2 + \beta_2 \varepsilon^4 + \cdots), \tag{18}$$

$$2cc_g = c_0^2(1 + \gamma_1 \varepsilon^2 + \gamma_2 \varepsilon^4 + \cdots). \tag{19}$$

The expansion (19) is for $2cc_g$ rather than for c_g^2 because it affords a certain convenience, as later developments will show.

Esthetics would demand, perhaps, that all quantities be made dimensionless. Yet, as the free-surface boundary condition (11) indicates, the calculation will be long and involved, and the dimensionless form of (11) may be quite burdensome. Keeping things in their dimensional forms also provides a certain check on the calculation, for when a mistake is made so that an equation becomes nonhomogeneous in dimension, that mistake will be detected. Thus one is prepared to pay the price that all the α's, β's, and γ's are dimensional, and have different dimensions when their numerical subscripts vary. Expansions (18) and (19) are in ε rather than a for a good reason that will appear later. Indeed, one will arrive at two closed formulas in terms of ε for c^2 and cc_g.

The expansion for ϕ is

$$\phi = a\phi_1 + a^2\phi_2 + a^3\phi_3 + \cdots, \tag{20}$$

in which ϕ_1, ϕ_2, etc. may themselves be sums involving coefficients containing powers of ε/a. These sums will not be exhibited now. As the calculations proceed, one will obtain the various terms in each of ϕ_1, ϕ_2, etc.

One starts by taking

$$\phi_1 = \hat{S}e^{-i\hat{Y}} + \hat{S}^*e^{-i\hat{Y}^*}, \tag{21}$$

where the asterisks indicate complex conjugates, and

$$\hat{S} = \operatorname{sech} \hat{X}. \tag{22}$$

It is immediately clear that $\hat{S}$ has singularities at $\hat{X} = \pm i(2n+1)\pi/2$. Those corresponding to the $+$ sign are outside of the liquid. The remaining singularities can be removed, as explained in Yih [11]. This removal has negligible effect on the free-surface condition if k/ε is large compared with 1, as is the case for the phenomenon under study here. Higher singularities created at higher approximations can be similarly removed (Yih, [11]). At $y = 0$, (21) reduces to

$$\phi_1 = 2S \cos Y, \tag{23}$$

where

$$S = \operatorname{sech} X, \qquad X = \varepsilon(x - c_g t), \qquad Y = k(x - ct), \tag{24}$$

Using (21), one obtains, at $y = 0$,

$$I_1(a\phi_1) = a[2(gk - k^2 c^2 + \varepsilon^2 c_g^2)S \cos Y - 2\varepsilon(g - 2kcc_g)ST \sin Y - 4\varepsilon^2 g^2 S^3 \cos Y]. \tag{25}$$

When evaluating I_2 and I_3, it is time-saving to remember that when no differentiation with respect to y is involved, one can use (23) directly and there is no need to invoke (21), and when differentiations with respect to y are involved, it is time-saving to replace ϕ_{yy} by $-\phi_{xx}$ whenever possible, for then one can again use (23) instead of (21). Since the calculation for I_2 and I_3 is lengthy, it will be presented in two subsections, to improve clarity.

4.1. Calculation for I_2. The following results for the various components of $I_2(\phi_1)$ can be readily verified, with the understanding that all the derivatives of ϕ_1 are evaluated at $y = 0$:

$$\phi_{1t} = 2kcS \sin Y + 2\varepsilon c_g ST \cos Y, \tag{26}$$
$$\phi_{1x} = 2kS \sin Y + 2\varepsilon ST \cos Y, \tag{27}$$

in which

$$T = \tanh X.$$

For the y-derivative of ϕ_1, one has to use (21), and the result is

$$\phi_{1y} = -2\varepsilon ST \sin Y + 2kS \cos Y, \tag{28}$$

which is again evaluated at $y = 0$. The calculation of $I_2(\phi_1)$ can now proceed in a straightforward manner. Detailed results for the various terms in I_2 will be given here for the convenience of anyone wishing to check the present calculations. First,

$$\phi_{1t}\phi_{1x} = -2[k^2 cS^2(1 - \cos 2Y) + \varepsilon k(c + c_g)S^2 T \sin 2Y + \varepsilon^2 c_g(S^2 - S^4)(1 + \cos 2Y)],$$

so that

$$(\phi_{1t}\phi_{1x})_x = -4k^3 cS^2 \sin 2Y + 4\varepsilon k^2 cS^2 T - 4\varepsilon k^2(2c + c_g)S^2 T \cos 2Y + T_h, \tag{29}$$

where T_h denotes higher-order terms given by

$$T_h = 4\varepsilon^2 k(c + 2c_g)S^2 \sin 2Y - 2\varepsilon^2 k(3c + 5c_g)S^4 \sin 2Y + 4\varepsilon^3 c_g(S^2 T - 2S^4 T)(1 + \cos 2Y).$$

For the next group of terms in I_2 one has

$$\phi_{1x}^2 + \phi_{1y}^2 = 4S^2[k^2 + \varepsilon^2(1 - S^2)], \tag{30}$$

so that

$$\left(\frac{\phi_{1x}^2 + \phi_{1y}^2}{2}\right)_t = 4\varepsilon c_g(k^2 + \varepsilon^2 - 2\varepsilon^2 S^2)S^2 T. \tag{31}$$

From (26) and (28) one has

$$\phi_{1t}\phi_{1ty} = 2k^3 c^2 S^2(1 - \cos Y) + 2\varepsilon k^2 c(c + 2c_g)S^2 T \sin 2Y + O(\varepsilon^2), \tag{32}$$

so that

$$(\phi_{1t}\phi_{1ty})_t = -4k^4 c^3 S^2 \sin 2Y + 4\varepsilon k^3 c^2 c_g S^2 T - 4\varepsilon k^3 c^2(c + 3c_g)S^2 T \cos 2Y + O(\varepsilon^2). \tag{33}$$

From (29), (31), and (33) one obtains

$$I_2(\phi_1) = 4\varepsilon k^2 c S^2 T + O(\varepsilon^2),$$

or

$$I_2(a\phi_1) = 4\varepsilon a^2 k^2 c S^2 T + O(\varepsilon^2 a^2). \tag{34}$$

4.2. Annihilation of $I_2(a\phi_1)$. One now seeks a function W so that (at $y = 0$)

$$\left(g\frac{\partial}{\partial y} + \frac{\partial^2}{\partial t^2}\right)W = -4\varepsilon a^2 k^2 c S^2 T, \tag{35}$$

with the higher-order terms in (34) neglected. It can be readily verified that

$$W = -\frac{a^2 k^2 c}{g}\left[i(\hat{S}^2 - \hat{S}^{*2}) + \frac{2\varepsilon c_g^2}{g}(\hat{S}^2\hat{T} + \hat{S}^{*2}\hat{T}^*)\right], \tag{36}$$

from which one obtains, for $y = 0$,

$$W_t = O(\varepsilon^2 a^2), \quad W_x = O(\varepsilon^2 a^2), \quad W_{yt} = O(\varepsilon^2 a^2), \quad W_y = -\frac{4\varepsilon a^2 k^2 c}{g}S^2 T.$$

The contribution of W to I_2 is, when W is added to ϕ_1 given by (21),

$$\tilde{I}_2(a\phi_1, W) = [(\phi_{1t}W_x + \phi_{1x}W_t)_x + (\phi_{1x}W_x + \phi_{1y}W_y)_t - \frac{1}{g}(\phi_{1t}W_{ty} + \phi_{1ty}W_t)_t]$$

$$= (\phi_{1y}W_y)_t + O(\varepsilon^3 a^3) = -\frac{8\varepsilon a^3 k^4 c^2}{g}S^3 T \sin Y + O(\varepsilon^3 a^3) \tag{37}$$

if $I_2(W)$, being of higher order in a, is neglected at this stage of approximation. The amount given by (37) will be added to $I_3(a\phi_1)$ to be calculated below.

4.3. Calculation of $I_3(a\phi_1)$. Since the calculation is lengthy, it will be divided into several portions.

We have

$$I_3(a\phi_1) = a^3 I_3(\phi_1),$$

$$I_3(\phi_1) = \frac{1}{2}\left[J_1 - \frac{1}{g}(J_{21} + J_{22}) + \frac{1}{g^2}J_3\right], \tag{38}$$

in which

$$J_1 = \left\{\phi_{1x}(\phi_{1x}^2 + \phi_{1y}^2)\right\}_x, \tag{39}$$

$$J_{21} = (\phi_{1t}^2\phi_{1x})_{xy}, \qquad J_{22} = \left\{\phi_{1t}(\phi_{1x}^2 + \phi_{1y}^2)\right\}_{ty}, \tag{40}$$

$$J_3 = (\phi_{1t}^2\phi_{1ty})_{yt}. \tag{41}$$

From (27) and (30), one obtains

$$\phi_{1x}(\phi_{1x}^2 + \phi_{1y}^2) = -8k^3S^3 \sin Y - 8\varepsilon k^2 S^3 T \cos Y + O(\varepsilon^2),$$

so that

$$J_1 = -8k^4S^3 \cos Y + 32\varepsilon k^3 S^3 T \sin Y + O(\varepsilon^2). \tag{42}$$

For J_{21}, one writes first of all

$$J_{21} = (H + K)_x, \tag{43}$$

where

$$H = 2\phi_{1t}\phi_{1ty}\phi_{1x}, \qquad K = \phi_{1t}^2\phi_{1yx}. \tag{44}$$

From (32) and (27) one has, with O now meaning "terms containing",

$$H = -12k^4c^2S^3 \sin Y - 8\varepsilon k^3 c(c + c_g)S^3 T \cos Y + O(\varepsilon^2, \varepsilon \cos 3Y, \sin 3Y), \tag{45}$$

in which the terms containing $\cos 3Y$ or $\sin 3Y$ do not contribute at this stage of approximation. From (28) one has

$$\phi_{1xy} = -2k^2S \sin Y - 4\varepsilon kST \cos Y + O(\varepsilon^2), \tag{46}$$

and from this and (26) one obtains, with O used as in (45),

$$K = -6k^4c^2S^3 \sin Y - 4\varepsilon k^3 c(c + c_g)S^3 T \cos Y + O(\varepsilon^2, \varepsilon \cos 3Y, \sin 3Y). \tag{47}$$

When H is added to K, and the result substituted into (43), one has

$$J_{21} = -18k^5c^2S^3 \cos Y + 6\varepsilon k^4 c(11c + 2c_g)S^3 T \sin Y + O(\varepsilon^2, \varepsilon \cos 3Y, \sin 3Y). \tag{48}$$

In calculating J_{22}, one notes first of all that differentiation with respect to y is more troublesome, since it requires the form for ϕ_1 in terms of the complex variable z. Therefore one seeks to replace ϕ_{1yy} by $-\phi_{1yy}$ whenever possible, and writes

$$J_{22} = (M + N)_t, \tag{49}$$

$$M = \phi_{1ty}(\phi_{1x}^2 + \phi_{1y}^2), \qquad N = 2\phi_{1t}(\phi_{1x}^2\phi_{1xy} - \phi_{1y}\phi_{1xx}). \tag{50}$$

From (30) and (32) one has

$$M = 8k^4cS^3 \sin Y + 8\varepsilon k^3(c + c_g)S^3 T \cos Y + O(\varepsilon^2).$$

From (27), (28), and (46),

$$\phi_{1x}\phi_{1xy} - \phi_{1y}\phi_{1xx} = 4k^3S^2 + O(\varepsilon^2),$$

and this gives, with (26),

$$N = 16k^4cS^3 \sin Y + 16\varepsilon k^3 c_g S^3 T \cos Y + O(\varepsilon^2).$$

With M and N so determined, (49) gives

$$J_{22} = -13k^5c^2S^3 \cos Y + 8\varepsilon k^4 c(12c_g + c)S^3 T \sin Y + O(\varepsilon^2).$$ (51)

Adding (51) to (48), one has

$$J_{21} + J_{22} = -42k^5c^2S^3 \cos Y + 2\varepsilon k^3 c(37c + 54c_g)S^3 T \sin Y + O(\varepsilon^2).$$ (52)

For J_3, first write (again to substitute ϕ_{1xx} for ϕ_{1yy})

$$J_3 = (P - Q)_t,$$ (53)

where

$$P = 2\phi_{1t}\phi_{1ty}^2, \qquad Q = \phi_{1t}^2\phi_{1txx}.$$ (54)

From (28) one has

$$\phi_{1ty} = \phi_{1yt} = 2k^2cS \sin Y + 2\varepsilon k(c + c_g)ST \cos Y + O(\varepsilon^2),$$

which gives, together with (32),

$$P = 12k^5c^3S^3 \sin Y + 4\varepsilon k^4 c^2(2c + 3c_g)T \cos Y + O(\varepsilon^2, \varepsilon \cos 3Y, \sin 3Y).$$ (55)

From (27) one obtains

$$\phi_{1xxx} = -2k^3cS \sin Y - 2\varepsilon k^2(2c + c_g)ST \cos Y + O(\varepsilon^2),$$

and this, together with (26), gives

$$Q = -6k^5c^3S^3 \sin Y - 2\varepsilon k^4 c^2(2c + 3c_g)S^3 T \cos Y + O(\varepsilon^2, \varepsilon \cos 3Y, \sin 3Y).$$ (56)

Substituting (55) and (56) into (53), one has, upon neglecting terms that do not contribute at this stage of approximation,

$$J_3 = -18k^6c^4S^3 \cos Y + 12\varepsilon k^5c^3(c + 6c_g)S^3 T \sin Y.$$ (57)

Finally, substituting (42), (52), and (57) into (38), one has,

$$I_3(\phi_1) = \frac{1}{2}\left[k^4\left(-8 + \frac{42kc^2}{g} - 18\frac{k^2c^4}{g^2} \right)S^3 \cos Y \right.$$
$$\left. + \varepsilon k^3\left\{ 32 - \frac{kc(74c + 108c_g)}{g} + \frac{12k^2c^3(c + 6c_g)}{g^2} \right\} S^3 T \sin Y \right],$$ (58)

upon neglecting terms that do not contribute at this stage of approximation.

Since, from (18) and (19),

$$c^2 = c_0^2 + O(a^2) \quad \text{and} \quad c_g = c_0/2 + O(a^2),$$

(58) can be written

$$I_3(\phi_1) = 8k^4S^3 \cos Y - 48\varepsilon k^3S^3 T \sin Y,$$ (59)

upon neglecting terms of higher orders.

Equations (37) and (59) give the result

$$\tilde{I}_2(a\phi_1, W) + I_3(a\phi_1) = 8a^3k^4S^3 \cos Y - 56\varepsilon a^3k^3S^3 T \sin Y,$$ (60)

with higher-order terms neglected.

CHIA-SHUN YIH

5. Treatment of the residue. The residue in the free-surface boundary condition, given by the sum of (25) and (60), is to be removed, and in the removal the variations of c, c_g, and ε with the amplitude (for the velocity potential) a are to be determined.

The equation (11) must be satisfied for various powers of S and T multiplied to $\cos Y$ or $\sin Y$. But now (11) reduces to

$$I_1(a\phi_1) + \tilde{I}_2(a\phi_1, W) + I_3(a\phi_1) = 0, \tag{61}$$

since $I_2(a\phi_1)$ has been annihilated by the introduction of W (which, as will be seen, constitutes part of ϕ_2). The last term in (60), which appears in (61), needs to be annihilated. For this purpose one notes that

$$\left(g\frac{\partial}{\partial y} + \frac{\partial^2}{\partial t^2}\right)(\widehat{S}\widehat{T}e^{-i\widehat{Y}}) = A\widehat{S}\widehat{T}e^{-i\widehat{Y}} + i\varepsilon B(-\widehat{S}\widehat{T}^2 + \widehat{S}^3)e^{-i\widehat{Y}} - 6\varepsilon^2 c_g^2\widehat{S}^3\widehat{T}e^{-i\widehat{Y}}, \tag{62}$$

in which

$$A = gk - k^2c^2 + \varepsilon c_g^2, \qquad B = g - 2kcc_g. \tag{63}$$

To annihilate the last term in (60), which appears in (61), one adds the following term to ϕ:

$$Z = -\frac{14i}{3\varepsilon c_g^2}a^3k^3(\widehat{S}\widehat{T}e^{-i\widehat{Y}} - \widehat{S}^*\widehat{T}^*e^{i\widehat{Y}^*}). \tag{64}$$

From (64), (62), and the complex conjugate form of (62), one has, upon taking $y = 0$ on the right-hand side of the equation,

$$\left(g\frac{\partial}{\partial y} + \frac{\partial^2}{\partial t^2}\right)Z = 56\varepsilon a^3k^3S^3T\sin Y - \frac{28A}{3\varepsilon c_g^2}a^3k^3ST\sin Y + \frac{14B}{3c_g^2}a^3k^3(-2S + 4S^3)\cos Y. \tag{65}$$

Thus, as the last term in (60) is annihilated, other terms are created. Recalling (25), one has, from (61),

$$2A - \frac{28}{3c_g^2}a^2k^3B = 0, \tag{66}$$

$$-2\varepsilon B - \frac{28}{3\varepsilon c_g^2}a^2k^3A = 0, \tag{67}$$

$$-4\varepsilon^2 c_g^2 + 8a^2k^4 + \frac{56}{3c_g^2}a^2k^3B = 0. \tag{68}$$

Equations (66) and (67) give, since they are obviously not linearly dependent, $A = 0 = B$, or

$$k^2c^2 = gk + \varepsilon^2 c_g^2, \qquad 2kcc_g = g, \tag{69}$$

and (68) gives then

$$\varepsilon^2 = \frac{2a^2k^4}{c_g^2}. \tag{70}$$

With higher-order terms neglected, this gives

$$\varepsilon^2 = \frac{8a^2k^4}{c_0^2} = \frac{8a^2k^5}{g}. \tag{71}$$

Equations (69) and (71) are the main results sought. It is important now to examine just to what order of a the calculation has been carried out. Note that the last term in (60) is of $O(a^4)$, and the concern arises that it is retained while other terms of $O(a^4)$ are neglected. But a close examination of the entire analytical procedure reveals that fourth-order terms can only arise from two sources:

(i) Equations (3) and (4), not accounted for in (11),

(ii) Other fourth-order terms in (11).

From source (i) one cannot obtain terms of $O(a^4)$ that contain $\sin Y$ or $\cos Y$ as a factor. From (ii) one can obtain terms of $O(a^4)$ by differentiation of $\widehat{S}$ or $\widehat{T}$ with respect to y, or S or T with respect to x or t, and, of course, also terms of fourth or higher orders by iteration. But the only term of fourth order obtained in this way that contains the factor $\sin Y$ or $\cos Y$ is the last term in (60). Since that term is important in establishing the second equation in (69), one can say that, in effect, the calculation has been carried to the fourth order in a, as far as the determinations of c and c_g are concerned. Indeed, the arguments in the following paragraph will establish that (69) stands intact at any order of approximation.

Denote the differential operator on the left-hand side of (65) by L_0. A simple calculation shows that

$$L_0(\widehat{S}^3\widehat{T}e^{-i\widehat{Y}}) = (A + 8\varepsilon^2 c_g^2)\widehat{S}^3\widehat{T}e^{-i\widehat{Y}} - 20\varepsilon^2 c_g^2\widehat{S}^5\widehat{T}e^{-i\widehat{Y}} + i\varepsilon B(-3\widehat{S}^3 + 4\widehat{S}^5)e^{-i\widehat{Y}},$$

$$(72)$$

$$L_0(\widehat{S}^3 e^{-i\widehat{Y}}) = (A + 8\varepsilon^2 c_g^2)\widehat{S}^3 e^{-i\widehat{Y}} - 3i\varepsilon B c_g^2\widehat{S}^3\widehat{T}e^{-i\widehat{Y}} - 12\varepsilon^2 c_g^2\widehat{S}^5 e^{-i\widehat{Y}}. \qquad (73)$$

Suppose one has a term (C real)

$$2CS^5 T \sin Y$$

to annihilate in (17). Since this is equal to

$$iC(\widehat{S}^3\widehat{T}e^{-i\widehat{Y}} - \widehat{S}^{*3}\widehat{T}^* e^{-i\widehat{Y}^*})_{y=0},$$

one can use (72), and add a term of the form (C_1 is another real constant)

$$iC_1(\widehat{S}^5\widehat{T}e^{i\widehat{Y}} - \widehat{S}^{*5}\widehat{T}^* e^{i\widehat{Y}^*})$$

to ϕ to accomplish the purpose. But then one creates terms containing the factors

$$(i\widehat{S}^3\widehat{T}, \widehat{S}^3, \widehat{S}^5)e^{i\widehat{Y}}$$

and their complex conjugates. The term containing $\widehat{S}^3$, and its complex conjugate, go toward a higher-order approximation for ε^2, as a continuation of (68). The term containing $i\widehat{S}^3\widehat{T}$, and its complex conjugate, are removed by the process already illustrated by (62) to (69), and would only possibly contribute to the determination of ε^2. The terms containing $\widehat{S}^5$ and $(\widehat{S}^*)^5$ can be annihilated by using (73). In that process terms containing $\widehat{S}^3$ and $\widehat{S}^3\widehat{T}$ and their complex conjugates will be created, as has been shown. But these will only contribute to the further determination of ε^2. Throughout the process of residue annihilation, the arguments leading from (66) and (67) to (69) are unaffected. Now that one has shown (69) is valid for all orders of approximation, it is worthwhile to obtain c^2 and c_g^2 explicitly in terms of ε from (69). The results are

$$c^2 = \frac{c_0^2}{2}\left[1 + \left\{1 + (\varepsilon/k)^2\right\}^{1/2}\right],$$ (74)

$$c_g^2 = \frac{c_0^2}{2}\,\frac{1}{1 + \left\{1 + (\varepsilon/k)^2\right\}^{1/2}}.$$ (75)

From (74) the β's in (18) can be readily determined if needed. As to (19), the second equation in (69) shows that all γ's are zero. An expansion of c_g^2 in a power series in ε can be readily obtained from (75) if needed. That c_g decreases as ε increases (or as the amplitude increases) may seem strange, but this is not the first instance of such a situation. See Whitham ([10], p. 526, formula for the group velocity V).

6. Results for ϕ_2. With W and Z determined by (36) and (64), respectively, the ϕ_2 in (20) is determined, and is

$$\phi_2 = (W + Z)/a^2.$$ (76)

7. The shape of the group. The shape of the wave group is given by η, which can be evaluated from (6) or (8). To calculate η to $O(a^3)$, one has to include terms containing $\sin 3Y$ and $\cos 3Y$. This can be done but is lengthy. Here η will be given to $O(a^2)$ only. For this purpose one notes that on $y = 0$ (36) gives

$$W = O(a^2\varepsilon) = O(a^3),$$

and (64) gives

$$Z = -\frac{28}{3\varepsilon c_g^2}a^3 k^3 ST \sin Y.$$ (77)

To $O(a^2)$ then, (9) and (32) give, upon use of (20), (21), (30), (36), (76), and (77),

$$-g\eta = 2akc_0 S \sin Y + 2a\varepsilon c_g ST \cos Y + 2a^2 k^2 S^2 \cos 2Y + \frac{28a^3 k^4 c}{3\varepsilon c_g^2} ST \cos Y.$$

When c and c_g are replaced by c_0 and $c_0/2$ respectively, and (16) and (71) are used, one has

$$-g\eta = 2akc_0 S \sin Y + \frac{17}{3}a\varepsilon c_0 ST \cos Y + 2a^2 k^2 S^2 \cos 2Y,$$ (78)

in which ε is given by (71).

The leading item of η is (Fig. 1)

$$\eta = -\alpha S \sin Y,$$

where

$$\alpha = \frac{2akc_0}{g} = \frac{2a}{c_0}$$ (79)

is the amplitude of the group to $O(a)$, and is related to ε by

$$\varepsilon = \sqrt{2}k^2\alpha.$$ (80)

Thus the group is shorter for a larger amplitude and for a shorter basic wavelength.

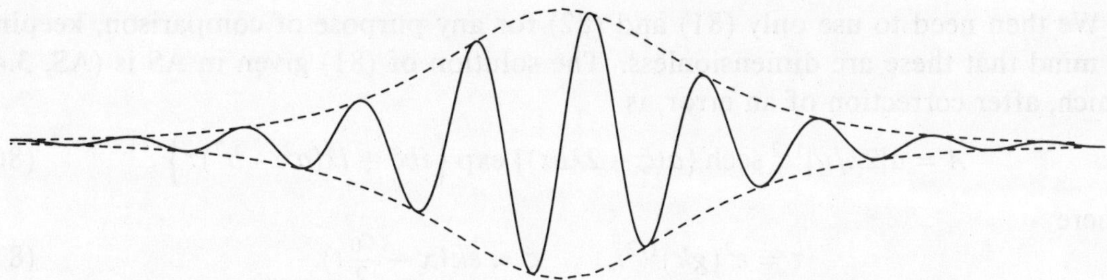

FIG. 1. Sketch of the gravity-wave group

8. Comparison with previous results. For the study of dispersive-wave groups and their stability, many previous investigators have derived the cubic Schrödinger equation (CBE). These are cited in the introduction of this paper. Among these, Hasimoto and Ono [8] derived it for gravity waves in a liquid of constant depth, and Djordjević and Redekopp [6] and Ablowitz and Segur ([2], henceforth referred to as AS) derived it for capillary-gravity waves in water of constant depth. In a later paper, Djordjević and Redekopp ([7], henceforth referred to as DR) derived it for gravity-capillary waves in water of slowly varying depth. From the results of these authors, among others, a CBE for gravity waves in water of infinite depth can be readily obtained. The coefficients of the CBE vary with the authors, and it is useful to reconcile the differences before comparing the results presented in this paper with their results.

The CBE obtained by Hasimoto and Ono [8] and that in AS, when capillary effects are neglected and the water depth is infinite and after a sign error in the definition of τ in (AS, 2.22) is corrected, are the same, except that the former is in dimensional and the latter is in dimensionless terms. The latter is (AS, p. 702)

$$iA_\tau + \lambda A_{\xi\xi} = \nu |A|^2 A, \tag{81}$$

in which A is no longer the A defined by (63), and

$$\lambda = -\tfrac{1}{8}, \qquad \nu = 2. \tag{82}$$

The form of CBE obtained by Djordjević and Redekopp ([6], [7]) is dimensional, and when reduced to the case of gravity waves in water of infinite depth, is

$$iA_\xi + \lambda A_{\tau\tau} = \nu |A|^2 A, \tag{83}$$

where

$$\lambda = -\frac{1}{g}, \qquad \nu = \frac{4k^4}{g}. \tag{84}$$

Ablowitz and Segur's τ and ξ correspond to ξ and τ in (83). The differences in the values of λ and ν are the result of differences in the scaling schemes. If the ξ in DR is doubled and the τ in DR is halved, as a close examination of the scaling schemes used in AS and DR would suggest, the new λ and ν for the DR form would be

$$\lambda = -\frac{1}{8g}, \qquad \nu = \frac{2k^4}{g}, \tag{85}$$

which then agree with (82), apart from the appearance of k and g in (85) as the consequence of the fact that (83) is in dimensional terms.

We then need to use only (81) and (82) for any purpose of comparison, keeping in mind that these are dimensionless. The solution of (81) given in AS is (AS, 3.4) which, after correction of an error, is

$$A = a|2\lambda/\nu|^{1/2} \operatorname{sech}\left\{a(\xi - 2\lambda b\tau)\right\} \exp\left\{ib\xi + i\lambda(a^2 - b^2)\tau\right\}, \tag{86}$$

where

$$\tau = \varepsilon^2(gk)^{1/2}t, \qquad \xi = \varepsilon k\left(x - \frac{c_0}{2}t\right). \tag{87}$$

In (AS, 3.4), the $2b\tau$ should be $2\lambda b\tau$, as in (86). The solution (86) is valid only for $\lambda/\nu < 0$, as is the case here, In regard to notation, the c_g in AS has been changed to $c_0/2$ in (87). The symbols x, t, g, and k mean the same things in AS as here, but a and ε mean different things, and λ, ν, b, τ, and ξ are not used in this paper. The A in AS is the dimensionless form of the $\tilde{A}$ in AS. My a therefore corresponds to their $A\varepsilon$, and my ε to their $a\varepsilon$. My α in (79) corresponds to their $2(2\lambda/\nu)^{1/2}a\varepsilon$, the factor 2 being there because $2A_{\max}\varepsilon$ is the amplitude of the dominant term in their ϕ. From (80),

$$\frac{\alpha}{\varepsilon} = \frac{1}{\sqrt{2}k^2}. \tag{88}$$

The k^2 in this equation arises because dimensional quantities are used here. The corresponding ratio in AS, from (AS, 3.4), is

$$\frac{2A_{\max}\varepsilon}{a\varepsilon} = 2|2\lambda/\nu|^{1/2}. \tag{89}$$

Since this is dimensionless, one equates this to $1/\sqrt{2}$ in (88), and thereby obtains

$$\nu = 2,$$

since $\lambda = -1/8$. This agrees with (82).

In AS, the authors did not say what their a is. To arrive at the dependence of c with amplitude, it is necessary to determine their a. This can be done from the definition of ε in (AS, 2.13a), which is

$$\varepsilon = k\hat{a}, \tag{90}$$

where $\hat{a}$ is the dimensional amplitude of the surface displacement. It was denoted by a in (AS, 2.13a). But since a is used in (AS, 3.4) to denote something else, I have supplied the symbol $\hat{a}$ to avoid confusion. This $\hat{a}$ is then given by

$$\hat{a} = \frac{2\varepsilon}{k}A_{\max}, \tag{91}$$

where the right-hand side is in AS notation, except the subscript. Comparing (90) with (91), one has

$$A_{\max} = \frac{1}{2}.$$

But from (86)

$$A_{\max} = \frac{a}{2\sqrt{2}}.$$

Therefore

$$a = \sqrt{2}. \tag{92}$$

As Ablowitz and Segur said in AS, one may take b in (86) equal to zero without loss in generality. Doing so, and combining (86) with the exponential factor assumed in AS for the basic waves, one has

$$2A \exp ik(x - c_0 t) = \operatorname{sech} a\xi \exp ik\left\{x - c_0\left(1 + \frac{\varepsilon^2}{4}\right)t\right\}, \tag{93}$$

which immediately shows that

$$c = c_0\left(1 + \frac{\varepsilon^2}{4}\right), \tag{94}$$

where, one emphasizes, ε is in AS notation. On the other hand, (69) and (71) give, to the order $O(\varepsilon^2)$ and in my notation,

$$c = c_0\left(1 + \frac{\varepsilon^2}{8k^2}\right) = c_0\left(1 + \frac{a^2 k^3}{g}\right). \tag{95}$$

Since my $a^2 k^3/g$ is the $A_{\max}^2 \varepsilon^2$ or $\varepsilon^2/4$ in AS, this formula is in agreement with (94). In this connection note that for Stokesian waves

$$c = c_0\left(1 + \frac{k^2 a^2}{2}\right) = c_0\left(1 + \frac{\varepsilon^2}{4k^2}\right). \tag{96}$$

There is no reason to expect agreement between (95) and (96).

If b is assumed different from zero, a straightforward calculation shows that the right-hand side of (93) becomes

$$\operatorname{sech}\left[ak'\varepsilon\left\{x - (c_g)_0'\left(1 - \frac{3b^2\varepsilon^2}{8}\right)t\right\}\right] \exp ik'\left\{x - c_0'\left(1 + \frac{\varepsilon^2}{4}\right)t\right\} \tag{97}$$

if terms of $O(\varepsilon^2)$ are dropped from the exponent and terms of $O(\varepsilon^4)$ are dropped from the argument of the sech function. In (97),

$$k' = (1 + b\varepsilon)k, \qquad c_0' = (g/k')^{1/2} = 2(c_g)_0'.$$

To arrive at (97), one needs only to use the formulas obtained from the Taylor expansion (on going from k' to k),

$$kc_0 = k'c_0'\left(1 - \frac{b\varepsilon}{2} + \frac{3b^2\varepsilon^2}{8}\right) + O(\varepsilon^3), \tag{98}$$

$$c_0 = 3c_0'\left(1 - \frac{b\varepsilon}{2} + \frac{b^2\varepsilon^2}{8}\right) + O(\varepsilon^3). \tag{99}$$

It must *not* be argued from (97) that

$$c_g' = (c_g)_0'\left(1 - \frac{3b^2\varepsilon^2}{8}\right),$$

for the term of $O(\varepsilon^3)$ in the argument of the sech function in (97) would contribute terms of $O(\varepsilon^4)$ in the calculation, since the A given by (86) is to be multiplied by ε in the AS analysis, and that analysis has been carried only to terms of $O(\varepsilon^3)$. Throwing away terms of $O(\varepsilon^3)$ in the argument of the sech function in (97), one recovers the right-hand side of (93), with k replaced by k' and the c_0 and $(c_g)_0$ replaced by c_0'

182   CHIA-SHUN YIH

and $(c_g)'_0$. Thus the CBE approach used in AS and indeed by all previous authors does not and cannot determine the effect of amplitude on c_g. For that determination one has to carry out the calculation to $O(\varepsilon^4)$, and that is what has been done in this paper.

In summary, the CBE approach does not provide a result for the variation of the group velocity with amplitude, for comparison with the result on c_g in this paper. Wherever comparisons are possible, e.g., in regard to the form of the wave envelope or the dependence of c (phase velocity of the basic waves) on the amplitude, agreement is found between the results of this paper and previous results obtained by the CBE approach.

The wave group found here may be considered the result of instability of Stokesian waves, as suggested by Hasimoto and Ono [8], who cited the computations of Chu and Mei [5] and of others to support that suggestion.

9. Interaction of wave groups. Let there be two wave groups, denoted by the subscripts 1 and 2, respectively, and let (with $i = 1$ or 2)

$$X_i = \varepsilon_i(x - c_{gi}t - \xi_i), \qquad\qquad Y_i = k_i(x - c_i t - x_i),$$
$$S_i = \operatorname{sech} X_i, \qquad\qquad T_i = \tanh X_i,$$
$$\hat{X}_i = \varepsilon_i(x + iy - c_{gi}t - \xi_i), \qquad \hat{S}_i = \operatorname{sech} \hat{X}_i, \quad \text{etc.,}$$

and let

$$c_{g1} \neq c_{g2}.$$

The ξ_i and x_i are mere phase indicators. For the two groups,

$$\phi = a_1\phi_1 + a_2\phi_2 + a_1^2\phi_{11} + a_1 a_2\phi_{12} + a_2^2\phi_{22} + a_1^3\phi_{111} + a_1^2 a_2\phi_{112} + a_1 a_2^2\phi_{122} + a_2^3\phi_{222} + \cdots.$$

The terms with only 1 for indices are for the first group and those with only indices 2 are for the second group. All other terms are interaction terms. From the analysis presented in the preceding sections, it is evident that ϕ_1 contains $\hat{S}_1$ and $\hat{S}_1^*$, and ϕ_2 contains $\hat{S}_2$ and $\hat{S}_2^*$. Nonlinear interaction will give rise to second-order terms containing $\hat{S}_1\hat{S}_2$, $\hat{S}_1\hat{S}_2^*$, and their complex conjugates, in what has been called the residue. These will be multiplied to exponential functions containing, among others, the factor $\exp(k_1 + k_2)y$, with positive k_1 and k_2. Because of the presence of the operator

$$L_0 = g\frac{\partial}{\partial y} + \frac{\partial^2}{\partial t^2}$$

in I_1 defined by (12), annihilation of these terms in the residue will call forth second-order terms containing the same $\hat{S}$-factors to constitute ϕ_{12}, and the process continues as indicated in the analysis presented in the foregoing sections. When finally (11) is satisfied at any order of approximation, one is left with three sets of terms: those purely for the first group, those purely for the second group, and hybrid terms, for ϕ or for the displacement η. The hybrid terms contain both $\hat{S}_1$ (or its complex conjugate), and $\hat{S}_2$ (or its complex conjugate), and possibly $\hat{T}_1$, $\hat{T}_2$ and their complex conjugates as well. Thus in time they must vanish everywhere, because $c_{g1} \neq c_{g2}$, and where $\hat{S}_1$ is of order 1 the factor $\hat{S}_2$ will vanish as time increases, and vice versa.

The conclusion is then that the two groups will interact and emerge intact, with not even a shift of phase for either group after interaction, and that the interaction terms eventually vanish everywhere. Recall that in the present analysis c_g varies with both k and ε. Whatever k and ε are, it is always the group with the greater c_g that overtakes the slower group. That is for overtaking. For head-on collision c_{g1} can be equal to c_{g2}.

I am aware that researchers using the CBE have asserted that collision of wave groups leaves the group shapes intact but with "possible" phase shifts after collision. But since the CBE applies only to wave groups with the same basic wavenumber k, and the solution of the CBE for any wave group for a given k gives the same linear group velocity for that k, there can be no overtaking in the first place. As to head-on collision, the foregoing analysis seems to rule out any phase shifts of wave groups after collision. Note that the arguments for no phase shifts given in this paper do not apply to ordinary solitary waves, which definitely suffer phase shifts after collision.

Since normal reflection can be considered as equivalent in all physical aspects to the head-on collision of two identical wave groups propagating in opposite directions, one concludes that a gravity-wave group is reflected by a vertical boundary normal to its path with no change of shape, no shift in phase, and no change of group velocity when it is considered as a continuation of its mirror image after collision.

10. Conclusions. From the foregoing analysis one reaches the following conclusions:

1. A procedure has been devised by which the permanent shape of a group of gravity waves in deep water and the attending irrotational flow can be systematically determined to any order of approximation.

2. The phase velocity c of the individual waves in any group and the group velocity c_g are determined by two closed formulas, (74) and (75), in terms of the group wavenumber ε. These formulas remain intact for all orders of approximation, although ε^2 varies as a power series in a^2 (starting with that power), where a is proportional to the amplitude of the waves.

3. The phase velocity c increases with ε and the group velocity c_g decreases with ε in such a way that their product is constant. The increase of c with ε is in agreement with the corresponding result from the cubic-Schrödinger-equation approach. But since that approach, being an analysis to the third order of the amplitude only, is incapable of determining the dependence of the group velocity c_g on the amplitude, no comparison can be made with the CBE approach in regard to c_g.

4. The group wavenumber ε, given by (80), is proportional to the amplitude of the surface displacement and to k^2, k being the wavenumber of the basic waves.

5. Collision of groups of gravity waves leaves the groups intact, with not even any phase shifts. In particular, a group approaching a vertical boundary normal to its velocity of advance will be, after the transients have died out, just the continuation of its mirror image across the boundary.

Acknowledgment. This work has been supported by the Fluid Dynamics Program of the Office of Naval Research, Under Contract N00014-87-C-0194. It is also a great pleasure to acknowledge the benefit of several discussions with my colleague Professor J. Hammack, who brought the papers of several authors to my attention.

REFERENCES

[1] Mark J. Ablowitz and H. Segur, *Asymptotic solutions of the Korteweg-deVries equation*, Studies in Appl. Math. **57**, 13–44 (1976/77)

[2] Mark J. Ablowitz and H. Segur, *On the evolution of packets of water waves*, J. Fluid Mech. **92**, 691–715 (1979)

[3] D. J. Benney and A. C. Newell, *The propagation of nonlinear wave envelopes*, J. Math. and Phys. **46**, 133–139 (1967)

[4] D. J. Benney and G. J. Roskes, *Wave instabilities*, Studies in Appl. Math. **48**, 377 (1969)

[5] Vincent H. Chu and Chiang C. Mei, *The nonlinear evolution of Stokes waves in deep water*, J. Fluid Mech. **47**, 337 (1971)

[6] V. D. Djordjević and Larry G. Redekopp, *On two-dimensional packets of capillary-gravity waves*, J. Fluid Mech. **79**, 703–714 (1977)

[7] V. D. Djordjević and Larry G. Redekopp, *On the development of packets of surface gravity waves moving over an uneven bottom*, J. Appl. Math. and Phys. **29**, 950 (1978)

[8] H. Hasimoto and H. Ono, *Nonlinear modulation of gravity waves*, J. Phys. Soc. Japan **33**, 805 (1972)

[9] H. Lamb, *Hydrodynamics*, Dover, New York, 1945

[10] G. G. Whitham, *Linear and Nonlinear Waves*, Wiley, New York, 1974

[11] Chia-Shun Yih, *A solitary group of two-dimensional deep-water waves*, Quart. Appl. Math. **45**, 177–183 (1987)

[12] V. E. Zakharov, *Stability of periodic waves of finite amplitude on the surface of a deep fluid*, Sov. Phys. J. Appl. Mech. Tech. Phys. **4**, 86 (1968)

QUARTERLY OF APPLIED MATHEMATICS
VOLUME XLVII, NUMBER 3
SEPTEMBER 1990, PAGES 581–599

NONLINEAR GROUPS OF GRAVITY-CAPILLARY WAVES

By

CHIA-SHUN YIH

The University of Florida, Gainesville, Florida

Abstract. Nonlinear groups of gravity-capillary waves in deep water are investigated by a systematic direct approach that can be applied to nonlinear groups of other dispersive waves. Two formulas in closed form expressing the variations of the phase velocity c of the basic waves and of their group velocity c_g with the amplitude of the waves are obtained. These are in terms of the wavenumber ε of the envelope and ε^2 can be determined by the present approach as a power series in a^2, if $2a$ represents the amplitude of the waves. To the order of approximation achieved here, ε^2 is determined as a multiple of a^2. If k is the wavenumber of the basic waves, g is the gravitational acceleration, ρ is the density of the fluid, $\widehat{T}$ is surface tension, and $\beta = \widehat{T}k^2/\rho g$, then wave groups are possible for

$$0 \le \beta < 0.1547 \quad \text{or} \quad \beta > \frac{1}{2},$$

although the analysis is valid only when β is not near $\frac{1}{2}$. The phase velocity increases with the amplitude in the former interval for β and decreases with the amplitude in the latter interval. The group velocity c_g decreases with the amplitude in the former interval for β, or for $\frac{1}{2} < \beta < 1$, but increases with the amplitude if $\beta > 1$. When the results of this paper are compared with the results of previous authors, wherever comparison is possible, complete agreement is found. (Previous authors did not give the variation of c_g with the amplitude.)

1. Introduction. In a previous paper [1] I have given a direct calculation of nonlinear gravity-wave groups that can be carried out to any order of approximation. The results of that analysis were compared with previous results obtained by other authors by a different approach, and wherever comparison could be made agreement was found. However, since my calculation was carried to the order $O(a^3\varepsilon)$, where $2a$ is the amplitude of the velocity potential and ε the wavenumber, so to speak, of the envelope, I was able to give the variation of the group velocity with amplitude. Furthermore, the cubic Schrödinger equation that previous investigators derived and used to obtain the group envelope is invariably based on one particular wavenumber of the basic waves, and for that reason cannot be used to investigate the interaction

Received December 1, 1989.

©1990 Brown University

CHIA-SHUN YIH

of two wave groups of different wavenumbers for the basic waves, although it can be used to study the interaction of two wave groups of the same basic wavenumber but different amplitudes. My approach allows the investigation of two interacting wave groups of different wavenumbers for the basic waves. Moreover, my approach, while rather cumbersome, as nonlinear calculations often are, is systematic and can be carried to any order of approximation.

For these reasons I have judged it desirable and worthwhile to use my approach to study nonlinear groups of gravity-capillary waves in deep water. Here, however, the procedure in [1] must be considerably modified, because the Bernoulli equation, applied to the free surface, now contains terms involving the surface tension and derivatives of the surface displacement. This makes it impossible to eliminate η (the surface displacement) between the dynamic condition and the kinematic condition for the free surface by a simple substitution of η obtained from the former into the latter, as was possible in [1]. A new systematic approach is herein devised, which will have a wide application to other nonlinear groups of dispersive waves.

The calculation is carried out to $O(a^3 \varepsilon)$, where, as in [1], $2a$ is the basic amplitude (that is, of the linear part) of the velocity potential and ε is the wavenumber of the envelope. The main results are the determination of ε^2 as a multiple of a^2 and two formulas, in closed form, for the phase velocity c of the basic waves and for their group velocity c_g as functions of the amplitude of the waves. These formulas are in terms of ε^2, which can be determined as a power series of a^2 by higher approximations. Interaction of wave groups is briefly discussed.

When the results of this paper are compared with the results of Ablowitz and Segur [2] and of Djordjević and Redekopp [3], complete agreement is found wherever comparison is possible. (These authors did not give the variation of the group velocity with amplitude.) In view of the vast difference in approach between this work and the work of these authors, and in view of the tremendous amount of calculations necessary in this work and in theirs, the complete agreement is remarkable and gratifying.

2. Formulation of the differential system. Consider a train of gravity-capillary waves with the amplitude vanishing at infinity. The fluid motion is assumed two-dimensional and irrotational, and the depth of the fluid is assumed infinite. The free surface at $x = \pm\infty$ is at $y = 0$, which is the x-axis, and the individual waves and their envelope are supposed to propagate in the direction of increasing x.

Since the flow is assumed irrotational, there exists a velocity potential ϕ, the gradient of which is the velocity. The equation of continuity then gives the Laplace equation

$$\phi_{xx} + \phi_{yy} = 0, \tag{1}$$

where subscripts indicate partial differentiation. At the free surface,

$$y = \eta(x, t), \tag{2}$$

where η is the displacement of that surface from its undisturbed position. The kinematic condition at the free surface, requiring the equality of two expressions of the vertical velocity, is

$$\eta_t + \phi_x \eta_x = \phi_y. \tag{3}$$

The Bernoulli equation is, at the free surface,

$$\phi_t + g\eta + \frac{\phi_x^2 + \phi_y^2}{2} + \frac{p}{\rho} = 0, \tag{4}$$

where g is the gravitational acceleration, t is the time, ρ is the density of the fluid, and p is the pressure just below the free surface. Equation (4) implies that the pressure at the free surface for $x = \pm\infty$ is taken to be zero for convenience. The pressure just above the free surface is then everywhere zero, with any variation of it due to air motion neglected. Then the p in (4) is given by

$$p = -\widehat{T}\eta_{xx}(1 + \eta_x^2)^{-3/2}, \tag{5}$$

in which $\widehat{T}$ denotes surface tension.

The calculation will be carried to the fourth order of the amplitude at most. Indeed, it will be carried out to the orders $O(a^3)$ and $O(a^3\varepsilon)$, where $2a$ is the amplitude of the velocity potential, and ε is the wavenumber of the envelope of the wave train, which is assumed small and will be shown to be of the order $O(a)$. Thus one can combine (4) and (5) into

$$g\eta = -L\phi + \sigma\eta_{xx}\left(1 - \frac{3}{2}\eta_x^2\right), \tag{6}$$

where

$$L\phi = \phi_t + \frac{1}{2}(\phi_x^2 + \phi_y^2), \qquad \sigma = \frac{\widehat{T}}{\rho}. \tag{7}$$

Equation (6) is to be used in conjunction with (3), which will be rewritten in the form

$$\eta_t = \phi_y - \phi_x \eta_x. \tag{8}$$

The final boundary condition is

$$\phi \to 0 \quad \text{as } y \to -\infty. \tag{9}$$

Note that (4) ignores viscous effects, which require a boundary layer at the free surface, called the stress layer. The p in (4) then is the pressure just at the lower edge of that layer. Since the stress layer is thin (because both the phase velocity of the waves and their group velocity are large enough to make the Reynolds number large if the fluid is water), its effects are negligible, and one can proceed on the assumption of irrotational motion for the entire fluid.

The differential system governing the dynamics of the wave train then consists of (1), (6), (8), and (9), with $L\phi$ and σ defined by (7).

3. The solution of the differential system. Since ϕ satisfies (1), one can assume it to be the real part of an analytic function of the complex variable

$$z = x + iy,$$

and, as in [1], it is convenient to use the symbols $\hat{X}$ and $\hat{Y}$ defined by

$$\hat{X} = \varepsilon(z - c_g t), \qquad \hat{Y} = k(z - ct), \tag{10}$$

in which k is the wavenumber of the basic waves and ε that of their envelope, c is the phase velocity of the waves and c_g their group velocity. The value of c and c_g given by the linear theory are

$$c_0 = (gk^{-1} + \sigma k)^{1/2}, \qquad (c_g)_0 = \frac{1}{2c_0}\left(\frac{g}{k} + 3\sigma k\right). \tag{11}$$

Given k, the main task is to determine c, c_g, and ε as functions of a, which is half the amplitude of ϕ. The expansions used are, as in [1],

$$\phi = a\phi_1 + a^2\phi_2 + a^3\phi_3 + \cdots, \tag{12}$$

$$\varepsilon^2 = a^2(\alpha_1 + \alpha_2 a^2 + \alpha_3 a^4 + \cdots), \tag{13}$$

$$c^2 = c_0^2(1 + \beta_1\varepsilon^2 + \beta_2\varepsilon^4 + \cdots), \tag{14}$$

$$2cc_g = 2c_0 c_{g0}(1 + \gamma_1\varepsilon^2 + \gamma_2\varepsilon^4 \cdots). \tag{15}$$

As it will be shown later, the amplitude of ϕ_1 is 2. Since a, when made dimensionless (i.e., expressed in units of $c_0 k^{-1}$), is supposed to be small, $2a$ is the principal part of the amplitude of ϕ, and is considered its nominal amplitude.

If σ is assumed zero, (6) gives an expression of η in terms of ϕ, which, when substituted into (8), provides a single free-surface condition in terms of ϕ. Upon expanding ϕ in a McLaurin series in powers of η and repeatedly using (6), with $\hat{T} = 0$, one obtains a single free-surface condition in terms ϕ and its derivatives, all evaluated at $y = 0$. This was done in [1], but the simplicity of this procedure is lost when surface tension is taken into account. One now needs an additional expansion

$$\eta = a\eta_1 + a^2\eta_2 + \cdots, \tag{16}$$

and proceeds systematically from the lowest-order terms in a to higher and higher orders.

From (6) and (8), the free-surface condition will now be developed in a form that can be used for calculation to any order of approximation. Using (6), one obtains

$$g\phi_y - \phi_x(g\eta_x) = g\phi_y + \phi_x(L\phi)_x - \sigma\phi_x\left\{\eta_{xx}\left(1 - \frac{3}{2}\eta_x^2\right)\right\}_x. \tag{17}$$

On the other hand, (6) gives

$$g\eta_t = -(L\phi)_t + \sigma\left\{\eta_{xx}\left(1 - \frac{3}{2}\eta_x^2\right)\right\}_t. \tag{18}$$

The left-hand side of (17) and (18) are equal on account of (8). Hence

$$g\phi_y + (L\phi)_t + \phi_x(L\phi)_x - \sigma Q = 0, \tag{19}$$

where

$$Q = \eta_{txx} - \frac{3}{2}(\eta_x^2\eta_{xx})_t + \phi_x\eta_{xxx}. \tag{20}$$

A term

$$-\frac{3}{2}\phi_x(\eta_x^2\eta_{xx})_x \tag{21}$$

has been omitted from Q because it is of $O(a^4)$, and because it will not affect the results to the desired order of approximation.

In four sub-sections that follow one will develop the four terms on the left-hand side of (19), which will be the main equation one works with.

3.1. *The term* $g\phi_y$. A power-series expansion gives

$$\phi_y = \phi_y(0) + \phi_{yy}(0)\eta + \frac{1}{2}\phi_{yyy}(0)\eta^2 + \cdots , \tag{22}$$

in which $\phi_y(0)$ means ϕ_y evaluated at $y = 0$ for any x and t. On account of (1), (12), and (16) this can be written as

$$\phi_y = a\phi_{1y} + a^2(\phi_{2y} - \phi_{1xx}\eta_1)$$
$$+ a^3\left\{\phi_{3y} + (\phi_{2yy}\eta_1 + \phi_{1yy}\eta_2) - \frac{1}{2}\phi_{1yxx}\eta_1^2\right\}, \tag{23}$$

in which all the derivatives of ϕ on the right-hand side are now evaluated at $y = 0$.

3.2. *The terms in* $(L\phi)_t$. Before one differentiates $L\phi$ with respect to t, one expands the terms in it, in order to evaluate $L\phi$ at $y = \eta$. Thus,

$$\phi_t = a\phi_{1t} + a^2(\phi_{2t} + \phi_{1ty}\eta_1) + a^3\left(\phi_{2ty}\eta_1 + \phi_{1ty}\eta_2 - \frac{1}{2}\phi_{1txx}\eta_1^2\right), \tag{24}$$

in which

$$-\phi_{txx} = \phi_{tyy},$$

on account of (1). All the derivatives of ϕ on the right-hand side of (24) are evaluated at $y = 0$. Furthermore,

$$\frac{1}{2}(\phi_x^2 + \phi_y^2) = \frac{1}{2}\{a^2(\phi_{1x}^2 + \phi_{1y}^2) + 2a^3(\phi_{1x}\phi_{1xy}\eta_1 - \phi_{1y}\phi_{1xx}\eta_1 + \phi_{1x}\phi_{2x} + \phi_{1y}\phi_{2y})\}, \tag{25}$$

in which again the derivatives of ϕ on the right-hand side are evaluated at $y = 0$, and (1) has again been applied. The reason for preferring $-\phi_{xx}$ to ϕ_{yy} is that derivatives with respect to x can be performed after y has been put to zero—a great convenience, as subsequent calculations will show.

Combining (24) and (25), one has

$$(L\phi)_t = a\phi_{1tt} + a^2\left\{\phi_{2t} + \phi_{1ty}\eta_1 + \frac{1}{2}(\phi_{1x}^2 + \phi_{1y}^2)\right\}_t$$
$$+ a^3\left(\phi_{2ty}\eta_1 + \phi_{1ty}\eta_2 - \frac{1}{2}\phi_{1txx}\eta_1^2 + \phi_{1x}\phi_{1xy}\eta_1\right.$$
$$\left. - \phi_{1y}\phi_{1xx}\eta_1 + \phi_{1x}\phi_{2x} + \phi_{1y}\phi_{2y}\right)_t. \tag{26}$$

3.3. *The terms in* $\phi_x(L\phi)_x$. Using (24) and (25) again, and

$$\phi_x = a\phi_{1x} + \alpha^2(\phi_{2x} + \phi_{1xy}\eta_1) + \cdots ,$$

                                    CHIA-SHUN YIH

one obtains

$$\phi_x(L\phi)_x = a^2\phi_{1x}\phi_{1xt} + a^3\left[\phi_{2x}\phi_{1xt} + \phi_{1xt}\phi_{1xy}\eta_1\right.$$

$$\left.+\phi_{1x}\left\{\phi_{2t} + \phi_{1ty}\eta_1 + \frac{1}{2}(\phi_{1x}^2 + \phi_{1y}^2)\right\}_x\right]$$

$$= a^2\phi_{1x}\phi_{1xt} + a^3\left[(\phi_{1x}\phi_{2x})_t + (\phi_{1x}\phi_{1yx})_t\eta_1\right.$$

$$\left.+\phi_{1x}\phi_{1ty}\eta_{1x} + \frac{1}{2}\phi_{1x}(\phi_{1x}^2 + \phi_{1y}^2)_x\right]. \qquad (27)$$

Again, all terms on the right-hand side of (27) are evaluated at $y = 0$.

3.4. *The terms in* Q. The first term on the right-hand side of (20) is, by virtue of (8),

$$\eta_{txx} = (\phi_y - \phi_x\eta_x)_{xx} = \phi_{yxx} - (\phi_x\eta_x)_{xx}, \qquad (28)$$

where all the derivatives of ϕ are still evaluated at $y = \eta$. Expansion of ϕ_{yxx} gives

$$\phi_{yxx} = a\phi_{1yxx} + a^2\{\phi_{2y} - (\phi_{1xx}\eta_1)\}_{xx}$$

$$+ a^3\left\{\phi_{3y} - \phi_{1xx}\eta_2 - \phi_{2xx}\eta_1 - \frac{1}{2}\phi_{1yxx}\eta_1^2\right\}_{xx}, \qquad (29)$$

in which (1) is applied whenever applicable, and all the derivatives of ϕ on the right-hand side are evaluated at $y = 0$. As to the last term in (28), one has

$$-(\phi_x\eta_x)_{xx} = -a^2(\phi_{1x}\eta_{1x})_{xx}$$

$$-a^3(\phi_{1x}\eta_{2x} + \phi_{2x}\eta_{1x} + \phi_{1xy}\eta_1\eta_{1x})_{xx}. \qquad (30)$$

Combining (29) with (30), one obtains the expression for η_{txx}. But one need not write this out, since later the terms in Q as given by (20) will be combined.

The next term in Q is simply, to $O(a^3)$,

$$-\frac{3}{2}(\eta_x^2\eta_{xx})_t = -\frac{a^3}{2}(\eta_{1x}^3)_{xt}, \qquad (31)$$

and the last term is

$$\phi_x\eta_{xxx} = a^2\phi_{1x}\eta_{1xxx} + a^3(\phi_{2x}\eta_{1xxx} + \phi_{1x}\eta_{2xxx} + \phi_{1xy}\eta_1\eta_{1xxx}). \qquad (32)$$

Combining (28) with (31) and (32), one obtains, with the help of (29) and (30),

$$Q = aQ_1 + a^2Q_2 + a^3Q_3, \qquad (33)$$

where

$$Q_1 = \phi_{1yxx}, \qquad (34)$$

$$Q_2 = -\{(\phi_{1xx}\eta_1)_{xx} + \phi_{1xxx}\eta_{1x} + 2\phi_{1xx}\eta_{1xx}\} + \phi_{2yxx}$$

$$= -\{(\phi_{1xx}\eta_1)_{xx} + (\phi_{1xx}\eta_{1x})_x + \phi_{1xx}\eta_{1xx}\} + \phi_{2yxx}, \qquad (35)$$

$$Q_3 = -\left\{\left(\phi_{1x}\eta_2 + \phi_{2x}\eta_1 + \frac{1}{2}\phi_{1yx}\eta_1^2\right)_{xxx} + \frac{1}{2}(\eta_{1x}^3)_{xt}\right.$$

$$\left.- (\phi_{1x}\eta_{2xxx} + \phi_{2x}\eta_{1xxx} + \phi_{1xy}\eta_1\eta_{1xxx})\right\} + \phi_{3yxx}. \qquad (36)$$

4. Calculation for terms containing a as a factor. The first calculation is for terms that contain a as a factor. The terms may be of orders $O(a)$, $O(a\varepsilon)$, $O(a\varepsilon^2)$, or $O(a\varepsilon^3)$. The working equation for all the calculations for all orders is always (19), with its four groups of terms given by (23), (26), (27), and (33), supplemented by (34), (35), and (36). For the starting calculation, one collects terms containing a as a factor in (23), (26), and (33), and obtains

$$L_0\phi_1 = g\phi_{1y} + \phi_{1tt} - \sigma\phi_{1yxx}. \tag{37}$$

In addition to (10), one now defines

$$X = \varepsilon(x - c_g t), \qquad Y = k(x - ct), \tag{38}$$

and

$$\widehat{S} = \operatorname{sech}\widehat{X}, \qquad \widehat{T} = \tanh\widehat{X}, \qquad S = \operatorname{sech}X, \qquad T = \tanh X. \tag{39}$$

Note that it is immediately clear that $\widehat{S}$ and $\widehat{T}$ have singularities at the points $\widehat{X} = \pm i(2n + 1)\pi/2$. Those corresponding to the $+$ sign are outside the liquid, and cause no difficulty. The remaining singularities can be removed, as shown in Yih [4]. This removal has very little effect on the free-surface conditions if k/ε is large compared with 1, as is the case for the phenomenon under investigation here. Higher singularities created at higher approximations can be similarly removed [4]. Now let

$$\phi_1 = \widehat{S}e^{-i\widehat{Y}} + \widehat{S}^* e^{i\widehat{Y}^*}, \tag{40}$$

so that, at $y = 0$,

$$\begin{aligned}
\phi_1 &= 2S\cos Y, \\
\phi_{1y} &= 2kS\cos Y - 2\varepsilon ST\sin Y, \\
\phi_{1x} &= -2kS\sin Y - 2\varepsilon ST\cos Y, \\
\phi_{1tt} &= (-2k^2c^2 + 2\varepsilon^2 c_g^2)S\cos Y + 4k\varepsilon cc_g ST\sin Y \\
&\quad - 4(\varepsilon c_g)^2 S^3\cos Y, \\
\phi_{1yxx} &= (-2k^3 + 6k\varepsilon^2)S\cos Y + (6k^2 - 2\varepsilon^2)\varepsilon ST\sin Y \\
&\quad - 12k\varepsilon^2 S^3\cos Y + 12\varepsilon^3 S^3\sin Y.
\end{aligned} \tag{41}$$

Then

$$L_0\phi_1 = 2AS\cos Y - 2\varepsilon BST\sin Y + \varepsilon^2(12\sigma k - 4c_g^2)S^3\cos Y$$
$$- 12\sigma\varepsilon^3 S^3 T\sin Y, \tag{42}$$

where

$$A = gk + \sigma k^3 - k^2c^2 + \varepsilon^2(c_g^2 - 3\sigma k), \tag{43}$$

$$B = g + 3\sigma k^2 - 2kcc_g - \sigma\varepsilon^2. \tag{44}$$

In (41) and (42), some higher-order terms which are unnecessary for the main purpose of this paper are exhibited, to give an indication of why they are unnecessary. For instance, it will become clear that the $2\varepsilon^2 c_g^2$ term in ϕ_{1tt} and the term $6k\varepsilon^2$ in ϕ_{1yxx} in (41) merely lead to higher-order determination of ε^2 in terms of a^2. Subsequent development will show that $A = 0 = B$.

To obtain η_1, one uses

$$\eta_{1t} = \phi_{1y}$$

and integrates by parts repeatedly to obtain

$$\eta_1 = 2(E_1 S \sin Y + \varepsilon E_2 ST \cos Y + \varepsilon^2 E_3 S^3 \sin Y) + O(\varepsilon^3), \tag{45}$$

in which

$$E_1 = -\frac{1}{c} - \frac{\varepsilon^2}{k^2 cr}(1 - r), \qquad E_2 = \frac{1}{kc}(1 - r), \qquad E_3 = \frac{2}{k^2 cr}(1 - r),$$

where

$$r = c_g / c. \tag{46}$$

Again some unnecessary terms are included in η_1. In subsequent calculations, one needs only to take

$$\eta_1 = \frac{2}{c} \left\{ -S \sin Y + \frac{\varepsilon}{k}(1 - r)ST \cos Y \right\}. \tag{47}$$

5. Calculation for ϕ_2 and η_2. Taking terms containing a^2 as a factor in (21), (26), (27), and (33), and applying (19), one has, with all terms on the right-hand side evaluated at $y = 0$,

$$L_0 \phi_2 = T_{21} + T_{22} + T_{23} + T_{24} + T_{25} + T_{26} + T_{27}, \tag{48}$$

where

$$L_0 = g \frac{\partial}{\partial y} + \frac{\partial^2}{\partial t^2} - \sigma \frac{\partial^3}{\partial y \, \partial x^2}, \tag{49}$$

$$\begin{aligned}
&T_{21} = g\phi_{1xx}\eta_1, && T_{22} = -(\phi_{1ty}\eta_1)_t, \\
&T_{23} = -\tfrac{1}{2}(\phi_{1x}^2 + \phi_{1x}^2)_t, && T_{24} = -\phi_{1x}\phi_{1xt}, \\
&T_{25} = -\sigma(\phi_{1xx}\eta_1)_{xx}, && T_{26} = -\sigma(\phi_{1xx}\eta_{1x})_x, \\
&T_{27} = -\sigma\phi_{1xx}\eta_{1xx}.
\end{aligned}$$

From (41) and (46),

$$T_{21} = \frac{2gk^2}{c} \left[S^2 \sin 2Y - \frac{\varepsilon}{k}S^2 T\{1 + r - (3 - r)\cos 2Y\} \right],$$

$$T_{22} = -4k^3 c \left[S^2 \sin 2Y + \frac{\varepsilon}{k}S^2 T\{-r + (2 + r)\cos 2Y\} \right],$$

$$T_{23} = -4k^2 \varepsilon cr S^2 T,$$

$$T_{24} = 2k^3 c \left[S^2 \sin 2Y - \frac{\varepsilon}{k}S^2 T\{r - (2 + r)\cos 2Y\} \right],$$

$$T_{25} = \frac{8k^4 \sigma}{c} \left[S^2 \sin 2Y - \frac{\varepsilon}{k}(5 - r)S^2 T \cos 2Y \right],$$

$$T_{26} = \frac{4k^4 \sigma}{c} \left[S^2 \sin 2Y + \frac{\varepsilon}{k}S^2 T\{1 + (5 - r)\cos 2Y\} \right],$$

$$T_{27} = \frac{2k^4 \sigma}{c} \left[S^2 \sin 2Y - \frac{\varepsilon}{k}S^2 T\{-1 + r + (-5 + r)\cos 2Y\} \right].$$

Upon collection of terms, (48) becomes

$$L_0\phi_2 = C_{21}S^2 \sin 2Y + C_{22}S^2 T + C_{23}S^2 T \cos 2Y, \tag{50}$$

where

$$C_{21} = \frac{2k^2}{c}(-kc^2 + g + 7\sigma k^2),$$

$$C_{22} = \frac{2\varepsilon k}{c}\{(3-r)\sigma k^2 - g(1+r) - kc^2 r\},$$

$$C_{23} = \frac{2\varepsilon k}{c}\{7(5-r)\sigma k^2 - (2kc^2 + kc^2 r - 3g + gr)\}.$$

Before using (50) for ϕ_2, it is advantageous to simplify the C's. This is done by anticipating the results

$$A = 0 = B, \tag{51}$$

where A and B are given by (43) and (44). For the purpose at hand it is permissible and desirable to ignore the terms of $O(\varepsilon^2)$ in (43) and (44), which will give terms of $O(a^3\varepsilon^2)$ when the final step in determining ε^2 in terms of a^2 is taken. Then, using (51), one obtains, after some substitutions,

$$C_{21} = \frac{12\sigma k^4}{c}, \tag{52}$$

$$C_{22} = \frac{4\varepsilon k g}{c}, \tag{53}$$

$$C_{23} = \frac{12\varepsilon\sigma k^3}{c}(5-r) = \frac{6\varepsilon k g}{c}\frac{\beta(9+7\beta)}{1+\beta}, \tag{54}$$

where

$$\beta = \frac{\sigma k^2}{g}. \tag{55}$$

One now proceeds to calculate ϕ_2. For this purpose define

$$\phi_{20} = -i(\widehat{S}^2 - \text{c.c.}) \tag{56}$$

$$\phi_{21} = -i\{\widehat{S}^2 \exp(-i2\widehat{Y}) - \text{c.c.}\}, \tag{57}$$

$$\phi_{22} = \{\widehat{S}^2 \widehat{T} \exp(-i2\widehat{Y}) + \text{c.c.}\}, \tag{58}$$

where c.c. denotes the complex conjugate of the preceding quantity.

Direct calculations show that, at $y = 0$ and with terms of $O(\varepsilon^2)$ neglected,

$$L_0\phi_{20} = -4\varepsilon g S^2 T, \tag{59}$$

$$L_0\phi_{21} = 4kg(1-2\beta)S^2 \sin 2Y + 4\varepsilon g(1-6\beta)S^2 T \cos 2Y, \tag{60}$$

$$L_0\phi_{22} = -4kg(1-2\beta)S^2 T \cos 2Y + O(\varepsilon). \tag{61}$$

With these results,

$$\phi_2 = \frac{k}{c}\left(\phi_{20} + \alpha_{21}\phi_{21} + \frac{\varepsilon}{k}\alpha_{22}\phi_{22}\right), \tag{62}$$

where

$$\alpha_{21} = \frac{3\beta}{1 - 2\beta}, \tag{63}$$

$$\alpha_{22} = -\frac{3\beta(7 - \beta - 2\beta^2)}{2(1 + \beta)(1 - 2\beta)^2}. \tag{64}$$

Note that the last term in (60) adds to the burden of the last term in (50), when the first term on the right-hand side of (50) is taken care of. That is why (64) is what it is, to account for that additional burden and to take care of the last term in (50). The factor ε in the last term of (62) shows why it is permissible to drop the term of $O(\varepsilon)$ in (61).

With ϕ_2 defined by (62), one is now in a position to calculate η_2. For that purpose, and for the purpose of later calculations, one lists some useful results below, evaluated at $y = 0$:

ϕ_{20} and all its derivatives with respect to x or t are zero,

$$(\phi_2)_y = -4\varepsilon S^2 T,$$

$$(\phi_{20})_{yxx} = O(\varepsilon^3),$$

$$\phi_{21} = -2S^2 \sin 2Y,$$

$$(\phi_{21})_y = -4kS^2 \sin 2Y - 4\varepsilon kS^2 T \cos 2Y,$$

$$(\phi_{21})_x = -4kS^2 \cos 2Y + 4\varepsilon S^2 T \sin 2Y,$$

$$(\phi_{21})_{xx} = 8k^2S^2 \sin 2Y + 16\varepsilon kS^2 T \cos 2Y,$$

$$(\phi_{21})_{xt} = -8k^2cS^2 \sin 2Y - 8\varepsilon kc(1 + r)S^2 T \cos 2Y,$$

$$\phi_{22} = 2S^2 T \cos 2Y,$$

$$(\phi_{22})_y = 4kS^2 T \cos 2Y,$$

$$(\phi_{22})_x = -4kS^2 T \sin 2Y,$$

$$(\phi_{22})_{xx} = -8kS^2 T \cos 2Y,$$

$$(\phi_{22})_{xt} = 8kcS^2 T \cos 2Y.$$

Again, terms of $O(\varepsilon)$ in ϕ_{22} and its derivatives are omitted, because they ultimately produce terms of $O(a^3\varepsilon^2)$ in the crucial calculation for ε^2 in terms of a^2. Note the coefficient of ϕ_{22} in (62).

One now calculates η_2 from

$$\eta_{2t} = \phi_{2y} + \phi_{1yy}\eta_{1x} - \phi_{1x}\eta_{1x} = \phi_{2y} - (\phi_{1x}\eta_1)_x \tag{65}$$

which comes from (8). With the results for ϕ_{20}, ϕ_{21}, and ϕ_{22} given in the foregoing, (65) becomes

$$\eta_{2t} = -\frac{4k^2}{c}(\alpha_{21} + 1)S^2 \sin 2Y + \frac{2k\varepsilon}{c}\theta S^2 T \cos 2Y, \tag{66}$$

where

$$\theta = 2\alpha_{22} - 2\alpha_{21} - 6 + 2r. \tag{67}$$

The solution of (66) is, by successive approximation,

$$\eta_2 = -\frac{2k}{c^2}(\alpha_{21} + 1)S^2 \cos 2Y - \frac{\varepsilon}{c^2}\{\theta + 2(\alpha_{21} + 1)r\}S^2 T \sin 2Y. \tag{68}$$

For brevity, one will write this as

$$\eta_2 = \frac{2k}{c^2}\left(E_{21}S^2 \cos 2Y + \frac{\varepsilon}{k}E_{22}S^2 T \sin 2Y\right), \tag{69}$$

where

$$E_{21} = -(\alpha_{21} + 1), \qquad E_{22} = -\left(\frac{\theta}{2} + r(\alpha_{21} + 1)\right). \tag{70}$$

6. Calculation of terms containing a^3 as a factor. Consider now the terms that contain a^3 or $a^3\varepsilon$ as a factor in (19). Again, for clarity, it is desirable to consider these terms in each of the terms on the left-hand side of (19). The calculation will be more detailed for the first term of (19), to show how the detailed calculation is done. Once the way of calculation is illustrated, the presentation will be much briefer.

6.1. *Terms from* $g\phi_y$. Leaving the term ϕ_{3y} aside for the moment, the first term containing a^3 as a factor is

$$\phi_{2yy}\eta_1 = -\phi_{2xx}\eta_1,$$

since ϕ_2 does satisfy the Laplace equation. As can be readily verified, on $y = 0$,

$$\phi_{2xx} = \frac{8k^3}{c}\left\{\alpha_{21}S^2 \sin 2Y + \frac{\varepsilon}{k}(2\alpha_{21} - \alpha_{22})S^2 T \cos 2Y\right\},$$

so that

$$-\phi_{2xx}\eta_1 = \frac{8k^3}{c}[\alpha_{21}S^3(\cos Y - \cos 3Y)$$
$$+ \frac{\varepsilon}{k}S^3 T\{\alpha_{21}(1 - r)(\sin 3Y + \sin Y)$$
$$+ (2\alpha_{21} - \alpha_{22})(\sin 3Y - \sin Y)\}].$$

Of this, the terms involving $\sin Y$ or $\cos Y$ are

$$[[-\phi_{2xx}\eta_1]] = \frac{8k^3}{c}[\alpha_{21}S^3 \cos Y + \frac{\varepsilon}{k}\{\alpha_{22} - \alpha_{21}(1 + r)\}S^3 T \sin Y], \tag{71}$$

in which the double brackets on the left-hand side mean "terms containing $\sin Y$ or $\cos Y$ in the quantity indicated in the brackets." Equation (71) is tabulated in Table 1, for convenience. The other terms in (23), except ϕ_{3y}, are also entered in Table 1 after multiplication by g.

6.2. *Terms from* $(L\phi)_t$. One now considers the terms in the last parenthesis in (26). The method of calculation being illustrated in Sec. 6.1, one now merely records the results. In Table 2, the results for $L\phi$ are recorded.

In forming the sum in Table 2, the definition of θ by (67) has been used, so that

$$\alpha_{21}(2r + 1) + \frac{\theta}{2} = 2r\alpha_{21} + \alpha_{22} + 3r - 2.$$

$$\textbf{TABLE 1.}\ \text{Terms associated with}\ a^3\ \text{in}\ g\phi_y.$$

	$S^3 \cos Y$	$S^3 T \sin Y$
$g[[-\phi_{2xx}\eta_1]]$	$\dfrac{8k^3 g}{c^2}\alpha_{21}$	$\dfrac{8k^2 \varepsilon g}{c^2}\{\alpha_{22} - \alpha_{21}(1+r)\}$
$g[[-\phi_{1xx}\eta_2]]$	$\dfrac{-2k^3 g}{c^2}(\alpha_{21}+1)$	$-\dfrac{2k^2 \varepsilon g}{c^2}\left\{\dfrac{\alpha_{22}}{2} + (1+r)\alpha_{21} - 1 + 2r\right\}$
$\dfrac{g}{2}[[-\phi_{1yxx}\eta_1^2]]$	$\dfrac{k^3 g}{c^2}$	$-\dfrac{k^2 \varepsilon g}{c^2}(7+2r)$
Sum	$\dfrac{k^3 g}{c^2}(6\alpha_{21}-1)$	$\dfrac{k^2 \varepsilon g}{c^2}\{7\alpha_{22} - 10(1+r)\alpha_{21} - 5 - 6r\}$

$$\textbf{TABLE 2.}\ \text{Terms associated with}\ a^3\ \text{in}\ L\phi.$$

	$S^3 \sin Y$	$S^3 T \cos Y$
$[[\phi_{2ty}\eta_1]]$	$\dfrac{8k^3}{c}\alpha_{21}$	$\dfrac{4k^2 \varepsilon}{c}(4\alpha_{21}r - 2\alpha_{22})$
$[[\phi_{1ty}\eta_2]]$	$\dfrac{2k^3}{c}(\alpha_{21}+1)$	$-\dfrac{2k^2 \varepsilon}{c}\left\{(\alpha_{21}+1)(2r+1) + \dfrac{\theta}{2}\right\}$
$[[\phi_{1x}\phi_{2x} + \phi_{1y}\phi_{2y}]]$	$-\dfrac{8k^3}{c}\alpha_{21}$	$-\dfrac{2k^2 \varepsilon}{c}(4 - 4\alpha_{22})$
$\dfrac{1}{2}[[\phi_{1txx}\eta_1^2]]$	$\dfrac{3k^3}{c}$	$\dfrac{2k^2 \varepsilon}{c}\left(2 - \dfrac{r}{2}\right)$
$\dfrac{1}{2}[[(\phi_{1x}^2 + \phi_{1y}^2)_y\eta_1]]$	$-\dfrac{8k^3}{c}$	$-\dfrac{8k^2 \varepsilon}{c}(1 - r)$
Sum	$\dfrac{k^3}{c}(2\alpha_{21}-3)$	$\dfrac{2k^2 \varepsilon}{c}\left(6r\alpha_{21} - \alpha_{22} + \dfrac{1}{2}r - 4\right)$

One now has

$$
\begin{aligned}
[[(L\phi)_t]] &= \left[\frac{k^3}{c}(2\alpha_{21} - 3)S^3 \sin Y \right. \\
&\qquad \left. + \frac{2k^2 \varepsilon}{c}\left(6r\alpha_{21} - \alpha_{22} + \frac{1}{2}r - 4\right) S^3 T \cos Y\right]_t \\
&= -k^4(2\alpha_{21} - 3)S^3 \cos Y \\
&\qquad + k^3 \varepsilon(18r\alpha_{21} - 2\alpha_{22} - 8r - 8)S^3 T \sin Y \\
&= k^4\left[(3 - 2\alpha_{21})S^3 \cos Y \right. \\
&\qquad \left. + \frac{\varepsilon}{k}(18r\alpha_{21} - 2\alpha_{22} - 8r - 8)S^3 T \sin Y\right].
\end{aligned}
\tag{72}
$$

6.3. *Terms from* $\phi_x(L\phi)_x$. Results for these terms, shown in (27), are summarized in Table 3.

6.4. *Terms in* Q. The terms in Q defined by (20) which have a^3 as a factor are in Q_3 defined in (36). Again neglecting ϕ_3 for the moment, one computes the terms in the braces in (36). First, the terms within the first parenthesis in (36) are summarized in Table 4.

Let

$$
I = \left[\left[\phi_{1x}\eta_2 + \phi_{2x}\eta_1 + \frac{1}{2}\phi_{1yx}\eta_1^2\right]\right].
$$

TABLE 3. Terms associated with a^3 in $\phi_x(L\phi)_x$.

	$S^3 \cos Y$	$S^3 T \sin Y$
$[[\frac{1}{2}\phi_{1z}(\phi_{1x}^2 + \phi_{1y}^2)_x]]$	0	$8k^3\varepsilon$
$[[(\phi_{1x}\phi_{1xy})_t\eta_1]]$	$4k^4$	$-8k^3\varepsilon(2r+1)$
$[[(\phi_{1x}\phi_{2x})_t]]$	$4k^4\alpha_{21}$	$-4k^3\varepsilon(3r\alpha_{21} - \alpha_{22})$
$[[\phi_{1x}\phi_{1yt}\eta_{1x}]]$	$2k^4$	$8k^3\varepsilon(r-1)$
Sum	$k^4(6 + 4\alpha_{21})$	$-4k^3\varepsilon(2r + 2 + 3r\alpha_{21} - \alpha_{22})$

TABLE 4. Terms in the first parenthesis of (36).

	$S^3 \sin Y$	$S^3 T \cos Y$
$[[\phi_{1x}\eta_2]]$	$-\frac{2k^2}{c^2}(\alpha_{21} + 1)$	$\frac{2k\varepsilon}{c^2}\{(\alpha_{21} + 1)(1 + r) + \frac{\theta}{2}\}$
$[[\phi_{2x}\eta_1]]$	$-\frac{4k^2}{c^2}\alpha_{21}$	$\frac{4k\varepsilon}{c^2}(\alpha_{22} - \alpha_{21}r)$
$\frac{1}{2}[[\phi_{1yx}\eta_1^2]]$	$-\frac{3k^2}{c^2}$	$-\frac{k\varepsilon}{c^2}(4 - 2r)$
Sum	$-\frac{k^2}{c^2}(6\alpha_{21} + 5)$	$\frac{k\varepsilon}{c^2}\{4r - 2 + 2(1 - r)\alpha_{21} + 4\alpha_{22} + \theta\}$

Then

$$I_{xxx} = -\frac{k^5}{c^2}\left[-(6\alpha_{21} + 5)S^3 \cos Y\right.$$

$$+ \frac{\varepsilon}{k}\{3(6\alpha_{21} + 5)(-3S^2 T)(-\sin Y)\}$$

$$\left. + \frac{\varepsilon}{k}\{2(r - 1)\alpha_{21} - 4\alpha_{22} + 2 - 4r - \theta\}S^3 T \sin Y\right]$$

$$= \frac{k^5}{c^2}\left[(6\alpha_{21} + 5)S^3 \cos Y\right.$$

$$\left. - \frac{\varepsilon}{k}\{(52 + 2r)\alpha_{21} - 4\alpha_{22} + 47 + 4r - \theta\}S^3 T \sin Y\right].$$

Upon use of (67), this becomes, finally,

$$I_{xxx} = \frac{k^5}{c^2}\left[(6\alpha_{21} + 5)S^3 \cos Y - \frac{\varepsilon}{k}\{(54 + 2r)\alpha_{21} - 6\alpha_{22} + 53 - 6r\}S^3 T \sin Y\right],$$

and this is recorded in Table 5, where the other terms in $[[-Q_3]]$ are also recorded.

Summarizing the results in the last lines of Tables 1, 3, and 5, and in (72), one has the final Table 6.

In Table 6 c^2 can be identified with the c_0^2 defined in (11), which is

$$c_0^2 = \frac{g}{2}(1 + \beta),$$

where β is defined by (55). Then, with the help of (63) and (64), a straightforward calculation gives

$$S_1 = \frac{k^4}{(1 + \beta)(1 - 2\beta)}(8 + \beta + 2\beta^2). \tag{73}$$

There is no need to carry out S_2 in more detail for the purpose at hand.

$$\text{TABLE 5. Terms in } -Q_3.$$

	$S^3\cos Y$	$S^3 T\sin Y$
I_{xxx}	$\frac{k^5}{c^2}(6\alpha_{21}+5)$	$\frac{\varepsilon k^4}{c^2}\{(54+2r)\alpha_{21}-6\alpha_{22}+53-6r\}$
$\frac{1}{2}[[(\eta_{1x}^3)_{xt}]]$	$-\frac{3k^5}{c^2}$	$\frac{3\varepsilon k^4}{c^2}(5+2r)$
$[[-\phi_{1x}\eta_{2xxx}]]$	$-\frac{16k^5}{c^2}(\alpha_{21}+1)$	$\frac{8\varepsilon k^4}{c^2}\{(6-2r)\alpha_{21}-2\alpha_{22}+10-4r\}$
$[[-\phi_{2x}\eta_{1xxx}]]$	$\frac{4k^5}{c^2}\alpha_{21}$	$\frac{4\varepsilon k^4}{c^2}(-\alpha_{21}+\alpha_{22}+4-r)$
$[[-\phi_{1xy}\eta_1\eta_{1xxx}]]$	$-\frac{2k^5}{c^2}$	$-\frac{\varepsilon k^4}{c^2}(6-4r)$
Sum $=[[-Q_3]]$	$\frac{k^5}{c^2}(6\alpha_{21}+16)$	$-\frac{\varepsilon k^4}{c^2}\{(10+18r)\alpha_{21}+6\alpha_{22}-52+20r\}$

$$\text{TABLE 6. Summary of results associated with } a^3.$$

	$S^3\cos Y$	$S^3 T\sin Y$
$[[g\phi_y]]$	$\frac{k^3 g}{c^2}(6\alpha_{21}-1)$	$\frac{\varepsilon k^2 g}{c^2}\{-10(1+r)\alpha_{21}+7\alpha_{22}-5-6r\}$
$[[(L\phi)_t]]$	$k^4(-2\alpha_{21}+3)$	$\varepsilon k^3\{18r\alpha_{21}-2\alpha_{22}-8-8r\}$
$[[\phi_x(L\phi)_x]]$	$k^4(4\alpha_{21}+6)$	$-4\varepsilon k^3\{3r\alpha_{21}-4\alpha_{22}+2+2r\}$
$[[-\sigma Q]]$	$-\frac{\sigma k^5}{c^2}(6\alpha_{21}+16)$	$-\frac{\varepsilon\sigma k^4}{c^2}\{(10+18r)\alpha_{21}+6\alpha_{22}-52+20r\}$
Sum	S_1	S_2

7. Determination of ε^2 as a function of a^2. The third-order terms of the left-hand side of (19) that contains the factors $S^3\cos Y$ and $S^3 T\sin Y$ have now been determined to be

$$a^3 S_1 S^3\cos Y + a^3 S_2 S^3 T\sin Y, \tag{74}$$

and one is in a position to determine ε^2 in terms of a^2. For this purpose one returns to (42), which, after multiplication by a, gives the terms in (19) containing a as a factor, as can be seen from (37). It is then clear that (74) should be combined with the last two terms in (42), after (42) is multiplied by a. (See (12).) Collecting the terms containing the factor $S^3\cos Y$ in (74) and (42), after the factor a is added to it, one has

$$a\varepsilon^2(12\sigma k - 4c_g^2) + a^3 S_1 = 0. \tag{75}$$

In this one can set c_g^2 equal to $(c_g)_0^2$, committing discrepancies of higher orders to be taken care of in later approximations if necessary. Then, using (11), one obtains

$$\varepsilon^2 = \frac{a^2 k^5}{g}\frac{8+\beta+2\beta^2}{(1-6\beta-3\beta^2)(1-2\beta)}, \tag{76}$$

and

$$\varepsilon^2(c_g^2 - 3\sigma k) = \frac{a^2 k^4}{4}\frac{8+\beta+2\beta^2}{(1+\beta)(1-2\beta)}, \tag{77}$$

which can be used in (43) to calculate the variation of c^2 with a^2, to the present order of approximation. Since ε^2 must be positive, it is evident that the solution for wave groups considered here is restricted to those values of β that make it so in (76).

Collecting the terms containing the factor $S^3 T \sin Y$ in (42), after it has been multiplied by a, and in (74), one has

$$(-12 a \varepsilon^3 \sigma + a^3 S_2) S^3 T \sin Y. \tag{78}$$

The question immediately arises: Why is (78) not set equal to zero to determine ε^2? This question does not arise for pure gravity waves, since $\sigma = 0$ for that case. But it does now. And the two determinations of ε^2, from (77) and from (78), would not give the same results. The answer to this question is that the term (78) can be annihilated by the same procedure as in [1], whereas if an attempt is made to annihilate a term with the factor $S^3 \cos Y$ and the coefficient equal to the left-hand side of (75), one is obliged to add a term to ϕ that has the factor $S \cos Y$. In other words ϕ_1 would change its amplitude, and that amplitude is not to be tampered with. Therefore (75) is used to determine ε^2, and (78) is to be annihilated.

At this juncture it is prudent to check (77) and (78) against the corresponding results for pure gravity waves, by putting σ or β equal to zero in S_1 and S_2 in (74), and compare it with (60) of [1], which will be denoted by [1, (60)] for convenience. Doing so, one finds, upon putting c^2 equal to c_0^2,

$$S_1 = 8k^4, \qquad S_2 = -32 \varepsilon k^3. \tag{79}$$

The result for S_1 agrees with [1, (60)], but the number corresponding to 32 in (79) is 56 in [1, (60)]. Close examination of [1, (59)] shows that a factor of $\frac{1}{2}$ in [1, (58)] had been overlooked, and the number 48 in [1, (59)] should be 24. Correction of that error changes the number 56 in [1, (60)] to 32, in agreement with (79). The oversight has no effect whatever on the main results and all the conclusions of [1], but I take this opportunity to present the corrigenda for the errors that arose from that oversight. Apart from the corrections mentioned above, all the numbers divisible by 7 in [1, (64)] down to [1, (68)], as well as in [1, (77)] and the equation in [1] following [1, (77)], should be multiplied by $\frac{4}{7}$. In [1, (78)], 17 should be 11. Corrections for some unrelated misprints in [1] are: (a) In the last term of the line 6 from the bottom of p. 170 of [1], a plus sign should be added between ϕ_x^2 and ϕ_y^2. (b) In the last term of [1, (25)], g^2 should be c_g^2. (c) In [1, (37)], the factor a should be added after the first two equality signs, and $\varepsilon^3 a^3$ should be $\varepsilon^2 a^3$. (d) In [1, (63)], ε should be ε^2.

The annihilation of the term (78) is similar to the same process in [1]. It involves adding a term like Z in [1] to ϕ, and results in (51). Consequently (75) or (76) is not affected by this annihilation. The main results are then (76) and

$$k^2 c^2 = gk + \sigma k^3 + \varepsilon^2 (c_g^2 - 3\sigma k), \tag{80}$$

$$2k c c_g = g + 3\sigma k^2 - \sigma \varepsilon^2. \tag{81}$$

Equation (76) determines ε^2 to the order of approximation achieved in this paper.

Higher-order approximations will determine ε^2 as a power series in a^2. But (80) and (81) in terms of ε^2 will remain valid to any order of approximation.

As in [1], the terms of $O(a^3)$ in (19) containing $S^3 \cos 3Y$ or $S^3 T \sin 3Y$, as appear in the equation before (71) and in the calculation for Secs. 6.2, 6.3, and 6.4 though not recorded in those sections, can be annihilated without affecting (80) and (81). Indeed, higher approximations will leave (80) and (81) intact, although they will improve (76) and determine ε^2 as a power series of a^2. This is the reason why it is not necessary to determine ϕ_3 for the purposes of this paper.

8. Comparison with existing results. The results obtained in this paper can be compared with the results obtained by Ablowitz and Segur [2], which was referred to as AS in [1], and the results of Djordjević and Redekopp [3], referred to as DR in [1]. The abbreviations will continue to be used in this paper.

First, AS (p. 697, last two lines) noted that their results were equivalent to those of DR, except for the correction of a misprint. Examination of (AS 2.24d) also reveals a misprint: The factor $(2 - \sigma^2)$ in that equation should be $(3 - \sigma^2)$. However, that misprint was truly a mere misprint; the results on p. 698 of AS are correct. One then needs only compare the results of this paper with those of AS. For this purpose focus on (AS 3.4), in which, as AS said, b can be taken to be zero.

When ω_0/ω in the definition of λ in AS (equation for λ_∞ on p. 698 of AS) is equated to my $(1 + \beta)^{1/2}$,

$$\lambda = -\frac{1}{8}\frac{1 - 6\beta - 3\beta^2}{(1 + \beta)^{3/2}}, \tag{82}$$

where my β has replaced $\tilde{T}$ in AS. Furthermore (AS 3.4) also shows

$$|2\lambda/\nu|^{1/2}a = A_{\max}, \tag{83}$$

in which ν is the X_∞ on p. 698 of AS, and

$$\frac{2\lambda}{\nu} = -\frac{(1 - 6\beta - 3\beta^2)(1 - 2\beta)}{8 + \beta + 2\beta^2}. \tag{84}$$

The solution (AS 3.4) is valid only if $2\lambda/\nu$ is negative. This agrees with the requirement that the ε^2 in (76) be positive, and limits the possibility of having a gravity-capillary wave train to the β-values satisfying

$$0 \leq \beta < \frac{-3 + \sqrt{12}}{3} = 0.1547 \quad \text{or} \quad \beta > \frac{1}{2}. \tag{85}$$

When either of these inequalities is satisfied, my ϕ_1 has the same envelope as the AS solution (AS 3.4). This can be seen by noting the definition of ξ in (AS 2.22), and that the $a\varepsilon$ in AS corresponds to my ε. The former is, in AS notation entirely,

$$a\varepsilon = \frac{A_{\max}\varepsilon}{|2\lambda/\nu|^{1/2}} \tag{86}$$

and my ε is given by (76). Taking into account that the velocity scale used in AS is $(g/k)^{1/2}$ and the length scale is k^{-1}, and that their $A_{\max}\varepsilon$ is dimensionless and corresponds with my dimensional a, one has (the right-hand in my notation)

$$A_{\max}\varepsilon = \frac{ak^{3/2}}{g}. \tag{87}$$

Then, in view of (84), with $2\lambda/\nu$ negative, one sees that, apart from being dimensional, the $a\varepsilon$ in AS is exactly my ε given by (76), showing agreement of the form of the envelope of ϕ_1 with the envelope of A in (AS 3.4).

Now one looks at the variation of the phase velocity c with the amplitude. In the AS solution (AS 3.4), the last factor can be combined with the factor

$$\exp(i\theta) = \exp[i(kx - \omega t)] \tag{88}$$

in (AS 2.15a) to obtain, in view of the definition of τ in (AS 2.22),

$$c = \frac{\omega}{k}\left\{1 - \lambda a^2 \varepsilon^2 \frac{(gk)^{1/2}}{\omega}\right\}. \tag{89}$$

In (89), c is in my notation and the rest in AS notation, except one has equated k with κ in AS, because only two-dimensional waves are considered. Recalling (85), and hence that λ is negative, as is $2\lambda/\nu$, and using (84), (86), and (β and c_0 in my notation)

$$\frac{\omega}{k} = c_0, \qquad \frac{(gk)^{1/2}}{\omega} = (1 + \beta)^{-1/2},$$

one can write (89) as

$$c = c_0\left(1 + \frac{A_{\max}^2 \varepsilon^2}{8} \frac{8 + \beta + 2\beta^2}{(1 + \beta)^2(1 - 2\beta)}\right), \tag{90}$$

or, in view of (87),

$$c = c_0\left(1 + \frac{a^2 k^3}{8g} \frac{8 + \beta + 2\beta^2}{(1 + \beta)^2(1 - 2\beta)}\right), \tag{91}$$

now entirely in my notation.

On the other hand c is given by (80) in my analysis, and is

$$c = c_0\left\{1 + \frac{\varepsilon^2(c_g^2 - 3\sigma k)}{k^2 c_0^2}\right\}. \tag{92}$$

When $(c_g)_0$ is used for c_g, committing an error of $O(\varepsilon^4)$, this is, upon use of (11) and (77),

$$c = c_0\left(1 + \frac{a^2 k^3}{8g} \frac{8 + \beta + 2\beta^2}{(1 + \beta)^2(1 - 2\beta)}\right), \tag{93}$$

which agrees with (91) exactly. This agreement is remarkable in view of the vast difference between the approach of AS and mine, and in view of the tremendous amount of detailed calculation in their work and in mine. From (95), it can be seen that c increases or decreases with the amplitude accordingly as $\beta < \frac{1}{2}$ or $B > \frac{1}{2}$. The analysis is not valid in the neighborhood of $\beta = \frac{1}{2}$.

As to the group velocity, one first uses (11) to reduce (92) to the form

$$c = c_0 \left(1 + \frac{\varepsilon^2}{k^2}\frac{1 - 6\beta - 3\beta^2}{8(1 + \beta)^2}\right), \tag{94}$$

and then uses (94) in (81) to obtain

$$c_g = (c_g)_0 \left[1 - \frac{\varepsilon^2}{k^2}\left(\frac{1 - 6\beta - 3\beta^2}{8(1 + \beta)^2} + \frac{\beta}{1 + 3\beta}\right)\right]. \tag{95}$$

One emphasizes that (81) is good to any order of approximation. To $O(\varepsilon^2)$, one has (95). When the first inequality in (85) holds, c_g always *decreases* with the amplitude. Since the parenthesis containing β is equal to

$$\frac{(1 - \beta)(\beta^2 + 6\beta + 1)}{8(3\beta^3 + 7\beta^2 + 5\beta + 1)}, \tag{96}$$

it is clear that c_g decreases with ε^2 for

$$\frac{1}{2} < \beta < 1,$$

but increases with β when $\beta > 1$.

Since AS and DR did not go beyond the third order in the amplitude in their calculation, their approach has not produced any information on the variation of the group velocity with amplitude.

9. Interaction of gravity-capillary wave trains. Consider normal (that is, not oblique) interaction between two trains of gravity-capillary waves. The cases of interaction are: overtaking of one wave train by another, head-on collision of one wave train with another, and reflection of a wave train from a vertical wall normal to its path. The last case is a special case of head-on collision. By using the arguments in [1], one concludes that in all cases of normal interaction each of the two wave trains involved will regain its integrity after interaction, without even a shift of phase either in basic waves or in their envelope.

10. Conclusions. From the foregoing the following conclusions may be drawn:

a. A systematic approach has been devised to construct gravity-capillary wave trains to any degree of approximation.

b. Whenever comparison is possible, the results of this paper have been compared with the results of previous workers (AS and DR) who treated the same subject, and complete agreement has been found. The areas of comparison include the criterion of existence of gravity-capillary wave trains (when $0 \le \beta < 0.1547$ or $\beta > \frac{1}{2}$), the shape of the envelope, and the variation of the phase velocity of the basic waves with amplitude. The agreement is remarkable in view of the vast difference of my approach from theirs, and in view of the great amount of detailed calculation in my work and in theirs.

c. Two closed formulas, (80) and (81), give the variation of the phase velocity c of the basic waves and the group velocity c_g with the wavenumber ε of the envelope. The quantity ε^2 can be expressed as a power series in a^2 and determined by successive approximations.

d. Gravity-capillary wave trains exist for β-values satisfying

$$0 \le \beta < 0.1547 \quad \text{or} \quad \beta > \frac{1}{2}.$$

e. The phase velocity c of the basic waves increases with amplitude when $\beta < 0.1547$, but decreases with amplitude when $\beta > \frac{1}{2}$.

f. The group velocity c_g decreases with amplitude when

$$\beta < 0.1547 \quad \text{or} \quad \frac{1}{2} < \beta < 1,$$

but increases with amplitude when $\beta > 1$.

g. Previous investigators of gravity-capillary wave trains have carried their calculations to the third order of the amplitude, and therefore have not been able to produce any results on the variation of the group velocity with amplitude.

Acknowledgment. This work has been sponsored by the Fluid Dynamics Program of the Office of Naval Research under Contract N00014-87-C-0194. This sponsorship is very much appreciated.

REFERENCES

[1] Chia-Shun Yih, *Nonlinear gravity-wave groups*, Quart. Appl. Math. 47, 167–184 (1989)

[2] Mark J. Ablowitz and H. Segur, *On the evolution of packets of water waves*, J. Fluid Mech. 92, 691–715 (1979)

[3] V. D. Djordjević and Larry G. Redekopp, *On two dimensional packets of capillary-gravity waves*, J. Fluid Mech. 79, 703–714 (1977)

[4] Chia-Shun Yih, *A solitary group of two-dimensional deep-water waves*, Quart. Appl. Math. 45, 177–183 (1987)

Part D
Jets, Plumes and Diffusion

Temperature Distribution in a Steady, Laminar, Preheated Air Jet

By CHIA-SHUN YIH,[1] VANCOUVER, B. C., CANADA

This paper contains an exact closed solution for the temperature distribution in a preheated air jet when the flow is steady and laminar. Both the two-dimensional and the axially symmetrical cases have been treated. The solution is immediately applicable to other similar problems of diffusion.

INTRODUCTION

THE velocity distribution in a steady laminar air jet issuing from either a slit or a small hole in a plane wall was obtained in 1933 by Schlichting[2] who used the boundary-layer equations as the equations of motion. In 1937 Bickley[3] gave a closed solution for the axial-symmetry case. In the present paper the air issuing from the opening is supposed to have a temperature difference from the air surrounding the jet, and the resulting temperature distribution is sought. If the additional velocity induced by the nonuniformity of temperature distribution is small as compared with the velocity obtained for isothermal jets, it can be neglected and the velocity distribution can be assumed to be practically the same as obtained by Schlichting and Bickley. Under this assumption, the equation for temperature distribution can be solved easily.

It should be noted that the solution is directly applicable not only to precooled air jets but also to problems where some property other than heat is undergoing diffusion. For instance, if oxygen is being discharged through a small slit or a small hole into an open space filled with nitrogen, the concentration of oxygen at different points in the jet can be obtained directly from the corresponding solution by making the necessary changes of physical constants.

It may be remarked that although the true line or point source cannot be realized, the solutions are still valid at a distance sufficiently large as compared with the dimension of the opening.

TWO-DIMENSIONAL CASE

In a plane perpendicular to the slit, the trace of the slit is taken as the origin, the center line of the air jet the x-axis, and the trace of the wall as the y-axis. The velocities in the x- and y-directions are, respectively, denoted by u and v. Using ψ for the stream function, ν for the kinematic viscosity, ρ for the density, and $M = \int_{-\infty}^{\infty} \rho u^2 dy$ for the momentum flux per unit length of the slit, the Schlichting-Bickley solution of the system (with proper boundary conditions)

$$\left. \begin{aligned} u \frac{\partial u}{\partial x} + v \frac{\partial u}{\partial y} &= \nu \frac{\partial^2 u}{\partial y^2} \\ u = \frac{\partial \psi}{\partial y}, \quad v &= -\frac{\partial \psi}{\partial x} \end{aligned} \right\} \quad \ldots \ldots \ldots \ldots [1]$$

gives

$$u = \left(\frac{3M^2}{32\rho^2 \nu x} \right)^{1/3} \operatorname{sech}^2 \xi \ldots \ldots \ldots \ldots [2]$$

$$v = \left(\frac{M\nu}{6\rho x^2} \right)^{1/3} (2\xi \operatorname{sech}^2 \xi - \tanh \xi) \ldots \ldots \ldots [3]$$

where

$$\xi = \left(\frac{M}{48\rho\nu^2} \right)^{1/3} \frac{y}{x^{2/3}}$$

Denoting by T_0 the original temperature of the free space into which the heated air jet is discharged, by T the temperature at any point of the free space, and by θ the quantity $(T - T_0)/T_0$, the equation for temperature distribution can be written

$$u \frac{\partial \theta}{\partial x} + v \frac{\partial \theta}{\partial y} = \alpha \left(\frac{\partial^2 \theta}{\partial x^2} + \frac{\partial^2 \theta}{\partial y^2} \right) \ldots \ldots \ldots \ldots [4]$$

where $\alpha = k/(\rho c_v)$ is the thermometric conductivity, k being the thermal conductivity and c_v the specific heat at constant volume. Assuming, as in the case of velocity, that $\partial^2 \theta/\partial x^2$ is uniformly small as compared with $\partial^2 \theta/\partial y^2$ (the assumption being justifiable a posteriori) Equation [4] can be written

$$u \frac{\partial \theta}{\partial x} + v \frac{\partial \theta}{\partial y} = \alpha \frac{\partial^2 \theta}{\partial y^2} \ldots \ldots \ldots \ldots [5]$$

The flux of temperature difference per unit length of the slit with T_0 as the datum temperature, is defined to be

$$H = \int_{-\infty}^{\infty} u(T - T_0) dy = T_0 \int_{-\infty}^{\infty} u\theta dy \ldots \ldots \ldots [6]$$

which, in view of the steadiness of motion, must be independent of x. A dimensional analysis shows that θ must be a function of the three dimensionless quantities $H/(T_0\nu)$, $(\rho\nu^2)/(Mx)$, and ξ. In order that the right side of Equation [6] can be reduced to H, it is readily seen that θ must be of the following functional form

$$\theta = \left(\frac{H}{T_0\nu} \right) \left(\frac{\rho\nu^2}{Mx} \right)^{1/3} t(\xi) \ldots \ldots \ldots \ldots [7]$$

where the function $t(\xi)$ is to be determined from Equation [5].

Substitution of Equations [2], [3], and [7] in [5] gives, after simplification

$$-2\sigma[t(\xi) \operatorname{sech}^2 \xi + t'(\xi) \tanh \xi] = t''(\xi) \ldots \ldots [8]$$

where $\sigma = \nu/\alpha$ is the Prandtl number. As $t'(0) = 0$, integration of Equation [8] gives

[1] Department of Mathematics, University of British Columbia.

[2] "Laminare Strahlensbreitung," by H. Schlichting, *Zeitschrift der Angewandte Mathematik und Mechanik*, vol. 13, 1933, pp. 260–263.

[3] "The Plane Jet," by W. G. Bickley, *Philosophical Magazine*, series 7, vol. 23, 1937, pp. 727–731. The foregoing papers are available in condensed form in S. Goldstein's "Modern Developments in Fluid Dynamics," Great Britain Aeronautical Research Committee, Oxford, England, vol. 1, 1938, pp. 145–148.

Presented at the National Conference of the Applied Mechanics Division, Purdue University, Lafayette, Ind., June 22–24, 1950, of THE AMERICAN SOCIETY OF MECHANICAL ENGINEERS.

Discussion of this paper should be addressed to the Secretary, ASME, 29 West 39th Street, New York, N. Y., and will be accepted until January 10, 1951, for publication at a later date. Discussion received after the closing date will be returned.

NOTE: Statements and opinions advanced in papers are to be understood as individual expressions of their authors and not those of the Society. Manuscript received by the Applied Mechanics Division July 25, 1949. Paper No. 50—APM-5.

$$t'(\xi) = -2\sigma t(\xi) \tanh \xi$$

A second integration then yields

$$t(\xi) = C \operatorname{sech}^{2\sigma}\xi \dots\dots\dots\dots\dots [9]$$

where C is to be determined from Equation [6]. Substitution of Equations [9] and [7] in [6] gives

$$C = \frac{1}{(36)^{1/2} \int_0^\infty \operatorname{sech}^{2+2\sigma}\xi d\xi} \dots\dots\dots [10]$$

Equation [7] then becomes

$$\theta = \frac{CH}{T_0}\left(\frac{\rho}{M\nu x}\right)^{1/2} \operatorname{sech}^{2\sigma}\xi$$

or

$$T - T_0 = CH\left(\frac{\rho}{M\nu x}\right)^{1/2} \operatorname{sech}^{2\sigma}\xi \dots\dots\dots [11]$$

where C is given by Equation [10]. For $\sigma = 1$, $C = 0.455$. For air under normal conditions $\sigma = 0.733$, and by numerical integration $C = 0.421$.

It may be noted that when $\sigma = 1$, the solution for θ is of exactly the same functional form with respect to ξ as that for u, as it should be, since Equations [5] and the first of Equations [1] are exactly the same for $\nu = \alpha$. From Equation [11] the use of the boundary-layer Equation [5] can be justified a posteriori.

Axially Symmetrical Case

In a plane containing the center line of the jet, the opening is taken as the origin and the center line of the jet as the x-axis from which r is measured in a radial direction. The longitudinal and radial velocities are denoted by u and v, respectively. Using ψ now for Stokes' stream function, Schlichting's solution of the system (with proper boundary conditions)

$$\left.\begin{array}{l} u\dfrac{\partial u}{\partial x} + v\dfrac{\partial u}{\partial r} = \dfrac{\nu}{r}\dfrac{\partial}{\partial r}\left(r\dfrac{\partial u}{\partial r}\right) \\[2mm] u = \dfrac{1}{r}\dfrac{\partial \psi}{\partial r}, \quad v = -\dfrac{1}{r}\dfrac{\partial \psi}{\partial x} \end{array}\right\} \dots\dots\dots [12]$$

gives

$$u = \frac{3}{8\pi}\frac{M}{\rho\nu x}\frac{1}{\left(1 + \dfrac{1}{4}\eta^2\right)^2} \dots\dots\dots [13]$$

$$v = \frac{1}{4}\left(\frac{3M}{\pi\rho}\right)^{1/2}\frac{1}{x}\frac{\eta\left(1 - \dfrac{1}{4}\eta^2\right)}{\left(1 + \dfrac{1}{4}\eta^2\right)^2} \dots\dots\dots [14]$$

where

$$\eta = \frac{1}{4}\left(\frac{3M}{\pi\rho\nu^2}\right)^{1/2}\frac{r}{x}$$

M now being the total momentum flux and is equal to $\int_0^\infty 2\pi r\rho u^2 dr$. Retaining the meanings of T_0, α, and θ, and under the assumption that $\partial^2\theta/\partial x^2$ is uniformly small as compared with

$$\frac{1}{r}\frac{\partial}{\partial r}\left(r\frac{\partial\theta}{\partial r}\right)$$

the equation for temperature distribution can be written as

$$u\frac{\partial\theta}{\partial x} + v\frac{\partial\theta}{\partial r} = \frac{\alpha}{r}\frac{\partial}{\partial r}\left(r\frac{\partial\theta}{\partial r}\right) \dots\dots\dots [15]$$

The total flux of temperature difference, with T_0 as the datum temperature, is defined to be

$$H = \int_0^\infty 2\pi r u(T - T_0)dr = 2\pi T_0\int^\infty r u\theta dr \dots\dots [16]$$

which, in view of the steadiness of motion, must be independent of x. A dimensional analysis shows that θ must be a function of the three dimensionless quantities

$$\frac{H}{T_0\nu x}, \quad \frac{M}{\rho\nu^2}, \quad \text{and } \eta$$

In order that the right side of Equation [16] can be reduced to H, it is readily seen that θ must be of the following functional form

$$\theta = \frac{H}{T_0\nu x}t(\eta) \dots\dots\dots\dots\dots [17]$$

where the function $t(\eta)$ is to be determined from Equation [15].

Substitution of Equations [13], [14], and [17] in Equation [15] gives, after simplification

$$\frac{-2\eta t(\eta)}{\left(1 + \dfrac{1}{4}\eta^2\right)^2} - \frac{\eta^2 t'(\eta)}{1 + \dfrac{1}{4}\eta^2} = \frac{1}{\sigma}[t'(\eta) + \eta t''(\eta)]$$

which can be immediately integrated to

$$\frac{-\eta^2 t(\eta)}{1 + \dfrac{1}{4}\eta^2} = \frac{\eta t'(\eta)}{\sigma}$$

the constant integration being zero, since $t(\eta)$ and $t'(\eta)$ are both finite for $\eta = 0$. A second integration yields

$$t(\eta) = \frac{C}{\left(1 + \dfrac{1}{4}\eta^2\right)^{2\sigma}} \dots\dots\dots\dots [18]$$

By substitution of Equations [17] and [18] in [16], C can be readily determined to be $(1 + 2\sigma)/(8\pi)$. Equation [17] then becomes, by virtue of Equation [18]

$$\theta = \frac{1 + 2\sigma}{8\pi}\frac{H}{T_0\nu x}\frac{1}{\left(1 + \dfrac{1}{4}\eta^2\right)^{2\sigma}}$$

or

$$T - T_0 = \frac{1 + 2\sigma}{8\pi}\frac{H}{\nu x}\frac{1}{\left(1 + \dfrac{1}{4}\eta^2\right)^{2\sigma}} \dots\dots\dots [19]$$

It may be noted that when $\sigma = 1$, the solution for θ is of exactly the same functional form with respect to η as that for u, as it should be, since Equation [15] is exactly the same as the first of Equations [12] for $\nu = \alpha$. From Equation [19], the use of the boundary-layer Equation [15] can be justified a posteriori.

Conclusion

The temperature distributions of a two-dimensional and an axially symmetrical preheated air jet, when the flow is steady and laminar, are given in closed forms by Equations [11] and [19], respectively, where the symbols M and H have different meanings as defined in the foregoing for each case.

FREE CONVECTION DUE TO A POINT SOURCE OF HEAT

by Chia-Shun Yih

Associate Professor, Civil Engineering Department, Colorado Agricultural and Mechanical College

ABSTRACT

A point source of heat is considered to be situated in an infinite plane above which the atmosphere was originally isothermal and at rest, and the resulting steady temperature and velocity distribution are sought. As can be observed from the behavior of smoke from a burning cigarette, the flow caused by the heat source is laminar at first, then at some height above it becomes unstable, and the subsequent flow is turbulent. The interdependent distributions of temperature and velocity are obtained in the laminar zone by solving a pair of simultaneous differential equations, and in the turbulent zone by systematic experimentation guided by a dimensional analysis. The transition from laminar to turbulent flow is also investigated. The results are applicable to similar problems of diffusion.

THEORETICAL INVESTIGATION

IN the analysis of the present problem it has been assumed that the temperature variation should be, on the one hand, small enough for the physical properties of the fluid to be considered constant, and, on the other, large enough to permit the effect of dissipation and kinetic energy variation upon the temperature to be neglected. Under this assumption, denoting by T the absolute temperature and by γ the specific weight, it can readily be shown from the well known equation of state for perfect gases

$$\frac{p}{\gamma} = RT \tag{1}$$

that

$$\frac{\Delta T}{T_o} = \frac{-\Delta \gamma}{\gamma_o} \tag{2}$$

where $\Delta T = T - T_o$, $\Delta \gamma = \gamma - \gamma_o$, T_o is the original temperature, and γ_o is the corresponding specific weight.

In fact a linear relation between ΔT and $\Delta \gamma$ similar to Equation [2] can be obtained for any fluid for small variations in T. As will be seen later, the equations of motion and of heat diffusion are linear with respect to T or ΔT.

Therefore Equation [2] permits the use of $\Delta \gamma$ instead of ΔT as a dependent variable.

Taking the heat source as origin, and x and r as vertical and radial coordinates, the vertical velocity will be denoted by u and the radial velocity by v. As the convectional heat flux must be constant for all values of x from continuity and ΔT and $\Delta \gamma$ are connected by Equation [2], the quantity

$$G = -\int_o^\infty 2\pi r u \Delta \gamma \, dr \tag{3}$$

must be independent of x and is in fact a measure of the strength of the heat source. The dependent variables are $\Delta \gamma$, u and v, and the independent variables are G, ρ, μ, x and r, where ρ and μ are the mass density and the dynamic viscosity of the fluid, respectively. Since u and v are connected by the equation of continuity which will appear later, it is sufficient to study $\Delta \gamma$ and u. A dimensional analysis of the pertinent variables then yields the two following relations for the distributions of u and $\Delta \gamma$:

$$\frac{\rho x u^3}{G} \quad F_1 \left(\frac{\rho^2 x^2 G}{\mu^3}, \frac{r}{x} \right) \tag{4}$$

$$\frac{x^5 \Delta \gamma^3}{\rho G^2} = F_2 \left(\frac{\rho^2 x^2 G}{\mu^3}, \frac{r}{x} \right) \tag{5}$$

where $\dfrac{\rho^2 x^2 G}{\mu^3}$ is essentially the cube of Reynolds number, $\dfrac{\rho x u^3}{G}$ a differential Froude number, and $\dfrac{x^5 \Delta \gamma^3}{\rho G^2}$ its reciprocal. In laminar flow all three parameters in each of these relations will be significant. In trubulent flow, since the effect of molecular viscosity is small compared with the eddy viscosity, they may be simplified to

$$\frac{\rho x u^3}{G} = F_3 \left(\frac{r}{x} \right) \tag{6}$$

$$\frac{x^5 \Delta \gamma^3}{\rho G} = F_4 \left(\frac{r}{x} \right) \tag{7}$$

Reprinted from *Proc. First U. S. Congr. Appl. Mech.* (1951) 941–947.

whereby similarity between different horizontal sections is tacitly assumed.

An exhaustive study of stability should include the initial disturbance as an important variable. Assuming, in the present case, that no special care is taken to eliminate or to impart initial disturbances, the height h at which transition from the laminar to the turbulent zone occurs is a function only of ρ, μ, and G. The sole pertinent parameter for stability is thus seen to be $\dfrac{\rho^2 h^2 G}{\mu^3}$, and the only possible dimensionless equation is

$$\frac{\rho^2 h^2 G}{\mu^3} = \text{Constant} \qquad [8]$$

where indeed the stability parameter is essentially the cube of the critical Reynolds number. It must be remembered, however, that as the critical Reynolds number for stability of flow in pipes varies over a considerable range when the change is from laminar to turbulent, depending on the initial disturbances, so should the present stability parameter $\dfrac{\rho^2 h^2 G}{\mu^3}$ be expected to vary over at least a comparable range, since there is no reason for constancy of the initial disturbances.

In the following the laminar case and the turbulent case will be discussed in more detail.

(a) *Laminar case.*

Assuming the hydrostatic pressure of the atmosphere to be essentially undisturbed by the flow caused by the heat source and $\dfrac{\partial^2 u}{\partial x^2}$ and $\dfrac{\partial^2 T}{\partial x^2}$ to be negligible as compared respectively with $\dfrac{1}{r}\dfrac{\partial}{\partial r}\left(r\dfrac{\partial u}{\partial r}\right)$ and $\dfrac{1}{r}\dfrac{\partial}{\partial r}\left(r\dfrac{\partial T}{\partial r}\right)$, the equation of motion and the equation for heat diffusion can be written, respectively, as

$$u\frac{\partial u}{\partial x} + v\frac{\partial u}{\partial r} = \frac{\nu}{r}\frac{\partial}{\partial r}\left(r\frac{\partial u}{\partial r}\right) + g\left(\frac{T - T_o}{T_o}\right)$$

and

$$u\frac{\partial T}{\partial x} + v\frac{\partial T}{\partial r} = \frac{a}{r}\frac{\partial}{\partial r}\left(r\frac{\partial T}{\partial r}\right)$$

where $a = \dfrac{\kappa}{\rho c_p}$ is the thermal diffusivity, κ being the thermal conductivity, and c_p the specific heat at constant pressure. From Equation [2] the above equations can be written

$$u\frac{\partial u}{\partial x} + v\frac{\partial u}{\partial r} = \frac{\nu}{r}\frac{\partial}{\partial r}\left(r\frac{\partial u}{\partial r}\right) - g\frac{\Delta\gamma}{\gamma_o} \qquad [9]$$

$$u\frac{\partial \Delta\gamma}{\partial x} + v\frac{\partial \Delta\gamma}{\partial r} = \frac{a}{r}\frac{\partial}{\partial r}\left(r\frac{\partial \Delta\gamma}{\partial r}\right) \qquad [10]$$

Neglecting compressibility, the equation of continuity is

$$\frac{\partial}{\partial x}(ru) + \frac{\partial}{\partial r}(rv) = 0 \qquad [11]$$

Equations [9], [10], and [11] can then be solved simultaneously with the boundary conditions that

u, v, and $\Delta\gamma$ vanish at $r = \infty$

u and v vanish at $x = 0$ except at the origin

v, $\dfrac{\partial \Delta\gamma}{\partial r}$, and $\dfrac{\partial u}{\partial r}$ vanish at $r = 0$

Equation [11] is satisfied by the use of the Stokes' stream function ψ such that

$$u = \frac{1}{r}\frac{\partial \psi}{\partial r}, \quad v = -\frac{1}{r}\frac{\partial \psi}{\partial x} \qquad [12]$$

To convert the partial differential Equations [9] and [10] into ordinary ones, the following forms are found adequate:

$$\Delta\gamma = -\frac{G\rho}{x\mu}\,\theta(\eta) \qquad [13]$$

$$\psi = 4\nu\, x\, f(\eta) \qquad [14]$$

where

$$\eta = \left(\frac{\rho^2 G}{\mu^3}\right)^{\frac{1}{4}} \frac{r}{x^{\frac{1}{2}}}$$

Equations [12] and [14] give;

$$u = 4\left(\frac{G}{\mu}\right)^{\frac{1}{2}} \frac{f'}{\eta} \qquad [15]$$

$$v = 2\left(\frac{\mu G}{\rho^2}\right)^{\frac{1}{4}} x^{-\frac{1}{2}} \left(f' - \frac{2f}{\eta}\right) \qquad [16]$$

where the primes denote differentiation with respect to η. Substitution of Equations [13], [15], and [16] into [9] and [10] gives the simultaneous differential equations

$$(1 - 4f)\frac{d}{d\eta}\left(\frac{f'}{\eta}\right) = f''' + \eta\theta \qquad [17]$$

$$f = -\frac{1}{4\sigma}\frac{\theta'}{\theta}\,\eta \qquad [18]$$

where $\sigma = \dfrac{\nu}{a}$ is the Prandtl number and has the value

736

0.73 for air under normal conditions. The boundary conditions, except the one that $v = 0$ when $x = 0$ which will be discussed later, are substituted by the following:

$$\theta(\infty) = \theta'(\infty) = 0$$

$$f(0) = f'(0) = \theta'(0) = 0 \qquad [19]$$

$$f(\infty) = \text{a finite number}$$

Still another boundary condition is furnished by Equation [3], which can be put in the following dimensionless form:

$$\int_0^\infty f' \, \theta \, d\eta = \frac{1}{8\pi} \qquad [20]$$

The differential system consisting of Equations [17], [18], [19] and [20] is difficult to solve for arbitrary values of σ. But when σ has the values 1 and 2, solutions in closed forms can be obtained.

When $\sigma = 1$ it may be assumed that

$$f(\eta) = B\left(1 - \frac{1}{1 + A\eta^2}\right) \qquad [21]$$

Substitution of Equation [21] into [18] and integration give:

$$\theta(\eta) = \frac{C}{(1 + A\eta^2)^{2B}} \qquad [22]$$

With these functional forms for f and θ, Equations [17], [18], and [19] are satisfied if $B = \frac{3}{2}$ and $C = 24A^2$. Equation [20] can then be integrated to yield $C = \frac{1}{3\pi}$ from which $A = \frac{1}{6\sqrt{2\pi}}$. With these values for A, B, and C, Equations [13] and [14] become, by virtue of Equations [21] and [22]

$$-\frac{\mu x \Delta\gamma}{G\rho} = \frac{1}{3\pi\left(1 + \frac{\eta^2}{6\sqrt{2}\pi}\right)^3} \qquad [23]$$

and

$$\psi = 6\nu x \frac{\eta^2}{6\sqrt{2}\pi + \eta^2} \qquad [24]$$

from which

$$\left(\frac{\mu}{G}\right)^{1/2} u = \frac{\sqrt{2}}{\sqrt{\pi}\left(1 + \frac{\eta^2}{6\sqrt{2}\pi}\right)^2} \qquad [25]$$

and

$$\left(\frac{\rho^2 x^2}{\mu G}\right)^{1/4} v = -\frac{6\eta^3}{\left(6\sqrt{2\pi} + \eta^2\right)^2} \qquad [26]$$

When $\sigma = 2$ it can be similarly shown that

$$f = 1 - \frac{1}{1 + \dfrac{\sqrt{5}}{8\sqrt{2\pi}}\,\eta^2}$$

and

$$\theta = \frac{5}{8\pi} \frac{1}{\left(1 + \dfrac{\sqrt{5}}{8\sqrt{2\pi}}\,\eta^2\right)^3}$$

and results similar to Equations [23] to [26] can be readily obtained.

For air which has a Prandtl number of 0.73 under normal conditions, the solution corresponding to $\sigma = 1$ can be used to give a close approximation. For $\sigma = 1$ the value of v at $x = 0$ can be shown to be $-\frac{6\nu}{r}$. This has a value of only 0.03 foot per second at $r = 0.05$ foot (ν being taken to be 0.00025 square foot per second for air) and varies inversely with r, so that the boundary condition $v = 0$ at $x = 0$ is approximately satisfied. This approximation will not introduce large errors if x is not extremely small. That the boundary-layer equations are valid can also be verified a posteriori from Equations [23] and [25].

The patterns of streamlines and isotherms in the laminar case are shown in Figs. 1 and 2, respectively. The parameters used are dimensionless.

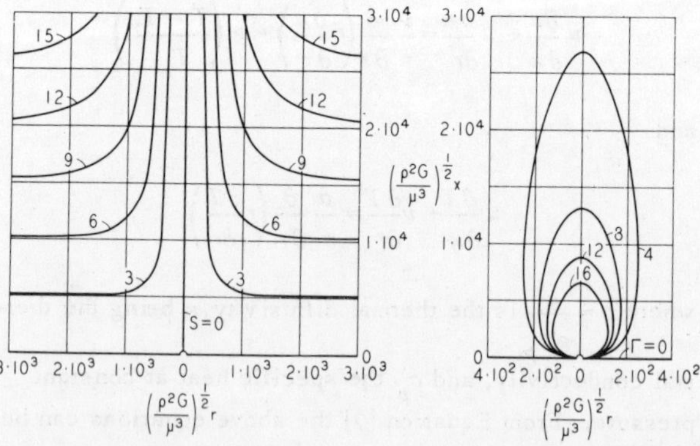

Fig. 1. DIMENSIONLESS PLOT FOR STREAMLINES. LAMINAR CASE. $S = 10^{-4}\left(\dfrac{\rho^4 G}{\mu^5}\right)^{1/2}\psi$

Fig. 2. DIMENSIONLESS PLOT FOR ISOTHERMS. LAMINAR CASE. $\Gamma = -10^6\left(\dfrac{\mu^5}{\rho^4 G^3}\right)^{1/2}\Delta\gamma$

(b) Turbulent case

The exact analysis of heat transfer in turbulent flow depends on an exact knowledge of the properties of turbulence pertaining to the specific problem studied, which no theory at present can predict and concerning which any future theory must be more or less descriptive. Therefore, any formal analysis of the turbulent case necessitates an assumption for the mixing length or some statistical property of the turbulence, the validity of which cannot be ascertained a priori. In view of this, and realizing that the chief purpose of the present investigation is to determine the macroscopic characteristics of free convection due to a point source of heat rather than to study the pertaining mechanism of turbulence, it is evident that an experimental determination ab initio of the functional relationships between the pertinent dimensionless parameters will be more direct and reliable. Writing Equations [6] and [7] in the modified forms

$$\left(\frac{\rho x}{G}\right)^{1/3} u = S_1\left(\frac{r}{x}\right) \qquad [27]$$

$$-\left(\frac{x^5}{\rho G^2}\right)^{1/3} \Delta\gamma = S_2\left(\frac{r}{x}\right) \qquad [28]$$

there is obtained then a guide for experimentation with which relatively few systematic experiments should suffice to show the validity of the basic assumptions and to yield the desired functional relationships.

From Equation [27], the stream function is

$$\psi = \int_o^r r u\, dr = \int_o^r \left(\frac{G}{\rho}\right)^{1/3} r\, x^{-1/3} S_1\left(\frac{r}{x}\right) dr = \left(\frac{G x^5}{\rho}\right)^{1/3} S_3\left(\frac{r}{x}\right)$$

or

$$\left(\frac{\rho}{G x^5}\right)^{1/3} \psi = S_3\left(\frac{r}{x}\right)$$

When $S_1\left(\frac{r}{x}\right)$ is known, $S_3\left(\frac{r}{x}\right)$ may be found by integration

and the discharge through a horizontal section at an elevation x is

$$Q = 2\pi\left(\frac{G x^5}{\rho}\right)^{1/3} S_3(\infty)$$

The momentum and energy fluxes can also be derived, as shall be done later. Knowing the stream function, v can be found from the equation

$$v = -\frac{1}{r}\frac{\partial\psi}{\partial x}$$

The principle of conservation of momentum requires that

$$\frac{d}{dx}\int_o^\infty 2\pi r \rho u^2\, dr = -\int_o^\infty 2\pi r \Delta\gamma\, dr \qquad [29]$$

Therefore $S_1\left(\frac{r}{x}\right)$ and $S_2\left(\frac{r}{x}\right)$ in Equations [27] and [28] should be such that Equation [29] is satisfied.

EXPERIMENTAL INVESTIGATION

The experiments were conducted in an air-tight room of considerable size with a ceiling high enough (11 feet) not to affect the region where the measurements were taken. At the center of the room the heat source, realized by a low flame, was placed at the same level as a low transite table 8 feet in diameter. Vertical guides and a horizontal traversing mechanism permitted measurements to be made over an elevation range of 6 feet in an axial plane. The measuring elements were remotely controlled to prevent disturbance of the flow.

The low flame was supplied alternatively by two Bunsen burners of 1-inch and 3/16-inch diameters, respectively, which could be connected to a gas tank through a pressure regulator; the flame height could be controlled by a valve in the connecting tube. Temperature differences were measured with a copper-constantan thermocouple with its cold junction placed far away from the heat source, used in connection with a potentiometer which could be read to 0.002 millivolt. The quantity $\Delta\gamma$ could be calculated from the temperature measurement by Equation [2]. The data obtained could then be arranged according to Equations [27] and [28].

For longitudinal velocity measurement the hot-wire method was first tried. The attempt was not successful because, aside from complications due to the temperature distribution of the field, the hot-wire method suffered from both insensitivity and inaccuracy at the prevailing low velocities. Soap bubbles were also tried in connection with various photographic techniques, but as the motion of the bubbles relative to the surrounding air could neither be eliminated nor ascertained, the idea had to be abandoned. Finally a properly calibrated midget anemometer was used which had a lower measurable limit of about 0.2 foot per second and an effective diameter of about 1 5/16 inches, and was adequate for velocity measurement when the convection region was fairly well spread out. After $\Delta\gamma$ and u had been measured, G could be computed from Equation [3]. Measurements in the turbulent zone were carried out over a range from $3(10)^{-4}$ to $40(10)^{-4}$ pounds per second for G and one from 3.3 to 6.0 feet for x.

To determine the stability parameter $\dfrac{\rho^2 b^2 G}{\mu^3}$, b was indicated by the breaking point of the smoke of a cigarette placed near the heat source, and G could be obtained by adding the G of the heat source, obtained by making one temperature measurement in the turbulent zone and computing from the plot of $-\left(\dfrac{x^5}{\rho G^2}\right)^{1/3} \Delta\gamma$, to that of the cigarette, obtained by careful calorimetry and observation of the burning rate.

Although no special steps had been taken to eliminate initial disturbances, considerable time had been allowed for the air to calm down before b was measured. When b varied over a range, only the highest value had been recorded. Thus the b measured was not the lower limit of the stability height. In fact, from the smoothness of the streamlines (visualized by the smoke) indicating small initial disturbances, the h measured should be near the higher limit.

Due to the fact that the midget anemometer was too large and not sensitive enough for velocity measurement in the laminar zone, only the temperature distribution was measured in the laminar case. The G of the heat source was obtained in the same way as in the investigation of stability, and the data could be arranged according to Equation [13].

DISCUSSION OF RESULTS

In the laminar zone, owing to the finite diameter of the flame, the variations of the density and dynamic viscosity of the fluid, and the extreme concentration and unsteadiness of the convection current, the experimental data obtained are too inaccurate to indicate more than the correct order of magnitude

Measurements of h and G in the determination of the stability parameter showed that

$$\frac{\rho^2 h^2 G}{\mu^3} = 9.10^9$$

the small variation of $h^2 G$ for constant μ and ρ being illustrated by Fig. 3. From the smoothness of the streamlines indicated by the smoke, the effect of the natural initial disturbances was seen to be uniformly small throughout the range of experiments.

After measurements of velocity and temperature for

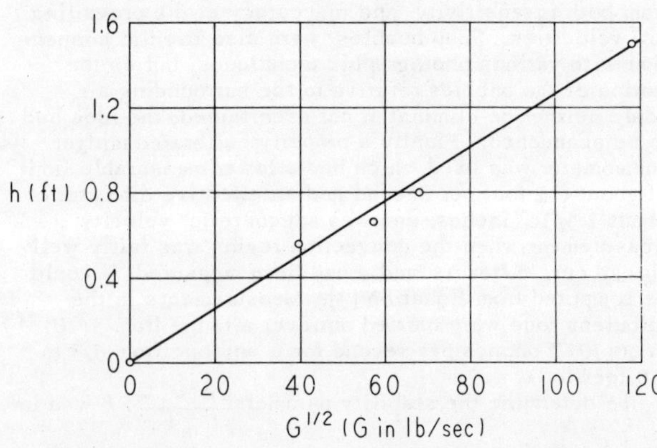

Fig. 3. VARIATION OF THE STABILITY HEIGHT h WITH G.

different values of x and G were taken in the turbulent zone, quantities $\left(\dfrac{\rho x}{G}\right)^{\!1/3} u$ and $-\left(\dfrac{x^5}{\rho G^2}\right)^{\!1/3}\Delta\gamma$, where G was obtained by integration, were plotted against $\dfrac{r}{x}$, according to the dimensional analysis. The temperature distribution is shown in Fig. 4 and is seen to follow closely the graph of the empirical formula

$$-\left(\frac{x^5}{\rho G^2}\right)^{1/3}\Delta\gamma = 11.0\, e^{-\frac{1}{2}\left(\frac{r}{0.084\,x}\right)^2} \qquad [30]$$

and the velocity distribution shown in Fig. 5 is seen to follow closely the graph of the empirical formula

$$\left(\frac{\rho x}{G}\right)^{1/3} u = 4.7\, e^{-\frac{1}{2}\left(\frac{r}{0.072\,x}\right)^2} \qquad [31]$$

When Equations [30] and [31] are substituted in Equation [29], the left side has a value of $0.48\,(G^2\rho x)^{1/3}$ and the right side has a value of $0.49\,(G^2\rho x)^{1/3}$, indicating close agreements between the experimental results and the requirements of the momentum equation.

From Equation [31] the stream function is found from integration to be

$$\psi = 0.0244\left(\frac{G x^5}{\rho}\right)^{1/3}\left[1 - e^{-\frac{1}{2}\left(\frac{r}{0.072\,x}\right)^2}\right] \qquad [32]$$

from which the radial velocity is found to be

$$v = -\frac{1}{r}\frac{\partial\psi}{\partial x}$$

$$= \frac{-0.0244}{r}\left(\frac{G x^2}{\rho}\right)^{1/3}\left\{\frac{5}{3} - e^{-\frac{1}{2}\left(\frac{r}{0.072\,x}\right)^2}\left[\frac{5}{3}+\left(\frac{r}{0.072\,x}\right)^2\right]\right\} \qquad [33]$$

The discharge through a horizontal section is

$$Q = 2\pi\,(0.0244)\left(\frac{G x^5}{\rho}\right)^{1/3} = 0.153\left(\frac{G x^5}{\rho}\right)^{1/3} \qquad [34]$$

The momentum flux is

$$M = 0.36\,(G^2\rho)^{1/3}\, x^{4/3} \qquad [35]$$

and the energy flux is

$$E = \frac{1}{2}\int_0^\infty 2\pi\,r\,\rho\,u^3\,dr = 0.566\,G x \qquad [36]$$

when the radial velocity component v is neglected.

The patterns of the streamlines and isotherms in the turbulent case are shown in Fig. 6 and 7, respectively. In order to make the parameters dimensionless, a standard length is required. The only one that can be used is the stability height h. But h, as can be seen from Equation [8], has the same dimension as $\left(\dfrac{\mu^3}{\rho^2 G}\right)^{1/2}$. This accounts for the appearance of μ in the dimensionless parameters used in Figs. 6 and 7.

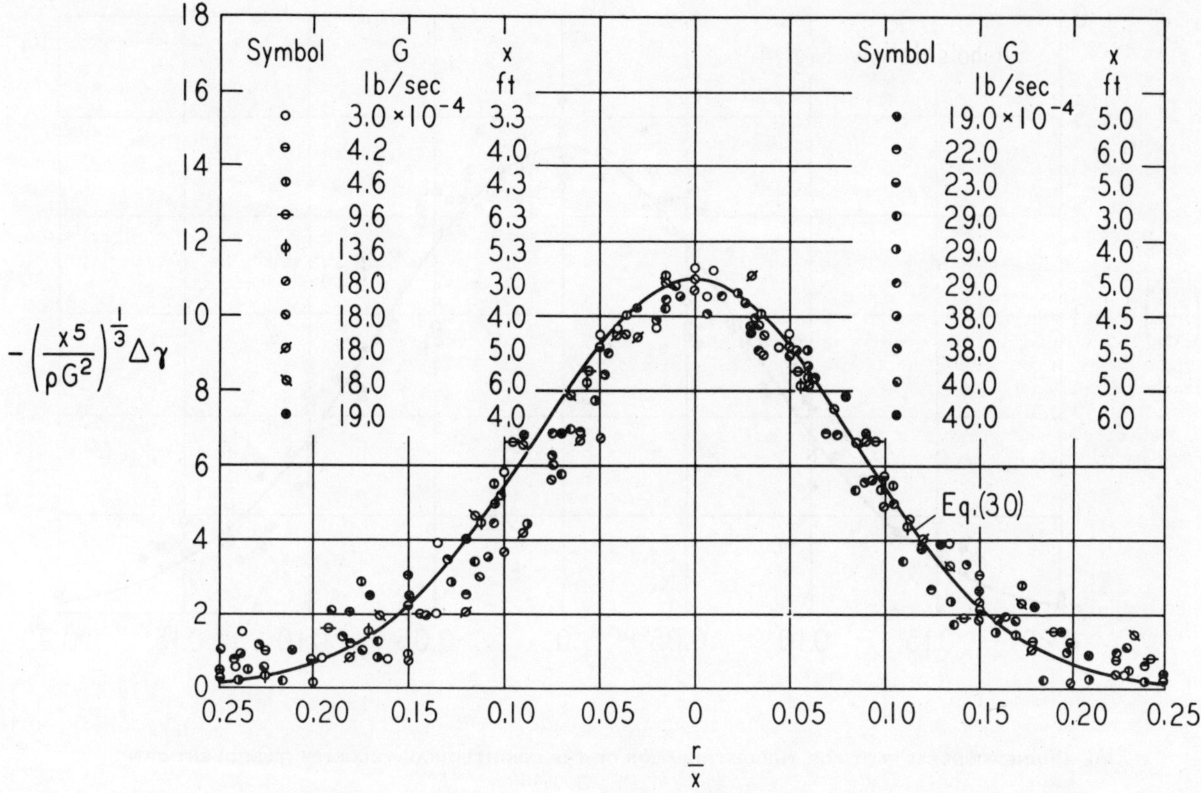

Fig. 4. DIMENSIONLESS PLOT FOR THE DISTRIBUTION OF $\Delta\gamma$. TURBULENT CASE.

It is adequate to mention in this discussion that the quantity G has been considered in the theoretical investigation to be due to the heat source alone, of which it is a measure. In the experiments, however, since a true point source of heat of sufficient strength to induce a perceptible convection cannot be realized, a flame, which has a finite dimension and is at once a heat source, a mass source, and a momentum source, has been used. It is believed that at the elevations where measurements were made, the effect of the finite dimension, the mass-source character, and the momentum-source character of the flame is negligible. Noteworthy is the fact that the flames used were all very low and did not have a large initial discharge or a large initial momentum.

CONCLUSION

If a point source of heat of constant strength is located in the horizontal boundary plane of a semi-infinite space originally isothermal and at rest, once the convection is established the rises in velocity and temperature at any point in the field will be functions of position, the strength of the source, the initial temperature, and the physical properties of the fluid. From the investigation it can be concluded that:

(1) In the laminar zone, Equations [23] to [26] obtained for $\sigma = 1$, furnish a close approximation. The patterns of the streamlines and isotherms are shown in Figs. 1 and 2 respectively.

(2) If no particular care is taken either to eliminate or to impart initial disturbances, the stability parameter will be approximately

$$\frac{\rho^2 h^2 G}{\mu^3} = 9.10^9$$

where h is the greatest height at which instability occurs in still air. The constancy of $h^2 G$ for essentially constant ρ and μ is shown in Fig. 3.

(3) In the turbulent zone, information is furnished by Equations [30] to [36]. The patterns of the streamlines and isotherms are shown in Figs. 6 and 7 respectively.

As in the experiments the heat source was realized by a flame which was also a mass source and a momentum source, the resulting convection was indeed not due to the heat source alone. The effect of the mass source and the momentum source, however, is believed to be negligible at sufficiently high elevations.

ACKNOWLEDGMENTS

This paper is based upon a thesis submitted by the writer to the Graduate College of the State University of Iowa in August, 1948, in partial fulfillment of the requirements for the Ph. D. degree. The experimental project was sponsored jointly by the Iowa Institute of Hydraulic Research and the Office of Naval Research under the supervision of Dr. Hunter Rouse.

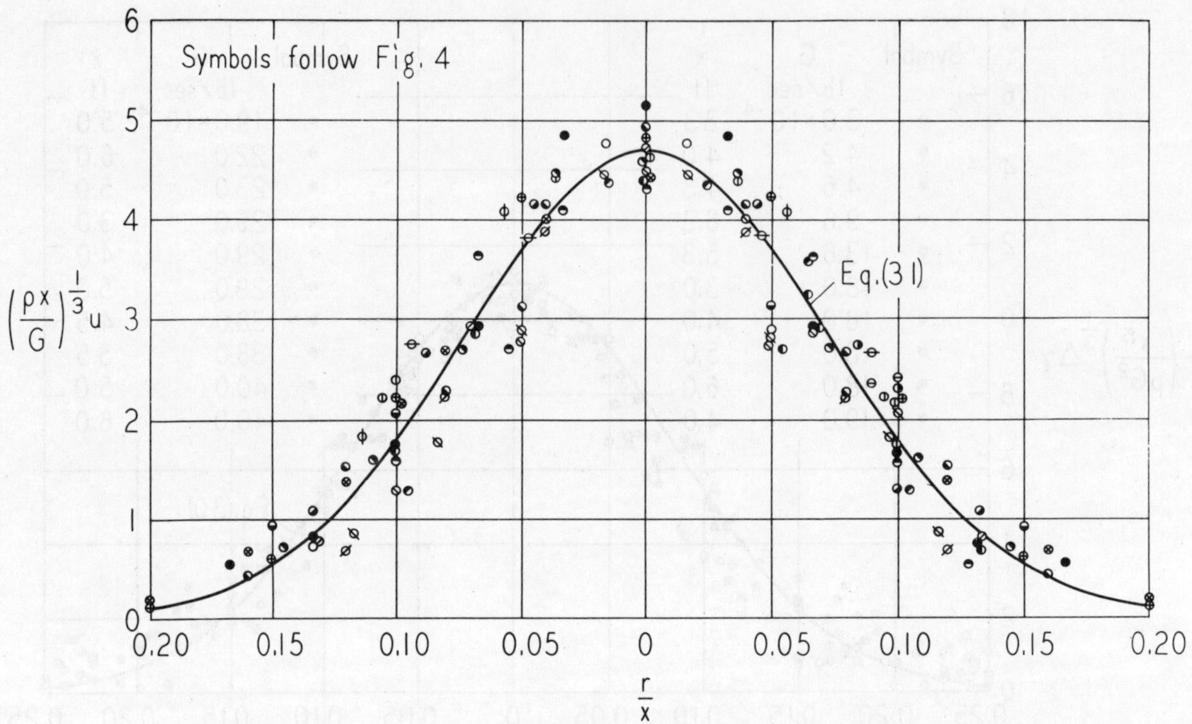

Fig. 5. DIMENSIONLESS PLOT FOR THE DISTRIBUTION OF THE LONGITUDINAL VELOCITY. TURBULENT CASE.

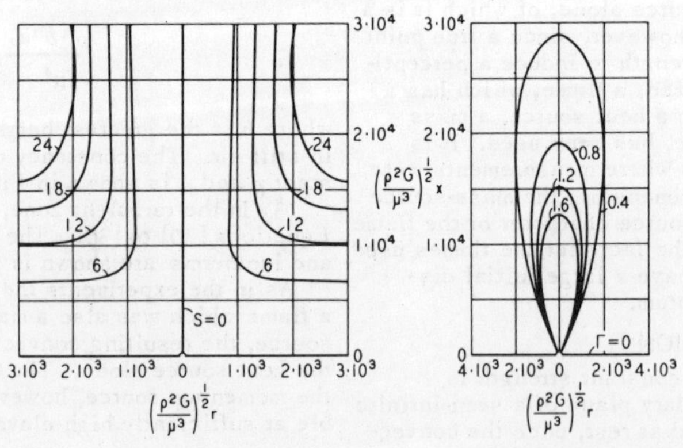

Fig. 6. DIMENSIONLESS PLOT FOR STREAMLINES. TURBULENT CASE.

$$S = 10^{-4} \left(\frac{\rho^4 G}{\mu^5}\right)^{\frac{1}{2}} \psi$$

Fig. 7. DIMENSIONLESS PLOT FOR ISOTHERMS. TURBULENT CASE.

$$\Gamma = -10^6 \left(\frac{\mu^5}{\rho^4 G^3}\right)^{\frac{1}{2}} \Delta \gamma$$

Transactions, American Geophysical Union   Volume 33, Number 1   February 1952

ON A DIFFERENTIAL EQUATION OF ATMOSPHERIC DIFFUSION

Chia-Shun Yih

Abstract--Exact closed solutions of the following equation of diffusion
$$y^m (\partial c/\partial x) = D \partial (y^n \partial c/\partial y)/\partial y$$
where m and n are considered to be independent, are obtained for the following cases:
(1) diffusion from a line-source embedded in a smooth surface; (2) diffusion from a
smooth surface; (3) vapor concentration in the wake of an evaporating surface. The
solutions for Cases (1) and (2) belong to the similarity-solution category. Dimensional analysis has been used in the systematic search for such solutions in as concise a
manner as possible. The solution for Case (3) can be obtained from those for Cases
(1) and (2). Diffusion in Couette flow is given as an example.

Introduction--O. G. SUTTON [1934] developed a theory of atmospheric diffusion from a smooth
surface on the assumption that the distribution of the mean velocity is

$$u = u_1 (y/y_1)^m \dots\dots\dots\dots\dots\dots\dots\dots\dots\dots (1)$$

where y is the elevation above the ground, and u_1 corresponds to the particular elevation y_1. From
the power distribution of the velocity, Sutton was able to show that the exchange coefficient $A(y)$
follows the power law

$$A(y) = A_1 (y/y_1)^n \dots\dots\dots\dots\dots\dots\dots\dots\dots\dots (2)$$

where n = 1 - m, and where again A_1 corresponds to y_1. Sutton's equation of diffusion is then

$$y^m (\partial c/\partial x) = K \partial (y^{1-m} \partial c/\partial y)/\partial y \dots\dots\dots\dots\dots\dots (3)$$

where $K = A_1 y_1^{2m-1}/u_1$ and where c is the vapor concentration at any point, x being measured
downwind from the leading edge of the evaporation surface or from a line source embedded in the
smooth surface. Eq. (3) has been extensively treated by O. G. SUTTON [1934], W. G. L. SUTTON
[1943], and FROST [1946]. In the present paper m and n are considered to be independent, and
the solution of the generalized equation

$$y^m (\partial c/\partial x) = D \partial (y^n \partial c/\partial y)/\partial y \dots\dots\dots\dots\dots\dots (4)$$

where $D = A_1 y_1^{m-n}/u_1$ is given for each of the three cases cited in the abstract. Since m and n
are assumed to be independent, the validity of the solutions contained in the present paper, depends only on the adequacy of the power-function representations of u and $A(y)$, and not on the
validity of Sutton's theory.

As a special feature of the present investigation, dimensional considerations will be utilized
in searching for a similarity-solution (Ähnlichkeitslösung). These, in conjunction with considerations of the powers of x, A_1, u_1, and y_1, will afford in a systematic way the most adequate transformations to be made in Cases (1) and (2) such that the solutions will be the simplest.

Diffusion from a line source embedded in a smooth surface--Eq. (4) is to be solved with the
following boundary conditions:

(a) $\partial c/\partial y = 0$ at $y = 0$
(b) $c \to c_0$ as $y \to \infty$
(c) $c \to c_0$ as $x \to 0$ for $y > 0$

and with the continuity equation

(d) $\int_0^\infty u (c - c_0) \, dy = Q = constant$

where c_0 is the ambient vapor concentration, and Q is the strength of the line source per unit length. The first boundary condition stipulates that the ground is impervious to vapor. The pertinent variables are, in this case, the following: $c, c_0, Q, A_1, u_1, y_1, x, y$. A dimensional analysis yields the relationship

$$(c - c_0)/c_0 = F \ (Q/A_1 c_0, \ u_1 x/A_1, \ y_1/x, \ y/x)$$

where $u_1 x/A_1$ is a Reynolds number.

To obtain a similarity solution, assume

$$\psi = (c - c_0)/c_0 = (Q/A_1 c_0) \ (u_1 x/A_1)^p \ (y_1/x)^q \ f[(u_1 x/A_1)^r \ (y_1/x)^s \ y/x] \ldots\ldots\ldots (5)$$

where the exponents p, q, r, and s are to be determined, and where the function f is to be determined from the diffusion equation and the boundary conditions. The last equation is a special form of the general relationship resulting from the dimensional analysis, but has the most general form for a similarity solution. Significantly, the effect of y is felt only through the new variable in the bracket, while the effect of x is felt not only through that variable, but also through the two factors preceding the function f. Substituting (5) in (4) and demanding equal powers in A_1, y_1, u_1, and x, one obtains values of r and s as follows

$$r = 1/(m - n + 2) \qquad s = (n - m)/(m - n + 2)$$

which are independent of the values of p and q. The values of p and q are obtained from condition (d), the satisfaction of which requires that

$$p = (n - 1)/(m - n + 2) \qquad q = (n + m)/(m - n + 2)$$

Thus, a similarity solution is possible with the transformation

$$\psi = (Q/A_1 c_0) \ (A_1^{1-n} y_1^{n+m}/u_1^{1-n} x^{m+1})^{1/(m-n+2)} \ f[(u_1 y_1^{n-m}/A_1 x)^{1/(m-n+2)} y] \ldots\ldots (6)$$

Substituting (6) into (4), one obtains the dimensionless equation

$$- [(m + 1)/(m - n + 2)] \eta^m f - [1/(m - n + 2)] \eta^{m+1} f' = d \ (\eta^n f')/d\eta \ldots\ldots\ldots (7)$$

where the primes denote differentiation with respect to the new variable

$$\eta = (u_1 \ y_1^{n-m}/A_1 x)^{1/(m-n+2)} \ y \ldots\ldots\ldots\ldots\ldots\ldots (8)$$

The boundary conditions become

(a) $f \ (0) = 0$
(b) and (c) $f \ (\infty) = 0 \quad$ if $\quad m - n + 2 > 0$

and the continuity condition becomes

$$(d) \int_0^\infty \eta^m \ f d\eta = 1 \ldots\ldots\ldots\ldots\ldots\ldots\ldots\ldots\ldots\ldots\ldots\ldots\ldots (9)$$

A first integration of (7) yields

$$- [1/(m - n + 2)] \ \eta^{m+1} f = \eta^n f'$$

the constant of integration being zero since both f and f' are finite at $\eta = 0$. A second integration gives

$$f = K \exp (- \eta^{(m-n+2)}/(m - n + 2)^2) \ldots\ldots\ldots\ldots\ldots (10)$$

where K is determined from (9) and is given by

$$K^{-1} = \int_0^\infty \eta^m \exp [- \eta^{m-n+2}/(m-n+2)^2] \ d\eta = (m-n+2)^{(m+n)/(m-n+2)} \ \Gamma[(m+1)/(m-n+2)] \ldots (11)$$

This integral is convergent since $m > 0$. Eq. (6), (10), and (11) then constitute the solution.

<u>Diffusion from a smooth surface</u>--Denoting by c_S the saturated vapor concentration at the evaporation surface, (4) is in this case to be solved with the following boundary conditions:

(a) $c = c_S$ at $y = 0$
(b) $c = c_O$ at $y = \infty$
(c) $c = c_O$ at $x = 0$ for $y > 0$

In this case the parameter containing the unknown c is

$$\theta = (c_S - c)/(c_S - c_O) \quad\dots\dots\dots\dots\dots\dots\dots\dots\dots (12)$$

and the parameter $Q/(A_1 c_O)$ is eliminated from consideration. Since the vapor flux is no longer constant, the integral condition (d) of the last section no longer exists. Hence, the values of p and q, which are determined by that condition, shall now be chosen to satisfy the boundary conditions listed above. Since condition (b) requires that $\theta = 1$ at $y = \infty$ irrespective of the values of A_1, y_1, u_1, and x, the values of p and q must both be zero.

Substituting therefore

$$\theta = h(\eta) \quad\dots\dots\dots\dots\dots\dots\dots\dots\dots\dots (13)$$

into (4) where c can be replaced by θ, one has

$$- \eta^{m+1} h'/(m - n + 2) = \eta^n h'' + n \eta^{n-1} h' \quad\dots\dots\dots\dots (14)$$

where the primes denote differentiation with respect to η which is defined by (8). The boundary conditions are now

(a) $h(0) = 0$
(b) and (c) $h(\infty) = 1$ if $m - n + 2 > 0$

Eq. (14) may be written

$$- \eta^{m-n+1}/(m - n + 2) - n/\eta = h''/h'$$

a first integration of which gives

$$h' = B \eta^{-n} \exp\left[- \eta^{m-n+2}/(m - n + 2)^2\right] \quad\dots\dots\dots\dots\dots (15)$$

A second integration yields the solution

$$h = B \int_0^\eta \eta^{-n} \exp\left[- \eta^{m-n+2}/(m - n + 2)^2\right] d\eta$$
$$= B \, \Gamma\left[(-n + 1)/(m - n + 2), \eta^{m-n+2}/(m - n + 2)^2\right] (m - n + 2)^{(-m-n)/(m-n+2)} \quad\dots\dots (16)$$

where $\Gamma(a,y) = \int_0^y x^{a-1} e^{-x} dx$ is the incomplete gamma function and where B is determined by $h(\infty) = 1$ and is given by

$$B^{-1} = \int_0^\infty \eta^{-n} \exp\left[- \eta^{m-n+2}/(m - n + 2)^2\right] d\eta$$
$$= \Gamma\left[(-n + 1)/(m - n + 2)\right] (m - n + 2)^{(-m-n)/(m-n+2)} \quad\dots\dots\dots\dots (17)$$

where $\Gamma(a) = \Gamma(a, \infty)$ is the gamma function. Eq. (12), (13), (16), and (17) then constitute the solution, so long as $n > 1$ so that the integrals in (16) and (17) exist. Eq. (16) may be written

$$h = \Gamma\left[(-n + 1)/(m - n + 2), \eta^{m-n+2}/(m - n + 2)^2\right]/\Gamma\left[(-n + 1)/(m - n + 2)\right] \quad\dots (16a)$$

<u>Vapor concentration in the wake of an evaporating surface</u>--The solution for this case can be obtained from the results of the last two sections by realizing that the evaporating surface can be considered as a collection of line sources the strengths of which are determined from the local rates of evaporation and that both the evaporation surface and the dry surface can then be considered as impervious to vapor.

The strength of the elemental line source at $x = \lambda$ is

$$(c_s - c_o)(A_1/y_1^n) \lim_{y \to 0} (y^n \, \partial h/\partial y) \, d\lambda = (c_s - c_o) \, G \lim_{\eta \to 0} (\eta^n h') \, d\lambda = (c_s - c_o) GB d\lambda \ldots (18)$$

where

$$G = (A_1^{m+1} u_1^{1-n}/\lambda^{1-n} y_1^{m+n}){}^{1/(m-n+2)}$$

Substituting the expression in (18) for Q in (6), one has

$$d\psi = d[(c-c_o)/c_o] = [(c_s-c_o)/c_o] B (1/\lambda^{1-n} (x-\lambda)^{m+1})^{1/(m-n+2)} f\left\{ [u_1 y_1^{n-m}/A_1 (x-\lambda)]^{1/(m-n+2)} y \right\} d\lambda \ . \ (19)$$

as the contribution of the elemental line-source to the value of $\psi = (c - c_o)/c_o$ at any value of x. If the evaporation surface has a downwind length b, then for $x > b$ one has, on integrating 19

$$(c - c_o)/(c_s - c_o) = B \int_0^b (1/\lambda^{1-n} (x - \lambda)^{m+1})^{1/m-n+2} f(\xi) \, d\lambda \ldots (20)$$

where

$$\xi = [u_1 y_1^{n-m}/A_1 (x - \lambda)]^{1/(m-n+2)} y \ldots (21)$$

and were f is given by (10).

<u>Diffusion in Couette flow</u>--As an example for the theory developed in the previous sections, one considers the diffusion in Couette flow. Here $m = 1$, $n = 0$, and $A = \alpha = $ constant, where α is the vapor diffusivity.

The solution for the case of a line source is, from (6), (8), (10), and (11)

$$(c - c_o)/c_o = (Q/\alpha c_o) (\alpha y_1/u_1 x^2)^{1/3} K \exp(-\eta^3/9)$$

$$= (Q/\alpha c_o) (\alpha y_1/u_1 x^2)^{1/3} \exp(-\eta^3/9)/3^{1/3} \, \Gamma(2/3) \ldots (22)$$

where

$$\eta = (u_1/y_1 \, \alpha x)^{1/3} y \ldots (23)$$

The solution for the evaporating surface is, from (12), (13), (16), and (17)

$$(c_s - c)/(c_s - c_o) = B \int_0^\eta e^{-\eta^3/9} \, d\eta = \Gamma(1/3, \eta^3/9)/\Gamma(1/3) \ldots (24)$$

where η is given by (23).

From (10), (17), (20), and (21), the vapor concentration in the wake of the evaporating surface of length b is

$$(c - c_o)/(c_s - c_o) = BK \int_0^b [1/\lambda(x - \lambda)^2]^{1/3} e^{-\xi^3/9} \, d\lambda$$

$$= [1/\Gamma(1/3) \Gamma(2/3)] \int_0^b [1/\lambda (x - \lambda)^2]^{1/3} e^{-\xi^3/9} \, d\lambda \ldots (25)$$

where

$$\xi = [u_1/y_1 \, \alpha (x - \lambda)]^{1/3} y \ldots (26)$$

It should be noted that since in this case $n = 0$, $A(0) = \alpha$ is different from zero and the singularity at $\eta = 0$ for h' in (15) does not exist, so that there is no objections to the theory based on physical considerations.

<u>Remarks</u>--It should be noted that along any generalized parabola

$$y = \beta x^{1/(m-n+2)}$$

12   **CHIA-SHUN YIH**   **[Trans. AGU, V. 33 - 1]**

the value for $(c_S - c)/(c_S - c_O)$ is the same for the case of diffusion from a smooth surface, and that on any two generalized parabolas of the above type the values of $(c - c_O)/c_O$ bear the same ratio for any value of x for the case of diffusion from a line source. These facts provide the reason why the related solutions are called similarity-solutions. The solution represented by (20), however, does not belong to the similarity-solution category.

Acknowledgment--This work has been done in connection with an ONR project (Contract No. N90nr-82401) in which the Civil Engineering Department of the Colorado Agricultural and Mechanical College is currently engaged.

References

FROST, R., Turbulence and diffusion in the lower atmosphere, Proc. R. Soc., v. A186, pp. 20-35, 1946.

SUTTON, O. G., Wind structure and evaporation in a turbulent atmosphere, Proc. R. Soc., v. A146, pp. 701-722, 1934.

SUTTON, W. G. L., On the equation of diffusion in a turbulent medium, Proc. R. Soc., v. A182, pp. 48-75, 1943.

Colorado Agricultural and Mechanical College,
     Fort Collins, Colorado

(Communicated manuscript received April 30, 1951;
open for formal discussion until July 1, 1952.)

Transactions, American Geophysical Union   Volume 33; Number 3   June 1952

SIMILARITY SOLUTION OF A SPECIALIZED DIFFUSION EQUATION

C. S. Yih

Abstract--The differential equation of diffusion when the wind velocity and the vertical and lateral diffusivities are power functions of height is

$$y^m \, \partial c/\partial x = D_1 \, \partial (y^n \, \partial c/\partial y)/\partial y + D_2 \, y^k \, \partial^2 c/\partial z^2$$

where x, y, and z are measured respectively in the down-wind, vertical, and cross-wind directions, and D_1 and D_2 are physical constants defined in the text. Exact solution of this equation for the case of a point source and for m = k is presented in this paper. In the systematic search for this solution, dimensional analysis has been utilized to the optimum advantage. Although the solution is restricted to the special case m = k, it shows the important characteristics of atmospheric diffusion from a point source.

Introduction--Two-dimensional diffusion, when the wind velocity and the vertical diffusivities are power functions of height, has been extensively treated by O. G. SUTTON [1934], W. G. L. SUTTON [1943], FROST [1946], CALDER [1949], and YIH [1952]. Three-dimensional diffusion where lateral diffusivity must be considered has been treated by DAVIS [1947, 1950], and by O. G. SUTTON [1947] in the case of a point source, on the assumption that the variation of the wind velocity with height may be neglected. Thus in comparison with the two-dimensional phenomenon, the three-dimensional one has apparently received insufficient attention.

This paper is concerned with the atmospheric diffusion from a point source when the wind velocity and the vertical and lateral diffusivities are power functions of height, the exponents (m, n, k in the following) being at first left completely free. A mathematical solution is found possible for the special case

$$m = k$$

The differential system--With the origin at the point source, and the directions of x, y, and z defined as in the abstract, if the variation of wind velocity u with y (vertical) is expressed by

$$u/u_1 = (y/y_1)^m \dotfill (1)$$

where u_1 is the wind velocity at y_1 and if the vertical and lateral diffusivities are respectively

$$A_v = A_1 \, (y/y_1)^n \dotfill (2)$$

$$A_\ell = A_2 \, (y/y_1)^k \dotfill (3)$$

where again A_1 and A_2 correspond to the height y_1, the equation of diffusion

$$u \, \partial c/\partial x = \partial(A_v \, \partial c/\partial y)/\partial y + \partial(A_\ell \, \partial c/\partial z)/\partial z \dotfill (4)$$

can be written as

$$y^m \, \partial c/\partial x = D_1 \partial(y^n \, \partial c/\partial y)/\partial y + D_2 \, y^k \, \partial^2 c/\partial z^2 \dotfill (5)$$

where c is the concentration of the quantity under diffusion and

$$D_1 = A_1 \, y_1^{m-n}/u_1 \qquad D_2 = A_2 \, y_1^{m-k}/u_1 \dotfill (6)$$

The differential equation (5) is to be solved with the following boundary conditions

$$
\begin{aligned}
&\text{(a) } \partial c/\partial y = 0 &&\text{at} &&y = 0 \\
&\text{(b) } \partial c/\partial z = 0 &&\text{at} &&z = 0 \\
&\text{(c) } c \to c_0 &&\text{as} &&y \to \infty \\
&\text{(d) } c \to c_0 &&\text{as} &&|z| \to \infty \\
&\text{(e) } c \to c_0 &&\text{as} &&x \to 0 \text{ for } y > 0 \\
&\text{(f) } c \to c_0 &&\text{as} &&x \to 0 \text{ for } z > 0
\end{aligned}
$$

and the integral continuity equation

$$(g) \int_{-\infty}^{\infty} \int_{0}^{\infty} u \, (c - c_0) \, dy \, dz = Q = \text{constant}$$

where c_0 is the ambient concentration, and Q is the strength of the point source. Condition (a) stipulates that the ground is impervious to the quantity under diffusion, and (b) follows from symmetry and can be replaced by the more general condition that c should be an even function with respect to z

The solution--To facilitate the systematic search for a similarity solution (Ähnlichkeits-lösung), a dimensional analysis will be performed first, which, in conjunction with considerations of the powers of x, A_1, A_2, u_1, and y_1, will afford the most adequate transformation to be made in order that the solution will be the simplest. The pertinent variables are

$$c, c_0, Q, A_1, A_2, u_1, y_1, x, y, z$$

A dimensional analysis yields the relationship

$$(c - c_0)/c_0 = F \ (Q/A_1 c_0 x, \ u_1 x/A_1, \ u_1 x/A_2, \ y_1/x, \ y/x, \ z/x) \ \dots\dots\dots \ (7)$$

To obtain a similarity solution, one makes the following substitution:

$$\phi = (c - c_0)/c_0 = (Q/A_1 c_0 x) \ (u_1 x/A_1)^{\alpha} \ (u_1 x/A_2)^{\beta} \ (y_1/x)^{\gamma} \ f \ (\eta, \zeta) \dots\dots \ (8)$$

where

$$\eta = (u_1 x/A_1)^{p} \ (y_1/x)^{q} \ y/x \ \dots\dots\dots\dots\dots\dots\dots \ (9)$$

$$\zeta = (u_1 x/A_2)^{r} \ (y_1/x)^{s} \ z/x \ \dots\dots\dots\dots\dots\dots\dots \ (10)$$

and where the exponents α, β, γ, p, q, r, and s are to be determined. Before proceeding further with the solution, it may be noticed here that the power of $Q/A_1 c_0 x$ is unity in consideration of condition (g), and that a pair of fixed values for η and ζ defines a space curve which is the intersection of two parabolic cylinders

$$y = K_1 \ x^{1+q-p} \ \dots\dots\dots\dots\dots\dots\dots\dots\dots \ (11)$$

$$z = K_2 \ x^{1+s-r} \ \dots\dots\dots\dots\dots\dots\dots\dots\dots \ (12)$$

The set of all the curves defined by (11) and (12) for various values of K_1 and K_2 will be dense in the three-dimensional space under consideration. On any two such curves, the values of ϕ will always bear the same ratio for any value of x. This is the reason why the solution having the form of (8) is called a similarity-solution.

One now proceeds to determine the exponents in (8), (9), and (10). Substituting (8) in (5) and requiring equal powers in u_1, y_1, and x and equal joint powers in A_1 and A_2 one has

$$p = 1/(m - n + 2) \qquad q = (n - m)/(m - n + 2) \dots\dots\dots\dots \ (13)$$

$$r = (k - n + 2)/2 \, (m - n + 2) \qquad s = (k - m)/(m - n + 2) \dots\dots\dots\dots \ (14)$$

so that

$$2p - q - 1 = 0 \dots\dots\dots\dots\dots\dots\dots\dots \ (15)$$

$$2r - s - 1 = 0 \dots\dots\dots\dots\dots\dots\dots\dots \ (16)$$

The exponents α, β, and γ are left undetermined by this procedure, and will be determined by condition (g) which gives, after (8) has been substituted into it

        C. S. YIH   [Trans. AGU, **V. 33 - 3**]

$$\alpha + \beta + 1 - p\,(m + 1) - r = 0$$
$$- m - q\,(m + 1) - s + \gamma = 0$$
$$-1 - \alpha + p\,(m + 1) = 0$$
$$- \beta + r = 0$$
$$(m + 1)\,(- p + q + 1) + (- r + s + 1) + \alpha + \beta - \gamma - 1 = 0$$

and

$$\int_{-\infty}^{\infty} \int_{0}^{\infty} \eta^m\, f\,(\eta, \zeta)\, d\eta\, d\zeta = 1 \quad \dots\dots\dots\dots\dots\dots\dots \quad (17)$$

The five equations given by condition (g) involving the unknown exponents α, β, γ are not independent, and are satisfied by

$$\beta = r \quad \dots\dots\dots\dots\dots\dots\dots\dots\dots \quad (18)$$

$$\alpha = p\,(m + 1) - 1 \quad \dots\dots\dots\dots\dots\dots\dots \quad (19)$$

$$\gamma = m + s + q\,(m + 1) \quad \dots\dots\dots\dots\dots\dots \quad (20)$$

so that

$$\alpha + \beta - \gamma - 1 = - \,[p\,(m + 1) + r] \quad \dots\dots\dots\dots\dots \quad (21)$$

With the exponents given in (13), (14), (18), (19), and (20) in terms of m, n, and k, substitution of (8) in (5) results in the following equation

$$(\alpha + \beta - \gamma - 1)\,f + (p - q - 1)\,\eta\,f_\eta + (r - s - 1)\,\zeta\,f_\zeta$$
$$= \eta^{n-m}\,f_{\eta\eta} + n\,\eta^{n-m-1}\,f_\eta + \sigma^{-1-2r}\,\eta^{k-m}\,f_{\zeta\zeta} \quad \dots\dots\dots\dots \quad (22)$$

where

$$\sigma = A_2/A_1$$

and where subscripts denote partial differentiations. In virtue of (15), (16), and (21), (22) can be written

$$- \,[p\,(m + 1) + r]\,f - p\,\eta\,f_\eta - r\,\zeta\,f_\zeta = \eta^{n-m}\,f_{\eta\eta} + n\,\eta^{n-m+1}\,f_\eta + \sigma^{-s}\,\eta^{k-m}\,f_{\zeta\zeta} \quad \dots \quad (23)$$

This is the differential equation that has to be solved in general. For the case m = k, make the transformation

$$\xi = \sigma^{s/2}\,\zeta \quad \dots\dots\dots\dots\dots\dots\dots\dots\dots \quad (24)$$

(23) can now be written.

$$- \,[p\,(m + 1) + r]\,f - p\,\eta\,f_\eta - r\,\xi\,f_\xi = \eta^{n-m}\,f_{\eta\eta} + n\,\eta^{n-m-1}\,f_\eta + f_{\xi\xi} \quad \dots\dots \quad (25)$$

(25) being in a form suitable for separation of variables, one assumes

$$f = Y\,(\eta)\, Z\,(\xi) \quad \dots\dots\dots\dots\dots\dots\dots\dots \quad (26)$$

Substitution into (25) gives

$$- \,[p\,(m + 1) + r] - p\,\eta\, Y'/Y - (\eta^{n-m}\, Y'' + n\,\eta^{\,n-m-1}\, Y')/Y = Z''/Z + r\,\xi\, Z'/Z = \lambda$$

which can be written into the two separate equations

$$[p\,(m + 1) + r + \lambda]\, Y + p\,\eta\, Y' + (\eta^{n-m}\, Y'' + n\,\eta^{n-m-1}\, Y') = 0 \quad \dots\dots\dots \quad (27)$$

$$Z'' + r\,\xi\, Z' - \lambda\, Z = 0 \quad \dots\dots\dots\dots\dots\dots\dots \quad (28)$$

where the primes denote ordinary differentiation, with respect to η for Y and with respect to ξ for Z. The boundary conditions for (27) are

$$\text{(h) } Y'(0) = 0$$
$$\text{(i) } Y(\infty) = 0$$

and those for (28) are

$$\text{(j) } Z'(0) = 0$$
$$\text{(k) } Z(\infty) = 0$$

One first considers the system (28), (j), and (k). A first integration gives

$$Z' + r\,\xi\,Z - (\lambda + r)\int_0^{\xi} Z\,d\xi = 0 \ldots\ldots\ldots\ldots\ldots\ldots (28a)$$

the lower limit being chosen equal to zero since $Z'(0) = 0$. As $\xi \to \infty$, one has $Z \to 0$, $Z' \to 0$, and

$$\int_0^{\infty} Z\,d\xi \neq 0 \ldots\ldots\ldots\ldots\ldots\ldots\ldots\ldots (29)$$

since otherwise the integral in (17) would vanish. On the other hand, $\int_0^{\infty} Z\,d\xi$ should be finite on account of (17). Consequently, if Z behaves as ξ^{-b} for large ξ, b must be larger than one so that $\xi Z \to 0$ as $\xi \to \infty$. If Z vanishes exponentially as $\xi \to \infty$, then also $\xi Z \to 0$ as $\xi \to \infty$. These are the only ways in which Z can vanish at infinity, and for each of these cases the first two terms of (28) vanish while the third one does not unless $\lambda = -\dot{r}$ on account of (29). The satisfaction of (28) and (k) therefore requires

$$\lambda = -r \ldots\ldots\ldots\ldots\ldots\ldots\ldots\ldots (30)$$

Thus there is only one single value for the parameter λ. With (30), integration of (28) gives

$$Z = K \exp(-r\,\xi^2/2) \ldots\ldots\ldots\ldots\ldots\ldots\ldots (31)$$

where K is an arbitrary constant to be determined by (17). Substituting (30) into (27) and multiplying throughout by η^m, one has

$$[(m+1)/(m-n+2)]\,\eta^m\,Y + [1/(m-n+2)]\,\eta^{m+1}\,Y' + (\eta^n\,Y'' + n\,\eta^{n-1}\,Y') = 0$$

a first integration of which gives

$$[1/(m-n+2)]\,\eta^{m+1}\,Y + \eta^n\,Y' = 0$$

the constant of integration being zero since $Y'(0) = 0$ and $Y(0)$ is finite. A second integration gives

$$Y = \exp\left[-\eta^{m-n+2}/(m-n+2)^2\right] \ldots\ldots\ldots\ldots\ldots\ldots (32)$$

the constant factor being absorbed in K of (31).

The constant K can be determined by (17) which can be written as

$$K\sigma^{-s/2}\int_{-\infty}^{\infty}\int_0^{\infty}\eta^m\exp\left[-\eta^{m-n+2}/(m-n+2)^2 - r\,\xi^2/2\right]d\eta\,d\xi = 1 \ldots\ldots (33)$$

Evaluation of (33) gives

$$\sigma^{-s/2}\,(2\pi/r)^{1/2}\int_0^{\infty}\eta^m\exp\left[-\eta/(m-n+2)^2\right]d\eta = 1$$

or

$$(m-n+2)^{1-2a}\,K\,\sigma^{-s/2}\,(2\pi/r)^{1/2}\,\Gamma(a) = 1$$

which gives

                         C. S. YIH   [Trans. AGU, V. 33 - 3]

$$K = \sigma^{s/2} (r/2\pi)^{1/2} (m - n + 2)^{2a-1} / \Gamma(a) \quad \dots\dots\dots\dots\dots \quad (34)$$

where

$$a = (m + 1)/(m - n + 2) \quad \dots\dots\dots\dots\dots\dots \quad (35)$$

and

$$\Gamma(a) = \int_0^\infty w^{a-1} e^{-w} \, dw$$

is the gamma function.

Equations (31), (32), (34), and (35) give the function f by means of (26), which in conjunction with (24) and (8), yields the solution. The exponents α, β, γ, p, q, r, and s being given in terms of m, n, and k·by (13), (14), (18), (19), and (20), and σ having been defined to be A_2/A_1. As has been stated, the exponents n and m = k (and in fact also the parameter σ) are left free to be determined by measurements. The case of n = 1 - m has been treated by DAVIS [1950, pp. 71-73].

Acknowledgment--This work has been done in connection with an ONR project (Contract No. N90nr - 82401) of the Civil Engineering Department of the Colorado Agricultural and Mechanical College.

References

CALDER, K. L., Q. J. Mech. and Appl. Math., v. 2, p. 153, 1949.

DAVIS, R. D., Proc. R. Soc., ser. A, v. 190, p. 232, 1947.

DAVIS, R. D., Three-dimensional turbulence and evaporation in the lower atmosphere, I and II, Q. J. Mech. and Appl. Math., v. 3, pt. 1, pp. 51-73, 1950.

FROST, R., Turbulence and diffusion in the lower atmosphere, Proc. R. Soc., ser. A, v. 186, pp. 20-35, 1946.

SUTTON, O. G., Wind structure and evaporation in a turbulent atmosphere, Proc. R. Soc., ser. A, v. 146, pp. 701-722, 1934.

SUTTON, O. G., Q. J. R. Met. Soc., v. 73, p. 257, 1947.

SUTTON, W. G. L., On the equation of diffusion in a turbulent medium, Proc. R. Soc., ser. A, v. 182, pp. 48-75, 1943.

YIH, C. S., On a differential equation of atmospheric diffusion, Trans. Amer. Geophys. Union, v. 33, pp. 8-12, 1952.

Civil Engineering Department,
Colorado A. and M. College,
Fort Collins, Colorado

(Communicated manuscript received September 10, 1951;
open for formal discussion until November 1, 1952.)

Särtryck ur Tellus nr 3, 1952

Gravitational Convection from a Boundary Source

By HUNTER ROUSE, C. S. YIH, and H. W. HUMPHREYS

Iowa Institute of Hydraulic Research, State University of Iowa, Iowa City

(Manuscript received 18 June, 1952)

Abstract

Elementary analyses of the mean patterns of free convection from a line source and a point source are presented without regard to the specific means by which the gravitational action is produced. The derived functional relationships are then verified and completed through use of velocity and temperature measurements above sources of heat, the generalized form of the results permitting characteristics of the mean flow to be determined over a considerable range of the primary variables. These results should enable meteorologists to evaluate the role of the basic convective process in the more complex movements of the atmosphere.

Introductory Remarks

Atmospheric disturbances are generally so complex in nature that the relative importance of the various factors which they involve can be appraised only by investigating the effect of each factor independently. In conducting an analysis of this nature, one often notes a close similarity between particular aspects of meterological and other flow occurrences, indicating that experience gained in related fields can be adapted to the problem in question. A case in point is the phenomenon of large-scale thermal updrafts in the atmosphere, one aspect of which is the comparatively simple process of gravitational or "free" convection from a boundary source, recently studied experimentally at the Iowa Institute of Hydraulic Research. The writers believe that the results of this investigation will permit meteorologists to evaluate the role of the basic convective mechanism in atmospheric phenomena.

Free convection due to a point source of heat is very simply illustrated by the plume of smoke which rises from a cigarette in otherwise stagnant air. Because of the buoyancy of the heated air in the immediate vicinity of the burning end, a continuous upward current is induced, with a corresponding radial inflow for reasons of continuity. While the initial steadiness of the smoke filament indicates purely laminar motion for a considerable distance above the heat source, the flow thereafter becomes unstable and the filament breaks up into the eddying clouds normally associated with turbulent motion. After the onset of turbulence, the effect of the convection upon the surrounding fluid becomes far more pronounced, the molecular shear and heat transfer of the initial laminar motion becoming dwarfed in scale by the macroscopic mixing action. Whereas the magnitude of the velocity along the vertical axis is then rapidly di-

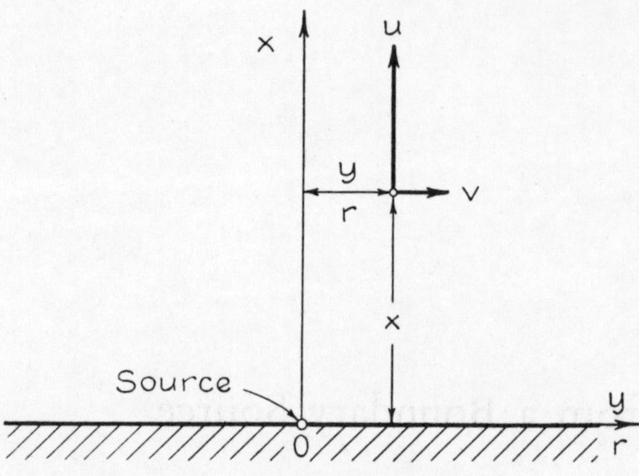

Fig. 1. Definition sketch.

minished, the angle of radial diffusion (and hence the rate of radial entrainment) is accordingly increased.

Although free convection of this nature is usually produced by a source of heat, it is the gravitational rather than the thermal aspects of the flow which are fundamental to the phenomenon. Indeed, essentially the same convection pattern can be produced in a liquid instead of a gas, and without any temperature change whatever. For example, the atmosphere may be replaced by a large body of water, and liquid having a different specific gravity may be introduced at a constant rate at a point on either horizontal boundary — a lighter liquid at the bottom or a heavier one at the top. In each event a similar pattern of convection will result, provided only that the local changes in density are relatively small in magnitude.

In the following pages an approximate analysis is made of the mean pattern of free convection from both a line source and a point source, without regard to the specific means of producing the gravitational action. Experimental evidence is then introduced to verify and complete the derived functional relationships, and generalized diagrams are presented to permit evaluation of the primary flow characteristics over a considerable range of the parameters involved.

Theoretical Analysis of the Mean Flow

If it is assumed that the scale of the initial laminar zone is small compared with that of the subsequent zone of turbulent convection,

notation for either two-dimensional flow over a line source or axially symmetric flow over a point source may be reduced to that shown schematically in Fig. 1. Herein the origin O represents the location of either source. The local mean component of velocity in the vertical direction x is denoted by u, and that in the lateral direction y or radial direction r is denoted by v.

In addition to the mean velocity of convection above the source, there will also be a mean local change $\Delta \gamma$ in the weight density of the fluid. This entails, to be sure, a comparable change in the mass density ϱ. However, the following analysis is based upon the assumption that, whereas the unit buoyant force $-\Delta \gamma$ is sufficiently great to produce vertical acceleration, the corresponding variation in the mass density of the fluid undergoing acceleration is sufficiently small, in comparison with the density itself, to be neglected.

The foregoing assumption as to constancy of the density makes it possible to proceed in close accordance with the elementary analysis of flow in boundary layers, jets, and wakes. Three additional approximations are thus involved: the pressure intensity is assumed to be hydrostatically distributed throughout the field of motion; transverse forces are ignored in comparison with those in the vertical direction; and turbulent mixing in the vertical direction is ignored in comparison with that in the horizontal. The fundamental equations of motion thus reduce to the equation of continuity and simplified equations of vertical acceleration and diffusion. The development of the relationships describing convection above a line source will be described in some detail, but for purposes of brevity only the results will be indicated for the case of axial symmetry.

Under the foregoing assumptions, the equation of vertical acceleration in two-dimensional flow reduces to

$$\varrho u \frac{\partial u}{\partial x} + \varrho v \frac{\partial u}{\partial y} = -\Delta \gamma + \frac{\partial \tau}{\partial y} \qquad (1)$$

in which the intensity of vertical shear τ is proportional to the mean product of the turbulent velocity components u' and v':

$$\tau = -\varrho \overline{u' v'}$$

The equation of continuity is simply

$$\frac{\partial u}{\partial x} + \frac{\partial v}{\partial y} = 0 \qquad (2)$$

Finally, the equation of diffusion of the quantity $\Delta\gamma$ has the form

$$u\frac{\partial(\Delta\gamma)}{\partial x} + v\frac{\partial(\Delta\gamma)}{\partial y} = -\frac{\partial w}{\partial y} \qquad (3)$$

in which the rate of lateral diffusion w due to turbulence is proportional to the mean product of the eddy scale l and the lateral velocity of fluctuation:

$$w = -\overline{v'l}\,\frac{\partial(\Delta\gamma)}{\partial y}$$

Since $u = 0$ at $y = \infty$, $v = 0$ at $y = 0$, and $\tau = 0$ at $y = 0$ and $y = \infty$, integration of Eq. (1), through use of Eq. (2), over a horizontal plane from the axis to infinity results in the following form of the momentum relationship:

$$\frac{d}{dx}\int_0^\infty \varrho u^2\,dy = -\int_0^\infty \Delta\gamma\,dy \qquad (4)$$

This states that the vertical gradient of the momentum flux is equal to the buoyancy of a horizontal stratum of unit thickness. As $\Delta\gamma=0$ at $y = \infty$ and $w = 0$ at $y = 0$ and at $y = \infty$, a similar integration of Eq. (3) leads to the following expression for the constancy of the incremental weight flux past all successive planes:

$$\frac{d}{dx}\int_0^\infty u\,\Delta\gamma\,dy = 0 \qquad (5)$$

Finally, after multiplication of each term of Eq. (1) by u, integration of the resulting expression by parts, with the help of Eq. (1), yields the following form of the energy relationship:

$$\frac{d}{dx}\int_0^\infty \frac{\varrho u^3}{2}\,dy = -\int_0^\infty u\,\Delta\gamma\,dy - \int_0^\infty \tau\frac{\partial u}{\partial y}\,dy \qquad (6)$$

Because the quantity v^3 is negligible in comparison with u^3, this relationship states that the vertical gradient of the flux of kinetic energy is equal to the rate at which work is done by the buoyant force less the rate at which work is done by the turbulent shear. The last term at the same time represents the rate at which energy is lost to the mean motion through the generation of turbulence.

Although no indication is given as to the form of the functional relationships for u, $\Delta\gamma$, and τ which will satisfy these three necessary conditions, the customary hypothesis of dynamic similarity of the mean (and turbulent) motion at all elevations permits each of the relationships to be considered of the same form for every value of x. It is thus finally assumed that

$$\frac{u}{u_{\max}} = f(\eta) \qquad \frac{\Delta\gamma}{\Delta\gamma_{\max}} = g(\eta) \qquad \frac{\tau}{\varrho u_{\max}^2/2} = h(\eta)$$

Herein $\eta = y/\sigma$, the quantity σ representing some linear characteristic of the velocity profile $u = u(y)$, such as the value of y at which the ratio $u/u_{\max}$ has some arbitrary magnitude.

Inasmuch as the unknown functions f, g, and h are independent of elevation, any power or combination thereof must also be constant with x. It is hence convenient to formulate a series of pertinent integrals for substitution into the three primary relationships which the functions must satisfy:

$$I_1 = \int_0^\infty f\,d\eta \qquad I_2 = \int_0^\infty f^2\,d\eta \qquad I_3 = \int_0^\infty f^3\,d\eta$$

$$I_4 = \int_0^\infty g\,d\eta \qquad I_5 = \int_0^\infty fg\,d\eta \qquad I_6 = \int_0^\infty h\frac{df}{d\eta}\,d\eta$$

Introduction of these terms into Eqs. (4), (5), and (6) permits the latter to be rewritten as

$$\frac{d}{dx}\left(I_2\varrho u_{\max}^2\sigma\right) = -I_4\Delta\gamma_{\max}\sigma$$

$$I_5 u_{\max}\Delta\gamma_{\max}\sigma = C_x$$

$$\frac{d}{dx}\left(I_3\frac{\varrho u_{\max}^3}{2}\sigma\right) = -C_x - I_6\frac{\varrho u_{\max}^3}{2}$$

Simultaneous solution of these relationships will yield the following significant results:

$$\sigma = \frac{I_4\,I_6\,x}{2\,I_2\,I_5 - I_3\,I_4} \sim x$$

$$u_{max} = \left(\frac{C_x}{\varrho}\,\frac{I_3\,I_4 - 2\,I_2\,I_5}{I_2\,I_5\,I_6}\right)^{1/3} \sim x^0$$

$$\varDelta\gamma_{max} = -\left(C_x\varrho^{1/2}\,\frac{I_3\,I_4 - 2\,I_2\,I_5}{I_2\,I_5\,I_6}\right)^{2/3}\frac{I_2}{I_4\,x} \sim x^{-1}$$

Evidently, no matter what forms the distribution curves may take, the convection zone will expand linearly with elevation; the maximum velocity (and hence the velocity along any line of constant y/x) will be independent of elevation; and the maximum incremental weight density (and hence that along any line of constant y/x) will vary inversely with elevation.

With this information it is possible to reach corresponding conclusions as to the variation of the volume flux Q, the momentum flux M, the kinetic-energy flux E, the unit buoyant force F, and the flux W of the incremental weight above a source of length L. Thus, per unit length of source,

$$\frac{Q}{L} = 2\int_0^\infty u\,dy \sim x \qquad \frac{M}{L} = 2\int_0^\infty \varrho\,u^2\,dy \sim x$$

$$\frac{E}{L} = 2\int_0^\infty \frac{\varrho\,u^3}{2}\,dy \sim x \qquad \frac{F}{L} = -2\int_0^\infty \varDelta\gamma\,dy \sim x^0$$

$$\frac{W}{L} = 2\int_0^\infty u\,\varDelta\gamma\,dy = 2C_x$$

Herefrom it is seen that the flux of volume, the flux of momentum, and the flux of kinetic energy must increase continuously with elevation, for the force producing the convective motion is the same at all successive levels. As the flux of the incremental weight is also the same at every level, the quantity W must indicate the output of the source.

The corresponding analysis of the axially symmetric pattern of convection above a point source proceeds in a closely comparable manner. The resulting integral equations of momentum, diffusion, and energy have the forms

$$\frac{d}{dx}\int_0^\infty \varrho\,u^2\,r\,dr = -\int_0^\infty \varDelta\gamma\,r\,dr \qquad (7)$$

$$\frac{d}{dx}\int_0^\infty u\,\varDelta\gamma\,r\,dr = 0 \qquad (8)$$

$$\frac{d}{dx}\int_0^\infty \frac{\varrho u^3}{2}\,r\,dr = -\int_0^\infty u\,\varDelta\gamma\,r\,dr - \int_0^\infty \tau\frac{\partial u}{\partial r}\,r\,dr \qquad (9)$$

Through the assumption of dynamic similarity of the mean flow at all elevations it is found that

$$\sigma \sim x \qquad u_{max} \sim x^{1/3} \qquad \varDelta\gamma_{max} \sim x^{-5/3}$$

The following expressions are then obtained:

$$Q = 2\pi\int_0^\infty u\,r\,dr \sim x^{5/3} \qquad M = 2\pi\int_0^\infty \varrho u^2\,r\,dr \sim x^{4/3}$$

$$E = 2\pi\int_0^\infty \frac{\varrho u^3}{2}\,r\,dr \sim x \qquad F = -2\pi\int_0^\infty \varDelta\gamma\,r\,dr \sim x^{1/3}$$

$$W = 2\pi\int_0^\infty u\,\varDelta\gamma\,r\,dr = 2\pi\,C_x'$$

Owing to the differences between these expressions and their counterparts for the two-dimensional case, basically different relationships are indicated for the flux of the several characteristic quantities past successive planes above a point source. Although the convection pattern again expands linearly with height above the source, the maximum velocity (and hence that for any constant value of r/x) now decreases continuously, and the incremental weight density decreases even more rapidly. On the other hand, the buoyant force on a stratum of unit thickness becomes steadily greater with increasing elevation, and Q, M, and E all increase at different rates. Once again, however, the flux of the incremental weight is the same at all elevations, so that W

must be equivalent to the output of the source.

Experimental Procedure and Results

In any experimental program to determine explicit relationships for either two-dimensional or axially symmetric convection from a boundary source, there are evidently four variables which can be controlled independently — two coordinate positions, the mass density of the fluid, and the strength of the source. These four quantities govern the magnitudes of such dependent variables as velocity, weight density, shear, turbulence, and their various combinations. While all of these factors would be of interest in a complete investigation of the phenomenon, attention is focused in the present study upon the major characteristics of the mean motion: the velocity component u and the change $\Delta\gamma$ in weight density. The resulting functional relationships between the dependent and independent variables for the two types of source can be indicated schematically as follows:

$$\begin{aligned} u \\ \Delta\gamma \end{aligned} = f_{1-4}\left(x,\ \frac{\gamma}{r},\ \varrho,\ \frac{W/L}{W}\right)$$

Inasmuch as five variables involving three fundamental dimensions appear in each of these four functions, it is to be expected that the dimensionless form of each will contain only two terms. Thus, for two-dimensional conditions, the relationships may be expressed as

$$\frac{u}{(W/L\varrho)^{1/3}} = \varphi_1\left(\frac{\gamma}{x}\right)$$

$$\frac{\Delta'\gamma}{(\varrho W^2/L^2 x^3)^{1/3}} = \varphi_2\left(\frac{\gamma}{x}\right)$$

For conditions of axial symmetry, the counterparts of these expressions are

$$\frac{u}{(W/\varrho x)^{1/3}} = \varphi_3\left(\frac{r}{x}\right)$$

$$\frac{\Delta\gamma}{(\varrho W^2/x^5)^{1/3}} = \varphi_4\left(\frac{r}{x}\right)$$

In each instance the grouping of terms is seen to be in accordance with the general relationships obtained analytically.

Experiments with heated air to determine the forms of these functions were conducted in closed rooms, particular care being required in the study of axially symmetric conditions to eliminate all sources of disturbance. In this instance the room was approximately circular in plan and had a diameter of 25 feet and an overall height of 11 feet. The heat source was placed at the midpoint of a centrally located platform 8 feet in diameter and a few inches in height. For the two-dimensional study the flow was confined between two parallel walls 4 feet high, 8 feet long, and 4 feet apart, and the source was placed across the midsection of a low platform extending the length of the walls. The heat sources in both cases consisted of recessed gas burners yielding low, blue flames approaching as nearly as practicable the desired point and line concentrations.

Measurements of the temperature distribution were made by means of a copper-constantan thermocouple, with its cold junction placed well away from the heat source, in combination with a potentiometer reading to 0.002 millivolt. Velocity indications were obtained with a specially constructed vane anemometer $1^1/_4$ inch in diameter, the jewel bearings of which permitted the indication of velocities as low as 0.2 foot per second. These instruments were mounted alternately on remotely controlled traversing mechanisms.

The rates of heat output from both the line and the point source were evaluated from the measured distributions of velocity and temperature according to the following thermal counterparts of the equations for W/L and W:

$$\frac{H}{L} = 2c_p\,\varrho \int\limits_0^\infty u\,\Delta T\,d\gamma \tag{10}$$

$$H = 2\pi\,c_p\,\varrho \int\limits_0^\infty u\,\Delta T\,r\,dr \tag{11}$$

for the closely approximate condition that $\Delta\gamma/\gamma = -\Delta T/T$, the corresponding value of W in either case was computed from the resulting conversion equation,

$$W = -\frac{gH}{c_p T} \tag{12}$$

Supplementary tests performed during the axially symmetric study were directed toward

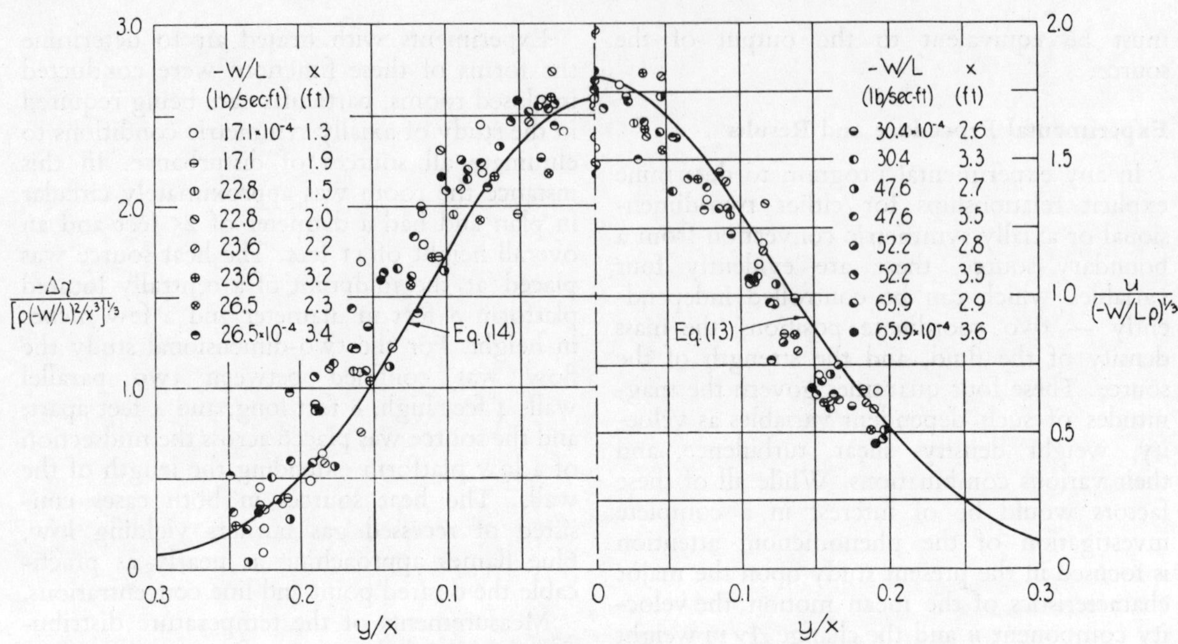

Fig. 2. Distribution functions for two-dimensional convection.

determination of the level at which, under ordinary circumstances, the initial laminar flow could be expected to become unstable. Because of the low rates of heat input required to yield readily measurable conditions of transition, it was necessary to use as the limiting heat source a burning cigarette (from a package carefully calibrated for rate of heat release), the smoke serving as a convenient tracing agent. The critical Reynolds number determined in this manner was of the form

$$\mathbf{R}_c = \frac{x_c}{\sqrt{\varrho v^3/(-W)}} \approx 10^5$$

in which v is the kinematic viscosity. As can be determined herefrom, the critical height x_c was small in every case for which detailed measurements were made.

All velocity and temperature traverses were carried entirely across the convection zone, the plotted curves being essentially symmetrical about the maximum but often indicating a slight deviation of the flow from the vertical. In analyzing the results, the reference axis was adjusted to agree with the axis of symmetry. Upon reduction of data to the pertinent dimensionless forms, composite plots were made of velocity and weight distributions for both the two-dimensional

and the axially symmetric cases, to verify the assumed similarity of flow at different levels and with different strengths of source and to determine the explicit distribution functions. For ease in comparison as well as economy of space, these plots are shown in half section: in Fig. 2 for two dimensions and in Fig. 3 for axial symmetry.

At once apparent is the appreciable scatter of points which seems to typify experimental studies of this nature — in part because of the difficulty of precise measurement and in part because of the sensitivity of such flow to slight disturbances. The scatter is not appreciably systematic, however, nor is it difficult to construct mean curves to indicate the distribution functions. The curves shown are normal-probability functions which best fit the data and at the same time satisfy Eqs. (4) and (5), and Eqs. (7) and (8), respectively. At least as a first approximation, there seems little doubt that the plotted curves describe the basic free-convection phenomenon. To be remarked, however, is the fact that use of the Gaussian function — not to mention the simplified analysis itself — loses significance as y/x or r/x becomes large.

If the probability curves plotted in Fig. 2 are assumed to represent the true distributions of u and $\Delta \gamma$, the corresponding expressions

GRAVITATIONAL CONVECTION FROM A BOUNDARY SOURCE

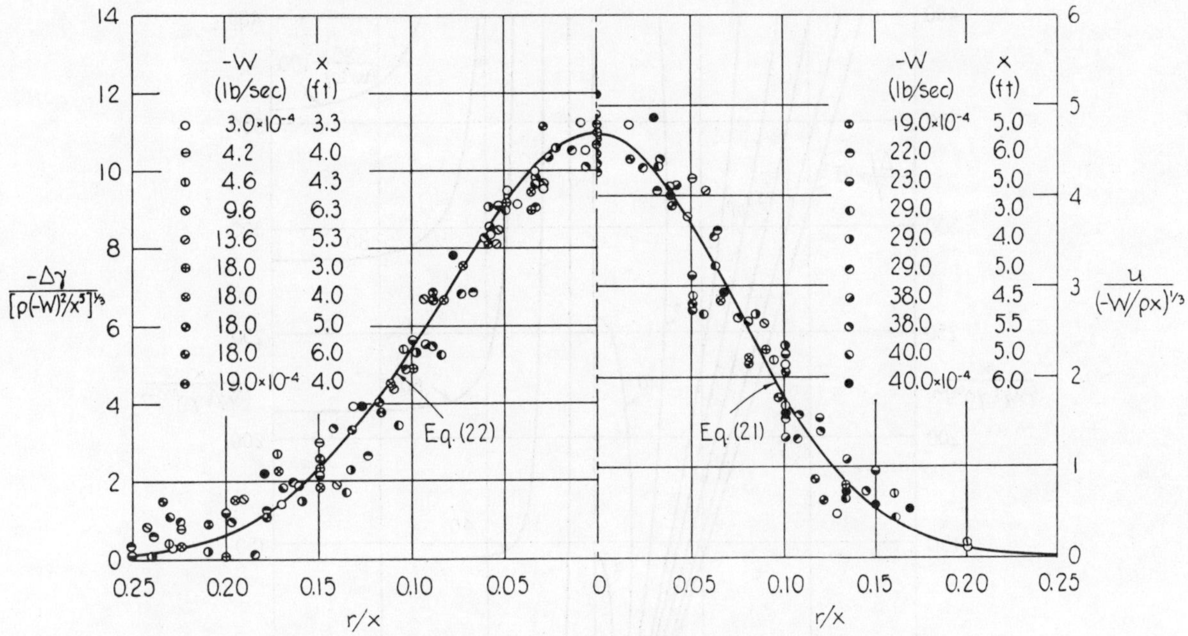

Fig. 3. Distribution functions for axially symmetric convection.

$$u = 1.80 \left(\frac{-W/L}{\varrho}\right)^{1/3} exp\left(-32\frac{y^2}{x^2}\right) \quad (13)$$

$$\Delta\gamma = -2.6\left[\frac{\varrho(-W/L)^2}{x^3}\right]^{1/3} exp\left(-41\frac{y^2}{x^2}\right) (14)$$

can be used conveniently to evaluate other characteristics of the mean pattern of motion. Thus, since $\psi = \int u\,dy$, the stream function is expressible implicitly as

$$\psi = 1.80 \left(\frac{-W/L}{\varrho}\right)^{1/3} \int_0^y exp\left(-32\frac{y^2}{x^2}\right) dy \quad (15)$$

in which values of the integral are obtainable from probability tables. The lateral velocity of entrainment just beyond the diffusion zone, otherwise available from the condition that $v = -\partial\psi/\partial x$, is instead computed from the expression $2v_e = -d(Q/L)/dx$ as

$$v_e = \mp\, 0.28 \left(\frac{-W/L}{\varrho}\right)^{1/3} \quad (16)$$

Specific relationships for Q, M, E, and F per unit length of source are obtained by integration as follows:

$$\frac{Q}{L} = 0.57 \left(\frac{-W/L}{\varrho}\right)^{1/3} x \quad (17)$$

$$\frac{M}{L} = 0.72 \left(\frac{-W}{L}\right)^{2/3} \varrho^{1/3} x \quad (18)$$

$$\frac{E}{L} = 0.53 \frac{-W}{L} x \quad (19)$$

$$\frac{F}{L} = 0.72 \left(\frac{-W}{L}\right)^{2/3} \varrho^{1/3} \quad (20)$$

For conditions of axial symmetry these expressions take the following forms:

$$u = 4.7 \left(\frac{-W}{\varrho x}\right)^{1/3} exp\left(-96\frac{r^2}{x^2}\right) \quad (21)$$

$$\Delta\gamma = -11.0\left[\frac{\varrho(-W)^2}{x^5}\right]^{1/3} exp\left(-71\frac{r^2}{x^2}\right) \quad (22)$$

$$\psi = 0.024\left(\frac{-Wx^5}{\varrho}\right)^{1/3}\left[1-exp\left(-96\frac{r^2}{x^2}\right)\right] \quad (23)$$

$$v_e = -0.041 \left(\frac{-W}{\varrho}\right)^{1/3}\frac{x^{2/3}}{r} \quad (24)$$

$$Q = 0.153 \left(\frac{-W}{\varrho}\right)^{1/3} x^{5/3} \quad (25)$$

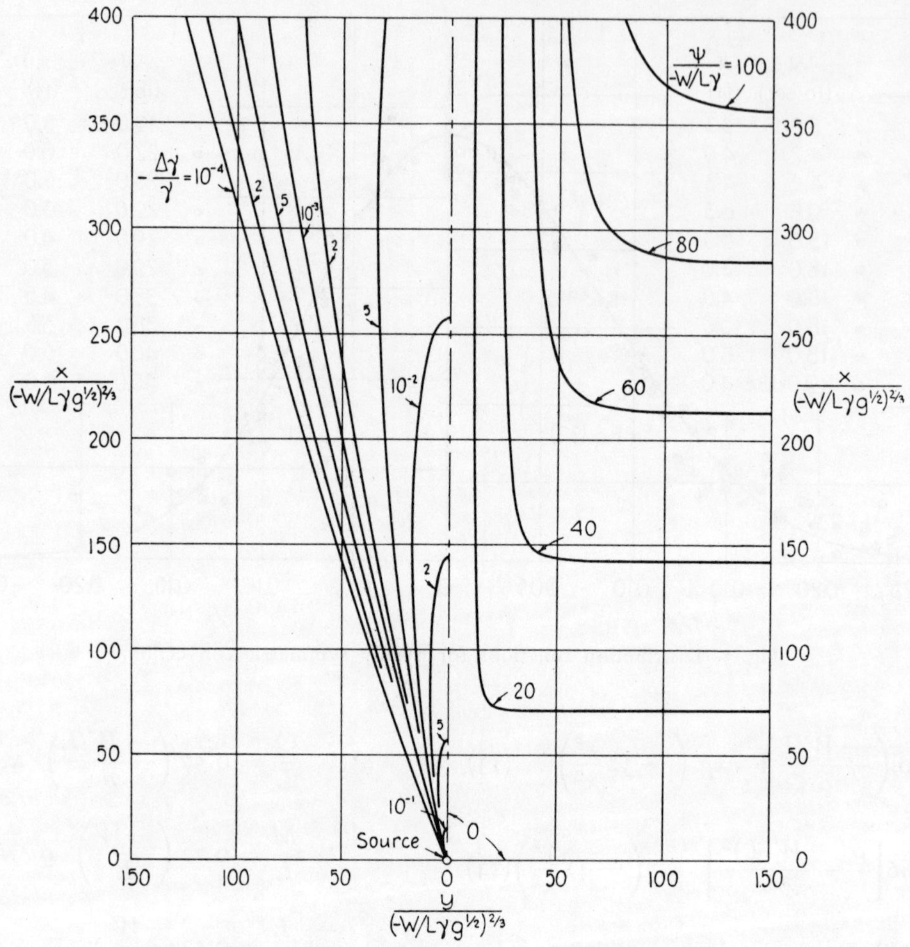

Fig. 4. Convection pattern over a line source.

$$M = 0.36\,(-W)^{2/3}\,\varrho^{1/3}\,x^{4/3} \tag{26}$$

$$E = 0.57\,(-W)\,x \tag{27}$$

$$F = 0.49\,(-W)^{2/3}\,\varrho^{1/3}\,x^{1/3} \tag{28}$$

So far as the mean flow is concerned, it remains only to indicate in generalized coordinates the pattern of stream lines and lines of constant incremental weight for the two cases. This, however, requires three rather than two dimensionless groups of variables in each instance — the additional variable which is needed being a characteristic length to serve as a reference coordinate. Such a length is found in the quantity $(W/L\gamma g^{1/2})^{2/3}$ for two dimensions, and in the corresponding quantity $(W/\gamma g^{1/2})^{2/5}$ for axial symmetry. Upon introduction of these quantities, the dimensionless coordinate relationships for ψ and $\Delta\gamma$ become, for the line source,

$$\frac{\psi}{W/L\gamma} = \varphi_5 \left[\frac{x}{(W/L\gamma g^{1/2})^{2/3}},\ \frac{y}{(W/L\gamma g^{1/2})^{2/3}} \right]$$

$$\frac{\Delta\gamma}{\gamma} = \varphi_6 \left[\frac{x}{(W/L\gamma g^{1/2})^{2/3}},\ \frac{y}{(W/L\gamma g^{1/2})^{2/3}} \right]$$

and, for the point source,

$$\frac{\psi}{W/\gamma} = \varphi_7 \left[\frac{x}{(W/\gamma g^{1/2})^{2/5}},\ \frac{r}{(W/\gamma g^{1/2})^{2/5}} \right]$$

$$\frac{\Delta\gamma}{\gamma} = \varphi_8 \left[\frac{x}{(W/\gamma g^{1/2})^{2/5}},\ \frac{r}{(W/\gamma g^{1/2})^{2/5}} \right]$$

The corresponding plots of stream lines and lines of constant incremental weight are shown in half section in Figs. 4 and 5.

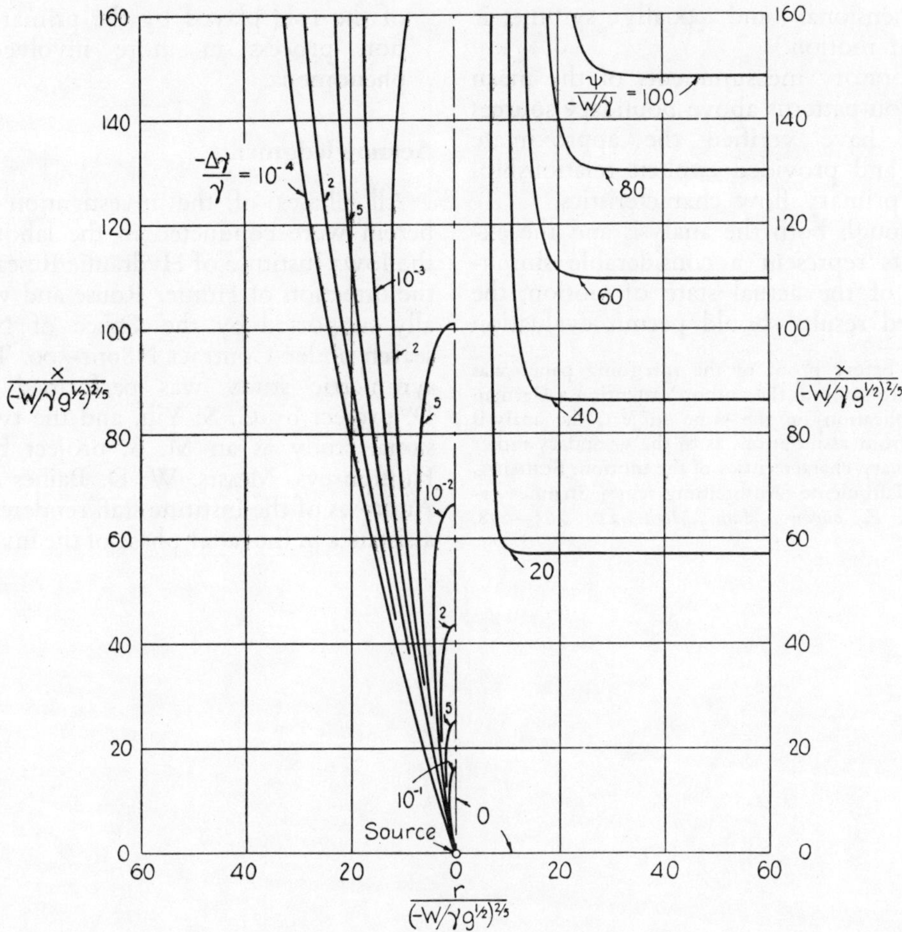

Fig. 5. Convection pattern over a point source.

As can be seen at once from these undistorted diagrams, the zones of pronounced vertical motion and change in weight density are concentrated about the area of symmetry and expand only slowly with elevation. Because of the fact that the measurements were restricted to these zones and that the analysis itself is not exact, the outlying portions of the stream-line patterns are purely schematic. Aside from this qualitative indication of the pattern of inflow, the diagrams are considered to represent with good approximation the basic characteristics of convection at any scale. They may readily be interpolated or extrapolated, as all curves in any diagram are geometrically similar by virtue of the dynamic similarity of the convection mechanism at successive elevations.

Conclusions

From the foregoing analytical and experimental studies of gravitational convection from both a line source and a point source, the following conclusions may be drawn:

(1) The motivating force in gravitational convection is the positive or negative buoyancy of the fluid, and the primary characteristics of the convection pattern can hence be analyzed without regard to the means whereby the buoyant effect is produced.

(2) Through use of an approximate method of analysis similar to that for boundary layers, wakes, and jets, it is possible to express as proportionalities the mean characteristics of gravitational convection for both

two-dimensional and axially symmetric turbulent motion.[1]

(3) Laboratory measurements of the mean convection patterns above boundary sources of heat have verified the approximate analysis and provided explicit relationships for the primary flow characteristics.

(4) Although both the analysis and the experiments represent a considerable simplification of the actual state of motion, the correlated results should permit evaluation of the role played by the primary convection process in more involved natural phenomena.

Acknowledgments

All phases of the investigation described herein were conducted in the laboratories of the Iowa Institute of Hydraulic Research under the direction of Hunter Rouse and were partially supported by the Office of Naval Research under Contract N8onr-500. The axially symmetric study was performed as a Ph. D. project by C. S. Yih, and the two-dimensional study as an M. S. project by H. W. Humphreys. Messrs. W. D. Baines and M. F. Andrews of the Institute staff rendered valuable assistance in the latter phase of the investigation.

---

[1] Shortly before proof of the foregoing paper was received, there came to the authors' attention a German wartime publication on the same subject, the analysis proceeding from assumptions as to the secondary rather than the primary characteristics of the motion: SCHMIDT, W., 1941, Turbulente Ausbreitung eines Stromes erhitzter Luft, *Z. angew. Math. Mech.* **21**, 265—278, 351—363.

FREE CONVECTION DUE TO BOUNDARY SOURCES

Chia-Shun Yih

State University of Iowa
Iowa City, Iowa

INTRODUCTION

In the past decade a number of investigations on free convection have been carried out at the Iowa Institute of Hydraulic Research. Although the unsurmountable difficulty involved in the proper simulation of atmospheric stratification imposes a limitation on the meteorological applications of the results obtained, it is believed that these results are nevertheless applicable to small elevations above the ground under favorable conditions, and that they should throw some light on the understanding of convective phenomena in a stratified atmosphere. Therefore, the salient features of these results are presented in the following sections.

FREE CONVECTION DUE TO A POINT SOURCE OF HEAT

As one of the efforts to gain a fundamental understanding of atmospheric convection, an investigation has been made (1) of the characteristics of free convection due to a point source of heat. Specifically, the point source is considered to be situated in an infinite plane above which the atmosphere was originally isothermal and at rest, and the resulting mean temperature and velocity distributions are sought. The vertical variation of density in the ambient atmosphere is neglected. As can be observed from the behavior of smoke from a burning cigarette, the flow caused by the heat source is laminar at first, then at some height above it becomes unstable, and the subsequent flow is turbulent. The two regimes of flow and the transition from one to the other will be discussed separately.

In the analysis of the present problem it has been assumed that the temperature variation should be small enough for the physical properties of the fluid to be considered constant. Under this assumption, if T denotes the absolute temperature and γ the specific weight, it can be shown from the well known equation of state for perfect gases

$$\frac{p}{\gamma} = RT \tag{1}$$

that

$$\frac{\Delta T}{T_0} = -\frac{\Delta \gamma}{\gamma_0}, \tag{2}$$

where T_0 is the ambient temperature, γ_0 the corresponding specific weight, $\Delta T = T - T_0$, and $\Delta \gamma = \gamma - \gamma_0$. In fact the proportionality between ΔT and $\Delta \gamma$ for small variations in T is quite independent of the equation of state, and can be obtained for any fluid. Since ΔT and $\Delta \gamma$ are connected by Eq. (2), $\Delta \gamma$ can be used as a dependent variable instead of ΔT.

Taking the heat source as origin, and x and r as vertical and radial coordinates, one denotes the vertical velocity by u and the radial velocity by v. Since the convectional heat flux must be constant for all values of x because of continuity, and since ΔT and $\Delta \gamma$ are related by Eq. (2), the quantity

$$G = -\int_0^\infty 2\pi r u \Delta \gamma \, dr \tag{3}$$

must be independent of x and is in fact a measure of the strength of the heat source. The constancy of G can be demonstrated by integrating the energy equation with the aid of the

117

Reprinted from *Fluid Models in Geophysics* (Proc. of the First Symp. on the Use of Models in Geophysical Fluid Dynamics) held at the Johns Hopkins University (September 1–4, 1953) 117–133.

                        Chia-Shun Yih

equation of continuity and the boundary condition at infinity for ΔT or $\Delta \gamma$, but since it is intuitively quite clear, a demonstration is not necessary. With G properly defined, the independent variables can be taken to be G, ρ, μ, x, r and α, where ρ is the density, μ the dynamic viscosity, and α the thermal diffusivity defined as $k/\rho c_p$, k being the thermal conductivity and c_p being the specific heat at constant pressure. The dependent variables are $\Delta \gamma$, u, and v. But since u and v are connected by the equation of continuity, it is sufficient to study $\Delta \gamma$ and u. A dimensional analysis of the pertinent variables then yields the following two relationships:

$$\frac{\rho x \mu^3}{G} = F_1 \left(\frac{\rho^2 x^2 G}{\mu^3}, \frac{r}{x}, \sigma \right), \tag{4}$$

$$\frac{x^5 \Delta \gamma^3}{\rho G^2} = F_2 \left(\frac{\rho^2 x^2 G}{\mu^3}, \frac{r}{x}, \sigma \right), \tag{5}$$

in which $\sigma = \mu/\rho\alpha$ is the Prandtl number. In laminar flow all three parameters appearing on the right side of Eq. (4) or (5) are significant in the determination of the dependent parameter. In turbulent flow, since the effect of molecular viscosity is small compared with the eddy viscosity, and since, in the experiments performed, air has been used as the working fluid, the relationship can be simplified to:

$$\frac{\rho x \mu^3}{G} = F_3 \left(\frac{r}{x} \right), \tag{6}$$

$$\frac{x^5 \Delta \gamma^3}{\rho G^2} = F_4 \left(\frac{r}{x} \right). \tag{7}$$

Although the effect of the Prandtl number is not included in Eqs. (6) and (7), it is believed that for fully turbulent flow the effect of the Prandtl number is secondary, so that the relationships obtained from experiments with air are applicable to other fluids.

An exhaustive study of stability should include the wave number of the disturbance as an important variable. However, if one is not concerned with the height at which a disturbance of a certain wave number becomes unstable but with the maximum height at which disturbances of all wave numbers are stable, then with h denoting that height, a dimensional analysis with h, G, ρ, μ, and α yields

$$\frac{\rho^2 h^2 G}{\mu^3} = F_5(\sigma)$$

which, for air, assumes the form

$$\frac{\rho^2 h^2 G}{\mu^3} = \text{constant}. \tag{8}$$

It must be remembered, however, that since the initial disturbances are not controlled in amplitude or frequency, the stability parameter, which is essentially the cube of a Reynolds number, may be expected to vary over a range comparable to that of the critical Reynolds number in boundary-layer flow.

The functional form of F_1, F_2, F_3, and F_4 and the constant in Eq. (8) are the principal objects of the investigation.

Laminar Case

Although convection currents occurring in the atmosphere are mostly turbulent, the laminar case is interesting because a mathematical solution of the pertinent equations brings out very clearly the interdependence of the temperature and velocity distributions, thus revealing the rather intricate mechanism of free convection. Moreover, mathematical solutions for problems of free convection are extremely rare. For these reasons, it is believed worthwhile to discuss the laminar case of the present problem in some detail.

Free Convection Due to Boundary Sources   119

Assuming the hydrostatic pressure of the atmosphere to be essentially undisturbed by the flow caused by the heat source and $\dfrac{\partial^2 u}{\partial x^2}$ to be negligible as compared with $\dfrac{1}{r}\dfrac{\partial}{\partial r}\left(r\dfrac{\partial u}{\partial r}\right)$, one can write the equation of motion as

$$u\frac{\partial u}{\partial x}+v\frac{\partial u}{\partial r}=\frac{\nu}{r}\frac{\partial}{\partial r}\left(r\frac{\partial u}{\partial r}\right)-g\frac{\Delta\gamma}{\gamma_0}, \tag{9}$$

where g is the gravitational acceleration and ν is the kinematic viscosity. In virtue of Eq. (2), the equation for heat diffusion (the energy equation), can be written

$$u\frac{\partial\Delta\gamma}{\partial x}+v\frac{\partial\Delta\gamma}{\partial y}=\frac{\alpha}{r}\frac{\partial}{\partial r}\left(r\frac{\partial\Delta\gamma}{\partial r}\right) \tag{10}$$

if $\partial^2\Delta\gamma/\partial x^2$ is neglected in comparison with $\dfrac{1}{r}\dfrac{\partial}{\partial r}\left(r\dfrac{\partial\Delta\gamma}{\partial r}\right)$. The equation of continuity is

$$\frac{\partial}{\partial x}(ru)+\frac{\partial}{\partial r}(rv)=0. \tag{11}$$

Equations (9), (10), and (11) are to be solved with the boundary conditions that

$$u,\ v,\ \text{and}\ \Delta\gamma\ \text{vanish at}\ r=\infty,$$
$$u\ \text{and}\ v\ \text{vanish at}\ x=0\ \text{except at the origin, and}$$
$$v,\ \frac{\partial\Delta\gamma}{\partial r},\ \text{and}\ \frac{\partial u}{\partial r}\ \text{vanish at}\ r=0.$$

Equation (11) permits the use of the Stokes stream function ψ such that

$$u=\frac{1}{r}\frac{\partial\psi}{\partial r};\qquad v=-\frac{1}{r}\frac{\partial\psi}{\partial x}. \tag{12}$$

Then, with the substitutions

$$\Delta\gamma=-\frac{G\rho}{x\mu}\theta(\eta), \tag{13}$$

and

$$\psi=4\nu x f(\eta), \tag{14}$$

in which

$$\eta=\left(\frac{\rho^2 G}{4\mu^3}\right)^{1/4}\frac{r}{x^{1/2}}, \tag{15}$$

Eqs. (9) and (10) become

$$(1-4f)\frac{d}{d\eta}\left(\frac{f'}{\eta}\right)=f'''+\eta\theta \tag{16}$$

and

$$f=-\frac{1}{4\sigma}\frac{\theta'}{\theta}\eta. \tag{17}$$

The boundary conditions, except the one that $v=0$ at $x=0$, which will be discussed later, are substituted by the following:

$$\theta(\infty)=0,$$
$$f(0)=f'(0)=\theta'(0)=0, \tag{18}$$
$$f(\infty)=\text{a finite number}.$$

The integral condition for the heat flux as expressed by Eq. (3) now assumes the form

$$\int_0^\infty f'\theta\,d\eta=\frac{1}{8\pi}. \tag{19}$$

                                    Chia-Shun Yih

The differential system consisting of Eqs. (16) to (19) is difficult to solve for arbitrary values of σ. But for $\sigma=1$ and $\sigma=2$, solutions in closed forms can be obtained.

For $\sigma=1$,

$$\frac{\psi}{4\nu x}=f(\eta)=\frac{3}{2}\,\frac{\eta^2}{6\sqrt{2\pi}+\eta^2} \tag{20}$$

and

$$-\frac{\mu x\Delta\gamma}{G\rho}=\theta(\eta)=\frac{1}{3\pi\left(1+\dfrac{\eta^2}{6\sqrt{2\pi}}\right)^3}. \tag{21}$$

From Eqs. (12), (15), and (20), one obtains

$$\left(\frac{\mu}{G}\right)^{\frac{1}{2}}u=\frac{2f'}{\eta}=\frac{1}{\sqrt{2\pi}\left(1+\dfrac{\eta^2}{6\sqrt{2\pi}}\right)^2}, \tag{22}$$

$$\left(\frac{\rho^2 x^2}{\mu G}\right)^{\frac{1}{4}}v=\sqrt{2}\left(f'-\frac{2f}{\eta}\right)=-\frac{3\sqrt{2}\,\eta^3}{(6\sqrt{2\pi}+\eta^2)^2}. \tag{23}$$

It is interesting to note that for $\sigma=1$ the temperature distribution is more concentrated than the vertical velocity distribution, as can be seen from Eqs. (21) and (22). This marks a sharp distinction between laminar free convection due to a point source of heat and laminar forced convection of a heated jet. In the latter case (2), the ratio of the spread of the longitudinal velocity to that of the temperature rise is, roughly speaking, equal to σ.

For $\sigma=2$,

$$\frac{\psi}{4\nu x}=f(\eta)=\frac{\sqrt{5}\,\eta^2}{8\sqrt{2\pi}+\sqrt{5}\,\eta^2}, \tag{24}$$

$$-\frac{\mu x\Delta\gamma}{G\rho}=\theta(\eta)=\frac{5}{8\pi\left(1+\dfrac{\sqrt{5}}{8\sqrt{2\pi}}\,\eta^2\right)^4}, \tag{25}$$

$$\left(\frac{\mu}{G}\right)^{\frac{1}{2}}u=\frac{2f'}{\eta}=\frac{\sqrt{5}}{2\sqrt{2\pi}\left(1+\dfrac{\sqrt{5}}{8\sqrt{2\pi}}\,\eta^2\right)^2}, \tag{26}$$

and

$$\left(\frac{\rho^2 x^2}{\mu G}\right)^{\frac{1}{4}}v=\sqrt{2}\left(f'-\frac{2f}{\eta}\right)=-\frac{10\sqrt{2}\,\eta^3}{(8\sqrt{2\pi}+\sqrt{5}\,\eta^2)^2}. \tag{27}$$

In this case the exponent in Eq. (25) is 4 and the corresponding one in Eq. (26) is 2, so that the ratio of the exponents is 2, which happens to be equal to σ, as in the case of forced convection (2).

From a comparison of the two solutions with previous ones for forced convection, it is seen that for σ less than 2 the effect of buoyancy is to sharpen the curve for temperature distribution in relation to that for longitudinal-velocity distribution.

For air, which has a Prandtl number of 0.73 under normal conditions, the solution corresponding to $\sigma=1$ can be used to give a close approximation. For $\sigma=1$ the value of v at $x=0$ can be shown to be $-3\sqrt{2}\nu/r$. This has a value of only 0.02 foot per second at $r=0.05$ foot (ν being taken to be 0.00025 square foot per second for air), and varies inversely with r, so that the boundary condition $v=0$ at $x=0$ is approximately satisfied. This approximation will not introduce large errors if x is not extremely small. That the boundary-layer equations are valid can also be verified a posteriori from Eqs. (21) and (22). Similar remarks apply to the case in which $\sigma=2$.

Equations (21), (22), (25), and (26) are plotted in Fig. 1. It can be seen that the temperature and velocity distributions are more concentrated for the larger Prandtl number, and that the effect of Prandtl number on the temperature is more pronounced. The patterns of streamlines and isotherms for laminar free convection with Prandtl number 1 are shown in Fig. 2. The parameters used are dimensionless. Measurements for the laminar case have not been made.

Turbulent Case

The exact analysis of heat transfer in turbulent flow depends on an exact knowledge of the properties of turbulence pertaining to the specific problem studied, which no theory at present can predict and concerning which any future theory must be more or less descriptive. Therefore, any formal analysis of the turbulent case necessitates an assumption for the mixing length or some statistical property of the turbulence, the validity of which cannot be ascertained a priori. In view of this, and realizing that the chief purpose of the present investigation is to determine the macroscopic characteristics of free convection due to a point source of heat rather than to study the pertaining mechanism of turbulence, it is evident that an experimental determination ab initio of the functional relationships between the pertinent dimensionless parameters will be more direct and reliable.

The experiments were conducted in an air-tight room of considerable size with a ceiling high enough (11 feet) for its effect on the region where the measurements were taken to be negligible. At the center of the room the heat source, realized by a low flame, was placed at the same level as a low transite table 8 feet in diameter. Vertical guides and a horizontal traversing mechanism permitted measurements to be made over an elevation range of 6 feet in an axial plane. The measuring elements were remotely controlled to prevent disturbance of the flow.

The low flame was supplied alternatively by two Bunsen burners of 1-inch and $\frac{3}{16}$-inch diameters, respectively, which could be connected to a gas tank through a pressure regulator; the flame height could be controlled by a valve in the connecting tube. Temperature differences were measured with a copper-constantan thermocouple with its cold junction placed far away from the heat source, used in connection with a potentiometer which could be read to 0.002 millivolt. The quantity $\Delta\gamma$ could be calculated from the temperature measurement by Eq. (2). The data obtained could then be arranged according to Eqs. (6) and (7).

For longitudinal-velocity measurement the hot-wire method was first tried. The attempt was not successful because, aside from complications due to the temperature distribution of the field, the hot-wire set used suffered from both insensitivity and inaccuracy at the prevailing low velocities. Soap bubbles were also tried in connection with various photographic techniques, but as the motion of the bubbles relative to the surrounding air could neither be eliminated nor ascertained, the idea had to be abandoned. Finally, a properly calibrated midget anemometer was used which had a lower measurable limit of about 0.2 foot per second and an effective diameter of about $1\frac{5}{16}$ inches and was adequate for velocity measurement when the convection region was fairly well spread out. After $\Delta\gamma$ and u had been measured, G could be computed from Eq. (3). Measurements in the turbulent zone were carried out over a range from $3(10)^{-4}$ to $40(10)^{-4}$ pounds per second for G and from 3.3 to 6.0 feet for x.

The experimental results show that the explicit relationships for Eqs. (6) and (7) are, respectively,

$$\left(\frac{\rho x}{G}\right)^{1/3} u = 4.7 \exp\left[-\frac{1}{2}\left(\frac{r}{0.072\,x}\right)^2\right] \tag{28}$$

and

$$-\left(\frac{x^5}{\rho G^2}\right)^{1/3} \Delta\gamma = 11.0 \exp\left[-\frac{1}{2}\left(\frac{r}{0.084\,x}\right)^2\right], \tag{29}$$

Chia-Shun Yih

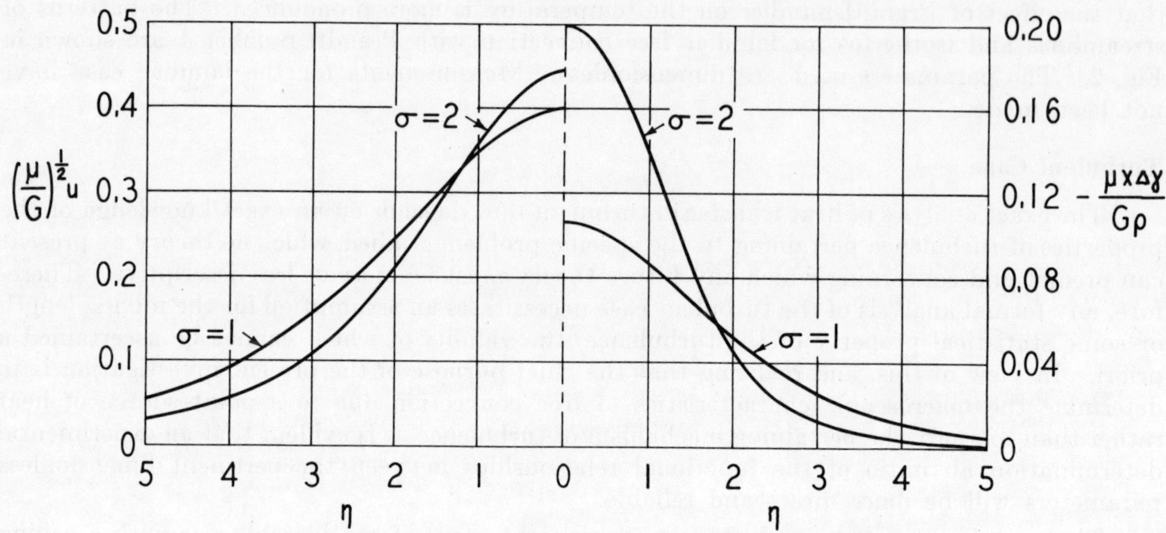

Figure 1—Distribution functions for laminar convection over a point source.

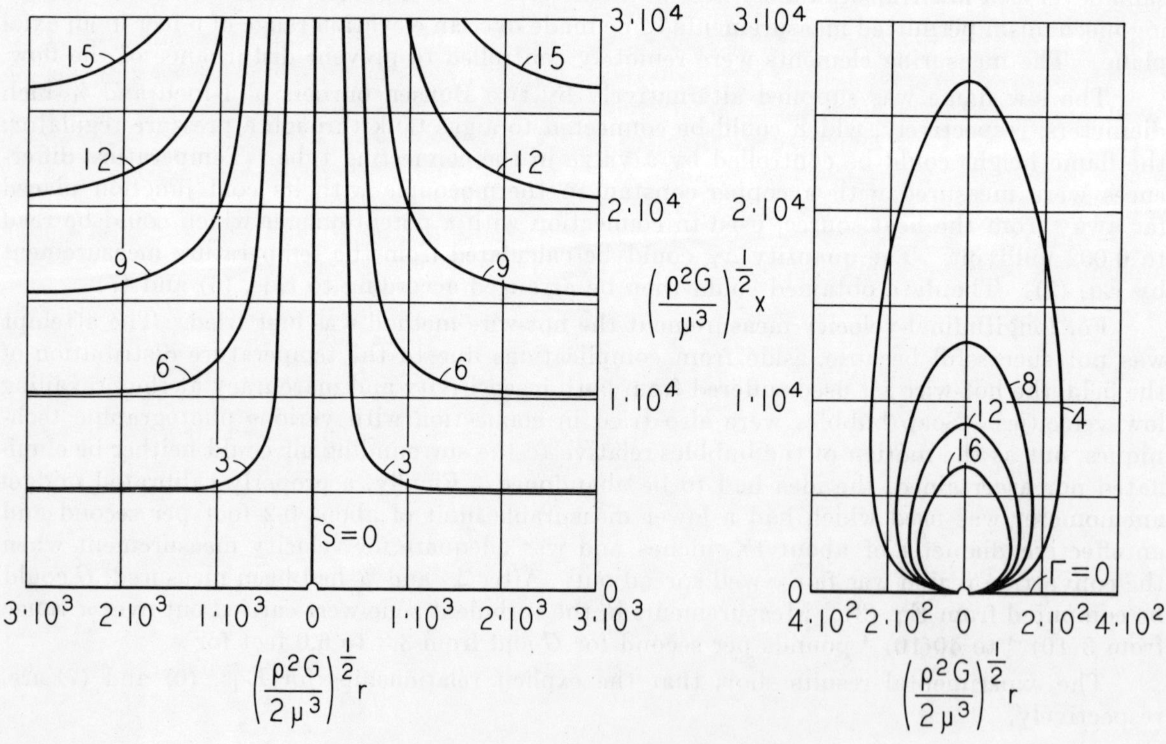

Figure 2—Convection pattern over a point source—laminar case

$$S = 10^{-4} \left(\frac{\rho^4 G}{\mu^5}\right)^{1/2} \psi, \qquad \Gamma = -10^6 \left(\frac{\mu^5}{\rho^4 G^3}\right)^{1\,2} \Delta\gamma.$$

Free Convection Due to Boundary Sources 123

from which ψ, v, the mass flux (through a horizontal section), the momentum flux, and the energy flux can be readily derived. Equations (28) and (29) are represented graphically in Fig. 3 and the patterns of streamlines and isotherms for the turbulent case are shown in Fig. 4, in dimensionless terms. Naturally, neither these patterns nor the distribution functions are valid at a region very close to the heat source.

The principle of conservation of momentum requires that

$$\frac{d}{dx}\int_0^\infty 2\pi r\rho u^2 dr = -\int_0^\infty 2\pi r\Delta\gamma dr, \tag{30}$$

which can be obtained by integrating the equation of motion, but is intuitively quite clear. From the results obtained, the left side of Eq. (30) has the value $0.48(G^2\rho x)^{1/3}$, and the right side has a value of $0.49(G^2\rho x)^{1/3}$, so that the requirement of the momentum equation is approximately satisfied.

In a previous work by Schmidt (3), calculations were made to obtain the temperature and velocity distributions from Prandtl's momentum-transfer theory and Taylor's vorticity-transfer theory. In each case an assumption had to be made concerning the mixing length and, as usual, a constant involved in this assumption had to be determined a posteriori from experiment. Though this constant could be chosen so that the result obtained agreed with experiment fairly well, recent investigations have shown that the structure of turbulence in a field of flow may be, and in general is, totally different from that dictated by any assumption concerning the mixing length. From Schmidt's experimental data for one value of $G(0.00219$ lb/sec) it can be shown that his standard deviations corresponding to 0.072 and 0.084 in Eqs. (28) and (29) are respectively 0.105 and 0.099, and that his coefficients corresponding to 4.7 and 11.0 in the same equations are respectively 2.7 and 13.7. Whereas these figures show agreement in the orders of magnitude, the discrepancy between 4.7 and 2.7 is quite large. This is perhaps partially due to the fact that in the writer's experiments a low flame was used, which was a source of momentum and of mass as well as of heat. On the other hand, Schmidt's experimental data, unlike the writer's, do not satisfy the momentum equation. According to his data, the right side of Eq. (30) is about 2.6 times as large as the left side, the discrepancy amounting to 160 percent.

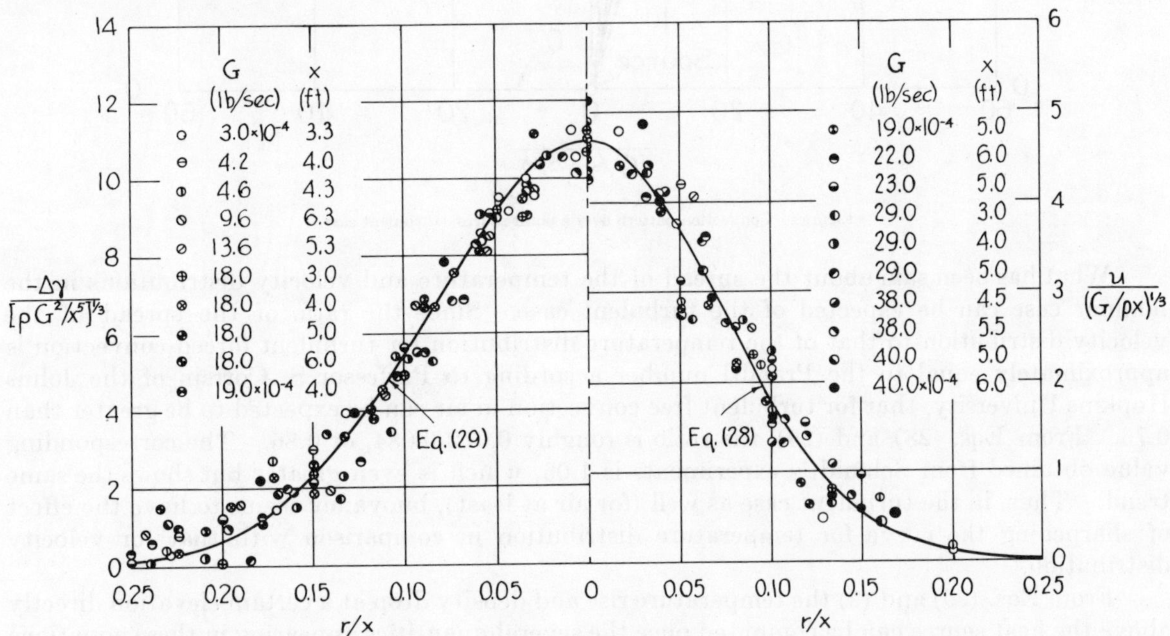

Figure 3—Distribution functions for turbulent convection over a point source.

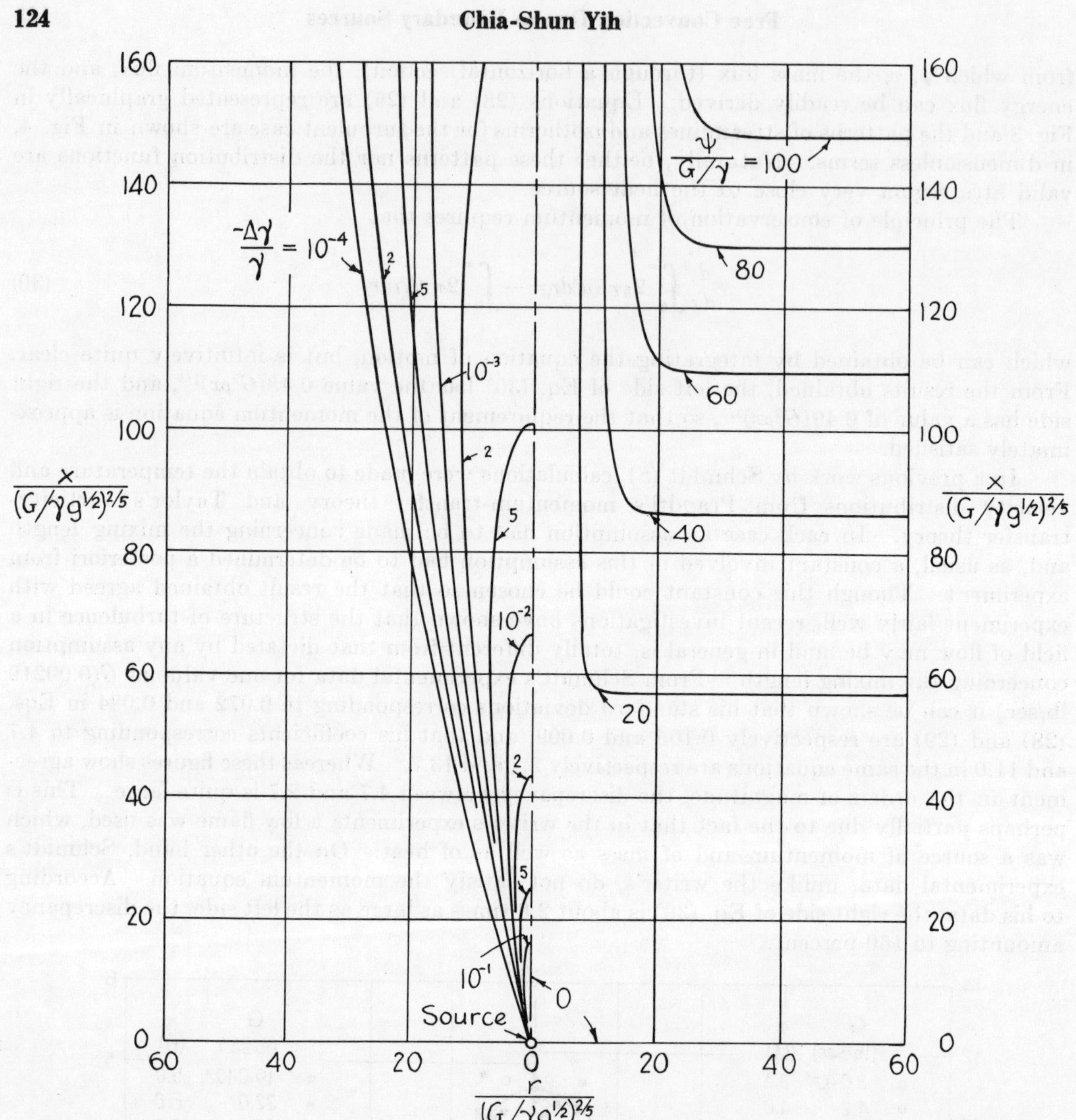

Figure 4—Convection pattern over a point source—turbulent case.

What has been said about the spread of the temperature and velocity distributions in the laminar case can be expected of the turbulent case. Since the ratio of the spread of the velocity distribution to that of the temperature distribution for turbulent forced convection is approximately equal to the Prandtl number according to Professor S. Corrsin of the Johns Hopkins University, that for turbulent free convection in air can be expected to be greater than 0.73. From Eqs. (28) and (29), the ratio is roughly 0.072/0.084, or 0.86. The corresponding value obtained from Schmidt's experiments is 1.06, which is even greater but shows the same trend. Thus, in the turbulent case as well (for air at least), buoyancy seems to have the effect of sharpening the curve for temperature distribution in comparison with that for velocity distribution.

From Eqs. (29) and (2) the temperature rise and density drop at a certain elevation directly above the heat source can be computed once the several quantities appearing in these equations are given. Admittedly, the validity of the results depends on the relative degree to which the condition that the ambient atmosphere be essentially isothermal and homogeneous is fulfilled. If the ambient lapse rate is known, the ambient temperature and density differences (from the values taken near the ground) at the same elevation can be computed in the usual way by the aid of the hydrostatic condition. If these changes are small compared with those computed from Eqs. (29) and (2), the results embodied in Eqs. (28) and (29) can be considered to be applicable up to the elevation at which the comparison is made. In general, the stronger the heat source, the higher the elevation below which the results can be applied.

Stability

To determine the stability parameter $\dfrac{\rho^2 h^2 G}{\mu^3}$, h was indicated by the breaking point of the smoke of a cigarette placed near the heat source, and G could be obtained by adding the G of the heat source, obtained by making one temperature measurement in the turbulent zone and computing from the plot of $-\left(\dfrac{x^5}{\rho G^2}\right)^{1/3}\Delta\gamma$, to that of the cigarette, obtained by careful calorimetry and observation of the burning rate.

The results of experiments show that

$$\frac{\rho^2 h^2 G}{\mu^3}=9\times10^9 \tag{31}$$

the small variation of $h^2 G$ for constant μ and ρ being illustrated by Fig. 5.

Although no special steps had been taken to eliminate initial disturbances, considerable time had been allowed for the air to calm down before h was measured. From the smoothness of the streamlines indicated by the smoke, the natural initial disturbances were seen to be uniformly small thoroughout the range of experiments. Since it could not be ascertained that disturbances of all frequencies existed, the stability parameter obtained is perhaps higher than what it should be according to the definition of the stability height h.

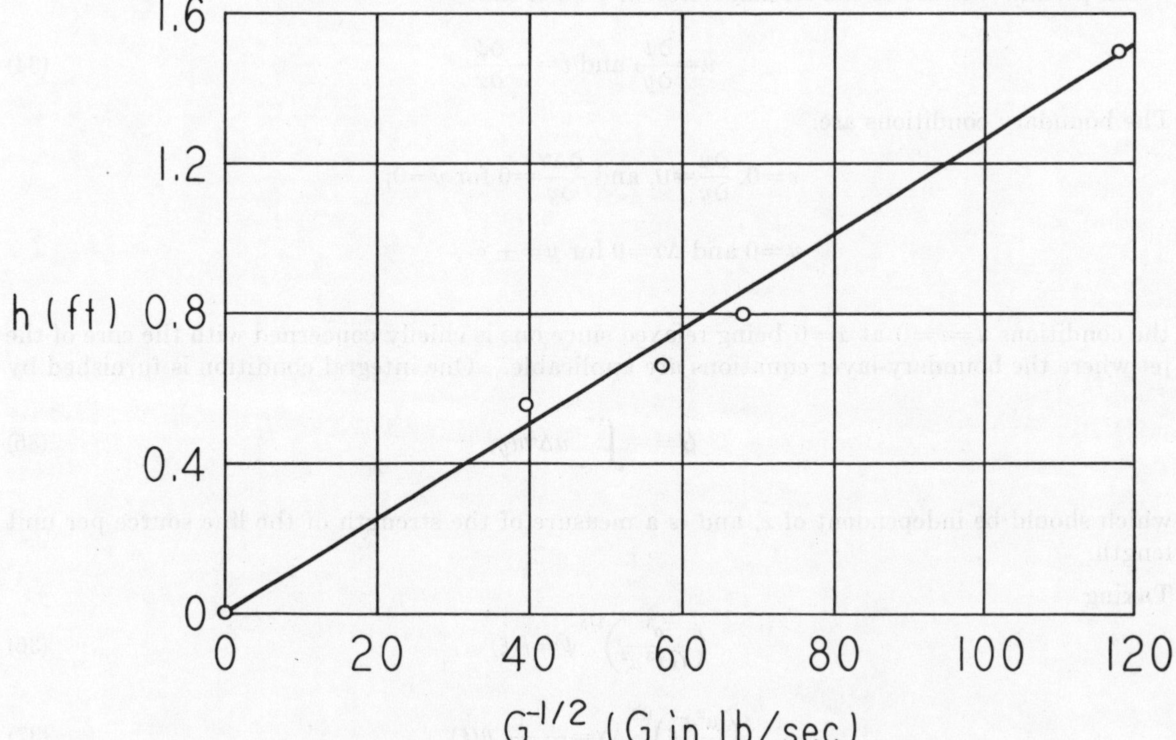

Figure 5—Variation of the stability height h with G for convection over a point source.

FREE CONVECTION DUE TO A LINE SOURCE OF HEAT

After the project on free convection due to a point source of heat was completed, investigation of the corresponding two-dimensional problem was undertaken at the Iowa Institute—not only to gain further fundamental understanding of free-convection phenomena, but also with a view to obtaining pertinent data in connection with a method of fog dispersal used for the landing of aircraft in England during the war. The analysis of the problem for the laminar and the turbulent cases bears much similarity to that of its axisymmetric counterpart. The solutions for the laminar case were completed at the Colorado A and M College.

Laminar Case

Under the same assumptions as for the axisymmetric case, two mathematical solutions in closed forms for $\sigma = \frac{5}{9}$ and $\sigma = 2$ have been found for the laminar case. Since the original article (4) contains a few numerical errors, it is particularly desirable to present here the corrected versions of the solutions.

In a vertical plane perpendicular to the line source, the trace of the line source is taken as the origin, and the vertical and horizontal lines issuing therefrom are taken as the x and y axes, respectively. If u and v are used to denote the velocity components in the x and y directions, the equation of motion and the diffusion equation can be written in their boundary-layer forms:

$$u\,\frac{\partial u}{\partial x} + v\,\frac{\partial u}{\partial y} = \nu\,\frac{\partial^2 u}{\partial y^2} - g\,\frac{\Delta\gamma}{\gamma_0}, \tag{32}$$

$$u\,\frac{\partial \Delta\gamma}{\partial x} + v\,\frac{\partial \Delta\gamma}{\partial y} = \alpha\,\frac{\partial^2 \Delta\gamma}{\partial y^2}. \tag{33}$$

The equation of continuity is

$$\frac{\partial u}{\partial x} + \frac{\partial v}{\partial y} = 0,$$

which permits the use of the stream function ψ such that

$$u = \frac{\partial \psi}{\partial y}, \text{ and } v = -\frac{\partial \psi}{\partial x}. \tag{34}$$

The boundary conditions are:

$$v = 0, \ \frac{\partial u}{\partial y} = 0, \text{ and } \frac{\partial \Delta\gamma}{\partial y} = 0 \text{ for } y = 0;$$

$$u = 0 \text{ and } \Delta\gamma = 0 \text{ for } y = \pm\infty,$$

the conditions $u = v = 0$ at $x = 0$ being relaxed since one is chiefly concerned with the core of the jet where the boundary-layer equations are applicable. One integral condition is furnished by

$$G = -\int_{-\infty}^{\infty} u\Delta\gamma\,dy, \tag{35}$$

which should be independent of x, and is a measure of the strength of the line source per unit length.

Taking

$$\left(\frac{\rho^3}{Gx^3\mu^2}\right)^{1/5}\psi = f(\xi) \tag{36}$$

$$\left(\frac{\mu^2 x^3}{\rho^3 G^4}\right)^{1/5}\Delta\gamma = -\frac{1}{125}\,\theta(\xi) \tag{37}$$

Free Convection Due to Boundary Sources

in which

$$\xi=\frac{1}{5}\left(\frac{\rho^2 G}{\mu^3 x^2}\right)^{1/5} y \tag{38}$$

and using Eqs. (34), one can transform Eqs. (32), (33), and (35) into the following forms:

$$f'f'-3ff''=f'''+\theta, \tag{39}$$

$$\theta f'+f\theta'=-\frac{\theta''}{3\sigma}, \tag{40}$$

$$\int_{-\infty}^{\infty} f'\theta d\xi=125. \tag{41}$$

The boundary conditions can now be written

$$f(0)=f''(0)=\theta'(0)=0,$$
$$f'(\pm\infty)=\theta(\pm\infty)=0. \tag{42}$$

For $\sigma=\frac{5}{9}$, the differential system consisting of Eqs. (39) to (42) is satisfied by

$$f(\xi)=2.24 \tanh 1.863\xi, \quad \theta(\xi)=41.99 \operatorname{sech}^2 1.863\xi \tag{43}$$

and for $\sigma=2$, by

$$f(\xi)=1.69 \tanh 2.505\xi, \quad \theta(\xi)=70.20 \operatorname{sech}^4 2.505\xi. \tag{44}$$

With the functions $f(\xi)$ and $\theta(\xi)$ given, Eqs. (34) and (36) to (38) constitute the solution. In particular, one has, for $\sigma=5/9$,

$$5\left(\frac{\rho u}{G^2 x}\right)^{1/5} u=f'(\xi)=4.16 \operatorname{sech}^2 1.863\xi, \tag{45}$$

and for $\sigma=2$,

$$5\left(\frac{\rho u}{G^2 x}\right)^{1/5} u=f'(\xi)=4.23 \operatorname{sech}^2 2.505\xi. \tag{46}$$

For $\sigma=0.733$, which is the case for air under normal conditions, Mr. E. Bendor of the Imperial College of London has found an approximate solution by numerical integration. The results are plotted in Fig. 6 together with those for Prandtl numbers 5/9 and 2. It is seen

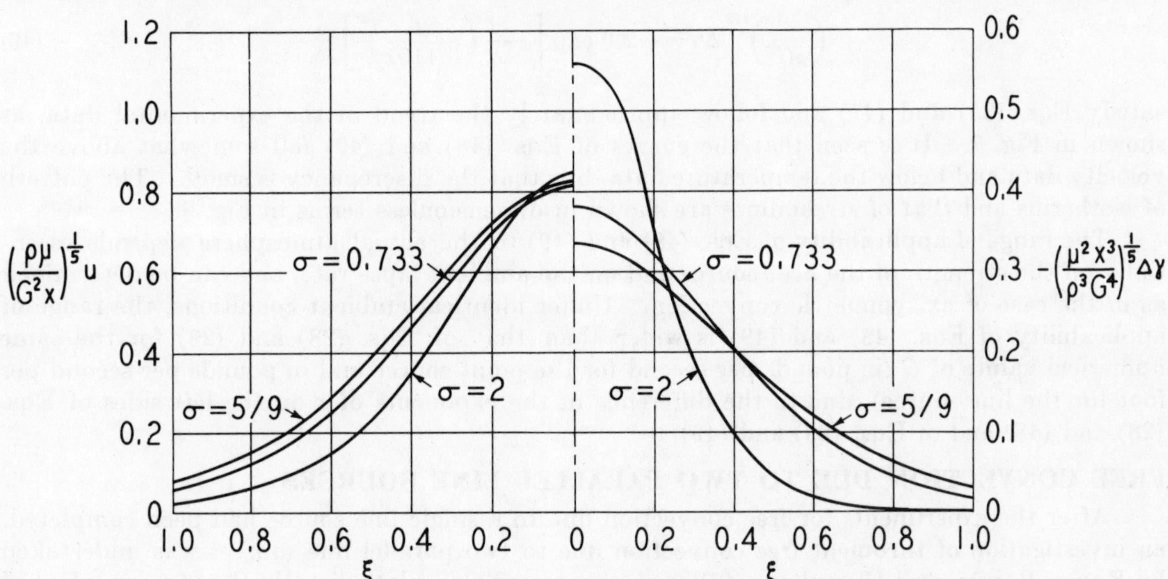

Figure 6—Distribution functions for laminar convection over a line source.

that, although Mr. Bendor's value for the velocity parameter at $\xi=0$ is not between the corresponding values for Prandtl numbers 5/9 and 2, as it should be, his solution shows the correct general trend. Here again, as in the case of the point source, the larger the Prandtl number, the more concentrated the temperature and velocity distributions, the effect of Prandtl number on the temperature distribution being more pronounced.

From a comparison of the three known solutions obtained with the corresponding solutions for forced convection (2), it can be concluded that, up to $\sigma=2$ at least, the effect of buoyancy is again to sharpen the temperature distribution curve in comparison with the velocity distribution curve.

The patterns of isotherms and streamlines can be easily obtained, but since they do not differ greatly in general character from the corresponding ones for the case of the point source, there is no need to present them.

Turbulent Case

A dimensional analysis similar to that performed for the case of the point source yields, for turbulent flow,

$$\left(\frac{\rho}{G}\right)^{1/3} u = F_6\left(\frac{y}{x}\right),$$

$$\left(\frac{x^3}{\rho G^2}\right)^{1/3} \Delta\gamma = F_7\left(\frac{y}{x}\right).$$

If the functions F_6 and F_7 are determined, the stream function, the discharge across a horizontal section, the momentum flux and the energy flux can be obtained by integration. The forms of F_6 and F_7 should be such that both Eq. (35) and the momentum equation

$$\frac{d}{dx}\int_{-\infty}^{\infty} \rho u^2 dy = -\int_{-\infty}^{\infty} \Delta\gamma dy \tag{47}$$

are satisfied.

Using the same experimental technique as for the case of the point source, Humphreys (5) found that

$$\left(\frac{\rho}{G}\right)^{1/3} u = 1.80 \exp\left[-\frac{1}{2}\left(\frac{y}{0.125x}\right)^2\right] \tag{48}$$

and

$$\left(\frac{x^3}{\rho G^2}\right)^{1/3} \Delta\gamma = -2.6 \exp\left[-\frac{1}{2}\left(\frac{y}{0.110x}\right)^2\right] \tag{49}$$

satisfy Eqs. (35) and (47) and follow approximately the trend of the experimental data, as shown in Fig. 7. It is seen that the curves of Eqs. (48) and (49) fall somewhat above the velocity data and below the temperature data, but that the discrepancy is small. The pattern of isotherms and that of streamlines are shown in dimensionless terms in Fig. 8.

The range of applicability of Eqs. (48) and (49) to the actual atmosphere depends essentially on the strength of the heat source and on the ambient lapse rate, and can be determined as in the case of axisymmetric convection. Under identical ambient conditions, the range of applicability of Eqs. (48) and (49) is wider than that of Eqs. (28) and (29) for the same numerical values of G (in pounds per second for the point source and in pounds per second per foot for the line source), due to the difference in the exponents of x on the left sides of Eqs. (28) and (48) and of Eqs. (29) and (49).

FREE CONVECTION DUE TO TWO PARALLEL LINE SOURCES

After the experiments for free convection due to a single line source had been completed, an investigation of turbulent free convection due to two parallel line sources was undertaken by Rouse, Baines, and Humphreys (6) in an endeavor to simulate directly the afore-mentioned method of fog dispersal used in England during the war.

Free Convection Due to Boundary Sources 129

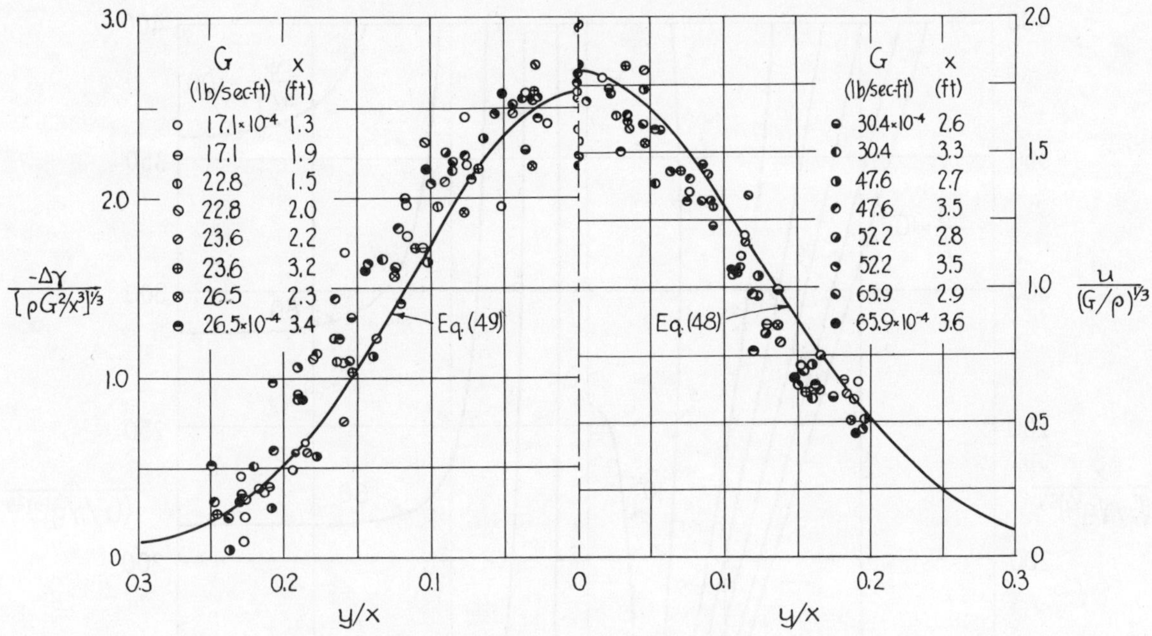

Figure 7—Distribution functions for turbulent convection over a line source.

If, in a plane perpendicular to the line sources, the origin is taken on the boundary mid-way between the sources and the vertical and horizontal lines issuing therefrom are taken as the x- and y-axes, and if, as before, u and v denote the velocity components in the x- and y-directions, the quantity

$$G=\int_0^{\infty} u\Delta\gamma\,dy, \tag{50}$$

in which $\Delta\gamma$ has the same meaning as before, is again a constant and is a measure of the strength of each of the line sources per unit length. If the distance between the sources is denoted by $2y_0$, then from a dimensional analysis the following relationships can be obtained:

$$\left(\frac{\rho}{G}\right)^{1/3} u=\phi_1\left(\frac{x}{y_0},\frac{y}{y_0}\right),$$

$$-\left(\frac{y_0^3}{\rho G^2}\right)^{1/3} \Delta\gamma=\phi_2\left(\frac{x}{y_0},\frac{y}{y_0}\right).$$

The explicit forms of the functions ϕ_1 and ϕ_2 are the chief objects sought in the investigation. The forms of ϕ_1 and ϕ_2 should be such that both Eqs. (50) and (47) are satisfied.

The methods of measurement were the same as used in connection with free convection due to a point source of heat. The results obtained are shown in Fig. 9, in which smooth curves have been drawn to approximate the trend of the data, and at the same time to satisfy Eqs. (50) and (47). It is seen that, in each case investigated, these curves fall somewhat above the velocity data and below the temperature data. This discrepancy was probably due in part to effects of radiation on the thermocouple indication and in part to the fact that the temperature differences were not always small (the average maximum reading was about 60° F. above room temperature). Since previous studies had not disclosed a satisfactory method of shielding, and a detailed evaluation of thermodynamic effects was not considered compatible with the elementary nature of the project, the results were accepted without further correction, and by correlation of the data from all runs the systematic sequences of curves satisfying Eqs. (50) and (47) and shown in Fig. 10 were obtained.

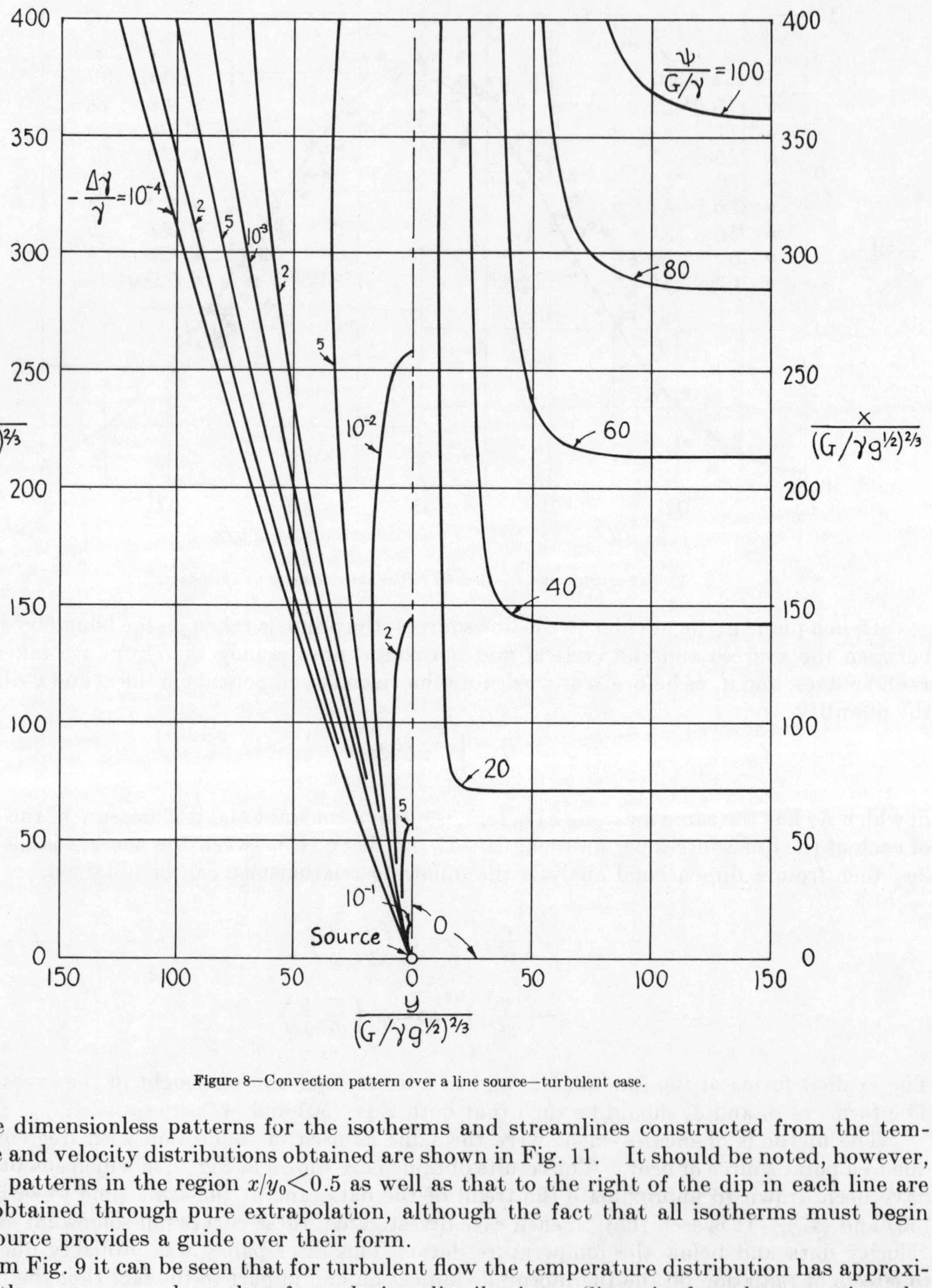

Chia-Shun Yih

Figure 8—Convection pattern over a line source—turbulent case.

The dimensionless patterns for the isotherms and streamlines constructed from the temperature and velocity distributions obtained are shown in Fig. 11. It should be noted, however, that the patterns in the region $x/y_0 < 0.5$ as well as that to the right of the dip in each line are results obtained through pure extrapolation, although the fact that all isotherms must begin at the source provides a guide over their form.

From Fig. 9 it can be seen that for turbulent flow the temperature distribution has approximately the same spread as that for velocity distribution. Since in forced convection the temperature distribution would have a wider spread than that for the velocity distribution, it is seen that, once again, the effect of buoyancy is to sharpen the temperature curve in comparison with the velocity curve. Remarkable also is the fact that at any elevation greater than 0.5 y_0 the temperature and longitudinal velocity decrease monotonically from $y=0$ outwards, showing no rise above the sources. This indicates a strong inward current near the boundary as a result of the rising of the fluid in the central core.

Free Convection Due to Boundary Sources

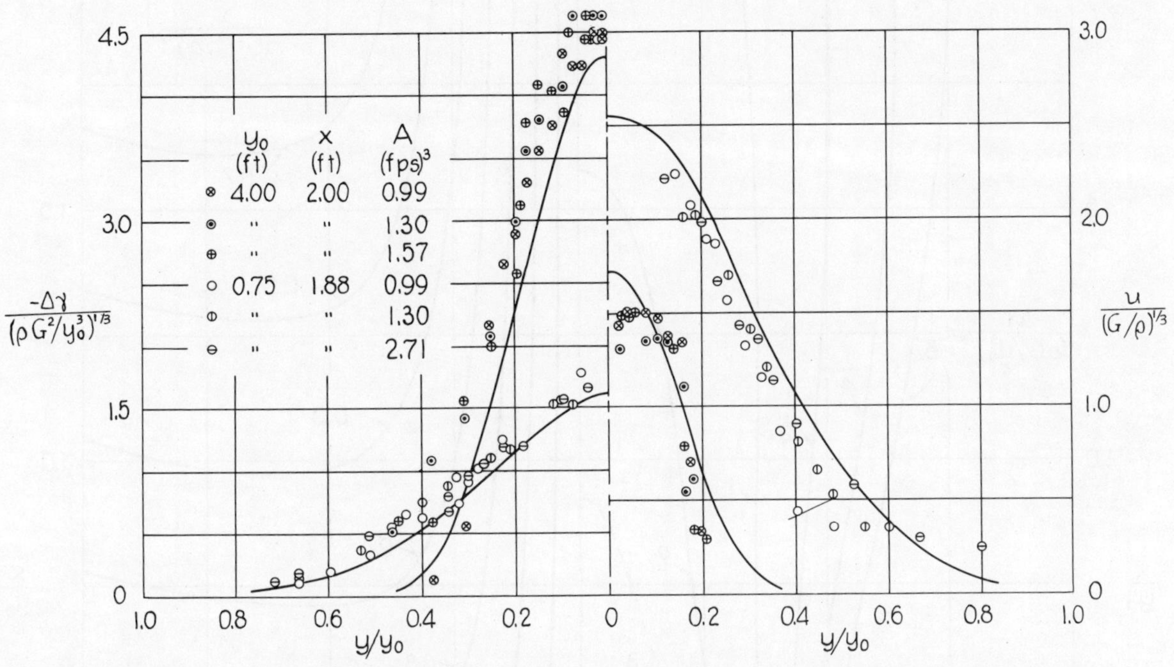

Figure 9—Typical experimental results for turbulent convection over parallel line sources.

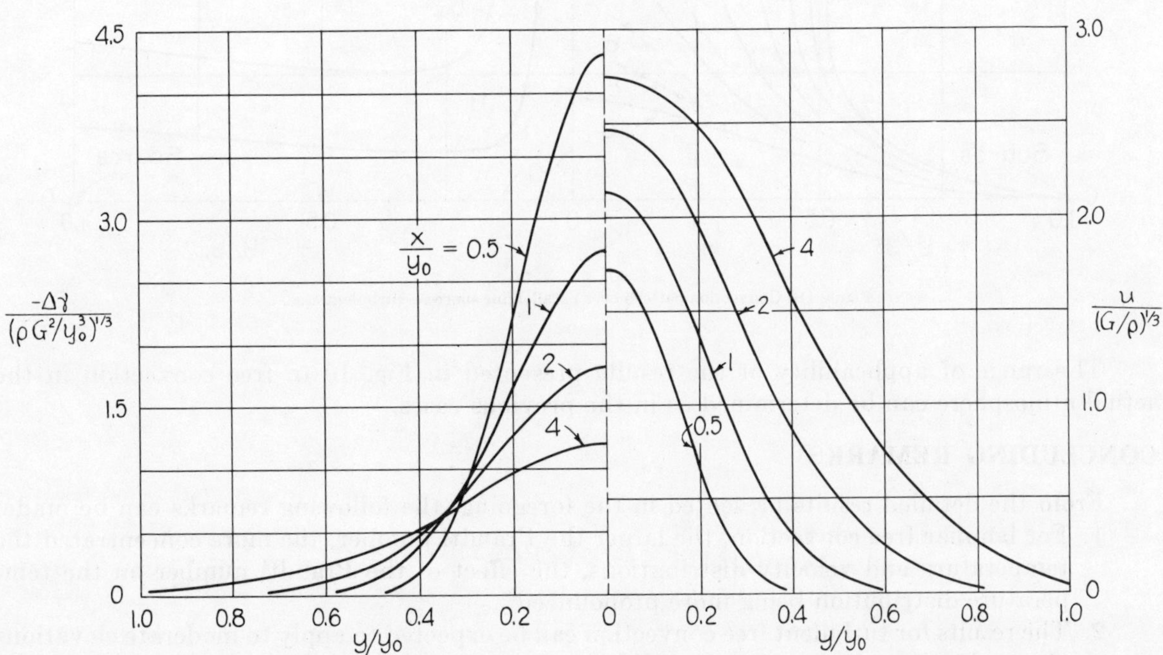

Figure 10—Generalized distribution functions for turbulent convection over parallel line sources.

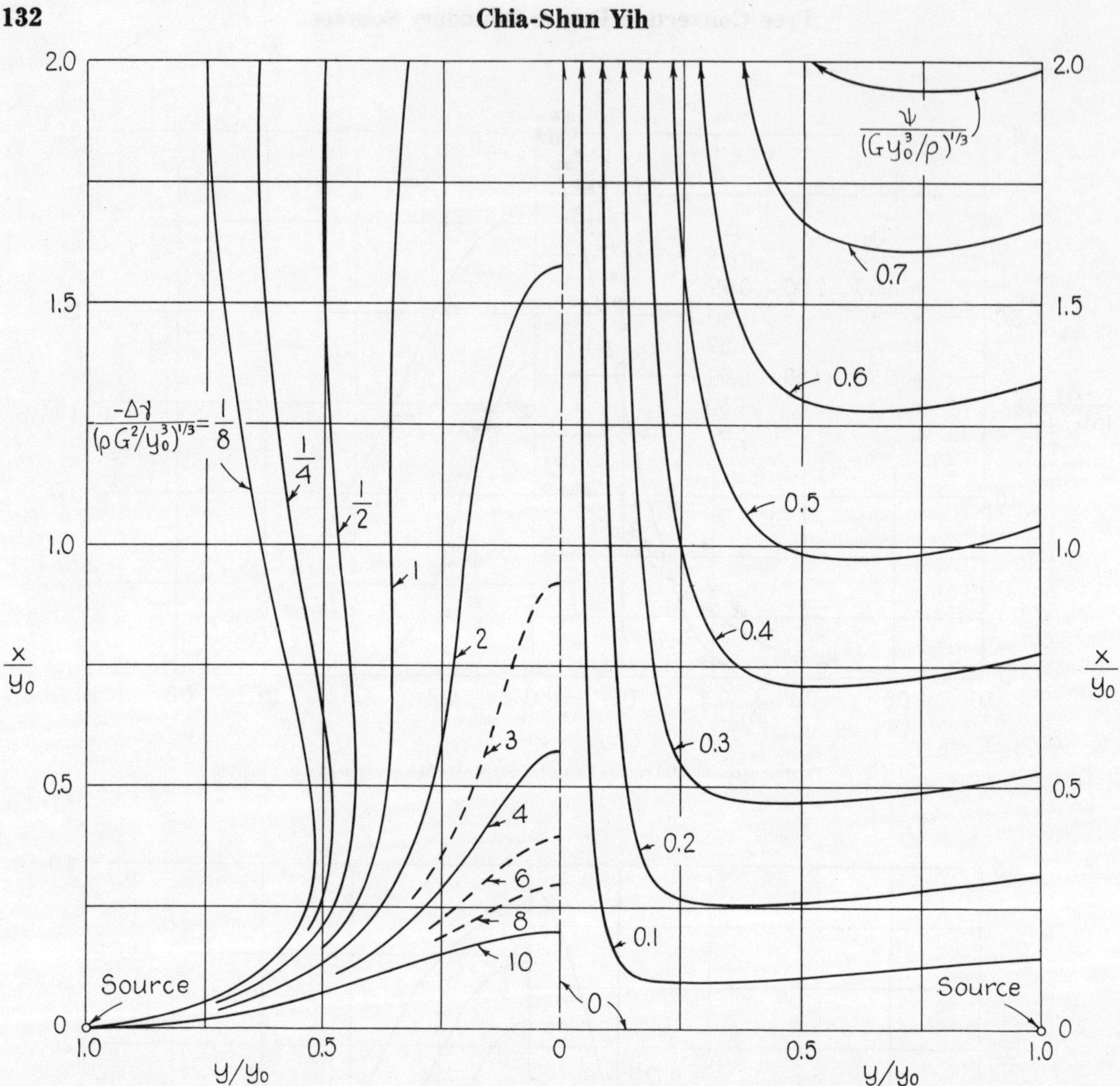

Figure 11—Convection pattern over parallel line sources—turbulent case.

The range of applicability of the results presented in Fig. 10 to free convection in the actual atmosphere can be determined as in the previous cases.

CONCLUDING REMARKS

From the detailed results presented in the foregoing, the following remarks can be made:

1. For laminar free convection, the larger the Prandtl number, the more concentrated the temperature and velocity distributions, the effect of the Prandtl number on the temperature distribution being more pronounced.

2. The results for turbulent free convection can be expected to apply to moderate elevations above the ground, particularly if the stability of the atmosphere is not great and the boundary source is strong. The range of applicability can be determined approximately from these results in each case once the lapse rate of the ambient atmosphere and the strength of the heat source are given.

3. The effect of thermal buoyancy, which characterizes free convection, is to concentrate the temperature distribution in relation to the velocity distribution. This is true for both laminar and turbulent cases, and for both two-dimensional and axisymmetric flow.

ACKNOWLEDGMENTS

All phases of the present investigation were partially supported by the Office of Naval Research.   The two closed solutions for laminar free convection from a line source were obtained at the Colorado Agricultural and Mechanical College under Contract N9onr–82401.   All the other results contained in this paper (except, of course, those explicitly quoted from Schmidt and Bendor) were obtained at the Iowa Institute of Hydraulic Research under Contract N8onr–500.   Mr. Bendor pointed out a few numerical mistakes in the author's original solutions for the laminar cases.

REFERENCES

1 **Yih, C. S.,** "Free Convection due to a Point Source of Heat," Proc. 1st U. S. Nat. Congr. Appl. Mech. 941–947, June 1951

2 **Yih, C. S.,** "Temperature Distribution in a Steady, Laminar, Preheated Air Jet," J. Appl. Mech. 17:381–382, December 1950

3 **Schmidt, W.,** "Turbulente Ausbreitung eines Stromes erhitzter Luft," Z. Angew. Math. Mech. 21: 265–278, 351–363, 1941

4 **Yih, C. S.,** "Laminar Free Convection due to a Line Source of Heat," Trans. A. G. U. 33 (No. 5): 669–672, October 1952

5 **Rouse, H., Yih, C. S.,** and **Humphreys, H. W.,** "Gravitational Convection from a Boundary Source," Tellus 4 (No. 3): 201–210, August 1952

6 **Rouse, H., Baines, W. D.,** and **Humphreys, H. W.,** "Free Convection over Parallel Sources of Heat," Proc. Phy. Soc. B LXVI: 393–399, 1952

Reprinted from JOURNAL OF THE AERONAUTICAL SCIENCES
Copyright, 1954, by the Institute of the Aeronautical Sciences and reprinted by permission of the copyright owner

JANUARY, 1954   VOLUME 21, No. 1

Temperature Distribution in Laminar Stagnation-Point Flow with Axisymmetry

CHIA-SHUN YIH*

Iowa Institute of Hydraulic Research, State University of Iowa

ABSTRACT

Based on the velocity distribution given by Homann in 1936 for the laminar incompressible flow near a stagnation point in axisymmetric flow, solutions for the following cases of forced convection are obtained:

(a) A point source of heat is situated at the stagnation point on an insulated boundary.

(b) The difference between the temperature of the boundary and the ambient temperature varies as an arbitrary power of the distance from the stagnation point.

(c) The temperature rise is a result of viscous dissipation alone.

Solutions for practical cases are obtained by combining the result for case (c) with that for case (a) or (b).

Numerical results are given for all three cases for various parametric values of the Prandtl Number, with special emphasis on the Prandtl Number 0.7, which applies approximately to air under normal conditions.

(1) INTRODUCTION

THE VELOCITY DISTRIBUTION in laminar stagnation flow with axisymmetry was obtained by Homann[1] in 1936. Since his solution is one of the rare exact solutions of the Navier-Stokes equations of motion, it seems desirable to study the temperature distribution in the fluid for various boundary conditions—on the assumption that the velocity distribution given by Homann is essentially undisturbed by the nonhomogeneous temperature of the fluid.

With the velocity distribution determined from the Homann solution, the energy equation can be solved for various boundary conditions. Temperature rise due to viscous shear can be discussed separately.

(2) VELOCITY DISTRIBUTION

Since the velocity distribution obtained by Homann is to be used in the calculations, a brief résumé of his solution is necessary. If the stagnation point on the bounding plane is taken as the origin and if r and z are, respectively, the radial distance from the origin and the vertical distance from the boundary (see Fig. 1), then the Navier-Stokes equations of motion are

$$u\frac{\partial u}{\partial r} + w\frac{\partial u}{\partial z} = -\frac{1}{\rho}\frac{\partial p}{\partial r} + \nu\left(\frac{\partial^2 u}{\partial r^2} + \frac{1}{r}\frac{\partial u}{\partial r} - \frac{u}{r^2} + \frac{\partial^2 u}{\partial z^2}\right) \quad (1)$$

$$u\frac{\partial w}{\partial r} + w\frac{\partial w}{\partial z} = -\frac{1}{\rho}\frac{\partial p}{\partial z} + \nu\left(\frac{\partial^2 w}{\partial r^2} + \frac{1}{r}\frac{\partial w}{\partial r} + \frac{\partial^2 w}{\partial z^2}\right) \quad (2)$$

in which u and w are the velocity components in the r- and z-directions, respectively; ρ and ν are, respectively, the density and the kinematic viscosity of the fluid; and p is the pressure. The equation of continuity is

$$(\partial/\partial r)\,(ru) + (\partial/\partial z)\,(rw) = 0$$

which permits the use of the Stokes stream function ψ such that

$$u = \frac{1}{r}\frac{\partial\psi}{\partial z}, \qquad w = -\frac{1}{r}\frac{\partial\psi}{\partial r} \quad (3)$$

If one takes

$$\psi = (\beta\nu/2)^{1/2}r^2 f(\eta)$$
$$\eta = (2\beta/\nu)^{1/2}z \quad (4)$$

in which β is a constant, one obtains from Eq. (3)

$$u = \beta r f'(\eta), \qquad w = -(2\beta\nu)^{1/2}f(\eta) \quad (5)$$

where the prime denotes differentiation with respect to η. Since β is so far not specified, one can take $f'(\infty) = 1$. The radial velocity just outside of the boundary layer is then $u_1 = \beta r$, and

$$-\frac{1}{\rho}\frac{\partial p}{\partial r} = u_1\frac{\partial u_1}{\partial r} = \beta^2 r \quad (6)$$

It then follows, from Eq. (1), that

Received June 16, 1953.
* Research Engineer.

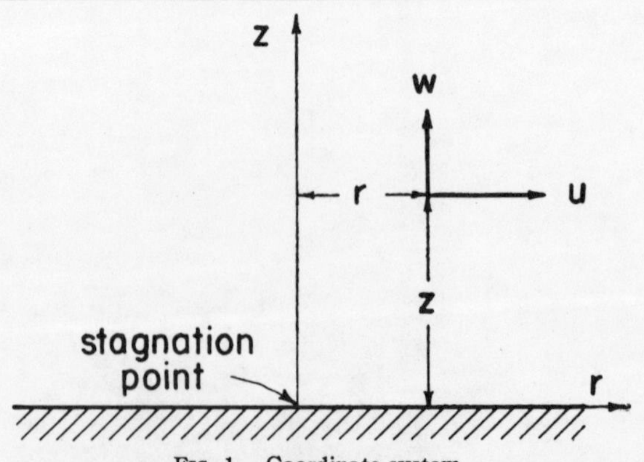

FIG. 1. Coordinate system.

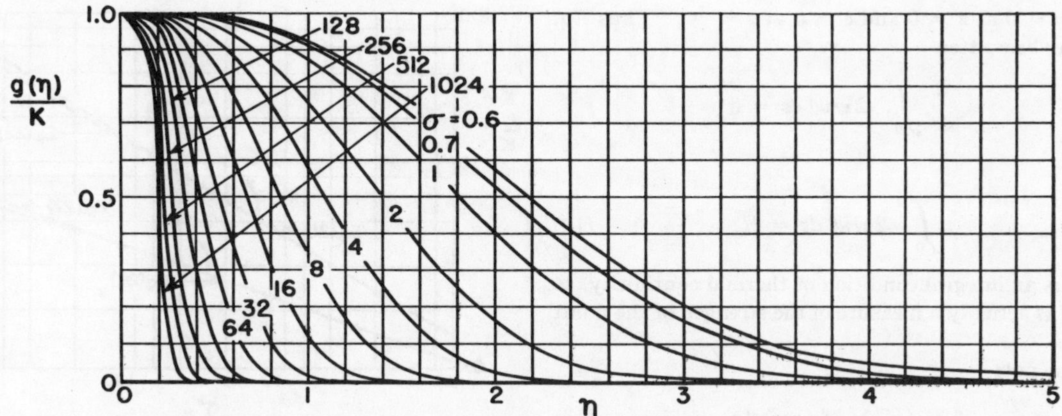

FIG. 2.   Graphical representation of Eq. (20) for various Prandtl Numbers.

$$f'^2 - 2ff'' = 1 + 2f''' \qquad (7)$$

which is to be solved with proper boundary conditions. After f is obtained, one can integrate Eqs. (2) and (6) and obtain an expression for the pressure. The equation obtained and solved by Homann differs from Eq. (7) only in that the coefficient of f''' is 1 in Homann's equation instead of 2, because of the absence of the constant 2 in the expressions assumed by Homann for ψ and η. The foregoing slightly modified treatment was used by Frössling[2] and is presented because Frössling's numerical solution is to be used in the present paper, owing to its greater accuracy.

(3) The Energy Equation

For liquids, the energy equation is (page 606, reference 3)

$$\rho J c_v \frac{DT}{Dt} = Jk\nabla^2 T + \Phi \qquad (8)$$

in which J is Joule's value, T is the absolute temperature, c_v is the specific heat at constant volume, k is the thermal conductivity, Φ is the dissipation function, $DT \div Dt$ is the substantial derivative of T, and $\nabla^2 T$ is the Laplacian of T. For gases, the work done by pressure cannot be neglected even if the dilatation of the velocity vector is small, and the energy equation is of the following form (page 607, reference 3):

$$\rho J c_p \frac{DT}{Dt} = Jk\nabla^2 T + \left(\Phi + \frac{Dp}{Dt}\right) \qquad (9)$$

in which c_p is the specific heat at constant pressure.

If α is defined to be $k/\rho c$, c standing for c_v for liquids and for c_p for gases, and if the nonhomogeneous terms are disregarded, Eqs. (8) and (9) can be represented by the single equation

$$DT/Dt = \alpha\nabla^2 T \qquad (10)$$

A solution of Eq. (10) is a complementary solution of Eq. (8) or (9). The complete solution is obtained by adding to it a particular solution. In the following, the complementary solution will be obtained first, and the particular solution will be discussed separately.

(4) Diffusion from a Point Source of Heat

Neglecting the temperature change due to pressure and viscous dissipation, the temperature rise in the fluid due to a point source of heat situated at the stagnation point can be calculated from Eq. (10), which for steady flow and for the particular coordinates chosen assumes the form

$$u\frac{\partial T}{\partial r} + w\frac{\partial T}{\partial z} = \alpha\left(\frac{\partial^2 T}{\partial r^2} + \frac{1}{r}\frac{\partial T}{\partial r} + \frac{\partial^2 T}{\partial z^2}\right) \qquad (11)$$

For small thermal diffusivity the last equation can be written for the thermal boundary layer as

$$u(\partial T/\partial r) + w(\partial T/\partial z) = \alpha(\partial^2 T/\partial z^2) \qquad (12)$$

If the ambient temperature is designated as T_0, the dimensionless quantity

$$\theta = (T - T_0)/T_0 \qquad (13)$$

can be conveniently used instead of T in Eq. (12):

$$u(\partial\theta/\partial r) + w(\partial\theta/\partial z) = \alpha(\partial^2\theta/\partial z^2) \qquad (14)$$

If the boundary is impervious to heat, $\partial\theta/\partial z$ vanishes at $z = 0$. Then multiplying Eq. (14) by $2\pi r$ and integrating with respect to z, one has

$$\int_0^\infty 2\pi r u \frac{\partial\theta}{\partial r}\,dz + \int_0^\infty 2\pi r w \frac{\partial\theta}{\partial z}\,dz = \alpha\frac{\partial\theta}{\partial z}\bigg]_0^\infty = 0 \qquad (15)$$

since $\partial\theta/\partial z$ vanishes also at $z = \infty$. By partial integration and from Eq. (3), the second integral above can be written

$$\int_0^\infty 2\,\pi r w \frac{\partial\theta}{\partial z}\,dz = 2\pi r w\theta\bigg]_0^\infty + 2\pi\int_0^\infty \theta\frac{\partial^2\psi}{\partial r\partial z}\,dz = 2\pi\int_0^\infty \theta\frac{\partial(ru)}{\partial r}\,dz$$

ince $w = 0$ at $z = 0$ and $\theta = 0$ at $z = \infty$. Thus Eq. (15) can be written

$$\frac{\partial}{\partial r} \int_0^\infty 2\pi r u \theta \, dz = 0$$

or

$$\int_0^\infty 2\pi r u \theta \, dz = H \qquad (16)$$

which is an integral condition of thermal continuity, so that H is actually a measure of the strength of the point source.

If one puts

$$\theta = (H/\sqrt{2\beta\nu}\ \pi r^2)g(\eta) \qquad (17)$$

Eq. (14) becomes, from Eq. (5),

$$-\sigma(f'g + fg') = g'' \qquad (18)$$

in which σ is the Prandtl Number ν/α, and Eq. (16) becomes

$$\int_0^\infty f'g \, d\eta = 1 \qquad (19)$$

The solution of Eq. (18) with the boundary conditions $g(\infty) = 0$, $g'(0) = 0$ is

$$g = K \exp\left(-\sigma \int_0^\eta f \, d\eta\right) \qquad (20)$$

in which K is determined from Eq. (19):

$$K^{-1} = \int_0^\infty f' \exp\left(-\sigma \int_0^\eta f \, d\eta\right) d\eta \qquad (21)$$

Since f is already given by Frössling,[2] the last two equations constitute the solution for Eq. (18), and Eqs. (13) and (17) give the temperature distribution. The function $g(\eta)/K$ is plotted in Fig. 2 for various values of the Prandtl Number. The quality K computed from Eq. (21) is plotted in Fig. 3 against the Prandtl Number. The dependence of K on σ can be expressed approximately by the formula

$$K = 0.886\sigma^{0.6} \qquad (22)$$

almost up to $\sigma = 1,024$, the highest Prandtl Number considered.

(5) DIFFUSION FROM BOUNDARY

If θ varies as an arbitrary power of r on the boundary, one can write

$$\theta = a_n(\beta/\nu)^{n/2} r^n g_n(\eta) \qquad (23)$$

in which n is any arbitrary positive number and a_n an arbitrarily assigned constant. Substitution of Eqs. (5) and (23) into Eq. (14) results in the equation

$$g_n'' + \sigma[fg_n' - (n/2)f'g_n] = 0 \qquad (24)$$

to be solved with the boundary conditions $g_n(0) = 1$,

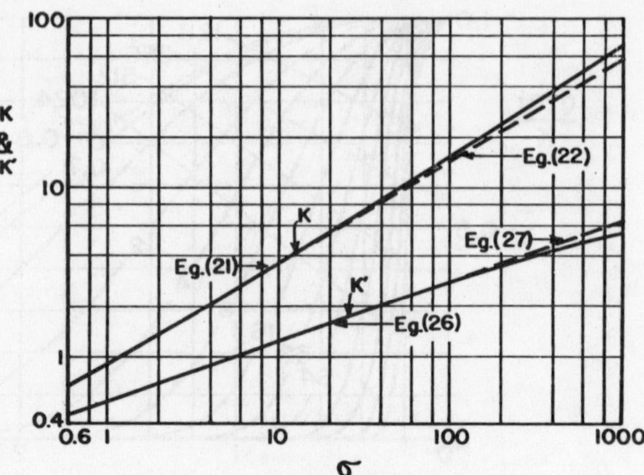

FIG. 3. Graphical representation of Eqs. (21), (22), (26), and (27).

$g_n(\infty) = 0$, the function f being already given by Frössling.[2]

For constant temperature at the boundary, $n = 0$, and the condition $g_0(0) = 1$ amounts to taking

$$a_0 = (T_1 - T_0)/T_0$$

in which T_0 is the ambient temperature and T_1 is the temperature at the boundary. The solution of Eq. (24) for $n = 0$ satisfying the boundary conditions is

$$g_0(\eta) = K' \int_\eta^\infty e^{-\sigma \int_0^\eta f \, d\eta} \, d\eta \qquad (25)$$

in which

$$K'^{-1} = \int_0^\infty e^{-\sigma \int_0^\eta f \, d\eta} \, d\eta \qquad (26)$$

The function g_0 given by Eq. (25) is plotted in Fig. 4 for various values of the Prandtl Number. Since the rate of heat transfer from the plate is given by

$$h = -k \left.\frac{\partial T}{\partial z}\right]_{z=0} = k \left(\frac{2\beta}{\nu}\right)^{1/2} (T_1 - T_0)g_0'(0) =$$

$$k \left(\frac{2\beta}{\nu}\right)^{1/2} (T_1 - T_0)K'$$

it seems desirable to express the quantity K' as a function of the Prandtl Number. The values of K' calculated from Eq. (26) for different Prandtl Numbers are plotted in Fig. 3, from which it is seen that the dependence of K' on σ can be expressed by the formula

$$K' = 0.539\sigma^{0.36} \qquad (27)$$

up to $\sigma = 258$, with slight deviation for higher Prandtl Numbers. It should be noted that, for $n = 0$, the left side of Eq. (23) is independent of r, and Eq. (11) coincides with Eq. (14), the solutions of which are thus exact solutions of the homogeneous energy equation. Noteworthy also is the fact that the solution for $\sigma = 0.7$ represents the first term of the Frössling expansion[2] for the temperature distribution in the laminar bound-

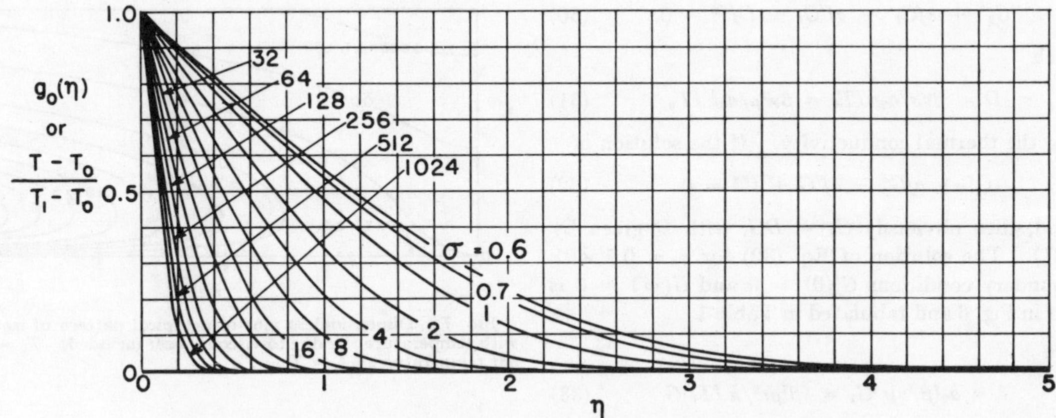

FIG. 4.   Graphical representation of Eq. (25) for various Prandtl Numbers.

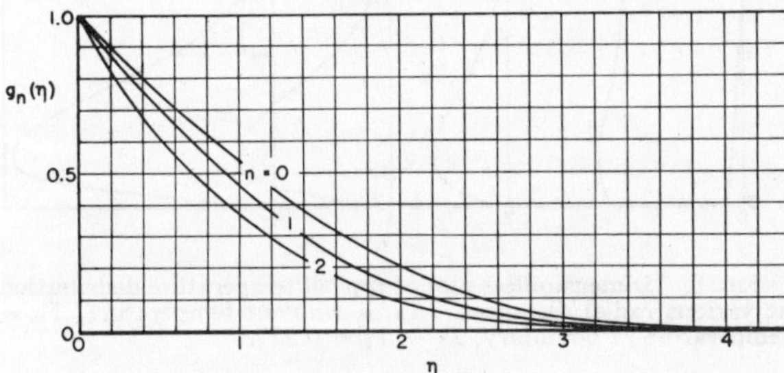

FIG. 5.   Solutions of Eq. (24) for $n = 0$, 1, and 2 for Prandtl Number 0.7.

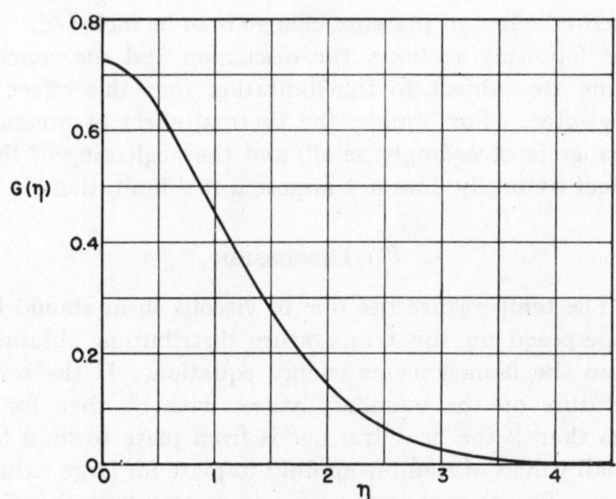

FIG. 6.   Solution of Eq. (32) for $\sigma = 0.7$.

ary layer of a blunt-nosed body with a uniform temperature on the surface exposed to air.

For $n = 1$ and 2, the solutions are obtained for the Prandtl Number 0.7 only and are plotted in Fig. 5, together with the solution for $n = 0$ and the same Prandtl Number.   For the purpose of calculating the heat transfer from the boundary for $n = 1$ and 2, it may be noted that

$$g_1'(0) = 0.582, \quad g_2'(0) = 0.845$$

Since Eq. (24) is linear in g_n, numerical solutions for higher values of n can be easily obtained if needed. Naturally, θ can vary as a fractional power of r, and if θ varies as a sum of powers or as a convergent power series of r, its solution can be obtained by superposition.

(6) TEMPERATURE RISE DUE TO VISCOUS DISSIPATION

The dissipation function is

$$\Phi = \mu \left[2 \left(\frac{\partial u}{\partial r} \right)^2 + 2 \left(\frac{u}{r} \right)^2 + 2 \left(\frac{\partial w}{\partial z} \right)^2 + \left(\frac{\partial u}{\partial z} + \frac{\partial w}{\partial r} \right)^2 \right]$$

which, from Eq. (6), can be written

$$\Phi = 12\mu\beta^2 f'^2 + 2\beta^3 \rho r^2 f''^2 \tag{28}$$

From Eq. (28) it can be seen that, for small viscosity and values of r which are not too small, the first term on the right is negligible compared with the second term, especially in the boundary layer where f and f' are small.   This situation fails to hold only at large values of z.   One should remember, however, that the Homann flow is not realistic at large values of z, since in reality the boundary is finite in extent and the flow is uniform $(u = 0)$ at large z.   Consequently, in actual flows the first term on the right of Eq. (28) is negligible at large values of z also, so that it can be neglected entirely except for small values of r.   Thus the nonhomogeneous terms to be considered in an approximate solution of Eq. (8) can be taken to be the second term on the right of Eq. (28), which is the term $\mu(\partial u/\partial z)^2$ usually used.

Since the nonhomogeneous term varies as the square of r, it should be included in the energy equation for θ given by Eq. (23), with $n = 2$ and G_2 replacing g_2 in order to distinguish between the particular and the complementary solutions.   Substituting Eqs. (13), (23), and

$$\Phi = 2\beta^3 \rho r^2 f''^2 \tag{29}$$

into Eq. (8) or (9), one obtains the equation

$$G_2'' + \sigma f G_2' - \sigma f' G_2 + D f''^2 = 0 \qquad (30)$$

in which

$$D = \beta \nu \sigma / a_2 c J T_0 = \beta \nu^2 \rho / a_2 k J T_0 \qquad (31)$$

k being the thermal conductivity. If the solution of

$$G'' + \sigma f G' - \sigma f' G + f''^2 = 0 \qquad (32)$$

is found, then obviously $G_2 = DG$, with D given by Eq. (31). The solution of Eq. (32) for $\sigma = 0.7$ with the boundary conditions $G'(0) = 0$ and $G(\infty) = 0$ is plotted in Fig. 6 and tabulated in Table 1.

Since

$$\theta = a_2(\beta/\nu)r^2 G_2 = (\beta^2 \mu r^2/k J T_0)G \qquad (33)$$

and $G(0) = 0.726$, the temperature rise at the boundary (assumed insulated) is

$$T_e - T_0 = 0.726 \beta^2 \mu r^2/kJ \qquad (34)$$

in which T_e can be called the eigen-temperature at the boundary.

To determine the thermal effects of pressure change, it is necessary to calculate

$$Dp/Dt = u(\partial p/\partial r) + w(\partial p/\partial z)$$

Since

$$-(1/\rho)\,(\partial p/\partial r) = u_1(\partial u_1/\partial r) = \beta^2 r$$

and, from Eq. (2),

$$w\frac{\partial w}{\partial z} = -\frac{1}{\rho}\frac{\partial p}{\partial z} + \nu\frac{\partial^2 w}{\partial z^2}$$

w being independent of r from the second of Eqs. (5), it follows from Eqs. (5) that

$$Dp/Dt = 4\mu\beta^2(f^2f' + ff'') - \rho\beta^3 r^2 f'$$

so that

$$\Phi + (Dp/Dt) = 4\mu\beta^2(f^2f' + ff'' + 3f'^2) + \rho\beta^3 r^2(2f''^2 - f')$$

It can be seen that even if, for vanishingly small viscosity, one neglects the three terms containing μ explicitly, the term $-\rho\beta^3 r^2 f'$ still remains to be considered, as well as that given in Eq. (29). For small values of η, the value of f' is small compared with $2f''^2$. But at the edge of the boundary layer the reverse is true. To account for the temperature change due to pressure variation as well as dissipation, it is therefore necessary (and sufficient for small viscosity) to take

$$\rho\beta^3 r^2\,(2f''^2 - f')$$

as the nonhomogeneous terms. The resulting equation corresponding to Eq. (30) is

$$G_2'' + \sigma f G' - \sigma f' G_2 + D[f''^2 - (f'/2)] = 0$$

Since $f'(\infty) = 1$ and $f''(\infty) = 0$, this equation is incompatible with the boundary condition $G_2(\infty) = 0$.

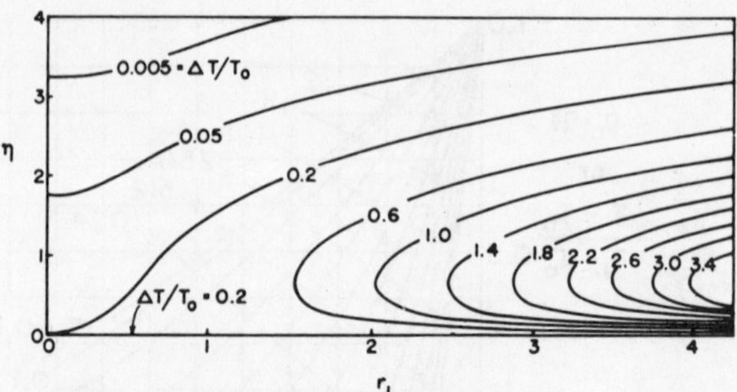

FIG. 7. Dimensionless plot of a typical pattern of isotherms with temperature rise due to viscous shear included. $T_0 =$ ambient temperature, $\Delta T = T - T_0$.

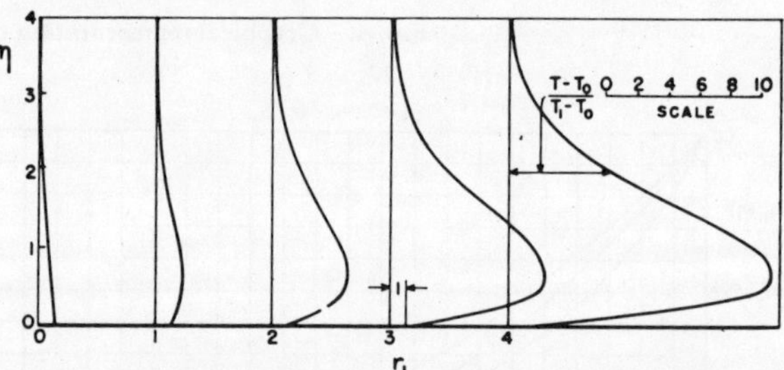

FIG. 8. Dimensionless plot of typical temperature distribution at various radial distances. $T_0 =$ ambient temperature, $T_1 =$ temperature at boundary, $T_1 - T_0 = 0.2T_0$.

Thus a realistic solution for the temperature distribution in Homann flow cannot be obtained for gases if the thermal effect of pressure change is to be included. In the following sections, the discussion and the conclusions are subject to the limitation that this effect is neglected. For liquids, the thermal effect of pressure change is exceedingly small, and the neglecting of this effect naturally does not impose a real limitation.

(7) DISCUSSION

The temperature rise due to viscous shear should be superposed on the temperature distribution obtained from the homogeneous energy equation. If the temperature on the boundary varies with r^n, then for n less than 2 the heat transfer is from plate to fluid for small values of r and from fluid to plate for large values of r. The reverse is true if n is greater than 2. For $n = 2$, the heat transfer is either always from plate to fluid or always from fluid to plate, or, if the temperature on the boundary is exactly the eigen-temperature, there is no heat transfer between boundary and fluid.

For constant temperature at the boundary, the temperature distribution is obtained by superposition,

$$\frac{T - T_0}{T_0} = \frac{T_1 - T_0}{T_1}\,g_0(\eta) + r_1^2 G(\eta) - 0.726 r_1^2 g_2(\eta)$$

in which

$$r_1^2 = \beta^2 \mu r^2/k J T_0$$

TABLE 1

Solution of Eq. (32) for Prandtl Number 0.7

η	G	η	G
0.0	0.7263	3.0	0.0263
0.2	0.7091	3.2	0.0173
0.4	0.6663	3.4	0.0111
0.6	0.6058	3.6	0.0070
0.8	0.5349	3.8	0.0043
1.0	0.4595	4.0	0.0025
1.2	0.3846	4.2	0.0015
1.4	0.3139	4.4	0.0008
1.6	0.2501	4.6	0.0004
1.8	0.1945	4.8	0.0002
2.0	0.1478	5.0	0.0001
2.2	0.1097	5.2	0.0001
2.4	0.0795	5.4	0.0000
2.6	0.0563	5.6	0.0000
2.8	0.0389		

and the last term involving g_2 is added to achieve uniform temperature on the boundary. Writing $\Delta T = T - T_0$, $AT_0 = T_1 - T_0$, one has

$$\Delta T/T_0 = Ag_0(\eta) + r_1^2[G(\eta) - 0.726g_2(\eta)]$$

from which the isotherms can be drawn in the plane of r_1 and η. In Fig. 7 the pattern of isotherms corresponding to $A = 0.2$ is shown. The temperature distribution at various values of r_1 is shown in Fig. 8, in which it is seen that the temperature rise due to dissipation becomes more and more pronounced as r_1 increases and is predominant for large values of r_1.

(8) Conclusions

In laminar stagnation flow with axisymmetry, the temperature distribution in the fluid due to a point source of heat situated at the stagnation point is given by Eqs. (13), (17), (20), and (21). The function $g(\eta)$ is plotted in Fig. 2. For a general class of concentric heating of the boundary, the temperature distribution is given by Eqs. (13) and (23) and by the solutions of Eq. (24) for various values of n. The solution of Eq. (24) for constant temperature on the boundary ($n = 0$) is given by Eq. (25) and is shown graphically in Fig. 4 for various values of the Prandtl Number. The dependence of the constants K and K' in Eqs. (20) and (25) on the Prandtl Number is shown in Fig. 3, the functional relationships being described approximately by Eqs. (22) and (27). For $n = 1$ and 2, the solutions of Eq. (24) are given graphically in Fig. 5 for Prandtl Number 0.7. Temperature rise due to dissipation is given by Eqs. (13) and (33), in which the function G is given graphically in Fig. 6 for Prandtl Number 0.7, and is tabulated in Table 1. This temperature rise is to be superposed on that which results from the solution of the homogeneous energy equation. With the thermal effect of the change of pressure neglected, a typical pattern of isotherms for constant temperature at the plate is shown in Fig. 7, and the vertical temperature distribution at various distances from the stagnation point is shown in Fig. 8.

References

[1] Homann, F., *Der Einfluss grosser Zähigkeit bei der Strömung um den Zylinder und um die Kugel*, ZAMM, Vol. 16, p. 153, 1936.

[2] Frössling, N., *Verdunstung, Wärmeübertragung und Geschwindigkeitsverteilung bei zweidimensionaler und rotationssymmetrischer laminarer Grenzschichtströmung*, Lunds Univ. Arsskr. N. F. 36, No. 4, pp. 1–32, 1940.

[3] Goldstein, S., *Modern Developments in Fluid Dynamics*, Vol. II; Oxford University Press, 1938.

Turbulent buoyant plumes

Chia-Shun Yih

Department of Applied Mechanics and Engineering Science, The University of Michigan, Ann Arbor, Michigan 48109
(Received 26 January 1977; final manuscript received 11 April 1977)

The velocity and temperature distributions in turbulent buoyant induced by a line source or point source of heat are calculated by assuming the eddy viscosity and eddy diffusivity to be constant in any cross section of the plume. Two solutions in closed forms are obtained for the two-dimensional plume, corresponding to turbulent Prandtl number σ equal to 2/3 and 2. Two such solutions are also obtained for the round plume, corresponding to σ equal to 1.1 and 2. The solution for $\sigma = 2/3$ is compared with previous measurements for two-dimensional plumes, and the solution for $\sigma = 1.1$ is compared with previous measurements for the axisymmetric plume. The analytical and experimental results agree well in the two-dimensional case, and satisfactorily in the axisymmetric case.

I. INTRODUCTION

It is well known that when a flow is turbulent the as yet un-resolved problem of closure prevents any rigorous analytical solution for the velocity field. In attempting to give approximate analytical solutions for turbulent flows, Prandtl[1] gave a mixing-length theory which Tollmien[2] applied to the calculation of the velocity distribution in jets. When compared with the experimental results of Förthmann,[3] Kuethe,[4] and Reichardt,[5] the calculated results of Tollmien for the velocity are invariably less than (although not by much) the measured values over the central part of the jet. A more serious objection to the application of the mixing-length theory to jets is that the curvature of the velocity profile must necessarily be infinite at the center of the jet. In other words, the velocity profile has a cusp there. It is strange that this fact has never been pointed out before. Tollmien,[2] who solved the equation for the velocity distribution in the jet *numerically*, naturally could not have noticed this point.

In 1942, Prandtl[6] proposed a simpler theory for the calculation of the velocity profile in jets and wakes. This was probably suggested by the experimental results of Reichardt.[5] Immediately afterwards, Görtler[7] applied this simpler theory to the calculation of velocity distributions in two-dimensional and round jets. The results of his calculations agree much better with all the experimental results in the core of the jets, but near the edge or edges of the jets Tollmien's calculations with the mixing-length theory seem to give better agreement. This is perhaps not surprising, for it is near walls and other regions (such as the edge of a jet) of significant variation of turbulent-transport coefficients that the mixing-length theory can be expected to give better results. The simpler theory of Prandtl presumes a constant eddy viscosity at each jet cross section, varying only with the longitudinal distance along the jet. The greatest virtue of this simpler theory is that there is no infinite curvature of the velocity profile at the center of the jet, and its greatest advantage is the simplicity with which it can be applied, as so well demonstrated by Görtler.[7]

Confirmation of the *validity* of the simpler theory of Prandtl in the core of jets (indeed in the core of wakes or pipe flows) came from Laufer's measurements,[8] which clearly showed that the eddy viscosity in the core of turbulent flow in a circular pipe is constant, although it varies drastically near the wall of the pipe, and that it varies with the Reynolds number. We now know that Prandtl's simpler theory can be confidently applied to the core of jets, wakes, and flows in pipes and channels, with the expectation that near the edges of jets and wakes and near the walls of pipes and channels the theory cannot be expected to give good results.

In this paper, we shall apply Prandtl's simpler theory to the calculation of velocity and temperature distributions of turbulent buoyant plumes, much as Görtler has applied it to the calculation of the velocity distribution in turbulent jets. After the analyses are given, the calculated results will be compared with the available experimental results of Schmidt,[9] Rouse *et al.*,[10] and Yih.[11,12]

II. TURBULENT TWO-DIMENSIONAL BUOYANT PLUME

Let x be measured vertically upward from a line source of heat along the center of the buoyant plume above that source. With the location of the source as the origin, y is measured in a horizontal direction normal to the line source. We shall use u and v to denote the velocity components in the directions of increasing x and y, respectively, g to denote the gravitational acceleration, ϵ to denote the kinematic eddy viscosity, σ to denote the Prandtl number for turbulent flow, i.e., the ratio of ϵ to the eddy diffusivity. The ambient atmosphere will be assumed uniform, with a constant specific weight γ_0, and the difference between the specific weight γ in the plume and γ_0 will be denoted by $\Delta\gamma$. Then, the boundary-layer forms of the equation of motion and the equation of heat diffusion are

$$uu_x + vu_y = \epsilon u_{yy} - g\Delta\gamma/\gamma_0, \tag{1}$$

and

$$u\frac{\partial}{\partial x}\Delta\gamma + v\frac{\partial}{\partial y}\Delta\gamma = \epsilon\sigma^{-1}\frac{\partial^2}{\partial y^2}\Delta\gamma. \tag{2}$$

In (1) the subscripts x and y indicate partial differenti-

     Copyright © 1977 American Institute of Physics

ation. In writing (1), it is tacitly assumed that the pressure distribution in the entire atmosphere is hydrostatic. The equation of continuity is

$$u_x + v_y = 0, \tag{3}$$

so that a stream function ψ exists, in terms of which

$$u = \psi_y, \quad v = -\psi_x. \tag{4}$$

The boundary conditions for u and $\Delta\gamma$ are

$$v = u_y = 0 = (\partial/\partial y)\Delta\gamma \text{ at } y = 0, \tag{5}$$

$$\psi \text{ is finite and } \Delta\gamma = 0 \text{ at } y = \pm\infty. \tag{6}$$

Let the strength of the line source per unit length be measured by G, so that

$$G = -\int_{-\infty}^{\infty} u\Delta\gamma \, dy, \tag{7}$$

if longitudinal diffusion is neglected, as in (2). Indeed, using (3), (5), and (6), we can obtain (7) by integrating (2).

A dimensional analysis shows that $x(G/\rho)^{1/3}$ has the dimension of kinematic viscosity. Hence, we can assume, in the spirit of Prandtl's simplified theory,

$$\epsilon = \lambda x(G/\rho)^{1/3}, \tag{8}$$

where ρ is the density of the ambient fluid and λ is a dimensionless constant to be determined from experimental data. With (8), it can easily be verified that a similarity solution is possible if we make the following transformation:

$$\psi = (G/\rho)^{1/3} x f(\eta), \tag{9}$$

$$\Delta\gamma = -x^{-1}(\rho G^2)^{1/3}\theta(\eta), \tag{10}$$

$$\eta = y/x. \tag{11}$$

Equations (4) and (9) give

$$u = (G/\rho)^{1/3} f'(\eta), \quad v = -(G/\rho)^{1/3}(f - \eta f'). \tag{12}$$

Then, (1) and (2) become, after some straightforward calculations,

$$-ff'' = \lambda f''' + \theta, \tag{13}$$

$$-\sigma(\theta f)' = \lambda \theta''. \tag{14}$$

The boundary conditions become

$$f(0) = 0, \quad f''(0) = 0, \quad \theta'(0) = 0. \tag{15}$$

$$f(\pm\infty) \text{ is finite}, \quad \theta(\pm\infty) = 0. \tag{16}$$

Let

$$f = A \tanh B\eta; \tag{17}$$

then, (14) gives

$$\theta = C \operatorname{sech}^m B\eta, \quad m = A\sigma/B\lambda. \tag{18}$$

There are two possible solutions. In case 1, (13) is satisfied if

$$\sigma = 2/3, \quad A = 3B\lambda, \quad m = 2, \quad C = 6B^4\lambda^2. \tag{19}$$

The integral relation (7) now has the form

$$\int_{-\infty}^{\infty} f'\theta \, d\eta = 1. \tag{20}$$

Equations (17), (18), (19), and (20) give, after some calculations,

$$AC = 3/4.$$

Then, (19) gives

$$24B^5\lambda^3 = 1, \tag{21}$$

which determines B in terms of λ. Then, A and C are also determined in terms of λ, by (19).

In case 2, a similar calculation gives

$$\sigma = 2, \quad 128B^5\lambda^3 = 15, \quad A = 2B\lambda, \quad C = 15/32B\lambda, \tag{22}$$

by which A, B, and C are determined in terms of λ.

It is not known what effect the molecular Prandtl number would have on the "turbulent" Prandtl number, but the latter must be closer to 1 than the former. Indeed, we should be quite contented with a solution with $\sigma = 1$. The closest σ for which we have a solution in closed form is 2/3. We shall use the solution to compare with existing data and to determine λ. Since

$$u = (G/\rho)^{1/3} AB \operatorname{sech}^2 B\eta,$$

the point of inflection of the velocity profile is at

$$B\eta = 0.881.$$

The measurement of Rouse et al.[10] gave

$$\left(\frac{\rho}{G}\right)^{1/3} u = 1.80 \exp\left[-\frac{1}{2}\left(\frac{\eta}{0.125}\right)^2\right].$$

$$\left(\frac{x^3}{\rho G^2}\right)^{1/3} \Delta\gamma = -2.6 \exp\left[-\frac{1}{2}\left(\frac{\eta}{0.110}\right)^2\right].$$

Thus, at the point of inflection of the experimental velocity profile $\eta = 0.125$, so that we obtain

$$B = 7.051.$$

Then, for case 1, where $\sigma = \frac{2}{3}$, we obtain from (21) and (19), very closely,

$$\lambda = 0.01337, \quad A = 0.282, \quad AB = 1.99, \quad C = 2.66.$$

Comparing 1.99 with 1.80 and 2.66 with 2.6, we see that it is rather reassuring that the calculation could produce rather good agreement, considering that our σ is not 1 but $\frac{2}{3}$. Near the edge of the plume however, the similarity solution gives consistently higher velocities and temperatures than the experimental values of Rouse et al.[10]

III. TURBULENT ROUND BUOYANT PLUME

The point source of heat is now the origin. The x axis is still vertical, but the radial cylindrical coordinate r now replaces y, so that the symbol v now denotes the radial velocity component. The meaning of u is unchanged. The equation of motion and the equation of heat diffusion are now, respectively,

$$uu_x + vu_r = \frac{\epsilon}{r}\frac{\partial}{\partial r}(ru_r) - g\frac{\Delta\gamma}{\gamma_0}, \tag{23}$$

$$u\frac{\partial}{\partial x}\Delta\gamma + v\frac{\partial}{\partial r}\Delta\gamma = \frac{\epsilon}{\sigma r}\frac{\partial}{\partial r}\left(r\frac{\partial}{\partial r}\Delta\gamma\right). \tag{24}$$

The equation of continuity is

$$\frac{\partial}{\partial r}(rv) + \frac{\partial}{\partial x}(ru) = 0,$$

which allows the use of Stokes' stream function ψ, in terms of which

$$u = (1/r)\psi_r, \quad v = -(1/r)\psi_x. \tag{25}$$

The boundary conditions are

$$u_r = 0 = v = (\partial/\partial r)\Delta\gamma \text{ at } r = 0, \tag{26}$$

$$\psi \text{ is finite and } \Delta\gamma = 0 \text{ at } r = \infty. \tag{27}$$

The flux G is now defined by

$$G = -2\pi \int_0^\infty ru\Delta\gamma \, dr . \tag{28}$$

A dimensional analysis shows that the eddy viscosity can be taken to be

$$\epsilon = \lambda(Gx^2/\rho)^{1/3} \tag{29}$$

according to Prandtl's simplified theory for jets. As in (2), we have used ϵ/σ for the eddy diffusivity for heat.

With (29), the differential system consisting of (23), (24), (26), and (27) allows a similarity solution if we make the following transformation:

$$\psi = 3\lambda(Gx^5/\rho)^{1/3}f(\eta), \tag{30}$$

$$-\Delta\gamma = 3\lambda^2(\rho G^2/x^5)^{1/3}\theta(\eta), \tag{31}$$

$$\eta = r/x.$$

Then,

$$u = 3\lambda(G/\rho x)^{1/3}f'/\eta, \tag{32a}$$

$$v = \lambda(G/\rho x)^{1/3}(3f' - 5f/\eta), \tag{32b}$$

and (23) and (24) become, respectively,

$$(1 - 5f)(f'/\eta)' - f'^2/\eta = f''' + \eta\theta, \tag{33}$$

$$-5\sigma(f\theta)' = (\eta\theta')'. \tag{34}$$

The boundary conditions become

$$f(0) = f'(0) = \theta'(0) = 0, \tag{35}$$

$$f(\infty) \text{ is finite}, \quad \theta(\infty) = 0. \tag{36}$$

We try a solution of the form

$$f = B[1 - (1 + A\eta^2)^{-1}] , \tag{37}$$

which gives, by virtue of (34) and the boundary conditions on θ, the results

$$\theta = C/(1 + A\eta^2)^m, \quad m = 5\sigma B/2. \tag{38}$$

Again, there are two possible solutions. In case 1,

$$B = \tfrac{12}{11}, \quad \sigma = 1.1, \quad m = 3, \quad C = \frac{1536A^2}{121}. \tag{39}$$

The number A can be related to λ through the dimensionless form of (28)

$$18\pi\lambda^3 \int_0^\infty f'\theta \, d\eta = 1. \tag{40}$$

From (40) we obtain

$$C\lambda^3 = 11/54\pi, \quad A^2\lambda^3 = 1331/82942\pi. \tag{41}$$

Thus, only λ needs to be determined experimentally.

In case 2,

$$B = \tfrac{4}{5}, \quad \sigma = 2, \quad m = 4, \quad C = 256A^2/25. \tag{42}$$

Use of (40) gives

$$C\lambda^3 = 25/72\pi, \quad A^2\lambda^3 = 625/18432\pi. \tag{43}$$

Again, the results for $\sigma = 1.1$ (case 1) can be compared with available experimental results. Equation (32a) can now be written as

$$u = \left(\frac{G}{\rho x}\right)^{1/3} \frac{6\lambda AB}{(1 + A\eta^2)^2} .$$

At the point of inflection of this u profile,

$$\eta = (5A)^{-1/2}.$$

The measurements of Yih[11,12] gave

$$\left(\frac{\rho x}{G}\right)^{1/3} u = 4.7\exp\left[-\frac{1}{2}\left(\frac{\eta}{0.072}\right)^2\right] , \tag{44}$$

$$-\left(\frac{x^5}{\rho G^2}\right)^{1/3}\Delta\gamma = 11.0\exp\left[-\frac{1}{2}\left(\frac{\eta}{0.084}\right)^2\right] . \tag{45}$$

Thus,

$$(5A)^{-1/2} = 0.072, \quad A = 38.58,$$

and (41) and (39) then give, in turn,

$$\lambda = 0.0151. \quad 6\lambda AB = 3.8.$$

The value 3.8 is somewhat below the 4.7 in (44). It is quite possible that the anemometer used by Yih was too clumsy and not sufficiently accurate, and that the experimental value 0.072 for the η at the inflection point is too small. The lack of a computer to take accurate mean values of u was also a source of error. (Yih read the mean by eye.) Perhaps more accurate measurements would give a maximum value for the left-hand side of (44) closer to 4. As to $\Delta\gamma$, we have, from (31),

$$-\Delta\gamma = (\rho G^2/x^5)^{1/3}3\lambda^2C(1 + A\eta^2)^{-3}.$$

The value $3\lambda^2C$ can be calculated from the first equation in (41), since λ is known, and we have

$$3\lambda^2C = 12.88,$$

compared with the experimental value of 11. In spite of the lack of good agreement, it is still rather reassuring that the values are as close as they are. Again, near the edge of the plume the theoretical values for the velocity and the temperature are consistently higher than the experimental values, which are represented by (44) and (45).

It is also satisfying that the λ for the two-dimensional plume and the λ for the axisymmetric plume are very close to each other.

We now compare the analytic results with Schmidt's experimental data,[9] which can be summarized in the formulae (44) and (45), with 2.7 and 13.7 replacing 4.7 and 11.0, respectively, and 0.105 and 0.099 replacing 0.072 and 0.084, respectively. Thus,

$$(5A)^{-1/2} = 0.105, \quad A = 18.14 ;$$

and (41) and (39) give

$$\lambda = 0.0025, \quad 6\lambda AB = 2.96, \quad 3\lambda^2C = 7.78.$$

The figure 2.96 is quite near 2.7, but 7.78 is quite far from 13.7. The lack of good agreement may be related to the fact that Schmidt's data do not satisfy the momentum equation obtained by integrating (23) from $r = 0$ to $r = \infty$.

ACKNOWLEDGMENT

This work was supported by the Office of Naval Research.

[1]L. Prandtl, Z. Angew. Math. Mech. 5, 136 (1925).
[2]W. Tollmien, Z. Angew. Math. Mech. 6, 468 (1926).
[3]E. Förthmann, Ing. -Arch. 5, 42 (1934).
[4]A. M. Kuethe, J. Appl. Mech. 2, 87 (1935).
[5]H. Reichardt, VDI-Forschungsh. 414 (1942).
[6]L. Prandtl, Z. Angew. Math. Mech. 22, 241 (1942).
[7]H. Görtler, Z. Angew. Math. Mech. 22, 244 (1942).
[8]J. Laufer, N. A. C. A. Technical Note 2954 (1953).
[9]W. Schmidt, Z. Angew. Math. Mech. 21, 265 (1941); 21, 351 (1941).
[10]H. Rouse, C.-S. Yih, and H. W. Humphrey, Tellus 4, 201 (1952).
[11]C.-S. Yih, in *Proceedings of the 1st U. S. National Congress of Applied Mechanics*, edited by E. Sternberg (American Society of Mechanical Engineers, New York, 1951), p. 941.
[12]C.-S. Yih, in *Proceedings of the 1st Symposium on the Use of Models in Geophysical Fluid Dynamics* (Government Printing Service, Washington, 1956), p. 117.

Proc. 12th Symposium of Naval Hydrodynamics, 1978

Buoyant Plumes in a Transverse Wind

Chia-Shun Yih
The University of Michigan
Ann Arbor, Michigan

ABSTRACT

With the rise in energy needs and the consequent
proliferation of cooling towers (not to mention
smoke stacks) on the one hand, and society's
enchanced concern with the environment on the other,
the study of buoyant plumes caused by heat sources
in a transverse wind has become important. Buoyant
plumes may also occur in the ocean, such as when
a deeply submerged heat source moves horizontally
in it. The fluid mechanics involved in buoyant
plumes is very nearly the same, be they atmospheric
or submarine.

In this paper a similarity solution for turbulent
buoyant plumes due to a point heat source in a
transverse wind is presented. By a set of transformations the mathematical dimension of the
problem is reduced from 3 to 2. Analytical solutions
for the first and second approximations are obtained
for the temperature and velocity fields. The
solution exhibits the often observed pair of longitudinal counter-rotating vortices. As a result of
buoyancy, the point of highest temperature and the
"eyes" of the vortices at any section normal to
the wind direction continuously rise as the longitudinal distance from the heat source increases.

1. INTRODUCTION

As industry expands and energy needs rise, the
buoyant plumes caused by ever-increasing cooling
towers and smoke stacks have become an important
concern for societies anxious to protect their
environment. Much effort has been expanded on the
so-called numerical modeling of the phenomenon
of plumes both in the United States and in Europe.
In most of the numerical studies, the eddy viscosity
is assumed constant, and its value is chosen to
make the results agree with whatever gross observations are available. The power of modern computers
has made it possible to obtain numerical solutions

for partial differential equations with very
irregular data, such as wind and temperature profiles
in the atmosphere. On the other hand, one can
only carry out a number of these special solutions,
and while the power of the computer makes computation possible it also makes the intermediate steps
so opaque that one can only have faith in the
accuracy of the results and the correctness of the
programing; and one can attempt to interpret the
results and understand the phenomenon only at the
very end, when numerical results are available.
One can hardly see, for example, the effects of
changing one single parameter of the problem, without
giving that parameter several values and going to
the computer again and again. It is in view of
this condition that even people most concerned with
the immediate applicability of calculated results
desire a certain measure of transparency in the
analysis of the phenomenon.

At the same time systematic and detailed experiments on buoyant plumes in transverse winds, with
temperature and velocity measurements, are lacking.
This being so, it seems that an analytical solution
of the problem is most desirable and timely, even
if it must of necessity be constructed by assuming
certain quantities (such as the turbulence level
in the plume) on the basis of whatever related
experimental results are available. The assumed
quantities (or quantity) will appear in the analysis
as unspecified coefficients (or coefficient, as in
this analysis), to be determined by experiments
later. In the present work only one coefficient
related to the turbulence level is left unspecified,
to be determined by future experiments. But the
probable range in which it lies is given.

The solution is based on a set of transformations
that reduces the mathematical dimension of the
phenomenon from 3 to 2 is thus characterized by the
striking feature of similarity between cross sections
normal to the wind direction. The laws of decay
of the temperature and velocity fields are given
in simple, explicit terms. Thus, apart from the

608

quantitative predictions that this analysis is
intended to furnish, I hope that the general features
of the solution will be found especially useful.

2. THE DIFFERENTIAL EQUATIONS

The two basic assumptions underlying the analysis
are that the longitudinal velocity component in
the direction of the wind is constant and that an
eddy viscosity, ε, is constant in any cross section
normal to the wind direction. It can be shown that
the first assumption ceases to be true only at
stages of approximations later than those arrived
at in the present analysis, and its violation is
therefore not very important. The second assumption
mentioned above has been made in all analytic
solutions for turbulent jets and plumes, according
to Prandtl's simplified theory. These solutions
are well known. See, for example, the paper by
Yih (1977) on turbulent plumes for the latest
application of that theory. One feels reassured
that for a calculation of the mean temperature and
velocity fields, this theory can again be used.

We shall take the direction of the wind to be
the direction of increasing x, and the z direction
to be vertically upward. The y direction will then
be a horizontal direction transverse to the x direction. In general ε depends on x, y, and z. But it
has been repeatedly shown before in other studies
of jets and plumes that in their core, ε can be
taken as constant at a constant value of x, and
that only at their outer edges does the nonuniformity
in the y-z plane introduce some errors in the
calculated mean quantities. (Very far away from
the jets and plumes the value of ε is immaterial
for the determination of the temperature and velocity
distributions). Accepting these outer-edge errors,
which are fairly small, we shall take ε to be a
function of x only, apart from the parameters of
the problem to be defined later. We note that if
an eddy viscosity is used to determine the velocity
distribution in turbulent flow in a circular pipe,
Laufer's (1953) measurements show that in the core,
that is, away from the narrow region near the pipe
wall, ε is nearly constant.

The equations of motion are then, with subscripts
denoting partial differentiations,

$$U v_x + v v_y + w v_z = - \frac{1}{\rho} p_y + \varepsilon (v_{yy} + v_{zz}), \qquad (1)$$

$$U w_x + v w_y + w w_z = - \frac{1}{\rho} p_z - g\theta + \varepsilon (w_{yy} + w_{zz}), \qquad (2)$$

in which U is the wind velocity, assumed constant,
v and w are the velocity components in the directions
of increasing y and z, respectively, ρ is the
density, p is the pressure, and g is the gravitational acceleration. The variable θ is defined by

$$\theta = \frac{\Delta \rho}{\rho}, \qquad (3)$$

where $\Delta \rho$ is the variation of the density from the
ambient density ρ, assumed constant. Thus the
Boussinesq approximation has been used in Eqs. (1)
and (2). Since θ is small and the pressure variation in the plume, though important for determination of the flow field, is unimportant in the determination of $\Delta \rho$ from the temperature variation by
the equation of state, θ can also be written, by
virtue of the equation of state of ideal gases.

$$\theta = - \frac{\Delta T}{T},$$

where ΔT is the temperature variation and T the
ambient temperature. For a liquid, the relationship
between $\Delta \rho$ and ΔT is still linear if θ is small,
and the constant of proportionality is determined
by the property of the liquid.

We shall assume the eddy viscoity for heat
diffusion to be the same as that for momentum
diffusion. This may not be strictly true, for the
turbulent Prandtl number may be slightly different
from 1. The effect of this difference, if any, is
not of great importance in our attempt to determine
the mean temperature and velocity fields. The
equation for heat diffusion can then be written in
the form

$$U \theta_x + v \theta_y + w \theta_z = \varepsilon (\theta_{yy} + \theta_{zz}). \qquad (4)$$

Longitudinal diffusion of heat or of momentum is
ignored in Eq. (1), (2), and (4). This is justified
in the same way as in other works that use the
boundary-layer theory.

The equation of continuity is, since the longitudinal velocity component is assumed constant,

$$v_y + w_z = 0. \qquad (5)$$

The heat source, located at the origin, is
measured by the quantity

$$G = - \int_{-\infty}^{\infty} \int_{-\infty}^{\infty} U\theta \, dy \, dz. \qquad (6)$$

Note that solid boundaries are assumed to be far
away from the source, so that their effects are
negligible. Equations (1), (2), (4), (5), and (6),
with appropriate boundary conditions, govern the
phenomenon under investigation.

The equation of continuity (5) allows the use
of a stream function ψ in terms of which v and w
can be expressed:

$$v = \psi_z, \qquad w = -\psi_y. \qquad (7)$$

By cross-differentiation of Eqs. (1) and (2), we
obtain the vorticity equation

$$U \hat{\zeta}_x + v \hat{\zeta}_y + w \hat{\zeta}_z = \varepsilon (\hat{\zeta}_{yy} + \hat{\zeta}_{zz}) - g\theta_y, \qquad (8)$$

in which $\hat{\zeta}$ is the x component of the vorticity and
is given by

$$\hat{\zeta} = w_y - v_z = -(\psi_{yy} + \psi_{zz}). \qquad (9)$$

3. THE FORM OF THE EDDY VISCOSITY

We assume the terms in Eqs. (1) or (2) or (4) to
be of the same order of magnitude. In particular,
this means that the diffusive and the convective
terms are of the same order of magnitude in any of
these equations. It also means that in Eq. (2) the
buoyancy term is of the same order of magnitude as
the convective and diffusive terms for w. This
assumption underlies all existing analytical studies

of jets and plumes and can be regarded as amply justified.

Comparing the first and last terms in Eq. (2), then, we have

$$\varepsilon \sim \frac{U\ell_z^2}{\ell_x}, \tag{10}$$

in which ℓ_x and ℓ_z are the length scales for the x and z directions. Comparing the first term in Eq. (2) with the term $g\theta$, we have

$$\theta \sim \frac{Uw}{g\ell_x}, \tag{11}$$

where θ and w stand for the magnitudes of θ and w, rather than θ and w rigorously, as they do also in the following proportionalities. Equation (6) gives, further,

$$\theta \sim \frac{G}{U\ell_z^2}, \tag{12}$$

if we take ℓ_y and ℓ_z to be equal. From proportionalities (11) and (12) we have, after some rearrangement,

$$w\ell_z \sim \frac{gG\ell_x}{U^2\ell_z}. \tag{13}$$

But surely

$$\varepsilon \sim w\ell_z. \tag{14}$$

Hence

$$\varepsilon \sim \frac{gG\ell_x}{U^2\ell_z}. \tag{15}$$

From proportionalities (10) and (15) we have

$$\ell_z^3 \sim \frac{gG}{U^3} \ell_x^2 = \frac{gG}{U^3} x^2, \tag{16}$$

since the ℓ_x, the scale of x, is just x. Thus (12), (13), (14), and (16) give

$$\ell_z \sim x^{2/3}, \quad \varepsilon \sim x^{1/3}, \quad w \sim x^{-1/3}, \quad \theta \sim x^{-4/3}.$$

These results are unaffected when other comparisons are made between terms in either Eq. (1), (2), (4), or (5).

From porportionalities (15) and (16) we have

$$\varepsilon = \frac{\alpha}{U}(g^2G^2x)^{1/3}, \tag{17}$$

where α is a dimensionless constant to be determined experimentally or estimated from known values of ε in similar phenomena. We shall leave it free throughout our analysis. Equation (17) gives the form of ε to be used in this paper.

It seems strange at first sight that ε should vary inversely as U. I believe that the interpretation of $\varepsilon \sim U^{-1}$ is that ε increases with the time that is required for the wind to travel a unit distance in the x direction, because turbulence needs time to develop.

4. THE TRANSFORMATIONS AND THE DIFFERENTIAL SYSTEM TO BE SOLVED

The transformations to be used to obtain similarity solutions are already suggested by (12), (13), and (16) and are

$$\theta = -\frac{U}{3\alpha} \left(\frac{G}{g^2}\right)^{1/3} x^{-4/3} h(\eta,\zeta), \tag{18}$$

$$(v,w) = \frac{1}{3\alpha} \left(\frac{Gg}{x}\right)^{1/3} (V,W), \tag{19}$$

$$(\eta,\zeta) = \frac{U}{(3\alpha)^{1/2}} (Ggx^2)^{-1/3} (y,z). \tag{20}$$

Then the equation of continuity (5) becomes

$$V_\eta + W_\zeta = 0,$$

and Eqs. (7) become

$$V = \Psi_\zeta, \qquad W = -\Psi_\eta, \tag{21}$$

in which Ψ is the dimensionless stream function related to ψ by

$$\psi = \frac{1}{(3\alpha)^{1/2}U} (G^2g^2x)^{1/3} \Psi(\eta,\zeta). \tag{22}$$

Equation (9) now takes the form

$$\xi = W_\eta - V_\zeta = -(\Psi_{\eta\eta} + \Psi_{\zeta\zeta}), \tag{23}$$

where ξ is the dimensionless vorticity component in the x direction.

With the transformations (18), (19), and (20), Eq. (4) becomes

$$Lh = \lambda(Vh_\eta + Wh_\zeta), \tag{24}$$

where L is the linear operator defined by

$$L = \frac{\partial^2}{\partial\eta^2} + \frac{\partial^2}{\partial\zeta^2} + 2\eta\frac{\partial}{\partial\eta} + 2\zeta\frac{\partial}{\partial\zeta} + 4, \tag{25}$$

and

$$\lambda = (3\alpha^3)^{-1/2}. \tag{26}$$

Equation (8) now has the form

$$(L - 1)\xi = -h_\eta + \lambda(V\xi_\eta + W\xi_\zeta). \tag{27}$$

Equations (23), (24), and (27) are the final equations governing the dynamics of the plume in a transverse wind. They are to be solved with the boundary conditions

(i) $h_\eta = 0$, $\xi = 0$, $\Psi = 0$, and $\Psi_{\eta\eta} = 0$ at $\eta = 0$.

(ii) $h = 0$, $\xi = 0$, $\Psi = 0$ at $\eta = \pm\infty$ or $\zeta = \pm\infty$.

Boundary conditions (i) correspond to symmetry with respect to the ζ axis, and conditions (ii) ensure that there is no temperature variation and no

610

velocity components v and w at infinity. The integral relation (6) now takes the form

$$\int_{-\infty}^{\infty} \int_{-\infty}^{\infty} h \, d\eta \, d\zeta = 1, \qquad (28)$$

The mathematical problem is now completely specified.

5. THE METHOD OF SOLUTION

The mathematical problem just formulated can be solved numerically once λ is known. But considerable effort is required for this solution, since there are three second-order partial differential equations to be solved, two of which are nonlinear. It is true that computers can deal with nonlinearities, but the domain is infinite, and some estimate has to be made of how far to go in the numerical computation. Furthermore the integral condition (28) can only be imposed after the computations are done for h, and this makes the computation very cumbersome.

For arbitrarily large values of λ an analytical solution is extremely difficult because the nonlinearities present formidable difficulties. We shall attempt a power-series solution of the form

$$\left. \begin{array}{l} h = h_0 + \lambda h_1 + \lambda^2 h_2 + \ldots , \\[4pt] \xi = \xi_0 + \lambda \xi_1 + \lambda^2 \xi_2 + \ldots , \\[4pt] \Psi = \Psi_0 + \lambda \Psi_1 + \lambda^2 \Psi_2 + \ldots \end{array} \right\} \qquad (29)$$

The success or failure of this approach depends not only on the value of λ, but also on the magnitudes of h_1/h_0, h_2/h_1, etc. Thus we need to make an estimate of the range of λ, and we have to find out how fast h_n, ξ_n, and Ψ_n decrease as n increases. Furthermore, even the estimate of λ cannot be made without knowing the magnitudes of Ψ_0. It turns out that a reasonable estimate of λ is

$$30 < \lambda < 50.$$

Using Eq. (29), we shall show in the following sections that h_1/h_0, ξ_1/ξ_0, and Ψ_1/Ψ_0 are all of the order of 10^{-2}. Thus, if $\lambda = 30$, stopping at the second approximation, that is, at the terms with the first power in λ, would introduce an error of about 10%, if we assume, as we evidently can, that the ratio 10^{-2} would apply to $(h_{n+1})/h_n$ etc. for n equal and greater than 1. If $\lambda = 50$ this error would be about 25 to 30 percent, and it would be necessary to go to at least the λ^2 terms to reduce the error to less than 15%.

We shall delay the presentation of the estimate of λ until later and shall proceed with the solution according to the approach in Eq. (29). In awaiting the experimental determination of λ, we shall carry out the solution to the second approximation.

6. THE FIRST APPROXIMATION

The first approximation is governed by the equations

$$L h_0 = 0, \qquad (30)$$

$$(L - 1) \xi_0 = -h_{0_\eta}, \qquad (31)$$

$$\Psi_{0_{\eta\eta}} + \Psi_{0_{\zeta\zeta}} = -\xi_0, \qquad (32)$$

with the boundary conditions (i) and (ii) stated before which we need not repeat here.

The solution of Eq. (30) is

$$h_0 = Ce^{-(\eta^2 + \zeta^2)},$$

and application of the integral condition (28) on h_0 gives the value $1/\pi$ for C, so that

$$h_0 = \frac{1}{\pi} e^{-r^2}, \qquad (33)$$

where

$$r^2 = \eta^2 + \zeta^2.$$

Then the solution of Eq. (31) is

$$\xi_0 = -\frac{2}{3\pi} \eta e^{-r^2} = -\frac{2}{3\pi} \cos\theta \cdot re^{-r^2},$$

where

$$\theta = \tan^{-1} \frac{\zeta}{\eta}.$$

Given ξ_0, Eq. (32) can be easily integrated by separation of the variables r and θ. The result is

$$\Psi_0 = -\frac{\cos\theta}{6\pi r} (1 - e^{-r^2}). \qquad (34)$$

The isotherms given by Eq. (32) are just concentric circles. But the streamlines given by Eq. (34) are already interesting. They are shown in Figure 1, which shows two very prominent vortices, with the vorticity pointing in the x direction. Thus the first approximation already shows the prominent features of the flow pattern in any plane normal to the x axis. Note that both the flow pattern and the temperature field are symmetric

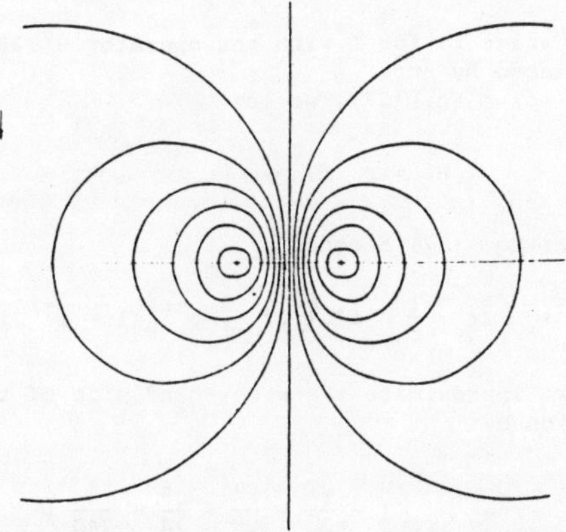

FIGURE 1. Flow pattern from the first approximation. The horizontal axis is the η axis, the vertical axis the ζ axis, and the arrow indicates the direction of the gravitational acceleration. The value of $6\cdot\Psi_0$ is zero on the ζ axis. It increases toward the left and decreases toward the right. The increments (or decrements) are all 0.1.

with respect to the ζ axis, and that both h_0 and Ψ_0 vanish at infinity, as desired.

The maximum vorticity is 0.09 and is at the point

$$\eta = 1/\sqrt{2}, \quad \zeta = 0,$$

at which both V and W are zero. The maximum vertical velocity is $1/6\pi$ and is at the origin. The maximum absolute value of Ψ_0 is $0.63817/6\pi$, which occurs at $\vartheta = 0$ or π, $r = 1.1225$.

7. THE SECOND APPROXIMATION

The equation for h_1 is

$$Lh_1 = V_0 h_{0\eta} + W_0 h_{0\zeta}, \tag{35}$$

where V_0 and W_0 are the velocity components from the first approximation. The right-hand side of Eq. (35) can be written in polar coordinates as

$$\frac{1}{r} \frac{\partial}{\partial\theta}\Psi_0 \cdot \frac{dh_0}{dr}.$$

Hence Eq. (35) can be written as

$$Lh_1 = - \frac{\sin \theta}{3\pi^2 r} e^{-r^2} (1 - e^{-r^2}),$$

where L, in its polar-coordinate form, is

$$L = \frac{\partial^2}{\partial r^2} + \frac{1}{r} \frac{\partial}{\partial r} + \frac{1}{r^2} \frac{\partial^2}{\partial\theta^2} + 2r \frac{\partial}{\partial r} + 4.$$

Writing

$$h_1 = \frac{\sin \theta}{3\pi^2} H_1 (r), \tag{36}$$

we have

$$L_1 H_1 = - \frac{e^{-r^2}}{r} (1 - e^{-r^2}), \tag{37}$$

if we write L_n for L with the operator $\partial^2/\partial\theta^2$ in L replaced by $-n^2$.

To solve Eq. (37), we let

$$H_1 = r^{-1} f, \tag{38}$$

so that Eq. (37) becomes

$$f'' + \left(2r - \frac{1}{r}\right) f' + 2f = -e^{-r^2}(1 - e^{-r^2}). \tag{39}$$

Then we approximate the right-hand side of this equation by

$$-r^2 e^{-r^2} \left(1 - \frac{r^2}{2} + \frac{r^4}{6} - \frac{r^6}{24} + \frac{r^8}{240}\right). \tag{40}$$

The greatest error occurs at $r = 1.8$, but it is less than 6.5% of the maximum value of the quantity approximated. Up to $r = 1.2$ the approximation is excellent. It is expected that the local errors around $r = 1.8$ will be diffused out when Eq. (39)

is integrated and will introduce negligible errors in the result. After (40) is substituted into Eq. (39), the latter is solved by repeated use of the following formula for various values of n:

$$\left[\frac{d^2}{dr^2} + \left(2r - \frac{1}{r}\right) \frac{d}{dr} + 2\right] \left(r^n e^{-r^2}\right)$$
$$= r^{n-2}[n(n-2) - 2(n-1)r^2]e^{-r^2}.$$

The result for f is put into Eq. (38), and we have

$$H_1 = r \left(\frac{193}{630} - \frac{61}{1260} r^2 + \frac{11}{1260} r^4 - \frac{5}{3024} r^6 \right.$$
$$\left. + \frac{1}{4320} r^8\right) e^{-r^2}. \tag{41}$$

The function H_1 is tabulated in Table 1. A look at h_1 given by Eq. (36) then reveals that the temperature is increased in the upper half of the $\eta-\zeta$ plane and decreased in the lower-half plane, making the isotherms more widely spaced in the upper-half plane and more crowded in the lower-half plane.

The tabulated values of H_1 show a very smooth variation of H_1 with r, verifying the expectation that the local irregular variation of (40) is diffused away when Eq. (39) is solved with (40) replacing its right-hand side.

The next step is to solve

$$(L - 1)\xi_1 = -h_{1\eta} + V_0\xi_{0\eta} + W_0\xi_{0\zeta}. \tag{42}$$

A simplification is possible before we attempt to solve Eq. (42). Differentiating Eq. (35), we have

$$(L + 2)h_{1\eta} = V_0 h_{0\eta\eta} + W_0 h_{0\eta\zeta} + V_{0\eta}h_{0\eta}$$
$$+ W_{0\eta}h_{0\zeta}. \tag{43}$$

Let

$$\xi_1 = \frac{h_{1\eta}}{3} + q. \tag{44}$$

Then Eq. (42) becomes

$$(L - 1)q + (L + 2) \frac{h_{1\eta}}{3} = \frac{1}{3} (V_0 h_{0\eta\eta} + W_0 h_{0\eta\zeta}), \tag{45}$$

since

$$\xi_0 = \frac{1}{3} h_{0\eta}.$$

By virtue of (43), Eq. (45) becomes

$$(L - 1)q = - \frac{1}{3} (V_{0\eta}h_{0\eta} + W_{0\eta}h_{0\zeta}). \tag{46}$$

But

$$V_{0\eta} = (\Psi_0)_{\zeta\eta}, \quad W_{0\eta} = -(\Psi_0)_{\eta\eta},$$

so that $\Psi_{0\eta}$ is a stream function for the fictitious velocity field $(V_{0\eta}, W_{0\eta})$, and we can write Eq. (46) as

612

TABLE 1 Values of H_1, S, and F; for $r > 4$, $-100F = 5.04\ r^{-2}$

r	0.1	0.2	0.3	0.4	0.5	0.6	0.7	0.8	0.9	1.0
$100H_1$	3.03	5.85	8.28	10.19	11.48	12.14	12.20	11.75	10.89	9.76
$-100S$	0.25	0.97	2.06	3.39	4.80	6.12	7.23	8.00	8.41	8.43
$-100F$	0.03	0.11	0.24	0.41	0.60	0.80	1.00	1.17	1.32	1.44

r	1.1	1.2	1.3	1.4	1.5	1.6	1.7	1.8	1.9	2.0
$100H_1$	8.47	7.13	5.84	4.65	3.62	2.74	2.04	1.48	1.06	0.75
$-100S$	8.11	7.51	6.70	5.79	4.83	3.91	3.07	2.34	1.73	1.25
$-100F$	1.52	1.56	1.57	1.55	1.51	1.45	1.38	1.30	1.22	1.13

r	2.1	2.2	2.3	2.4	2.5	2.6	2.7	2.8	2.9	3.0
$100H_1$	0.53	0.38	0.27	0.19	0.14	0.11	0.08	0.06	0.05	0.03
$-100S$	0.88	0.61	0.42	0.29	0.20	0.14	0.11	0.08	0.06	0.05
$-100F$	1.05	0.98	0.90	0.84	0.78	0.73	0.68	0.63	0.59	0.56

r	3.1	3.2	3.3	3.4	3.5	3.6	3.7	3.8	3.9	4.0
$100H_1$	0.02	0.02	0.01	0.01	0.01	0.00				
$-100S$	0.04	0.03	0.02	0.02	0.01	0.01	0.01	0.00		
$-100F$	0.52	0.49	0.46	0.44	0.41	0.39	0.37	0.35	0.33	0.32

$$(L - 1)q = -\frac{1}{3r}\ \frac{\partial}{\partial\theta}\ \Psi_{0\eta} \cdot \frac{dh_0}{dr}\ .$$

Remembering that

$$\frac{\partial}{\partial\eta} = -\frac{\sin\theta}{r}\ \frac{\partial}{\partial\theta} + \cos\theta\ \frac{\partial}{\partial r}\ ,$$

and with Ψ_0 and h_0 given by Eqs. (34) and (32), we have, finally,

$$(L - 1)q = \frac{2}{9\pi^2}\ \sin 2\theta\ \left[e^{-r^2}\left(1 + \frac{1}{r^2}\right) - \frac{1}{r^2}\right] e^{-r^2}. \tag{47}$$

To solve this, let

$$q = \frac{2}{9\pi^2}\ \sin 2\theta \cdot r^{-2}k.$$

Then Eq. (47) becomes

$$\hat{L}k \equiv k'' + \left(2r - \frac{3}{r}\right)k'' - k = e^{-r^2}[e^{-r^2}(r^2 + 1) - 1], \tag{48}$$

where $\hat{L}$ is the linear operator defined by (48). It is advantageous to write the right-hand side of (48) as

$$e^{-2r^2}\left(r^2 + \frac{7}{8}\right) - \frac{7}{8}\ e^{-r^2} + \frac{1}{8}\ e^{-r^2}(e^{-r^2} - 1), \tag{49}$$

for

$$\hat{L}\left(\frac{1}{8}\ e^{-2r^2} - \frac{7}{24}\ e^{-r^2}\right) = e^{-2r^2}\left(r^2 + \frac{7}{8}\right) - \frac{7}{8}\ e^{-r^2},$$

and the last member of (49) can be approximated by one eighth of (40). By repeated use of the formula

$$\hat{L}(r^n e^{-r^2}) = r^{n-2}[n(n - 4) - (2n - 3)r^2]e^{-r^2}$$

for various values of n, we can then find the solution for (48), and the final result for q is

$$q = \frac{2}{9\pi^2}\ \sin 2\theta \cdot Q, \tag{50}$$

with

$$Q = \frac{1}{8r^2}\ e^{-r^2}(e^{-r^2} - 1) - e^{-r^2}\left(-\frac{1}{8} + \frac{116}{9945}\ r^2\right.$$
$$\left. - \frac{133}{95472}\ r^4 - \frac{11}{42432}\ r^6\right.$$
$$\left. - \frac{1}{32640}\ r^8\right). \tag{51}$$

With h_1 given by (36) and (41) and therefore with $h_{1\eta}$ known, (44), (50), and (51) give

794

$$\xi_1 = \frac{1}{9\pi^2} \sin 2\theta \cdot S(r), \qquad (52)$$

where

$$S(r) = e^{-r^2} \left[\frac{1}{4r^2} (e^{-r^2} - 1) + \frac{1}{4} - \frac{105283}{278460} r^2 \right.$$

$$+ \frac{114713}{1670760} r^4 - \frac{3517}{247520} r^6$$

$$\left. + \frac{181}{68544} r^8 - \frac{1}{4320} r^{10} \right].$$

$$(53)$$

The values of $S(r)$ are tabulated in Table 1, from which it can be seen that the maximum absolute value of S occurs at about $r = 0.95$ and is about 0.847. Since S is negative throughout, inspection of Eq. (52) shows that the maximum value of ξ_1 is at

$$r = 0.95, \qquad \theta = \frac{3\pi}{4},$$

and its minimum value (negative) at

$$r = 0.95, \qquad \theta = \frac{\pi}{4}.$$

The effect of S is to reduce the strenths of the vorticity for the lower-half plane, but to augment them in the upper-half plane, thus to raise the eyes of the vortices.

Finally, Ψ_1 is to be found from

$$\Psi_{1\eta\eta} + \Psi_{1\zeta\zeta} = \left(\frac{\partial^2}{\partial r^2} + \frac{1}{r} \frac{\partial}{\partial r} + \frac{1}{r^2} \frac{\partial^2}{\partial\theta^2} \right) \Psi_1 = -\xi_1.$$

Let

$$\Psi_1 = \frac{\sin 2\theta}{9\pi^2} F(r). \qquad (54)$$

Then

$$F'' + \frac{1}{r} F' - \frac{4}{r^2} F = -S(r).$$

Two integrations by the method of variation of parameters (since a complimentary solution of F is simply r^2) gives, with due regard for the boundary conditions,

$$F = -r^2 \int_\infty^r \left[r^{-5} \int_0^r r^3 S dr \right] dr$$

$$= \frac{1}{4} \left[r^{-2} \int_0^r r^3 S dr - r^2 \int_\infty^r r^{-1} S dr \right], \qquad (55)$$

which is given in Table 1 also. The calculations for the second approximation have now been accomplished.

8. ESTIMATE OF λ

The terms involving ε in Eq. (2) have their origin in the Reynolds stress terms

$$\frac{\partial}{\partial y} (v'w') \text{ and } \frac{\partial}{\partial z} (w'^2),$$

where the primes indicate turbulent quantities. The terms were originally on the left-hand side of Eq. (2). The nonlinear terms on the left-hand side of Eq. (2) can be written as

$$\frac{\partial}{\partial y} (vw) + \frac{\partial}{\partial z} (w^2).$$

Thus the ratio of

$$\frac{\partial}{\partial z} (w^2) \text{ and } \frac{\partial}{\partial z} (w'^2)$$

is the ratio of

$$\frac{\partial}{\partial z} (w^2) \text{ and } -\varepsilon w_{zz},$$

and this ratio has the magnitude of

$$-\lambda w^2/W_\zeta .$$

The magnitude of W_0 is $1/6\pi$, and the magnitude of $W_{0\zeta}$ is $0.267/3\pi$, which is the maximum value of $W_{0\zeta}$ along the η axis. Thus, approximately,

$$\frac{\lambda}{0.267(12\pi)} = \frac{1}{s}, \qquad (56)$$

where s is the square of w'/w. The convection in the bent plume is like the convection in a two-dimensional plume, since the plume is bent by the wind to a nearly horizontal position. The measurements of Kotsovinos (1977) for the plane plume give the value 0.2 to s. This is considered by some people to be too high. But for the problem under investigation s may be even higher, because any swaying or deformation of the vortices would contribute a good deal to turbulence. Thus using 0.2 for s in Eq. (56) would *overestimate* λ. Using 0.2 for s, we obtain from Eq. (2)

$$\lambda = 48.5.$$

This is probably too high. My estimate of λ is that it is somewhere in the range

$$30 < \lambda < 40.$$

The value 30 for λ corresponds to a value of 0.34 for s.

Let us now see what errors would be committed for h, Ψ, and ξ by stopping at the second approximation. For $\lambda = 30$, the errors (in ratio of the

614

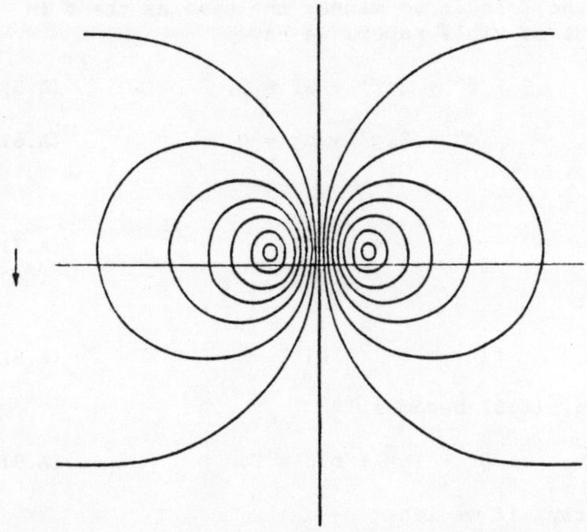

FIGURE 2. Flow pattern from the second approximation. The η axis is horizontal and the ζ axis vertical. The arrow indicates the direction of the gravitational acceleration. The value of $6\pi\Psi$ is, starting from the ζ axis and going to the curves on the right, respectively, 0, -0.1, -0.2, -0.3, -0.4, -0.5, -0.6, and -0.65. The values of $6\pi\Psi$ on the curves to the left of the ζ axis have corresponding absolute values but are positive.

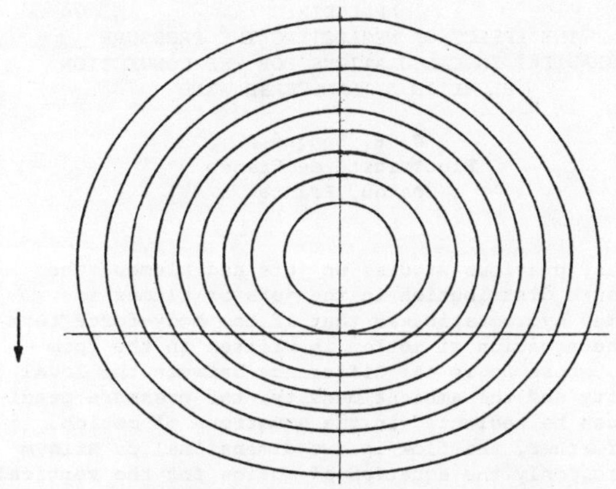

FIGURE 3. Isotherms from the second approximation. The η axis is horizontal and the ζ axis vertical. The arrow indicates the direction of the gravitational acceleration. The value of πh is 1.1 on the smallest closed curve and 0.3 on the outermost curve. The increments are 0.1.

estimated* maximum value of the terms neglected to the maximum value of the computed quantity) are, respectively, less than 15%, 3%, and 10%. For λ = 40 these percentage errors are, respectively, 25%, 5%, and 18%. The most interesting thing to note is that Ψ is the most accurately calculated quantity. Figure 2 shows the flow pattern in a plane normal to the x axis, and Figure 3 shows the isotherms therein, all for λ = 30. The flow pattern in Figure 2 can be regarded as sufficiently accurate to be representative of the actual flow pattern in a plane normal to the x axis. As expected, the hottest point and the "eyes" of the vortices occur at positive values of ζ. That is to say, the plume rises according to the $x^{2/3}$ law. After the present work was done, I found that this law had recently been verified experimentally by Wright (1977), although he did not measure the detailed velocity and temperature distributions in the plume.

If later measurements show λ is larger than 30, higher approximations would be necessary.

9. DISCUSSION

It is perhaps surprising that the analysis shows that the results in dimensionless terms are independent of the parameter Gg^2/U^5. The explanation is that the velocity (v,w) far downwind from the heat source becomes vanishingly small, and whatever the value of U, the transverse wind is asymptotically *always strong*.

Near the heat source the flow indeed depends very much on the magnitude of U. The plume may rise high in a weak wind before being bent sufficiently for the present theory to apply. In using the present theory it is always necessary to determine a virtual position for the heat source, which for small value of U can be considerably higher than its actual position.

ACKNOWLEDGMENT

This work was partially supported by the Office of Naval Research. The subject of this work was suggested to me by my friend Dr. Michel Hug, Director of the Department of Equipment, Electricity of France, through Mr. F. Boulot of the National Hydraulics Laboratory at Chatou, France, during my brief sojourn there in the summer of 1977. Their interest in this work, as well as the interest of Dr. A. Daubert, director of that laboratory, is very much appreciated. The work, begun at Chatou, was substantially improved and finished during the tenure of my Humboldt Award, at the University of Karlsruhe. To the Humboldt Foundation and my Karlsruhe hosts I should like to express my sincere appreciation.

REFERENCES

Kotsovinos, N. E. (1977). Plane turbulent buoyant jets. Part 2. Turbulence structure. *J. Fluid Mech. 81*, 45-62 (see P. 52, Figure 7).

Laufer, J. (1953). The structure of turbulence in fully developed pipe flow. *NACA Tech. Note 2954*.

Wright, S. J. (1977). *Report KH-R-36, Keck Laboratory, California Institute of Technology*.

Yih, C.-S. (1977). Turbulent buoyant plumes. *Phys. Fluids 20*, 1234-1237.

*On the basis that h_1/h_0 and $(h_{n+1})/h_n$ are of the same order of magnitude and that the same is true for Ψ and ζ

APPENDIX:
THE EFFECT OF NEGLECTING THE PRESSURE
GRADIENT IN CALCULATIONS FOR THE CONVECTION
PLUME IN A TRANSVERSE WIND

J. P. Benqué
Electricité de France
Chatou, France

In many previous studies on jets and plumes, the pressure distribution in the jets or plumes is assumed hydrostatic, so that if the body-force term in the equation of motion is written in the form $-g\Delta\rho$, where $\Delta\rho$ is the difference between the local density and the ambient density, the pressure gradient can be neglected in the equations of motion. If, further, the flow is two dimensional or axisymmetric, only the equation of motion for the vertical velocity component is then needed. After that velocity component is determined, the equation of continuity can be used to determine the other velocity component.

In the preceding paper by Yih, the assumption that the x component of the velocity is constant leaves only two other velocity components to be determined, and it is tempting to adopt the usual procedure of neglecting the pressure gradient. Yih has resisted that temptation. But it is useful to see what effects such a neglect would have on the flow and to determine whether in the problem treated by Yih such a neglect is allowable. This Appendix is devoted to this question.

If the pressure distribution is assumed hydrostatic and the usual procedure is followed, one will drop Eq. (1) and retain Eq. (2), with the first term on its right-hand side dropped. [Equation numbers in Yih's paper are retained.] Equations (3) to (7) will remain but (8) and (9) will not be needed.

Following Yih's development and using his notation, then, we have, as the dimensionless equations to solve, (24) and

$$(L - 3)W = -h + \lambda(VW_\eta + WW_\zeta). \qquad (A.1)$$

Using the λ-series (29), we have again (33) for the solution of h_0. The equation for W_0, obtained from (A.1), however, is now

$$(L - 3)W_0 = -h_0. \qquad (A.2)$$

The solution of this equation, satisfying all the boundary conditions for W stated in Yih's paper, is

$$W_0 = \frac{1}{3\pi} e^{-r^2} = \frac{1}{3\pi} e^{-\eta^2 - \zeta^2}. \qquad (A.3)$$

Although it can be readily verified that Eq. (A.3) satisfies Eq. (A.2), it is not obvious that Eq. (A.3) is the unique solution. We shall show in the following that it indeed is the unique solution. The complementary solution W_{0c} of Eq. (A.2) satisfies

$$(L - 3)W_{0c} = 0 \qquad (A.4)$$

and must be even in both η and ζ. Let

$$W_{0c} = f(\eta)g(\zeta),$$

where the f is in no manner the same as the f in Eq. (38) of Yih's paper, we have

$$f'' + 2\eta f' + af = 0, \qquad (A.5)$$

$$g'' + 2\zeta g' + bg = 0, \qquad (A.6)$$

where

$$a + b = 1. \qquad (A.7)$$

Now let

$$f(\eta) = e^{-\eta^2/2}\beta(\eta). \qquad (A.8)$$

Then Eq. (A.5) becomes

$$\beta'' - (\eta^2 + b)\beta = 0. \qquad (A.9)$$

Similarly, if we let

$$g(\zeta) = e^{-\zeta^2/2}\gamma(\zeta).$$

Then

$$\gamma'' - (\zeta^2 + a)\gamma = 0. \qquad (A.10)$$

Because of Eq. (A.7), a or b must be positive. Let b be positive. (The argument is strictly similar if a is positive.) Because of the symmetry with respect to the ζ axis,

$$\beta'(0) = 0.$$

Then Eq. (A.9) shows that β will approach infinity as η^2 approaches infinity, if $\beta(0)$ is not zero. [If $\beta(0) = 0$ then $\beta = 0$ throughout.] To see how $f(\eta)$ behaves at infinity, it is necessary to see how $\beta(\eta)$ behaves asymptotically. A simple calculation shows that the two solutions of Eq. (A.9) behave, for large values of η^2, like

$$\exp\left[-\int_0^\eta (\eta^2 - a - 2)^{\frac{1}{2}}d\eta\right] \quad \text{and} \quad \exp\left[\int_0^\eta (\eta^2 - a)^{\frac{1}{2}}d\eta\right].$$

As we have seen, β must contain the second solution since β approaches infinity as $\eta^2 \to \infty$. Using the second solution as the dominant term (a constant multiplier being understood), and recalling that

$$(\eta^2 - a)^{\frac{1}{2}} = \eta - \frac{a}{2\eta} + 0\left(\frac{1}{\eta^2}\right),$$

we see from Eq. (A.8) that for large η^2

$$f(\eta) \sim |\eta|^{-a/2}, \qquad (A.11)$$

which can be seen to satisfy Eq. (A.5) asymptotically. If a is negative, (A.11) shows that $f(\eta)$, and therefore W_{0c}, cannot satisfy the condition on W_0 at infinity. If a is positive, it must be less than 1, because of (A.7) and because b is positive. Then if W_0 contains W_{0c},

616

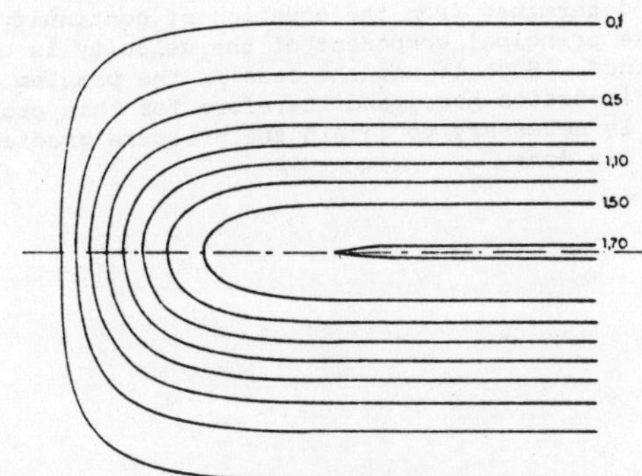

FIGURE A.1. Flow pattern for $(V_1 W_1)$. $\Delta 6\pi \Psi_1 = 0.2$.

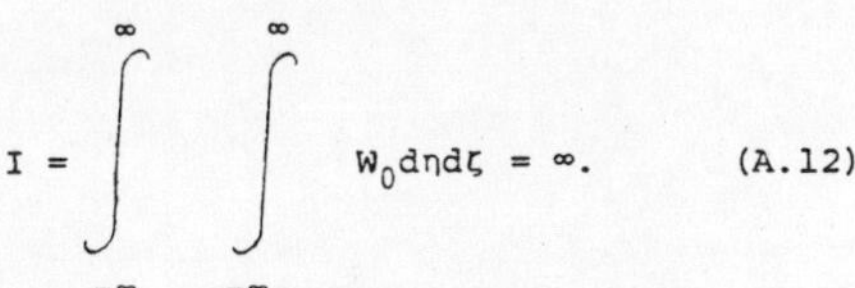

$$I = \int_{-\infty}^{\infty} \int_{-\infty}^{\infty} W_0 \, d\eta \, d\zeta = \infty. \tag{A.12}$$

But this cannot be true, because integration of (A.2), by parts if necessary, gives

$$-3I = -\int_{-\infty}^{\infty} \int_{-\infty}^{\infty} h_0 \, d\eta \, d\zeta = -1,$$

so that

$$I = \frac{1}{3}.$$

Hence W cannot contain a multiple of W_{0c}, and Eq. (A.3) is the unique solution.

Then the equation of continuity gives

$$V_0 = \frac{2}{3\pi} \int_0^{\eta} \zeta e^{-(\eta^2 + \zeta^2)} d\eta, \tag{A.13}$$

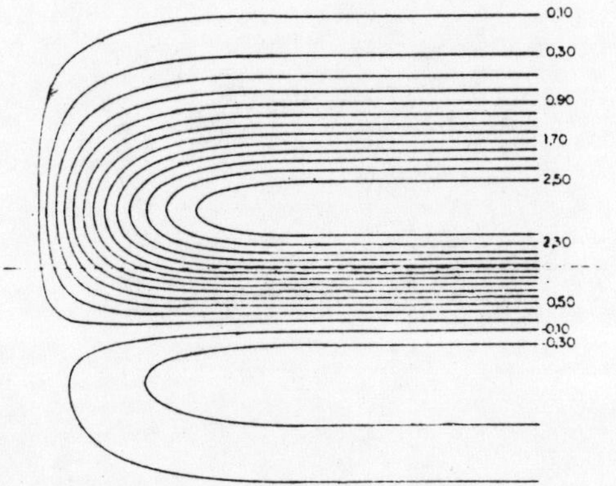

FIGURE A.2. Flow pattern for $(V_0 + \lambda V_1,\ W_0 + \lambda W_1)$. $\Delta 6\pi_1 = 0.2$.

which shows that at $|\eta| = \infty$, V_0 does not vanish. We must then, if we adopt the procedure of neglecting the pressure gradient, not demand that V_0 vanish at infinity, but instead demand

$$\frac{\partial V_0}{\partial \eta} = 0 \text{ at } |\eta| = \infty. \tag{A.14}$$

This boundary condition for V_0 must, for consistency, be demanded of V, i.e., of V_1, V_2, etc., as we proceed to higher and higher approximations.

In this connection we can also see that it is not possible to add a multiple of W_{0c} to the W_0 given by Eq. (A.3) to make V_0 vanish at infinity. For, in order to make V_0 vanish at infinity, the only possibility is to add to the W_0 given by Eq. (A.3) a multiple of

$$W_{0c} = e^{-\zeta^2} f(\eta), \tag{A.15}$$

where f satisfies

$$f'' + 2\eta f' - f = 0.$$

That means

$$a = -1,$$

and Eq. (A.11) gives

$$f(\eta) \sim |\eta|^{\frac{1}{2}},$$

which makes W_{0c}, and therefore W_0 if it contains W_{0c}, infinite at $|\eta| = \infty$. Any other dependence of W_0 on ζ than $\exp(-\zeta^2)$ would, of course, not make V_0 vanish at infinity, for the part of V_0 that arises from W_{0c} would not be able to cancel out Eq. (A.13) at $|\eta| = \infty$.

Hence W_0 and V_0 are uniquely given by Eqs. (A.3) and (A.13). Using them in

$$Lh_1 = V_0 h_{0\eta} + W_0 h_{0\zeta}, \tag{A.16}$$

and

$$(L - 3)W_1 = -h_1 + V_0 W_{0\eta} + W_0 W_{0\zeta}, \tag{A.17}$$

we find that

$$W_1 = \frac{h_1}{3}. \tag{A.18}$$

I have computed h_1 numerically from Eq. (A.16) and the boundary conditions, and therefore W_1. The velocity component, V_1, is then found from the equation of continuity. The flow pattern corresponding to (V_1, W_1) is given in Figure A.1, where the streamlines are shown, with $\Psi_1 = 0$ on the ζ axis and $\Delta 6\pi \Psi_1 = 0.2$.

Then the flow field for

$$V = V_0 + \lambda V_1 \text{ and } W = W_0 + \lambda W_1$$

is shown in Figure A.2, with $\lambda = 30$, where the $\Delta 6\pi \Psi = 0.2$.

It is clear that the "streamlines" do not close to form closed eddies, as in the figures of Yih's paper. Thus the effect of the pressure gradient cannot be neglected in the problem studied by Yih.

In past studies of jets and plumes, where the

pressure gradient has been successfully neglected, the velocity component other than the one retained is one order of magnitude smaller than the one retained. Thus the equation of motion for it can be neglected together with the gradient of (the dynamic part of) the pressure, and the flow pattern can be determined from the equation of continuity once the principal component of the velocity is determined. Such is not the case in the problem under discussion here, and therefore for this problem it is necessary to retain the pressure gradient, as Yih has done.

16336   JUNE 1981   EM3

SIMILARITY SOLUTIONS FOR TURBULENT JETS AND PLUMES

By Chia-Shun Yih[1]

INTRODUCTION

At this stage of development of research in civil engineering, when the use of digital computers is increasingly prevalent—sometimes, regrettably, to the point of replacing the use of the best analog computer available (the laboratory)—analytical work on turbulent flows especially needs insight, care, a constant regard for experimental evidence, and a drive for a sense of unity. In this paper attention will be focused on turbulent jets and plumes that allow solutions characterized by similarity laws, and it is hoped that the formulation, the solutions, and the analyses will not only furnish specific results for and understanding of the phenomena studied, but will also contribute to the aforementioned requirements at a time when they are especially needed.

This paper is the basis of a lecture given at the third ASCE Engineering Mechanics Division Specialty Conference held at the University of Texas at Austin in September 1979. The paper is dedicated to my mentor Hunter Rouse, who has been interested in jets and plumes all his professional life. The lecture at Austin, on the other hand, was given in honor of my friend and former colleague Louis Landweber, at the occasion of his retirement.

After known similarity solutions for jets and mixing streams are briefly presented for the sake of comparison and to add weight to the body of turbulent flows that admit such solutions, a new similarity solution for turbulent jets in a transverse wind is presented. Then vertical buoyant plumes (hereafter called plumes for brevity), round or two-dimensional, are considered, and their solutions given and analyzed. Finally, the problem of three-dimensional plumes in a transverse wind, which is of importance to our atmospheric environment, is considered and its solution given. The three main conclusions of this paper are:

1. The use of eddy viscosity produces very good agreement with available

[1]Stephen P. Timoshenko Univ. Prof. of Fluid Mech., The Univ. of Michigan, Ann Arbor, Mich. 48109.

Note.—Discussion open until November 1, 1981. Separate discussions should be submitted for the individual papers in this symposium. To extend the closing date one month, a written request must be filed with the Manager of Technical and Professional Publications, ASCE. Manuscript was submitted for review for possible publication on July 10, 1979. This paper is part of the Journal of the Engineering Mechanics Division, Proceedings of the American Society of Civil Engineers, ©ASCE, Vol. 107, No. EM3, June, 1981.

experimental results for mean-velocity and mean-temperature distributions. Furthermore, a check with available turbulence measurements for round jets and plumes gives support to the validity of the eddy-viscosity approach.

2. When the eddy viscosity is expressed as a function of the product of the maximum mean velocity at any section and the distance at which the velocity falls to one half of that maximum, this fraction (or coefficient) is about 0.037 for two-dimensional jets, 0.030 for half jets, 0.026 for round jets, about 0.051 for plane plumes, and 0.039 for round plumes. It is remarkable that these coefficients vary in such a narrow range. For bent-over jets and plumes no experimental results exist to allow evaluation of this coefficient, but it will probably be much larger.

3. Whenever the geometry allows similarity of the flow (and the temperature field for plumes), turbulence is conducive to similarity, and moreover endows the word "similarity" with the richer meaning that the velocity and temperature fields are not only mathematically but also dynamically similar between any two cross sections.

TURBULENT PLANE JETS

There exist many experimental and analytical works on turbulent jets and turbulent mixing of two streams (hereafter called half jets for brevity). These were mostly done in Germany from the early 1920s to the early 1950s, and, with a few exceptions, from 1935 to the early 1950s in this country. Most of the references are given in Schlichting's book (13). Recent work on floating plumes has been done by Engelund (3). Here we shall give specific references only when our analyses touch upon the results contained therein.

We start with a consideration of two-dimensional turbulent jets. Consider a fluid issuing from a slit in a wall into infinite space filled with the same fluid. In a plane perpendicular to the slit the trace of the slit will be taken to be the origin, and the trace of the wall the y-axis. The line passing through the origin and normal to the wall is the x-axis. It is well known that when the width of the slip approaches zero it is possible to have a line source of momentum as the discharge goes to zero. If u and v denote the time-mean velocity components in the directions of increasing x and y, respectively, and u' and v' denote the velocity fluctuations, the Reynolds equation for the x direction is

$$\rho\left(\frac{\partial}{\partial x}u^2 + \frac{\partial}{\partial y}uv + \frac{\partial}{\partial x}\overline{u'u'} + \frac{\partial}{\partial y}\overline{u'v'}\right) = \mu\left(\frac{\partial^2 u}{\partial y^2} + \frac{\partial^2 u}{\partial x^2}\right) \quad \ldots \ldots \ldots (1)$$

in which the term representing the gradient of the pressure has been neglected; μ = the viscosity; and ρ = the density of the fluid. The equation of continuity (with subscripts henceforth denoting partial differentiation) is

$$u_x + v_y = 0 \ldots \ldots \ldots \ldots \ldots \ldots \ldots \ldots \ldots \ldots \ldots \ldots \ldots \ldots \ldots \ldots \ldots \ldots \ldots (2)$$

The quantities $\overline{u'u'}$ and $\overline{u'v'}$, where the bars mean time averages, are the Reynolds stresses. In arriving at Eq. 1, Eq. 2 and the equation for continuity for u' and v', of the same form as Eq. 2, have been used. Integrating Eq. 1 with respect to y from minus infinity to plus infinity, and noting that both

u and the turbulent quantities must vanish at the limits of integration, we have

$$\frac{\partial}{\partial x}\left[\int \rho\left(u^2 + \overline{u'^2}\right) dy + \mu\left(v_{-\infty} - v_\infty\right)\right] = 0 \dots\dots\dots\dots\dots\dots (3)$$

in which the limits of integration are omitted and where the term involving μ originates from the term μu_{xx} in Eq. 1 after Eq. 2 has been used. We are then left with the result, if the term involving μ is neglected

$$\rho \int \left(u^2 + \overline{u'^2}\right) dy = M \dots\dots\dots\dots\dots\dots\dots\dots (4)$$

in which M = the momentum flux, and is independent of x. In most previous works the contribution of the Reynolds stress to M is neglected, but it can be as much as 7% of M for round jets, and as high as 20%–25% for turbulent two-dimensional plumes, as we shall see later.

Let us now consider u as a function of M, ρ, μ, x and y. Since only M, μ, and ρ contain the dimension of mass, we shall replace them by their ratios M/ρ and μ/ρ, which we shall denote by K and v respectively, in a dimensional analysis which gives

$$\left(\frac{x}{K}\right)^{1/2} u = F_1\left(\frac{Kx}{v^2}, \frac{y}{x}\right) \dots\dots\dots\dots\dots\dots (5)$$

Now the usual, and indeed correct, way to interpret Eq. 5 is that when Kx/v^2, which is a Reynolds number squared, is very large, molecular viscosity is not important and thus that parameter can be omitted from the last equation to give

$$\left(\frac{x}{K}\right)^{1/2} u = F_1\left(\frac{y}{x}\right) \dots\dots\dots\dots\dots\dots\dots\dots (6)$$

which can serve as a guide for experimentation. But stopping here in the interpretation of Eq. 5 and the use of Eq. 6 is to deprive oneself of an important perception concerning the eddy viscosity and thus of a tool for giving a similarity solution to the problem, the existence of which is already suggested by Eq. 6.

Indeed, from Eq. 5 we see immediately that $(Kx)^{1/2}$ has the dimension of a kinematic viscosity, which can be used as the scale of the eddy viscosity ϵ. If we use ϵ as an unknown and ignore the effects of molecular viscosity, we have

$$(Kx)^{-1/2} \epsilon = F_2\left(\frac{y}{x}\right) \dots\dots\dots\dots\dots\dots\dots\dots (7)$$

If further we ignore the variation of the left-hand side with y, which we cannot possibly specify analytically, we have

$$\epsilon = \lambda (Kx)^{1/2} \dots\dots\dots\dots\dots\dots\dots\dots\dots\dots (8)$$

in which λ = a constant. With this, the equation of motion becomes, if further longitudinal turbulent diffusion is neglected

$$uu_x + vu_y = \epsilon u_{yy} \dots\dots\dots\dots\dots\dots\dots\dots\dots\dots (9)$$

which has the same form as the corresponding equation for the laminar case, and the solution of which was given numerically by Schlichting (13) and analytically by Bickley (2). When the angle of spread measured by Reichardt (11) is used, and ϵ is expressed in terms of the maximum velocity at any section of constant x and $b_{1/2}$, which is half of the width between points where the velocity drops to half of the maximum, the result is

$$\epsilon = 0.037\, b_{1/2}\, U \quad\ldots\ldots\ldots\ldots\ldots\ldots\ldots\ldots\ldots\ldots\ldots\ldots (10)$$

This gives a value of 0.0116 for the λ in Eq. 8. The results so far presented in this section are well known, but it is not as well recognized that there is a contribution of the turbulence to the momentum flux, and that the form of the eddy viscosity can be derived. Above all—and this is one of the most important points I wish to make in this paper—it has not been generally recognized, if recognized at all, that turbulence *ensures* the existence of a similarity solution when the geometry allows it (as in this case), and that one has not picked a form for the eddy viscosity just to get a similarity solution. It is also interesting that the velocity field and the eddy viscosity can be determined from just one measured quantity, i.e., the angle of spread of the jet if K is known.

The contribution of the turbulent term in Eq. 4 to the momentum flux M can be found once u'^2 is known. Kotsovinos (8) has measured this quantity for two-dimensional jets, and the turbulent term in Eq. 4 is about 6% of the other term on the left-hand side of Eq. 4 so that

$$\rho \int u^2 \, dy = 0.94 M \quad\ldots\ldots\ldots\ldots\ldots\ldots\ldots\ldots\ldots\ldots\ldots\ldots (11)$$

This is true, however, only if the velocity u measured with a hotwire is truly the time mean of the instantaneous longitudinal velocity. When u is measured by inertial methods, such as by a Pitot tube or a vane anemometer, the result obtained is really the root-mean-square of that instantaneous velocity, namely $(u^2 + u'^2)^{1/2}$. In that case the measured mean velocity flux is exactly M. But since the similarity solution is for the mean velocity rather for the root-mean-square velocity, comparison of the latter with the theoretical u suffers from a lack of strict correspondence of the quantities compared. The effect of this disparity is small if the turbulent part in Eq. 4 is small. Note also that if Eq. 11 is used the velocity components given by Schlichting (13) for two-dimensional turbulent jets should be multiplied by 0.97. Since the comparisons for the mean velocity are usually presented in terms of $u/u_{\max}$, they are not affected by this multiplication, and the 3% reduction in the theoretical $u_{\max}$ is so small that it is probably within the range of the spread of experimental results. The smallness of u'^2 compared with u^2 justifies the neglect of the longitudinal-diffusion term in Eq. 9.

The comments made in the foregoing paragraph are relevant to all the following sections, and we shall not repeat the analysis except where it is desirable to do so to give the magnitude of the contribution of the turbulent part to the momentum or temperature flux.

TURBULENT HALF JETS

Consider now the turbulent mixing of two streams, the upper one of which flows at velocity U_1 at infinite y, and the lower one of which flows at velocity U_2 at negative infinite y. The two streams meet at the origin, and the line starting from this origin and going in the direction of U_1 or U_2 at infinite y is the x-axis. Here, instead of a kinematic momentum flux K we have U_1 and U_2, and it is convenient, though not at all necessary, to use $U_1 + U_2$ as the velocity scale. Again neglecting the effects of molecular viscosity, one has instead of Eq. 5

$$\frac{u}{(U_1 + U_2)} = F_3\left(\frac{U_1}{U_2}, \frac{y}{x}\right) \quad\dotfill\quad (12)$$

and instead of Eq. 7

$$\frac{\epsilon}{U_1 x} = F_4\left(\frac{U_1}{U_2}, \frac{y}{x}\right)$$

But to write this is to ignore the origin of turbulence, for the difference $U_1 - U_2$ is solely responsible for the mixing and the turbulence, and a much more perceptive expression for the eddy viscosity is

$$\frac{\epsilon}{(U_1 - U_2)x} = F_4\left(\frac{y}{x}\right) \quad\dotfill\quad (13)$$

Again ignoring the variation of ϵ with y we have

$$\epsilon = \lambda x(U_1 - U_2) \quad\dotfill\quad (14)$$

With this, Görtler (7) reduced the boundary-layer equation of motion to the well-known Blausius equation for flow over a flat plate, again neglecting longitudinal turbulent diffusion and the longitudinal pressure gradient. His solution, valid only if $U_1 - U_2$ is small compared with $U_1 + U_2$, was used by Schlichting to compare with the measurements of Reichardt (11) for $U_2 = 0$. The agreement was good but fortuitous. Since the Blasius equation is also obtained for the laminar case for which the boundary conditions are also identical (although, of course, the spatial variable is not y/x for the laminar case), and since Lock (10) has solved the laminar case without Görtler's assumption, his results should have been used to compare with Reichardt's measurements. When we do so, we find that the agreement is rather less good, the value for u/U_1 is almost 0.6 from Lock's calculations, while the experimental value is about 0.5. Using Reichardt's measurements for the spread angle and Görtler's calculated results, Schlichting got an expression for the eddy viscosity. Using $b_{1/2}$ now to denote the breadth across which the velocity varies from $U_1/4$ to $3U_1/4$, Schlichting's expression for the eddy viscosity can be replaced, upon using Reichardt's experimental results, by

$$\epsilon = 0.030\, b_{1/2}(U_1 - U_2) \quad\dotfill\quad (15)$$

which corresponds to the value 0.00137 for λ in Eq. 14.

Turbulent Round Jets

The development for round jets is similar to that for two-dimensional jets, except that the difference in geometry demands that Eqs. 4, 5, 6, and 7 be replaced by

$$2\pi \int_0^\infty r(u^2 + \overline{u'^2})\, dr = \frac{M}{\rho} = K \quad\quad\quad\quad\quad\quad\quad\quad\quad (16)$$

$$K^{-1/2} xu = F_5\left(\frac{K}{\nu^2}, \frac{r}{x}\right) \quad\quad\quad\quad\quad\quad\quad\quad (17)$$

$$K^{-1/2} xu = F_5\left(\frac{r}{x}\right) \quad\quad\quad\quad\quad\quad\quad\quad\quad (18)$$

$$K^{-1/2} \epsilon = F_6\left(\frac{r}{x}\right) \quad\quad\quad\quad\quad\quad\quad\quad\quad (19)$$

in which x is measured from the origin of the jet along the axis of symmetry of the jet; and r is measured radially from that axis. Ignoring, of necessity, the variation of ϵ with r, we write Eq. 19 in the simplified form

$$\epsilon = \lambda K^{1/2} \quad\quad\quad\quad\quad\quad\quad\quad\quad\quad\quad\quad (20)$$

With Eq. 20 substituted into the equation of motion to give turbulent-diffusion terms in replacement of the Reynolds-stress terms, an equation similar to Eq. 9 is obtained. It was solved by Schlichting (13), albeit in unnecessarily complicated forms. When compared with the measurements of Reichardt (11), good agreement was found for

$$\epsilon = 0.0256\, r_{1/2}\, U \quad\quad\quad\quad\quad\quad\quad\quad\quad\quad (21)$$

in which U is again the maximum velocity at any section normal to the jet axis; and $r_{1/2}$ the distance across which the velocity u falls from U to half of U. This result gives the value 0.0165 to λ in Eq. 20.

The measurements of Gibson (6) show that the contribution of turbulence to the momentum flux K in Eq. 16 is about 7%. The same comments as those made after Eq. 11 for two-dimensional jets can be made here also, and will not be repeated. Finally, we note that Prandtl's original mixing-length theory gave ϵ the form

$$\epsilon = \rho l^2 \left|\frac{dU}{ds}\right| \quad\quad\quad\quad\quad\quad\quad\quad\quad\quad (22)$$

in which $s = y$ for two-dimensional jets and r for round jets. Using this, Tollmien (14) gave mean-velocity distributions for both two-dimensional and round jets, which agree fairly well with Reichardt's measurements, except that near the jet axis the theoretical results are consistently too low. This writer (20) has already noted the more serious fault of Eq. 22, which gives a cusp to the velocity profile at the jet axis—an undesirable consequence of Prandtl's original mixing-length theory not noticed before and not revealed by Tollmien's numerical calculations.

Since Gibson (6) has given the measurements for the Reynolds stress $\rho\,\overline{u'v'}$, we have now an excellent opportunity to test the validity of using the eddy viscosity. From Figs. 1 and 2 of Gibson's paper (6), we obtain near the jet axis

$$\frac{\overline{u'v'}}{U^2} = 0.078 \frac{r}{r_{1/2}}$$

Using the U given by Schlichting's solution, we have

$$\overline{u'v'} = 2.59 Kx^{-2} \left(\frac{r}{r_{1/2}}\right) \quad\ldots\ldots\ldots\ldots\ldots\ldots \quad (23)$$

near the axis. The value calculated from Schlichting's solution is, near the jet axis

$$\overline{u'v'} = -\epsilon \frac{dU}{dr} = 1.41 Kx^{-2} \left(\frac{r}{r_{1/2}}\right) \quad\ldots\ldots\ldots\ldots \quad (24)$$

Thus, the result given by Eq. 23 is considerably greater than that given by Eq. 24, although not quite twice the latter. So it appears that the use of the eddy viscosity gives good agreements with the mean-velocity profile only fortuitously. However, near the jet axis the velocity gradient is small, and this discrepancy may not be important. At $r = r_{1/2}$, where the velocity gradient is near the maximum, the experimental value of $\overline{u'v'}$ is, from Gibson's figures (6)

$$\overline{u'v'} = 0.86 Kx^{-2} \quad\ldots\ldots\ldots\ldots\ldots\ldots\ldots\ldots \quad (25)$$

whereas its value from the analytical solution is

$$\overline{u'v'} = 0.82 Kx^{-2} \quad\ldots\ldots\ldots\ldots\ldots\ldots\ldots\ldots \quad (26)$$

The closeness of 0.82 to 0.86 must be considered a triumph for the concept and the use of the eddy viscosity. This writer believes that this is the first time that this much used concept has been given a test, though the data have been available for a long time.

Taking stock for straight jets, we see from Eqs. 10, 15, and 21 that the coefficients in the formulas vary in a remarkably narrow range. The corresponding values for λ in Eqs. 8, 14, and 20, however, vary in a much wider range, with the λ for the half jet much smaller. This shows the superiority of expressing ϵ in terms of U and $b_{1/2}$ or $r_{1/2}$.

TURBULENT THREE-DIMENSIONAL JETS IN TRANSVERSE WIND

Consider a three-dimensional jet issuing vertically at the origin into a horizontal wind with velocity U. (Note the new usage of U.) The direction of the x-axis is the direction of the wind, that of the y-axis is the horizontal direction normal to the x-axis, and the z-axis is directed vertically upward. The velocity components in the directions of increasing x, y, and z will be denoted by u, v, and w, respectively.

The two basic assumptions of the analysis are that the velocity component u can be replaced by the constant U, and that an eddy viscosity ϵ independent of y and z can be used. If p denotes the pressure and ρ the density, and if the diffusion of momentum in the x-direction is neglected when compared with the diffusion of momentum in the directions of y and z, the equations of motion are

$$Uv_x + vv_y + wv_z = -\frac{1}{\rho}p_y + \epsilon(v_{yy} + v_{zz}) \quad\dots\dots\dots\dots (27)$$

$$Uw_x + vw_y + ww_z = -\frac{1}{\rho}p_z + \epsilon(w_{yy} + w_{zz}) \quad\dots\dots\dots\dots (28)$$

From these, the vorticity equation is obtained upon elimination of p:

$$U\hat{\xi}_x + v\hat{\xi}_y + w\hat{\xi}_z = \epsilon(\hat{\xi}_{yy} + \hat{\xi}_{zz}) \quad\dots\dots\dots\dots\dots (29)$$

in which $\quad \hat{\xi} = w_y - v_z \quad\dots\dots\dots\dots\dots\dots\dots (30)$

The equation of continuity is

$$v_y + w_z = 0 \quad\dots\dots\dots\dots\dots\dots\dots\dots (31)$$

which permits the use of a stream function ψ, in terms of which

$$v = \psi_z, \quad w = -\psi_y \quad\dots\dots\dots\dots\dots\dots (32)$$

The flow is symmetric with respect to the xy-plane.

The boundary condition at infinity in the yz-plane is that v, w, and p vanish there. Using Eq. 31 to write the left-hand side of Eq. 28 as

$$Uw_x + (vw)_y + (w^2)_z$$

and then integrating Eq. 28 in the yz-plane, we obtain

$$\frac{d}{dx}M = 0 \quad\dots\dots\dots\dots\dots\dots\dots\dots\dots (33)$$

in which apart from a constant factor ρ

$$M = \int_{-\infty}^{\infty}\int_{-\infty}^{\infty} Uw\,dy\,dz \quad\dots\dots\dots\dots\dots\dots (34)$$

is the flux of vertical momentum in the x direction (or through the yz-plane). Eq. 33 indicates that M is a constant. If the assumption $u = U$ is not made, replacing U by u in the equations of motion and in Eq. 34 will still give a constant M but there will then be a contribution of turbulence to M. In consistency with the assumption of constant U, one ignores the contribution from turbulence.

For the problem posed, then, the independent variables are the coordinates U and M. We shall see that ϵ is not an independent variable.

To proceed further we need the form of ϵ. To discover it, we compare the first and last terms in Eqs. 27 and 28 and demand they be of the same order of magnitude and obtain

$$\frac{\epsilon}{l^2} \sim \frac{U}{x} \quad\dots\dots\dots\dots\dots\dots\dots\dots\dots (35)$$

in which l = the length scale in the yz-plane; and x = the length scale for the x direction. On the other hand, Eq. 34 gives

$$wl^2 \sim \frac{M}{U} \quad\dots\dots\dots\dots\dots\dots\dots\dots\dots (36)$$

in which w is now used to denote the scale of w and v. The root-mean-square of the turbulent velocity can be assumed to be proportional to w and the scale of turbulence proportional to l, so that

$$\epsilon \sim wl \quad\quad\quad\quad\quad\quad\quad\quad\quad\quad\quad\quad\quad\quad\quad\quad (37)$$

Then Eqs. 36 and 37 give

$$l^3 \sim \frac{Mx}{U^2} \quad\quad\quad\quad\quad\quad\quad\quad\quad\quad\quad\quad\quad\quad\quad (38)$$

so that $\quad \epsilon \sim \left(\frac{M^2}{Ux}\right)^{1/3}$

We shall take $\quad \epsilon = \alpha \left(\frac{M^2}{Ux}\right)^{1/3} \quad\quad\quad\quad\quad\quad\quad\quad\quad (39)$

in which $\alpha = $ a dimensionless constant to be determined from experiment or to be estimated from experience with related problems concerning jets.

The neglect of the dependence of ϵ on y and z is consistent with all previous analyses using Prandtl's simplified theory. See Görtler (7), the writer (20), and others, who have used that theory to predict successfully the forms of velocity and temperature distributions in jets and plumes.

From Eq. 38 we obtain immediately for the coordinates the transformation

$$(\eta, \zeta) = (6\alpha)^{-1/2} \left(\frac{U^2}{Mx}\right)^{1/3} (y, z) \quad\quad\quad\quad\quad\quad\quad (40)$$

and Eqs. 36 and 37 suggest the transformation for the velocity components

$$(v, w) = (6\alpha)^{-1} \left(\frac{MU}{x^2}\right)^{1/3} (V, W) \quad\quad\quad\quad\quad\quad\quad (41)$$

in which V and W depend only on η, ζ, and α. The powers of 6α in Eqs. 40 and 41 are used to simplify the final equations to be given as follows. We note here that the 1/3-power law of the rise of the jet implied by Eq. 40 was already found by Scorer (15) by other arguments, but Eq. 40 is otherwise new, and Eq. 41 is entirely new.

With these transformations Eq. 32 becomes

$$V = \Psi_\zeta \quad \text{and} \quad W = -\Psi_\eta \quad\quad\quad\quad\quad\quad\quad\quad\quad (42)$$

in which $\Psi = $ the dimensionless stream function. The dimensionless vorticity (in the x direction) is defined by

$$\xi = W_\eta - V_\zeta$$

which can be written as

$$\xi = -(\Psi_{\eta\eta} + \Psi_{\zeta\zeta}) \quad\quad\quad\quad\quad\quad\quad\quad\quad\quad (43)$$

Eq. 3 now has the form

$$(L + 2)\xi = \lambda (V\xi_\eta + W\xi_\zeta) \quad\quad\quad\quad\quad\quad\quad\quad\quad (44)$$

in which $\quad L = \dfrac{\partial^2}{\partial \eta^2} + \dfrac{\partial^2}{\partial \zeta^2} + 2\eta \dfrac{\partial}{\partial \eta} + 2\zeta \dfrac{\partial}{\partial \zeta} + 4$ . . . . (45)

and $\quad \lambda = (6\alpha^3)^{-1/2}$ . . . . (46)

Eqs. 17 and 18 can be combined to give the single equation

$$(L + 2)\nabla^2 \Psi = \lambda(\Psi_\zeta \nabla^2 \Psi_\eta - \Psi_\eta \nabla^2 \Psi_\zeta) \qquad (47)$$

which can be solved, numerically if necessary, once λ is given, whatever value λ has.

The boundary conditions are:

(i) $W = 0 = V$ (or $\quad \Psi_\zeta = 0 = \Psi_\eta$) at $\quad r^2 = \infty$;

(ii) $V = 0 = W_\eta$ (or $\quad \Psi_\zeta = 0 = \Psi_{\eta\eta}$) at $\quad \eta = 0$

in which $\quad r^2 = \eta^2 + \zeta^2$ . . . . (48)

In addition to (i) and (ii), there is the integral condition

$$\text{(iii)} \quad \int_{-\infty}^{\infty} \int_{-\infty}^{\infty} W \, d\eta \, d\zeta = 1$$

The formulation for the similarity solution is now complete. This formulation and the following solution are both new.

The differential equations to be solved are Eqs. 43 and 44, or 47, and the boundary and integral conditions are (i), (ii), and (iii). The method of solution depends on the magnitude of λ. With no experimental data to guide us in the determination of λ, we shall adopt the following procedure. The differential system will be solved by a power expansion in λ for Ψ and carry the solution to the second approximation and give the flow pattern for a value of λ for which the solution is valid. After experimental results are available, we shall see what value λ indeed has. If it is small enough for the second approximation to be sufficient, no further work is needed. Otherwise we need to carry the solution further, or else abandon the method altogether and give a numerical solution instead.

For this scheme we shall use Eqs. 43 and 44 instead of Eq. 47. The power expansion is

$$\Psi = \Psi_0 + \lambda \Psi_1 + \lambda^2 \Psi_2 + \ldots \qquad (49)$$

Correspondingly, we have

$$\xi = \xi_0 + \lambda \xi_1 + \lambda^2 \xi_2 + \ldots \qquad (50)$$

Substituting Eq. 40 into Eq. 44, we have for the first approximation

$$(L + 2)\xi_0 = 0 \qquad (51)$$

In polar coordinates (r, θ), in which r is given by Eq. 48 and

$$\theta = \arctan \frac{\zeta}{\eta} \qquad (52)$$

the operator L can be written as

$$L = \frac{\partial^2}{\partial r^2} + \frac{1}{r}\frac{\partial}{\partial r} + \frac{1}{r^2}\frac{\partial^2}{\partial \theta^2} + 2r\frac{\partial}{\partial r} + 4 \quad \dots \dots \dots \dots (53)$$

The solution of Eq. 51 in polar coordinates is

$$\xi_0 = C\cos\theta\,(re^{-r^2}) \quad \dots \dots \dots \dots \dots (54)$$

Then Ψ_0 is obtained from Eq. 43, or, in polar coordinates from

$$\left(\frac{\partial^2}{\partial r^2} + \frac{1}{r}\frac{\partial}{\partial r} + \frac{1}{r^2}\frac{\partial^2}{\partial \theta^2}\right)\Psi_0 = -\xi_0 \quad \dots \dots \dots \dots (55)$$

the solution of which is

$$\Psi_0 = \frac{C}{4r}\cos\theta\,(1 - e^{-r^2}) \quad \dots \dots \dots \dots (56)$$

The constant C is determined by (iii), since W_0 is known once Ψ_0 is known. We have then

$$C = -\frac{4}{\pi}$$

The flow pattern determined by Ψ_0 is shown in Fig. 1.

Taking the coefficients of λ in Eq. 44 after Eq. 50 has been substituted into it, we obtain

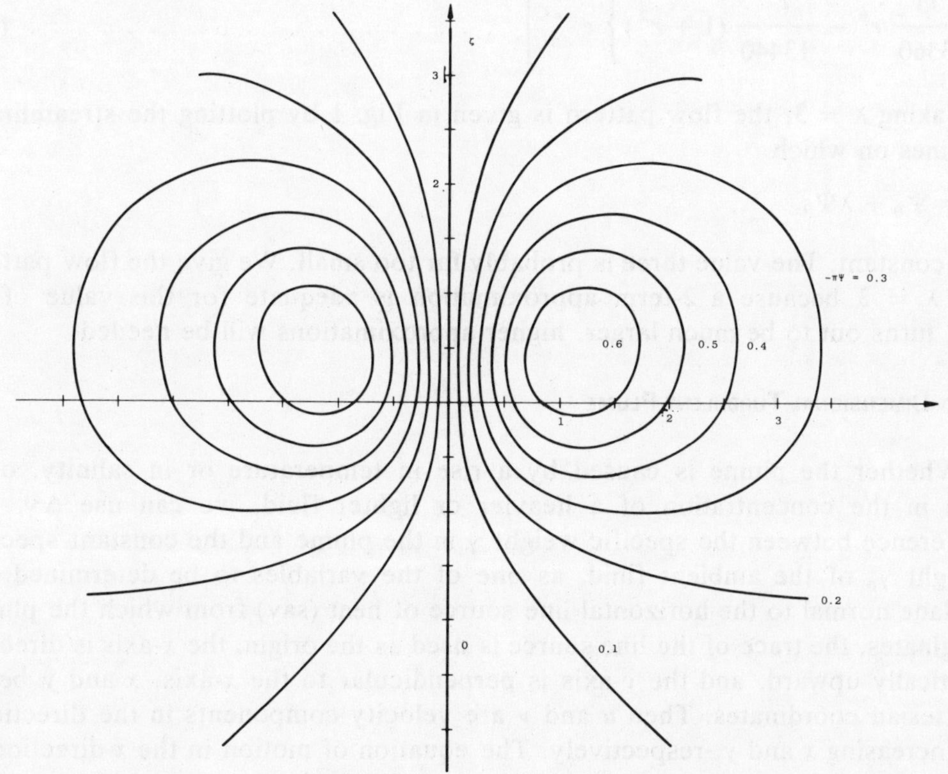

FIG. 1.—Flow Pattern for Vertical Momentum Jet in Transverse Wind, in Terms of Dimensionless Variables (Two-Term Approximation)

$$(L + 2)\xi_1 = \frac{4 \sin 2\theta}{\pi^2} e^{-r^2} [1 + r^{-2}(e^{-r^2} - 1)] \quad \dots \dots \dots \quad (57)$$

Using in Eq. 57 the approximation

$$e^{-r^2} - 1 = -r^2 + \frac{r^4}{2} - \frac{r^6}{6} + \frac{r^8}{24} - \frac{r^{10}}{240}$$

and employing a straightforward method of solution, we find

$$\xi_1 = \frac{4}{\pi^2} \sin 2\theta \, S(r) \quad \dots \dots \dots \dots \dots \dots \quad (58)$$

in which $\quad S(r) = r^4 e^{-r^2} \left(-\frac{67}{420} + \frac{19}{1260} r^2 - \frac{1}{420} r^4 + \frac{1}{3360} r^6 \right) \quad \dots \dots \quad (59)$

Then the equation for Ψ_1 is Eq. 55 with the subscripts zero changed to 1, and we find by the method of variation of parameters

$$\Psi_1 = \frac{4}{\pi^2} \sin 2\theta \, F(r) \quad \dots \dots \dots \dots \dots \quad (60)$$

in which $\quad F(r) = r^{-2} \left[-\frac{139}{840} + \left\{ \frac{139}{840} (1 + r^2) + \frac{245}{10080} r^4 \right. \right.$

$$\left. \left. -\frac{11}{3360} r^6 - \frac{r^8}{13440} (1 + r^2) \right\} e^{-r^2} \right] \quad \dots \dots \dots \dots \quad (61)$$

Taking $\lambda = 3$, the flow pattern is given in Fig. 1 by plotting the streamlines, or lines on which

$$\Psi = \Psi_0 + \lambda \Psi_1$$

are constant. The value three is probably far too small. We give the flow pattern for $\lambda = 3$ because a 2-term approximation is adequate for this value of λ. If λ turns out to be much larger, higher approximations will be needed.

Two-Dimensional Turbulent Plume

Whether the plume is caused by a rise in temperature or in salinity, or a rise in the concentration of a heavier or lighter fluid, we can use $\Delta\gamma$, the difference between the specific weight γ in the plume and the constant specific weight γ_0 of the ambient fluid, as one of the variables to be determined. In a plane normal to the horizontal line source of heat (say) from which the plume originates, the trace of the line source is used as the origin, the x-axis is directed vertically upward, and the y-axis is perpendicular to the x-axis, x and y being Cartesian coordinates. Then u and v are velocity components in the directions of increasing x and y, respectively. The equation of motion in the x-direction is

$$(u^2 + \overline{u'^2})_x + (uv + \overline{u'v'})_y = -g \frac{\Delta\gamma}{\gamma_0} \quad \dots \dots \dots \dots \quad (62)$$

in which g = the gravitational acceleration, and the pressure distribution in the plume is assumed to be the same as the hydrostatic pressure distribution in the ambient fluid. The equation of heat diffusion can be replaced by

$$(u\Delta\gamma + u'\Delta\gamma')_x + (v\Delta\gamma + v'\Delta\gamma')_y = 0 \qquad \ldots \ldots \ldots \ldots \ldots \quad (63)$$

In Eqs. 62 and 63, the equation of continuity has been used and viscous effects are neglected. Integrating Eq. 63 in the y direction, we have

$$\int (u\Delta\gamma + \overline{u'\Delta\gamma'})\, dy = \text{constant} = -G, \quad \text{say} \ldots \ldots \ldots \ldots \quad (64)$$

in which the limits of integration are understood to be minus infinity and plus infinity.

Because of the equation of continuity, which is identical with Eq. 2, we can use a stream function ψ, in terms of which

$$u = \psi_y, \quad v = -\psi_x \ldots \ldots \ldots \ldots \ldots \ldots \ldots \ldots \ldots \quad (65)$$

Ignoring the effects of molecular viscosity, one can obtain by a dimensional analysis

$$\psi = (G/\rho)^{1/3} x f(\eta) \ldots \ldots \ldots \ldots \ldots \ldots \ldots \ldots \ldots \quad (66)$$

$$\Delta\gamma = -x^{-1}(\rho G^2)^{1/3}\theta(\eta) \ldots \ldots \ldots \ldots \ldots \ldots \ldots \quad (67)$$

$$\left(\frac{\rho}{G}\right)^{1/3} x^{-1}\epsilon = \text{function of } \eta \ldots \ldots \ldots \ldots \ldots \ldots \ldots \quad (68)$$

in which ϵ = the eddy viscosity; ρ is the density of the ambient fluid; and

$$\eta = y/x \ldots \ldots \ldots \ldots \ldots \ldots \ldots \ldots \ldots \ldots \ldots \ldots \quad (69)$$

If the variation of ϵ with y is ignored, Eq. 68 is replaced by

$$\epsilon = \lambda x \left(\frac{G}{\rho}\right)^{1/3} \ldots \ldots \ldots \ldots \ldots \ldots \ldots \ldots \ldots \ldots \quad (70)$$

Now we shall use the concept of eddy viscosity and eddy diffusivity, ignore the terms representing the longitudinal Reynolds stress or the longitudinal turbulent diffusion, and write Eqs. 62 and 63 in the forms

$$uu_x + vu_y = \epsilon u_{yy} - \frac{g\Delta\gamma}{\gamma_0} \ldots \ldots \ldots \ldots \ldots \ldots \ldots \quad (71)$$

and $\quad u(\Delta\gamma)_x + v(\Delta\gamma)_y = \epsilon\sigma^{-1}(\Delta\gamma)_{yy} \ldots \ldots \ldots \ldots \quad (72)$

in which σ = the "turbulent" Prandtl number, i.e., the ratio of kinematic eddy viscosity to eddy diffusivity. With Eqs. 66, 67, and 70, Eqs. 71 and 72 become

$$-ff'' = \lambda f''' + \theta \ldots \ldots \ldots \ldots \ldots \ldots \ldots \ldots \ldots \ldots \quad (73)$$

$$-\sigma(\theta f)' = \lambda\theta'' \ldots \ldots \ldots \ldots \ldots \ldots \ldots \ldots \ldots \ldots \quad (74)$$

The boundary conditions are

$$f(0) = 0, \quad f''(0) = 0, \quad \theta'(0) = 0 \ldots \ldots \ldots \ldots \ldots \quad (75)$$

$$f(\pm\infty) \text{ is finite}, \quad \theta(\pm\infty) = 0 \ldots \ldots \ldots \ldots \ldots \quad (76)$$

Eqs. 75 are conditions of symmetry, and Eqs. 76 are conditions of finiteness of discharge at any section of constant x and the vanishing of $\Delta\gamma$ at infinity.

For $\sigma = 2/3$, which is not far from the desired value one (although it may not be exactly one), the solutions for f and θ have been given by the writer (20), and are

$$f = A \tanh B\eta, \quad \theta = C \operatorname{sech}^2 B\eta \quad\quad\quad (77)$$

in which the constants are related by

$$A = 3\lambda B, \quad C = 6\lambda^2 B^4 \quad\quad\quad (78)$$

If we ignore for the moment the turbulent part of G defined by Eq. 64, we have

$$\int_{-\infty}^{\infty} f'\theta\, d\eta = 1$$

which gives $\quad AC = 3/4 \quad\quad\quad (79)$

Once λ is given (from experimental data), Eqs. 78 and 79 determine A, B, and C completely. The longitudinal velocity is then given by

$$u = \left(\frac{G}{\rho}\right)^{1/3} f'(\eta) = AB(G/\rho)^{1/3} \operatorname{sech}^2 \eta \quad\quad\quad (80)$$

For $\lambda = 0.0134$, $B = 7.051$, and a comparison of the theoretical results with the experimental results of Humphrey presented in Ref. 12 shows very good agreement, the value of AB being 1.99 from the theory, as compared with the experimental value of 1.80 of Humphrey (12), and the value of C being 2.66 from the theory, as compared with Humphrey's experimental value of 2.6. Indeed, there is agreement in the velocity and θ profiles throughout the range of the experimental points, despite the fact that the theoretical results are for $\sigma = 2/3$ and not for $\sigma = 1$.

According to Kotsovinos' measurements (8), there is a significant contribution, of the order of 25%, of turbulence to the momentum flux. However, his measurements for $(\overline{u'^2})^{1/2}$ show a trapezoidal distribution. Near the important central core it varies little with y/x. Since it does not vary with x except through y/x, this means the contribution of the term $\partial(\overline{u'^2})/\partial x$ to the equation of motion is very small, even if we accept the abnormally high value of $\overline{u'^2}$. Thus the use of the eddy viscosity and the neglect of the term just mentioned are not precluded by the high value of $\overline{u'^2}$.

To give a test for ϵ, as we have done for round jets, we need the measurements of $\overline{u'v'}$. Unfortunately Kotsovinos did not attempt to measure this. Nor did he measure the correlation of longitudinal velocity fluctuations and temperature fluctuations, so that we do not yet know the degree to which turbulence contributes to the heat flux. It would be most welcome if these measurements could be provided in the future.

We note, finally, that using $\lambda = 0.0134$ and the experimental results given for $b_{1/2}$ in Rouse et al. (12), we obtain

$$\epsilon = 0.051 b_{1/2} u_{\max} \quad\quad\quad (81)$$

in which $u_{\max}$ = the maximum u (at the center plane) at any section of constant x; and $b_{1/2}$ has the same meaning as for plane jets.

ROUND TURBULENT PLUME

With the point source of bouyancy as the origin, the vertical axis of symmetry is the x-axis, from which r is measured radially. The meaning of u remains the same, but now v denotes the radial velocity component. With the same assumption on the pressure as for two-dimensional plumes, Eq. 62 is replaced by a corresponding one in cylindrical coordinates, and the dy in Eq. 64 is replaced by $2\pi r dr$. We continue to call the specific-weight flux-G.

The equation of continuity is now

$$(ru)_x + (rv)_r = 0$$

which allows us to use Stokes' stream function ψ and write

$$u = \frac{1}{r}\psi_r, \quad v = -\frac{1}{r}\psi_x$$

The three equations corresponding to Eqs. 66, 67, and 70, obtained by the writer (20), using dimensional analysis, are

$$\psi = 3\lambda \left(\frac{Gx^5}{\rho}\right)^{1/3} f(\eta) \quad \ldots \ldots \ldots \ldots \ldots \ldots \ldots \quad (82)$$

$$-\Delta\gamma = 3\lambda^2 \left(\frac{\rho G^2}{x^5}\right)^{1/3} \theta(\eta) \quad \ldots \ldots \ldots \ldots \ldots \ldots \quad (83)$$

$$\epsilon = \lambda \left(\frac{Gx^2}{\rho}\right)^{1/3} \quad \ldots \ldots \ldots \ldots \ldots \ldots \ldots \ldots \ldots \quad (84)$$

in which ρ = the ambient density and

$$\eta = r/x$$

Using the eddy viscosity ϵ, the equation of motion and the diffusion equation are now

$$(1 - 5f)\left(\frac{f'}{\eta}\right)' - \frac{f'^2}{\eta} = f''' + \eta\theta \quad \ldots \ldots \ldots \ldots \quad (85)$$

$$-5\sigma(f\theta)' = (\eta\theta')' \quad \ldots \ldots \ldots \ldots \ldots \ldots \ldots \quad (86)$$

Again, longitudinal diffusion of momentum or of heat is neglected. The boundary conditions are

$$f(0) = f'(0) = \theta'(0) = 0; \quad f(\infty) \text{ is finite}, \quad \theta(\infty) = 0$$

Apart from the obvious conditions at infinity, the conditions at $r = 0 = \eta$ are all conditions of symmetry.

For $\sigma = 1.1$, which is not far from the desirable value of one, the writer (20) found the exact solution:

$$f = \frac{12}{11}\left(1 - \frac{1}{1 + A\eta^2}\right) \quad \cdots \quad (87)$$

$$\theta = \frac{C}{(1 + A\eta^2)^3} \quad \cdots \quad (88)$$

in which $\quad C = \dfrac{1536}{121} A^2$

If the turbulent part of G is ignored, the integral condition on specific-weight flux is

$$18\pi\lambda^3 \int_0^\infty f'\,\theta\,d\eta = 1$$

which gives $\quad C\lambda^3 = \dfrac{11}{54\pi}$

Thus, once λ is known, C and A can be determined. Since the exact solution is for $\sigma = 1.1$, which is very near the value one generally accepted, it can be used for comparisons with experimental results.

For $\lambda = 0.0191$ the theoretical result for θ agrees with the temperature measurements of the writer (18), presented also in Rouse et al. (12), whereas for $\lambda = 0.0168$ the theoretical result for u agrees fairly well with the velocity measurements of the writer, although the theoretical result is too low near the center line and somewhat too high near the edge of the plume. Recently, George et al. (5) did some measurements with a computer-aided hot wire, and found values at the center line for $\pi_1 \equiv (\rho x/G)^{1/3} u$ and $\pi_2 \equiv -(x^5/\rho G^2)^{1/3} \cdot \Delta\gamma$ to be 3.4 and 9.1, respectively. When these are compared with the writer's corresponding figures 4.7 and 11.0, and the figures 2.7 and 13.7 derived from Schmidt's measurements (14), one sees that 3.4 is almost the mean of 2.7 and 4.7, and 11.0 almost the mean of 9.1 and 13.7. When one takes $\lambda = 0.0191$, one obtains a nearly perfect fit of the theoretical result for π_1 with the experimental points in the paper of George et al. (5), whereas the agreement between theoretical and experimental results from Ref. 5 for π_2 is very good only for r/x equal or greater than 0.75. For smaller values of r/x the theoretical points (for $\lambda = 0.0191$) are above the experimental ones of George et al., with the maximum value of 10.2 for the parameter at the center line, as compared with 9.1 given by George et al.

In a paper yet to be presented (1), which George has kindly sent to me, some new measurements by him and by his assistants Beuther and Capp on round plumes are given. The maximum value for π_1 is now revised to 3.6, and the maximum value for π_2 to 9.5. Furthermore, on the preprint he sent me be noted that the value of his F_o (proportional to G/ρ here) used in presenting his data of π_1 and π_2 is about 20% too high. If we take account of this we obtain the adjusted values of 3.85 and 10.83 for the maximum values of π_1 and π_2, respectively. The latter is now very close to the writer's figure of 11, although the former is still some 18% smaller than 4.7.

If we take the two solutions given by the writer for $\sigma = 1.1$ and $\sigma = 2$, all for $\lambda = 0.016$, we can use the forms of the solutions for $\sigma = 1.1$ and extrapolate to get, for $\sigma = 1$, the maximum values for π_1 and π_2, and the value for A. These are 3.7, 11.3, and 33.7, respectively. Since George et al. (5) and Beuther et al. (1) have found the value 33 for A satisfactory for agreement with their data, and the values 3.7 and 11.3 are not far from the values 3.85 and 10.83 obtained by Beuther et al., one may propose

$$\pi_1 = \frac{3.7}{(1 + 33.7\eta^2)^2}; \quad \pi_2 = \frac{11.3}{(1 + 33.7\eta^2)^3} \quad \cdots \cdots \quad (89)$$

to be used whenever a self-consistent solution agreeing with the most recent experimental data is required.

Finally, we note that from the measurements of George et al. (5) and Beuther et al., (1), the contribution of turbulence to the momentum-flux integral is about 6.3%, and the contribution of turbulence to the heat-flux integral is about 4.8%. These contributions are thus rather small for round plumes at least.

Finally, we note that using $\lambda = 0.016$ and the result of George et al. for $r_{1/2}$ and u_{max}, we have

$$\epsilon = 0.039 \, r_{1/2} u_{max} \quad \cdots \cdots \cdots \cdots \quad (90)$$

in which $r_{1/2}$ has the same meaning as for round jets; and u_{max} = the maximum u (at the center line) for any section of constant x. The coefficient 0.039 is somewhat smaller than the 0.051 in Eq. 81 (for plane plumes).

But the most significant test is provided by the $\overline{u'v'} \, (\rho/Gx)^{2/3}$ measured by Beuther et al. (1), which varies almost linearly from 0–0.365 (after adjustment by reducing their F_o by 20%, when η varies from 0–0.08. This is to be compared with $-\lambda(d\pi_1/d\eta)$ given by the theoretical result Eq. 89, which varies almost linearly from 0–0.355 when η varies from 0–0.08. The agreement is remarkable. Beyond $\eta = 0.08$, the theoretical Reynolds stress is somewhat higher than the experimental one, but their trends of decrease toward zero for large η is quite the same.

TURBULENT PLUME IN TRANSVERSE WIND

Of particular importance to the maintenance of environmental quality is the behavior of turbulent plumes in a transverse wind. We shall take the point source of heat to be the origin, and measure x downwind from it, z vertically upward, and y in the horizontal direction normal to the x direction. The velocity in the direction of increasing x will be denoted by U, and will be assumed constant. This assumption is increasingly valid as x increases, and does not introduce significant errors in the analysis. Then, with v and w denoting the velocity components in the directions of increasing y and z, and p denoting the pressure, the equations of motion are

$$Uv_x + vv_y + wv_z = -\frac{1}{\rho}p_y + \epsilon(v_{yy} + v_{zz}) \quad \cdots \cdots \quad (91)$$

$$Uw_x + vw_y + ww_z = -\frac{1}{\rho}p_z - g\theta + \epsilon(w_{yy} + w_{zz}) \quad \cdots \cdots \quad (92)$$

in which ϵ = the eddy viscosity and

$$\theta = \frac{\Delta \rho}{\rho} \quad \ldots \ldots \ldots \ldots \ldots \ldots \ldots \ldots \ldots \ldots \ldots \ldots \ldots \ldots \ldots \quad (93)$$

where $\Delta\rho$ = the variation of the density from the ambient density ρ, assumed constant. Thus the Boussinesq approximation has been used in Eqs. 90 and 91. By virtue of the equation of state for ideal gases

$$\theta = -\frac{\Delta T}{T}$$

in which ΔT = the temperature variation; and T = the ambient temperature. For a liquid, the relationship between $\Delta\rho$ and ΔT is still linear if θ is small, and the constant of proportionality is determined by the property of the liquid.

We shall assume the eddy viscosity for heat diffusion to be the same as that for momentum diffusion. This may not be strictly true, but the difference between the two is known to be small. The equation for heat diffusion can then be written in the form

$$U\theta_x + v\theta_y + w\theta_z = \epsilon(\theta_{yy} + \theta_{zz}) \quad \ldots \ldots \ldots \ldots \ldots \ldots \ldots \quad (94)$$

Longitudinal diffusion of heat or of momentum is ignored in Eqs. 90, 91, and 93.

The equation of continuity is still Eq. 31, and we can still use Eq. 32. The heat source, located at the origin, is measured by the quantity

$$G = -\int_{-\infty}^{\infty} \int_{-\infty}^{\infty} U\theta \, dy \, dz \quad \ldots \ldots \ldots \ldots \ldots \ldots \ldots \ldots \ldots \ldots \ldots \quad (95)$$

if solid boundaries are assumed to be far away from the source. In consistency with the assumption that the longitudinal velocity u is the constant U, the contribution of turbulence to the θ flux is ruled out. Adjustments can be made if later experimental research shows that the contribution is not negligible. Eqs. 91, 92, 94, and 95, with the appropriate boundary conditions, govern the phenomenon of turbulent plumes in a transverse wind.

By cross differentiation of Eqs. 91 and 92, we obtain the vorticity equation

$$U\hat{\xi}_x + v\hat{\xi}_y + w\hat{\xi}_z = \epsilon(\hat{\xi}_{yy} + \hat{\xi}_{zz}) - g\theta_y \quad \ldots \ldots \ldots \ldots \ldots \ldots \quad (96)$$

in which $\hat{\xi}$ = the x component of the vorticity and is given by

$$\hat{\xi} = w_y - v_z = -(\psi_{yy} + \psi_{zz}) \quad \ldots \ldots \ldots \ldots \ldots \ldots \ldots \ldots \quad (97)$$

The determination of ϵ by the writer (21) is similar to that presented in the section on turbulent jets in a transverse wind, and the process will not be repeated here. Instead, we give ϵ and the accompanying transformations of the writer (21) here:

$$\epsilon = \frac{\alpha}{U}(g^2 G^2 x)^{1/3} \quad \ldots \ldots \ldots \ldots \ldots \ldots \ldots \ldots \ldots \ldots \ldots \ldots \quad (98)$$

$$\theta = -\frac{U}{3\alpha}\left(\frac{G}{g^2}\right)^{1/3} x^{-4/3} h(\eta, \zeta) \quad \ldots \ldots \ldots \ldots \ldots \ldots \ldots \quad (99)$$

$$(v, w) = \frac{1}{3\alpha} \left(\frac{Gg}{x} \right)^{1/3} (V, W) \quad \dots \dots \dots \dots \dots \dots \quad (100)$$

$$(\eta, \zeta) = \frac{U}{(3\alpha)^{1/2}} (Ggx^2)^{-1/3} (y, z) \quad \dots \dots \dots \dots \dots \quad (101)$$

The power law given by Eq. 101 was first stated by Scorer (15), and has been experimentally verified by Wright (17). Eq. 100 is equivalent to the transformation for the stream function ψ:

$$\psi = \frac{1}{(3\alpha)^{1/2} U} (G^2 g^2 x)^{1/3} \Psi(\eta, \zeta) \quad \dots \dots \dots \dots \dots \quad (102)$$

In terms of the dimensionless stream function Ψ, the velocity components V and W are given by

$$V = \Psi_\zeta; \quad W = -\Psi_\eta \quad \dots \dots \dots \dots \dots \dots \dots \dots \quad (103)$$

and the dimensionless longitudinal vorticity by

$$\xi = W_\eta - V_\zeta = -(\Psi_{\eta\eta} + \Psi_{\zeta\zeta}) \quad \dots \dots \dots \dots \dots \quad (104)$$

Eq. 93 now becomes

$$Lh = \lambda(Vh_\eta + Wh_\zeta) \quad \dots \dots \dots \dots \dots \dots \dots \quad (105)$$

in which L is the linear operator defined by Eq. 45 or 53, and

$$\lambda = (3\alpha^3)^{-1/2} \quad \dots \dots \dots \dots \dots \dots \dots \dots \dots \quad (106)$$

Eq. 96 now has the form

$$(L - 1)\xi = -h_\eta + \lambda(V\xi_\eta + W\xi_\zeta) \quad \dots \dots \dots \dots \dots \quad (107)$$

Eqs. 105, 106, and 107 are the final equations governing the dynamics of the plume in a transverse wind. They are to be solved with the boundary conditions

(i) $h_\eta = 0$, $\quad \xi = 0$, $\quad \Psi = 0$, $\quad$ and $\quad \Psi_{\eta\eta} = 0$ $\quad$ at $\quad \eta = 0$

(ii) $h = 0$, $\quad \xi = 0$, $\quad \Psi = 0$ $\quad$ at $\quad \eta = \pm\infty$ $\quad$ or $\quad \zeta = \pm\infty$

Boundary conditions (i) correspond to symmetry with respect to the ζ-axis, and conditions (ii) ensure that there is no temperature variation and no velocity components v and w at infinity. The integral relation 95 now takes the form

$$\int_{-\infty}^{\infty} \int_{-\infty}^{\infty} h\,d\eta\,d\zeta = 1 \quad \dots \dots \dots \dots \dots \dots \dots \quad (108)$$

The mathematical problem is now formulated and it can be solved numerically once λ is known. But considerable effort is required for this solution, since there are three second-order partial differential equations to be solved, two of which are nonlinear. Furthermore, the domain is infinite, and some estimate has to be made of how far to go in the numerical computation, and Eq. 108 can only be imposed after the computations are done for h, and this makes the computation very cumbersome.

For arbitrarily large values of λ an analytical solution is very difficult because the nonlinearities present formidable difficulties. We shall attempt a power-series solution of the form

$$h = h_0 + \lambda h_1 + \lambda^2 h_2 + ...; \quad \xi = \xi_0 + \lambda\xi_1 + \lambda^2\xi_2 + ...;$$

$$\Psi = \Psi_0 + \lambda\Psi_1 + \lambda^2\Psi_2 + ... \quad\quad\quad\quad\quad\quad (109)$$

The success or failure of this approach depends not only on the value of λ, but also on the magnitudes of h_1/h_0, h_2/h_1, etc. Thus we need to make an estimate of the range of λ, and we have to find out how fast h_n, ξ_n, and Ψ_n decrease as n increases. Furthermore, even the estimate of λ cannot be made without knowing the magnitudes of Ψ_0. The writer (21) has estimated λ to be between 30 and 50. But this estimate may be too optimistic. If λ is as high as 100, one has to go to the fourth approximation at least. We shall give h up to and including the term $\lambda^2 h_2$, and ξ and Ψ up to the first order term in λ only. If future experimental research indicate the need for higher approximations, these can then be carried out.

The solutions obtained by the writer (21) are, in the order that one obtains them:

$$h_0 = \frac{1}{\pi} e^{-r^2}$$

$$\text{in which} \quad r^2 = \eta^2 + \zeta^2;$$

$$\xi_0 = -\frac{2}{3\pi}\eta e^{-r^2} = -\frac{2}{3\pi}\cos\theta\,(re^{-r^2})$$

$$\text{where} \quad \theta = \tan^{-1}\frac{\zeta}{\eta};$$

$$\Psi_0 = -\frac{\cos\theta}{6\pi r}(1 - e^{-r^2});$$

$$h_1 = \frac{\sin\theta}{3\pi^2} H_1(r)$$

$$\text{with} \quad H_1 = r\left(\frac{193}{630} - \frac{61}{1,260}r^2 + \frac{11}{1,260}r^4 - \frac{5}{3,024}r^6 + \frac{1}{4,320}r^8\right)e^{-r^2}$$

$$\xi_1 = \frac{1}{9\pi^2}\sin 2\theta\,[S(r)]$$

$$\text{in which} \quad S(r) = e^{-r^2}\left[\frac{1}{4r^2}(e^{-r^2} - 1) + \frac{1}{4} - \frac{105,283}{278,460}r^2 + \frac{114,713}{1,670,760}r^4\right.$$

$$\left. - \frac{3,517}{247,520}r^6 + \frac{181}{68,544}r^8 - \frac{1}{4,320}r^{10}\right]$$

$$\text{and} \quad \Psi_1 = \frac{\sin 2\theta}{9\pi^2} F(r)$$

with $$F = -r^2 \int_\infty^r \left[r^{-5} \int_0^r r^3\,S\,dr \right] dr = \frac{1}{4} \left\{ r^{-2} \int_0^r r^3\,S\,dr - r^2 \int_\infty^r r^{-1}\,S\,dr \right\}$$

The writer (21) did not proceed beyond this stage of approximation. The next term in the expansion of h has now been calculated, and is

$$h_2 = h_{2,0} + \cos 2\theta\, h_{2,2}$$

in which $$h_{2,0} = \frac{1}{36\pi^3} H_{2,0}; \quad h_{2,2} = \frac{1}{36\pi^3} H_{2,2}$$

and $$H_{2,0} = e^{-2r^2} \left(-\frac{76}{7,791} + \frac{103}{31,164} r^2 - \frac{557}{1,160,640} r^4 + \frac{1}{8,640} r^6 \right)$$

$$+ e^{-r^2} \left[-0.04045 - \frac{61}{2,520} r^2 + \frac{11}{5,040} r^4 - \frac{5}{18,144} r^6 \right.$$

$$\left. + \frac{1}{34,560} r^8 + \frac{193}{630} \int_0^r \frac{1}{r} (1 - e^{-r^2})\, dr \right]$$

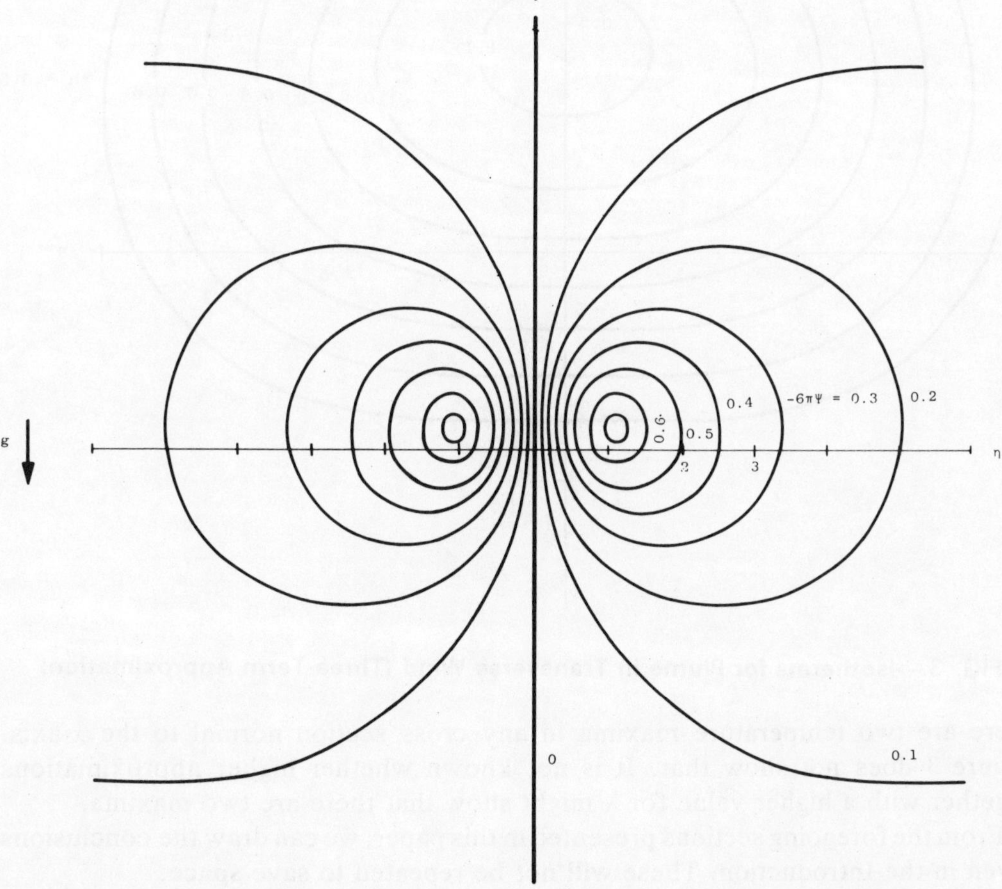

FIG. 2.—Flow Pattern for Plume in Transverse Wind, in Terms of Dimensionless Variables (Two-Term Approximation) the Figure for the Smallest Closed Streamline is 0.65

$$H_{2,2} = e^{-r^2}(0.03411\,r^2 - 0.04609\,r^4 + 0.01704\,r^6 - 0.00567\,r^8 + 0.00054\,r^{10})$$

The determination of the expression for $H_{2,2}$ involves a step of numerical approximation.

The flow pattern obtained by taking two terms for Ψ in Eq. 109 is shown in Fig. 2, and the temperature distribution obtained by taking three terms for h in Eq. 109 is shown in Fig. 3. These figures are all for $\lambda = 30$.

It has been found by some numerical computations on the assumption of constant eddy viscosity throughout, i.e., without even an x dependence, that

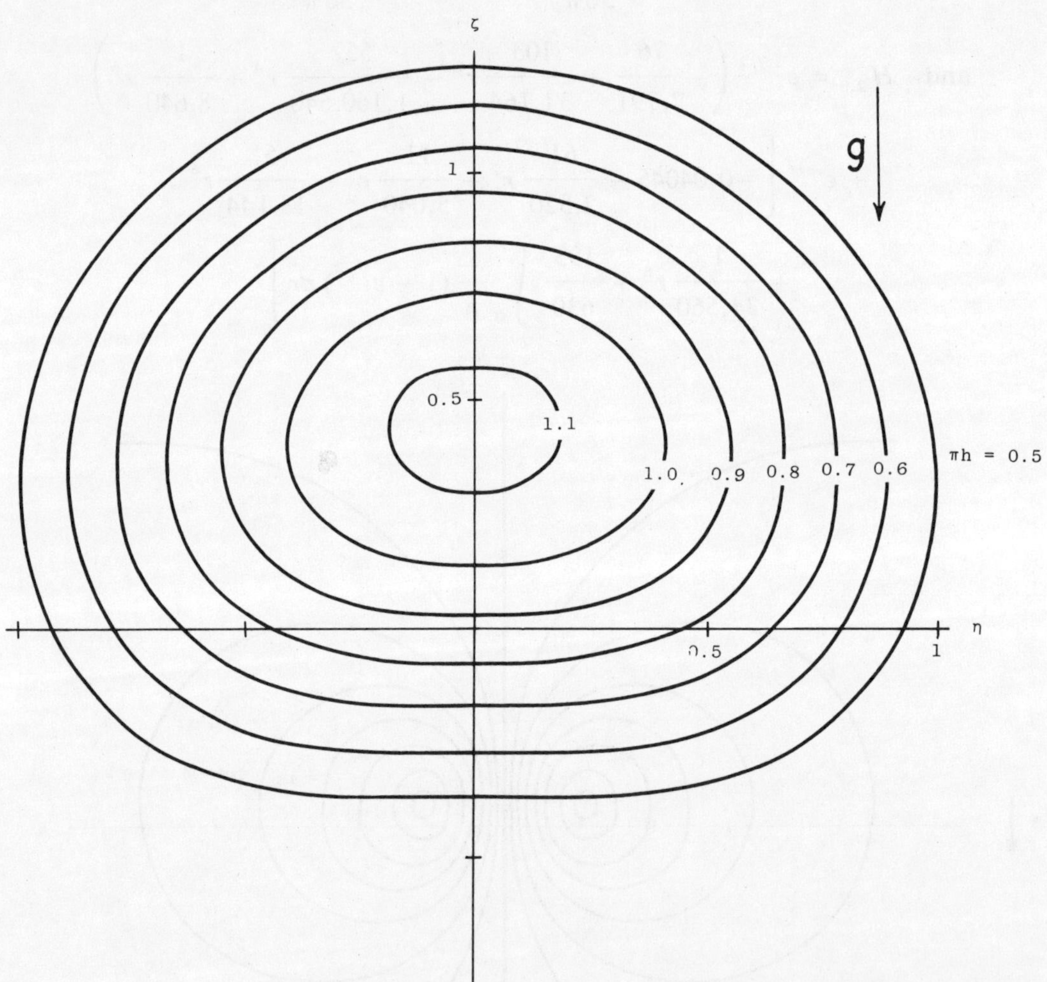

FIG. 3.—Isotherms for Plume in Transverse Wind (Three-Term Approximation)

there are two temperature maxima in any cross section normal to the x-axis. Figure 3 does not show that. It is not known whether higher approximations together with a higher value for λ might show that there are two maxima.

From the foregoing sections presented in this paper, we can draw the conclusions given in the Introduction. These will not be repeated to save space.

Acknowledgment

This work has been supported by the Office of Naval Research.

APPENDIX I.—REFERENCES

1. Beuther, P. D., Capp, S. P., and George, W. K., "Momentum and Temperature Balance Measurements in an Axisymmetric Turbulent Plume," presented at the Aug. 6–8, 1979, Joint ASME-AIChE 18th National Heat Transfer Conference, held at San Diego Calif.

2. Bickley, W., "The Plane Jet," *Philosophical Magazine*, London, England, Series 7, Vol. 23, 1937, pp. 727–731.

3. Engelund, F., "Hydraulics of Surface Buoyant Jet," *Journal of the Hydraulics Division*, ASCE, Vol. 102, No. HY9, Proc. Paper 12409, Sept., 1976, pp. 1315–1325.

4. Foerthmann, E., "Ueber turbulente Strahlausbreitung," *Ingenieur—Archiv.*, Vol. 5, 1934, p. 42, or NACA TM789, 1936.

5. George, W. K., Jr., Alpert, R. L., and Tominini, F., "Turbulence Measurements in an Axisymmetric Buoyant Plume," *International Journal of Heat Transfer*, Vol. 20, 1977, pp. 1145–1154.

6. Gibson, M. M., "Spectra of Turbulence in a Round Jet," *Journal of Fluid Mechanics*, Vol. 15, 1963, pp. 161–173.

7. Görtler, H., "Berechnung von Aufgaben der freien Turbulenz auf Grund eines neuen Naeherungsansatzes," *Zeitschrift fuer Angewandte Mathematik und Mechanik*, Berlin, East Germany, Vol. 22, 1942, pp. 244–254.

8. Kotsovinos, N. E., "Plane Turbulent Buoyant Jets. Part 2. Turbulent Structure," *Journal of Fluid Mechanics*, Vol. 81, 1977, pp. 45–62.

9. Kotsovinos, N. E., and List, E. J., "Plane Turbulent Buoyant Jets. Part 1. Integral Properties," *Journal of Fluid Mechanics*, Vol. 81, 1977, pp. 25–44.

10. Lock, R. C., "The Velocity Distribution in the Laminar Boundary Layer between Parallel Streams," *Quarterly Journal of Mechanics and Applied Mathematics*, Vol. 4, 1951, pp. 42–63.

11. Reichardt, H., "Gesetzmaessigkeiten der freien Turbulenz," *Zeitschrift fuer Angewandte Mathematik und Mechanik*, Vol. 21, 1941, p. 257.

12. Rouse, H., Yih, C.-S., and Humphreys, H. W., "Gravitational Convection from a Boundary Source," *Tellus*, Vol. 4, 1952, p. 201.

13. Schlichting, H., *Boundary Layer Theory*, McGraw-Hill, Book Co., Inc., New York, N.Y., 1960.

14. Schmidt, W., "Turbulente Ausbreitung eines Stromes erhitzter Luft, 1. Teil und 2. Teil," *Zeitschrift fuer Angewandte Mathematik und Mechanik*, Vol. 21, 1941, pp. 265–278, and pp. 351–363.

15. Scorer, R. S., "The Behavior of Chimney Plumes," *International Journal of Pollution*, Vol. 1, 1959, pp. 198–220.

16. Tollmien, W., "Berechnung turbulenter Ausbreitungsvorgaenge," *Zeitschrift fuer Angewandte Mathematik und Mechanik*, Vol. 6, 1926, pp. 468–478.

17. Wright, S. J., Report KH-R-36, Keck Laboratory, California Institute of Technology, Pasadena, Calif., 1977.

18. Yih, C.-S., "Free Convection due to a Point Source of Heat," *Proceedings of the First U.S. National Congress Applied Mech.*, June, 1951, pp. 941–947.

19. Yih, C.-S., "Free Convection due to Boundary Sources," *Fluid Models in Geophysics, Proceedings of the 1st Symposium on the Use of Models in Geophysical Fluid Dynamics*, The Johns Hopkins University, Baltimore, Md., R. R. Long, ed., 1953, pp. 117–133.

20. Yih, C.-S., "Turbulent Buoyant Plumes," *Physics of Fluids*, Vol. 20, 1977, pp. 1234–1237.

21. Yih, C.-S., "Buoyant Plumes in a Transverse Wind," with an appendix by J. B. Benqué, *Proceedings of the 12th Symposium on Naval Hydrodynamics*, 1978.

APPENDIX II.—NOTATION

The following symbols are used in this paper:

A, B, C = numerical coefficients:

$$b_{1/2} = \text{half of width of plane jet or plume between points where velocity is half maximum velocity;}$$

$F, H_1, H_{2,0}, H_{2,2}, S$ = functions of r;

f = function of dimensionless variable η;

g = gravitational acceleration;

h = dimensionless temperature in plume in transverse wind;

K = kinematic momentum flux;

L, L_n = operators in r;

M = momentum flux, but used for K for jets in wind;

p = pressure;

r, x = dimensionless cylindrical coordinates;

$r_{1/2}$ = radius of point in round jet or plume where velocity is half of maximum velocity;

T = ambient temperature;

U = uniform velocity of wind, or maximum velocity in jet at cross section;

U_1, U_2 = asymptotic velocities in half jets;

u, v, w = velocity components;

u_{max} = maximum u at section of constant x;

V, W = dimensionless velocity components;

x, y, z = Cartesian coordinates;

α, λ = dimensionless coefficients;

γ = specific weight of ambient fluid;

ΔT = variation from T;

$\Delta \gamma$ = variation from γ;

$\Delta \rho$ = variation from ρ;

ϵ = kinematic eddy viscosity;

η = dimensionless variable y/x or r/x;

η, ζ = dimensionless coordinates y/x and z/x;

θ = dimensionless temperature;

μ = viscosity;

ν = kinematic viscosity;

ξ = dimensionless x component of vorticity;

$\hat{\xi}$ = x component of vorticity;

ρ = density;

σ = turbulent Prandtl number;

Ψ = dimensionless stream function; and

ψ = stream function.

Round buoyant laminar and turbulent plumes

Chia-Shun Yih

The University of Michigan, Ann Arbor, Michigan 48109

Feng Wu

China University of Science and Technology, Hofei, Anhni, China

(Received 21 August 1980; accepted 17 February 1981)

Two approximate solutions, which become exact for Prandtl numbers 1 and 2, are given for laminar round plumes for arbitrary Prandtl number σ. The first of these gives a very accurate solution for laminar found plumes in air, for which $\sigma = 0.73$, and the second provides a good solution for laminar round plumes in water, for which $\sigma = 6.7$. Two approximate solutions, which become exact for turbulent Prandtl numbers 1.1 and 2, respectively, are given for turbulent round plumes. The one which becomes exact at $\sigma = 1.1$ is used to give a highly accurate solution for $\sigma = 1$, which, for an eddy-viscosity coefficient λ equal to 0.0156, provides a remarkably good agreement with the experimental data of Beuther, Capp, and George, Jr.

I. INTRODUCTION

The problem of round laminar buoyant plumes was in an unstratified environment studied as early as 1937 by Zel'dovich.[1] Independently, Yih[2,3] developed the differential equations for a similarity solution of the problem, and he gave two exact solutions for the differential system consisting of those equations, the boundary conditions, and an integral condition; one for Prandtl number $\sigma = 1$, and one for $\sigma = 2$. Later, other researchers, unaware of Yih's work also studied the problem, but produced nothing new. Thus to this day, solutions for round laminar buoyant plumes for other Prandtl numbers are still unavailable. Especially desirable are the solutions for air, with $\sigma = 0.73$, and for water, with $\sigma = 6.7$.

The problem of round turbulent buoyant plumes was investigated by Schmidt[4], and later Rouse, unaware of Schmidt's work, suggested the problem to this writer. Rouse was the first to give, explicitly and completely, the dimensionless parameters which, when experimentally determined, would give the description of the phenomenon. The Iowa measurements were recorded in three papers,[2,3,5] and it was only in recent years that other measurements with more elaborate and therefore, presumably, more accurate instruments were made by George and his associates.[6] We shall later take the most recent measurements of Beuther, Capp, and George, Jr.[7] and compare them with our analytical results.

The first analytical results for turbulent plumes were given by Yih,[8] and these were shown to agree well with the Iowa measurements made nearly three decades ago. However, Yih's "exact" solutions for round turbulent plumes are for (turbulent) Prandtl numbers 1.1 and 2, and although the turbulent Prandtl number must be around 1, there is no reason to expect it to be 1.1. It is desirable to have a solution for turbulent Prandtl numbers in the neighborhood of 1, in order to provide an analytical basis for comparison with the recent measurements of Beuther, Capp, and George, Jr.[7]

In this paper, we shall present approximate solutions for laminar round plumes for any Prandtl number.

These are especially accurate when the Prandtl number is near 1, as for air. We shall also present approximate solutions for turbulent round plumes for (turbulent) Prandtl numbers around 1, and compare our analytical results with the measurements of Beuther *et al.*[7]

Furthermore, we shall give rigorous results for the asymptotic behavior of the angle of spread of laminar round plumes for large Prandtl numbers, and we shall give a set of transformations that leave the differential system (excepting the integral condition) invariant, which are useful for any accurate numerical calculation for a given Prandtl number, since one can ignore the integral condition first, carry out the numerical calculation, and then apply the set of transformations to satisfy the integral conditions. All the results given in this paper, excepting the existing results explicitly cited, are new and not previously available.

We note here that plumes in stratified environments were investigated by Morton, Taylor, and Turner[9] using the concept of entrainment.

II. ROUND LAMINAR PLUMES

A brief account of the formulation of the problem is necessary in order to facilitate the presentation of the new results. We shall take the heat source as the origin, use x and r as vertical and radial coordinates, and denote the velocity components in the directions of increasing x and r by u and v, respectively. The gravitational acceleration is denoted by g, and acts in the direction of decreasing x. If $\Delta \rho$ is the variation of the density of the fluid as a result of temperature rise due to the heat source, we can, for temperature rises small compared with the absolute temperature of the surrounding fluid, use $\Delta \rho$ instead of the temperature rise ΔT as a dependent variable. For convenience, we choose to use

$$\Delta \gamma = g \Delta \rho$$

instead of ΔT. The density and viscosity of the ambient fluid will be denoted by ρ and μ, respectively, and the kinematic viscosity μ/ρ will be denoted by ν, as usual.

© 1981 American Institute of Physics

Since the pressure variation in the plume is assumed to be small compared with the pressure (assumed hydrostatic) in the ambient fluid, we can use the thermal diffusivity at constant pressure. We denote it by α, and the Prandtl number ν/α by σ.

Assuming the hydrostatic pressure of the atmosphere to be essentially undisturbed by the flow caused by the heat source and $\partial^2 u/\partial x^2$ to be negligible as compared with $r^{-1}\partial\,(r\,\partial u/\partial r)/\partial r$, one can write the equation of motion as

$$u\frac{\partial u}{\partial x} + v\frac{\partial u}{\partial r} = \frac{\nu}{r}\frac{\partial}{\partial r}\left(r\frac{\partial u}{\partial r}\right) - g\frac{\Delta\gamma}{\gamma_0}\,, \tag{1}$$

where $\gamma_0 = \rho g$. The equation for heat diffusion (the energy equation), can be written

$$u\frac{\partial\Delta\gamma}{\partial x} + v\frac{\partial\Delta\gamma}{\partial r} = \frac{\alpha}{r}\frac{\partial}{\partial r}\left(r\frac{\partial\Delta\gamma}{\partial r}\right), \tag{2}$$

if $\partial^2\Delta\gamma/\partial x^2$ is neglected in comparison with $r^{-1}\partial\,(r\,\partial\Delta\gamma/\partial r)/\partial r$. The equation of continuity is

$$\frac{\partial}{\partial x}(ru) + \frac{\partial}{\partial r}(rv) = 0\,. \tag{3}$$

Equations (1)–(3) are to be solved with the boundary conditions that; u, v, and $\Delta\gamma$ vanish at $r=\infty$; u and v vanish at $x=0$ except at the origin, and v, $\partial\Delta\gamma/\partial r$, and $\partial u/\partial r$ vanish at $r=0$. Equation (3) permits the use of Stokes' stream function ψ so that

$$u = \frac{1}{r}\frac{\partial\psi}{\partial r}\,, \quad v = -\frac{1}{r}\frac{\partial\psi}{\partial x}\,. \tag{4}$$

Multiplying (2) by $2\pi r\,dr$ and integrating from zero to infinity, using the boundary conditions that $\partial\Delta\gamma/\partial r$ is zero at $r=0$ and $\Delta\gamma = 0$ at infinity, we find that the following quantity is independent of x:

$$G = -\int_0^\infty 2\pi r u\,\Delta\gamma\,dr\,. \tag{5}$$

Indeed, G is a measure of the strength of the heat source. Then, with the substitutions

$$\Delta\gamma = -(G\rho/x\mu)\theta(\eta)\,, \tag{6}$$

and

$$\psi = 4\nu x f(\eta)\,, \tag{7}$$

in which

$$\eta = (\rho^2 G/4\mu^3)^{1/4}(r/x^{1/2})\,, \tag{8}$$

Eqs. (1) and (2) become

$$(1 - 4f)\frac{d}{d\eta}\left(\frac{f'}{\eta}\right) = f''' + \eta\theta\,, \tag{9}$$

and (after one integration and application of the boundary conditions)

$$f = -(1/4\sigma)(\theta'/\theta)\eta\,. \tag{10}$$

In obtaining (9), γ_0/g has been equated to the ambient density ρ. The boundary conditions are now

$$\theta(\infty) = 0\,,$$

$$f(0) = f'(0) = \theta'(0) = 0\,, \tag{11}$$

$$f(\infty) = C\,,$$

where C is any finite number. The integral condition for the heat flux as expressed by (5) now assumes the form

$$\int_0^\infty f'\theta\,d\eta = \frac{1}{8\pi}\,. \tag{12}$$

We note in passing that the definition of η by (8) shows that the term $\nu\partial^2 u/\partial x^2$ neglected in comparison with the first term of the right-hand side of (1) is justified for $Gx^2/\mu\nu^2 \gg 1$, as can readily be shown.

A. Exact solutions for round laminar plumes

For Prandtl numbers 1 and 2, Yih[2,3] obtained exact solutions of the differential system consisting of (9) to (12). For $\sigma = 1$:

$$\frac{\psi}{4\nu x} = f(\eta) = \frac{3}{2}\frac{\eta^2}{6\sqrt{2\pi} + \eta^2}\,, \tag{13}$$

$$-\frac{\mu x\Delta\gamma}{G\rho} = \theta(\eta) = \frac{\eta^2}{3\pi(1 + \eta^2/6\sqrt{2\pi})^3}\,, \tag{14}$$

$$\left(\frac{\mu}{G}\right)^{1/2}u = \frac{2f'}{\eta} = \frac{1}{\sqrt{2\pi}(1 + \eta^2/6\sqrt{2\pi})^2}\,, \tag{15}$$

$$\left(\frac{\rho^2 x^2}{\mu G}\right)^{1/4}v = \sqrt{2}\left(f' - \frac{2f}{\eta}\right) = -\frac{3\sqrt{2}\eta^3}{(6\sqrt{2\pi} + \eta^2)^2}\,. \tag{16}$$

For $\sigma = 2$:

$$\frac{\psi}{4\nu x} = f(\eta) = \frac{\sqrt{5}\eta^2}{8\sqrt{2\pi} + \sqrt{5}\eta^2}\,, \tag{17}$$

$$-\frac{\mu x\Delta\gamma}{G\rho} = \theta(\eta) = \frac{5}{8\pi[1 + (\sqrt{5}/8\sqrt{2\pi})\eta^2]^4}\,, \tag{18}$$

$$\left(\frac{\mu}{G}\right)^{1/2}u = \frac{2f'}{\eta} = \frac{\sqrt{5}}{2\sqrt{2\pi}[1 + (\sqrt{5}/8\sqrt{2\pi})\eta^2]^2}\,, \tag{19}$$

$$\left(\frac{\rho^2 x^2}{\mu G}\right)^{1/4}v = \sqrt{2}\left(f' - \frac{2f}{\eta}\right) = -\frac{10\sqrt{2}\eta^3}{(8\sqrt{2\pi} + \sqrt{5}\eta^2)^2}\,. \tag{20}$$

B. New solutions

The new solutions we shall present here are not exact, but they cover the entire range of Prandtl numbers. When the Prandtl number is near 1 or 2, for which exact solutions exist, they give a high degree of accuracy. But, the term neglected is a fixed small portion of a term retained, while both are proportional to $\Delta\sigma$, which is the difference between the actual Prandtl number σ and 1, or 2, as the case may be. In this sense, the relative error is of the same order of magnitude for all Prandtl numbers, and the solutions given here are reliable approximate solutions, which, at the least, would assist in any accurate numerical solution of the problem for any Prandtl number.

First, we shall briefly describe the obvious approach, which was the first that came to mind but which in the end proved laborious and inferior to the vastly simpler and reliable method finally used. Expanding f and θ in a power series of $\Delta\sigma$ and using f_0 and θ_0 to denote the exact solution at $\sigma = 1$ or 2, as the case may be, we have

$$f = f_0 + \Delta\sigma f_1 + (\Delta\sigma)^2 f_2 + \ldots,$$

$$\theta = \theta_0 - \Delta\sigma\theta_1 + (\Delta\sigma)^2\theta_2 + \ldots. \tag{21}$$

Then, substituting these expansions in (9) and (10) and

collecting equal powers of $\Delta\sigma$, we obtained a sequence of simultaneous equations for (f_1, θ_1), (f_2, θ_2), etc. For f_1 and θ_1, we found, after considerable effort and trials, that the following expansions are appropriate:

$$f_1 = \ln X \left(\sum_{n=1}^{\infty} A_n X^{-n-1} \right) + \sum_{n=1}^{\infty} B_n (1 - X^{-1}) X^{1-n},$$

$$\theta_1 = \ln X \left(\sum_{n=1}^{\infty} C_n X^{-n-4} \right) + \sum_{n=1}^{\infty} D_n X^{-n-2}, \tag{22}$$

where

$$X = 1 + A\eta^2, \tag{23}$$

A being a constant to be determined by the integral condition (12) afterward. (In practice, we used $A = 1$ for the determination of the coefficients in the expansions, and determined the actual A by a transformation to be presented later in this paper.) But, the first several coefficients obtained for each series are large compared with the corresponding coefficient in the exact solution, and both series converge very slowly. We calculated up to 22 terms. Even then, the results obtained by taking only terms of order $\Delta\sigma$ are already not satisfactory for $\Delta\sigma = 0.25$, indicating that terms of order $(\Delta\sigma)^2$ or even $(\Delta\sigma)^3$ are necessary. This outcome discouraged us from proceeding further with this approach.

The final method adopted is simple, direct, and, if one accepts the errors the order of magnitude of which is known *a priori*, reliable.

1. Solution based on exact solution for $\sigma = 1$

For any σ, let

$$f = (3/2\sigma)(1 - X^{-1}), \tag{24}$$

where X is given by (23), in which A is to be determined later. Substituting (24) into (10) and integrating, we have

$$\theta = C X^{-3}. \tag{25}$$

Substituting (24) and (25) into (12), we find

$$C = \sigma/3\pi. \tag{26}$$

To determine A, we substitute (24) and (25) into (9), and obtain

$$(24/\sigma^2)[3 - 2\sigma + 3(\sigma-1)X^{-1}]A^2 X^{-3} = C X^{-3}, \tag{27}$$

from which it is obvious that an exact solution exists for $\sigma = 1$. For any σ, we write (27) as

$$(24 A^2/\sigma^2)[(3 - 2\sigma) + 3(\sigma - 1)\beta]X^{-3} + R = C X^{-3}, \tag{28}$$

where

$$R = (72 A^2/\sigma^2)(\sigma - 1)(X^{-4} - \beta X^{-3}) \tag{29}$$

is the residual, and β is a constant to be determined so as to make

$$\left| \beta X^{-3} - X^{-4} \right|$$

as small as possible in the core of the plume.

The temperature distribution is given by (25). The point of inflection of X^{-3} is at $X = 8/7$, or $A\eta^2 = 1/7$.

If we require that the *relative* (to X^{-4}) error $\beta X - 1$ at the origin be equal and of opposite sign to its value at $A\eta^2 = 2/7$ (twice its value at the point of inflection of the plume), we have

$$\beta = \tfrac{7}{8}. \tag{30}$$

The difference between βX^{-3} and X^{-4} is shown in Fig. 1.

Then, ignoring the residue R in (28), we have

$$C = [(9 + 15\sigma)/\sigma^2]A^2, \tag{31}$$

which, in combination with (26), gives

$$A = \sigma[\sigma/9\pi(5\sigma + 3)]^{1/2}. \tag{32}$$

Then (23)–(26), and (32) constitute the solution.

2. Solution based on exact solution for $\sigma = 2$

For σ near 2 or greater than 2, a more accurate approximate solution can be obtained if it is based on the exact solution for $\sigma = 2$.

With X defined by (23), we take

$$f = (2/\sigma)(1 - X^{-1}). \tag{33}$$

Then, the solution of (10) is

$$\theta = C X^{-4}. \tag{34}$$

Substituting (33) and (34) into (12), we obtain, whatever the value of A may be in the definition (23) of X,

$$C = 5\sigma/16\pi. \tag{35}$$

To find A as a function of σ, we substitute (33)–(35) into (9), and obtain

$$-\frac{16}{\sigma} A^2 \left[4\left(1 - \frac{2}{\sigma}\right) X^{-3} + \left(\frac{8}{\sigma} - 6\right) X^{-4} \right] = \frac{5\sigma}{16\pi} X^{-4}. \tag{36}$$

Again, equating X^{-3} to $\beta^{-1} X^{-4}$, where β is now $10/11$, we obtain from (36)

$$A^2 = \frac{25\sigma^3}{1024\pi(2\sigma + 1)}. \tag{37}$$

Then (23), (33), (34), (35), and (37) constitute the solution.

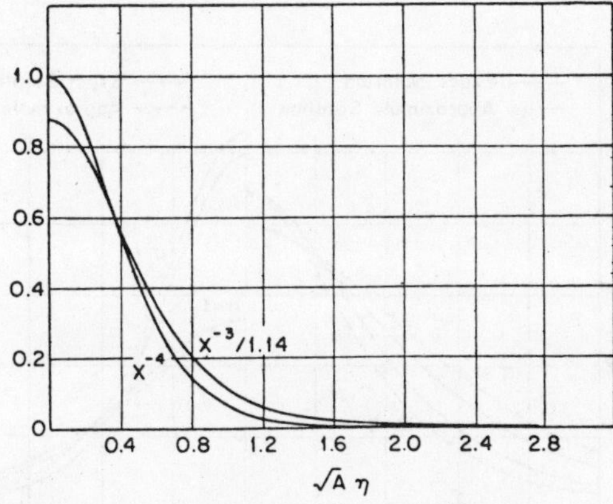

FIG. 1. Approximation of X^{-4} by $\beta^{-1} X^{-3}$, $\beta = 8/7$.

C. Comparisons of approximate and exact solutions

In the approximate solutions just presented, the error committed arises from, and only from, approximating X^{-4} by $7X^{-3}/8$, or X^{-3} by $1.1X^{-4}$. If we call the approximate solution based on the exact solution for $\sigma=1$ the first approximate solution and that based on the exact solution for $\sigma=2$ the second approximate solution, then the first approximate solution is increasingly accurate as σ approaches 1 and is exact at $\sigma=1$, and the second approximate solution is increasingly accurate as σ approaches 2 and is exact at $\sigma=2$.

In Fig. 2, the first approximate solution evaluated at $\sigma=2$ is compared with the exact solution for $\sigma=2$, and the second approximate solution evaluated at $\sigma=1$ is compared with the exact solution for $\sigma=1$. It is seen that as σ is increased from 1, the first approximate solution overestimates the temperature and underestimates the velocity, and that as σ decreases from 2, the second approximate solution underestimates the temperature and (except for a small region near the axis of symmetry) overestimates the velocity. Or, to put it loosely, the approximate solutions overestimate the temperature and underestimate the velocity as the Prandtl number σ increases from the σ on which they are based, and the opposite is true when σ decreases.

But, the striking feature of Fig. 2 is that the approximate solutions give rather good predictions for both the velocity and the temperature, and that the temperature predictions are especially accurate. The rather good approximations obtained when σ varies from 1 to 2 are all the more remarkable when one notes that at $\eta=0$ (or $X=1$) the R in (28), which is neglected, is, for $\sigma=2$, 18% of the entire left-hand side of (28), and yet in Fig. 2 the maximum discrepancy between the exact and approximate solutions for $\sigma=2$ is only about 7% for $\eta \leqslant 1.5$, and that the absolute value of the error is never more than 7% of the maximum value for velocity or for temperature (at the axis of symmetry). When σ varies from 2 to 1 and (36) is used, the left-hand side of (36) varies, at $\eta=0$ (or $X=1$), by fully 28% when X^{-3} is replaced by $1.1X^{-4}$, and yet the agreement between the exact solution and the approximate solutions for $\sigma=1$ is even better, both for the velocity and the temperature distributions, than the agreement between the exact and approximate solutions for $\sigma=2$.

These comparisons of approximate and exact solutions at $\sigma=1$ and $\sigma=2$ indicate that there is good agreement between the approximate solutions even when the Prandtl number is doubled or halved, especially for the temperature distribution (Fig. 2). This agreement is due largely to the fact that the temperature equation (10) is integrated exactly, once one accepts (24), and that the integral conditions are exactly satisfied by (26). The only approximation is the neglect of R in (28), and we can give an estimate of the error in the results introduced by the neglect for the important case of $\sigma = 0.73$.

For $\sigma=0.73$ and at $\eta=0$, at which R is a maximum, the ratio of R to the entire left-hand side of (28) is 0.133. Thus, the maximum error in A computed from (31), where C is given by (26), is 6.4%, and the error in $A^{1/2}$ is 3.2%, at most. The actual error is probably smaller, since R changes sign at $A^{1/2}\eta=0.374$, and since R can be regarded as a vertical momentum source, so that from the physical point of view the effects due to negative values of R and those due to its positive values are mutually compensating to a certain extent. The constant $A^{1/2}$ determines the angle of spread of the plume, and is the only constant to be determined by the approximate solution. That it can be in error by 3.2% at most for $\sigma=0.73$ is certainly reassuring, in spite of the arbitrariness of the approximation of X^{-4} by $7X^{-3}/8$. For σ nearer 1 than 0.73, the results are even more accurate.

D. Approximate solutions for air and for water

Since the Prandtl number of air is 0.73, which is near 1, a good approximate solution for air is the first approximate solution, which is shown in Fig. 3 together with the exact results for $\sigma=1$, for comparison. From our discussion of the results shown in Fig. 2, the true velocity curve for $\sigma=0.73$ should lie somewhat below the velocity curve shown in Fig. 3 for $\sigma=0.73$, and the true temperature curve should be somewhat above the temperature curve shown in Fig. 3 for $\sigma=0.73$. But these corrections, especially for the temperature curve, are small because σ is quite near 1. We refrain from making further refinements and consider the

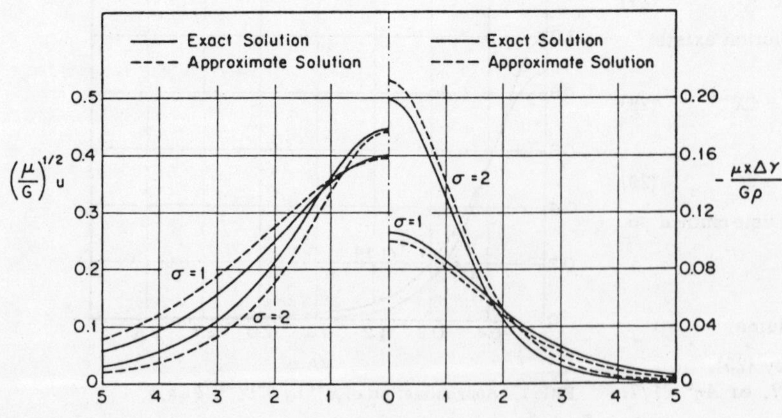

FIG. 2. Comparison of approximate and exact solutions for laminar round plumes for $\sigma=1$ and $\sigma=2$. The abscissa is η.

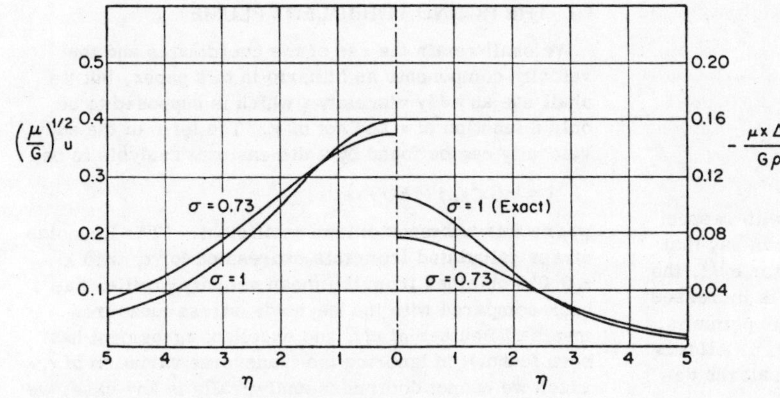

FIG. 3. Velocity and temperature (represented by $\Delta\gamma$) distributions in laminar round plumes for $\sigma = 1$ and $\sigma = 0.73$ (for air).

results given in Fig. 3 as sufficiently accurate.

For water $\sigma = 6.7$, the left-hand side of (36) varies by 20% when X^{-3} is replaced by $1.1 X^{-4}$ in our approximate solution. Judging by the corresponding percentage (28%) when the same is done for $\sigma = 1$, and the rather good agreement shown in Fig. 2 between the exact and approximate solutions for $\sigma = 1$, we venture to assert with some confidence that the second approximate solution (the one that becomes exact for $\sigma = 2$) can be used for $\sigma = 6.7$. Upon using (33)–(35), and (37), as well as (6) and (7), we obtain Fig. 4 for $\sigma = 6.7$. From our discussion in Sec. II C, we can expect the true velocity curve for $\sigma = 6.7$ to be somewhat above the one shown, and the true temperature curve to be somewhat below the one shown. In the core of the plume, we do not expect a relative error of more than a few percent.

There being no exact solution for σ greater than 2, we are obliged to give an error estimate for the approximate solution given by (33)–(35), and (37), when it is applied to water, of which $\sigma = 6.7$.

We note again that, once (33) is accepted, (34) is an exact solution of (10) and the integral condition (12) is

exactly satisfied by (35). These facts contribute to the accuracy of the approximate solution mentioned here. The only approximation is made when we substitute X^{-4} for $X^{-3}/1.1$ in (36). The ratio of the residue

$$R = -\frac{64}{\sigma} A^2 \left(1 - \frac{2}{\sigma}\right)(X^{-3} - \beta^{-1} X^{-4})$$

to the entire left-hand side of (36) is, for $\sigma = 6.7$ and at the axis of symmetry, where R is largest, equal to -0.196. The error introduced in the determination of A^2 is then 24.5% at most, giving an error in $A^{1/2}$, which determined the spread angle, of 5.5% at most. The velocity u is proportional to A, and the error in A is 11.6% at most. For a more than threefold increase in σ (from 2–6.7), an approximate solution with these maximum errors (the actual errors must be less due to the compensative effects of positive and negative values of R) is certainly useful in giving a good estimate of the velocity and temperature fields.

E. Behavior of the solution for large σ

For large values of σ we can make the transformations

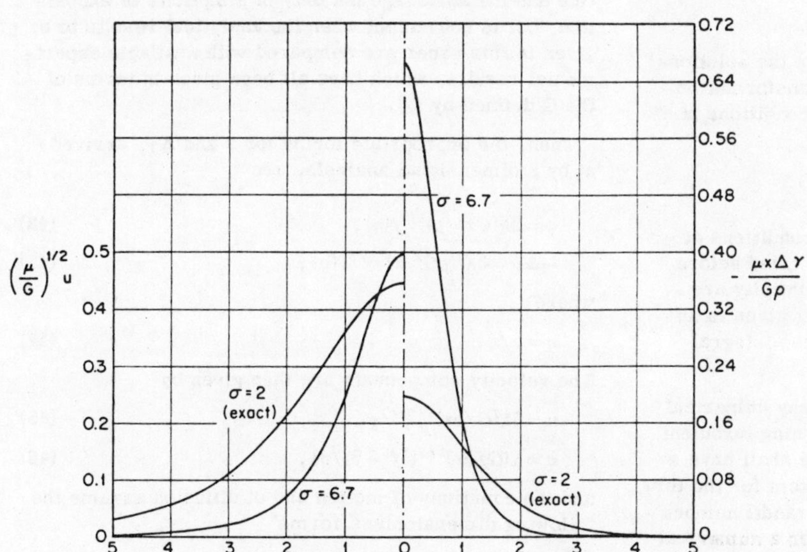

FIG. 4. Velocity and temperature (represented by $\Delta\gamma$) distributions in laminar round plumes for $\sigma = 2$ and $\sigma = 6.7$ (for water).

$$\hat{f} = \sigma f, \quad \hat{\theta} = \theta/\sigma, \quad \hat{\eta} = \sigma^{1/2}\eta .$$

Then, Eqs. (9), (10), and (12) become

$$\left(\frac{\hat{f}'}{\eta}\right)' = \hat{f}''' + \hat{\eta}\hat{\theta}, \quad \hat{f} = -\frac{1}{4}\frac{\hat{\theta}'}{\hat{\theta}}\hat{\eta} ,$$

$$\int_0^\infty \hat{f}\hat{\theta}d\hat{\eta} = \frac{1}{8\pi} ,$$

where the primes indicate differentiation with respect to $\hat{\eta}$. Since $\hat{f}$ and $\hat{\theta}$ depend only on $\hat{\eta}$, we can say that at any value of x if r is reduced by the factor $\sigma^{1/2}$, the function f is reduced by the factor σ and θ is increased by the factor σ. The rate of widening of the plume is, in this sense, inversely proportional to $\sigma^{1/2}$. All this is in agreement with (32) or (37), if we recall the definition (23) of X and the role of A in X.

F. A transformation indispensable for numerical calculations

If a numerical solution of the differential system consisting of (9)–(12) is attempted, one quickly sees that (12), being an integral condition the satisfaction of which can only be tested *after* the computation, would give rise to great difficulties. It would be nice if a solution satisfying (9)–(11) can be made to satisfy (12) by some transformation. Such a transformation will be given.

Suppose that a solution (f, θ) satisfies (9)–(11), but gives

$$\int_0^\infty f'\theta\,d\eta = \frac{1}{8\pi}\alpha^4 .$$

Then, let

$$f = f(\hat{\eta}), \quad \theta = \alpha^4\hat{\theta}(\hat{\eta}), \quad \hat{\eta} = \alpha\eta .$$

These substitutions leave (9) to (11) invariant in form, but give

$$\int_0^\infty f'\hat{\theta}d\hat{\eta} = \frac{1}{8\pi} ,$$

where $f' = df/d\hat{\eta}$. Thus, $f(\hat{\eta})$ and $\hat{\theta}(\hat{\eta})$ are the solutions of the differential system. With this transformation available, we can impose the following conditions at $\eta = 0$:

$$f(0) = 0 = f'(0), \quad \theta(0) = 1, \quad f''(0) = a .$$

The constant a is chosen to satisfy the conditions at $\eta = \infty$, and different values of it must be tried before one is found for which the conditions at infinity are satisfied. Then, the transformation just given is applied to get $f(\hat{\eta})$ and $\hat{\theta}(\hat{\eta})$, which satisfy the integral condition (12) as well as (9)–(11).

This transformation is also useful in any numerical solution of the differential system governing turbulent round plumes. But, as will be seen, we shall have a very good analytical solution of that system for the turbulent plume for which the (turbulent) Prandtl number is near 1, and thus shall have no need for a numerical solution at all.

III. THE ROUND TURBULENT PLUME

We shall retain the use of the coordinates and the velocity components as hitherto in this paper, but we shall use an eddy viscosity ϵ which is supposed to be only a function of x and not of r. The form of the eddy viscosity can be found by a dimensional analysis to be

$$\epsilon = \lambda(Gx^2/\rho)^{1/3}F(r/x) ,$$

where λ is a dimensionless coefficient. (The Reynolds stress calculated from this expression for ϵ, with $\lambda = 0.016$ obtained from the mean velocity profile, has been compared with the Reynolds-stress measurements of Beuther *et al.*,[7] and excellent agreement has been found.) In ignoring the transverse variation of ϵ, which we cannot determine analytically in any case, we are simply dropping $F(r/x)$ and assuming[8]

$$\epsilon = \lambda(Gx^2/\rho)^{1/3} . \tag{38}$$

Then, understanding u and v to be the time-mean velocity components at any point in space, the equation of motion and the diffusion equation are, respectively,

$$uu_x + vu_r = \frac{\epsilon}{r}\frac{\partial}{\partial r}(ru_r) - g\frac{\Delta\gamma}{\gamma_0} , \tag{39}$$

$$u\frac{\partial}{\partial x}\Delta\gamma + v\frac{\partial}{\partial r}\Delta\gamma = \frac{\epsilon}{\sigma r}\frac{\partial}{\partial r}\left(r\frac{\partial}{\partial r}\Delta\gamma\right) . \tag{40}$$

The equation of continuity is (3) and (4) can again be used, as well as the boundary conditions stated just after (3).

We note that, since the flow is turbulent, strictly speaking G is now given by

$$G = -2\pi\int_0^\infty r(u\Delta\gamma + \overline{u'\Delta\gamma'})dr , \tag{41}$$

where the primed quantities denote turbulent fluctuations. We assume the contribution of the turbulent part to be a definite fraction of G defined by (41), which indeed it is, and continue to use the nominal G defined by (5) to represent the strength of the source. This practice has the advantage not only of simplicity of exposition, but is convenient when the analytical results to be given in this paper are compared with available experimental results, which have all been given in terms of the G defined by (5).

Then, the appropriate forms for ψ and $\Delta\gamma$, arrived at by a dimensional analysis, are

$$\psi = 3\lambda(Gx^5/\rho)^{1/3}f(\eta) , \tag{42}$$

$$-\Delta\gamma = 3\lambda^2(\rho G^2/x^5)^{1/3}\theta(\eta) , \tag{43}$$

where

$$\eta = r/x . \tag{44}$$

The velocity components are then given by

$$u = 3\lambda(G/\rho x)^{1/3}f'/\eta , \tag{45}$$

$$v = \lambda(G/\rho x)^{1/3}(3f' - 5f/\eta) , \tag{46}$$

and the equations of motion and of diffusion assume the following dimensionless forms[8]

$$(1 - 5f)(f'/\eta)' - f'^2/\eta = f''' + \eta\theta , \tag{47}$$

$$-5\sigma(f\theta)' = (\eta\theta')', \tag{48}$$

where σ denotes the turbulent Prandtl number. The boundary conditions remain (11), and the integral condition (5) becomes

$$18\pi\lambda^3 \int_0^\infty f'\theta\, d\eta = 1. \tag{49}$$

A. Exact solutions for the round turbulent plume

The differential system consisting of (47) to (49) was solved exactly by Yih[8] for $\sigma = 1.1$ and $\sigma = 2$. The results are

$$f = B[1 - (1 + A\eta^2)^{-1}], \tag{50}$$

$$\theta = C/(1 + A\eta^2)^m, \tag{51}$$

in which, for $\sigma = 1.1$,

$$B = 12/11, \quad m = 3, \quad C = (1536/121)A^2. \tag{52}$$

From (49) we obtain

$$C\lambda^3 = 11/54\pi, \quad A^2\lambda^3 = 1331/82944\pi. \tag{53}$$

Thus, only λ needs to be determined experimentally.

For $\sigma = 2$,

$$B = \tfrac{4}{5}, \quad m = 4, \quad C = (256/25)A^2, \tag{54}$$

and use of (49) gives

$$C\lambda^3 = 25/72\pi, \quad A^2\lambda^3 = 625/18432\pi. \tag{55}$$

For comparison of experimental results, we note that

$$u\left(\frac{\rho x}{G}\right)^{1/3} = \frac{6\lambda AB}{(1 + A\eta^2)^2} = \frac{3\lambda f'}{\eta}. \tag{56}$$

B. Approximate solutions for the round turbulent plume

We can build approximate solutions upon the exact solutions for turbulent plumes in the same way as for laminar plumes. Expansions like (21) and (22), but without the logarithm terms, can be used, in principle, but converge very slowly and are, therefore, very cumbersome in practice. Instead, we approximate X^{-4} by βX^{-3} or X^{-3} by $\beta^{-1}X^{-4}$, as the case may be, where $\beta = 7/8$ or $\beta = 10/11$, respectively. With this approxi-

mation, we obtain two approximate solutions.

1. *The first approximate solution—based on the exact solution for $\sigma = 1.1$*. With a method strictly similar to that used in Sec. IIB, we obtain the approximate solution

$$f = \frac{6}{5\sigma}(1 - X^{-1}), \quad \theta = \frac{5\sigma}{27\pi\lambda^3}X^{-3}, \quad X = 1 + A\eta^2,$$

$$A^2 = \frac{5}{27\pi\lambda^3}\frac{\sigma^3}{2.16 + 12\sigma}, \tag{57}$$

where η is defined by (44). This solution is exact for $\sigma = 1.1$.

2. *The second approximate solution—based on the exact solution for $\sigma = 2$*. With the same definition for X, and by a method similar to that employed in Sec. IIB, we also have the approximate solution

$$f = \frac{8}{5\sigma}(1 - X^{-1}), \quad \theta = \frac{25\sigma}{144\pi\lambda^3}X^{-4}, \quad A^2 = \frac{625\sigma^2}{73728\pi\lambda^3}. \tag{58}$$

This solution is exact for $\sigma = 2$.

C. Comparison of approximate and exact solutions

In Fig. 5, the first approximate solution evaluated at $\sigma = 2$ is compared with the exact solution for $\sigma = 2$, and the second approximate solution evaluated at $\sigma = 1.1$ is compared with the exact solution for $\sigma = 1.1$. Again, although the change in σ is nearly double (or one-half) that for which the approximate solution is exact, it still gives satisfactory results. This gives us confidence that for σ equal to 1 or near 1, as it should be for turbulent flows, the first approximate solution will give very accurate results.

We can, indeed, give an estimate of the error introduced by the approximation of X^{-4} by $7/8X^{-3}$. We note first that the solution (57) satisfies (48) and (49) exactly, and that the approximation only affects (47). This approximation introduces a residue on the left-hand side of (47), after division by η, and for $\sigma = 1$ the ratio of the maximum value of this residue (at the axis of symmetry) to the value of the left-hand of (47) can be shown to be -0.051. The error in A^2 determined by

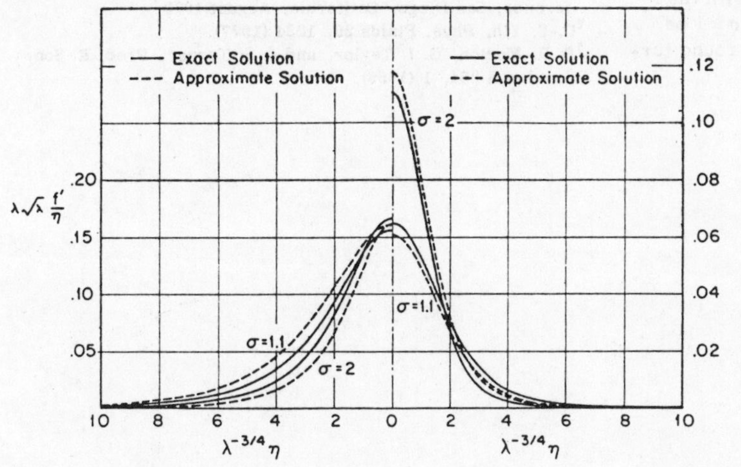

FIG. 5. Comparison of approximate and exact solutions for turbulent round plumes, for turbulent Prandtl numbers $\sigma = 1.1$ and $\sigma = 2$.

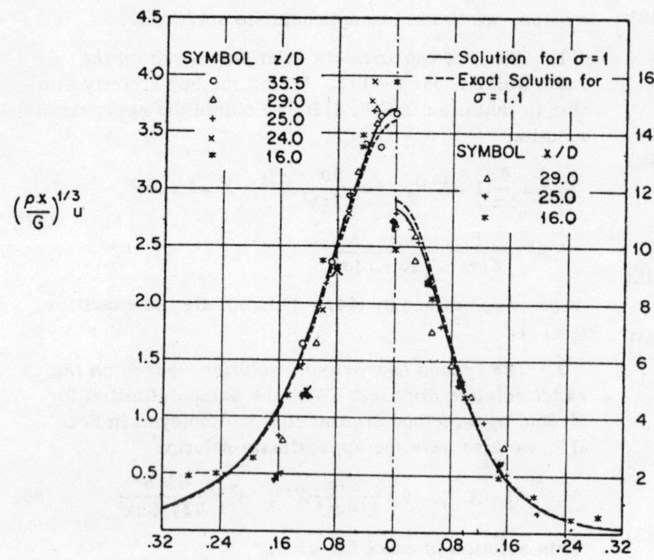

FIG. 6. Comparison of analytical results for turbulent Prandtl number 1 and $\lambda = 0.0156$ with the experimental data of Beuther *et al.*[7] The abscissa is η.

the last equation in (57) is thus 5.4% at most, and the error in $A^{1/2}$, which determines the spread angle of the plume is only 1.3% at most. The error in the vertical velocity is 2.7% at most. These maximum errors are certainly within the range of errors of any experimental data.

D. The proposed solution for round turbulent plumes

Taking solution (57) and fitting it to the data of Beuther, Capp, and George Jr.[7], we found that the best fit gives $\sigma = 1$, $\lambda = 0.0156$, $A = 33$. [In our comparison with the experimental data, we have taken into account the statement written on the reprint of their paper, which they kindly sent to us, that their F_0 (corresponding to our G) is 20% too high.] The comparison between the analytical curves for velocity and temperature distributions with their experimental data is shown in Fig. 6. The dotted curves are for $\sigma = 1.1$ and the same values of λ and A. It seems that the curves for $\sigma = 1$ give a slightly better fit than those for $\sigma = 1.1$, but that both the solid curves and the dotted ones fit the experimental data very well. We propose, then, that (57) with the above-mentioned values for λ and A and with $\sigma = 1$ be adopted as the solution for the problem of the round turbulent plume.

ACKNOWLEGMENT

This work has been supported by the Office of Naval Research.

[1]Ya. B. Zel'dovich, Zh. Eksp. Teor. Fiz. 7, 1963 (1937).
[2]C.-S. Yih, in *Proceedings of the 1st U. S. National Congress Applied Mechanics* (American Society of Mechanical Engineers, New York, 1951), p. 941.
[3]C.-S. Yih, in *Proceedings of Symposium on the Use of Models in Geophysical Fluid Mechanics* (Government Printing Office Washington, D.C., 1956), p. 117.
[4]W. Schmidt, Z. Angew. Math. Mech. 21, 265 (1941).
[5]H. Rouse, C.-S. Yih, and H. W. Humphreys, Tellus 4, 201 (1952).
[6]W. K. George, Jr., R. L. Alpert, and F. Tamanini, Int. J. Heat Mass Transfer 20, 1145 (1977).
[7]P. D. Beuther, S. P. Capp, and W. K. George, Jr., presented at the Joint ASME/AIChE 18th National Heat Transfer Conference, San Diego, California, August 1979.
[8]C.-S. Yih, Phys. Fluids 20, 1234 (1977).
[9]B. R. Morton, G. I. Taylor, and J. S. Turner, Proc. R. Soc. London A 234, 1 (1956).

Part E
General

AMERICAN SOCIETY OF CIVIL ENGINEERS

Founded November 5, 1852

TRANSACTIONS

Paper No. 2758

APPLICATIONS OF THE RELAXATION TECHNIQUE IN FLUID MECHANICS

By John S. McNown,[1] M. ASCE, En-Yun Hsu,[2] A. M. ASCE, and Chia-Shun Yih[3]

With Discussion by Messrs. Fred W. Blaisdell; Henry M. Paynter and Ronald F. Scott; Mladen Boreli; Turgut Sarpkaya; and John S. McNown, En-Yun Hsu, and Chia-Shun Yih

Synopsis

Problems in fluid mechanics of essentially irrotational flow are often so complex that numerical methods must be used in their resolution. A simple, yet generally useful method is the relaxation process, which is based on a network of values of the required function determined by means of the finite-difference theory. The numerical process is simple, and techniques are available for satisfying various types of boundary conditions. The computations are useful in solving problems of efflux and seepage and in analyzing flow through transitions or around submerged bodies. Examples of these various types have been solved, and the results are presented as illustrations of the process.

Introduction

Relaxation, a numerical method of integration, can be used to obtain solutions for a wide variety of problems which cannot be solved by standard methods. In using this method, a network of values is assumed for the function sought; the network is then systematically corrected as the errors are "relaxed." Based on the calculus of finite differences, this method was brought to fruition in England by R. V. Southwell and his associates[4]; it has been used in solving a variety of problems dealing with elasticity, heat transfer, and fluid mechanics.

Note.—Published, essentially as printed here, in July, 1953, as *Proceedings-Separate No. 223.* Positions and titles given are those in effect when the paper was received for publication.

[1] Associate Director, Iowa Inst. of Hydr. Research, State Univ. of Iowa, Iowa City, Iowa.
[2] Research Engr., Hydrodynamics Lab., California Inst. of Technology, Pasadena, Calif.
[3] Research Engr., Iowa Inst. of Hydr. Research, State Univ. of Iowa, Iowa City, Iowa.
[4] "Relaxation Methods in Theoretical Physics," by R. V. Southwell, Oxford Press, 1946.

Although only particular solutions can be obtained by such methods and although the computations are time consuming, relaxation methods are effective in cases for which general solutions cannot be obtained by direct methods.

Partial differential equations such as the Laplacian, the Poisson, and the biharmonic can be integrated by using the relaxation procedure. These equations are often encountered in engineering, and numerous general solutions have been obtained for simple boundary conditions. However, general solutions are usually unobtainable if the boundary conditions are complex. It is in such cases that numerical solutions are particularly valuable because in their application a complex boundary condition can be fulfilled almost as easily as a simple one. There is presented herein the method of solving only the Laplace equation, the one most frequently encountered in the analysis of fluid flow. Although this is the simplest of the several equations, the manner of solving it is nonetheless indicative of the general method. Applications of this differential equation are restricted to potential flows such as seepage, flow through boundary contractions, efflux through slots or orifices, certain types of wave motion, and flow over weirs. Only for two-dimensional flow patterns and axisymmetric flow patterns is it feasible to obtain solutions.

Resolution of any significant problem by the relaxation process will require at least many hours and perhaps several months, yet the individual steps in the process are few and easily mastered. These steps are presented subsequently in some detail, from the initially assumed network of values, through the elimination of residual errors and the advances to successively finer nets, to the eventual satisfaction of both the differential equation and the assigned boundary conditions. A number of applications are cited, the analyses having been conducted at the Iowa Institute of Hydraulic Research, State University of Iowa, at Iowa City.

FINITE DIFFERENCE THEORY

Essential Elements.—The goal in applying the relaxation method is to attain a network of values of a function which satisfies a given partial differen-

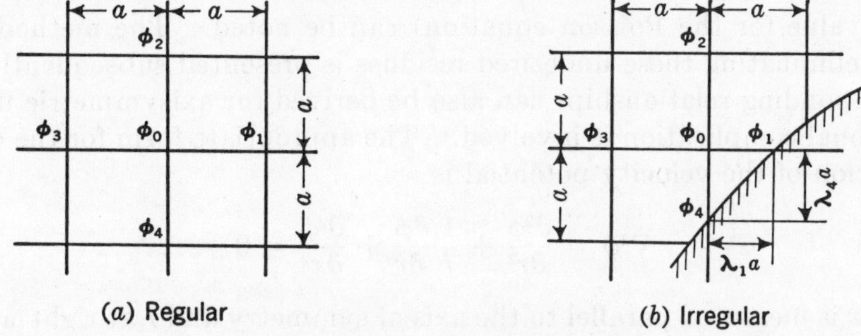

(a) Regular   (b) Irregular

FIG. 1.—PATTERN OF FUNCTION VALUES

tial equation at each point of a discrete network covering the region and which also satisfies a given set of boundary conditions. The number of points must be large enough (or the mesh fine enough) to make the assumption of a linear variation of the function between adjacent points justifiable. For such a network, the theory of finite differences can be successfully used.

An algebraic expression for the Laplacian of a particular function, such as the velocity potential ϕ, can be obtained quite simply. For example, in Fig. 1 (a), the approximate value of

$$\nabla^2 \phi = \frac{\partial^2 \phi}{\partial x^2} + \frac{\partial^2 \phi}{\partial y^2} \dots \dots \dots (1)$$

is sought for the central point in terms of the several values of ϕ in the immediate vicinity, the mesh being square and the lines spaced a distance a apart. If the coordinates of the central point are designated as x_0 and y_0, at the points $(x_0 + a/2, y_0)$ and $(x_0 - a/2, y_0)$,

$$\frac{\partial \phi}{\partial x} \approx \frac{\phi_1 - \phi_0}{a} \dots \dots \dots \dots \dots \dots (2a)$$

and

$$\frac{\partial \phi}{\partial x} \approx \frac{\phi_0 - \phi_3}{a} \dots \dots \dots \dots \dots \dots (2b)$$

respectively. The second partial derivative of ϕ can be obtained in a similar manner—

$$\frac{\partial^2 \phi}{\partial x^2} \approx \frac{\dfrac{\phi_1 - \phi_0}{a} - \dfrac{\phi_0 - \phi_3}{a}}{a} = \frac{\phi_1 + \phi_3 - 2\,\phi_0}{a^2} \dots \dots \dots (3a)$$

In the same way, one can obtain an expression for the second partial derivative with respect to y—

$$\frac{\partial^2 \phi}{\partial y^2} \approx \frac{\phi_2 + \phi_4 - 2\,\phi_0}{a^2} \dots \dots \dots \dots \dots (3b)$$

Finally, the equivalent form for Eq. 1 expressed in finite-difference form is

$$a^2 \nabla^2 \phi \approx \phi_1 + \phi_2 + \phi_3 + \phi_4 - 4\,\phi_0 \dots \dots \dots \dots (4)$$

Although Eq. 4 is an approximation, equality is closely approached as the spacing is reduced. For a given set of ϕ-values, either known or assumed, $a^2 \nabla^2 \phi$ can be evaluated from Eq. 4, and its difference from zero (or another assigned value for the Poisson equation) can be noted. The method of successively eliminating these undesired residues is presented subsequently.

Corresponding relationships can also be derived for axisymmetric flow, but an additional complication is involved. The appropriate form for the differential equation of the velocity potential is

$$\nabla^2 \phi = \frac{\partial^2 \phi}{\partial r^2} + \frac{1}{r}\frac{\partial \phi}{\partial r} + \frac{\partial^2 \phi}{\partial x^2} = 0 \dots \dots \dots \dots \dots (5)$$

in which x is measured parallel to the axis of symmetry and r at right angles to it. Although both the velocity potential and the stream function ψ for two-dimensional flow satisfy the same equation, the Stokes stream function, for axisymmetric flow, satisfies an equation similar to Eq. 5 but differing in the sign of the first-order term—

$$\frac{\partial^2 \psi}{\partial r^2} - \frac{1}{r}\frac{\partial \psi}{\partial r} + \frac{\partial^2 \psi}{\partial x^2} = 0 \dots \dots \dots \dots \dots \dots (6)$$

For the point (x_0, r_0), the value of $\partial\phi/\partial x$ is unchanged from the two-dimensional case (Fig. 1(a)); in addition,

$$\frac{\partial\phi}{\partial r} \approx \frac{\phi_2 - \phi_4}{2\,a} \dots\dots\dots\dots\dots\dots\dots (7)$$

If this value is substituted into Eq. 5, together with the finite-difference equivalents of the second partial derivatives,

$$a^2\,\nabla^2\,\phi = \phi_1 + \phi_2 + \phi_3 + \phi_4 - 4\,\phi_0 + \frac{1}{2\,n}\,(\phi_2 - \phi_4) = 0 \dots (8)$$

The corresponding form for ψ is

$$\psi_1 + \psi_2 + \psi_3 + \psi_4 - 4\,\psi_0 - \frac{1}{2\,n}\,(\psi_2 - \psi_4) = 0 \dots\dots\dots (9)$$

in which n is the number of subdivisions between the axis of symmetry and the point (x_0, r_0) and is denoted by r_0/a.

If the four neighboring points are not equidistant from a given point, such as a point near an irregular boundary, the forms of Eqs. 4, 8, and 9 must be modified. As shown in Fig. 1(b), the lengths of two of the legs on the star may be less than a. If these lengths are designated as $\lambda_1\,a$ and $\lambda_4\,a$, in which $0 < \lambda < 1$, the appropriate form for the Laplacian operator for two-dimensional flow is

$$a^2\,\nabla^2\,\phi \approx \frac{\phi_1}{\lambda_1} + \phi_2 + \phi_3 + \frac{\phi_4}{\lambda_4} - \phi_0\left(2 + \frac{1}{\lambda_1} + \frac{1}{\lambda_4}\right) \dots\dots\dots (10)$$

and for axisymmetric flow is

$$a^2\,\nabla^2\,\phi \approx \frac{\phi_1}{\lambda_1} + \phi_2 + \phi_3 + \frac{\phi_4}{\lambda_4} - \phi_0\left(2 + \frac{1}{\lambda_1} + \frac{1}{\lambda_4}\right) + \frac{\phi_2 - \phi_4}{n\,(1 + \lambda_4)} \dots (11)$$

For some problems it is preferable to use a reverse method in which the dependent and independent variables are interchanged. In two-dimensional potential flow, if ϕ and ψ are considered to be the independent variables, x and y satisfy the Reimann-Cauchy equations,

$$\frac{\partial x}{\partial \phi} = \frac{\partial y}{\partial \psi} \dots\dots\dots\dots\dots\dots\dots\dots\dots (12a)$$

and

$$\frac{\partial x}{\partial \psi} = -\frac{\partial y}{\partial \phi} \dots\dots\dots\dots\dots\dots\dots\dots\dots (12b)$$

from which follow the inverse Laplace equations,

$$\frac{\partial^2 x}{\partial \phi^2} + \frac{\partial^2 x}{\partial \psi^2} = 0 \dots\dots\dots\dots\dots\dots\dots (13a)$$

and

$$\frac{\partial^2 y}{\partial \phi^2} + \frac{\partial^2 y}{\partial \psi^2} = 0 \dots\dots\dots\dots\dots\dots\dots (13b)$$

654 RELAXATION TECHNIQUES

Eqs. 13 can, of course, be expressed in terms of finite differences in the afore-mentioned manner.

Because the region of interest in fluid flow can always be bounded by a pair of potential lines (on which ϕ is constant) and a pair of streamlines (on which ψ is constant), no irregular stars will be encountered if the $(\phi-\psi)$-plane is chosen for computation. This advantage sometimes compensates for the drawback that the values of x and y along some boundary are unknown (although related) functions of ϕ. As will be illustrated subsequently, the use of ϕ and ψ as independent variables is particularly advantageous if, as in free-jet problems, the boundary streamlines are not fixed a priori but are determined by trial from a double boundary condition.

RELAXATION TECHNIQUE

The relaxation process can be described as a method of systematic refinement of an assumed variation of a function. In addition to the special techniques for satisfying various boundary conditions, two principal procedures are required: (a) The reduction of the residues and (b) the subdivision of the network wherever the assumption of linear variation is found to be inaccurate.

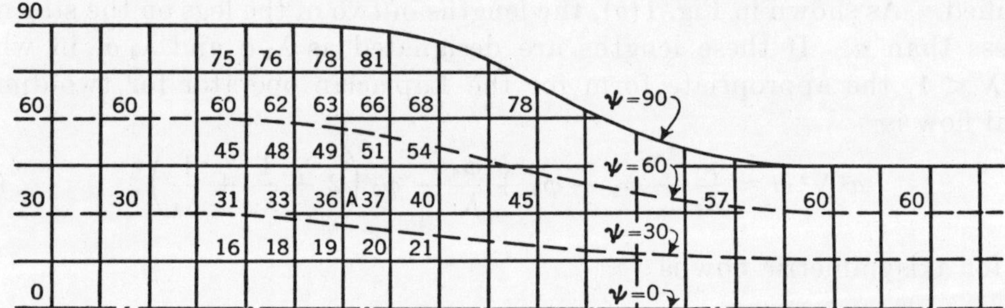

FIG. 2.—PRELIMINARY NET FOR A TWO-DIMENSIONAL TRANSITION

The region of flow is drawn to a large scale and subdivided into squares; approximate values of the function are then selected for each intersection. For example, in the two-dimensional transition shown in Fig. 2, values of the stream function can be estimated from sketched streamlines after arbitrary values of ψ (0 and 90 in this case) have been assigned for the center line and the boundary. The numerical values can be selected at will because the results are to be presented dimensionlessly in terms of the flow characteristics either upstream or downstream from the transition.

Using Eqs. 4 and 10, one can compute from the assumed values of the function the value of the residue for each of the intersections. For example, near point A in Fig. 2 the values could be as shown in Fig. 3, and the residues as recorded to the right of the intersections of the lines. At point A,

$$a^2 \nabla^2 \psi = R = 37 + 49 + 33 + 19 - 4(36) = -6.$$

The other values are similarly computed. In order to reduce the residues it is necessary to adjust repeatedly the many values of ψ.

For a regular star, one for which all four legs are equal in length, a unit increase of ψ at a given point will result in a decrease of 4 in the corresponding residue, as is apparent from Eqs. 4, 8, or 9. Thus, if ψ_A for Figs. 3 or 4 is decreased by 1, the residue is reduced from -6 to -2, as can be seen by referring to Eq. 4. In the same adjustment, the residues for each of the neighboring points are also decreased by 1 because ψ_A becomes ψ_4 in the computation of the residue at the point above, and so forth. The process is therefore continued in accordance with the simple star pattern shown at the left of Fig. 4(a) for the several possible cases. Because each change in ψ affects four other ψ-values directly and still others indirectly, the various values will have to be corrected many times. Large residues are first reduced without attempting to make them extremely small, refinement being sought only after all large discrepancies have been eliminated. In less than an hour of computation, one can obtain a familiarity with the simple process and a feeling for various short cuts, such as overcorrection and regional or block relaxation, for which simple formulas can be derived. In Fig. 5 there is shown a stage of computation following single

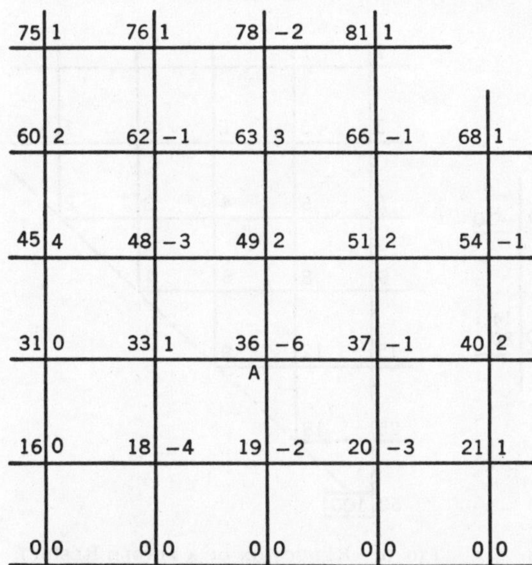

FIG. 3.—COMPUTATION OF INITIAL RESIDUES

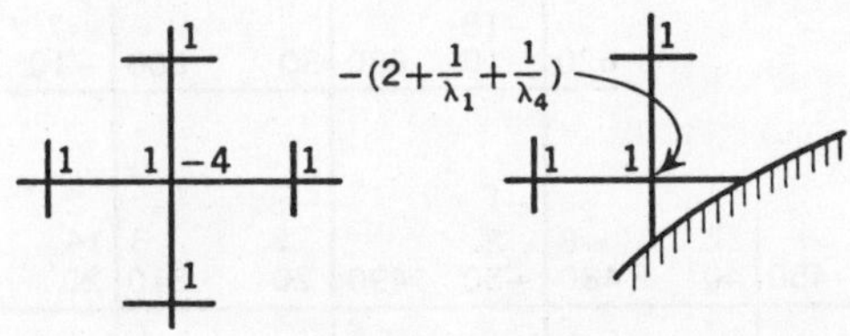

(a) Two-dimensional pattern

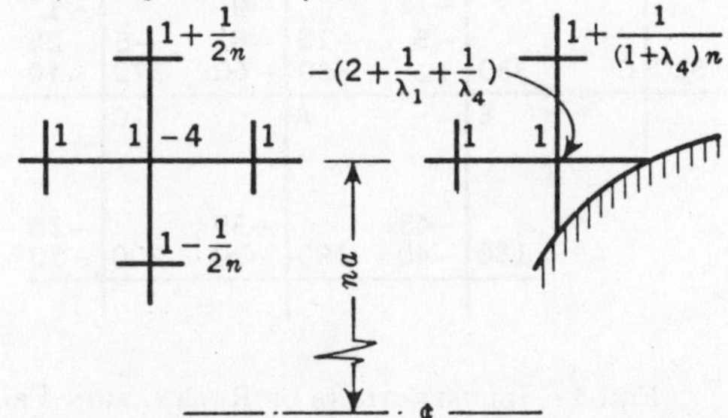

(b) Axisymmetric pattern

FIG. 4.—PATTERNS FOR RELAXATION

operations at each of points A to D (in alphabetical order). The original ψ-values were obtained from Fig. 3, the values having been multiplied by 10 to avoid the use of decimals.

Reduction of the residues to a negligible value on a coarse net, such as that shown in Fig. 2, is usually not sufficient because errors are likely to be made in the many numerical processes and because the net is too coarse for the assumption of linearity to apply. The errors can be found by recomputing all the residues from the corrected values of the function; a difference between the recomputed value and that obtained from the successive alteration indicates an error in computation. Thus, for point A in Fig. 5,

$$364 + 490 + 330 + 190 - 4(345) = -6$$

based on the revised values constitutes a check on several of the preceding computations.

656   RELAXATION TECHNIQUES

Such errors once found can usually be eliminated rather rapidly; hence they cause no particular trouble unless residues are checked too infrequently. If they occur at a distance from the boundary in a two-dimensional flow pattern, corrections can be made directly in accordance with a predetermined pattern (Fig. 6). In the preparation of Fig. 6, it was assumed that a residue (or error) of 100 was found for point A and that those residues (or errors) for all other points in the vicinity of point A were negligible. In reducing R_A to zero, one hundred and twenty-eight neighboring values of the function were found to be affected by at least as much as 1% of R_A. Of course, for local residues other than 100, proportional values can be used. The correction at any point is determined directly in terms of the coordinates of the points; that is, at a point three squares to the left and two squares below the point at which the error was made, the correction indicated in Fig. 6 would be 6% of the anomalous residue.

Because the initial grid is deliberately made coarse for simplicity, the variation of ψ in some regions is probably not linear. The existence of this undesirable

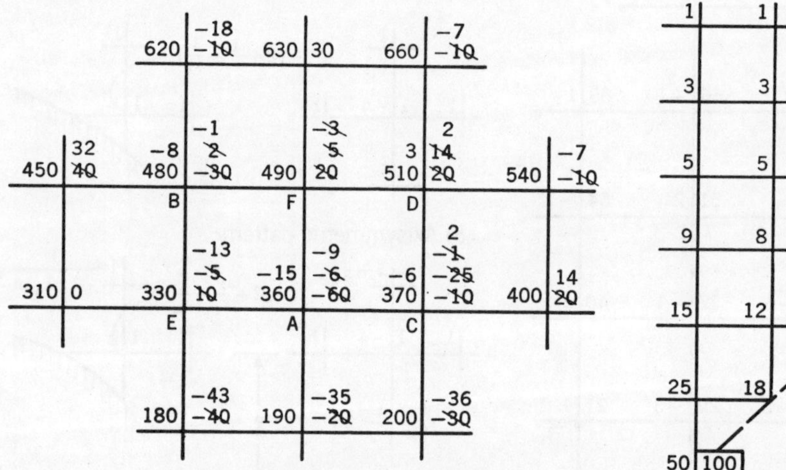

Fig. 5.—Illustrations of Relaxation Process   Fig. 6.—Reduction of a Single Residue

condition can be easily ascertained once the relaxation of the initial network has been satisfactorily completed. In a given region, a value of ψ can be obtained for the center of a square by averaging the four values at the corners (points A, C, D, and F in Fig. 5). If this is done for each of four squares with a common vertex, the four new values then can be averaged to give a second value for the common point. If this value—ψ'_A—differs significantly from ψ_A, a smaller spacing should be used. The necessary step, termed an advance to a finer net, need be taken only in the region for which nonlinearity is evident from such computations. If successively finer nets are used only as required, the work is kept to a minimum. Fortunately, the check for nonlinearity and the first step in an advance are the same. As the work progresses, it is desirable to add one or more zeros to each of the numbers, thereby permitting further reduction of the residues without resorting to decimals. Once again, some experience is required to attain an insight into the proper concepts for balancing the merits of additional refinements on a coarse net against those of an advance to a finer one.

Naturally, the relaxation technique that has been described also applies if ϕ and ψ are used as independent variables.

The accuracy of a given result can be judged only by computing velocity or pressure distributions along a boundary line or another arbitrarily selected line and determining whether they are both systematic and comparatively insensitive to further refinement. For this reason, it is desirable to make such computations at various stages. It may be known that a small region of nonlinearity remains; however, if further advance does not appreciably alter the computed distribution nearby, there is no need to continue.

BOUNDARY CONDITIONS

Little mention has been made of the method of satisfying a given set of boundary conditions because the procedure is actually a separate part of the problem and because a variety of techniques is required. For the transition in Fig. 2, no difficulty exists; the values of ψ along the solid boundary and center line are fixed, and the net is simply, if laboriously, extended to the right and left until the condition of constant velocity ($\psi = k\,y$) is satisfactorily approached. For other problems, however, special procedures are required.

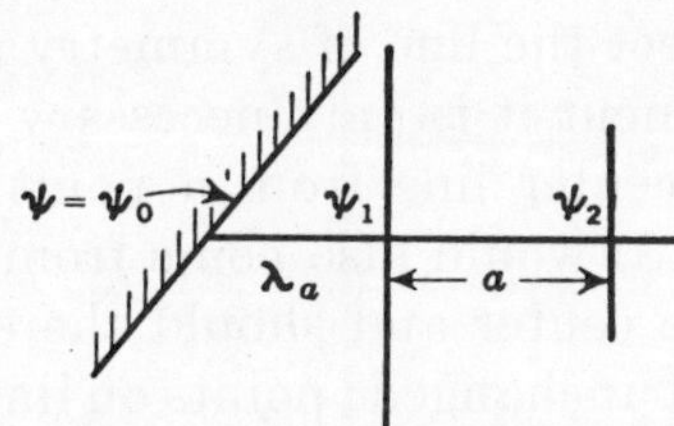

FIG. 7.—COMPUTATION OF $\partial\psi/\partial x$
AT A BOUNDARY

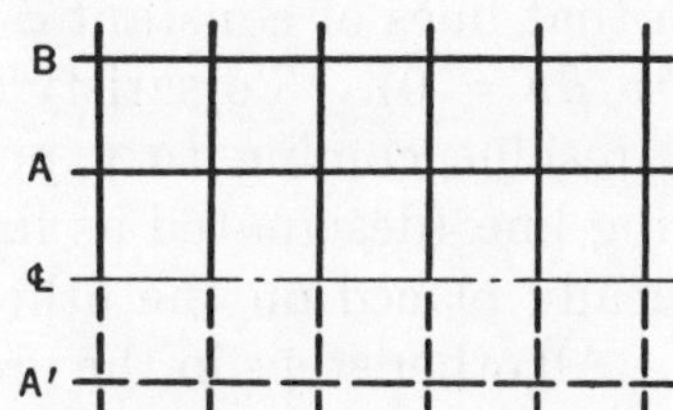

FIG. 8.—INDICATION OF
REFLECTION PRINCIPLE

Among such conditions are those specifying (a) symmetry at the boundary, (b) free streamlines with or without gravitational effects, (c) the free surface in a seepage problem, and (d) the special condition for the inverse method. In some cases, the velocity at the boundary must be evaluated before the boundary condition can be assessed.

Along a solid boundary, the function ϕ is a variable and ψ is a constant. If ϕ is used, the velocity v can be computed directly for the midpoint of each interval along the boundary from

$$v = -\frac{\partial\phi}{\partial s} \approx -\frac{\phi_1 - \phi_4}{a\sqrt{\lambda^2_1 + \lambda^2_2}} \quad\dots\dots\dots\dots\dots\dots(14)$$

in which s represents distance along a streamline and ϕ_1 and ϕ_4 are adjacent values along the boundary as shown in Fig. 1(b). If ψ is used, the normal gradient $\partial\psi/\partial n$ must be determined from $\partial\psi/\partial x$ (or $\partial\psi/\partial y$), which in turn is estimated from two values, one on the boundary and the other near the boundary. In such a case (Fig. 7),

$$v_y = \frac{\partial\psi}{\partial x} \approx \frac{\psi_1 - \psi_4}{\lambda_1\,a} \quad\dots\dots\dots\dots\dots\dots(15)$$

yields an approximation of the y-component of the velocity at a point which is a distance $\lambda_1 a/2$ away from the boundary. Even though the assumption of local linearity approaches the actual conditions, better results are obtained by using a finite-difference formula for the derivative at the boundary based on three ψ-values as illustrated in Fig. 7—

$$\frac{\partial \psi}{\partial x} \approx \frac{1 + \lambda}{\lambda} \; \frac{\psi_1 - \psi_0}{a} - \frac{\lambda}{1 + \lambda} \; \frac{\psi_2 - \psi_0}{a} \dots\dots\dots\dots (16)$$

Inclusion of more than three terms is unnecessary, the increased complexity of the computation not being accompanied by a significant increase in accuracy. Curvilinear extrapolation of this kind might seem unwarranted in a method which is based on the assumption of locally linear variation, but the resulting increased accuracy can obviate an advance to a finer net.

In the event that a flow pattern is symmetrical with respect to a center line, only one of the two halves need be determined, the line of symmetry being a streamline (as in Fig. 3). If ψ is used, the corresponding boundary condition is automatically fixed as it is for a solid boundary, and residues which would be transferred to points on such a boundary are ignored. If, however, the velocity potential is used, the boundary values are not known but are subject to the condition that lines of constant ϕ must intersect the line of symmetry at right angles ($\partial \phi/\partial n = 0$). To satisfy this requirement it is only necessary to note that any residue coming to a point on the center line from a point on the neighboring line (designated as line A in Fig. 8) would also come from line A' symmetrically placed on the other side of the center and should therefore be doubled. All other steps in the process remain unchanged; points on line B and on the center line are relaxed in the usual manner.

In the analysis of the patterns of flow occurring for various types of efflux, the free streamlines which are encountered necessitate special procedures. Along a free streamline the pressure is constant; thus, for irrotational flow the velocity is either constant (if gravitational effects are ignored) or proportional to the square root of the vertical distance below the line of total head (if gravitational effects are included). Initially the location of the free streamline is not known and it consequently must be assumed. The corresponding flow pattern is next determined by use of the relaxation process, and the velocities along the free streamlines are computed. Because the values obtained will not, in general, satisfy the specified boundary condition for the velocity, the assumed location of the free streamline must be changed and the process repeated. Because ψ is used in the direct method for this type of problem, the aforementioned method of evaluating $\partial \psi/\partial n$ by curvilinear extrapolation is extremely useful.

In the analysis of unconfined seepage through a porous medium, a somewhat different type of free streamline is encountered. Because the piezometric head (velocity potential) is generally used, two conditions are required: (a) At every point along the free streamline the pressure must be zero and (b) the normal component of velocity must be zero. Accordingly, after a trial curve has been drawn for the streamline bounding the flow, values can be assigned for ϕ which automatically satisfy the condition that $p = 0$—that is, that ϕ is equal to the elevation. After the corresponding complete network has been obtained, the second boundary condition can be checked, and a revised bounding line drawn as required. Once again, this process can be repeated, entirely or in part, until an acceptably correct result is obtained.

To check the imposed boundary condition or to evaluate the velocity along a curved or irregular boundary, $\partial\psi/\partial n$ is evaluated from $\partial\psi/\partial x$ or $\partial\psi/\partial y$. With reference to Fig. 7, $\partial\psi/\partial x$ is determined from Eq. 16 for the point on the bounding streamline. The value of $\partial\psi/\partial n$ is then determined from

$$v = \frac{\partial\psi}{\partial n} = \frac{1}{\sin\theta}\frac{\partial\psi}{\partial x} = \frac{1}{\cos\theta}\frac{\partial\psi}{\partial y} \dots\dots\dots\dots\dots\dots (17)$$

in which θ is the angle between the bounding streamline and the x-axis. For axisymmetric flow, the corresponding expression is

$$v = \frac{1}{r}\frac{\partial\psi}{\partial n} = \frac{1}{r\sin\theta}\frac{\partial\psi}{\partial x} = \frac{1}{r\cos\theta}\frac{\partial\psi}{\partial y} \dots\dots\dots\dots\dots\dots (18)$$

It should be noted that no sign convention need be defined because the direction of the velocity is never in question.

The treatment of the boundary condition—if ϕ and ψ are used as independent variables—can best be explained by an example. On the surface of a jet

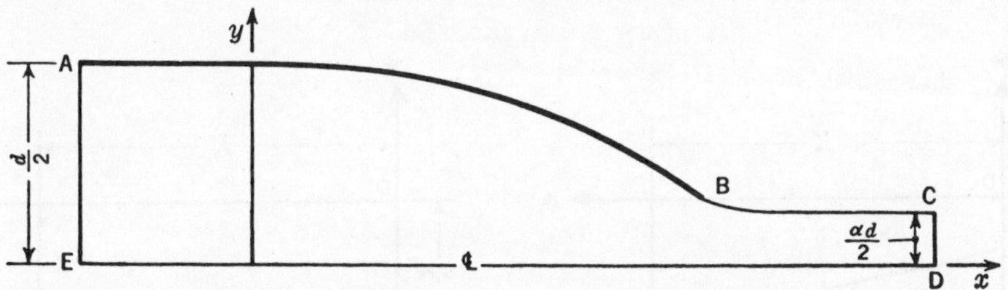

FIG. 9.—SCHEMATIC DIAGRAM FOR REVERSE METHOD

issuing from a two-dimensional nozzle, the pressure and magnitude of the velocity are constants; this condition will determine the shape of the jet. With reference to Fig. 9, it is sufficient to consider the region ABCDE, where line AE and line CD are comparatively far away from the contraction. Along line CD, ϕ can be assumed to be a constant, such as zero. The corresponding value for x can be taken from Fig. 9 and is denoted by X. Taking $\psi = 0$ along line ED, $\psi = -q/2$ along line ABC, q being the discharge per unit width of the nozzle. The value of ϕ along line AE can be taken to be a constant K large enough so that the flow upstream from line AE is essentially uniform; it should be remembered, however, that so far the corresponding value of x (denoted by X') has not been determined. Except for the somewhat complicated boundary conditions for x and y along line ABC, the conditions at the boundaries are

$$\text{for } \phi = 0: x = X \text{ (known)}, \quad y = -\alpha\psi\frac{d}{q}$$

$$\text{for } \phi = K: x = X' \text{ (unknown)}, \quad y = -\psi\frac{d}{q}$$

$$\text{and } \text{ for } \psi = 0: \frac{\partial x}{\partial\psi} = 0, \quad y = 0$$

in which d is the width of the nozzle at point A.

660   RELAXATION TECHNIQUES

Along line AB it would be possible to translate the condition $\partial\phi/\partial n = 0$ (n being measured in a direction normal to line AB) into one involving x or y as the unknowns, but the result would be extremely unwieldy. Instead, one requires the satisfaction of one of the Riemann-Cauchy equations (Eq. 12a), and that

$$x = x(\phi) \dotfill (19a)$$

and

$$y = y(\phi) \dotfill (19b)$$

must be equivalent to

$$y = f(x) \dotfill (20)$$

which describes the boundary AB.

The condition along line BC can be similarly formulated. One again demands the satisfaction of one of the relationships from Eqs. 12 along $\psi = -q/2$. However, instead of Eqs. 19, one requires that

$$\left(\frac{\partial x}{\partial \phi}\right)^2 + \left(\frac{\partial y}{\partial \phi}\right)^2 = \left(\frac{\alpha d}{q}\right)^2 \dotfill (21)$$

in which α is the ratio of the ultimate width of the jet to d.

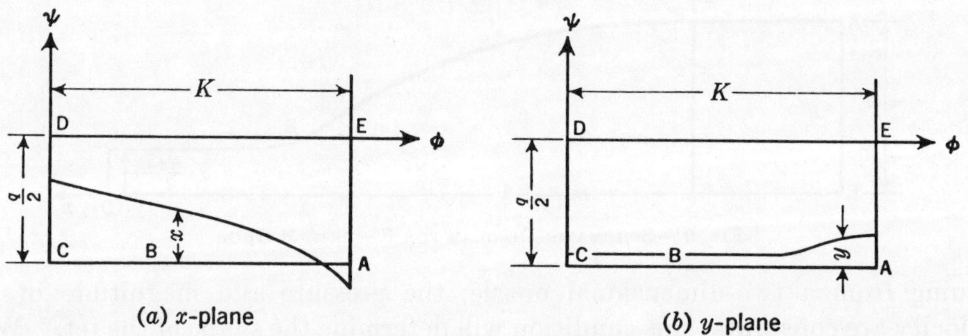

Fig. 10.—Work Sheets for the Evaluation of x and y

With reference to Fig. 10, the procedure is then as follows: Assuming $x(\phi)$ along line AC, one obtains X' and can locate point B at which x is known. From Eq. 20, the value of y along line AB can be obtained. The value of y from point B to point C is obtained by integrating Eq. 21 numerically, α being assumed such that y computed at C will be equal to $\alpha d/2$. With the value of y at point C given, the boundary condition for y at $\phi = 0$ is determined from the linear relationship between y and ψ along line CD.

After the relaxation procedure for y is completed, the result is checked against one of Eqs. 12. If this equation is not satisfied, $x(\phi)$ is corrected accordingly. The process is repeated until the equation is satisfied. Finally, x can be computed either by one relaxation process, or directly by using Eqs. 12.

In the assumption of $x(\phi)$ along line AC, it should be noted that $x(\phi)$ is asymptotically linear. At $\phi = 0$, $\partial x/\partial \phi$ is approximately equal to $-\alpha d/q$ and y is approximately equal to $\alpha d/2$. At $\phi = K$, $\partial x/\partial \phi$ is approximately equal to $-d/q$, and y is approximately equal to $d/2$. The final result of a computation for the two-dimensional nozzle with the boundary geometry given in Fig. 9 is presented subsequently.

After the various steps in the relaxation process have been completed, any required results can be obtained.   The shape of a free streamline is established in the process, the pressure and velocity distributions can be determined throughout space with reference to the pressure and velocity in a region of uniform flow, comparative quantities of seepage can be evaluated, and coefficients of discharge can be computed.   The one remaining question is the degree of accuracy obtained—a difficult question to answer.

There is no direct way to assess the accuracy other than to make determinations, for example, of velocity distributions from each of the various nets

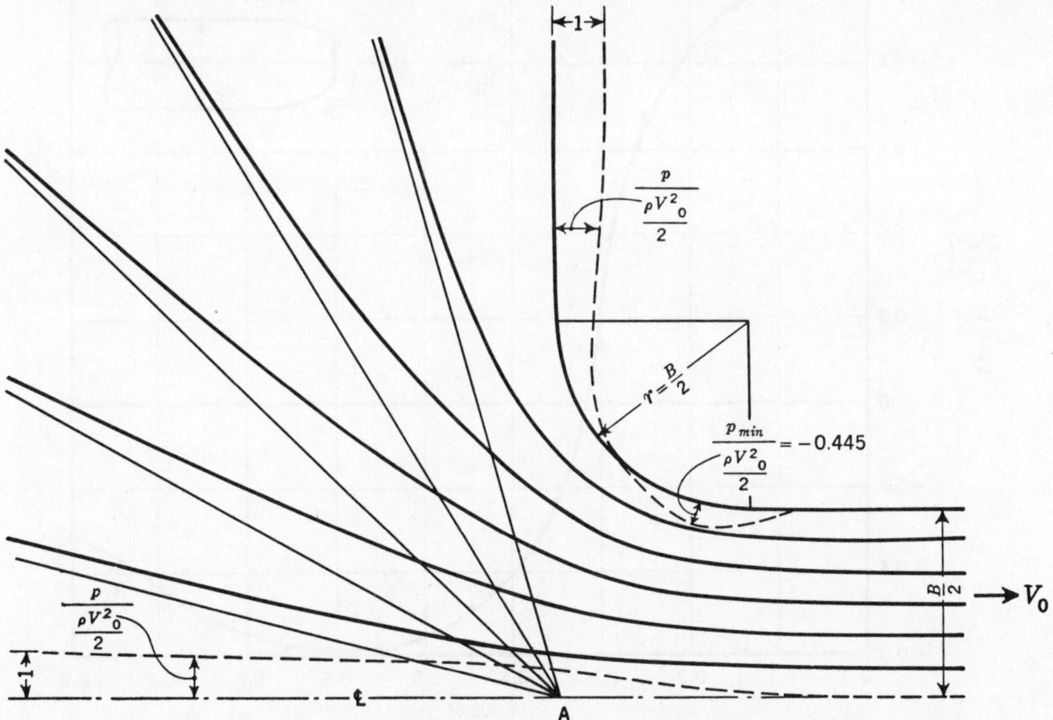

Fig. 11.—Two-Dimensional Curved Inlet

prepared.   If the change in this result following a particular refinement is comparatively small, one can conclude that the result is satisfactory.   Various methods of partly resolving this troublesome matter will become evident in each problem.   It is a significant fact that no two regions are entirely equivalent. In one region several subdivisions may be required; in another, none.   Furthermore, even sizable errors in the pattern at one point may have a very small effect at another.   As the entire process is time consuming, special care should be taken to assess the reliability of the results at each stage of the computation.

APPLICATIONS

The importance of the relaxation method is best indicated by its diversity of application.   This diversity is evident from the following series of examples for flow through boundary transitions, flow with a free surface, and seepage.   The patterns are two-dimensional or axisymmetric. Because the details of the computation procedure for the interior are similar in all problems, only in the satisfying of the boundary conditions do the problems differ significantly.

The results of computation of the flow through a two-dimensional inlet transition between a reservoir and a conduit are shown in Fig. 11; in this case the radius of rounding is equal to half the conduit width.   The distribution of pressure along the boundary is indicated, and representative streamlines are shown together with the radial lines which they approach asymptotically. The pattern of the flow some distance upstream of the inlet is identical to that

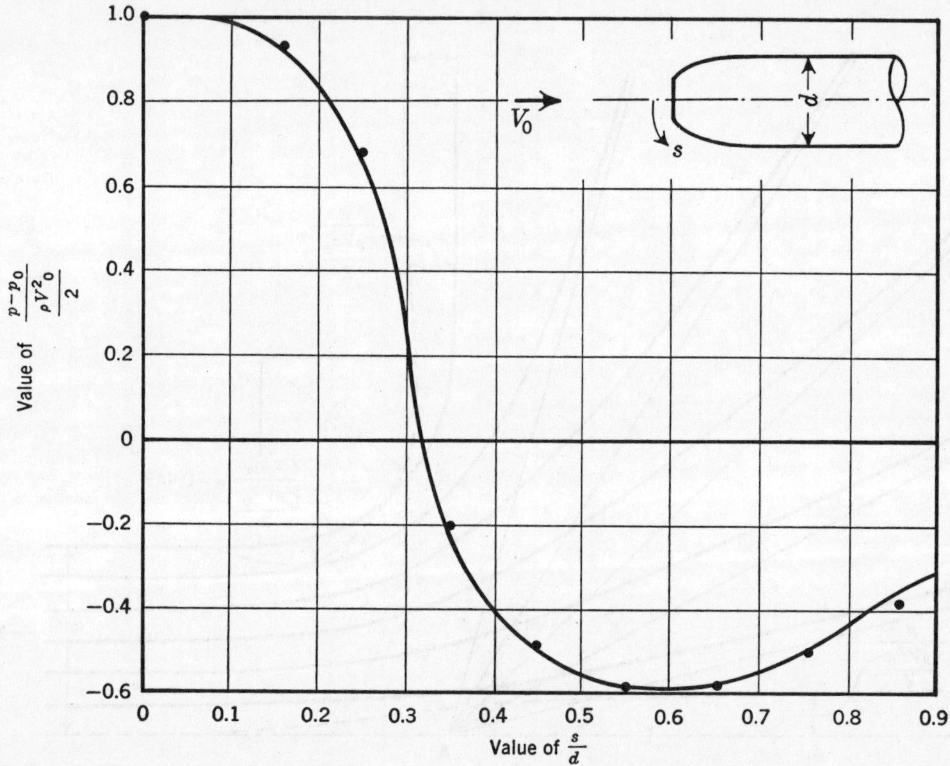

FIG. 12.—PRESSURE DISTRIBUTION FOR AXISYMMETRIC FLOW PAST A MODIFIED ELLIPSOIDAL HEAD FORM

for flow toward a sink at point A—the intersection of the projection of the vertical boundary and the axis of symmetry.   The result has been found to conform closely with that obtained from a different type of analysis and with that from an experiment.[5]

A second example is an internal boundary transition in axisymmetric flow. In a study of a series of head forms,[6] the pressure distribution was determined for a modified ellipsoidal form as indicated in Fig. 12.   In this study a comparison was made of the results obtained from the water tunnel with those computed numerically.   The correspondence is good from the point of stagnation to a

[5] "Pressure Distribution from Theoretical Approximations of the Flow Pattern," by John S. McNown and En-Yun Hsu, *Proceedings*, Heat Transfer and Fluid Mechanics Inst., 1949, pp. 65–76.

[6] "Cavitation and Pressure Distribution—Head Forms at Zero Angle of Yaw," by Hunter Rouse and John S. McNown, *Studies in Engineering Bulletin 32, No. 420*, State Univ. of Iowa, Iowa City, Iowa, 1948.

point somewhat beyond the region of minimum pressure. The dimensionless value for the minimum pressure is -0.57, which can be compared with a value of -0.74 for a hemispherical nose form. The significance of this comparison is that a body with the modified nose form could move at higher velocities without producing cavitation than could one with the hemispherical form. The effects of the boundary layer in this region are evidently very small.

Applications of the relaxation technique to the determination of flow patterns involving a free surface include problems of efflux, overflow, jet impingement, and steady cavity flow. Each of these is characterized by the existence of a boundary along which the pressure is constant. These problems

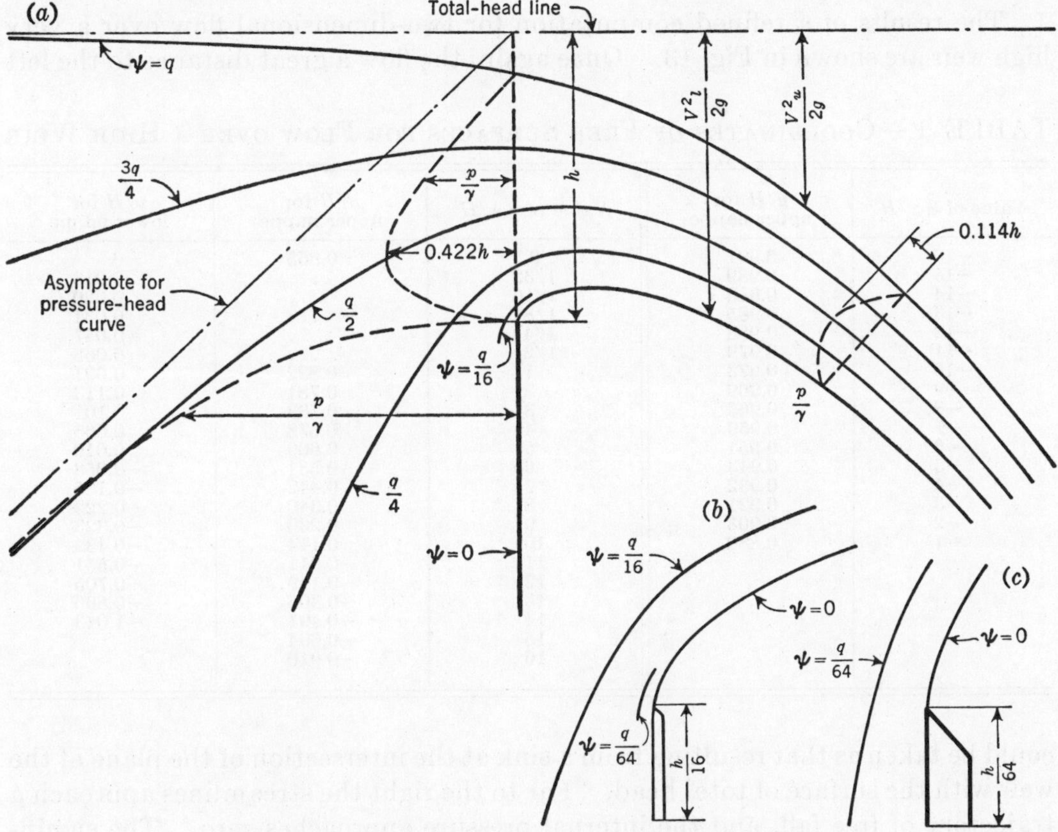

Fig. 13.—Pattern of Flow Over a Very High Weir

have been the subjects of several computations, which serve as further illustrations of the method.

From extensive computations, Hunter Rouse, M. ASCE, and A. H. Abul-Fetouh have presented[7] detailed information for efflux through an orifice symmetrically placed at the end of a circular conduit. The shape of the free jet, the pressure distribution along the solid boundary, and the coefficient of contraction were presented for various ratios of the diameter of the orifice to the diameter of the conduit. A comparison of the results with those for similar two-dimensional flows revealed remarkably close correspondence for the

[7] "Characteristics of Irrotational Flow Through Axially Symmetric Orifices," by Hunter Rouse and A. H. Abul-Fetouh, *Journal of Applied Mechanics*, Vol. 17, No. 4, 1950, pp. 421–426.

values of the contraction coefficient. Furthermore, the coefficients available from various experiments were found to follow essentially the same trend.

Overflow problems are indeterminable by ordinary methods of hydrodynamics because of the paramount importance of gravity. That is, surfaces of constant pressure are not, for these flows, also surfaces of constant velocity. Thus, even the classical method of the free-streamline theory is not applicable. Mr. Southwell has presented[4] a computation for the free overfall. D. Citrini has published[8] the results of a computation for a circular weir which are applicable to the design of a morning-glory spillway; Mr. Citrini obtained the pattern for the case in which the (horizontal) radius of curvature of the weir was ten times the total head on the weir.

The results of a refined computation for two-dimensional flow over a very high weir are shown in Fig. 13. Once again, the flow a great distance to the left

TABLE 1.—COORDINATES OF FREE SURFACES FOR FLOW OVER A HIGH WEIR

Value of $8\,x/H$	y/H for upper nappe	Value of $8\,x/H$	y/H for upper nappe	y/H for lower nappe
−16	0.991	0	0.855	0
−15	0.989	1/32	....	0.013
−14	0.988	1/16	....	0.020
−13	0.985	1/8	....	0.031
−12	0.983	1/4	....	0.047
−11	0.979	1/2	....	0.068
−10	0.973	1	0.822	0.091
−9	0.969	2	0.781	0.113
−8	0.965	3	0.733	0.101
−7	0.959	4	0.678	0.065
−6	0.951	5	0.609	0.010
−5	0.943	6	0.531	−0.058
−4	0.932	7	0.442	−0.135
−3	0.921	8	0.340	−0.222
−2	0.903	9	0.230	−0.323
−1	0.880	10	0.114	−0.432
		11	−0.011	−0.561
		12	−0.149	−0.705
		13	−0.305	−0.866
		14	−0.491	−1.043
		15	−0.694	
		16	−0.910	

could be taken as that resulting from a sink at the intersection of the plane of the weir with the surface of total head. Far to the right the streamlines approach a trajectory of free fall, and the internal pressure approaches zero. The significant region near the crest of the weir is shown at three different scales in the various parts of Fig. 13. The coefficient of discharge C_d in the conventional equation,

$$Q = C_d \sqrt{2\,g}\, L\, H^{\frac{3}{2}} \dots\dots\dots\dots\dots\dots\dots (22)$$

was found to be 0.408. This value, as it should be, is somewhat more than the value of 0.388 found by Mr. Citrini for the curved weir. Both free surfaces and representative internal streamlines are shown in Fig. 13. Because the shape of the former is significant in the design of spillways, coordinates of the two bounding curves in their ratio to the head are given in Table 1.

---

[8] "Un'esperienza di calcolo numerico; Lo stramazzo a pianta circulare," by D. Citrini, Rendicont Seminario Matematico e Fisico di Milano, Vol. XXI, 1951, pp. 125–147.

Perhaps the longest of all the computations described herein was that for axisymmetric flow with an internal boundary which was partly fixed and partly a steady-state cavity. Once again, this computation duplicated part of the experiments conducted in the water tunnel at the Iowa Institute[6] for cavitating

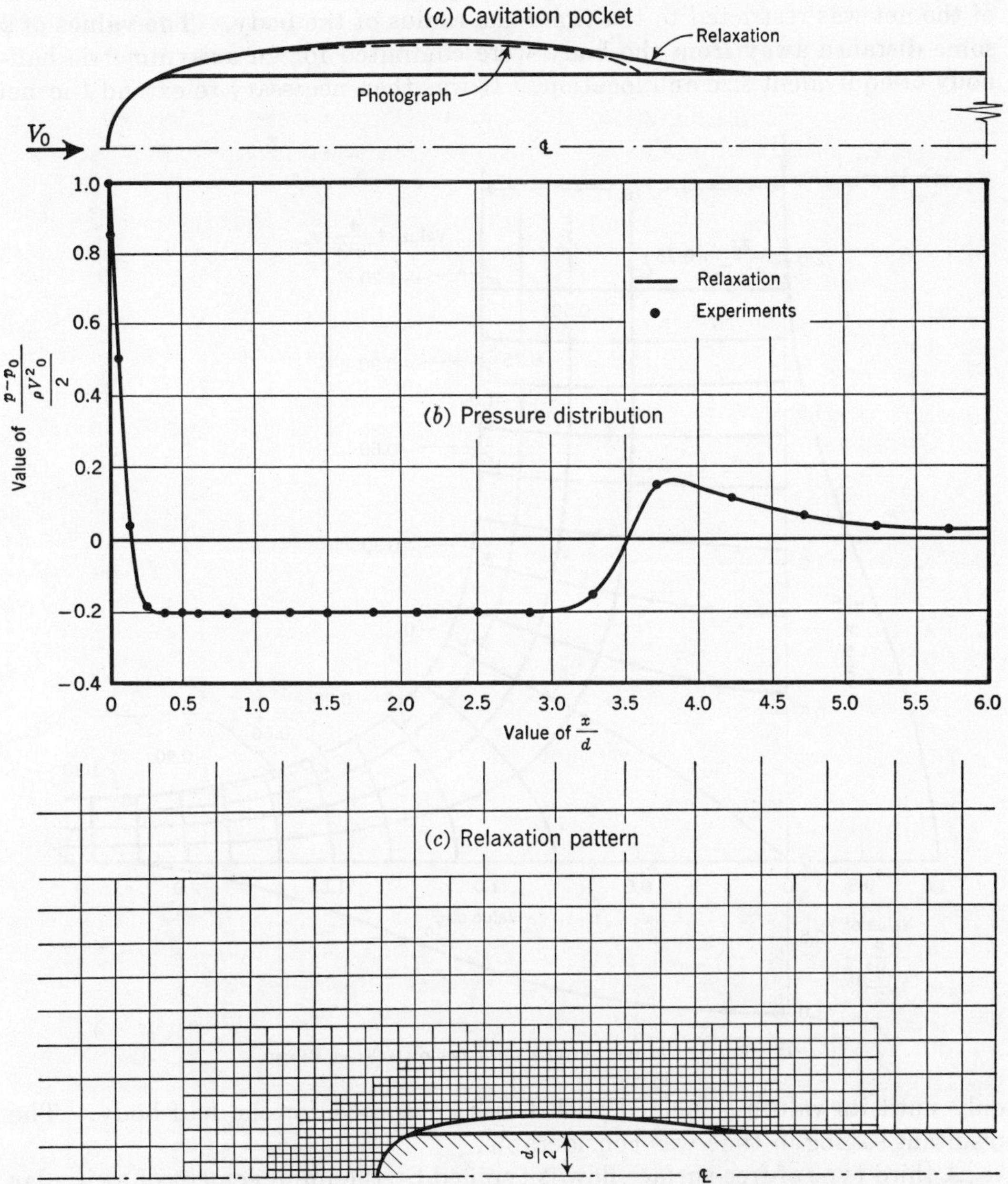

Fig. 14.—Flow with Cavitation for a Hemispherical Head Form

flow around a hemispherical head form mounted on a shaft of equal diameter. The cavitation index for this case was 0.2, a value that was so low that a large vapor cavity formed. The pressure distribution observed in the experiments[6] was imposed as an internal boundary condition, and the corresponding shape of the vapor cavity was determined by successive approximation.

In Fig. 14 there are shown (a) the observed and computed cavity profiles, (b) the pressure distribution, and (c) the pattern used for computation. Further details of the computation are available,[9] including the ψ-values at each of the intersections in Fig. 14(c). The conditions far upstream or far downstream were, of course, those for parallel flow. By use of an artifice, the radial extent of the net was restricted to ten times the radius of the body. The values of ψ some distance away from the body were computed for an axisymmetric half-body of equivalent size and location. It was then necessary to extend the net

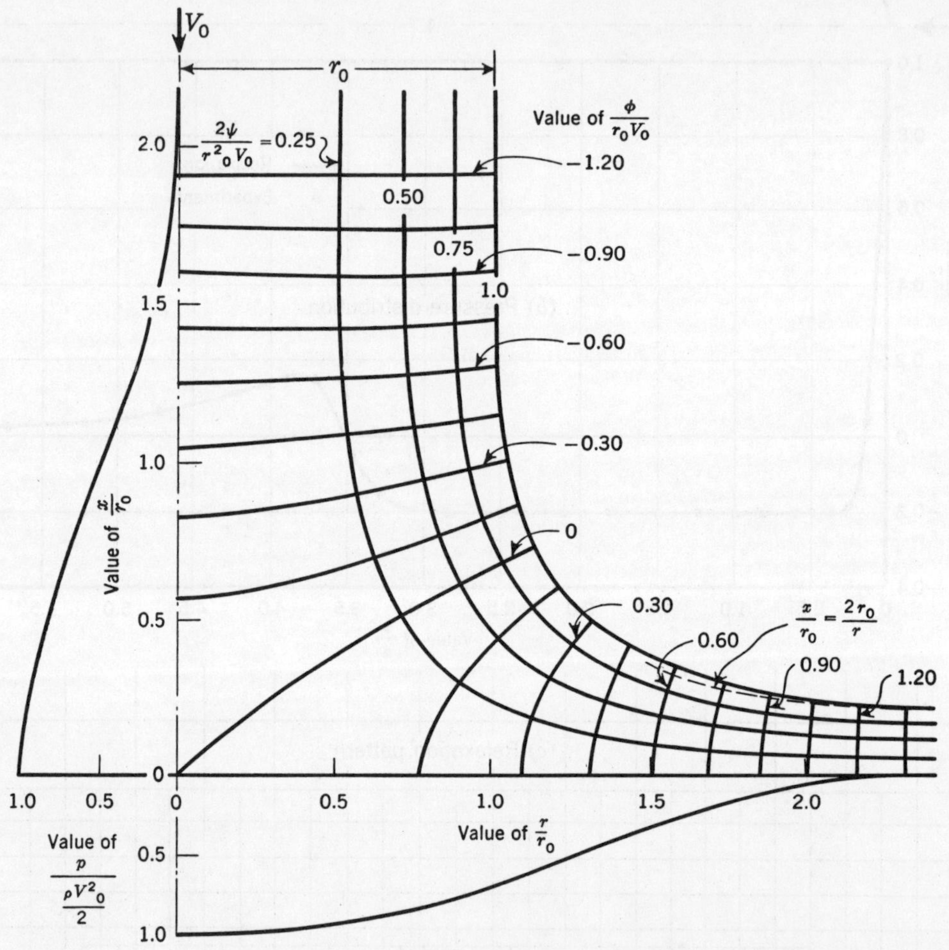

FIG. 15.—IMPINGEMENT OF A JET ON A FLAT PLATE

only until its values coincided with those computed for the half-body. The resultant saving in time was considerable.

A third type of free-surface flow is typified by the impingement of a circular jet on a plate normal to the jet axis, the topic of an investigation made by A. LeClerc.[10] In this study, the form of the free surface was determined by electrical analogy; only the internal flow pattern was evaluated by relaxation. The

[9] "Approximate Analyses Interrelating Pressure Distribution and Axisymmetric Body Form," by En-Yun Hsu, thesis presented to the State University of Iowa, at Iowa City, in 1950, in partial fulfilment of the requirements for the degree of Doctor of Philosophy.

[10] "Déviation d'un jet liquide par une plaque normale à son axe," by A. LeClerc, *La Houille Blanche*, Vol. 5, 1950, pp. 816–821.

velocity was assumed to be sufficiently high that the effect of gravity as well as that of viscosity could be neglected. The shape of the jet and representative streamlines, the variation of the pressure along the axis and along the plate, and the limiting curve for the free surface are shown in Fig. 15.

A characteristic application of the inverse method is shown in Fig. 16. The pattern of efflux from a curved two-dimensional nozzle is that which was also used in explaining the techniques. An arbitrary parabolic curve at the end of a parallel approach reduces the normal section at the region of efflux to one third of that of the approach. The curve is defined by

$$\frac{y}{b} = 3 - \frac{(x/b)^2}{18} \dots\dots\dots\dots\dots\dots\dots\dots\dots (23)$$

The contraction coefficient was found to be 0.75. It is of importance to note, once again, that regular stars are used throughout this computation even though both the solid boundary and the free boundary are curved.

Problems of seepage comprise a third group to which the methods of relaxation are applicable. As is well known, a consequence of the Darcy law is the

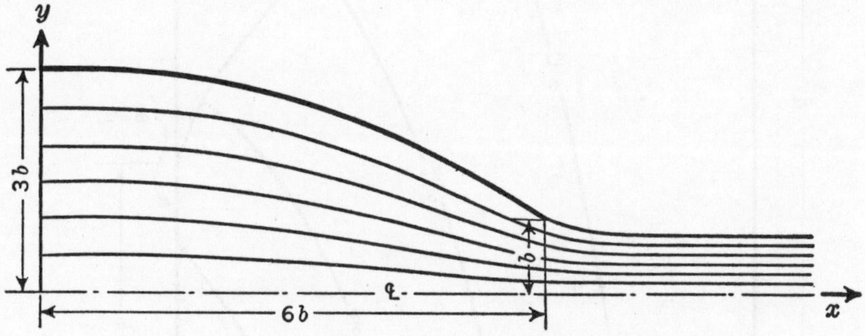

FIG. 16.—EFFLUX FROM A CURVED NOZZLE

applicability of potential theory to problems of laminar seepage. The pressure or the piezometric head acquires the role of the velocity potential, and the Laplace equation is hence applicable. Several examples of the application of the relaxation procedure to various types of seepage flows have been published; results of simply bounded structures have been presented for two-dimensional horizontal seepage through a monolith[11] and for various patterns of two-dimensional seepage into an excavation which is partly protected by impervious sheet piling.[12]

Applications to the more complex case of seepage with a free surface have been presented elsewhere[4,11], a refined version being presented in Fig. 17. These are cases for which, once again, the bounding streamline is initially unknown and can be determined only by trial and error. The two boundary conditions for the free surface are as follows: (a) The direction of the resultant velocity must coincide with that of the free streamline. (b) The free surface must be one of constant pressure. (That is, the piezometric head, which is ϕ, is equal to

[11] Discussion by John S. McNown of "The Significance of Pore Pressure in Hydraulic Structures," by L. F. Harza, *Transactions*, ASCE, Vol. 114, 1949, p. 245.

[12] "Seepage into Sheeted Excavation," by J. McNamee, *Geotechnique*, London, England, Vol. 4, December, 1949, pp. 227–241.

the elevation h.)   The second of these conditions was assumed for a trial curve, and a relaxation of the interior was completed.   Adjustment of the free surface was then made on the basis of the shortcomings with regard to the first condition.   Because the ϕ-function was used throughout, the boundary condition for the horizontal bottom line was that of orthogonality (or symmetry) and was fulfilled by the application of double residues as previously described.   The

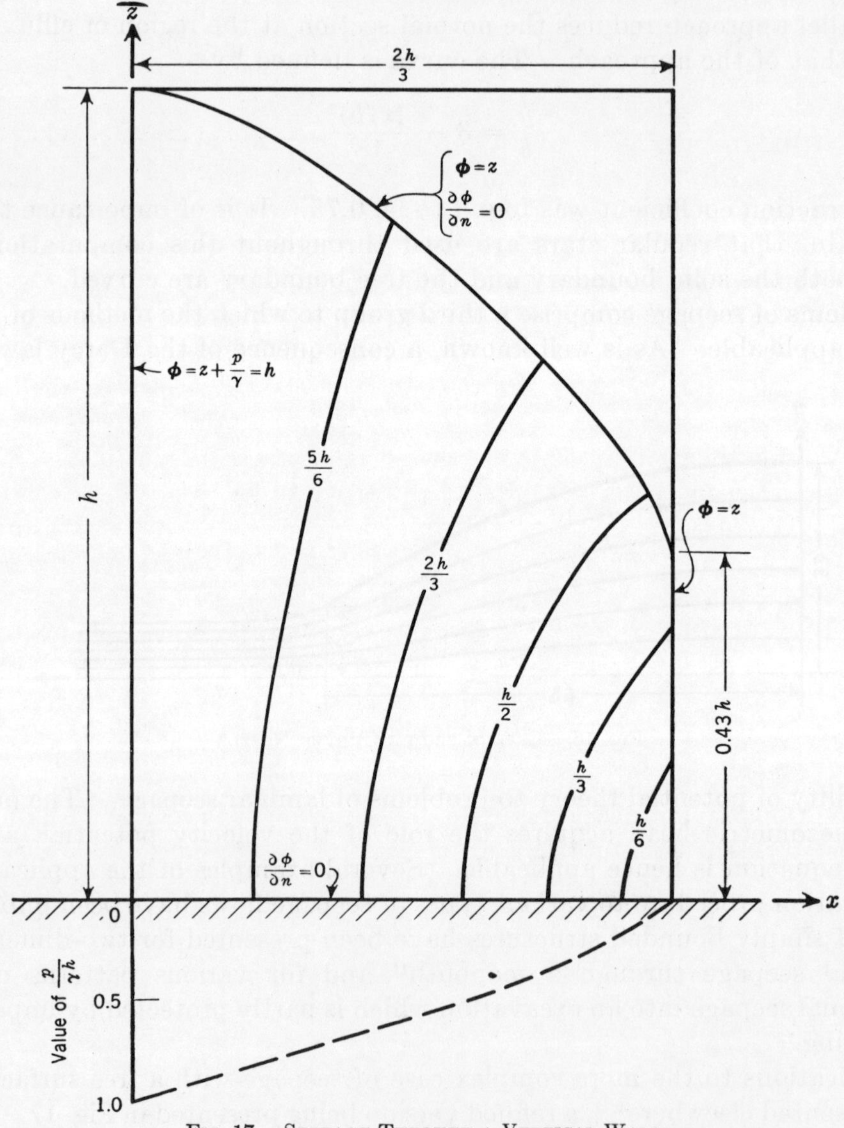

Fig. 17.—Seepage Through a Vertical Wall

value of ϕ is a constant on the upstream face but is equal to the elevation on the downstream face.

Although many problems of seepage in two dimensions can be obtained more satisfactorily by use of classical methods, only such a method as relaxation can be used for complex or curved boundaries.   In addition, axisymmetric flows—such as flow of ground water to a well—or the axisymmetric counterpart of the problem of seepage into an excavation[12] are beyond the scope of ordinary methods.

Conclusions

In the presentation both of the relaxation method and of examples in which it is utilized, the utility and flexibility of the process have been amply demonstrated. Fortunately, the technique can be quickly mastered, containing as it does only two basic parts. The mechanism of the internal reduction of residues is simple and extremely repetitive. The various boundary conditions are either assigned initially or met indirectly as a part of the process. An advantage of the method is that absolute accuracy is not a requirement; an occasional error once made will be caught and need not cause an excessive loss of time. Although the method is simple, it is not completely mechanical, so that the exercise of judgment and the introduction of suitable modifications of a given routine can greatly reduce the time required.

The method is restricted to the resolution of problems of essentially irrotational flows or flows for which the Reynolds number is quite small. It will not be and should not be considered as a replacement for the well-known analytical solutions characterizing classical hydrodynamics. Although still restricted to flows which are essentially two-dimensional or axially symmetric, its utility lies in the fact that within these limitations the relaxation process can be used regardless of the complexity of the boundary conditions. A small change in boundary form that might preclude the solving of an otherwise classical problem by standard methods presents no difficulty in its resolution by numerical methods. Because the engineering profession is constantly discovering many new applications for analyses of potential flows, the relaxation technique is recommended as a powerful adjunct to standard methods. The flow patterns presented herein are both useful in themselves and representative of the variety of problems which can be solved by relaxation.

Acknowledgments

Much of the work described herein was supported by the Office of Naval Research, Department of the Navy, under contract N8onr-500. Among those who assisted in the computations are S. Ince, J. M. ASCE (Fig. 11), W. Hsieh (Fig. 12), S. C. Liu (Fig. 13), Mr. Leclerc (Fig. 15), Turgut Sarpkaya, J. M. ASCE (Fig. 16), and Y. C. Soong, of the State University of Iowa. Mr. Rouse suggested or directed several of the studies.

DISCUSSION

Fred W. Blaisdell,[13] M. ASCE.—In describing the relaxation technique together with its advantages and its limitations, the authors have provided a distinct service to those who might consider the use of this "tool." The examples of the application of the relaxation technique are most interesting, and the comparisons with experimental data, where presented, show good agreement.

The writer has conducted a study of experimental data[14] on the form of the nappe emitting from a vertical, sharp-crested, suppressed weir. A general equation was obtained for that part of the nappe which was free-falling. This conforms to the region defined by the authors (under the heading, "Applications") where "Far to the right the streamlines approach a trajectory of free fall, and the internal pressure approaches zero."

TABLE 2.—Comparison of Nappe Surface Coordinates

| Value of $8\,x/H$ | Lower Nappe | | | | Upper Nappe | | | | Value of T/H |
| | y/H | | Eq. 25 | | y/H | | Eq. 25 | | |
	FWB[a]	MHY[b]	FWB[a]	MHY[b]	FWB[a]	MHY[b]	FWB[a]	MHY[b]	
4	+0.071	+0.065	...	...	+0.630	+0.678	...	...	...
5	+0.018	+0.010	−0.832	−0.832	+0.577	+0.609	−0.832	−0.576	...
6	−0.048	−0.058	−0.832	−0.576	+0.511	+0.531	−0.832	−0.704	...
7	−0.127	−0.135	−0.896	−0.640	+0.432	+0.442	−0.896	−0.832	0.577
8	−0.220	−0.222	−0.832	−0.896	+0.339	+0.340	−0.832	−0.512	0.562
9	−0.326	−0.323	−0.832	−0.512	+0.233	+0.230	−0.832	−0.384	0.553
10	−0.445	−0.432	−0.896	−1.280	+0.114	+0.114	−0.896	−0.576	0.546
11	−0.578	−0.561	−0.832	−0.960	−0.019	−0.011	−0.832	−0.832	0.550
12	−0.724	−0.705	−0.832	−1.088	−0.165	−0.149	−0.832	−1.152	0.556
13	−0.883	−0.866	−0.832	−1.024	−0.324	−0.305	−0.832	−1.920	0.561
14	−1.055	−1.043	−0.896	...	−0.496	−0.491	−0.896	−1.088	0.552
15	−1.241	...	−0.832	...	−0.682	−0.694	−0.832	−0.832	...
16	−1.440	...	...	...	−0.881	−0.910	...	...	...
Average			−0.849	−0.868			−0.849	−0.855	0.557 0.559[a]

[a] The writer, Fred W. Blaisdell.   [b] The authors, Messrs. McNown, Hsu, and Yih.

The data available to the writer indicate the free-fall region to include values of x/H in excess of 0.5. Therefore, the writer's results and Table 1 should yield comparable results when $x/H \geqq 0.5$; the comparison is made in Table 2. For the lower nappe there seems to be some trend to the differences between the writer's results and the authors' results. For the upper nappe, the differences are erratic and no trend can be detected.

A second comparison and test can also be applied. The general equation developed by the writer has the form:

$$\frac{y}{H} = C + \tan\theta\,\frac{x}{H} + \frac{S}{2}\left(\frac{x}{H}\right)^2 + \frac{T}{H} \quad\ldots\ldots\ldots\ldots\ldots (24)$$

[13] Project Supervisor, Agri. Research Service, U. S. Dept. of Agriculture, St. Anthony Falls Hydr. Lab., Minneapolis, Minn.

[14] "Equation of the Free-Falling Nappe," by Fred W. Blaisdell, *Proceedings-Separate No. 482*, ASCE, August, 1954.

The second differential of Eq. 24 is

$$\frac{d^2\left(\dfrac{y}{H}\right)}{d\left(\dfrac{x}{H}\right)^2} = S \dotfill (25)$$

Eq. 25 indicates that the second differences should be constant; these differences are given in Table 2. The lack of absolute constancy in the writer's second differences is caused by the fact that the nappe coordinates were recorded to only three significant figures. The writer's value for S is 0.850; there seems to be considerable variation in the second differences derived from the authors' data.

Still a third comparison and test can be applied to the data. The term T in Eq. 24 represents the vertical thickness of the nappe. This dimension is a constant because the horizontal velocity is constant where the nappe is free-falling. (For the lower nappe the term T is zero.) The nappe thickness in terms of H computed from the authors' data is given in Table 2. This nappe thickness can be compared with 0.559, the nappe thickness derived by the writer for the authors' boundary conditions.

The validity of comparing (y/H)-values is perhaps open to some question because either method of analysis could yield valid results from the basic data and assumptions, and one could not choose which method would give the most accurate values. However, the comparison within each group of data of nappe thickness and, more particularly, of the second differences should yield some information on the precision of the results. Based on the authors' presentation, it would seem that the relaxation technique should give identical nappe thicknesses for each value of x/H and identical second differences if the network were sufficiently subdivided. This does not seem to be completely substantiated by the writer's tests of the data.

HENRY M. PAYNTER,[15] J. M. ASCE, AND RONALD F. SCOTT.[16]—The definition of relaxation methods given by the authors does not appear to be complete. Rather than merely being techniques of numerical integration, relaxation methods are a mode of attack on any problem or set of relationships, be they graphic, algebraic, or numerical. Such methods constitute much the same approaches which have come to be termed "Hardy Cross" methods in the United States.[17] Essentially these methods involve the prior determination of the mutual influence patterns among the variables, followed by a systematic successive application of this pattern (stylus or matrix) to each and every equation of the system until the unbalances (residuals) are reduced to within the required tolerances.

---

[15] Asst. Prof. of Hydr. Eng., Massachusetts Inst. of Technology, Cambridge, Mass.

[16] Research Associate, Massachusetts Inst. of Technology, Cambridge, Mass.

[17] "The Relation of Analysis to Structural Design," by Hardy Cross, *Transactions*, ASCE, Vol. 101, 1936, p. 1363.

672 PAYNTER AND SCOTT ON RELAXATION TECHNIQUES

The general philosophy behind all such methods has been discussed fully.[18,19] Besides the treatise[4] cited by the authors, further details and special manipulations have been investigated by Mario G. Salvadori, M. ASCE, and Melvin L. Baron,[20] J. M. ASCE, J. B. Scarborough,[21] W. E. Milne,[22] and F. S. Shaw.[23]

The relaxation principle differs from simple iteration in that the personal judgment and insight of the individual can be exercised at each step of the process. Relaxation methods reduce to purely iterative procedures if this judgment factor is removed; this point is clearly brought out in the work of H. W. Emmons.[19]

It is also important to distinguish between steady-state solutions and transient solutions as they affect the applicability of different numerical approaches. The diffusion equation,

$$\frac{\partial \phi}{\partial t} = a \nabla^2 \phi \dots\dots\dots\dots\dots\dots (26)$$

reduces to the Laplace equation,

$$\nabla^2 \phi = 0 \dots\dots\dots\dots\dots\dots (27)$$

under steady conditions ($\partial \phi / \partial t = 0$). If, for example, it were desired to find the values of seepage flow through a dam during a drawdown of the reservoir or the values of the hydrostatic excess pore-water pressure during a soil-consolidation process, relaxation methods would not be appropriate. In these cases, iterative techniques, such as those used for thermal diffusion or soil-consolidation problems,[19,22,24,25] become useful.

In a similar manner, when the Poisson equation,

$$\nabla^2 \phi = f(x, y, z) \dots\dots\dots\dots\dots\dots (28)$$

is to be solved, there are certain cases in which, with the proper choice of grid and symmetry conditions, direct numerical solutions are often possible. The senior writer has studied such a case involving the cooling of a chemical reactor in which heat was generated uniformly and removed by a grillage of cooling tubes. In this case, a hexagonal grid was used, making maximum use of symmetry; the heat flow could be summed directly by computing outward from the tubes.

It is regretted that the authors did not "tie down" all the interesting features and consequences of the potential-flow solutions according to the manner in which the height of the seepage face is located—as 0.43 h, for example, in

<hr>

[18] "Numerical Methods of Analysis in Engineering," arranged by L. E. Grinter, Macmillan Co., New York, N. Y., 1949.

[19] "The Numerical Solution of Partial Differential Equations," by H. W. Emmons, *Quarterly of Applied Mathematics*, Vol. II, No. 3, October, 1944, p. 173.

[20] "Numerical Methods in Engineering," by Mario G. Salvadori and Melvin L. Baron, Prentice-Hall, New York, N. Y., 1952.

[21] "Numerical Mathematical Analysis," by J. B. Scarborough, 2d Ed., Johns Hopkins Press, Baltimore, Md., 1950.

[22] "Numerical Solution of Differential Equations," by W. E. Milne, John Wiley & Sons, Inc., New York, N. Y., 1953.

[23] "An Introduction to Relaxation Methods," by F. S. Shaw, Dover Publications, Inc., New York, N. Y., 1953.

[24] "Numerical Solution of Some Problems in the Consolidation of Clay," by R. E. Gibson and P. Lumb, *Proceedings*, Inst. of C. E., London, England, Pt. I, Vol. 2, No. 2, March, 1953.

[25] "Numerical Analysis of Consolidation Problems," by R. F. Scott, thesis presented to Massachusetts Inst. of Technology, Cambridge, Mass., in 1953, in partial fulfilment of the requirements for the degree of Master of Science.

Fig. 17.   However, even in this case the phreatic line (free-surface curve) can be located only very crudely by a graphical procedure.   Moreover, it would be most helpful to soils engineers and hydraulic engineers to have the effective conductance G of this wall expressed numerically—that is, a numerical value for the coefficient G in the expression,

$$Q = G\,k\,(L\,h)\,\frac{h}{b} = G\left(k\,\frac{L}{b}\right)h^2 \dots\dots\dots\dots\dots(29)$$

in which L is the length of the wall and k is the permeability.

Perhaps it is not realized at the time the solutions are performed that these results are the very answers engineers are seeking, and that such numbers can be obtained with precision only from the original computation sheets. For this reason many of those in the numerical-computation field prefer to publish the numerical values of the potential (or stream) function as deter-

TABLE 3.—WEIR DISCHARGE PROFILE

UPPER NAPPE				LOWER NAPPE			
Value of $8\,x/H$	Relaxation MHY[a]	Experiment USBR[b]	Difference	Value of $8\,x/H$	Relaxation MHY[a]	Experiment USBR[b]	Difference
−16	0.991	0.979	0.012	0	0	0	0
−12	0.983	0.972	0.011	$\frac{1}{2}$	0.068	0.066	0.002
− 8	0.965	0.958	0.007	1	0.091	0.096	0.005
− 4	0.932	0.921	0.011	2	0.113	0.112	0.001
0	0.855	0.845	0.010	3	0.101	0.102	0.001
4	0.678	0.670	0.008	4	0.065	0.070	0.005
8	0.340	0.344	0.004	5	0.010	0.021	0.011
16	−0.910	−0.905	0.005	6	−0.058	−0.046	0.012
				7	−0.135	−0.122	0.013
				8	−0.222	−0.214	0.008
				12	−0.705	−0.724	0.019

[a] The authors, Messrs. McNown, Hsu, and Yih.   [b] From reference 27.

mined at each point in the grid, together with the final unbalanced residual at each such point.

However, it should be noted that the authors and their co-workers have done a great service to the profession in publishing, for example, the table (Table 1) of coordinates of the upper and lower nappes corresponding to the relaxation solution for the free overflow from a high, sharp-crested, vertical weir.   In Table 3 the values from Table 1 are compared with values derived from experimental data obtained by the Bureau of Reclamation, United States Department of the Interior (USBR), and others.[26]   Over the range of values compared the fit is impressive; if the free surface of the relaxation solution was obtained (or at least refined) independently of this experimental information, the result constitutes a remarkable testimonial to the value of potential-flow methods in general, and relaxation procedures in particular, in obtaining basic design information for free-surface flow where viscous effects are not significant.

[26] "Studies of Crests for Overfall Dams," by J. N. Bradley, *Bulletin No. 3*, Pt. VI, Bureau of Reclamation, U. S. Dept. of the Interior, Washington, D. C., 1948.

The writers believe this point might be stressed to the advantage of analytical procedures.

The authors have restricted their attention to the use of uniform square grids or meshes. Whereas this may be justified because of space limitations, it may leave one with the incorrect impression that such a grid is to be preferred in most cases. Several other mesh systems are preferable for particular instances; a few, among others, are (*a*) nonuniform rectangular, (*b*) oblique, (*c*) triangular, and (*d*) hexagonal.

In connection with analog studies, R. H. MacNeal[27,28] has treated the problem in which completely nonuniform grids are used as shown in Fig. 18(*a*). It was proved by Mr. MacNeal that the best general values of distribution coefficients for such cases can be obtained by constructing what hydrologists would term a "Thiessen Polygon Network" of tributary influence areas around each node,[29] such as is shown in Fig. 18(*b*). From the sides of these polygons and from the distances between nodes, as indicated in Fig. 18(*c*), Mr. MacNeal

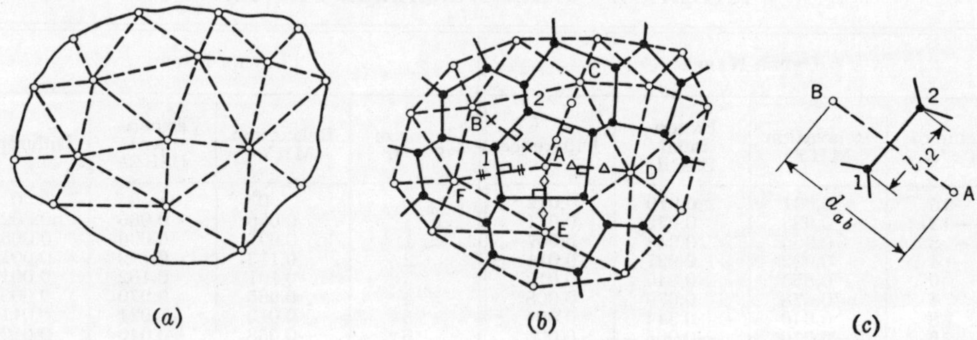

(a)   (b)   (c)

FIG. 18.—IRREGULAR MESHES

has shown that influence coefficients can be determined. These coefficients might be termed λ_{ab} which is equal to d_{ab}/l_{12}. Thus, the expression equivalent to Eq. 8 becomes

$$\frac{\phi_B}{\lambda_{ab}} + \frac{\phi_C}{\lambda_{ac}} + \frac{\phi_D}{\lambda_{ad}} + \frac{\phi_E}{\lambda_{ae}} + \frac{\phi_F}{\lambda_{af}} - \phi_A \left(\frac{1}{\lambda_{ab}} + \frac{1}{\lambda_{ac}} + \frac{1}{\lambda_{ad}} + \frac{1}{\lambda_{ae}} + \frac{1}{\lambda_{af}} \right) = 0 \ . \ . \ (30)$$

For the special case of square nets, the four λ-values are all unity, and Eq. 28 reduces to Eq. 8.

The foregoing techniques can be used to good advantage for all types of solutions, particularly where irregular boundaries or irregular symmetry conditions are involved. Mr. MacNeal has noted that all radial angles must be acute if negative resistance is to be avoided in passive electrical-resistor networks.

[27] "The Solution of Partial Differential Equations by Means of Electrical Networks," by R. H. Mac-Neal, thesis presented to California Inst. of Technology at Pasadena, Calif., in 1949, in partial fulfilment of the requirements for the degree of Doctor of Science.

[28] "An Asymmetrical Finite Difference Network," by R. H. MacNeal, *Quarterly of Applied Mathematics*, Vol. XI, No. 3, October, 1953.

[29] "Engineering Hydraulics," edited by Hunter Rouse, John Wiley & Sons, Inc., New York, N. Y., 1950, p. 276.

Iteration and relaxation methods demonstrate, as intermediate or end results, the solution at every point in the net and give a complete picture of heat or fluid flow or potential function distribution in the region considered. However, in many cases engineers are concerned only with the conditions at one or two points, and the distribution of the solution throughout the remainder of the area is not a matter of prime importance. In such cases, satisfactory solutions using these two methods consume considerable time in relation to the information desired, and some other approach would prove valuable.

Such an approach is offered by the Monte Carlo method,[22] or solution by random walks, in which a method of statistics is applied to the solution of partial differential equations.

Monte Carlo Method.—In order to illustrate the Monte Carlo method of estimating the stream function or potential function at a point in a fluid flowing irrotationally, a rectangular, two-dimensional bend is shown in Fig. 19(*a*). At a distance on each side of the corner equal to the width of the section, the flow was assumed to be uniform, and convenient values were assigned to the

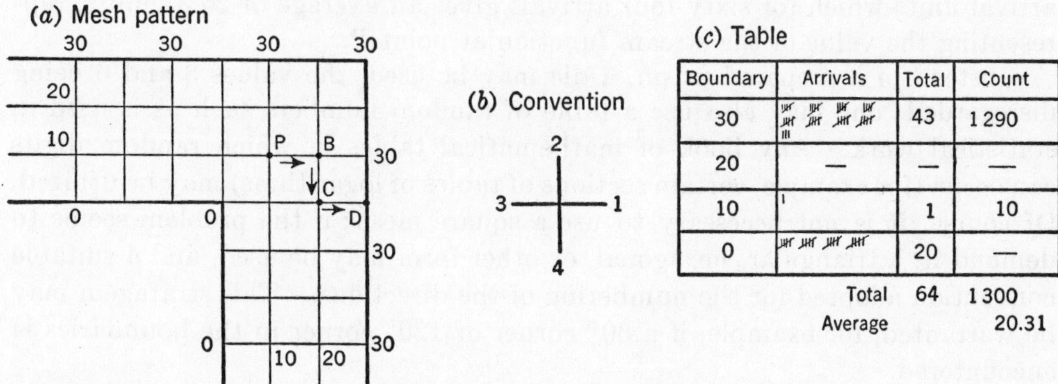

FIG. 19.—MONTE CARLO METHOD

streamlines. It will be seen from the solution of the problem that the actual position at which uniform flow is assumed has little effect on the result.

The section under investigation is covered with a square meshwork of some appropriate size. It will be obvious that the work required for a solution depends on the size of the mesh chosen; no method is known for determining the optimum size for a particular problem. The convention sketch in Fig. 19(*b*) is drawn beside the main diagram (Fig. 19(*a*)) to indicate the direction of travel assigned to each number from 1 to 4. The point P at which the stream function, in this case, is desired is then chosen (it may be noted that the position of this point may influence the original choice of the net) and can be considered the origin of all movement; a pencil point is placed there.

Briefly, the method proceeds as follows: A wooden prism of square cross section is obtained, and the four long sides are marked 1, 2, 3, and 4. The prism, as if it were a die, is then tossed onto a flat surface, and the number turning up is noted in order that the pencil may move from point P according to the convention in Fig. 19(*b*). Assuming that the number 1 turns up, the pencil is moved to point B. The prism is cast again, and 4 appears; the pencil is moved to point C. Another throw, and 1 appears once more; the pencil is now at point D, a point on the boundary, of value 30 units. Consequently, in the column marked 30 in the accompanying table, a check or tally is placed, and the pencil is returned to point P. The entire procedure is carried through again until a boundary is again reached, and the value is noted.

Eventually, for example, a total of from fifty to one hundred values are recorded. A count is made of the number of units from the column corresponding to each boundary point, and these counts are totaled. Division by the number of times the boundaries were encountered gives the desired value of the stream function at point P.

In the example demonstrated, it is seen that, out of a total of sixty-four boundary arrivals, forty three were on the outer boundary of value 30 units. Only one reached the 10-unit interpolated point; twenty reached the inner 0 boundary. In this case, the value of the stream function at point P would be

$$(43 \times 30) + (1 \times 10) + (20 \times 0) = 1,300$$

arrival units which for sixty-four arrivals gives an average of 20.31 units, representing the value of the stream function at point P.

Instead of a prepared prism, a die may be used, the values 5 and 6 being disregarded; one may also use a table of random numbers such as is used in statistical work. Any book of mathematical tables in which random digits can occur (for example, certain sections of tables of logarithms) may be utilized. Of course, it is not necessary to use a square mesh; if the problem seems to demand it, a triangular, hexagonal, or other form may be used, and a suitable convention adopted for the numbering of the directions. This stratagem may be warranted, for example, if a 60° corner or 120° corner in the boundaries is encountered.

If a three-dimensional problem is to be solved and a cubical mesh used, the new directions can be assigned the numbers 5 and 6; a tabular system of coordinates can be set up, with the values of the various boundaries being noted. It would then be necessary to check coordinates of each point arrived at to see if it coincided with a boundary.

From the example presented, it will be seen that the principal contributions to the final result are the values on the two boundaries immediately adjacent to the point and that the assumptions of parallel flow at a section some distance away from the bend play a very small part in the computations; this section could be pushed indefinitely outward without materially affecting the labor of solution.

Mr. Milne has stated[22] that the error (correct solution minus approximate solution) in a solution of this sort varies as $1/\sqrt{n}$ in which n is the number of arrivals at boundaries; this fact can be utilized in extrapolating to better solutions. To the writers' knowledge, not enough work has been done to correlate the optimum number of arrivals at boundary points with mesh dimensions in order to obtain reasonably accurate solutions. Further investigation of a mathematical nature, however, may give a correct indication.

MLADEN BORELI.[30]—As indicated by the variety of results obtained by the authors, the relaxation method is a powerful tool for solving engineering problems. Because the method is essentially one of successive approximations —so that the process involved is, of necessity, rather laborious—it is of great importance to explore all possibilities for reducing the necessary time to attain a certain specified accuracy. From the experience gained by use of the relaxation method to compute free-surface flow toward partly penetrating wells—a project which the writer undertook at the Polytechnic Institute of the University of Grenoble (France)—it is believed that the fineness of the mesh and hence the labor involved depend to a great extent on the treatment of the irregular stars and the singular points.

There are three ways in which irregular stars can occur: (a) They appear in the region where a finer mesh matches with a coarser one; (b) they appear at a fixed or free boundary; or (c) they are simply chosen under favorable conditions as a matter of preference. Wherever irregular stars are encountered, it is

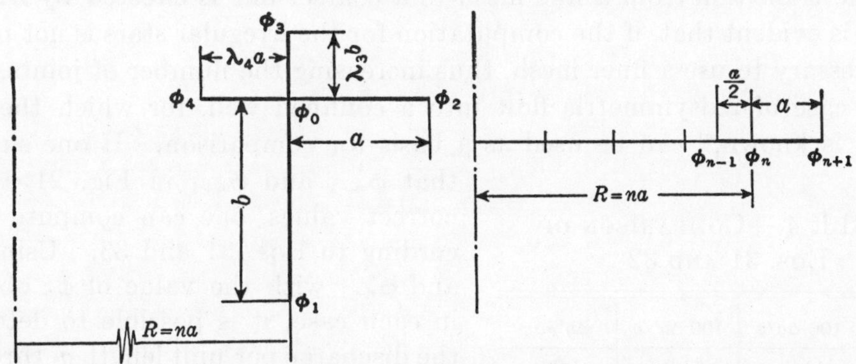

FIG. 20.—IRREGULAR STAR   FIG. 21.—AXISYMMETRIC FLOW

necessary to have a formula to determine residues. For an irregular star having legs of different lengths, as shown in Fig. 20, one can obtain from Eq. 10

$$a^2 \nabla^2 \phi = (\phi_2 - \phi_0) + \frac{\phi_4 - \phi_0}{\lambda_4} + \frac{\phi_2 - \phi_4}{n(1 + \lambda_4)}$$
$$+ \frac{a}{b}\left[(\phi_1 - \phi_0) + \frac{\phi_3 - \phi_0}{\lambda_3} \right] \ldots (31)$$

for the residue. On the other hand, using a Taylor expansion, there results

$$a^2 \nabla^2 \phi = \frac{1}{1 + \lambda_4}\left[(\phi_2 - \phi_0)\left(2 + \frac{\lambda_4}{n}\right) + \frac{\phi_4 - \phi_0}{\lambda_4}\left(2 - \frac{1}{n}\right) \right]$$
$$+ \frac{a^2}{b^2}\frac{2}{1 + \lambda_3} \cdot \left[(\phi_1 - \phi_0) + \frac{\phi_3 - \phi_0}{\lambda_3} \right] \ldots (32)$$

which, in spite of its apparently more complicated form, is no more difficult to apply than Eq. 31. A comparison of Eqs. 31 and 32, in connection with the ways in which irregular stars can occur, will show their relative merits.

[30] Assistant, Fluid Mech. Lab., Polytechnic Inst., Univ. of Grenoble, Grenoble, France; on leave from Hydrotechnic Inst., Serbian Academy of Sciences, Beograd, Yugoslavia.

Transition from a Coarser to a Finer Mesh.—For axisymmetric flow, the formula for the residue at the center of a regular star is

$$a^2 \, \nabla^2 \phi = \phi_1 + \phi_2 + \phi_3 + \phi_4 - 4\,\phi_0 + \frac{a}{2\,r}\,(\phi_2 - \phi_4) - 2 \sum_{n=2}^{\infty} \frac{a^{2n}}{2\,n!}$$

$$\times \left(\frac{\partial^{2n} \phi}{\partial r^{2n}} + \frac{\partial^{2n} \phi}{\partial z^{2n}} \right) - \frac{a}{r} \sum_{n=2}^{\infty} \frac{a^{2n-1}}{(2\,n-1)!} \frac{\partial^{2n-1} \phi}{\partial r^{2n-1}} \cdots (33)$$

The quantities on the right side of Eq. 33 which involve the derivatives of y can be denoted by ΔE. It is immediately clear that, if these derivatives are large and r is small, ΔE is not necessarily small. Thus, the greater the variation of the function ϕ and the smaller the values of r, the finer the mesh must be. This seems to have been universally recognized for the authors have shown that the fineness of the actual mesh used varies from region to region. Because the transition from a fine mesh to a coarser one is effected by irregular stars, it is evident that, if the computation for the irregular stars is not precise, it is necessary to use a finer mesh, thus increasing the number of joints.

The case of axisymmetric flow into a confined well, for which the exact solution is known,[31] can be used as a basis for comparison. If one supposes that ϕ_{n-1} and ϕ_{n+1} in Fig. 21 are the correct values, one can compute ϕ_n according to Eqs. 31 and 33. Using ϕ_{n-1} and ϕ_{n+1} with the value of ϕ_n obtained in each case, it is possible to determine the discharge per unit length q_1 through a cylindrical surface of radius $(n - \tfrac{1}{4})a$, and q_2 through a cylindrical surface of radius $(n + \tfrac{1}{2})a$. These discharges, in general, differ from the correct value q. The absolute values of the deviations of q_1 and q_2 as determined from Eq. 31 are denoted by Δq_1 and Δq_2, and their mean value is denoted by $\Delta q''$; the corresponding quantity computed from Eq. 32 is denoted by $\Delta q'$. Table 4 shows that for a specified accuracy the value of n corresponding to Eq. 31 is larger than that corresponding to Eq. 32, so that the latter equation is preferable to the former.

TABLE 4.—COMPARISON OF EQS. 31 AND 32

n	$100\,\Delta q/q$	$100\,\Delta q'/q$	$\Delta q'/\Delta q$
1	11.2	11.2	1.00
2	6.01	2.65	0.440
3	4.07	1.20	0.298
4	3.11	0.72	0.232
5	2.40	0.43	0.179
6	2.01	0.33	0.164

Boundary Conditions.—Irregular stars usually occur at the boundary, which may be fixed or free. For a free surface the boundary conditions can be checked only after all the residues have been eliminated. If the expressions for the residue are not correct, the free-surface position will not be correctly determined.

To make a further comparison of Eqs. 31 and 32, one may consider the region near the free surface in seepage flow. In addition to satisfying the Laplace equation, the potential function ϕ has to adhere to the conditions that

[31] "The Flow of Homogeneous Fluids Through Porous Media," by M. Muskat, 2d Ed., McGraw-Hill Book Co., Inc., New York, N. Y., 1946, p. 151.

at the free surface $\phi = z$ and $\partial\phi/\partial n = 0$, in which z is the elevation of the free surface and n is measured in a direction normal to the free surface. Because $\partial\phi/\partial n = 0$, it is possible to consider point A$'$ rather than point A (Fig. 22), thus eliminating one irregular leg and leaving only one leg of irregular length. Eq. 31 thus results in

$$a^2\,\nabla^2\phi = \phi_2 + \phi_4 - 2\,\phi_0 + \frac{\phi_2 - \phi_4}{2\,n} + \phi_1 - \phi_0 + \frac{\phi_3 - \phi_0}{\lambda_3}\dots\dots(34)$$

which becomes

$$a^2\,\nabla^2\phi = \phi_2 + \phi_4 - 2\,\phi_0 + \frac{\phi_2 - \phi_4}{2\,n} + \phi_1 - \phi_0 + a\sin^2\alpha\dots\dots(35)$$

because

$$\frac{\phi_3 - \phi_0}{\lambda_3} = a\sin^2\alpha\dots\dots\dots\dots\dots\dots(36)$$

Similarly, Eq. 32 results in

$$a^2\,\nabla^2\phi = \phi_2 + \phi_4 - 2\,\phi_0 + \frac{\phi_2 - \phi_4}{2\,n} + \frac{2}{1 + \lambda_3}\,(\phi_1 - \phi_0 + a\sin^2\alpha)\dots(37)$$

To make a cursory comparison of Eqs. 35 and 37, one can let $\lambda_3 \to 0$ and $\sin\alpha \to 0$. In the limit, Eqs. 35 and 37 should lead to the formula for the

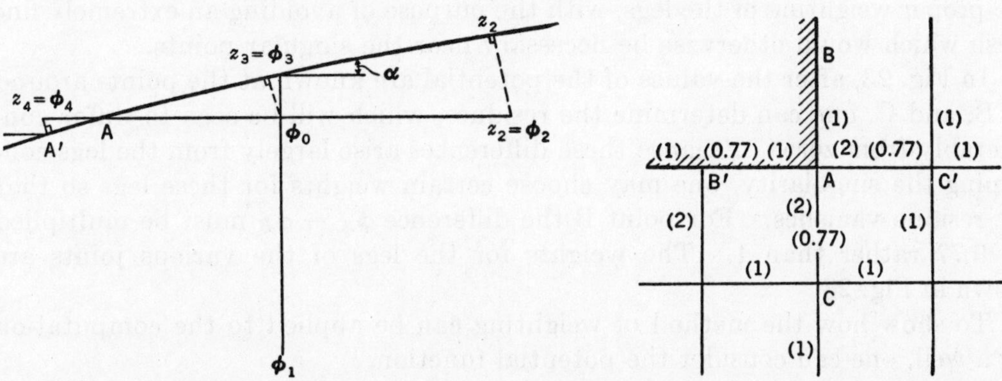

Fig. 22.—Eliminating an Irregular Leg   Fig. 23.—Weighting the Legs

residue at a joint located on a horizontal impermeable bed. This is the case with Eq. 37 but not with Eq. 35. The coefficient 2 appearing in the left side of Eq. 37 shows that the direction normal to the free surface is a privileged one— a property which is not displayed in Eq. 35. Because Eq. 35 is derived from Eq. 31 and Eq. 37 from Eq. 32, it is indicated that Eq. 32 is again preferable to Eq. 31.

The method of reflection used in Fig. 22 is not always convenient. One may use the ratio 2 to 1 for the lengths of the legs. If the joint is located on the surface, Eq. 32 leads to

$$a^2\,\nabla^2\phi = 2\left(\phi_1 + \phi_2 - 2\,\phi_0 + a\sin^2\alpha - a\sin\alpha\cos\alpha + \frac{a\sin\alpha\cos\alpha}{2\,n}\right)\dots(38)$$

whereas Eq. 31 results in

$$a^2 \nabla^2 \phi = \phi_1 + \phi_2 - 2\phi_0 + a \sin^2 \alpha - a \sin \alpha \cos \alpha + \frac{\phi_2 - \phi_0}{n} \dots (39)$$

Because the numerators of the fractions are approximately equal, the residue determined from Eq. 38 is twice that computed from Eq. 39.

Rectangular Meshes.—If the gradient of the unknown function can be judged a priori to be considerably larger in one direction than in the other, rectangular meshes can be used advantageously, with the long legs in the direction along which the gradient is small. Sometimes the number of joints involved can thus be reduced by from 30% to 40%. Evidently a more exact formula for the residue will be of considerable importance.

If, under favorable conditions, the mesh is made rectangular, with the longer legs twice as long as the shorter ones, Eq. 32 results in

$$a^2 \nabla^2 \phi = \phi_2 + \phi_4 - 2\phi_0 + \tfrac{1}{4}(\phi_1 + \phi_3 - 2\phi_0) + \frac{\phi_2 - \phi_4}{2n} \dots (40)$$

whereas the left side of the corresponding formula given by Eq. 32 is only half as great. Consequently, the difference is large.

On the basis of the foregoing comments on the formulas for the residue at the joint of an irregular star, it is of interest to note a method of treating the singular points in some detail. The method involved consists, essentially, in the proper weighting of the legs, with the purpose of avoiding an extremely fine mesh which would otherwise be necessary near the singular points.

In Fig. 23, after the values of the potential are known at the points around A, B, and C, one can determine the residues, which will be seen to differ considerably from zero. Because these differences arise largely from the legs containing the singularity, one may choose certain weights for these legs so that the residue vanishes. For point B the difference $\phi_A - \phi_B$ must be multiplied by 0.77 rather than 1. The weights for the legs of the various joints are shown in Fig. 23.

To show how the method of weighting can be applied to the computation for a well, one can consider the potential function,

$$\phi = L\,r^2 + M \log r + N \dots (41)$$

For this case

$$a^2 \nabla^2 \phi = 4\,L\,a^2 = (\phi_2 - \phi_0)\,\frac{a^2}{r^2}\,\frac{4}{k - m\,l} - (\phi_0 - \phi_4)\,\frac{a^2}{r^2}$$
$$\cdot \frac{4\,l}{k - m\,l} = (\phi_2 - \phi_0)\,A_l - (\phi_0 - \phi_4)\,B_l \dots (42)$$

in which

$$k = \left(\frac{r_2}{r_0}\right)^2 - 1 \dots (43a)$$

$$m = 1 - \left(\frac{r_4}{r_0}\right)^2 \dots (43b)$$

and

$$l = \frac{\log r_2 - \log r_0}{\log r_0 - \log r_4}. \dots\dots\dots\dots\dots\dots\dots (43c)$$

For the case shown in Fig. 21, one can obtain the following coefficients:

Value of n	Value of A_l	Value of B_l
1	1.7778	1.7778
2	1.5788	2.2255
3	1.5031	2.3716
4	1.4628	2.4443

It can be seen, therefore, that in each of the three cases in which irregular stars can occur Eq. 32 is preferable to Eq. 31. Moreover, by the use of proper weights considerable economy in labor can also be achieved in the vicinity of a singular point.

Turgut Sarpkaya,[32] J. M. ASCE.—The engineering profession is indebted to the authors for their informative presentation of the relaxation technique as it is applied to problems in fluid mechanics. The numerous examples of a practical nature are most valuable. It should be emphasized that both the direct and reverse relaxation methods, although by nature approximate and relatively time consuming, have distinct advantages over such approximate methods as the source-sink method[5] and the flow-net method.[33] Also of interest are (a) the applicability of the reverse method, (b) the application of the direct method to wave problems, (c) the accuracy of results, and (d) the treatment of sharp corners and singularities.

As was emphasized by the authors, the application of the direct relaxation method (using the $(x\,y)$-plane) to the problems in which some part of the boundary is exposed to constant pressure is not a rational approach because it is difficult to estimate to what extent the boundary should be changed between successive trials. However, the application of the reverse method, especially to free-jet problems, does provide a rational approach to the solution. The reverse method, as it is presented by the authors, has the advantage that the assumption of the variation of the potential with distance—that is, the assumption of an $x(\phi)$-curve—is made only once. The relaxation procedure for y is then completed, the results are checked against one of the Cauchy-Riemann equations, and a new $x(\phi)$-curve is obtained. This procedure eliminates the necessity of assuming another entirely arbitrary $x(\phi)$-relationship. It is recommended that the x-values for the final trial be computed with a relaxation similar to that for the y-values rather than determined directly from Cauchy-Riemann conditions.

The authors note that the relaxation method is applicable to certain types of wave motion. An example, the case of irrotational standing waves in a channel of constant depth and variable width, will be offered after the general

[32] Research Engr., Hydrodynamics Lab., Massachusetts Inst. of Technology, Cambridge, Mass.

[33] "Fluid Mechanics for Hydraulic Engineers," by Hunter Rouse, McGraw-Hill Book Co., Inc., New York, N. Y., 1938, p. 54.

procedure is explained. Many types of wave motion are essentially irrotational, and the motion can therefore be defined in terms of a velocity potential—

$$\phi = \psi(x, y) \cos \frac{2\pi t}{T} \cosh\left[k(h - z)\right] \dots\dots\dots\dots (44)$$

in which ϕ satisfies the Laplacian equation,

$$\nabla^2 \phi = 0 \dots\dots\dots\dots\dots\dots\dots\dots (45)$$

Also, if the amplitude of the motion is small, the condition for the free surface is

$$\frac{\partial^2 \phi}{\partial t^2} + g\,\frac{\partial \phi}{\partial z} = 0 \dots\dots\dots\dots\dots\dots (46)$$

in which z is taken as positive in the upward vertical direction. If the value of ϕ from Eq. 44 is substituted into Eq. 45, $\psi(x, y)$ is found to satisfy the criterion,

$$\psi_{xx} + \psi_{yy} + k^2\,\psi = 0 \dots\dots\dots\dots\dots (47)$$

Also, if Eq. 46 is to be satisfied,

$$\left(\frac{2\pi}{T}\right)^2 - k\,g\,\tanh k\,h = 0 \dots\dots\dots\dots (48)$$

These two relationships, Eqs. 47 and 48, are fundamental to this study as well as to studies of other physical problems. The goal of the analysis is the attainment of a solution that satisfies Eq. 47 and the boundary condition $\partial\phi/\partial n = 0$. Eq. 38 represents the relationship between the period of the wave, the depth of the water, and the parameter k. Eq. 47 can be written in the usual finite-difference form as

$$\sum_{i=1}^{4}\left(\frac{\psi_i}{x_i}\right) + \left[k^2 - \sum_{i=1}^{4}\left(\frac{1}{x_i}\right)\right]\psi_0 = R \dots\dots\dots\dots (49)$$

Hence, with k taken from Eq. 48 by trial, arbitrary ψ-values assigned, and $\sum_{i=1}^{4}\left(\frac{1}{x_i}\right)$-values computed, the relaxation process can be performed. After it is completed, the elevation η of the free surface is obtained from

$$\eta = \frac{2\pi}{g\,t}\cosh \psi_i\,(x, y) \dots\dots\dots\dots (50)$$

The troughs and crests of succeeding waves are obtained by connecting, respectively, locally maximum and minimum η-values.

An application of this result is shown in Fig. 24. A parabolic transition reduces the width of a rectangular, constant-depth channel to one fourth of its original width, as shown. The assumptions made were that the depth of the still water in the channel was 0.6 ft, k was equal to π ft^{-1}, and the period was 0.64 sec. In Fig. 24 there is shown the instantaneous pattern of the crests of standing waves in the channel. The amplitude of the wave, also indicated in Fig. 24, was found to be inversely proportional to the square root of the width, in accordance with Green's law.[34]   If constant depth can be assumed, the relaxation method can be applied in the analysis of seiche in irregularly shaped harbors, for which standard methods of analysis fail.

The authors caution that the accuracy of a given result can only be judged by computing the velocity or pressure distribution along a boundary or other arbitrarily selected lines.   However, the computation of velocities on a free

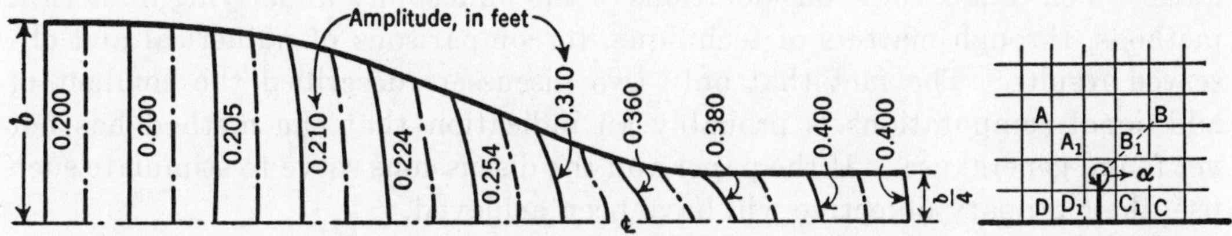

Fig. 24.—Trough and Crest Lines for Standing Waves   Fig. 25.—Sharp Corner

boundary even from a fine mesh—if the mesh size near the boundary is of the order of magnitude of the radius of curvature of the boundary—will not lead to an absolute check because of the variation of λ-values in the star.   If a star with a very small λ-value is to be considered, a formula for curvilinear extrapolation must be used.

The solution of certain practical problems may present difficult boundary conditions such as sharp corners which give rise to singularities of various types.   Special treatment is essential if the function approaches infinite values near the corner.   This difficulty can be overcome by the application of a somewhat more complicated method.

The solution of Eq. 45 can be expressed by the series,

$$\phi = \sum_{-\infty}^{+\infty} A_k\, r^n \cos n\theta \dots\dots\dots\dots\dots\dots\dots(51)$$

in which $n = \pi\, k/\alpha$, $(k = 0, \pm 1, \pm 2, \dots)$, and α is the angle of the sharp corner as is shown in Fig. 25.   For $\alpha = 2\pi$, ϕ takes the form:

$$\phi = A_0 + A_1\, r^{\frac{1}{2}} \cos \frac{\theta}{2} + A_2\, r \cos \theta + A_3\, r^{\frac{3}{2}} \cos \frac{3}{2}\theta + \dots \quad \dots\dots(52)$$

In Eq. 52 only the first four terms need be retained.   The units of r can be so chosen that $r = 1$ at points A, B, C, and D.   In terms of ϕ_A, ϕ_B, ϕ_C, and ϕ_D, which are known, one obtains the coefficients A_0, A_1, A_2, and A_3.   Using these coefficients ϕ_{A1}, ϕ_{B1}, ϕ_{C1}, and ϕ_{D1} can be expressed in terms of ϕ_A, ϕ_B, ϕ_C, and ϕ_D as follows:

$$\left.\begin{aligned}
\phi_{A1} &= 0.4572\, \phi_A + 0.2351\, \phi_B + 0.2093\, \phi_C + 0.0992\, \phi_D \\
\phi_{B1} &= 0.2351\, \phi_A + 0.5930\, \phi_B + 0.0992\, \phi_C + 0.0728\, \phi_D \\
\phi_{C1} &= 0.2093\, \phi_A + 0.0992\, \phi_B + 0.4572\, \phi_C + 0.2351\, \phi_D \\
\phi_{D1} &= 0.0992\, \phi_A + 0.0728\, \phi_B + 0.2351\, \phi_C + 0.5930\, \phi_D
\end{aligned}\right\} \dots\dots\dots(53)$$

---

[34] "Engineering Hydraulics," edited by Hunter Rouse, John Wiley & Sons, Inc., New York, N. Y., 1950, Chapter X, p. 738.

684   MCNOWN-HSU-YIH ON RELAXATION TECHNIQUES

The mathematical analysis for this method is available.[19,35]   Eqs. 53 are used at singular points; the relaxation procedure is performed in the usual manner, observing that Eqs. 53 hold at singular points.

JOHN S. McNOWN,[36] M. ASCE, EN-YUN HSU,[37] A. M. ASCE, AND CHIA-SHUN YIH.[38]—In the several discussions submitted, contributions have been made which range from considerations of the philosophy underlying numerical methods, through matters of technique, to comparisons of numerical and observed results.   The fact that only two discussers described the conduct of additional computations is probably an indication that the method has not yet found general use.   If the paper and the discussions serve to stimulate such use, their primary objective will have been achieved.

Mr. Blaisdell considered primarily the accuracy, or rather the consistency, of the numerical results for flow over a weir.   The results obtained from Eq. 24 and the relaxation method are remarkably close together.   Although Mr. Blaisdell characterized a part of the correspondence as erratic, Messrs. Paynter and Scott apparently found the general agreement between the results observed by the USBR[26] and those of the relaxation almost perfect.   Actually, these data[26] came to the writers' attention after the manuscript had been completed. Had they been used, reference would, of course, have been made to them.   In communications to the writers, Frank B. Campbell, M. ASCE, informed the writers of the existence of these data, and J. N. Bradley, A. M. ASCE, submitted a comparison similar to that of Messrs. Paynter and Scott.

A comparison between second differences can be misleading, particularly if one set is computed from a quadratic equation for which the second differences are inherently constant.   Because their order of magnitude in this computation is approximately $H/100$, presentation of the second differences as three-digit and four-digit numbers by Mr. Blaisdell is misleading.   Even for Eq. 24, the rounding-off process results in a sizable change.

The trend of the values for the thickness of the jet is more significant. However, the value of 4 for $8\,x/H$ is not large enough for the internal pressure to be ignored, as is clearly indicated in Fig. 13.   For $8\,x/H \approx 8$, the internal pressure head is still more than $H/10$.   Thus, the conditions of free fall assumed by Mr. Blaisdell are only approximately valid.   The fact that the observed thickness differs from the mean of the computed thicknesses by less than 1% seems quite remarkable.

Messrs. Paynter and Scott have objected to the absence of both a broader statement of the underlying philosophy of numerical methods and fuller numerical detail.   In their comment, "Rather than merely being techniques of numerical integration * * *," the word "merely" is the discussers' and not the

[35] "Relaxation Methods Applied to Engineering Problems," by D. W. de G. Allen, D. G. Christopherson, L. Fox, J. R. Green, H. Motz, F. S. Shaw, and R. V. Southwell, *Philosophical Transactions*, Royal Soc. of London (A), 1945, pp. 239, 367–385, 519–537.

[36] Associate Director, Iowa Inst. of Hydr. Research, State Univ. of Iowa, Iowa City, Iowa.

[37] Research Engr., Hydrodynamics Lab., California Inst. of Technology, Pasadena, Calif.

[38] Research Engr., Iowa Inst. of Hydr. Research, State Univ. of Iowa, Iowa City, Iowa.

writers'; their more general interpretation of the method is in accord with the writers' views.

Numerical details were included in the original paper more as illustrations of what can be done than as exhaustive solutions to practical problems. In this connection the computations for weir flow (Fig. 13) and for seepage (Fig. 17) are hardly comparable in significance. The former is a classic problem of considerable practical importance; the latter is an isolated example which is only illustrative of an infinite variety of boundary configurations. Furthermore, difficulties inherent in the presentation of the numerical results will be obvious to the reader. In the cavity flow (Fig. 14), for example, more than 1,300 values of the stream function were determined. To have elaborated in either of the somewhat opposing directions proposed by Messrs. Paynter and Scott would have unduly extended the paper.

Messrs. Boreli and Paynter and Scott described methods and conditions for which a mesh other than square is used. Some of these were also discussed in Mr. Southwell's work.[4] Aside from the square mesh, however, only the rectangular mesh which Mr. Boreli used to advantage in computing seepage toward wells is likely to be applicable to problems of fluid flow. The distantly related Monte Carlo method is interesting and perhaps useful for isolated applications.

Mr. Boreli's contention that Eq. 32 obtained by a Taylor expansion for the residue is often preferable to Eq. 31 is readily conceded. In fact, in using the relaxation technique to determine the cavity shape (Fig. 14), the formula from a Taylor expansion was used. It must be noted, however, that, if the second and higher derivatives of the unknown function are large and if the net is comparatively coarse, the superiority of Eq. 32 to Eq. 31 cannot be established, because Eq. 32 is then only a rough approximation. All one can say is that, as the net becomes finer, the accuracy of Eq. 32 is increased more rapidly than that of Eq. 31.

Mr. Boreli proposed a treatment of singular points by properly weighting the neighboring legs. Unfortunately, it was not mentioned how the weighting is to be determined. The treatment presented by Mr. Sarpkaya for the same purpose is simple and systematic and is a welcome contribution to this troublesome aspect of the relaxation technique.

Although it was stated (under the heading, "Introduction") that application of the relaxation method is feasible only for two-dimensional flows or axisymmetric flows, some studies[39,40] have included analyses of problems for which variations in all three dimensions are significant. S. K. Roy obtained[39] a rough approximation for flow through a transition from a reservoir to a rectangular conduit, and D. N. de G. Allen and S. C. R. Dennis demonstrated[40] a useful technique which is particularly well suited to problems for which the

---

[39] "Development of Three Dimensional Relaxation Processes for a Systematic Approach to Flow Analysis in Hydraulic Structures," by S. K. Roy, (in three parts), *Irrigation and Power*, Govt. of India Press, Simla, Vol. 9, No. 1, January, 1952.

[40] "The Application of Relaxation Methods to the Solution of Differential Equations in Three Dimensions," by D. N. de G. Allen and S. C. R. Dennis, I. Boundary Value Problems, *Quarterly Journal of Mechanics and Applied Mathematics*, Vol. IV, Pt. 2, June, 1951, pp. 199–208.

686 MCNOWN-HSU-YIH ON RELAXATION TECHNIQUES

third dimension is small compared to the others. A solution of acceptable accuracy for a three-dimensional flow with a free surface, as an extreme example, remains an exorbitant undertaking.

The discussers indicated that they share the writers' convictions as to the applicability and versatility of the relaxation technique. Mr. Sarpkaya's application of the method to problems of wave motion is additional evidence of its adaptability to a wide variety of potential flows. By their contributions, the discussers have expanded and reinforced various phases of the study.

Reprinted from
QUARTERLY OF APPLIED MATHEMATICS
Vol. XIII, No. 2, July, 1955

MAXIMUM ACCELERATION IN TWO-DIMENSIONAL STEADY FLOWS OF AN IDEAL FLUID*

BY CHIA-SHUN YIH (*Iowa Institute of Hydraulic Research*)

It is well known** that, in a domain free from singularities, the maximum speed in irrotational flows of an incompressible fluid occurs on the boundary of that domain. In this note, it will be proved that for two-dimensional irrotational flows of an incompressible fluid, the maximum magnitude of the acceleration in any singularity-free domain D must also occur on its boundary provided the flows are steady.

The acceleration components in the x- and y-directions are, respectively,

$$b = uu_x + vu_y , \tag{1}$$

$$c = uv_x + vv_y , \tag{2}$$

in which u and v are the x- and y-components of the velocity, and the subscripts denote partial differentiation. The equation of continuity is

$$u_x + v_y = 0 \tag{3}$$

and the equation expressing irrotationality is

$$u_y - v_x = 0. \tag{4}$$

From Eqs. (1) to (4) it immediately follows that the square of the magnitude of the acceleration is given by

$$a^2 = b^2 + c^2 = q^2(u_x^2 + u_y^2), \tag{5}$$

in which $q^2 = u^2 + v^2$.

If ϕ and ψ are respectively the velocity potential and the stream function of the given flow, the complex potential for that flow is

$$w(z) = \phi(x, y) + i\psi(x, y),$$

in which $w(z)$ is an analytic function free from singularities in the domain D. The well-known relation concerning the magnitude of the velocity is

$$q^2 = w'(w')^*, \tag{6}$$

in which the asterisk denotes the complex conjugate, and the primes denote ordinary differentiation. Since $w(z)$ is analytic in D, its derivative

$$w'(z) = -u + iv$$

is also analytic in D and represents a potential flow with velocity components u_x and u_y , concerning which the result analogous to (6) is

$$u_x^2 + u_y^2 = w''(w'')^*. \tag{7}$$

From (5) to (7), it follows that

$$a^2 = w'w''(w'w'')^* = (w'^2/2)'[(w'^2/2)']^* = q_1^2 \tag{8}$$

———
*Received Nov. 1, 1954. This work is supported by the Office of Naval Research under Contract No. N8onr–500.

**H. Lamb, *Hydrodynamics*, Dover, New York, 1945, p. 39 and p. 47.

in which q_1 is the velocity magnitude in the irrotational flow corresponding to the new complex potential $w'^2/2$. But it has been proved that the maximum value of q_1^2 in D occurs on its boundary, hence the same is true for a^2.

Since $w'w''$ is analytic in D, the result for the acceleration could have been reached through

$$a^2 = w'w''(w'w'')^*$$

in (8) by means of the well-known maximum-modulus theorem for analytic functions, without resorting to q_1 . However, since the corresponding result for the speed is often reached without the use of the maximum-modulus theorem, the present proof may seem preferable to some.

As a by-product of the proof, a means of evaluating the magnitude of the acceleration at any point in the field of flow is provided by (8), once $w(z)$ is known. Furthermore, since the acceleration is proportional to the gradient of the dynamic pressure, it follows from the present result that the maximum dynamic-pressure gradient in D must occur on its boundary.

The boundary of D is, of course, not necessarily a solid boundary. However, for ambiently uniform flows past arbitrarily shaped bodies, the maximum acceleration (or the maximum dynamic-pressure gradient) must occur on one of the solid boundaries. This can be seen by taking D as the entire domain outside the solid bodies. Its boundary then consists of the solid boundaries and a boundary at infinity. Since the acceleration at infinity is zero, the maximum acceleration must occur on one of the solid boundaries.

Reprinted from
QUARTERLY OF APPLIED MATHEMATICS
Vol. XIII, No. 4, January, 1956

SOLUTIONS OF THE HYPER-BESSEL EQUATION*

BY CHIA-SHUN YIH, (*State University of Iowa*)

In problems of hydrodynamic stability involving axial symmetry, it is sometimes necessary to find the solutions of a differential equation of the type

$$L_1^n f = 0$$

in which n is a positive integer, and (with $D \equiv d/dr$)

$$L_1 \equiv D^2 + r^{-1}D - r^{-2} - \lambda^2$$

is the Bessel operator of the first order. In this note, solutions of the equation

$$L_p^n f = 0 \tag{1}$$

in which

$$L_p \equiv D^2 + r^{-1}D - p^2 r^{-2} + k^2$$

will be given explicitly. The theorem one seeks to establish is the following: If p (taken to be positive for convenience) is not an integer, the solutions of Eq. (1) are $r^m J_{\pm(p+m)}(kr)$ in which $m = 0, 1, 2, \cdots, n-1$; otherwise they are $r^m J_{p+m}(kr)$ and $r^m N_{p+m}(kr)$, with m ranging over the same integers. The symbols J and N stand for the Bessel function and the Neumann function, respectively.

Proof: It is known that the solutions of $L_p f = 0$ are $J_{\pm p}(kr)$ for p not equal to an integer and $J_p(kr)$ and $N_p(kr)$ for p equal to an integer. Thus it suffices to show that if $r^s Z_{p+s}(kr)$ (in which Z stands for either J or N) satisfies $L_p^{s+1} f = 0$, then $r^{s+1} Z_{p+s+1}(kr)$ satisfies $L_p^{s+2} f = 0$, since the proof for $r^m J_{-(p+m)}(kr)$ is identical with that for $r^m Z_{p+m}(kr)$. This will be accomplished if one can show that $L_p r^{s+1} Z_{p+s+1}(kr)$ is equal to a constant times $r^s Z_{p+s}(kr)$. By straightforward differentiation one has

$$L_p r^{s+1} Z_{p+s+1}(kr) = r^{s+1} L_p Z_{p+s+1}(kr) + s(s+1) r^{s-1} Z_{p+s+1}(kr)$$

$$+ 2(s+1) r^s D Z_{p+s+1}(kr) + (s+1) r^{s-1} Z_{p+s+1}(kr)$$

$$= r^{s+1} L_p Z_{p+s+1}(kr) + (s+1)^2 r^{s-1} Z_{p+s+1}(kr)$$

$$+ 2(s+1) r^s D Z_{p+s+1}(kr).$$

But

$$L_p = L_{p+s+1} + \frac{2p(s+1) + (s+1)^2}{r^2}$$

and [1]

$$D Z_{p+s+1}(kr) = k\left[-\frac{p+s+1}{kr} Z_{p+s+1}(kr) + Z_{p+s}(kr) \right].$$

---

*Received May 14, 1955.

So

$$L_p r^{s+1} Z_{p+s+1}(kr) = r^{s+1} L_{p+s+1} Z_{p+s+1}(kr) + [2p(s+1) + (s+1)^2] r^{s-1} Z_{p+s+1}(kr)$$

$$+ (s+1)^2 r^{s-1} Z_{p+s+1}(kr) + 2(s+1) r^s k \left[-\frac{p+s+1}{kr} Z_{p+s+1}(kr) + Z_{p+s}(kr) \right]$$

$$= 2(s+1) kr^s Z_{p+s}(kr)$$

since

$$L_{p+s+1} Z_{p+s+1}(kr) = 0$$

by definition of Z.

Dr. Y. C. Fung of the California Institute of Technology communicated to the writer a different proof of the present result by means of Almansi's theorem [2] on hyperharmonic functions. His proof will not be presented here.

It may be noted that since [1]

$$Z_{p-1}(kr) + Z_{p+1}(kr) = \frac{2p}{kr} Z_p(kr) \tag{2}$$

and since by the theorem just proved $rZ_{p+1}(kr)$ and $Z_p(kr)$ are solutions of

$$L_p^2 f = 0, \tag{3}$$

it follows from Eq. (2) that $rZ_{p-1}(kr)$ is also a solution of Eq. (3). In fact, by repeated use of Eq. (2) and a similar one obtained by changing p to $-p$ in Eq. (2), it can be proved that if the m in the subscripts of the solutions given in the theorem is changed to $-m$, the results will still be solutions of Eq. (1). These solutions are of course not independent of the ones given in the statement of the theorem.

REFERENCES

[1] E. Jahnke and F. Emde, *Table of functions*, Dover Publications, New York, 1945, pp. 144-145
[2] E. Almansi, *Sull' integrazione dell' equazione differenziale* $\Delta^{2n} u = 0$, Annali di Matimatica, (III) **2** (1899)

Reprinted from
JOURNAL OF FLUID MECHANICS, Vol. 1, Part 3, p. 319, September 1956

Forces, moments, and added masses for Rankine bodies

By L. LANDWEBER and C. S. YIH
Iowa Institute of Hydraulic Research, State University of Iowa

(*Received* 25 *February* 1956)

SUMMARY

The dynamical theory of the motion of a body through an inviscid and incompressible fluid has yielded three relations: a first, due to Kirchhoff, which expresses the force and moment acting on the body in terms of added masses; a second, initiated by Taylor, which expresses added masses in terms of singularities within the body; and a third, initiated by Lagally, which expresses the forces and moments in terms of these singularities. The present investigation is concerned with generalizations of the Taylor and Lagally theorems to include unsteady flow and arbitrary translational and rotational motion of the body, to present new and simple derivations of these theorems, and to compare the Kirchhoff and Lagally methods for obtaining forces and moments. In contrast with previous generalizations, the Taylor theorem is derived when other boundaries are present; for the added-mass coefficients due to rotation alone, for which no relations were known, it is shown that these relations do not exist in general, although approximate ones are found for elongated bodies. The derivation of the Lagally theorem leads to new terms, compact expressions for the force and moment, and the complete expression of the forces and moments in terms of singularities for elongated bodies.

1. INTRODUCTION

In the decade from 1920 to 1930 there were published by Lagally, Munk, and Taylor a number of hydrodynamic theorems concerning the added masses of bodies moving through an inviscid fluid and the forces and moments acting upon them. These theorems enable the forces, moments, and added masses to be determined when the singularity distributions of sources, sinks, and doublets within the body, which may be considered to generate the potential flow about it, are known. Since, for the important class of elongated bodies, simple approximations to the singularity distributions are given directly in terms of the body shape, these theorems have furnished a powerful means of investigating the forces and moments acting on such bodies, especially near a free surface. Until recently, the scope of the aforementioned theorems has been limited: that of Taylor (1928) to only one kind of added-mass coefficient, and that of Lagally (1922) to steady flow only. Birkhoff (1953, p. 161) and Landweber (1956) have succeeded in generalizing

 L. Landweber and C. S. Yih

Taylor's theorem to apply to all the added-mass coefficients except those for pure rotation, and Cummins (1953) in generalizing Lagally's theorem to apply to cases of unsteady flows.

The Taylor theorem and its generalizations have heretofore been concerned with the added-mass coefficients corresponding to the motion of a single body in an otherwise undisturbed and unbounded fluid. The extension of the theorem to the important cases where external singularities and other boundaries are present is highly desirable.

Cummins was able to express the force and moment on a body in terms of the strengths of the singularities, except for one term in the expression for the moment—an integral over the surface of the body with integrand linear in the potential. As will be seen, this single unresolved term is intimately related to the missing relations in the generalization of Taylor's theorem. The discovery of the latter would complete the generalizations of both the Taylor and Lagally theorems.

The present work, then, has several purposes.

(1) The first is to extend the Taylor theorem to include cases with external singularities and boundaries and new results concerning the missing relations between added masses and singularities. The latter will be derived for ellipsoids and for elongated bodies, but it will be proved that such relations do not exist in general. Also the opportunity will be taken to present, new, short, and simple proofs of the theorem for both two and three dimensional flows.

(2) The second is to consolidate and extend Cummins' results and to present a simpler derivation of them. An important secondary motive for this part of the work is to popularize this powerful theorem, which in its present form has been applied only by Cummins himself.

(3) The third is to examine the interconnections, if any, between the Taylor theorem (relating added masses to singularities), the Lagally theorem (relating singularities to forces), and Kirchhoff's equations of motion (relating forces to added masses).

2. Formulation of the problem

We are concerned with the interactions of a fluid with a rigid body moving through it. The fluid is assumed to be incompressible and inviscid, the flow to be irrotational and, in general, unsteady. We shall suppose that the unsteadiness may be due to the time dependence of the linear or angular velocities of the body or to the presence of external boundaries or flow-producing mechanisms which may themselves be moving in an arbitrary manner.

The flow may be considered to be generated by singularities, and the singularities considered will be isolated sources or sinks, doublets, and continuously distributed sources or sinks. Continuous distributions of doublets are excluded from consideration because they can be replaced by corresponding ones of sources and sinks. The symbol m will denote the

Forces, moments, and added masses for Rankine bodies 321

strength of a source or sink, $\bar{\mu}$ (a vector) will describe both the strength and the orientation of a doublet, and σ will denote the volume or area density of continuously distributed sources or sinks.

Cartesian coordinates (fixed in the body) x_i $(i = 1, 2, 3)$ will be used, so that the position vector $\bar{r}$ is (x_1, x_2, x_3) with magnitude r. The components of the velocity vector $\bar{u}$ of the origin of coordinates will be denoted by (u_1, u_2, u_3) and the components of the angular velocity $\bar{\omega}$ will be designated alternatively by $(\omega_1, \omega_2, \omega_3)$ or by (u_4, u_5, u_6). The surface of the body will be denoted by S, and those surrounding the singularities inside S by S' collectively. The distance n normal to either S or S' is always directed out of that portion of the fluid with which one is concerned. The direction of n will be indicated by the unit vector $\bar{n}$ with components n_i $(i = 1, 2, 3)$, which are given by $n_i = \partial x_i / \partial n$.

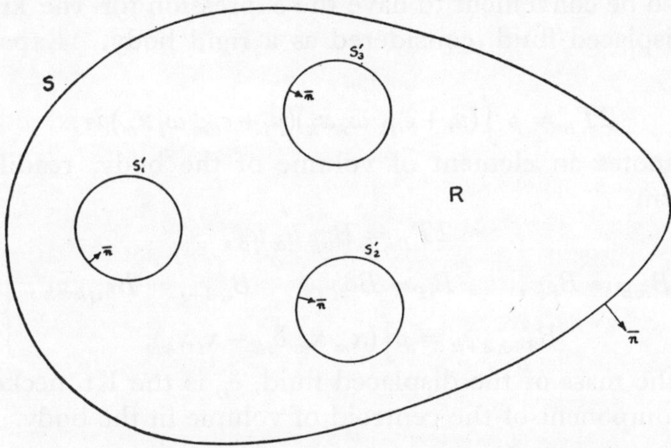

The kinematic boundary condition at a point on S is given by

$$- \frac{\partial \phi}{\partial n} = (\bar{u} + \bar{\omega} \times \bar{r}) \cdot \bar{n} = u_\alpha n_\alpha, \tag{1}$$

in which ϕ is the velocity potential satisfying the Laplace equation, and the components of $\bar{r} \times \bar{n}$ are denoted by (n_4, n_5, n_6). Here the summation convention has been adapted and the Greek subscripts range from 1 to 6. For convenience of presentation, Greek subscripts will range from 1 to 6, whereas Latin ones will range over 1, 2, and 3 only, unless otherwise stated or when summation signs are expressly used.

The velocity potential ϕ may be considered to be composed of a part due to the motion of the body alone, when all other boundaries and external flow producing mechanisms are at rest, expressible in the form $u_\alpha \phi_\alpha$ after Kirchhoff, and a part ϕ_0 due to the motions of the latter when the body is at rest, i. e.

$$\phi = u_\alpha \phi_\alpha + \phi_0. \tag{2}$$

Then, on S, from (1) and (2),

$$\frac{\partial \phi_0}{\partial n} = 0, \qquad - \frac{\partial \phi_0}{\partial n} = n_\alpha. \tag{3}$$

322   *L. Landweber and C. S. Yih*

The boundary condition (1) may also be expressed in the alternative form

$$v_i\, n_i = (u_i + \epsilon_{ijk}\, \omega_j\, x_k)n_i\,,$$

where $v_i = -\partial\phi/\partial x_i$ is the i-component of the velocity at a point of the fluid, and ϵ_{ijk} is zero if any two of the indices i, j, k are alike, and $+1$ or -1 according as the indices are in cyclic or anticyclic order. Hence, the boundary condition becomes

$$V_i\, n_i = 0, \qquad V_i = -v_i + u_i + \epsilon_{ijk}\, \omega_j\, x_k\,. \tag{4}$$

Since the coordinate axes are in motion, the Bernoulli equation for the pressure is, from Lamb (1932, p. 20),

$$\frac{p}{\rho} = \frac{\partial\phi}{\partial t} - W, \qquad W = \tfrac{1}{2}(u_j\, u_j + v_j\, v_j) - v_i(u_j + \epsilon_{jkl}\, \omega_k\, x_l), \tag{5}$$

where ρ is the density of the fluid.

It will also be convenient to have the expression for the kinetic energy T_B of the displaced fluid, considered as a rigid body. Expansion of the integrand in

$$2T_B = \rho \int (u_i + \epsilon_{ijk}\, \omega_j\, x_k)(u_i + \epsilon_{ilm}\, \omega_l\, x_m)d\tau,$$

where $d\tau$ denotes an element of volume of the body, readily yields the quadratic form

$$2T_B = B_{\alpha\beta}\, u_\alpha\, u_\beta\,, \tag{6}$$

$$\left. \begin{aligned} B_{\alpha\beta} = B_{\beta\alpha}\,, \qquad B_{ij} = B\delta_{ij}\,, \qquad B_{i,\,3+j} = B\epsilon_{ijk}\overline{x}_k\,, \\ B_{3+j,\,3+k} = \rho\!\int (x_m\, x_m\, \delta_{jk} - x_j\, x_k), \end{aligned} \right\} \tag{7}$$

where B is the mass of the displaced fluid, δ_{ij} is the Kronecker delta, and $\overline{x}_k$ is the k-component of the centroid of volume in the body.

3. Mathematical preliminaries

In this section will be collected various mathematical theorems and results which will be required in the subsequent sections.

3.1. *Potential functions*

Let ϕ be a potential function which satisfies Laplace's equation at points where no singularities are present, and which, in regions where there is a source distribution of strength σ, satisfies Poisson's equation

$$\frac{\partial^2\phi}{\partial x_i\, \partial x_i} = -4\pi\sigma. \tag{8}$$

In the neighbourhood of a point source of strength m at the point with coordinates x_{is}, the potential may be expressed in the form

$$\phi = \phi' + \frac{m}{r_s}, \qquad r_s^2 = (x_i - x_{is})(x_i - x_{is}), \tag{9}$$

or, since ϕ' is analytic in the neighbourhood of x_{is},

$$\phi = \frac{m}{r_s} + (\phi')_s + (x_i - x_{is})\left(\frac{\partial\phi'}{\partial x_i}\right)_s + \dots,$$

Forces, moments, and added masses for Rankine bodies 323

and similarly the velocity field is expressible in the form

$$v_i = -\frac{mn_i}{r_s^2} + (v_i')_s + (x_j - x_{js})\left(\frac{\partial v_i'}{\partial x_i}\right)_s + \ldots, \tag{11}$$

$$n_i = \frac{x_{is} - x_i}{r_s}, \qquad v' = -\frac{\partial \phi'}{\partial x_i}. \tag{12}$$

In the neighbourhood of a point doublet of vector strength $\bar{\mu}$ at the point x_{id}, the potential may be expressed in the form

$$\phi = \phi' - \frac{\mu_i n_i}{r_d^2}, \qquad n_i = \frac{x_{id} - x_i}{r_d}, \qquad r_d^2 = (x_i - x_{id})(x_i - x_{id}), \tag{13}$$

or, since ϕ' is analytic in the neighbourhood of x_{id},

$$\phi = -\frac{\mu_i n_i}{r_d^2} + (\phi')_d + (x_i - x_{id})\left(\frac{\partial \phi'}{\partial x_i}\right)_d + \ldots, \tag{14}$$

$$v_i = \frac{1}{r_d^3}(3\mu_j n_i n_j - \mu_i) + (v_i')_d + (x_j - x_{jd})\left(\frac{\partial v_i'}{\partial x_j}\right)_d + \ldots \tag{15}$$

3.2. *Gauss's and Green's theorems*

Let $\phi(x_1, x_2, x_3)$ be a function analytic in a region R and on its boundaries, where the region R is bounded externally by a closed surface S and internally by a set of spheres whose surfaces are collectively designated by S'. The sense of the normals to the boundaries outward from the region R is taken as positive.

We can now state Gauss's theorem in the form

$$\int \phi n_i \, dS = \int \frac{\partial \phi}{\partial x_i} \, d\tau - \int \phi n_i \, dS', \tag{16}$$

where the integral on the left extends over the surface of the outer boundary, the last integral over the surface of the spheres, and the first integral on the right is a volume integral over the region R. Also, if $\psi(x_1, x_2, x_3)$ is another function analytic in R and on its boundaries, we can state the second of Green's theorems in the form

$$\int\left(\phi\frac{\partial \psi}{\partial n} - \psi\frac{\partial \phi}{\partial n}\right) dS = \int\left(\phi\frac{\partial^2 \psi}{\partial x_i \partial x_i} - \psi\frac{\partial^2 \phi}{\partial x_i \partial x_i}\right) d\tau - \int\left(\phi\frac{\partial \psi}{\partial n} - \psi\frac{\partial \phi}{\partial n}\right) dS',$$

or, if ϕ satisfies Poisson's equation and ψ Laplace's equation,

$$\int\left(\phi\frac{\partial \psi}{\partial n} - \psi\frac{\partial \phi}{\partial n}\right) dS = 4\pi \int \psi\sigma \, d\tau - \int\left(\phi\frac{\partial \psi}{\partial n} - \psi\frac{\partial \phi}{\partial n}\right) dS'. \tag{17}$$

3.3 *Boundary conditions and the Bernoulli equation*

Various partial derivatives of the quantities V_i and W defined in (4) and (5) will be required. These are given in this section.

We readily obtain

$$\frac{\partial V_i}{\partial x_k} = -\frac{\partial v_i}{\partial x_k} + \epsilon_{ijk}\,\omega_j, \tag{18}$$

If ϕ satisfies Poisson's equation, we have, when $k = i$,

$$\frac{\partial V_i}{\partial x_i} = -4\pi\sigma. \tag{19}$$

324   *L. Landweber and C. S. Yih*

Next, if ϕ satisfies Poisson's equation, noting that $\partial v_i/\partial x_j = \partial v_j/\partial x_i$, and applying (19), we obtain

$$\frac{\partial W}{\partial x_i} = \frac{\partial}{\partial x_j}(-v_i V_j + \epsilon_{ijk}\,\phi\omega_k) - 4\pi\sigma v_i\,. \tag{20}$$

Then, from (27) we obtain

$$\epsilon_{ijk}\,x_j\frac{\partial W}{\partial x_k} = \epsilon_{ijk}\left[-\frac{\partial}{\partial x_l}(x_j\,v_k\,V_l) + V_j\,v_k - 4\pi\sigma x_j\,v_k - \epsilon_{klm}\,x_j\,v_l\,\omega_m\right].$$

But, substituting for V_j, and simplifying, we have

$$\epsilon_{ijk}(V_j\,v_k - \epsilon_{klm}\,x_j\,v_l\,\omega_m) = \epsilon_{ijk}(u_i\,v_k + \epsilon_{klm}\,\omega_j\frac{\partial\phi}{\partial x_l}\,x_m).$$

Hence

$$\epsilon_{ijk}\,x_j\frac{\partial W}{\partial x_k} = \epsilon_{ijk}\left[-\frac{\partial}{\partial x_l}(x_j\,v_k\,V_l) - u_j\frac{\partial\phi}{\partial x_k} - 4\pi\sigma x_j\,v_k + \epsilon_{klm}\,\omega_j\frac{\partial\phi}{\partial x_l}\,x_m\right]. \tag{21}$$

4. Added masses

If we consider the kinetic energy T of the fluid due to the motion of the body when all the other boundaries and flow-producing mechanisms are at rest, we have the well-known formula

$$2T = -\rho\int\phi\frac{\partial\phi}{\partial n}\,dS. \tag{22}$$

From (1) and (2) it follows that

$$2T = A_{\alpha\beta}\,u_\alpha\,u_\beta\,, \tag{23}$$

in which the added masses $A_{\alpha\beta}$ are given by

$$A_{\alpha\beta} = \rho\int\phi_\alpha\,n_\beta\,dS, \qquad A_{\alpha\beta} = A_{\beta\alpha}. \tag{24}$$

Can the added masses be expressed simply in terms of the singularities inside the body under consideration as some of them $(A_{\alpha i})$ were by Taylor, Birkhoff, and Landweber for a body moving in unbounded fluid? This is the chief concern of this section. In the following, two-dimensional and three-dimensional flows will be discussed separately. Two dimensional flows are discussed not only because the use of function-theoretic methods enables one to solve the problem for two dimensions from an entirely new approach and in a singularly simple manner, but also because *simple* relationships between $A_{\alpha\beta}$ and the singularities can be shown to be non-existent for pure rotations.

4.1. *Two-dimensional flows*

The complex variable z is defined, as usual, to be $x_1 + ix_2$. With every velocity potential ϕ_α ($\alpha = 1,\ 2,\ 6$ throughout the discussion for two-dimensional flows) one may associate a stream function ψ_α such that the

Forces, moments, and added masses for Rankine bodies   325

complex potential is $w_\alpha = \phi_\alpha + i\psi_\alpha$. Now, if s denotes the curvilinear distance along the body, we have $n_1 \, ds = dx_2$, $n_2 \, ds = -dx_1$, and since

$$\frac{\partial \psi_\alpha}{\partial s} = \frac{\partial \phi_\alpha}{\partial n} = -n_\alpha, \tag{25}$$

$$A_{\alpha 1} + iA_{\alpha 2} = \rho \oint \phi_\alpha \, n_1 \, ds + i\rho \oint \phi_\alpha \, n_2 \, ds = i\rho \oint \phi_\alpha \, dz$$

$$= -i\rho \left[\oint w_\alpha \, dz - i \oint \psi_\alpha \, dz \right] = -i\rho \oint w_\alpha \, dz - \rho \oint z n_\alpha \, ds.$$

Thus,

$$A_{\alpha 1} + B_{\alpha 1} + i(A_{\alpha 2} + B_{\alpha 2}) = -i\rho \oint w_\alpha \, dz, \tag{26}$$

in which

$$B_{\alpha 1} = \rho \oint x_1 \, n_\alpha \, ds, \qquad B_{\alpha 2} = \rho \oint x_2 \, n_\alpha \, ds. \tag{27}$$

By Gauss's theorem, we have

$$B_{ij} = B\delta_{ij}, \quad B_{61} = -B\bar{x}_2, \quad B_{62} = B\bar{x}_1, \tag{28}$$

where B is the mass of the displaced fluid per unit length of the body, and x_1, x_2 are the coordinates of the centroid of its area of section.

Equation (26) readily yields the generalized Taylor theorem. If there is a doublet of strength μ_α inside S, where in general μ_α is a complex number, there is a term $\mu_\alpha/(z - z_d)$ in w, and its contribution to the integral in (26) is $2\pi\mu_\alpha i$, by Cauchy's theorem; and if there is a source of strength m_α at $z_{\alpha s}$ inside S, there is a term $-m_\alpha \log(z - z_s)$ in w_α, and its contribution to the same integral is $2\pi m_\alpha z_s i$. Thus, extending the result to distributed sources and sinks of strength σ_α per unit area of section, we have

$$A_{\alpha 1} + B_{\alpha 1} + i(A_{\alpha 2} + B_{\alpha 2}) = 2\pi\rho \left[\int \sigma_\alpha z \, dA + \Sigma \, (m_\alpha z_s + \mu_\alpha) \right], \tag{29}$$

in which dA is an element of the area of section over which the integral extends. Equation (28) gives precisely the generalized Taylor theorem for two-dimensional flows.

What, then, about the added mass for pure rotation? The added mass in question is

$$A_{66} = \rho \oint \phi_6 \, n_6 \, ds = \rho \oint \phi_6 (x_1 n_2 - x_2 n_1) \, ds = -\rho \oint \phi_6 (x_1 \, dx_1 + x_2 \, dx_2)$$

$$= -\rho \mathscr{R} \left\{ \oint w_6 \, z^* dz \right\} + \rho \oint \psi_6 (x_2 \, dx_1 - x_1 \, dx_2),$$

where z^* is the complex conjugate of z. But, putting

$$F_1(s) = \int_0^s x_1 n_1 \, ds, \qquad F_2(s) = \int_0^s x_2 n_2 \, ds,$$

326   *L. Landweber and C. S. Yih*

integrating by parts, and applying (25), we have

$$\oint \psi_6(x_2\,dx_1 - x_1\,dx_2) = -\oint \psi_6(x_1\,n_1 + x_2\,n_2)\,ds$$

$$= -\oint (x_1\,n_2 - x_2\,n_1)(F_1 + F_2)\,ds - \psi_6(0)\oint (x_1\,n_1 + x_2\,n_2)\,ds$$

$$= \tfrac{1}{2}[(x_1^2 + x_2^2)_0 - 2\psi_6(0)]\oint (x_1\,n_1 + x_2\,n_2)\,ds$$

$$- \tfrac{1}{2}\oint (x_1^2 + x_2^2)(x_1\,n_1 + x_2\,n_2)\,ds,$$

where the index 0 denotes initial values along the path of integration. Applying Gauss's theorem, we obtain

$$\oint \psi_6(x_2\,dx_1 - x_1\,dx_2) = A[(x_1^2 + x_2^2)_0 - 2\psi_6(0)] - 2\int (x_1^2 + x_2^2)\,dA.$$

We may take $\psi_6(0) = 0$. Also, let r_g be the radius of gyration of the area, and let $r_0^2 = (x_1^2 + x_2^2)_0$. Then we have, finally,

$$A_{66} + B_{66} = \rho A(r_0^2 - r_g^2) - \rho\mathcal{R}\left\{\oint w_6\,z^*dz\right\}. \tag{30}$$

It is now seen, by expressing w_6 in terms of its singularities, that (30) gives a linear relation between A_{66} and their strength. If, for instance, among the singularities of w_6, there are doublets of strength μ_i at $z = z_i$, each would give rise to a term

$$-\rho\mu_i\mathcal{R}\left\{\oint \frac{z^*}{z - z_i}\,dz\right\}$$

which, however, cannot be expressed in the form $\mu_i f(z_1, z_2, \ldots)$ independent of the shape of the profile; for otherwise, as a consequence of Morera's theorem of complex variables, the integrand would be an analytic function, which it clearly is not. In this sense a simple relationship like those of (29) does not exist for A_{66}. The writers have laboured much and in vain in their endeavour to establish the missing simple relationships for pure rotations, and it was not until equation (30) was reached that they recognized the futility of their efforts.

4.2. *Three-dimensional flows*

For the fluid inside S and outside the small surface S' around the interior singularities, we can apply (17) to obtain

$$A_{j\alpha} = A_{\alpha j} = \rho\int \phi_\alpha\,n_j\,dS = \rho\int \phi_\alpha\frac{\partial x_j}{\partial n}\,dS$$

$$= \rho\int x_j\frac{\partial\phi_\alpha}{\partial n}\,dS + 4\pi\rho\int x_j\sigma_\alpha\,d\tau + \rho\int\left(x_j\frac{\partial\phi_\alpha}{\partial n} - \phi_\alpha\,n_j\right)dS', \tag{31}$$

where σ_α is the distributed source strength corresponding to ϕ_α. Here, as shown by Landweber (1956),

$$\rho\int x_j\frac{\partial\phi_\alpha}{\partial n}\,dS = -\rho\int x_j\,n_\alpha\,dS = -B_{\alpha j}. \tag{32}$$

Forces, moments, and added masses for Rankine bodies   327

Moreover, for the source,

$$\int x_j \frac{\partial \phi_\alpha}{\partial n} \, dS' = 4\pi \sum_s m_\alpha \, x_{js} \,. \tag{33}$$

For the doublet $\bar{\mu}_\alpha$, with components $\mu_{\alpha i}$, the potential is given by (13), from which, writing

$$x_j \frac{\partial \phi_\alpha}{\partial n} = x_j \frac{\partial \phi'_\alpha}{\partial n} - \frac{2x_{jd}\,\mu_{\alpha i}\,n_i}{r_d^3} + \frac{2\mu_{\alpha i}\,n_i\,n_j}{r_d^2} \,,$$

and noting that $\int x_j (\partial \phi'/\partial n) \, dS'$ vanishes in the limit as r_d approaches zero, and $\int n_i r_d^{-3} dS'$ and $\int n_i n_j r_d^{-2} \, dS'$ vanish because of anti-symmetry except when $i = j$ in the last integral, we have

$$\int x_j \frac{\partial \phi_\alpha}{\partial n} \, dS' = 2\mu_{\alpha j} \int \frac{n_j\,n_j}{r_d^2} \, dS' = \frac{4\pi}{3} \mu_{\alpha j} \,, \tag{34}$$

where j is not summed in the second member of (34). Next, considering $-\int \phi_\alpha n_i \, dS'$, the contribution to it by a source is zero, since its potential varies inversely as the radial distance r_s from it, whereas dS varies as r_s^2. The contribution of a doublet is

$$-\int \left(\phi' - \frac{\mu\alpha_i n_i}{r_d^2} \right) n_j \, dS' = \mu_{\alpha j} \int \frac{n_j\,n_j}{r_d^2} \, dS' = \frac{4\pi}{3} \mu_{\alpha j} \,. \tag{35}$$

Substituting (32) to (35) into (31), we obtain the generalized Taylor theorem

$$A_\alpha + B_{\alpha j} = 4\pi\rho \left[\int \sigma_\alpha x_j \, d\tau + \Sigma \, (m_\alpha x_{js} + \mu_{\alpha j}) \right]. \tag{36}$$

4.3. *Evaluation of 'missing' added-mass relations for an elongated body*

In this section simple expression for the added-mass coefficients for pure rotation in terms of the singularities within the body, will be derived for ellipsoids, and approximate ones for elongated bodies.

From (17) we have

$$\int \phi(x_j n_k + x_k n_j) \, dS = \int \phi \frac{\partial}{\partial n}(x_j x_k) \, dS$$

$$= \int x_j x_k \frac{\partial \phi}{\partial n} \, dS + 4\pi \int \sigma x_j x_k \, d\tau - \int \left[\phi(x_j n_k + x_k n_j) - x_j x_k \frac{\partial \phi}{\partial n} \right] dS'$$

$$= \int x_j x_k \frac{\partial \phi}{\partial n} \, dS + 4\pi \left[\int (\sigma x_j x_k \, d\tau + \Sigma \, (m x_j x_k + \mu_j x_k + \mu_k x_j) \right], \tag{37}$$

where the integrals over the spherical surfaces about the isolated singularities have been evaluated by a now familiar process and the subscripts s and d on the coordinates have been omitted in the last terms. Also for the first integral on the right in (37), we readily obtain from (3) and (16) the matrix of values

$$\rho \int x_j x_k \frac{\partial \phi_\alpha}{\partial n} \, dS = B'_{3+i,\alpha} \quad (\alpha = 4, 5, 6),$$

$$B'_{3+i,\,3+i} = -\rho \epsilon_{ijk} \int (\dot{x}_j^2 - x_k^2) \, d\tau, \tag{38}$$

$$B'_{3+i,\,3+k} = \rho \epsilon_{ijk} \int x_j x_k \, d\tau,$$

328   **L. Landweber and C. S. Yih**

where i, j, k are different and not summed.   Thus we may write

$$\left.\begin{array}{l} \rho \int \phi_\alpha(x_j\, n_k + x_k\, n_j)\, dS = B'_{3+i,\,\alpha} + 4\pi\rho\Sigma_{jk\alpha}\,, \\[12pt] \Sigma_{jk\alpha} = \int \sigma_\alpha\, x_j\, x_k\; d\tau + \Sigma\,(m_\alpha\, x_j\, x_k + \mu_{\alpha j}\, x_k + \mu_{\alpha k}\, x_j). \end{array}\right\} \qquad (39)$$

Also we have

$$A_{\alpha,\,3+i} = \rho \int \phi_\alpha\, n_{3+i}\, dS = \rho\epsilon_{ijk} \int \phi_\alpha\, x_j\, n_k\, dS. \qquad (40)$$

Consider the case of an ellipsoid rotating in an infinite fluid in which no other boundaries or singularities are present.   Then we have, from Lamb (1932, p. 154), when the coordinate axes are taken along the principal axes,

$$\phi_4 = C_4\, x_2\, x_3\,, \qquad \phi_5 = C_5\, x_3\, x_1\,, \qquad \phi_6 = C_6\, x_1\, x_2\,, \qquad (41)$$

where C_4, C_5, C_6 are constants, and hence, from (39), (40), and (16), for the case $\alpha = 6$, $i = 3$, we obtain

$$C_6\, B_{66} = B'_{66} + 4\pi\rho\Sigma_{126}$$
$$A_{66} = -C_6\, B'_{66}\,, \qquad (42)$$

or eliminating C_6,

$$A_{66} \cdot \frac{B_{66}}{B'_{66}} + B'_{66} = -4\pi\rho\Sigma_{126}\,. \qquad (43)$$

Similar expressions may be written by symmetry for A_{55} and A_{44}.   The coefficients A_{56}, A_{64}, A_{45} are zero for the chosen orientation of the coordinate axes.   Thus we have found simple relations between the rotational added-mass coefficients and the singularities for ellipsoids, albeit not as simple as those in (36).

When the x_1-axis of the ellipsoid is much greater than the others, and the x_2- and x_3-axes are nearly equal C_6 is very nearly 1, $A_{66} \doteq -B'_{66}$ from (42), and the left member of (43) may be written as

$$A_{66} - A_{66}\!\left(\frac{B_{66}}{B'_{66}} + 1\right) - B'_{66} \doteq A_{66} + B'_{66}\!\left(\frac{B_{66}}{B'_{66}} + 1\right) - B'_{66} = A_{66} + B_{66}\,,$$

which is of the form that an extension of (36) would suggest.

Next let us consider a body elongated in the direction of the x_1-axis with nearly elliptical sections in the planes $x_1 = $ constant.   From (39) we obtain directly and exactly

$$A_{66} - B'_{66} + 2\rho \int \phi_6\, x_2\, n_1\, dS = 4\pi\rho\Sigma_{126}\,. \qquad (44)$$

For an elongated body the third term on the left is small compared with the other terms, so that only a small error would be introduced by assuming an approximate value for ϕ_6 in that term.   Since the section is nearly elliptical, let us assume $\phi_6 \doteq C x_1 x_2$.   Then

$$2 \int \phi_6\, x_2\, n_1\, dS \doteq 2C \int x_2^2\, d\tau \doteq -2\frac{A_{66}}{B'_{66}} \int x_2^2\, d\tau\,,$$

whence, substituting into (44) and simplifying, we obtain

$$A_{66}\frac{B_{66}}{B'_{66}} + B'_{66} \doteq -4\pi\rho\Sigma_{126}. \qquad (45)$$

The corresponding formulae for A_{44} and A_{55} can be written down from symmetry. As in the case of the elongated ellipsoid, when the section is nearly circular we have also

$$A_{66} + B_{66} \doteq 4\pi\rho\, \Sigma_{126} \tag{46}$$

and similarly for A_{55}. For A_{44} the term corresponding to the integral in (44) is of the same order of magnitude as the others, so that the errors in the foregoing approximations would be greater than for A_{55} or A_{66}.

Similarly we have, from (39),

$$A_{56} - B_{56}' + 2\rho \int \phi_6\, x_1 n_3\, dS = 4\pi\rho\Sigma_{316} , \tag{47}$$

in which the third term may be expressed approximately in the form

$$2\rho \int \phi_6\, x_1 n_3\, dS \doteq 2\rho C \int x_1^2 x_2 n_3\, dS = 0.$$

Hence (47) becomes

$$A_{56} + B_{56} \doteq 4\pi\rho\, \Sigma_{316}. \tag{48}$$

An alternative relation for A_{56} may be derived by interchanging the roles of the indices, and similar expressions may be obtained for A_{64} and A_{45}. These as well as the relations for A_{44}, A_{55}, and A_{66} may be summarized in the form

$$\left.\begin{aligned}
A_{\alpha\alpha}\frac{B_{\alpha\alpha}}{B_{\alpha\alpha}'} + B_{\alpha\alpha}' &\doteq -(A_{\alpha\alpha} + B_{\alpha\alpha}) = -4\pi\rho\, \Sigma_{jk\alpha} \quad (\alpha = 3+i \neq 4), \\[2mm]
A_{\beta\gamma} + B_{\beta\gamma} &\doteq 4\pi\rho\epsilon_{ijk}\, \Sigma_{ik\gamma} \quad (\beta = 3+j, \quad \gamma = 3+k),
\end{aligned}\right\} \tag{49}$$

in which i, k are not summed and i, j, k are different.

4.4 *Linear and Angular Momentum*

It will be of interest to express the integrals $\rho \int \phi n_i\, dS$ and $\rho\epsilon_{ijk} \int \phi x_j n_k\, dS$ in terms of the added-mass coefficients and the singularities within the body. By applying Gauss's transformation to the region exterior to the body it is seen that the sums of such integrals over all the boundaries give the linear and angular momenta of the fluid.

The velocity potential, in the form given by (4), may be further resolved by writing

$$\phi_0 = \phi_0' + \phi_0'', \tag{50}$$

where ϕ_0' is the potential of the part of ϕ_0 due to external singularities, and ϕ_0'' that due to internal singularities. We have then, from (24),

$$\rho \int \phi n_i\, dS = u_\alpha A_{\alpha i} + \rho \int (\phi_0' + \phi_0'') n_i\, dS. \tag{51}$$

But, by Green's reciprocal theorem and (17),

$$\int \phi_0'\, n_i\, dS = \int x_i \frac{\partial \phi_0'}{\partial n}\, dS, \tag{52}$$

$$\int \phi_0''\, n_i\, dS = \int x_i \frac{\partial \phi_0''}{\partial n}\, dS + 4\pi \int \sigma_0\, x_i\, d\tau + \int \left(x_i \frac{\partial \phi_0''}{\partial n} - \phi_0''\, n_i \right) dS', \tag{53}$$

330   *L. Landweber and C. S. Yih*

where σ_0 is the strength of the distributed singularities within the body corresponding to ϕ_0. Thus, substituting (52) and (53) into (51), applying the boundary condition (3), and noting that the last integral over the spheres about the singularities is of the same form as that evaluated in (31), we obtain

$$\rho \int \phi n_i \, dS = u_\alpha A_{\alpha i} + 4\pi\rho \left[\int \sigma_0 x_i \, d\tau + \Sigma \, (m_0 x_i + \mu_0) \right], \tag{54}$$

where m_0 and μ_{0i} are the strengths of the sources and doublet components within the body corresponding to ϕ_0. Hence, applying (36), we obtain

$$\rho \int \phi n_i \, dS + u_\alpha B_{\alpha i} = 4\pi\rho \left[\int \sigma x_i \, d\tau + \Sigma \, (m x_i + \mu_i) \right], \tag{55}$$

where σ, m, and μ_i denote the totality of all the distributions and singularities within the body. This shows that the value of the momentum integral depends simply upon the internal singularities.

Next let us consider the angular momentum integral. Recalling the definition $n_{3+i} = \epsilon_{ijk} x_j n_k$, we have, putting $\beta = 3+i$, and applying (24) and (3),

$$\rho\epsilon_{ijk} \int \phi x_j n_k \, dS = \rho \int (u_\alpha \phi_\alpha + \phi_0) n_\beta \, dS$$

$$= u_\alpha A_{\alpha\beta} - \rho \int (\phi_0' + \phi_0'') \frac{\partial \phi_\beta}{\partial n} \, dS. \tag{56}$$

But, from (17), we have

$$\int \phi_0' \frac{\partial \phi_\beta}{\partial n} \, dS = \int \phi_\beta \frac{\partial \phi_0'}{\partial n} \, dS - 4\pi \int \sigma_\beta \phi_0' \, d\tau + \int \left(\phi_\beta \frac{\partial \phi_0'}{\partial n} - \phi_0' \frac{\partial \phi_\beta}{\partial n} \right) dS'.$$

Also, putting $\phi_\beta = \phi_\beta' + \phi_\beta''$, where ϕ_β' is the part of ϕ_β due to external singularities, and ϕ_β'' that due to the internal ones, we have from (17) and Green's reciprocal theorem

$$\int \phi_0'' \frac{\partial \phi_\beta}{\partial n} \, dS = \int \phi_\beta' \frac{\partial \phi_0''}{\partial n} \, dS + 4\pi \int \sigma_0 \phi_\beta' \, d\tau + \int \left(\phi_\beta' \frac{\partial \phi_0''}{\partial n} - \phi_0'' \frac{\partial \phi_\beta'}{\partial n} \right) dS',$$

$$\int \phi_0'' \frac{\partial \phi_\beta''}{\partial n} \, dS = \int \phi_\beta'' \frac{\partial \phi_0''}{\partial n} \, dS,$$

whence, applying the boundary condition (3), evaluating the integrals over S' by the usual procedure, and substituting into (56), we obtain

$$\rho\epsilon_{ijk} \int \phi x_j n_k \, dS = u_\alpha A_{\alpha\beta} + 4\pi\rho \left[\int (\sigma_\beta \phi_0' - \sigma_0 \phi_\beta') \, d\tau + \right.$$

$$\left. + \Sigma \, (m_\beta \phi_0' - m_0 \phi_\beta' - \mu_{\beta j} v_{0j}' + \mu_{0j} v_{\beta j}') \right] \tag{57}$$

or, substituting for $A_{j\beta}$ from (36), and applying (7),

$$\rho\epsilon_{ijk} \int \phi x_j n_k \, dS = B\epsilon_{ijk} u_j \bar{x}_k + 4\pi\rho \left\{ \int [\sigma_\beta(\phi_0' + u_j x_j) - \sigma_0 \phi_\beta'] \, d\tau + \right.$$

$$\left. + \Sigma \, [m_\beta(\phi_0' + u_j x_j) - m_0 \phi_\beta - \mu_{\beta j}(v_{0j} - u_j) + \mu_{0j} v_{\beta j}'] \right\} + \omega_j A_{3+i,\,3+j}. \tag{57\,a}$$

Forces, moments, and added masses for Rankine bodies 331

It will usually be convenient to choose the origin of coordinates so that the term $B\epsilon_{ijk}\,u_j\,\bar{x}_k$ vanishes, as is done in the equations of rigid body dynamics, where this term also occurs.

For the elongated bodies considered in the previous section we can substitute the approximate values given in (49) for $A_{3+i,\,3+j}$. Thus, applying the simpler of the approximate relations for A_{66}, we obtain

$$\rho\epsilon_{3jk}\int \phi x_j\,n_k\,dS = B\epsilon_{3jk}\,u_j\,\bar{x}_k - \omega_j\,B_{3+j,\,6} + 4\pi\rho[\int (\sigma_6\,\Omega_6 - \sigma_0\,\phi'_\beta)\,d\tau +$$

$$+ \Sigma\,(m_6\,\Omega_6 - m_0\,\phi'_\beta + \mu_{6j}\frac{\partial\Omega_6}{\partial x_j} + \mu_{0j}\,v'_{\beta j})], \quad (57\,\text{b})$$

$$\Omega_6 = \phi'_0 + u_j\,x_j - \omega_1\,x_2\,x_3 + \omega_2\,x_3\,x_1 - \omega_3\,x_1\,x_2,$$

and a similar expression for $i = 2$, with

$$\Omega_5 = \phi'_0 + u_j\,x_j + \omega_1\,x_2\,x_3 - \omega_2\,x_3\,x_1 - \omega_3\,x_1\,x_2.$$

For the case $i = 1$, the simpler approximation for A_{44} cannot be used so that the resulting expression for the moment of momentum integral would be more complex in form.

5. The generalized Lagally theorem

5.1. *Force on the body*

From (5), the force on the body is given by

$$F_i = -\int pn_i\,dS = -\rho\int\left(\frac{\partial\phi}{\partial t} - W\right)n_i\,dS$$

$$= -\rho\frac{d}{dt'}\int \phi n_i\,dS + \rho\int Wn_i\,dS, \quad (58)$$

where the prime in t' denotes that the variation with time is relative to a moving coordinate system.   But, from (16) and (20),

$$\int Wn_i\,dS = \int\frac{\partial W}{\partial x_i}\,d\tau - \int Wn_i\,dS'$$

$$= \int\frac{\partial}{\partial x_j}(-v_i\,V_j + \epsilon_{ijk}\,\phi\omega_k)\,d\tau - 4\pi\int \sigma v_i\,d\tau - \int Wn_i\,dS'.$$

Also, applying (4) and (16), we have

$$\int\frac{\partial}{\partial x_j}(-v_i\,V_j + \epsilon_{ijk}\,\phi\omega_k)\,d\tau = \epsilon_{ijk}\,\omega_k\int \phi n_j\,dS + \int(-v_i\,V_j + \epsilon_{ijk}\,\phi\omega_k)n_j\,dS'.$$

Hence, substituting into (58), we obtain

$$F_i = -\rho\frac{d}{dt'}\int \phi n_i\,dS + \rho\epsilon_{ijk}\,\omega_k\int \phi n_j\,dS - 4\pi\rho\int \sigma v_i\,d\tau +$$

$$+ \rho\int[(-v_i\,V_j + \epsilon_{ijk}\,\phi\omega_k)n_j - Wn_i]\,dS'. \quad (59)$$

The sum of the first two terms of (59) is seen to be the absolute time derivative of the momentum vector integral $-\rho\int \phi n_i\,dS$ for which values were

332   *L. Landweber and C. S. Yih*

given in (54) and (55). Thus, evaluating the integrals over S' by the usual procedure, we obtain the expression for the force

$$F_i = -\frac{d}{dt}(u_\alpha A_{\alpha i}) - 4\pi\rho\frac{d}{dt}\left[\int \sigma_0\, x_i\, d\tau + \Sigma\,(m_0\, x_i + \mu_{0i})\right] -$$
$$- 4\pi\rho\left[\int \sigma v_i\, d\tau + \sum\left(mv'_i - \tfrac{4}{3}\pi\sigma\mu_i + \mu_j\frac{\partial v'_i}{\partial x_j}\right)\right], \quad (60)$$

or, if (55) is used in (59), and (7) is applied to evaluate

$$u_\alpha B_{\alpha i} = u_j\, B_{ji} + \omega_j\, B_{3+j,i} = B(u_i + \epsilon_{ijk}\,\omega_j\,\bar{x}_k) = B\bar{u}_i\,,$$

where $\bar{u}_i$ is the i-component of the velocity of the centroid, then

$$F_i = B\frac{d\bar{u}_i}{dt} - 4\pi\rho\frac{d}{dt}\left[\int \sigma x_i\, d\tau + \Sigma(mx_i + \mu_i)\right] -$$
$$- 4\pi\rho\left[\int \sigma v_i\, d\tau + \sum\left(mv'_i - \tfrac{4}{3}\pi\sigma\mu_i + \mu_j\frac{\partial v'_i}{\partial x_j}\right)\right]. \quad (61)$$

If it is desired to use relative rather than absolute time derivatives, we may employ alternative expressions of which a typical one is

$$\frac{d}{dt}(\sigma x_i) = \frac{d}{dt'}(\sigma x_i) + \sigma\epsilon_{ijk}\,\omega_j\, x_k.$$

Furthermore, it should be noted that the strengths of the singularities occurring in (60) and (61) are those due to the superimposed effects of all the velocity components of both the body and external boundaries and flow-producing mechanisms, in contrast with the singularity strengths corresponding to unit magnitude of a single velocity component of the body which occur in the generalized Taylor formulas for the added masses.

It is important to observe that, in computing v'_i and $\partial v'_i/\partial x_j$ in (60) and (61), the contributions from all the internal singularities may be omitted. The reason for this is that the mutual contributions of the velocity fields of a pair of internal singularities to the expression for the force on the body are equal and opposite and hence annul each other. This introduces a significant simplification in the calculation of the force from these equations.

Equation (61) is essentially equivalent to the corresponding result by Cummins (1953). It differs from it in the following respects.

(1) A new term, $16\pi^2\rho\sigma\mu_i/3$, has appeared. This did not occur in the treatments of Lagally or Cummins because they did not consider the case of simultaneous occurrence of distributed and isolated singularities.

(2) The inertia term in Cummins' equation (8) and the terms of his equation (48) for the vector F_3 have been replaced by the first term of (61), which is seen to represent the inertia of the displaced fluid.

(3) The expression for the force has been expressed in a much more compact form.

Forces, moments, and added masses for Rankine bodies   333

5.2. *Moment on the Body*

The moment on the body is given, from (5), by

$$M_i = -\epsilon_{ijk} \int p x_j n_k \, dS = -\rho\epsilon_{ijk} \int \left(\frac{\partial\phi}{\partial t} - W\right) x_j n_k \, dS$$

$$= -\rho\epsilon_{ijk}\left[\frac{d}{dt'}\int \phi x_j n_k \, dS - \int W x_j n_k \, dS\right]. \tag{62}$$

From (16), (21), and (4), we obtain

$$\epsilon_{ijk}\int W x_j n_k \, dS = \epsilon_{ijk}\left[\int x_j \frac{\partial W}{\partial x_k} \, d\tau - \int W x_j n_k \, dS'\right]$$

$$= -\epsilon_{ijk}\left[u_j \int \phi n_k \, dS + \omega_j \int \phi n_{3+k} \, dS + 4\pi \int \sigma x_j v_k \, d\tau\right] -$$

$$- \epsilon_{ijk}\int (x_j v_k V_l n_l + u_j \phi n_k + \omega_j \phi n_{3+k} + W x_j n_k) \, dS'.$$

Hence, evaluating the integrals over S' by the already frequently applied procedure and putting

$$\epsilon_{ijk}\left[\frac{d}{dt'}\int \phi x_j n_k \, dS + \omega_j \int \phi n_{3+k} \, dS\right] = \epsilon_{ijk}\frac{d}{dt}\int \phi x_j n_k \, dS,$$

the expression for the moment becomes

$$M_i = -\rho\epsilon_{ijk}\left[\frac{d}{dt}\int \phi x_j n_k \, dS + u_j \int \phi n_k \, dS\right] + M_{iL}(v), \tag{63}$$

where $M_{iL}(v)$ denotes the Lagally moment for steady flow,

$$M_{iL}(v) = -4\pi\rho\epsilon_{ijk}\left[\int \sigma x_j v_k \, d\tau + \sum\left(m x_j v'_k + \mu_j v'_k + x_j \mu_l \frac{\partial v'_k}{\partial x_l} - \tfrac{4}{3}\pi\sigma x_j \mu_k\right)\right].$$

This differs from the expressions derived by Lagally and Cummins for steady flow in the appearance of the last term, because they did not consider the case in which distributed sources and isolated doublets are simultaneously present. Except for this term, (63) may be shown to be equivalent to the result derived by Cummins for unsteady flow. Cummins, however, did not succeed in expressing the moment of momentum integral in (63) in terms of singularities, so that its time derivative occurs explicitly in his final result. As in the case of the Lagally force, the contributions to v from internal singularities need not be considered in computing the Lagally moment since they annul each other in summation.

Now, substituting for the momentum and moment of momentum integrals in (63) from (55) and (57a), and noting from (7) that

$$-B\epsilon_{ijk}\frac{d}{dt}(u_j \bar{x}_k) + \epsilon_{ijk} u_j u_\alpha B_{\alpha k} = B\epsilon_{ijk}\bar{x}_j \frac{du_k}{dt},$$

we obtain

$$M_i = B\epsilon_{ijk}\bar{x}_j \frac{du_k}{dt} - \frac{d}{dt}(\omega_j A_{3+\alpha,\,3+j}) - 4\pi\rho\frac{d}{dt}\left\{\int [\sigma_\beta(\phi'_0 + u_j x_j) - \sigma_0 \phi'_\beta] \, d\tau + \right.$$

$$\left. + \Sigma\, [m_\beta(\phi'_0 + u\, x_j) - m_0 \phi'_\beta - \mu_{\beta j}(v'_{0j} - u_j) + \mu_{0j} v_{\beta j}]\right\} + M_{iL}(v - u), \tag{64}$$

where $\beta = 3+i$, and $M_{iL}(v-u)$ denotes the value of the Lagally moment when the velocity at the singularity relative to that of the body is used.

For elongated bodies with nearly ellipsoidal sections, substituting for $A_{3+i,\,3+j}$ from (49), we can obtain an approximate but complete expression for the moment in terms of singularities. Thus, applying (57b), we have

$$M_3 = B\epsilon_{3jk}\,\bar{x}_j\frac{du_k}{dt} + \frac{d}{dt}(\omega_j\,B_{3+j,\,6}) - 4\pi\rho\,\frac{d}{dt}\Bigg\{\int(\sigma_6\,\Omega_6 - \sigma_0\,\phi_6')\,d\tau\,+$$

$$+\,\Sigma\left[m_6\,\Omega_6 - m_0\,\phi_6' + \mu_{6j}\frac{\partial\Omega_6}{\partial x_j} + \mu_{0j}\,v_{6j}'\right]\Bigg\} + M_{iL}(v-u). \quad (64\,\mathrm{a})$$

A similar expression for M_2 can be written down by symmetry. In the application of (64) and (64 a) it will usually be convenient to make the first term vanish either by choosing the origin at a point of zero acceleration, or at the centroid, or at a point whose acceleration vector passes through the centroid.

6. Comparison of the results of Kirchhoff, Taylor and Lagally

Kirchhoff's equations of motion of a body through a fluid express the force and moment acting on a body in terms of its added masses. Since the generalized Taylor theorem expresses the added masses in terms of the singularities, it appears that, by substituting these expressions for the added masses into Kirchhoff's equations, it might be possible to derive identical formulas to those derived above for the forces and moments in terms of the singularities.

First let us consider one of Kirchhoff's equations (Lamb 1932, p. 168), for the case when the fluid is disturbed only by the motion of the body,

$$F_1 = -\frac{d}{dt'}\frac{\partial T}{\partial u_1} + u_6\frac{\partial T}{\partial u_2} - u_5\frac{\partial T}{\partial u_3}, \qquad 2T = A_{\alpha\beta}\,u_\alpha\,u_\beta, \qquad (65)$$

where T is the kinetic energy of the fluid and the prime denotes that the time derivative is taken relative to a moving coordinate system. Then

$$F_1 = -\frac{d}{dt'}(u_\alpha\,A_{\alpha 1}) - u_\alpha(u_5\,A_{\alpha 3} - u_6\,A_{\alpha 2}) = -\frac{d}{dt}(u_\alpha\,A_{\alpha 1}). \qquad (66)$$

On examining the expression for the corresponding term in (60), it is seen that the terms in the first bracket vanish since, in the present case, there are no external singularities and consequently no internal images of them. The terms in the second bracket vanish because the mutual contributions of the internal sources and doublets to the force on the body annul each other. Consequently, (60) and (66) are seen to be in agreement.

More generally, if it is supposed that other boundaries are present, but that only the given body is in motion, the force on the body due to the fluid may be obtained by applying Lagrange's equations (Lamb 1932, p. 188) in the form

$$F_i = -\frac{d}{dt}\frac{\partial T}{\partial u_i} + \frac{\partial T}{\partial \xi_i}, \qquad 2T = A_{\alpha\beta}\,u_\alpha\,u_\beta, \qquad (67)$$

Forces, moments, and added masses for Rankine Bodies 335

where ξ_i ($i = 1,2,3$) are the coordinates at the origin of the coordinate system attached to the body, relative to an inertial system. Then

$$F_i = -\frac{d}{dt}(u_\alpha A_{\alpha i}) + \frac{1}{2}\frac{\partial A_{\alpha\beta}}{\partial \xi_i} u_\alpha u_\beta. \tag{68}$$

Comparison of this result with (60), in which the first bracket vanishes in the present case since the external boundaries are at rest, shows that the two expressions for the force would be identical in form only if

$$\frac{\partial A_{\alpha\beta}}{\partial \xi_i} u_\alpha u_\beta = -8\pi\rho\left[\int \sigma v_i \, d\tau + \sum\left((mv'_i - \tfrac{4}{3}\pi\sigma\mu_i + \mu_j\frac{\partial v'_i}{\partial x_j})\right)\right],$$

or, putting $\sigma = u_\alpha \sigma_\alpha$, $v_i = u_\beta v_{\beta i}$, etc., only if

$$\frac{\partial A_{\alpha\beta}}{\partial \xi_i} = -8\pi\rho\left[\int \sigma_\alpha v_{\beta i} \, d\tau + \sum\left(m_\alpha v'_{\beta i} - \tfrac{4}{3}\pi\mu_{\alpha i}\sigma_\beta + \mu_{\alpha j}\frac{\partial v'_\beta}{\partial x_j}\right)\right]. \tag{69}$$

But substitution of the generalized Taylor formula for the added masses in terms of singularities into (68) does not seem to yield identically the generalized Lagally formula for the force; in fact, such a complete substitution could not be made since not all the added masses can be so expressed. Thus the method of Kirchhoff–Lagrange appears in general to furnish an alternative (and more limited) method of computing the forces on a body. Nevertheless, (69) must be valid, since the force may be obtained by either method, so that we have expressions for the gradients of the added masses in terms of the singularities.

It will be instructive to illustrate both methods by computing the force on a sphere A of radius a moving with velocity u_1 along the line of centres away from a fixed sphere B of radius b. Let c be the distance between centres at a given instant. Using the method of successive images, we begin with a doublet of strength $\mu_0 = \frac{1}{2}u_1 a^3$ at the centre of A. Its first image in B is a doublet of strength

$$\mu_1 = -\frac{b^3}{c^3}\mu_0 = -\frac{u_1 a^3 b^3}{2c^3}$$

at a distance $\xi_1 = c - b^2/c$ from the centre of A. This gives a second image in A, a doublet of strength

$$\mu_2 = -\frac{b^3}{\xi_1^3}\mu_1 = \frac{u_1 a^6 b^3}{2(c^2 - b^2)^3}.$$

To this order of approximation, from (36) the added mass A_{11} is

$$A_{11} = -B_{11} + 4\pi\rho\frac{\mu_0 + \mu_2}{u_1}, = \tfrac{2}{3}\pi\rho a^3\left[1 + \frac{3a^3 b^3}{(c^2 - b^2)^3}\right],$$

and (68) gives for the force

$$F_1 = -\frac{d}{dt}(u_1 A_{11}) + \tfrac{1}{2}u_1^2\frac{dA_{11}}{dc} = -\frac{d}{dt}(u_1 A_{11}) - \frac{6\pi\rho u_1^2 a^6 b^3 c}{(c^2 - b^2)^4}.$$

336   *L. Landweber and C. S. Yih*

In order to apply (60) we also need the velocity v', due to the first doublet image μ_1, along the line of centres,

$$v' = 2\mu_1(x - b^2/c)^{-3},$$

where x is distance measured from the centre of B.   Then

$$\frac{\partial v'}{\partial x} = \frac{3u_1\, a^3 b^3 c}{(xc - b^2)^4}.$$

In order to obtain the same order of approximation as above, we need compute only the force on the original doublet.   We obtain from (60)

$$F_1 = -\frac{d}{dt}(u_1\, A_{11}) - 4\pi\rho\mu_0\left(\frac{\partial v'}{\partial x}\right)_c = -\frac{d}{dt}(u_1\, A_{11}) - \frac{6\pi\rho u_1^2\, a^6 b^3 c}{(c^2 - b^2)^4},$$

which agrees with the result above.

The present work was conducted at the Iowa Institute of Hydraulic Research, State University of Iowa, under contract Nonr 1611 with the Office of Naval Research.   The authors wish to thank Milton Martin and Manfred Bottacini of the Institute for their careful reviews.   We are also pleased, here, to mention George Weinblum of the University of Hamburg, that most inspiring teacher, who pointed out the power of the Lagally theorem and new fields of research for many of us.

REFERENCES

BIRKHOFF, G. 1953 *Hydrodynamics*.   Princeton University Press.

CUMMINS, W. E. 1953 The forces and moments acting on a body moving in an arbitrary potential stream. *David Taylor Model Basin, Rep.* no. 708.

LAGALLY, M. 1922 Berechnung der Kräfte und Momente die strömende Flüssigkeiten auf ihre Begrenzung ausüben.   *Z. angew. Math. Mech.* **2,** 409.

LAMB, H. 1932 *Hydrodynamics*, 6th Ed.   Cambridge University Press.

LANDWEBER, L. 1956 On a generalization of Taylor's virtual mass relation for Rankine bodies. *Quart. Appl. Math.* **14,** 51.

TAYLOR, G. I. 1928 The energy of a body moving in an infinite fluid, with an application to airships. *Proc. Roy. Soc.* A, **120,** 13.

Note on "Forces, moments, and added masses for Rankine bodies"[*] by
L. Landweber and C. S. Yih, Journal of Fluid Mechanics, September, 1956.

Mr. K. Eggers of the Hamburg Institut fur Schiffbau has pointed out that the term $\frac{16}{3}\pi^2\rho\sigma\mu_i$ in the expression for the force in Eq. (61) of the paper by Yih and myself (Journal of Fluid Mechanics, Sept. 1956, p. 332) cannot of itself contribute to the force. If it did then a closed body, generated by a source-sink distribution of zero total strength in which a doublet was embedded, in steady motion in an infinite, unbounded fluid, would be subject to a force.

It is stated in the text following Eq. (61) that, in computing v_i' and $\partial v_i'/\partial x_j$ in (60) and (61), the contributions from all the internal singularities may be omitted. This statement should have been amplified to state that all the mutual contributions to the force (and moment) from internal singularities annul each other and may be omitted. In the case of a doublet of vector strength μ_i embedded in a source distribution σ, the term $\frac{16}{3}\pi^2\rho\sigma\mu_i$ appears as an internal interaction term between the doublet and the source distribution which we might expect would be cancelled when all the internal interactions are considered. It will now be shown how this occurs.

In the expression for the force F_1 we need consider only the terms

$$ -4\pi\rho\left[\int\sigma v_i\,d\tau - \sum\frac{4}{3}\pi\sigma\mu_i + \sum\mu_j\frac{\partial v_i'}{\partial x_j}\right] $$

Let the doublet μ_i be situated at the point $P(x_1, x_2, x_3)$ and let (ξ_1, ξ_2, ξ_3) denote the coordinates of a point when referring to the source distribution. Then the velocity v_i at a source element due to the doublet is

$$ v_i = \frac{3\mu_j(x_i-\xi_i)(x_j-\xi_j)}{r^5} - \frac{\mu_i}{r^3}, \qquad r^2 = (x_i-\xi_i)(x_i-\xi_i) $$

[*] Work sponsored by Office of Naval Research, Contract Nonr 1611.

-2-

and the contribution of the doublet to the force on the source distribution is

$$- 4\pi\rho \int_R \sigma \left[\frac{3\mu_j (x_i - \xi_i)(x_j - \xi_j)}{r^5} - \frac{\mu_i}{r^3} \right] d\tau, \quad d\tau = d\xi_1 d\xi_2 d\xi_3$$

where the region R is bounded internally by a small sphere about the point P. Next, the velocity at P due to the source distribution is

$$v_i = \int_{R+S'} \sigma (\xi_1, \xi_2, \xi_3) \frac{x_i - \xi_i}{r} d\tau$$

where S' denotes the volume of the small sphere about P, and

$$\frac{\partial v_i}{\partial x_j} = \int_{R+S'} \sigma \left[\frac{\delta_{ij}}{r^3} - \frac{3(x_i - \xi_i)(x_j - \xi_j)}{r^5} \right] d\tau$$

Hence the contribution of the source distribution to the force on the doublet is

$$- 4\pi\rho \int_{R+S'} \sigma \left[\frac{\mu_i}{r^3} - \frac{3\mu_j (x_i - \xi_i)(x_j - \xi_j)}{r^5} \right] d\tau$$

It is now seen that the integrands in the above two cases are equal and opposite and hence the integrals over the region R annul each other. The last integral over the small sphere S' is indeterminate, so that it will be evaluated by an alternative means.

For a sufficiently small sphere σ may be considered constant. Applying Gauss's theorem for the flux of fluid out of a sphere of radius r about P, we have

$$v_i = \frac{4}{3} \pi \sigma x_i$$

and

$$\mu_j \frac{\partial v_i}{\partial x_j} = \frac{4}{3} \pi \sigma \mu_i$$

Hence the contribution of the source distribution in the neighborhood of the doublet to the force on the doublet is $- \frac{16}{3} \pi^2 \rho \sigma \mu_i$. But this is equal and opposite to the remaining doublet - source distribution term, so that the total contribution from their interactions is zero, as was stated.

Thus it is seen that, when the internal interactions are omitted from the expression for the force (or moment), the term $\frac{16}{3} \pi^2 \rho \sigma \mu_i$ (and the corresponding one for the moment) will vanish.

L. Landweber

Stream functions
in three-dimensional flows

by Chia-Shun YIH

IOWA INSTITUTE OF HYDRAULIC RESEARCH, STATE UNIVERSITY OF IOWA (U.S.A.)

(Now at the University of Michigan)

Texte français, p. 439

Stream functions exist for general three-dimensional flows of a non-diffusive fluid except unsteady flows of a compressible fluid. Along a streamline, these functions are constant. A simple definition of the velocity in terms of the stream functions has been given whenever the latter exist. This definition includes all the known ones for special flows as special cases, and yields a simple relationship between the volume or mass discharge and the values of the stream functions, from which all the well-known ones for special flows can be immediately deduced. For unsteady flows of a compressible fluid three « path functions » exist in terms of which the density and the products of the density and the velocity components can be expressed — and in such a way that the equation of continuity is identically satisfied. The mass contained in three pairs of surfaces which are time-traces of the material surfaces (or hypersurfaces) corresponding to specific values of the " path functions " is shown to be the product of the three differences of these functions. An analogous development for vorticity (instead of velocity) results in a similar relationship between the circulation and the vorticity functions.

I. — INTRODUCTION.

In 1781, Lagrange [1] introduced the stream function for two-dimensional motion of an incompressible fluid. His method of attack was an entirely mathematical one, without any appeal to kinematics. Recognizing that the equation of continuity

$$u_x + v_y = 0$$

(in which u and v are velocity components in the directions of the cartesian coordinates x and y, respectively, and subscripts denote partial differentiation) is the analytic condition that $udy - vdx$ should be an exact differential, he denoted that differential by $- d\psi$, and thereby arrived at the now-well-known relationships between the velocity components and the function ψ :

$$u = - \psi_y, \qquad v = \psi_x \qquad (1)$$

Since the differential equation for a streamline is

$$udy - vdx = 0$$

or

$$d\psi = 0$$

the function ψ must be constant along a streamline. For this reason it is called the stream function.

Sixty-one years later, Stokes [2] invented the stream function ψ for axisymmetric flows of an incompressible fluid in precisely the same manner as Lagrange. Although in Stokes' original paper cylindrical coordinates were used, his stream function can also be used with spherical coordinates. The relationships between the velocity components and the stream function for cylindrical coordinates (r, φ, z) are

$$u = \frac{1}{r}\,\psi_z, \quad w = -\frac{1}{r}\,\psi_r \qquad (2)$$

and those for spherical coordinates (R, θ, φ) are

$$u = -\frac{1}{R^2 \sin \theta}\,\psi_\theta, \quad v = \frac{1}{R \sin \theta}\,\psi_R \qquad (3)$$

in which, as in Eq. (2), u, v, and w denote the velocity components in the directions of the three coordinates, in the order that these coordinates are mentioned. It is a simple matter to show that Eqs. (2) and (3) are entirely compatible if ψ is taken to be the same function of position.

Lagrange's stream function possesses the property that the discharge q per unit distance in the z-direction across an arc in the x - y plane is equal to the difference in its values at the end of the arc :

$$q = \psi_2 - \psi_1 \qquad (4)$$

Similarly, Stokes' stream function has the property that the discharge Q through an annulus is equal to 2π times the difference in its values at the rims of the annulus :

$$Q = 2\pi (\psi_2 - \psi_1) \qquad (5)$$

Two questions now naturally arise. For three-dimensional flows, do stream functions exist in terms of which the velocity components can be expressed? And, if so, does a general relationship between the discharge and these stream functions exist, which includes Eqs. (4) and (5) as special cases? Under the assumption that the fluid, if inhomogeneous, is not diffusive, the answers to these questions are positive not only for an incompressible fluid in steady or unsteady flow but also for a compressible fluid in steady flow. Furthermore, for unsteady flows of a compressible fluid, " path functions " corresponding to material surfaces exist in terms of which both the velocity components and the mass contained in a volume bounded by traces of these surfaces can be simply expressed.

II. — THE STREAM FUNCTIONS.

In presenting the stream functions, two ways are possible. One may define the velocity components rather artificially in terms of two functions in such a way that the equation of continuity is identically satisfied, and prove that along a streamline these functions are constant and can therefore be considered as stream functions. Or, alternatively, one may write the equations for the streamline and find the integrals thereof. Since these integrals are constant along the streamline, they are the stream functions desired. The definition of the velocity components in terms of the stream functions is easily obtained from the fact that the stream functions are integrals of the equations for the streamline. Whereas in the former procedure the satisfaction one experiences in identifying the functions used in the definition of the velocity components as stream functions is offset by the artificiality of this definition, the latter procedure avoids this artificiality but still yields a pleasant surprise. As will be shown presently, the definition of the velocity components in terms of stream functions which is arrived at very naturally, is such that the equation of continuity can be identically satisfied. Consequently, the latter procedure will be adopted.

If the velocity components in the directions of increasing x, y, and z are denoted by u, v and w, respectively, the equations for the streamlines are

$$\frac{dx}{u} = \frac{dy}{v} = \frac{dz}{w} \qquad (6)$$

All the integrals of these equations are represented by a system of equations of the form :

$$f(x, y, z) = a \qquad (7)$$

$$g(x, y, z) = b \qquad (8)$$

For any value of the constant a or b, Eq. (7) or (8) represents a stream surface in which streamlines are imbedded, and the intersections of the surfaces represented by Eq. (7) with those represented by Eq. (8) are precisely the streamlines. Thus it is clear that along any streamline the values of f and g are both constant. These functions will then be called the stream functions.

Of course the choice of these functions is not unique, and one can always choose a function $h(f, g)$ such that on a solid boundary h remains constant. That the surface

$$h(f, g) = \text{constant} \qquad (9)$$

is a stream surface follows from the fact that

Eq. (9) can be susbtituted for either Eq. (7) or Eq. (8) to furnish the solution of Eqs. (6) — a standard result in the theory of partial differential equations. Since a fixed boundary must be a stream surface also, Eq. (9) will represent a fixed boundary if it passes through the trace of that boundary for $x = x_0$, say. If this trace is the curve

$$C(y, z) = 0$$

which may be open or closed, one can solve for y and z in terms of f and g from the equations

$$f = f(x_0, y, z)$$
$$g = g(x_0, y, z)$$

and obtain

$$y = y(x_0, f, g)$$
$$z = z(x_0, f, g)$$

When these are substituted in $C(y, z)$, one obtains a function $h(f, g)$ which vanishes on the curve C at $x = x_0$, and hence on the solid boundary.

The use of two stream functions for irrotational flows was discussed by Prášil [3], who, however, did not relate them to the velocity components.

III. — DEFINITION OF VELOCITY BY STREAM FUNCTIONS FOR INCOMPRESSIBLE FLOWS.

Since the f-surfaces and g-surfaces contain the streamlines, their normals must be perpendicular to the streamlines. The direction numbers of these normals are (f_x, f_y, f_z) for the f-surfaces (with the subscripts denoting partial differentiation) and (g_x, g_y, g_z) for the g-surfaces, and the direction numbers of the streamlines are (u, v, w).

Thus

$$u f_x + v f_y + w f_z = 0 \qquad (10)$$

$$u g_x + v g_y + w g_z = 0 \qquad (11)$$

from which one obtains

$$u : v : w = (f_y g_z - f_z g_y) : (f_z g_x - f_x g_z) : (f_x g_y - f_y g_x) \qquad (12)$$

This immediately leads to

$$u = \lambda (f_y g_z - f_z g_y), \quad v = \lambda (f_z g_x - f_x g_z),$$
$$w = \lambda (f_x g_y - f_y g_x) \qquad (13)$$

in which λ is, for the time being, an arbitrary function of x, y, and z. Equation (12) can be written in vector form

$$\vec{v} = \lambda \begin{vmatrix} \vec{i} & \vec{j} & \vec{k} \\ f_x & f_y & f_z \\ g_x & g_y & g_z \end{vmatrix} = \lambda (\text{grad } f) \times (\text{grad } g) \qquad (14)$$

in which $\vec{v} = u\vec{i} + v\vec{j} + w\vec{k}$ is the vector velocity.

Whether the velocity components are well defined by Eqs. (13) or (14) depends on whether the equation of continuity is satisfied by the velocity components so defined. Since :

$$\text{div}(\text{grad } f) \times (\text{grad } g) = 0$$

one has (*)

$$u_x + v_y + w_z = \lambda_x (f_y g_z - f_z g_y)$$
$$+ \lambda_y (f_z g_x - f_x g_z) + \lambda_z (f_x g_y - f_y g_x)$$
$$= (u \lambda_x + v \lambda_y + w \lambda_z)/\lambda = u (\text{Log } \lambda)_x$$
$$+ v (\text{Log } \lambda)_y + (w \text{Log } \lambda)_z$$

If the equation of continuity for incompressible flow is to be satisfied, one must have :

$$u (\text{Log } \lambda)_x + v (\text{Log } \lambda)_y + w (\text{Log } \lambda)_z = 0$$

which shows that $\text{Log } \lambda$ satisfies the same equation as f and g [see Eqs. (10) and (11)]. Hence $\text{Log } \lambda$, and consequently λ, must be a function of f and g, and the definition of velocity in terms of stream functions becomes

$$\vec{v} = \lambda (f, g) (\text{grad } f) \times (\text{grad } g) \qquad (15)$$

It will now be shown that λ can be taken to be 1 without loss of generality. It F and G are functions of f and g, it can be readily shown by a direct calculation that

$$(\text{grad F}) \times (\text{grad G}) = (F_f G_g - F_g G_f) (\text{grad } f) \times (\text{grad } g)$$

This means that if

$$\lambda = F_f G_g - F_g G_f \qquad (16)$$

<hr>

(*) Under french notation, " Log " corresponds to neperian logarithms and to the american notation " ln ".

then

$$v = (\text{grad } F) \times (\text{grad } G)$$

in which the new λ is simply 1. For a given function $\lambda (f, g)$, $F (f, g)$ and $G (f, g)$ can be found such that Eq. (16) is satisfied. In fact, F can be so chosen as to make a solid boundary an F-surface, and Eq. (16) can be solved for G — and there still is a good deal of latitude in the choice of G, since Eq. (16) does not determine G uniquely. Thus, writing small letters for the corresponding capital ones in the last equation, one has

$$v = (\text{grad } f) \times (\text{grad } g) \qquad (14\,a)$$

or

$$u = f_y\,g_z - f_z\,g_y, \quad v = f_z\,g_x - f_x\,g_z,$$
$$w = f_x\,g_y - f_y\,g_x \qquad (13\,a)$$

Equations (13 a) were first written down without derivation by Clebsch [4], who did not identify the f and g as stream functions, and was not concerned with the question of whether taking λ to be one is unnecessarily restrictive — in fact, the factor λ did not appear at all in Clebsch's paper. The present work was done when the writer was not aware of Clebsch's result.

IV. — RELATIONSHIP BETWEEN DISCHARGE AND STREAM FUNCTIONS.

There exists a simple relationship between the discharge through a stream tube and the values of the stream functions on the walls bounding that tube. Let a surface intersecting the streamlines be called the $\varnothing$-surface for brevity. It is a known result in differential geometry that two families of curves orthogonal to each other can be introduced on such a surface. If this is done and if the coordinates are denoted by α and β, the square of a infinitesimal distance ds will be given by

$$ds^2 = h^2\,d\alpha^2 + k^2\,d\beta^2$$

in which h and k are functions of position on the $\varnothing$-surface, and give the metric for that surface. The discharge through a portion S of the $\varnothing$-surface bounded by the traces of

$$f\,(x, y, z) = f_1, \quad f\,(x, y, z) = f_2;$$
$$g\,(x, y, z) = g_1, \quad g\,(x, y, z) = g_2$$

is, from Eq. (14 a),

$$Q = \iint\limits_{S} \left(\frac{f_\alpha}{h}\,\frac{g_\beta}{k} - \frac{f_\beta}{k}\,\frac{g_\alpha}{h} \right) h\,k\,d\alpha\,d\beta = \iint\limits_{S} \frac{\partial\,(f, g)}{\partial\,(\alpha, \beta)}\,d\alpha\,d\beta$$

in which $(f_\alpha\,g_\beta - f_\beta\,g_\alpha)/hk$ is the velocity component normal to the $\varnothing$-surface, and

$$\frac{\partial\,(f, g)}{\partial\,(\alpha, \beta)} = f_\alpha\,g_\beta - f_\beta\,g_\alpha$$

is the Jacobian of transformation between the coordinates (α, β) and (f, g) on the $\varnothing$-surface. Hence, if the directions of increasing $(\alpha, \beta, \varnothing)$ and those of $(f, g, \varnothing)$ are all right-handed, one has

$$Q = \int\limits_{y_1}^{g_2} \int\limits_{f_1}^{f_2} df\,dg = (f_2 - f_1)\,(g_2 - g_1) \qquad (17)$$

which is the generalization of the relationship between discharges and values of stream functions for two-dimensional and axisymmetric flows.

V. — APPLICATION TO SPECIAL CASES.

For two-dimensional flow parallel to the z-plane, one may take

$$g = - z$$

and denote f by Lagrange's stream function ψ. Then Eq. (13 a) or (14 a) reduces to Eq (1), and, for unit thickness in the z-direction, Eq. (17) yields Eq. (4).

For flows with axial symmetry, one may take $g = -\varphi$ for either cylindrical coordinates or spherical coordinates, and denote f by Stokes' stream function ψ. Then Eq. (14 a) reduces to Eqs. (2) or (3), and for discharge through an annulus symmetrical with respect to the axis of symmetry (the z-axis or the axis of θ), Eq (17) reduces to Eq. (5).

VI. — EXTENSION TO FLOWS OF A HETEROGENEOUS OR COMPRESSIBLE FLUID.

For a heterogeneous fluid which is incompressible and non-diffusive, the density ρ remains constant on a path line, therefore (with t denoting time)

$$D\rho/Dt = \rho_t + u\rho_x + v\rho_y + w\rho_z = 0 \qquad (18)$$

The equation of continuity is

$$\rho_t + (\rho u)_x + (\rho v)_y + (\rho w)_z = 0 \qquad (19)$$

From Eqs. (18) and (19), one has again the usual equation of continuity :

$$u_x + v_y + w_z = 0$$

Since the equations for the streamlines remain the same, the developments for a homogeneous fluid apply here exactly, and no further comments are necessary.

If the fluid is compressible one can study only steady flows profitably. For such flows one can take

$$v = (1/\rho)\,(\text{grad } f) \times (\text{grad } g) \qquad (20)$$

It should be noted here that the equation of continuity is no longer the same as in the case of a homogeneous fluid, so ρ does not have to be a function of f and g, i.e., it does not have to remain constant on a streamline. Equation (19) — with the first term omitted — is then satisfied, and if one calculates the more significant mass discharge through the same sort of stream tube considered before, one has

$$M = \iint_S \rho\,\frac{1}{\rho}\,\frac{\partial\,(f,\,g)}{\partial\,(\alpha,\,\beta)}\,d\alpha\,d\beta$$

$$= \int_{g_1}^{g_2}\int_{f_1}^{f_2} df\,dg = (f_2 - f_1)\,(g_2 - g_1)$$

$$\qquad (21)$$

Examples of application to special flows (two-dimensional or axisymmetric) can again be given, but now the point is so clear that such a demonstration is hardly necessary.

Equations (20) and (21) were first discovered by Maeder and Woods [5], and independently discovered by the present writer.

VII. — PATH FUNCTIONS AND MATERIAL SURFACES.

Under the assumption of non-diffusivity the discussion is now complete except for unsteady flows of a compressible fluid. For such flows the differential equations for the path lines are

$$dt = \frac{dx}{u} = \frac{dy}{v} = \frac{dz}{w}$$

the solutions of which can be written as

$$f\,(x,\,y,\,z,\,t) = a \qquad (22)$$

$$g\,(x,\,y,\,z,\,t) = b \qquad (23)$$

$$h\,(x,\,y,\,z,\,t) = c \qquad (24)$$

Since the path lines are intersections of the surfaces described by Eqs. (22), (23), and (24), they must lie in these four-dimensional surfaces, which are therefore material surfaces. If Eqs. (23) and (24) are obtained from

$$\frac{dx}{u} = \frac{dy}{v} = \frac{dz}{w}$$

the surfaces described by them for a definite value of t are also instantaneous stream surfaces.

By arguments similar to those employed in Section 3, one may define the 4-vector (ρu, ρv, ρw, ρ) by

$$\rho u\,\vec{i},\,\rho v\,\vec{j},\,\rho w\,\vec{k},\,\rho\,\vec{1} = \begin{vmatrix} \vec{i} & \vec{j} & \vec{k} & \vec{1} \\ f_x & f_y & f_z & f_t \\ g_x & g_y & g_z & g_t \\ h_x & h_y & h_z & h_t \end{vmatrix} \qquad (25)$$

It can be shown in a straightforward manner that according to this definition the equation of continuity — Eq. (19) — is identically satisfied. Furthermore, at any instant $t = t_0$ the mass contained in a space V bounded by the three pairs of surfaces

$$f\,(x,\,y,\,z,\,t_0) = f_1 \qquad f\,(x,\,y,\,z,\,t_0) = f_2$$

$$g\,(x,\,y,\,z,\,t_0) = g_1 \qquad g\,(x,\,y,\,z,\,t_0) = g_2$$

$$h\,(x,\,y,\,z,\,t_0) = h_1 \qquad h\,(x,\,y,\,z,\,t_0) = h_2$$

is

$$M = \iiint\limits_{V} \begin{vmatrix} f_x & f_y & f_z \\ g_x & g_y & g_z \\ h_x & h_y & h_z \end{vmatrix} dx \, dy \, dz = \int\limits_{h_1 g_1 f_1}^{h_2 g_2 f_2}\!\!\!\iiint df \, dg \, dh = (f_2 - f_1)(g_2 - g_1)(h_2 - h_1) \tag{26}$$

This result is analogous to Eq. (17) or (21).

VIII. — REMARK.

Since the vanishing of the divergence of vorticity ω corresponds to the equation of continuity, and the equations of a vortex line correspond to those of a streamline (see [6]), the foregoing development applies equally well to the kinematics of vortex motion.

Remembering that the circulation Γ around a closed path C is equal to twice the integral of the component of the vorticity normal to a surface S bounded by C over that surface, one is led as before to

$$\Gamma/2 = (f_2 - f_1)(g_2 - g_1) \tag{27}$$

in which the functions f and g are now vorticity functions.

IX. — ACKNOWLEDGMENTS.

This work was partially supported by the Office of Naval Research under Contract No. N8onr-500 with the Iowa Institute of Hydraulic Research. The writer wishes to express his appreciation to Dr. Hunter Rouse and Dr. Louis Landweber, both of the Iowa Institute, for the interest they have shown.

BIBLIOGRAPHY

[1] LAGRANGE (J. L.). — Mémoire sur la théorie du mouvement des fluides, *Nouv. Mém. de l'Acad. de Berlin*, 1781 [*Œuvres*, iv, 720].

[2] STOKES (G. G.). — On the steady motion of incompressible fluids, *Camb. Trans.* vii, 1942 [Paper i, 1].

[3] PRASIL (F.). — *Technische Hydrodynamik*, Julius Springer, Berlin, 1926, pp. 48-56.

[4] CLEBSCH (A.). — Ueber eine allgemeine Transformation der hydrodynamischen Gleichungen, *Crelle* 54, p. 303, 1857.

[5] MAEDER (P. F.) and WOOD (A. D.). — Stream functions and transonic similarity in three-dimensional flow, *Technical Report WT-14, Division of Engineering, Brown University,* October 1954.

[6] LAMB (H.). — *Hydrodynamics*, Dover, New York, 1945, p. 428.

Reprinted from
QUARTERLY OF APPLIED MATHEMATICS
Vol. XVI, No. 2, July, 1958

MAXIMUM SPEED IN STEADY SUBSONIC FLOWS*

BY CHIA-SHUN YIH (*University of Michigan*)

The purpose of this note is to show that the maximum speed in a singularity-free region of any steady subsonic flow must occur on its boundary, provided the flow is isentropic and irrotational. The corresponding result for irrotational flows of an incompressible fluid is well known.

Since the flow under consideration is irrotational, the square of the speed q is given by

$$q^2 = \varphi_{,i}\varphi_{,i} \tag{1}$$

in which φ is the velocity potential, the summation convention is used, and, with Cartesian coordinates,

$$\varphi_{,i} = \frac{\partial \varphi}{\partial x_i}$$

is the jth component of the velocity vector—with the usual minus sign suppressed for convenience. The equation of continuity is, for steady flow,

$$(\rho\varphi_{,i})_{,i} = 0 \tag{2}$$

in which ρ is the density. The equations of motion are

$$(\ln \rho)_{,i} = -\frac{1}{2c^2} (q^2 + 2gx_3)_{,i} \tag{3}$$

if x_3 is measured in a direction opposite to that of the gravitational acceleration g, and c is the local speed of sound. Finally, the Bernoulli equation can be written in the form (with p indicating pressure)

$$c^2 = k \frac{p_0}{\rho_0} - \frac{k-1}{2} (q^2 + 2gx_3) \tag{4}$$

in which k is the ratio of the specific heat at constant pressure to that at constant volume, and the subscripts zero indicate that the quantities involved are taken at some point of reference, where the gas is at rest and from which x_3 is measured.

For a proof, it is sufficient to show that the Laplacian of q^2 is non-negative. Whereas this is easily done for irrotational flows of an incompressible fluid, it cannot be readily established for the flows under discussion. Professors D. Gilbarg (through his publications) and C. Truesdell (by oral communication) have indicated to the writer that

---

[6]G. Borg, Amer. J. Math. **71**, 68 (1949); see also P. Hartman and A. Wintner, *ibid.*, p. 209.
*Received April 18, 1957.

the non-negativeness of $\nabla^2 q^2$ can be replaced by that of

$$(b_{ij}(q^2)_{,ij}$$

if the matrix b_{ij} is positive definite. It will be seen that their suggestion provides one of the key steps to the following proof.

Taking the Laplacian of Eq. (1), one has

$$(q^2)_{,ii} = (\varphi_{,i}\varphi_{,i})_{,ii} = 2\varphi_{,ij}\varphi_{,ij} + 2\varphi_{,i}\varphi_{,iii} \, . \tag{5}$$

But Eq. (2) can be written as

$$\varphi_{,ii} + (\ln \rho)_{,i}\varphi_{,i} = 0$$

so that

$$\varphi_{,i}\varphi_{,iii} = -[(\ln \rho)_{,i}\varphi_{,i}]_{,i}\varphi_{,i} = -(\ln \rho)_{,i}\varphi_{,ii}\varphi_{,i} - (\ln \rho)_{,ii}\varphi_{,i}\varphi_{,i}$$

and Eq. (5) becomes

$$(q^2)_{,ii} = 2\varphi_{,ij}\varphi_{,ij} - 2(\ln \rho)_{,i}\varphi_{,ii}\varphi_{,i} - 2(\ln \rho)_{,ii}\varphi_{,i}\varphi_{,i} \, . \tag{6}$$

By virtue of Eqs. (3) and (4), one has

$$-2(\ln \rho)_{,ii}\varphi_{,i}\varphi_{,i} = \frac{1}{c^2}(q^2)_{,ii}\varphi_{,i}\varphi_{,i} + \frac{k-1}{2c^4}(q^2 + 2gx_3)_{,i}(q^2 + 2gx_3)_{,i}\varphi_{,i}\varphi_{,i} \, . \tag{7}$$

If

$$2\varphi_{,i}\varphi_{,ii} = (q^2)_{,i} \neq 0$$

then q^2 cannot be a maximum. Therefore, one can concentrate on the case

$$2\varphi_{,i}\varphi_{,ii} = (q^2)_{,i} = 0. \tag{8}$$

In this case Eq. (6) becomes, after substitution from Eqs. (7) and (8),

$$(q^2)_{,ii} - \frac{1}{c^2}\varphi_{,i}\varphi_{,i}(q^2)_{,ij} = 2\varphi_{,ij}\varphi_{,ij} + \frac{2g^2(k-1)}{c^4}\delta_{i3}\delta_{j3}\varphi_{,i}\varphi_{,i}$$

or

$$b_{ij}(q^2)_{,ij} = 2\varphi_{,ij}\varphi_{,ij} + \frac{2g^2(k-1)}{c^4}\delta_{i3}\delta_{j3}\varphi_{,i}\varphi_{,i} = \text{positive} \tag{9}$$

in which

$$b_{ij} = \delta_{ij} - \frac{1}{c^2}\varphi_{,i}\varphi_{,i} \, , \quad \text{and} \quad \delta_{ij} = \text{the Kronecker delta.} \tag{10}$$

Now since the flow is subsonic,

$$\frac{\varphi_{,\alpha}\varphi_{,\alpha}}{c^2} \leq 1.$$

Then obviously if

$$b'_{ij} = \frac{\varphi_{,\alpha}\varphi_{,\alpha}}{c^2}\delta_{ij} - \frac{1}{c^2}\varphi_{,i}\varphi_{,i} \tag{11}$$

is positive definite, b_{ij} must also be. The proof will therefore be complete if one can demonstrate that b'_{ij} is positive definite, i.e., the bilinear form $b'_{ij} u_i u_j$ is positive definite— u_1, u_2, and u_3 being any three real numbers. But

$$b'_{ij} u_i u_j = \frac{1}{c^2} \left[(u_1 \varphi_{,2} - u_2 \varphi_{,1})^2 + (u_2 \varphi_{,3} - u_3 \varphi_{,2})^2 + (u_3 \varphi_{,1} - u_1 \varphi_{,3})^2 \right]. \tag{12}$$

Thus b'_{ij} and therefore b_{ij} are positive definite, and Eq. (9) shows that the maximum value of q^2 must occur on the boundary of any singularity-free region.

Since the Bernoulli equation is

$$\frac{k}{k-1} \frac{p}{\rho} + \frac{q^2}{2} + g x_3 = \text{constant}$$

and the equation for isentropic change is

$$p \rho^{-k} = p_0 \rho_0^{-k} = \text{constant},$$

minimum pressure, minimum density, and (from the equation of state for perfect gases) minimum temperature are always associated with the maximum value of

$$q^2 + 2g x_3 .$$

If now one takes the Laplacian of $q^2 + 2g x_3$, one can show by a procedure strictly similar to the foregoing one that the maximum value of $q^2 + 2g x_3$ must occur on the boundary of any singularity-free region. Thus for any such region of a steady subsonic flow, the minimum density, pressure, or temperature must occur on the boundary, provided the flow is irrotational and isentropic.

The boundary of a singularity-free region is, of course, not necessarily a solid boundary. However, in the case of an ambiently uniform flow past closed solid bodies placed in an infinite fluid, one may compare a streamline at infinity with another not entirely at infinity. Both streamlines can be considered to originate and terminate at the same potential planes (on each of which φ is constant). Since there is variation of speed on the latter streamline, the maximum speed thereon must exceed the uniform fluid speed at infinity. This fact, plus the theorem for the speed just proved, shows that, for any ambiently uniform flow of the kind under discussion, the maximum speed must occur on one of the solid boundaries present in the flow if it is free from singularities—since the entire fluid space bounded by infinity and the solid boundaries can be taken to be the region under consideration.

A flow with uniform ambient velocity U past a solid body is physically the same as one caused by that body moving with velocity $- U$ in an otherwise quiescent infinite fluid, i.e., the distributions of pressure and density relative to the body must be the same for both cases. Thus, if gravity is ignored, the minimum density, pressure or temperature in a subsonic flow caused by a body moving steadily in an otherwise quiescent fluid must occur on the boundary of that body if the flow is isentropic, irrotational, and free from singularities.

Reprinted without change of pagination from the
Journal of Fluid Mechanics, *volume* 5, *part* 1, *pp.* 36–40, 1959

Two solutions for inviscid rotational flow with corner eddies

By CHIA-SHUN YIH

Department of Engineering Mechanics, University of Michigan

(Received 11 June 1958)

The steady rotational flow of an inviscid fluid in a two-dimensional channel or a circular tube toward a sink is treated. The velocity distribution at infinity is approximated by a cosine curve (which is nearly parabolic) for the two-dimensional case, and is taken as exactly parabolic for the axisymmetric case. The dependence of vorticity on stream-function is assumed to be everywhere the same as it is for streamlines coming from infinity upstream. The resulting linear equations of motion are solved exactly. The solutions show the rather unusual features of separating streamlines and regions of closed flow (corner eddies).

It is well known that, for a viscous fluid flowing in a channel or pipe with an abrupt contraction, eddies occur at the corners immediately preceding that contraction. The occurrence of such eddies, and their shape and size, are probably influenced strongly by the rotationality of the flow far upstream, and the intention in this note is to show two simple solutions which throw a little light on this influence. Since we are interested here in the effect of upstream vorticity only, the direct effect of viscosity will be ignored, although the distribution of vorticity far upstream will be assumed to be the same (or nearly so) as it would be for a fluid with viscosity. The particular flow to be studied is that of an inviscid homogeneous fluid in a long channel or pipe toward a sink in the middle of a wall across the channel. Under these assumptions, exact solutions of the governing differential systems (assumed to apply to the entire region of flow) will be seen to show the existence of separating streamlines and regions of closed flow or corner eddies. (For another instance of corner eddies, in stratified flow, see Yih (1958).) No singular surfaces occur in the flow (nor could they, in view of the assumption made about the dependence of vorticity on stream-function), and the solutions to be given are unlikely to represent the corresponding flow of a real fluid at large Reynolds number; this is part of the penalty for neglecting viscous forces entirely.

Two-dimensional flow into a line sink

In this section we consider steady two-dimensional flow in a long channel with half-width equal to unity terminating in a wall with a symmetrically placed line sink. The origin of a system of Cartesian co-ordinates is taken at the sink, with the centreline of the channel as the x-axis (see figure 1).

37   *Inviscid rotational flow with corner eddies*

If ψ is Lagrange's stream function, the equation governing steady two-dimensional flow of an inviscid fluid is

$$\nabla^2\psi \equiv \frac{\partial^2\psi}{\partial x^2} + \frac{\partial^2\psi}{\partial y^2} = f(\psi), \tag{1}$$

where $-f(\psi)$ represents the vorticity and depends on ψ alone. The velocity distribution far upstream from the sink should be parabolic if it is to be made the same as that for the laminar flow of a viscous fluid in a long channel. However, a parabolic distribution of the upstream velocity would make equation (1) non-linear and preclude the possibility of a simple solution. Since we are looking here

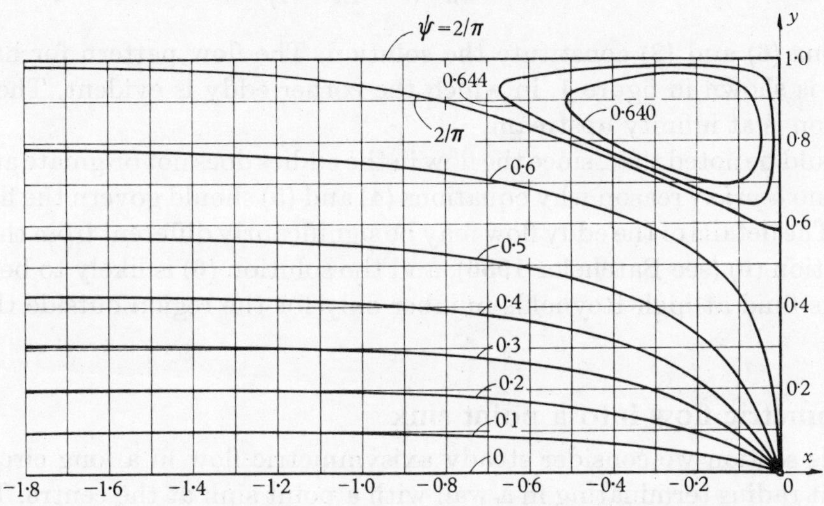

FIGURE 1. Pattern of two-dimensional flow into a sink.

for the effect of non-uniformity of the upstream velocity, a cosine distribution, which is nearly parabolic and makes equation (1) linear, can usefully be assumed. If the upstream velocity U is measured in terms of the centreline velocity $U_{\max}$, the dimensionless upstream velocity is then

$$u = U/U_{\max} = \cos \tfrac{1}{2}\pi y, \tag{2}$$

which vanishes at the walls ($y = \pm 1$). The corresponding (dimensionless) stream function far upstream is then

$$\psi = \int_0^y \cos \tfrac{1}{2}\pi y \, dy = (2/\pi) \sin \tfrac{1}{2}\pi y, \tag{3}$$

and the vorticity is

$$-\nabla^2\psi = \tfrac{1}{2}\pi \sin \tfrac{1}{2}\pi y = \tfrac{1}{4}\pi^2\psi. \tag{4}$$

Thus the function $f(\psi)$ is equal to $-\tfrac{1}{4}\pi^2\psi$ not only far upstream but everywhere, and equation (1) becomes

$$\nabla^2\psi = -\tfrac{1}{4}\pi^2\psi. \tag{5}$$

The boundary conditions on ψ are

   (i) $\psi \to (2/\pi)\sin \tfrac{1}{2}\pi y$ as $x \to -\infty$,

  (ii) $\psi = \pm(2/\pi)$ for $y = \pm 1$,

 (iii) $\psi = \mp(2/\pi)$ for $y \lessgtr 0$ and $x = 0$.

Solution of equation (5) by the method of separation of variables yields

$$\psi = (2/\pi)\sin\tfrac{1}{2}\pi y + \sum_{n=1}^{\infty} C_n \sin n\pi y \exp\{(n^2-\tfrac{1}{4})^{\frac{1}{2}}\pi x\}, \tag{6}$$

which satisfies (i) and (ii), and is an odd function of y. It is therefore only necessary to determine the C_n to satisfy

$$\sum_{n=1}^{\infty} C_n \sin n\pi y = (2/\pi)(1-\sin\tfrac{1}{2}\pi y) \quad (0 < y \leqslant 1), \tag{7}$$

which yields
$$C_n = \frac{4}{n\pi^2}\left(1 + \frac{\cos n\pi}{4n^2-1}\right). \tag{8}$$

Equations (6) and (8) constitute the solution. The flow pattern for half of the channel is shown in figure 1, in which the corner eddy is evident. The point of separation is at infinity upstream.

It should be noted that, since the flow in the eddies does not originate at infinity, there is no *a priori* reason why equations (4) and (5) should govern the flow in the eddies. The details of the eddy flow may be significantly different from those given by equation (6) (see Batchelor 1956), and the solution (6) is likely to be valid for a viscous fluid at high Reynolds number only for the region outside the corner eddies.

Axisymmetric flow into a point sink

In this section we consider steady axisymmetric flow in a long circular pipe with unit radius terminating in a wall with a point sink at the centre. The point sink will be taken to be the origin of a set of cylindrical co-ordinates, with the centreline of the pipe as the z-axis and with the radial distance therefrom denoted by r (see figure 2).

If ψ is now Stokes's stream function, steady axisymmetric flow of an inviscid fluid is governed by the equation

$$\frac{\partial^2\psi}{\partial r^2} - \frac{1}{r}\frac{\partial\psi}{\partial r} + \frac{\partial^2\psi}{\partial z^2} = r^2 F(\psi), \tag{9}$$

where $rF(\psi)$ represents the vorticity and F depends on ψ alone (Lamb 1945). The velocity distribution far upstream can here be assumed to be parabolic, as for the laminar flow of a viscous fluid in a long pipe, so that the dimensionless velocity far upstream is

$$w = W/W_{\max} = r^2 - 1. \tag{10}$$

The corresponding dimensionless stream function far upstream is

$$\psi = \tfrac{1}{2}r^2 - \tfrac{1}{4}r^4, \tag{11}$$

and the vorticity there is $-2r$. Thus the function F is constant (-2) far upstream and hence everywhere, and the equation governing the flow everywhere is

$$\frac{\partial^2\psi}{\partial r^2} - \frac{1}{r}\frac{\partial\psi}{\partial r} + \frac{\partial^2\psi}{\partial z^2} = -2r^2. \tag{12}$$

39   *Inviscid rotational flow with corner eddies*

The boundary conditions are

    (i) $\psi \to \frac{1}{2}r^2 - \frac{1}{4}r^4$ as $z \to \infty$,

    (ii) $\psi = \frac{1}{4}$ for $r = 1$,

    (iii) $\psi = \frac{1}{4}$ for $z = 0$ $(0 < r \leqslant 1)$.

Solution of equation (12) by the separation of variables yields

$$\psi = \tfrac{1}{2}r^2 - \tfrac{1}{4}r^4 + \sum_{n=1}^{\infty} C_n r J_1(\lambda_n r)\exp(-\lambda_n z) \tag{13}$$

which satisfies (i) and (ii) if λ_n are the zeros of $J_1(\lambda)$. The coefficients C_n are determined by the condition (iii), and we find

$$C_n = \frac{1}{2\lambda_n J_0^2(\lambda_n)}\left(1 + \frac{8J_0(\lambda_n)}{\lambda_n^2}\right) \tag{14}$$

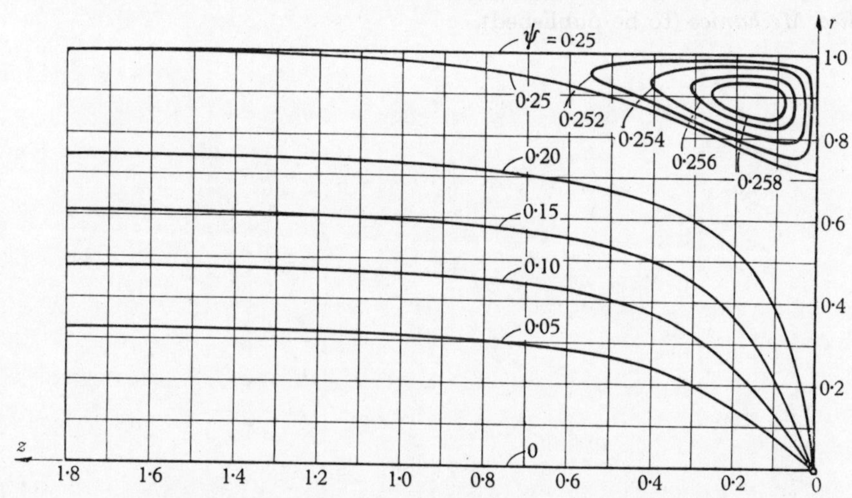

FIGURE 2. Pattern of axisymmetric flow into a sink.

by multiplying equation (13) (with $z = 0$) by $J_1(\lambda_m r)$, integrating between 0 and 1, and using the orthogonality of the functions $J_1(\lambda_n r)$. The detailed calculation for C_n involves integrations by parts and some known relationships for J_0 and J_1, and is omitted because it is straightforward. Equations (13) and (14) then constitute the solution.

The flow pattern for half of the meridianal plane is shown in figure 2, in which the ring-shaped corner eddy is evident. The point of separation is again at infinity. Again, the solution is strictly applicable to a fluid of small viscosity only outside the region of the ring eddy; equation (12) has been *assumed* to be valid for the whole field of flow, but the solution shows a region of closed flow where the vorticity is not determined by conditions far upstream and there is no *a priori* reason (other than convenience) why equation (12) should be applicable. We note that equation (12) does state that the vorticity is proportional to r everywhere, and therefore in the eddy in particular, which coincides with the exact result for flow with closed streamlines at high Reynolds number (Batchelor 1956); however, the constant of proportionality is also fixed by equation (12) and is unlikely to have here the value that would be required for a fluid with non-zero viscosity. As in the two-dimensional case, the flow shown in figure 2 is free from singular surfaces.

The computational assistance rendered by Mr Wei Lai and Mr Walter R. Debler is much appreciated. Mr Lai's assistance was made available to the author through a faculty research fund granted by the Rackham Graduate School of the University of Michigan. Mr Debler's assistance was supplied by the Office of Ordnance Research, U.S. Army.

REFERENCES

BATCHELOR, G. K. 1956 On steady laminar flow with closed streamlines at large Reynolds number. *J. Fluid Mech.* **1**, 117.

LAMB, H. 1945 *Hydrodynamics*. New York: Dover.

YIH, C.-S. 1958 On the flow of a stratified fluid. *Proc. Third U.S. National Congress of Applied Mechanics* (to be published).

—NOTES—

EFFECTS OF GRAVITATIONAL OR ELECTROMAGNETIC FIELDS ON FLUID MOTION*

By CHIA-SHUN YIH (*University of Michigan*)

Summary. It is shown in this paper that the effect of gravity on a stratified fluid is to inhibit steady motion in the direction of gravity; that, for small values of the magnetic viscosity, the effect of a main magnetic field is to make steady weak motions of a fluid independent of the distance along the lines of force; and that, again for small values of the magnetic viscosity, the effect of a uniform electric field is to make steady weak motions of a fluid rotationally symmetric with respect to an axis in the direction of the field. These results, together with a similar one of Proudman (1916) [1] for a fluid with general rotation, enable one to state that the effects of rotation, gravity, and electromagnetic fields (for small magnetic viscosity) are to endow the fluid with a certain anisotropic rigidity by "stiffening" it along the vorticity lines, the isopycnic surfaces or lines, or the lines of force, as the case may be. In the case of a weak steady motion or relative motion, this "stiffening" has the effect of reducing the *a priori* number of physical or at least mathematical dimensions of the motion by one.

1. Introduction. Since Proudman [1] showed that the effect of rotation on weak steady relative motion of an inviscid fluid is to make it two-dimensional, in the sense that the motion is independent of the distance along the axis of rotation, experiments performed by Taylor [2], Long [3], and others have largely supported his assertion. Recently, Gariél's experiments with a stratified fluid and Lehnert's with mercury have indicated similar effects of gravity and of a magnetic field, respectively. The purpose of this paper is to describe these effects, to predict the effect of an electric current on weak steady motions of a fluid, to explain all these effects mathematically and, as far as possible, to bring out their similarity to one another. The fluid is assumed to be inviscid and incompressible throughout and, in the case of an electromagnetic field, to have negligible magnetic viscosity.

2. Effect of rotation. For convenience of comparison and for completeness, Proudman's demonstration [1] of the effect of rotation will be briefly presented. If the general rotation of the fluid is Ω, the axis of rotation can be chosen to be the x-axis. Two other axes, both rotating with angular velocity Ω, can be chosen to provide a rotating cartesian frame of reference, with coordinates (x, y, z). The velocity components relative to this rotating frame in the directions of x, y and z will be denoted by u, v, and w respectively. The equations of motion are then (Morgan [4]):

$$\frac{Du}{Dt} = -\frac{\partial P}{\partial x}, \tag{1}$$

$$\frac{Dv}{Dt} - 2\Omega w = -\frac{\partial P}{\partial y}, \tag{2}$$

$$\frac{Dw}{Dt} + 2\Omega w = -\frac{\partial P}{\partial z}, \tag{3}$$

---

*Received August 2, 1957.

Reprinted from *Quart. Appl. Math.* **16** (1959) 409–415.

in which

$$\frac{D}{Dt} = \frac{\partial}{\partial t} + u \frac{\partial}{\partial x} + v \frac{\partial}{\partial y} + w \frac{\partial}{\partial z} ,$$

and

$$P = \frac{p}{\rho} - \frac{1}{2} \Omega^2(y^2 + z^2) + \phi \tag{4}$$

with p, ρ, and ϕ as the pressure, density, and the body-force potential, respectively. The equation of continuity is

$$\frac{\partial u}{\partial x} + \frac{\partial v}{\partial y} + \frac{\partial w}{\partial z} = 0. \tag{5}$$

For steady and weak relative motion, Eqs. (1) to (3) become

$$\frac{\partial P}{\partial x} = 0, \tag{6}$$

$$\frac{\partial P}{\partial y} = 2\Omega w, \tag{7}$$

$$\frac{\partial P}{\partial z} = -2\Omega v. \tag{8}$$

By cross-differentiation of Eqs. (7) and (8), it can be readily shown that

$$\frac{\partial v}{\partial y} + \frac{\partial w}{\partial z} = 0. \tag{9}$$

It follows from Eq. (5) that

$$\frac{\partial u}{\partial x} = 0. \tag{10}$$

Furthermore, by differentiation of Eqs. (7) and (8) with respect to x it can readily be seen with the aid of Eq. (6) that

$$\frac{\partial v}{\partial x} = 0, \qquad \frac{\partial w}{\partial x} = 0. \tag{11}$$

Equations (10) and (11) indicate that the motion is independent of x. Hence, the steady and weak relative motion is two-dimensional. In a loose way, one might say that the general rotation has endowed the fluid with a certain rigidity along the vorticity lines.

It can be readily shown that for symmetric motion the radial velocity component vanishes (so that the streamlines are spirals wound around circular cylinders). This situation can be directly compared with the vanishing of the vertical velocity component in the steady weak motion of a stratified fluid to be treated in the following section, for in the case of rotation one may imagine a virtual gravity acting in the radial direction, according to Mach and Einstein.

3. Effect of gravity.   One now turns to the effect of gravity on steady and weak motions of a stratified fluid. Let the z-axis be vertical. The equations of motion are

$$\rho \frac{Du}{Dt} = -\frac{\partial p}{\partial x}, \tag{12}$$

$$\rho \frac{Dv}{Dt} = -\frac{\partial p}{\partial y}, \tag{13}$$

$$\rho \frac{Dw}{Dt} = -\frac{\partial p}{\partial z} - g\rho, \tag{14}$$

in which D/Dt, as usual, stands for the substantial differentiation. The equation of incompressibility is

$$\frac{D\rho}{Dt} = 0 \tag{15}$$

which permits the equation of continuity to be given by Eq. (5).

The density can be expressed as the sum of a prevailing density ρ_1, which depends only on z, and a perturbation density ρ':

$$\rho = \rho_1(z) + \rho'. \tag{16}$$

For steady weak motion, Eqs. (12) and (13) become

$$\frac{\partial p}{\partial x} = 0, \qquad \frac{\partial p}{\partial y} = 0 \tag{17}$$

and hence, from Eqs. (14) and (16) one obtains

$$\frac{\partial \rho'}{\partial x} = 0, \qquad \frac{\partial \rho'}{\partial y} = 0. \tag{18}$$

Equations (17) and (18) are correct to the first order. But from Eqs. (15) and (16) it follows that

$$u \frac{\partial \rho'}{\partial x} + v \frac{\partial \rho'}{\partial y} + w \frac{d\rho_1}{dz} + w \frac{\partial \rho'}{\partial z} = 0 \tag{19}$$

so that, from Eqs. (18),

$$w = 0 \tag{20}$$

to the second order. Thus gravity inhibits steady velocity in the vertical direction, and if the disturbance is not strong enough, steady motion can occur in horizontal planes only. This situation is directly comparable to that for symmetric relative motion with general rotation, provided that that motion is steady and weak, as mentioned in the last section. In the present case, it is the isopycnic surfaces or lines that are "stiffened."

Another result comparable to Proudman's can also be obtained. If two-dimensional motion is considered to start with, so that v is zero, Eqs. (5) and (20) yield

$$\frac{\partial u}{\partial x} = 0. \tag{21}$$

Thus the motion will be one-dimensional, in the sense that the state of affairs does not change with x—in much the same way that Proudman's motion is independent of x. In both cases x is measured in a direction normal to that of gravitation or virtual gravitation created by rotation. The essential one-dimensional character of steady weak motions of a stratified fluid has been experimentally demonstrated by Gariél [5].

4. Effect of a magnetic field.   One now considers a uniform magnetic field $\mathbf{H}_0$ acting in the x-direction, and imagines a weak steady motion to take place in this field. The fluid is assumed to be homogeneous. The perturbation magnetic field will be denoted by $\mathbf{h}$, so that the total magnetic field is

$$\mathbf{H} = \mathbf{H}_0 + \mathbf{h}. \tag{22}$$

The vector equation of motion is (all electromagnetic variables being measured in emu), with $\mathbf{g}$ as the body force per unit mass,

$$\rho \frac{D\mathbf{v}}{Dt} = -\operatorname{grad} p + \rho\mathbf{g} + \mu\mathbf{j} \times \mathbf{H} \tag{23}$$

in which $\mathbf{v}$ is the velocity vector, μ is the magnetic permeability and $\mathbf{j}$ the current density. Since

$$\operatorname{curl} \mathbf{H} = 4\pi\mathbf{j}, \tag{24}$$

Eq. (23) may be written

$$\rho \frac{D\mathbf{v}}{Dt} = -\operatorname{grad} p' - \operatorname{grad}\left(\frac{\mu H^2}{8\pi}\right) + \operatorname{div}\left(\frac{\mu\mathbf{H}\mathbf{H}}{4\pi}\right) \tag{25}$$

in which

$$p' = p + \rho\phi \tag{26}$$

with ϕ again denoting the potential of the body force. The intensity $\mathbf{E}$ of the electric field is related to the magnetic field by

$$\operatorname{curl} \mathbf{E} = -\mu \frac{\partial \mathbf{H}}{\partial t}. \tag{27}$$

Furthermore, the current density, electric field, magnetic field, and velocity field are related by the equation

$$\mathbf{j} = \sigma(\mathbf{E} + \mu\mathbf{v} \times \mathbf{H}) \tag{28}$$

in which σ is the electric conductivity. The fluid being homogeneous, the equation of continuity is again given by Eq. (5).

Since the motion under consideration is weak and steady, Eq. (25) becomes, after linearization:

$$\frac{\partial p'}{\partial x} = 0, \tag{29}$$

$$\frac{\partial p'}{\partial y} = \frac{H_0}{4\pi}\left(\frac{\partial h_y}{\partial x} - \frac{\partial h_x}{\partial y}\right), \tag{30}$$

$$\frac{\partial p'}{\partial z} = \frac{H_0}{4\pi}\left(\frac{\partial h_z}{\partial x} - \frac{\partial h_x}{\partial z}\right). \tag{31}$$

From Eqs. (29) to (31) one obtains by cross differentiation

$$\frac{\partial}{\partial x} \operatorname{curl} \mathbf{h} = 0 \tag{32}$$

or, by virtue of Eq. (24),

$$\frac{\partial}{\partial x} \mathbf{j} = 0 \tag{33}$$

so that the current density is independent of x. Although Eq. (33) is not needed to prove the independence of the fluid flow on x, it contains a result which is worthy of note.

The linearized form of Eq. (28) is

$$j_x = \sigma E_x , \tag{34}$$

$$j_y = \sigma(E_y + \mu H_0 w), \tag{35}$$

$$j_z = \sigma(E_z - \mu H_0 v). \tag{36}$$

Since the motion under consideration is steady, Eq. (27) becomes

$$\text{curl } \mathbf{E} = 0. \tag{37}$$

From Eqs. (24) and (34) to (37) one obtains, by the aid of Eq. (5),

$$\frac{\partial}{\partial x} \mathbf{v} = \frac{\eta}{H_0} \nabla^2 \mathbf{h} \tag{38}$$

in which

$$\eta = (4\pi\mu\sigma)^{-1} \tag{39}$$

is the magnetic viscosity. If the magnetic viscosity is negligible, Eq. (38) becomes

$$\frac{\partial \mathbf{v}}{\partial x} = 0 \tag{40}$$

so that the motion does not change with x. Thus the magnetic field seems to have endowed the fluid with a certain rigidity, as if the material along the lines of forces had been stiffened to give the fluid a fibrous structure. If the motion is axisymmetric (e.g., if a sphere is towed through the fluid), from the equation of continuity one can easily show that the radial velocity is zero. The motion is then one dimensional in any meridianal plane or, if no revolving motion exists, even truly one-dimensional. It may be mentioned that for small values of the magnetic viscosity the lines of force always move with the fluid, or, to use Alfven's expression, are "frozen" into the material (Cowling [6], pp. 5–6). In the case of steady weak motions, the word "frozen" used by Alfven acquires a much stronger meaning, as explained above.

5. Effect of an electric current. Consider now a uniform electric current $\mathbf{j}_0$ flowing in the z-direction, with (r, θ, z) as the cylindrical coordinates. From Eq. (24) one obtains

$$H_\theta = 4\pi j_0 r \tag{41}$$

the other two components of the main magnetic field being zero. Eliminating $\mathbf{j}$ and $\mathbf{E}$ from Eqs. (24), (27), and (28), one obtains

$$\frac{\partial \mathbf{H}}{\partial t} = \text{curl } (\mathbf{v} \times \mathbf{H}) + \eta \nabla^2 \mathbf{H} \tag{42}$$

which, for steady motion and negligible magnetic viscosity, becomes

$$\text{curl } (\mathbf{v} \times \mathbf{H}) = 0. \tag{43}$$

To the first order, one has, with (u, v, w) for (v_r, v_θ, v_z),

$$\mathbf{v} \times \mathbf{H} = (-H_\theta w, 0, H_\theta u)$$

and

$$\operatorname{curl}(\mathbf{v} \times \mathbf{H}) = \left\{ \frac{1}{r} \frac{\partial}{\partial \theta}(H_\theta u), -\left[\frac{\partial}{\partial r}(H_\theta u) + \frac{\partial}{\partial z}(H_\theta w) \right], \frac{1}{r} \frac{\partial}{\partial \theta}(H_\theta w) \right\}. \tag{44}$$

From Eqs. (41), (43) and (44) it follows that

$$\frac{\partial u}{\partial \theta} = 0, \tag{45}$$

$$\frac{\partial(ru)}{\partial r} + \frac{\partial(rw)}{\partial z} = 0, \tag{46}$$

$$\frac{\partial w}{\partial \theta} = 0. \tag{47}$$

But the equation of continuity is

$$\frac{\partial(ru)}{\partial r} + \frac{\partial v}{\partial \theta} + \frac{\partial(rw)}{\partial z} = 0.$$

Thus Eq. (46) yields

$$\frac{\partial v}{\partial \theta} = 0 \tag{48}$$

which, together with Eqs. (45) and (47), states that the motion is independent of θ. The meaning of this statement can be fully realized physically by imagining an object to be towed slowly and steadily along a circular path about an axis parallel to the main electric current. According to the result just obtained, the fluid will be pushed along circular paths or along the lines of force of the main magnetic field induced by the main electric current. What has been said in the previous section about the "stiffening" of material along lines of force can be said in the present case also.

6. **Concluding remarks.** From the foregoing it may be concluded that, under the assumptions stated, the effects of rotation, gravity, or an electromagnetic field are to stiffen the fluid along the vorticity lines, isopycnic surfaces or lines, or lines of force, respectively. In the case of weak steady motions or relative motions, this "stiffening" has the effect of reducing the *a priori* number of physical or at least the mathematical dimensions of motion by one, in the various senses stated. In steady weak motions of a stratified fluid the velocity in the direction of gravity vanishes, and simple cases exist in which motion normal to vorticity lines or lines of forces are completely inhibited. For the motion of a conductive fluid due to the disturbance of an object slowly and steadily towed through it along a circular path, a torus-shaped mass of fluid will revolve around the axis of symmetry if a main uniform electric current is flowing longitudinally.

As already mentioned, the concept of a virtual gravitational field created by rotation helps to unify the understanding of many phenomena of fluid motion involving gravity and rotation.

7. **Acknowledgment.** This work is sponsored by the Office of Ordnance Research, U. S. Army.

Bibliography

1. J. Proudman, *On the motion of solids in a liquid possessing vorticity*, Proc. Roy. Soc. **A92**, 408-24 (1916)
2. Sir Geoffrey Taylor, *Experiments on the motion of solid bodies in rotating fluids*, Proc. Roy. Soc. **A104**, 213-18 (1923)
3. R. R. Long, *Steady motion around a symmetrical obstacle moving along the axis of a rotating fluid*, J. Met. **10**, 197-203 (1953)
4. G. W. Morgan, *A study of motions in a rotating liquid*, Proc. Roy. Soc. **A206**, 108-30 (1951)
5. Paul Gariél, *Recherches experimentales sur l'écoulement de couches superposées de fluides de densités differentes*, La Houille Blanche, No. 1, 56-64 (1949)
6. T. G. Cowling, *Magnetohydrodynamics*, Interscience, 1957

Reprinted without change of pagination from the
Proceedings of the Royal Society, A, *volume* 258, pp. 90–100, 1960

Finite two-dimensional cavities

By Chia-Shun Yih*

Department of Engineering Mechanics, University of Michigan

(*Communicated by Sir Geoffrey Taylor, F.R.S.*—*Received* 5 *April* 1960)

General formulae for generating unsteady potential flows characterized by the presence of a cavity (which can be finite in extent) are presented. The fluid at infinity is either in accelerative motion or at rest, but the two cases are essentially distinct. A class of solution is given explicitly for each case. Steady flows in a gravitational field are also investigated, and a class of solutions representing such flows past a finite cavity is given. Some of the solutions in these three classes have been carried out in detail.

1. Introduction

It is well known that finite cavities with a stagnation point are impossible in steady streaming flows if gravity is neglected. Von Kármán (1949) gave a solution for a two-dimensional accelerating flow past a plate with an attached finite cavity behind. This flow is different† from the flow caused by the motion of an accelerating plate with an attached cavity. Solutions for ambiently quiescent flows caused by accelerating bodies and characterized by the presence of a finite cavity have not previously been found. Nor do simple solutions exist for flows with finite cavities in the presence of a gravitational field, although Garabedian (1957) has given some mathematically elaborate solutions for bubbles rising in a liquid.

In this paper, two general formulae for generating unsteady flows with cavities are presented. The fluid at infinity is either in accelerative motion or at rest. With one of these formulae, a class of solutions containing von Kármán's solution as a limiting case is obtained. Another class of solutions for ambiently quiescent flows caused by an accelerating bubble (with the attached boundary) is obtained by the use of the other formula. Finally, a class of solutions for steady streaming flow past a finite cavity in a gravitational field is given. The details of some of the solutions in these three classes have been carried out.

2. Finite cavities in unsteady flows

Although the flow caused by an immersed solid body moving with constant velocity is unsteady, it can be rendered steady by adopting a frame of reference moving with the body. The pressure distribution over the body and, if there is a cavity, the shape of the cavity are entirely the same, whether fixed or moving co-ordinates are used. The same cannot be said of flows caused by accelerating bodies. The pressure distribution on an accelerating body and that on a stationary body in a stream flowing (and accelerating) in the opposite direction are different. If there is no cavity or free surface, the difference is simply $a\rho x$ in which a is the

---

* University of Cambridge, 1959–60.

† The difference seems to have escaped the serious attention of von Kármán, as can be seen from the two opening paragraphs of his paper (1949).

91   *Finite two-dimensional cavities*

acceleration, ρ the density of the fluid, and x the distance along the direction of motion of the body, measured from an arbitrary origin. The velocity of the flow caused by the accelerating body can, as always, be added to a uniform velocity to produce the velocity field for an accelerating flow streaming past the body, now considered fixed. However, if there is a cavity, the change in pressure $(a\rho x)$ would render a moving cavity unsuitable as a stationary cavity, and vice versa. Therefore in studying truly unsteady flows with a free surface, it is necessary to distinguish the case in which the body is accelerating from the case in which it is stationary.

(a) *Body and cavity stationary*

If the body is stationary and the cavity is constant in form, the velocity potential Φ can be written (von Kármán 1949)

$$\Phi = U(t)\,f(x, y), \tag{1}$$

in which $U(t)$ is the unsteady velocity at infinity, assumed to be in the direction of x, and x and y are Cartesian co-ordinates. The boundary of the body and the attached cavity form part of a streamline, on which we shall suppose, without loss of generality, the stream function to be zero. The dynamic condition on the boundary of the cavity is that the pressure p be constant. This can, without loss of generality, be expressed by

$$-\frac{\partial \Phi}{\partial t} + \tfrac{1}{2}(\Phi_x^2 + \Phi_y^2) = 0, \tag{2}$$

with subscripts indicating partial differentiation. In order that (2) be satisfied, the velocity U must satisfy the differential equation

$$-a + \lambda U^2 = 0, \tag{3}$$

in which $a = \mathrm{d}U/\mathrm{d}t$ is the acceleration of the fluid at infinity, and λ is a constant with the dimension of the reciprocal of a length. The Froude number based on U, a, and λ is $U^2\lambda/a$, and has the value 1. But since the relationship that λ bears to a physical length of the problem is as yet unknown, the meaningful Froude number for which a solution is possible is yet to be found. The solution of (3) is

$$U = \frac{U_0}{1 - U_0 \lambda t}, \tag{4}$$

in which U_0 is the value of U at $t = 0$. Now equations (1) to (3) yield

$$f_x^2 + f_y^2 = 2\lambda f. \tag{5}$$

If

$$f = \frac{\phi}{\lambda},$$

so that

$$\Phi = \frac{U}{\lambda}\,\phi, \tag{6}$$

then the dynamic condition on the surface of the cavity is, in terms of ϕ:

$$\phi_x^2 + \phi_y^2 = 2\lambda^2 \phi. \tag{7}$$

If ψ is complex conjugate of ϕ, then on the surface of the body and of the cavity

$$\psi = 0. \tag{8}$$

It is obvious that the solution for ϕ is the same if λ and therefore Φ change sign. Consequently, for every accelerating flow past a body and an attached cavity there is a decelerating flow in the opposite direction past the same body and the same attached cavity, as originally oriented.

The complex potential

$$w = \phi + i\psi$$

must be such that (7) and (8) are satisfied, and*

$$\mathrm{d}w/\mathrm{d}z = -\lambda \quad \text{as} \quad z \to \infty, \tag{9}$$

in which z is the complex variable $x + iy$. Furthermore, there must not be any singularities outside of the body and the cavity. A general transformation that satisfies (7) to (9) is, as can be easily verified,

$$2\lambda \frac{\mathrm{d}z}{\mathrm{d}w} = -H'(w) + i\left[\frac{2}{w} - (H'(w))^2\right]^{\frac{1}{2}}, \tag{10}$$

in which H' is subject to the condition that there should be no singularities in the fluid, and, like the square root of the bracket, must be real on the surface of the cavity. The prime on H' is used for consistency with later development, and could have been omitted here.

One class of solutions is furnished by (10) and

$$H'(w) = \left(\frac{w-A}{w-B}\right)^{\frac{1}{2}}, \tag{11}$$

in which A and B are real and positive. Equation (10) then becomes

$$2\lambda \frac{\mathrm{d}z}{\mathrm{d}w} = -\left(\frac{w-A}{w-B}\right)^{\frac{1}{2}} + i\left(-\frac{(w-\alpha)(w-\beta)}{w(w-B)}\right)^{\frac{1}{2}}, \tag{12}$$

in which α and β are the roots of the equation

$$w^2 - (2+A)w + 2B = 0. \tag{13}$$

We shall suppose

$$A \leqslant B, \quad \alpha < \beta < B. \tag{14}$$

If

$$\alpha < A < \beta, \tag{15}$$

close examination of (12) reveals that the body and cavity are of the form shown in figure 1a. If

$$\alpha < \beta < A < B, \tag{16}$$

the body and cavity are shown in figure 1b. In either case the stagnation points corresponding to $w = B$ can be brought to the same level (value of y) as the stagnation point for $w = 0$, by proper choices of A and B. If

$$A = B,$$

the body and cavity are shown in figure 4, and there is only one stagnation point (at $w = 0$).

---

* The convention $\mathrm{d}w/\mathrm{d}z = -u + iv$ is used here, u and v being velocity components in the directions of increasing x and y, respectively.

93 *Finite two-dimensional cavities*

The actual integration of (12) for the cases characterized by (15) and (16), though complicated in general, is not impossible. The integration for the particular case

$$\alpha = \beta < A < B \tag{17}$$

is indeed very simple. In this case

$$\alpha = \beta = \frac{2+A}{2}, \quad B = \frac{(2+A)^2}{8}, \tag{18}$$

and

$$2\lambda \frac{dz}{dw} = -\left(\frac{w-A}{w-B}\right)^{\frac{1}{2}} + i(w-\alpha)\left(-\frac{1}{w(w-B)}\right)^{\frac{1}{2}}, \tag{19}$$

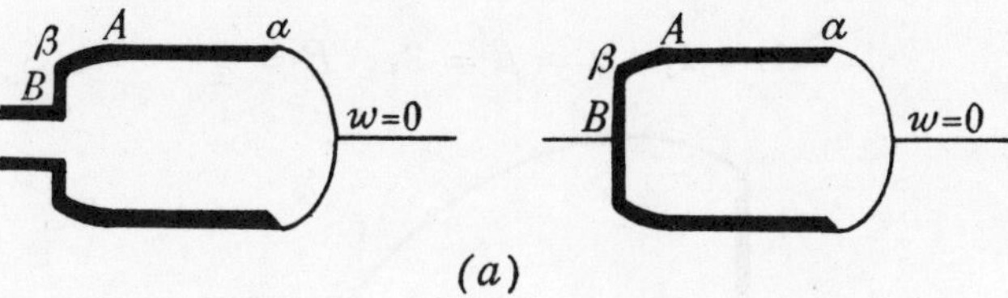

(a)

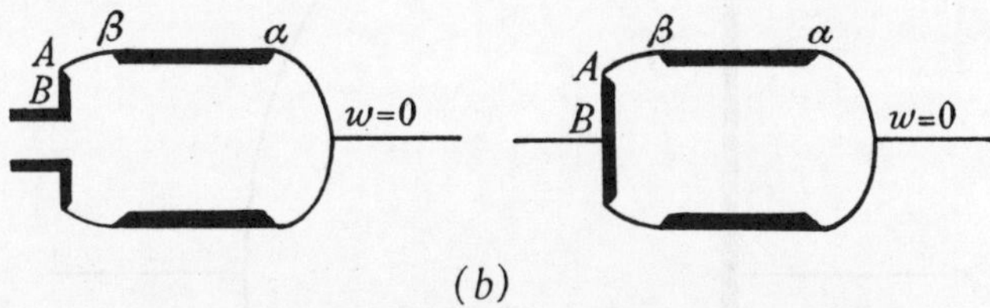

(b)

FIGURE 1. (a) Forms of boundary and cavity for $\alpha < A < \beta$.
(b) Forms of boundary and cavity for $\alpha < \beta < A$.

and the solid boundaries $\alpha\beta$ in figure 1b disappear. Integration of (19) yields the following parametric equation for the cavity shape:

$$z = \frac{1}{2\lambda}(I \pm iJ),$$

in which, form $w = 0$ to $w = A$,

$$I(w) = -\int_0^w \left(\frac{w-A}{w-B}\right)^{\frac{1}{2}} dw = -\int_0^w \left(\frac{A-w}{B-w}\right)^{\frac{1}{2}} dw$$

$$= (B-A)\left[\frac{\sqrt{\{(B-w)(A-w)\}}}{B-A} - \ln\left\{\sqrt{\left(\frac{B-w}{B-A}\right)} + \sqrt{\left(\frac{A-w}{B-A}\right)}\right\}\right]_0^w, \tag{20}$$

$$J(w) = \int_0^w (w-\alpha)\left(-\frac{1}{w(w-B)}\right)^{\frac{1}{2}} dw$$

$$= -\sqrt{\{w(B-w)\}} + \left(\frac{B}{2}-\alpha\right)\left[\sin^{-1}\left(1-\frac{2w}{B}\right) - \frac{\pi}{2}\right], \tag{21}$$

in which the positive value of the radical is to be taken, and the arc sine has a value between $-\frac{1}{2}\pi$ and $\frac{1}{2}\pi$. From $w = A$ to $w = B$, dz is purely imaginary, and for $w > B$ and $w < 0$, dz is real. Thus the streamline $\psi = 0$ consists of the surface of the cavity ($0 \leqslant w \leqslant A$) and straight lines. The distance from z_A to z_B can be obtained from

$$z_B - z_A = -\frac{1}{2\lambda}\int_A^B \left(\frac{w-A}{w-B}\right)^{\frac{1}{2}} dw + \frac{i}{2\lambda}\int_A^B (w-\alpha)\left(-\frac{1}{w(w-B)}\right)^{\frac{1}{2}} dw$$

$$= \frac{i}{2\lambda}\left[\frac{\pi}{4}\left(1-\frac{A}{2}\right)^2 + J(B) - J(A)\right]. \tag{22}$$

Chia-Shun Yih

The difference in the y-values of z_B and z_0 is

$$y_B - y_0 = \frac{1}{2\lambda}\left[\frac{\pi}{4}\left(1 - \frac{A}{2}\right)^2 - \left(-\frac{2+A}{2} + \frac{(2+A)^2}{16}\right)(-\pi)\right]$$

$$= \frac{\pi}{8\lambda}\left(\frac{A^2}{2} - 2A - 2\right). \tag{23}$$

Thus for
$$A = 2 + 2\sqrt{2}, \quad B = 3 + 2\sqrt{2} \quad \text{and} \quad \alpha = \beta = 2 + \sqrt{2}, \tag{24}$$

we have $y_B = y_0$, and the cavity is attached to a flat plate, as shown in figure 2. The form of the boundary and the cavity for the case

$$A = 4, \quad \alpha = \beta = 3, \quad B = \tfrac{9}{2} \tag{25}$$

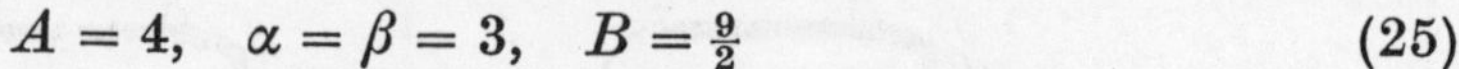

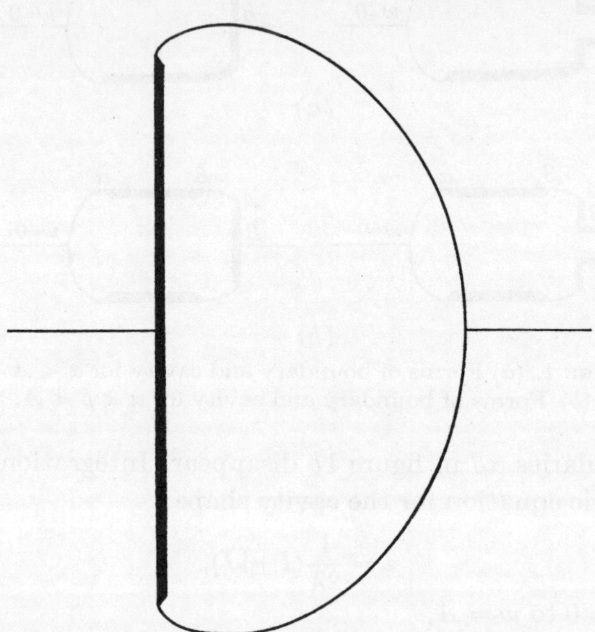

FIGURE 2. Finite cavity in unsteady flow past a stationary plate, for $\alpha = \beta < A = 2 + 2\sqrt{2}$.

is shown in figure 3. The flow past a flat plate with an attached cavity was first given by von Kármán (1949). The width of the plate is $2h$, with

$$h = \frac{1\cdot672}{\lambda} \tag{26}$$

approximately. The Froude number based on h is therefore

$$\frac{U^2}{ah} = \frac{\lambda U^2}{1\cdot672a} = 0\cdot598 \tag{27}$$

approximately, which agrees well with the figure $0\cdot596$ given by von Kármán. The Froude number U^2/ah for the flow described by figure 3 is $0\cdot625$, if $2h$ is the maximum width of the solid boundary.

The case $A = B$ is particularly simple, because H' is 1. The conformal mapping is given by

$$2\lambda\frac{\mathrm{d}z}{\mathrm{d}w} = -1 + \mathrm{i}\left(\frac{2}{w} - 1\right)^{\frac{1}{2}}, \tag{28}$$

95 *Finite two-dimensional cavities*

which can be integrated readily to yield, from $w = 0$ to $w = 2$ along $\psi = 0$ in the upper half of the w-plane,

$$2\lambda z = -w - i\,2\left(\frac{\sqrt{\{w(2-w)\}}}{2} - \cos^{-1}\sqrt{\frac{w}{2}} + \frac{\pi}{2}\right), \tag{29}$$

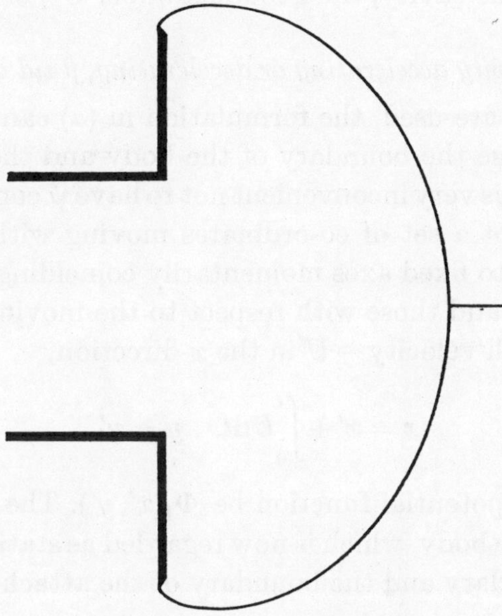

FIGURE 3. Finite cavity in unsteady flow past flanges of parallel plates, for $\alpha = \beta < A = 4$.

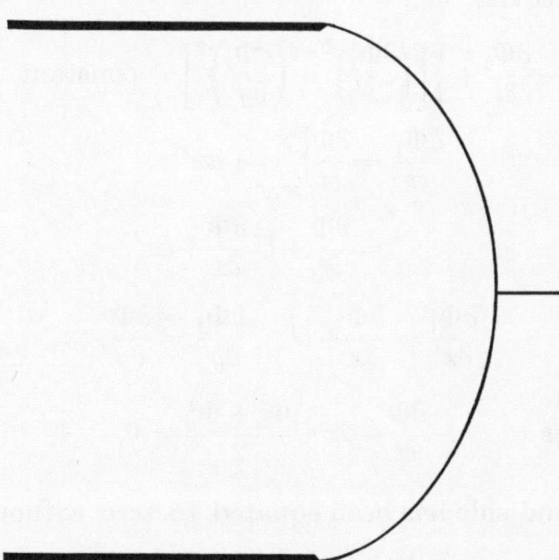

FIGURE 4. Finite cavity in unsteady flow past parallel plates (with cavity attached), or in flow caused by the unsteady motion of the plates (with cavity attached), or, after turned 90° counterclockwise, finite cavity in steady flow in a gravitational field.

in which the radicals indicate positive roots, and the value of the arc cosine is between 0 and $\frac{1}{2}\pi$. For the lower half of the w-plane and from $w = 0$ to $w = 2$ along $\psi = 0$, the sign of the imaginary part of (29) should be changed. The rest of the streamline $\psi = 0$ consists of straight lines. The form of boundary and the attached cavity is shown in figure 4. The values of z outside of the linear range

$$0 \leqslant w \leqslant 2$$

can be obtained by analytical continuation. If $2h$ is the distance between the parallel walls holding the cavity, the Froude number U^2/ah is $2/\pi$.

(b) *Body and cavity accelerating or decelerating, fluid at infinity at rest*

If fixed co-ordinates are used, the formulation in (a) can still be used, with the exception of (8), because the boundary of the body and the cavity is no longer a streamline. But since it is very inconvenient not to have ψ constant on the boundary, it is preferable to adopt a set of co-ordinates moving with the body. If the co-ordinates with respect to fixed axes momentarily coinciding with the moving axes are denoted by (x', y'), and those with respect to the moving axes by (x, y), and if the body is moving with velocity $-U$ in the x-direction,

$$x = x' + \int_0^t U \mathrm{d}t, \quad y = y'. \tag{30}$$

Let the instantaneous potential function be $\Phi_1(x', y')$. The potential with respect to axes moving with the body, which is now regarded as stationary in order to make ψ constant on its boundary and the boundary of the attached cavity, is

$$\Phi(x, y, t) = \Phi_1(x', y') - Ux'. \tag{31}$$

On the surface of the cavity

$$-\frac{\partial \Phi_1}{\partial t} + \frac{1}{2}\left[\left(\frac{\partial \Phi_1}{\partial x'}\right)^2 + \left(\frac{\partial \Phi_1}{\partial y'}\right)^2\right] = \text{constant}. \tag{32}$$

But since

$$\frac{\partial \Phi_1}{\partial t} = \frac{\partial \Phi}{\partial t}\bigg|_{x', y'} + ax'$$

$$= \frac{\partial \Phi}{\partial t} + U\frac{\partial \Phi}{\partial x} + ax' \tag{33}$$

and

$$\frac{\partial \Phi_1}{\partial x'} = \frac{\partial \Phi}{\partial x} + U, \quad \frac{\partial \Phi_1}{\partial y'} = \frac{\partial \Phi}{\partial y}, \tag{34}$$

equation (32) becomes

$$-\frac{\partial \Phi}{\partial t} - ax + \frac{\Phi_x^2 + \Phi_y^2}{2} = 0, \tag{35}$$

in which the right-hand side has been equated to zero without loss of generality. If again

$$\Phi(x, y, t) = Uf(x, y), \tag{36}$$

equation (35) becomes

$$a(f + x) + \frac{U^2}{2}(f_x^2 + f_y^2) = 0. \tag{37}$$

With

$$-a + \lambda U^2 = 0,$$

equation (4) is again valid, and equation (5) becomes

$$f_x^2 + f_y^2 = 2\lambda(f + x). \tag{38}$$

With
$$f = \frac{\phi}{\lambda}, \quad \Phi = \frac{U}{\lambda}\phi, \tag{39}$$

the equation corresponding to (7) is

$$\phi_x^2 + \phi_y^2 = 2\lambda^2(\phi + \lambda x). \tag{40}$$

On the surface of the body and the attached cavity, equation (8) is still valid, in which ψ is the complex conjugate of ϕ. With w defined as before, equation (9) is still to be satisfied. Once again, there should be no singularities in the physical plane outside of the body and the cavity.

The appropriate transformation is

$$2\lambda \frac{dz}{dw} = -H'(w) + i\left[\frac{4}{2w - H(w)} - H'^2(w)\right]^{\frac{1}{2}}, \tag{41}$$

in which the prime indicates differentiation with respect to w, both H' and the square root of the bracket must be real on the surface of the cavity, and H must be such that there are no singularities outside of the body and the cavity. One class of solutions is obtained by taking

$$H'(w) = \left(\frac{w - A}{w - B}\right)^{\frac{1}{2}}. \tag{42}$$

On the streamline $\psi = 0$ containing the surface of the cavity,

$$H(w) = \int_0^w \left(\frac{w - A}{w - B}\right)^{\frac{1}{2}} dw$$
$$= -(B - A)\left[\frac{\sqrt{\{(B - w)(A - w)\}}}{B - A} - \ln\left\{\sqrt{\left(\frac{B - w}{B - A}\right)} + \sqrt{\left(\frac{A - w}{B - A}\right)}\right\}\right]_0^w \tag{43}$$

from $w = 0$ to $w = A$, if $H(O) = 0$. From $w = A$ to $w = B$ along $\psi = 0$, for the upper half of the w-plane,

$$H(w) = H(A) + \int_A^w \left(\frac{w - A}{w - B}\right)^{\frac{1}{2}} dw = H(A) - i\int_A^w \left(\frac{w - A}{B - w}\right)^{\frac{1}{2}} dw$$
$$= H(A) + i(B - A)\left[\frac{\sqrt{\{(B - w)(w - A)\}}}{B - A} + \sin^{-1}\sqrt{\left(\frac{B - w}{B - A}\right)} - \frac{\pi}{2}\right], \tag{44}$$

in which, as in (43), the positive roots are to be used, the value of the arc sine is between zero and $\frac{1}{2}\pi$, and $H(A)$ is given in (43). From $w = A$ to $w = B$ along $\psi = 0$ in the lower half of the w-plane, the sign of the imaginary part in (44) should be changed. The value of $H(w)$ in the w-plane other than from $w = 0$ along $\psi = 0$ to $w = B$ is determined by analytic continuation.

It is evident that $2w - H(w)$ does not become infinite in the finite part of the w-plane. The point $w = A$ can be a point of infinite velocity only if the bracket in (41) also vanishes at $w = A$, or if $2A - H(A)$ is infinite. Since this is not the case there is no singular point in the entire physical plane outside of the body and the attached cavity.

The integration of (41) is in general impossible except by series expansion or by numerical means. The only readily integrable case is

$$B = A, \quad H'(w) = 1, \quad H(w) = w,$$

and

$$2\lambda \frac{\mathrm{d}z}{\mathrm{d}w} = -1 + \mathrm{i}\left(\frac{4}{w} - 1\right)^{\frac{1}{2}}. \tag{45}$$

From $w = 0$ to $w = 4$ along the streamline $\psi = 0$,

$$2\lambda z = -w \mp \mathrm{i}[\sqrt{\{w(4-w)\}} - 4\cos^{-1}\sqrt{\tfrac{1}{4}w} + 2\pi], \tag{46}$$

in which the upper and lower signs are to be taken for the upper and lower half of the w-plane, respectively, and the principal value of the arc cosine is taken. The form of the cavity is given parametrically by (46). Since (29) can be written in the form

$$\lambda z = -w_1 \mp \mathrm{i}[\sqrt{\{w_1(1-w_1)\}} - \cos^{-1}\sqrt{w_1} + \tfrac{1}{2}\pi], \tag{47}$$

with $w_1 = \tfrac{1}{2}w$, and (46) can be written in the form

$$\tfrac{1}{2}\lambda z = -w_2 \mp \mathrm{i}[\sqrt{\{w_2(1-w_2)\}} - \cos^{-1}\sqrt{w_2} + \tfrac{1}{2}\pi], \tag{48}$$

with $w_2 (= \tfrac{1}{4}w)$ also varying between 0 and 1, obviously the cavity represented by (46) is exactly the same as that represented by (29), except that it is twice as large. The shape is therefore the same as that shown in figure 4.

Although the actual integration of (41) is difficult if A is not equal to B, the general features of the shape of the body and cavity can be traced out by following the change of sign of the two quantities inside the radical signs in (41). The possible shapes are as shown in figures 1 to 3.

It remains to point out one most interesting fact concerning the direction of flow. If λ is kept at the same value, and hence ϕ in (40) is unchanged, but the sign of U is changed, then the sign of Φ is changed and the flow is reversed. But the velocity is still given by (4), except that the sign of U_0 is changed. Thus the same cavity is produced if the body reverses its direction of motion, with its speed decreasing.* The cavity is then in *front* of the body.

3. Finite cavities in a gravitational field

In two-dimensional steady flows in a gravitational field, the constancy of pressure in a cavity demands that on the surface of the cavity, where we shall suppose $\psi = 0$,

$$\phi_x^2 + \phi_y^2 + 2gy = 0, \tag{49}$$

in which the constant on the right-hand side is assumed to be zero without loss of generality. Richardson (1920) gave two formulae for generating such flows with a free surface. With

$$w = \phi + \mathrm{i}\psi$$

now being the unmodified (by a constant factor) complex potential, one of Richardson's formulae can be reduced to the form

$$\frac{\mathrm{d}z}{\mathrm{d}w} = \left[-\frac{1}{2gH(w)} - H'^2(w)\right]^{\frac{1}{2}} + \mathrm{i}H'(w), \tag{50}$$

---

* Thus the direction of acceleration is unchanged.

in which $H'(w)$ and the square root of the bracket must be real on the surface of the cavity, where $\psi = 0$. It is readily verified that (49) is satisfied. One class of solutions is obtained if

$$H' = \frac{1}{2V}\left(\frac{w-A}{w-B}\right)^{\frac{1}{2}}. \tag{51}$$

Apart from the factor $1/(2V)$, the function $H(w)$ is given for real values of w between $w = 0$ and $w = B$ by (43) and (44). Again, if $A \neq B$ the actual integration of (50) is difficult, but the possible shapes of the solid boundary and attached cavity can be traced by following the change of sign of the quantities under the radical signs (one of them in H') in (50) along a contour in the w-plane. The general features of these shapes are shown in figures 1 to 3, which should now be turned 90° counterclockwise. Again there are no singularities outside of the body and the cavity.

The case $A = B$ is the only case in which direct integration is possible. In this case

$$H'(w) = \frac{1}{2V}, \quad H(w) = \frac{w}{2V},$$

and

$$\frac{\mathrm{d}z}{\mathrm{d}w} = \frac{1}{2V}\left[\left(-\frac{4V^3}{gw}-1\right)^{\frac{1}{2}}+\mathrm{i}\right]. \tag{52}$$

The velocity at infinity is vertical and downward, of magnitude V. (Of course the flow can be reversed, but the orientation of the cavity must remain the same, with the stagnation point always the highest point of the cavity.) On the surface of the cavity, w varies from 0 to $-(4V^3)/g$ through real values. Integration of (52) yields the parametric equations for the form of the cavity

$$2Vz = \mathrm{i}w \mp \frac{4V^3}{g}\left[\sqrt{\{-w_3(w_3+1)\}}-\cos^{-1}\sqrt{(-w_3)}+\tfrac{1}{2}\pi\right], \tag{53}$$

in which the upper and lower signs are to be used for the upper and lower half of the w-plane, respectively,

$$w_3 = \frac{gw}{4V^3} \tag{54}$$

varies from 0 to -1, positive root is meant by the radicals, and the principal value of the arc cosine is taken. For w_3 greater than 0 or less than -1, the streamline $\psi = 0$ is straight and vertical. Since (53) can be written

$$\frac{gz}{2V^2} = \mathrm{i}w_3 \mp \left[\sqrt{\{-w_3(w_3+1)\}}-\cos^{-1}\sqrt{(-w_3)}+\tfrac{1}{2}\pi\right], \tag{55}$$

which is identical with (47) if z is multiplied by $(\mathrm{i}2\lambda V^2)/g$, and w_3 is changed to $-w_1$, the form of the solid boundary and the attached cavity is shown again in figure 4, except that the figure should be turned 90° counterclockwise. The solid boundaries are at a distance $2\pi V^2/g$ apart, so that the Froude number based on that width is $1/(2\pi)$. The depth of the cavity from the stagnation point to the base of the cavity is $2V^2/g$. The radius of curvature R at the crown is $4V^2/g$, so that V^2/gR is $\tfrac{1}{4}$.

It is of interest to compare the present result, so far as possible, with the findings of Davies & Taylor (1950), who measured the speed and shape of large bubbles rising in a liquid. They found that the upper part of the bubble is nearly spherical.

From figure 4 it is found that the middle portion of the cavity, covering $\frac{3}{4}$ of its entire length, is very nearly circular in shape ! Davies & Taylor assumed the velocity distribution of the liquid (relative to the moving bubble) over the upper part of the bubble to be the same as that of potential flow past a sphere (with which the upper part of the bubble coincides), and on this assumption found the values of V^2/gR (U^2/gR in their notation) to be $\frac{4}{9}$. A similar calculation for the two-dimensional case, demonstrated to the writer by Sir Geoffrey Taylor, yields

$$\frac{V^2}{gR} = \frac{1}{4},$$

in agreement with the exact result obtained here. There seems to be no reason why there should be such complete agreement, but this agreement does justify the assumption of Davies & Taylor. Finally, Davies & Taylor found that the rising bubble has a wake that moves bodily with it. The model presented here is characterized by two vertical solid boundaries, which can be considered to represent (roughly) the boundaries of the two-dimensional wake, in *qualitative* agreement with the finding of Davies & Taylor.

This work has been done during the tenure of a Senior Post-doctoral Fellowship granted by the National Science Foundation. The writer is grateful to Sir Geoffrey Taylor, F.R.S., for the interest he has shown in this work and for his kind encouragement.

REFERENCES

Davies, R. M. & Taylor, Sir Geoffrey 1950 *Proc. Roy. Soc.* A, **200**, 375–90.
Garabedian, P. R. 1957 *Proc. Roy. Soc.* A, **241**, 423.
Richardson, A. R. 1920 *Phil. Mag.* (6) **40**, 97–110.
von Kármán, Th. 1949 *Ann. Matemat. Pura Appl.* (IV) **29**, 247–9. Or *Collected works*, **4**, 396–8.

Reprinted from

THE PHYSICS OF FLUIDS   VOLUME 6, NUMBER 10   OCTOBER 1963

Velocity of a Fluid Mass Imbedded in Another Fluid Flowing in a Porous Medium

CHIA-SHUN YIH

The University of Michigan, Ann Arbor, Michigan, and Huyck Felt Company*
(Received 20 November 1962; revised manuscript received 16 May 1963)

The velocity of a fluid mass imbedded in another fluid, which is of a different viscosity and a different specific weight and flowing in a porous medium under a prevailing uniform pressure gradient, is investigated. The fluid mass may take the form of a circular or elliptic cylinder, a sphere, or an ellipsoid, and the orientation of the fluid mass, if not spherical, is completely arbitrary with respect to both the direction of the pressure gradient and that of gravity. Exact closed solutions are obtained. The results for two-dimensional flows are applicable to Hele–Shaw cells.

1. INTRODUCTION

IN this paper we deal with the velocity of a fluid mass imbedded in another fluid flowing in porous media. The fluid mass may take the form of a circular or elliptic cylinder, a sphere, or an ellipsoid. The viscosity and the specific weight of the fluid mass may differ from those of the ambient fluid, and the orientation of the cylinder, or of the ellipsoid, may be entirely arbitrary with respect to the direction of the prevailing pressure gradient and to the direction of gravity. Exact closed solutions for the velocity of the fluid mass are obtained for the cases of the elliptic cylinder and of the ellipsoid, and the solutions for a circular cylinder and for a sphere follow as special cases.

Polubarinova-Kochina and Falkovich[1] referred to solutions for the velocity in porous media of a fluid mass in the form of an ellipsoid of revolution. These solutions were presented in a more general form in the work of Taylor and Saffman,[2] who also considered the speed of a circular or elliptic bubble

moving in a Hele–Shaw cell. Their solutions for these two cases are for two-dimensional flows only, because the velocity normal to the walls of the Hele–Shaw cell is necessarily zero. These solutions were obtained as limiting cases of a bubble moving in a Hele–Shaw cell of finite width, as the width approaches infinity, and not in the direct way used in this paper. The solution of Taylor and Saffman for the velocity of the elliptic bubble is further specialized in that the motion of the bubble is parallel to either one of its axes.

The main justification for writing this paper is that the solution for the general ellipsoid and the general solution for the elliptic cylinder are new, as far as the writer is aware, and that they bring out the very interesting behavior of ellipsoidal or elliptic-cylindrical masses of fluid in porous media. A minor justification is that the solutions for all the cases, general or special, are presented in more direct and explicit forms than hiterto. In principle, the solution for the elliptic cylinder can be derived from the one for the general ellipsoid. But in practice this derivation is not simple. Therefore the solution for the elliptic cylinder has been derived separately.

The problems studied bear on the problem of ex-

---

* Permanent address.

[1] P. Y. Polubarinova-Kochina and S. B. Falkovich, Advances Appl. Mech. **2**, 153, 1951.

[2] Sir Geoffrey Taylor and P. G. Saffman, Quart. J. Mech. and Appl. Math. **12**, 265 1959.

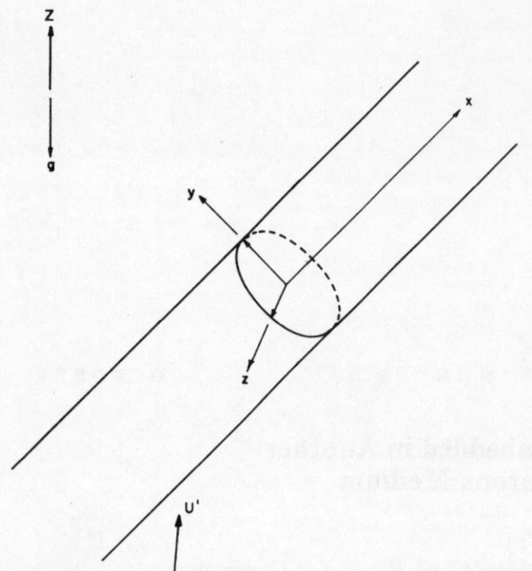

FIG. 1. Definition sketch for the case of an elliptic cylinder. The direction cosines of gravity is α, β, and γ. Those of U' are α', β', and γ'.

traction of oil from the ground in the presence of water, and on the problem of water removal encountered in the paper industry. In the latter problem, air and water are exuded from a felt carrying a wet paper sheet and passing through two rollers, and it is important to find out how much faster the air moves relative to the water through the porous media of felt and paper sheet.

2. GOVERNING DIFFERENTIAL SYSTEM

Cartesian coordinates x, y, and z will be used. The coordinate axes are fixed with respect to the fluid mass under consideration. The orientation of the axes will be specified in each case to be considered. The x' axis will be taken along the general direction of flow of the ambient fluid. The direction cosines of the x' axis with respect to the x, y, and z coordinates will be denoted by α', β', and γ'. The z axis will be taken in a direction opposite to that of the gravitational acceleration. Its direction cosines will be denoted by α, β, and γ.

Seepage flow of a fluid in porous media is governed by Darcy's law, which states that

$$\frac{\mu}{k}(u, v, w) = -\left(\frac{\partial}{\partial x}\, \frac{\partial}{\partial y}\, \frac{\partial}{\partial z}\right)(p + \rho g Z), \qquad (1)$$

in which μ is the viscosity of the fluid, ρ is its density, k is the permeability of the porous medium, assumed constant, p is the pressure, g is the gravitational acceleration, and u, v, and w are the velocity components in the directions of increasing x, y, and z,

respectively. The equation of continuity is, if the fluid is incompressible,

$$\frac{\partial u}{\partial x} + \frac{\partial v}{\partial y} + \frac{\partial w}{\partial z} = 0. \qquad (2)$$

If μ and k are constant, (1) and (2) can be combined to form the single equation

$$\left(\frac{\partial^2}{\partial x^2} + \frac{\partial^2}{\partial y^2} + \frac{\partial^2}{\partial z^2}\right)\phi = 0, \qquad (3)$$

in which

$$\phi = p + \rho g Z \qquad (4)$$

is a potential.

One remark needs to be made on the coordinates used. Since the porous medium is at rest, application of Darcy's law requires that the coordinates be fixed, otherwise (1) would give, for example, no pressure drop in uniform flow with a coordinate system moving with it. On the other hand, for the unsteady flows caused by moving bodies, such as are treated here, it is not convenient to use a coordinate system which is fixed once and for all. The dilemma is resolved by the use of *fixed* coordinates *coinciding instantaneously* with the coordinates most natural and convenient for the body. Since (3), the boundary conditions (as will be seen), and hence the solution are entirely independent of the history of the motion, the use of instantaneous coordinates is justified. However, these are, in concept, *fixed* coordinates.

The most important fact about (3) is that it is linear. One of the conditions at the boundary of two fluids in contact is that p should be continuous. From (4) it can be seen that this condition will be linear in ϕ, although not necessarily homogeneous in ϕ. The linearity of (3) and the boundary conditions allow solutions to be superposed, provided any nonhomogeneity of the boundary conditions in ϕ is properly taken into account. Since the interface of the two fluids is not specified *a priori*, it is necessary to have another boundary condition at the interface. That condition is a kinematic one, and follows from the fact that the velocity component normal to the interface must be the same for both fluids. Since the flow is governed by the Laplace equation, the tangential velocities at the interface will not be the same for the two fluids. In reality, the tangential velocity changes from one value for one fluid to another for the other fluid in a very short distance comparable to the pore size of the medium. Hence the slippage at the interface is an idealized situation closely representing reality.

3. VELOCITY OF A CYLINDRICAL MASS OF ELLIPTIC CROSS SECTION

The x axis will be assumed to coincide with the axis of the elliptic cylinder. The y axis coincides with the major axis, and the z axis with the minor axis of the ellipse

$$y^2/a^2 + z^2/b^2 = 1, \tag{5}$$

which describes the cross section of the elliptic cylinder under consideration.

Consider now a flow of the ambient fluid with velocity U' in the x' direction at infinity. The component of U' in the x direction is $U_1 = \alpha' U'$. Since

$$\partial Z/\partial x = \alpha,$$

the first of equations (1) can be written

$$(\mu/k)u = -\partial p/\partial x - \rho g\alpha.$$

For the ambient fluid,

$$-\partial p/\partial x = (\mu_1/k)U_1 + \rho_1 g\alpha.$$

For the fluid mass,

$$-\partial p/\partial x = (\mu_2/k)U_2 + \rho_2 g\alpha.$$

Hence the continuity of p at the interface demands that

$$U_2 = (\mu_1/\mu_2)U_1 + k(\rho_1 - \rho_2)g\alpha/\mu_2. \tag{6}$$

This is in fact true whatever the cross section of the cylinder. For $(\rho_1 - \rho_2)\alpha = 0$, (6) reduces to

$$U_2 = (\mu_1/\mu_2)U_1, \tag{7}$$

in agreement with the previous result of Yih.[3]

For the motion of the cylinder in the directions of y and z, it is advantageous to introduce the elliptic coordinates ξ and η. They are connected with y and z by

$$y + iz = c \cosh(\xi + i\eta),$$

or

$$y = c \cosh \xi \cos \eta, \qquad z = c \sinh \xi \sin \eta. \tag{8}$$

On the ellipse, $\xi = \xi_0$, because (5) and (8) coincide with

$$a = c \cosh \xi_0, \qquad b = c \sinh \xi_0,$$

which defines c and ξ_0 in terms of a and b. The flow caused by a velocity ΔV in the y direction relative to the ambient fluid can be described by

$$\phi + i\psi = Ce^{-(\xi + i\eta)},$$

in which ψ is the stream function, and is conjugate to ϕ. If, as it will turn out to be the case, the fluid cylinder moves as a solid body, the kinematic boundary condition on the ellipse is

$$\psi = -\Delta Vz + \text{constant},$$

<hr>

[3] C.-S. Yih, J. Fluid Mech. **10**, 133, 1961.

if ΔU, ΔV, and ΔW are the components of the velocity of the fluid mass *relative* to the ambient fluid. This condition follows from the requirement that the velocity component normal to the surface of the fluid mass must be the same for the mass and for the ambient fluid. Since

$$\psi = -Ce^{-\xi} \sin \eta,$$

this boundary condition is satisfied if

$$Ce^{-\xi_0} = \Delta Vc \sinh \xi_0.$$

Thus

$$C = \frac{\Delta Vbc}{a - b} = \Delta Vb\left(\frac{a + b}{a - b}\right)^{\frac{1}{2}},$$

and

$$\phi = Ce^{-\xi} \cos \eta.$$

On the ellipse

$$\phi = Ce^{-\xi_0} \cos \eta = \Delta V (\tanh \xi_0)y = \frac{b}{a} \Delta Vy. \tag{9}$$

Similarly, if the velocity in the z direction of the cylinder relative to the ambient fluid is ΔW,

$$\phi + i\psi = iDe^{-(\xi + i\eta)},$$

with

$$D = \Delta Wa[(a + b)/(a - b)]^{\frac{1}{2}},$$

and

$$\phi = (a/b)\Delta Wz. \tag{10}$$

The components of the velocity U' in the coordinate directions are $\alpha'U'$, $\beta'U'$, and $\gamma'U'$. These will be denoted by U_1, V_1, and W_1. Now, *on the ellipse*, with $\Delta V = V_2 - V_1$, restoring the factor μ/k,

$$\phi_1 = (\mu_1/k)[-V_1y + (V_2 - V_1)yb/a], \tag{11}$$

$$\phi_2 = -(\mu_2/k)V_2y, \tag{12}$$

if the elliptic cylinder is assumed to move as a solid body with velocity components U_2, V_2, and W_2. Continuity of p then demands that

$$(\mu_1/k)[-V_1y + (V_2 - V_1)yb/a] - \rho_1 g\beta y$$
$$= -(\mu_2/k)V_2y - \rho_2 g\beta y, \tag{13}$$

which gives

$$V_2 = \frac{\mu_1(a + b)}{\mu_1 b + \mu_2 a} V_1 + \frac{ak(\rho_1 - \rho_2)g\beta}{\mu_1 b + \mu_2 a}. \tag{14}$$

Similarly,

$$W_2 = \frac{\mu_1(a + b)}{\mu_1 a + \mu_2 b} W_1 + \frac{bk(\rho_1 - \rho_2)g\gamma}{\mu_1 a + \mu_2 b}. \tag{15}$$

The expression for U_2 is still given by (6). From (6), (14), and (15) it can be seen that the velocity of the cylinder is independent of its size, although it does depend on its shape.

If $\rho_1 = \rho_2$, then

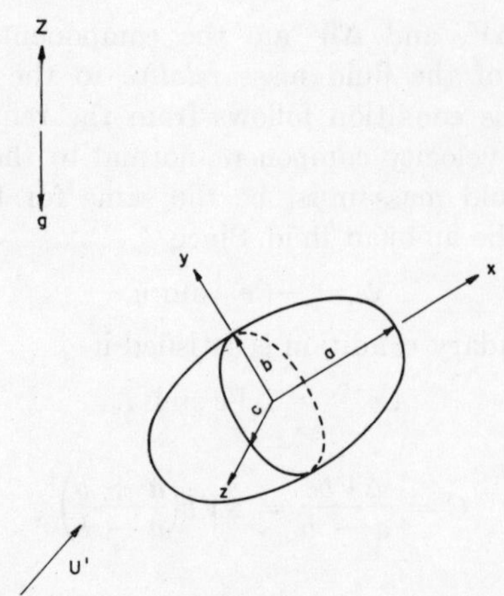

FIG. 2. Definition sketch for the case of an ellipsoid. The direction cosines of gravity and of U' remain the same as in Fig. 1.

$$\frac{W_2}{V_2} = \frac{\mu_1 b + \mu_2 a}{\mu_1 a + \mu_2 b} \frac{W_1}{V_1}$$

$$= \left[1 + \frac{(a-b)(\mu_2 - \mu_1)}{\mu_1 a + \mu_2 b} \right] \frac{W_1}{V_1}.$$

If $\mu_2 < \mu_1$, then since $a > b$, we have

$$W_2/V_2 < W_1/V_1$$

so that in the yz plane the cylinder will not move in the same direction with the ambient fluid, but will move more closely to the major axis of the ellipse. The reverse is true if $\mu_2 > \mu_1$. This is indeed a very interesting situation.

If $U' = 0$, then

$$U_2 : V_2 : W_2 = (\mu_1 b + \mu_2 a)\alpha : \mu_2 a\beta : \mu_2 b\gamma,$$

so that the cylinder will not move in the direction of gravity, but will have a velocity deviating from that direction toward the y axis, and even more toward the x axis. In other words, it will drift in such a way as to favor the axes of the cylinder in the order of their length: ∞, a, and b.

The solution for the special case of a circular cylinder can be derived from (13) and (14). The results are (6),

$$V_2 = \frac{2\mu_1}{\mu_1 + \mu_2} V_1 + \frac{k(\rho_1 - \rho_2)}{\mu_1 + \mu_2} g\beta, \qquad (16)$$

and

$$W_2 = \frac{2\mu_1}{\mu_1 + \mu_2} W_1 + \frac{k(\rho_1 - \rho_2)g\gamma}{\mu_1 + \mu_2}. \qquad (17)$$

For $\mu_2 = 0$ and $(\rho - \rho)\beta = 0$, $V = 2V$, in agreement with the result of Taylor and Saffman.[2]

From (6), (16), and (17), it can be seen that the velocity of the cylinder is entirely independent of its size, and that, when the ambient fluid is at rest (i.e.,

if $U' = 0$), the velocity of the cylinder is simply $k(\rho_1 - \rho_2)g/(\mu_1 + \mu_2)$, in the direction opposite to that of gravity if $\rho_1 > \rho_2$, and $k(\rho_2 - \rho_1)g/(\mu_1 + \mu_2)$ in the direction of gravity if $\rho_2 > \rho_1$.

4. THE VELOCITY OF AN ELLIPSOIDAL MASS

Let the coordinate axes be taken along the axes of the ellipsoid, and the origin be located at its center. Then the fluid mass is an ellipsoid the surface of which is described by

$$x^2/a^2 + y^2/b^2 + z^2/c^2 = 1, \qquad (18)$$

and the potentials for a velocity ΔU, ΔV, and ΔW of the ellipsoidal mass relative to the ambient fluid is, respectively,

$$\phi = \frac{abc}{2 - \alpha_0} \Delta U x \int_\lambda^\infty \frac{d\lambda}{(a^2 + \lambda)\Delta}, \qquad (19)$$

$$\phi = \frac{abc}{2 - \beta_0} \Delta V y \int_\lambda^\infty \frac{d\lambda}{(b^2 + \lambda)\Delta}, \qquad (20)$$

and

$$\phi = \frac{abc}{2 - \gamma_0} \Delta W z \int_\lambda^\infty \frac{d\lambda}{(c^2 + \lambda)\Delta}, \qquad (21)$$

in which

$$\alpha_0 = abc \int_0^\infty \frac{d\lambda}{(a^2 + \lambda)\Delta}, \quad \beta_0 = abc \int_0^\infty \frac{d\lambda}{(b^2 + \lambda)\Delta},$$

$$\gamma_0 = abc \int_0^\infty \frac{d\lambda}{(c^2 + \lambda)\Delta}, \qquad (22)$$

and

$$\Delta = [(a^2 + \lambda)(b^2 + \lambda)(c^2 + \lambda)]^{\frac{1}{2}}.$$

The coordinate λ is the first of the so-called ellipsoidal coordinates λ, μ, and ν, which are roots of the cubic equation in θ,

$$\frac{x^2}{a^2 + \theta} + \frac{y^2}{b^2 + \theta} + \frac{z^2}{c^2 + \theta} = 1,$$

for every point (x, y, z). For the ellipsoid given by (18), $\lambda = 0$ on the surface. On the assumption that the ellipsoid moves as a solid body, the kinematical boundary condition at the interface (that the normal velocity must be the same) is satisfied by the solutions (19), (20), and (21). On the ellipsoid,

$$\phi = \frac{\alpha_0}{2 - \alpha_0} \Delta U x, \quad \phi = \frac{\beta_0}{2 - \beta_0} \Delta V y, \quad \phi = \frac{\gamma_0}{2 - \gamma_0} \Delta W z,$$

for the three modes of motion. For the motion parallel to the x axis,

$$\phi = \frac{\mu_1}{k} \left[-U_1 x + \frac{\alpha_0}{2 - \alpha_0} (U_2 - U_1)x \right]$$

for the ambient fluid and

$$\phi = -(\mu_2/k)U_2 x$$

for the ellipsoidal fluid mass, assumed in solid body translation. Hence the continuity of pressure at the surface of the ellipsoid demands that

$$\frac{\mu_1}{k}\left[-U_1 x + \frac{\alpha_0}{2-\alpha_0}(U_2 - U_1)x\right] - g\rho_1\alpha x$$

$$= -(\mu_2/k)U_2 x - g\rho_2\alpha x, \qquad (23)$$

so that

$$U_2 = \frac{2\mu_1 U_1 + (2-\alpha_0)kg(\rho_1 - \rho_2)\alpha}{\alpha_0\mu_1 + (2-\alpha_0)\mu_2}. \qquad (24)$$

Similarly,

$$V_2 = \frac{2\mu_1 V_1 + (2-\beta_0)kg(\rho_1 - \rho_2)\beta}{\beta_0\mu_1 + (2-\beta_0)\mu_2}, \qquad (25)$$

and

$$W_2 = \frac{2\mu_1 W_1 + (2-\gamma_0)kg(\rho_1 - \rho_2)\gamma}{\gamma_0\mu_1 + (2-\gamma_0)\mu_2}. \qquad (26)$$

For the case $\rho_1 = \rho_2$,

$$U_2/U_1 > V_2/V_1 > W_2/W_1$$

if $\mu_2 < \mu_1$, and

$$U_2/U_1 < V_2/V_1 < W_2/W_1$$

if $\mu_2 > \mu_1$, since $\alpha_0 < \beta_0 < \gamma_0$. This is indeed a very amusing situation. For the case $U' = 0$, so that $U_1 = V_1 = W_1 = 0$,

$$U_2 : V_2 : W_2 = \frac{\alpha}{[\alpha_0/(2-\alpha_0)]\mu_1 + \mu_2} : \frac{\beta}{[\beta_0/(2-\beta_0)]\mu_1 + \mu_2} : \frac{\gamma}{[\gamma_0/(2-\gamma_0)]\mu_1 + \mu_2}.$$

Since $\alpha_0 < \beta_0 < \gamma_0$, the direction of the velocity of the ellipsoid will deviate from that of gravity toward the directions of the longer axes, i.e., toward the direction of y and even more toward the direction of x, whether μ_2 is greater or less than μ_1. The independence of the sign of $\mu_1 - \mu_2$ is due to the fact that the inequality of the three axes is not merely a measure of the inequality of the resistance to flow, as in the case $\rho_1 = \rho_2$, but is also a measure of the inequality of the motive force in the three directions, when $\rho_1 \neq \rho_2$.

For the special case of a sphere, $\alpha_0 = \beta_0 = \gamma_0 = \frac{2}{3}$. Hence (24)–(26) become

$$(U_2, V_2, W_2) = \frac{3\mu_1}{2\mu_2 + \mu_1}(U_1, V_1, W_1)$$

$$+ \frac{2kg(\rho_1 - \rho_2)}{2\mu_2 + \mu_1}(\alpha, \beta, \gamma). \qquad (27)$$

If $\mu_2 = 0$ and $\rho_1 = \rho_2$, $U_2 = 3U_1$, in agreement with Taylor and Saffman's result. If $U' = 0$, the sphere moves in the direction of gravity or in a direction opposite to it, according as $\rho_2 > \rho_1$ or $\rho_2 < \rho_1$. In either case the speed is

$$2kg\,|\rho_1 - \rho_2|/(2\mu_2 + \mu_1).$$

5. DISCUSSION

In Secs. 3 and 4, the fluid mass has been assumed to move as a solid body, hence without change of form, and a solution is possible because, in the case of an elliptic cylinder, y can be cancelled in (13), and, in the case of an ellipsoid, x can be cancelled in (23). These are very special situations, and the solutions obtained are very probably the only ones corresponding to solid-body motion of the fluid mass. For a mass of given volume (or given volume per unit length), the solution is obviously not unique, for the mass can take infinitely many shapes. The stability of the fluid motion corresponding to these solutions is another question. It is known that large flat masses moving broadside on are not stable, but circular masses in Hele–Shaw cells have been observed to preserve their form and to move as a solid body. Perhaps surface tension will make the masses describe here stable, provided they are not too large in any dimension.

6. APPLICATION TO HELE–SHAW CELLS

Since Hele–Shaw cells provide a means of experimentation on flows in porous media, it may be mentioned that the results of Sec. 3 can be verified in the laboratory by the use of a Hele–Shaw cell. The flow is necessarily two dimensional, since the axis of the cylinder is necessarily perpendicular to its direction of motion. The direction of gravity may be related in any arbitrary fashion to the direction of the general flow of the ambient fluid and to the direction of the axis of the cylinder. However, gravity effects in the direction of the cylinder must be ignored, since the walls of the cell prohibit any flow in that direction. The error is a small since the spacing of the walls of the cell is supposed to be so small that any change of hydrostatic pressure over the thickness is small compared with the change of pressure from place to place in the cell, in a plane parallel to the walls.

ACKNOWLEDGMENTS

The author wishes to thank Dr. D. Wicker, Mr. J. Hintermaier, and Mr. S. J. McNamara, all of Huyck Felt Company, for their interest in this problem, and for the stimulation of Mr. McNamara's experiments.

Reprinted from

THE PHYSICS OF FLUIDS VOLUME 7, NUMBER 5 MAY 1964

Hydraulic Jump in a Rotating Fluid

CHIA-SHUN YIH, H. E. GASCOIGNE, AND W. R. DEBLER

Department of Engineering Mechanics, University of Michigan, Ann Arbor, Michigan

(Received 18 March 1963; revised manuscript received 29 November 1963)

A hydraulic jump occurs in a layer of fluid flowing down the inner wall of a rotating cylinder when the downstream conditions are adequate. The theory of these jumps is presented, together with supporting experimental data. The results confirm the similarity between free-surface flows under general rotation (and hence centripetal acceleration) and free-surface flows in the presence of a gravitational field, and indicate that the hydraulic jump in a rotating fluid is just the counterpart of the ordinary hydraulic jump.

1. INTRODUCTION

IT has been generally recognized that the flows of a rotating fluid are, in many respects, similar to the flows of a stratified fluid in the presence of a gravitational field. Since a free surface is a surface of density discontinuity, which is a form of extreme stratification, there is also a similarity of flows of a rotating fluid with a free surface to free-surface flows in the gravitational field. A free surface in the rotating fluid is necessary to ensure similarity of its flow to a free-surface flow in the gravitational field because the quantity corresponding to a discontinuity in specific weight in the latter is a discontinuity in $\rho\Gamma^2$ in the former, ρ being the density and Γ the circulation of the flow along any circle in its domain located with axial symmetry. Thus the

counterpart of the ordinary hydraulic jump appears to be a hydraulic jump in a layer of liquid flowing down the inner wall of a rotating cylinder, and rotating with it. The analytical and experimental results are presented in this paper to provide yet another instance of the similarity of rotating flows and stratified flows.

The hydraulic jump in a swirling fluid has also been observed by Binnie.[1] But the tube he used was stationary, and his work was not primarily a study of the jump.

2. ANALYSIS

With reference to Fig. 1, b is the inner radius of the tube, d_1 is the depth of water upstream from

---

[1] A. M. Binnie, Proc. Roy. Soc. (London) **A270**, 452 (1962).

the jump, and d_2 the downstream depth. The pressure in the fluid upstream from the jump is

$$p_1 = \tfrac{1}{2}\rho\omega_1^2(r^2 - a_1^2) \qquad (\omega_1 = \omega), \qquad (1)$$

in which ω_1 is the angular speed of the rotating water film, and is equal to the angular speed ω of the rotating cylinder, r is the radial distance from the axis to the point at which the pressure is being considered, and $a_1 = b - d_1$. Downstream from the jump, the angular speed ω_2 of the fluid in general varies from one radial position to another. Two extreme situations may be considered. If viscous and turbulent mixings are ignored, Kelvin's theorem on the conservation of circulation enable one to compute ω_2 as a function of r, upon utilization of the equation of continuity and the assumption that the downstream velocity U_2 is constant. This would be a very unrealistic situation, because there is violent turbulent mixing at the jump, so that Kelvin's theorem cannot be valid. The other extreme condition is the condition of complete mixing, so that after the jump another *uniform* ω_2 exists, which can be computed from ω_1 by use of the conservation of the integrated angular momentum. Thus, on the assumption that ω_2 is uniform, the downstream pressure distribution is given by

$$p_2 = \tfrac{1}{2}\rho\omega_2^2(r^2 - a_2^2), \qquad (2)$$

in which $a_2 = b - d_2$. The total axial force acting at an upstream section (Section 1-1) is

$$P_1 = \int_{a_1}^{b} p_1 2\pi r \, dr = \tfrac{1}{4}\rho\pi\omega^2(b^2 - a_1^2)^2. \qquad (3)$$

The total axial force acting at downstream section (Section 2-2) is

$$P_2 = \int_{a_2}^{b} p_2 2\pi r \, dr = \tfrac{1}{4}\rho\pi\omega_2^2(b^2 - a_2^2)^2. \qquad (4)$$

The discharge is given by

$$Q = \int_{a_1}^{b} U_1 2\pi r \, dr = \int_{a_2}^{b} U_2 2\pi r \, dr, \qquad (5)$$

which is the equation of continuity. The downstream flow is very turbulent, so that U_2 can be assumed constant without appreciable error. If the upstream flow is also turbulent, U_1 can also be assumed constant, thus the equation of continuity can be written as

$$U_1(b^2 - a_1^2) = U_2(b^2 - a_2^2). \qquad (6)$$

The momentum flux through Section 1-1 is

$$M_1 = \int_{a_1}^{b} \rho U_1^2 2\pi r \, dr, \qquad (7)$$

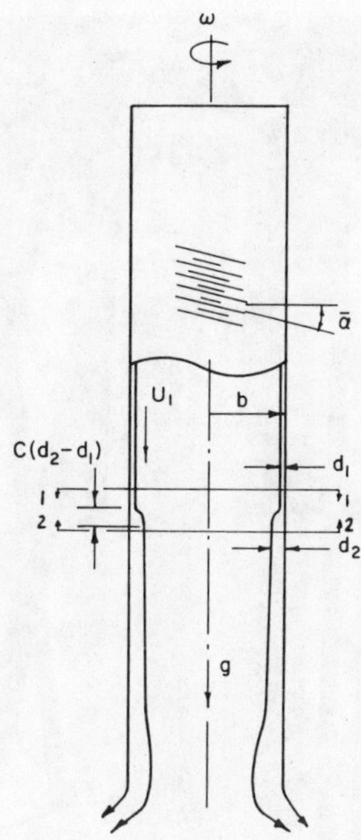

Fig. 1. Definition sketch.

and that through Section 2-2 is

$$M_2 = \int_{a_1}^{b} \rho U_2^2 2\pi r \, dr. \qquad (8)$$

Since U_1 and U_2 are assumed constant,

$$M_1 = \rho\pi U_1^2(b^2 - a_1^2), \qquad M_2 = \rho\pi U_2^2(b^2 - a_2^2). \qquad (9)$$

The fluxes of angular momenta are the same before and after the jump, since the torque exerted by the wall of the cylinder can be neglected. Thus

$$\int_{a_1}^{b} (\rho\omega r^2) U_1 2\pi r \, dr = \int_{a_1}^{b} (\rho\omega_2 r^2) U_2 2\pi r \, dr. \qquad (10)$$

Now ω is constant, and as explained before U_1, U_2, and ω_2 can be assumed constant. Thus (10) becomes

$$\rho\omega U_1(b^4 - a_1^4) = \rho\omega_2 U_2(b^4 - a_2^4). \qquad (11)$$

which can be reduced to

$$\omega(b^2 + a_1^2) = \omega_2(b^2 + a_2^2) \qquad (12)$$

by the use of (6).

The momentum equation applied to the fluid between Sections 1-1 and 2-2 is

$$P_1 - P_2 + W = M_2 - M_1, \qquad (13)$$

in which W is the weight of the body of fluid in the region of change of depth. If the inner radius of that body of fluid is assumed to vary linearly (with 3) from a_1 to a_2, and if the length of the jump is assumed

Fig. 2. A photograph of the apparatus used.

to be $c(a_1 - a_2)$, c being a constant of proportionality,

$$W = g\rho\pi(a_1 - a_2)[b^2 - \tfrac{1}{3}(a_1^2 + a_1 a_2 + a_2^2)]$$

$$= g\rho\pi(a_1 - a_2)[b^2 - a_1 a_2 - \tfrac{1}{3}(a_1 - a_2)^2]. \quad (14)$$

Equation (13) then becomes

$$\tfrac{1}{4}\rho\pi[\omega^2(b^2 - a_1^2)^2 - \omega_2^2(b^2 - a_2^2)]$$

$$+ g\rho\pi(a_1 - a_2)[b^2 - a_1 a_2 - \tfrac{1}{3}(a_1 - a_2)^2]$$

$$= \rho\pi[U_2^2(b^2 - a_2^2) - U_1^2(b^2 - a_1^2)]. \quad (15)$$

Now if (6) is used on the right-hand side, (12) is used to eliminate ω_2 and for simplicity one writes

$$\alpha_1 = \frac{a_1}{b}, \qquad \alpha_2 = \frac{a_2}{b}, \qquad F_1 = \frac{U_1}{\omega b}, \qquad G = \frac{g}{b\omega^2}.$$

One obtains, after simplifications,

$$(1 - \alpha_1^2\alpha_2^2)(1 - \alpha_2^2) = F_1^2(1 - \alpha_1^2)(1 + \alpha_2^2)$$

$$+ \frac{cG(1 - \alpha_2^2)(1 + \alpha_2^2)^2[3(1 - \alpha_1\alpha_2) - (\alpha_1 - \alpha_2)^2]}{3(\alpha_1 + \alpha_2)}. \quad (16)$$

This equation enables one to find α_2 for given values of α_1, F_1, G, and c.

In the experiments performed, d_1 and d_2 were very small compared with b. Hence a_1 and a_2 were nearly equal to b and so α_1 and α_2 were nearly equal to 1. Putting α_1 and α_2 equal to 1 except where differences are involved, one obtains from (16)

$$(1 - \alpha_1\alpha_2)(1 - \alpha_2) = 2F_1^2(1 - \alpha_1)$$

$$+ cG(1 - \alpha_2)[(1 - \alpha_1\alpha_2) - \tfrac{1}{3}(\alpha_1 - \alpha_2)^2]. \quad (17)$$

Now with

$$\eta = d_2/d_1 \quad \text{and} \quad F^2 = U^2/\omega^2 b d_1$$

one has

$$1 - \alpha_1\alpha_2 = (d_1/b)(1 + \eta), \quad (1 - \alpha_2) = (d_1/b)\eta.$$

$$F_1^2(1 - \alpha_1) = F_1^2(d_1/b)$$

and

$$(\alpha_1 - \alpha_2)^2 = (d_1^2/b^2)(\eta - 1)^2.$$

Thus (17) can be written as

$$\eta(\eta + 1)(1 - cG) + \tfrac{1}{3}\frac{d_1}{b}cG\eta(\eta - 1)^2 = 2F^2. \quad (18)$$

The depth ratio η had a maximum value of 10.7 in one test, and less than 10 on all the other tests, and d_1/b was very small. Thus, under the experimental conditions, the second term on the right-hand side can be neglected. The resulting equation can be solved simply. The solution is

$$\eta = \frac{d_2}{d_1} = \frac{1}{2}\left[-1 + \left(1 + \frac{8F^2}{1 - cG}\right)^{\frac{1}{2}} \right]. \quad (19)$$

Equations (17) and (18) are identical in substance,

Fig. 3. A photograph showing location of the jump and streaks in the flow.

and are approximations to (16). Equation (16) corresponds to the momentum equation in ordinary hydraulic-jump theory, except that the weight of the fluid in the region of variable depth plays a part here, but not in the ordinary hydraulic jump.

3. APPARATUS AND METHOD OF MEASUREMENT

The apparatus is shown in Fig. 2. The working section was a piece of transparent tube of polished cast resin about 50 in. long and 9 in. o.d. The wall was $\frac{1}{4}$ in. thick. The innersurface diameter had a variation of at most 0.012 in. The tube is supported by a rigid hub at the top and a rigid ring at the bottom. A rod running centrally from the top to the bottom carried a movable point gauge for measuring depths. A turntable fixed to the bottom ring supporting the transparent tube was driven by a variable-speed motor of 5 hp.

Water at 62°F was introduced into the tube through a rotating union threaded into the top hub from a head tank. The flow was regulated by needle valves through flow meters of the type of the Fischer–Porter rotometer. The flow meters were calibrated under test conditions and the variation of the discharge was within $\pm 1\%$ in each run. After entering the rotating union, the water was spread onto the inner wall of the best cylinder by a circular plate. Vertical uniform flow was established after approximately one tube diameter and a half.

At the bottom of the tube were efflux ports which could be opened or closed at will to adjust the location of the jump. The jump could be moved up the tube by reducing the opening at the bottom of the tube.

The angular speed of the turntable was measured electromagnetically and was maintained constant. The variation in each run was no more than 1 r.p.m., or about $\pm 0.1\%$ in the tests. This angular speed is the same as ω in the analysis. Figure 3 shows the location of the jump and streaks in the flow both upstream and downstream of the jump. Since ω was known and d_1 was small, the circumferential velocity upstream from the jump was known. Assuming the streaks were statistically the same as the streamlines, one could obtain the upstream surface velocity U_1 of the fluid in the axial direction from the inclination of the streaks.

[If the streaks are actually characteristics for surface waves, the effect of the assumption made here is to over-estimate U_1 and hence to underestimate d_1. In that case the experimental points in Fig. 4 should be shifted downward and to the

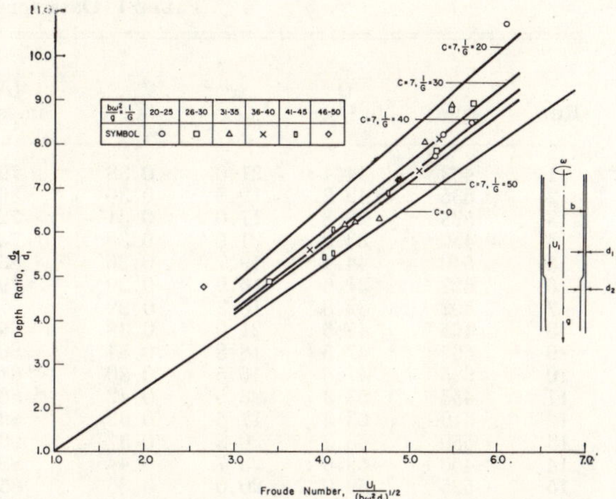

FIG. 4. Comparison of theoretical and experimental results.

right. The error introduced by the assumption would in that event increase with the speed of the surface waves, which in turn would depend on and probably increase with ω and d_1. If surface-wave speed greatly overshadows the actual speed of the fluid in determining the slope of the streaks, the streaks prior to the jump cannot be much steeper than those after it, since $d_2 > d_1$, and ω_2 is nearly equal to ω for the tests performed, according to (12). But the upstream streaks are much steeper than the downstream ones. Hence we believe the assumption made is not far wrong.]

From U_1 one can easily calculate d_1. The mean inclination of the streaks was obtained photographically with a variation of ± 0.50. Downstream from the jump the inclination of the streaks were too small to be useful as a reliable means of obtaining d_2, which was therefore measured with the point gauge. The error was approximately ± 0.007 in. The upstream depth was so small that the waviness of the free-surface would introduce a substantial percentage error in d_1 if measured with the point gauge. That was why the streaks were utilized upstream from the jump.

The length of the jump was observed to be between 0.5 and 1 in. in the tests.

4. DISCUSSION OF RESULTS

The results are shown in Table I and Fig. 4. As explained in Sec. 3, U_1 was computed from the inclination of the streaks on the upstream free surface. Since the upstream flow was assumed to be turbulent, this U_1 was considered to be the axial velocity in the major part of the upstream flow.

TABLE I. Data for rotating hydraulic jump.

Run	rpm	Q in.^{3}/sec	α deg	$\tan \alpha$	U_1 in./sec	d_1 in.	d_2 in.	F	$\dfrac{d_2}{d_1}$	R	$\dfrac{b\omega_1{}^2}{g}$
1	463	44.4	21.0	0.38	79	0.021	0.18	5.5	8.8	1400	25.8
2	535	42.2	19.8	0.36	86	0.018	0.16	5.5	8.9	1300	34.6
3	535	29.8	17.0	0.31	72	0.015	0.12	5.2	8.0	900	34.6
4	430	33.0	21.0	0.38	73	0.017	0.18	6.1	10.7	1000	22.4
5	540	44.4	19.7	0.36	86	0.019	0.16	5.3	8.1	1400	35.2
6	622	31.6	16.0	0.29	79	0.015	0.11	4.9	7.2	1000	47.1
7	592	32.8	16.3	0.29	77	0.016	0.11	4.7	6.9	1000	42.4
8	465	47.5	21.0	0.38	79	0.022	0.17	5.3	7.8	1500	26.2
9	565	47.5	18.8	0.34	86	0.021	0.15	4.9	7.2	1500	34.7
10	625	47.5	16.5	0.30	61	0.029	0.14	2.7	4.7	1500	47.2
11	455	53.3	23.0	0.42	86	0.023	0.21	5.7	9.2	1700	25.0
12	610	53.3	17.5	0.32	86	0.023	0.14	4.2	6.1	1700	45.0
13	550	53.3	20.2	0.37	90	0.022	0.16	5.1	7.4	1700	36.5
14	450	59.0	23.7	0.44	88	0.025	0.21	5.7	8.5	1900	24.5
15	525	59.0	20.0	0.36	85	0.026	0.16	4.6	6.3	1900	33.2
16	600	59.0	17.8	0.32	86	0.026	0.14	4.1	5.5	1900	43.6
17	450	64.2	23.5	0.43	87	0.028	0.23	5.4	8.2	2000	24.5
18	525	64.2	19.8	0.36	84	0.029	0.18	4.4	6.2	2000	33.2
19	600	64.2	18.0	0.32	87	0.028	0.15	4.0	5.4	2000	43.6
20	440	71.0	24.0	0.44	87	0.030	0.23	5.3	7.7	2200	23.6
21	525	71.0	20.0	0.36	85	0.031	0.19	4.3	6.1	2200	33.2
22	625	71.0	16.5	0.30	82	0.032	0.16	3.4	4.8	2200	47.2
23	575	76.2	18.7	0.34	87	0.033	0.18	3.8	5.6	2400	40.0

The Reynolds number

$$R = U_1 d_1 / \nu$$

based on the surface velocity was recorded in Table I, with $\nu = 1.2 \times 10^{-5}$ ft^2/sec. The values of R show that the judgment of turbulent upstream flow is not an unrealistic one. It is known that plane Poiseuille flow, which would be the upstream flow if it were laminar and the slight curvature effect were neglected, is unstable at a value 2000 for the Reynolds member based on the mean velocity, or 3000 for R. It is also known that a free surface tends to destabilize the flow. But it is important to remember the distinction between stability against surface waves and that against shear waves. For surface waves the flow is unstable at any Reynolds number however small, but at the same time it is shear-wave instability that is responsible for turbulence. In view of the fact that the Reynolds numbers recorded are from 930 to 2400, which are of the order of 3000, and considering that the flow was not free from turbulence as it entered the tube, the assumption of turbulent upstream flow was not unrealistic. With

Q as the discharge in cubic inches per second, d_1 was obtained from

$$d_1 = 0.0375 \, Q/U_1,$$

U_1 being measured in inches per second.

In Fig. 4 the data are plotted in a chart with F as the abscissa and d_2/d_1 as the ordinate. Equation (19) is plotted with $c = 0$, and also, for best fit at various values of G, for $c = 7$. This value for c is the same as for the length of the ordinary hydraulic jump. It can be seen that the agreement between the theoretical prediction and the experimental results is quite satisfactory.

In none of the experiments did the tube run completely full of water downstream from the jump. Choking downstream from jump can happen if the discharge is great enough, or the pipe small enough, or the downstream opening narrow enough. If that happens, the situation is similar to the ordinary hydraulic jump when the water surface downstream touches an upper lid, the thin-film approximation is invalidated, and the radial variation of ω_2 is quite uncertain.

J. Fluid Mech. (1965), *vol.* 23, *part* 2, *pp.* 261–271

On large-amplitude magnetohydrodynamics

By CHIA-SHUN YIH

Department of Engineering Mechanics, University of Michigan,
Ann Arbor, Michigan

(Received 13 December 1964)

Three results on the flow of an infinitely conducting and inviscid fluid are presented in this paper. The first result is that all steady flows with magnetic lines coincident with streamlines are reducible to flows without a magnetic field. The second result is on the establishment of a steady irrotational and current-free flow with coincident streamlines and magnetic lines. It throws some light on the controversy between Stewartson (1960) and Sears & Resler (1959) concerning the possibility of such a flow. The third result concerns the flow of a fluid through a circular cylinder of radius R into a point sink with strength m when the fluid carries a current of density j_0 at infinity. It is shown that the condition of uniform flow at infinity is impossible to maintain if a dimensionless number $(kR)^2$ involving the current density j_0 exceeds the value $(3 \cdot 831)^2$, and that the current has the effect of concentrating the flow near the centre line and of producing ring eddies which become longer and longer as $(kR)^2$ is increased. The dimensionless number $(kR)^2$ is defined to be

$$|2(\omega - \alpha\gamma) R/W(1-\alpha^2)|^2$$

with $\qquad \alpha = h_0/W, \quad \gamma = 2\pi j_0(\mu/4\pi\rho)^{\frac{1}{2}} \quad \text{and} \quad h_0 = H_0(\mu/4\pi\rho)^{\frac{1}{2}},$

in which ω and W are the uniform angular velocity and the velocity at infinity, H_0 is the uniform longitudinal magnetic field at infinity, ρ the density, μ the magnetic permeability, and j_0 the current density at infinity.

1. Preliminaries

This paper deals with the flow of an inviscid, incompressible, and infinitely conducting fluid in a magnetic field. Except in §4, Cartesian co-ordinates x_i $(i = 1, 2, 3)$ will be used. The corresponding velocity components will be denoted by u_i and the corresponding magnetic field components by H_i. As usual, the density of the fluid will be denoted by ρ, the pressure by p, the magnetic permeability by μ, the body force per unit mass by X_i, and the time by t. The magnetic permeability is assumed constant. The equations of motion are

$$\rho \frac{Du_i}{Dt} = -\frac{\partial}{\partial x_i}\left(p + \frac{\mu}{8\pi}H^2\right) + \rho X_i + \frac{\mu}{4\pi}H_\alpha\frac{\partial H_i}{\partial x_\alpha}, \tag{1}$$

and the magnetic-field equations are

$$\frac{DH_i}{Dt} = H_\alpha\frac{\partial u_i}{\partial x_\alpha}, \tag{2}$$

in which $\qquad \dfrac{D}{Dt} = \dfrac{\partial}{\partial t} + u_\alpha\dfrac{\partial}{\partial x_\alpha}, \quad H^2 = H_\alpha H_\alpha,$

262   *Chia-Shun Yih*

and repeated indices in the same term indicate summation of the terms as the dummy index runs through 1, 2 and 3. The vector forms of equations (1) and (2) will be useful. These are

$$\rho \frac{D}{Dt}\mathbf{v} = -\operatorname{grad} p + \rho\mathbf{X} + \mu\mathbf{j}\times\mathbf{H}, \quad 4\pi\mathbf{j} = \operatorname{curl}\mathbf{H}, \tag{1a}$$

and
$$\frac{\partial\mathbf{H}}{\partial t} = \operatorname{curl}(\mathbf{v}\times\mathbf{H}), \tag{2a}$$

in which $\mathbf{v}$ is the velocity, $\mathbf{X}$ the body force, $\mathbf{H}$ the field, and $\mathbf{j}$ the current density.

The equation of continuity is

$$\frac{D\rho}{Dt} + \rho\frac{\partial u_\alpha}{\partial x_\alpha} = 0, \tag{3}$$

in which ρ need not be constant. Since the fluid is incompressible,

$$D\rho/Dt = 0, \tag{4}$$

and (3) can be written as $\partial u_\alpha/\partial x_\alpha = 0.$ (5)

There is also an equation of continuity of the magnetic field, which is

$$\partial H_\alpha/\partial x_\alpha = 0. \tag{6}$$

This is in effect an initial condition which persists by virtue of equation (2a).

2. Steady magnetically reinforced flows

A steady magnetically reinforced flow is a steady flow in which the streamlines and magnetic lines are coincident. It will now be shown that, provided the fluid is inviscid, incompressible, and infinitely conducting, the totality of solutions for such flows is exactly the same as the totality of solutions for steady flows in the absence of a magnetic field. In other words, a steady magnetically reinforced flow is equivalent to and has the same pattern as some steady flow of an ideal fluid (which may be non-homogeneous) in the absence of a magnetic field. Note that for an infinitely conducting fluid the magnetic lines move with the fluid. Hence if streamlines and magnetic lines are coincident far upstream in a steady flow, they coincide everywhere, except possibly in regions of closed streamlines.

The above-stated theorem will now be proved. Since the flow is steady,

$$D/Dt = u_\alpha\,\partial/\partial x_\alpha,$$

and equations (1), (2) and (4) become

$$\rho u_\alpha\frac{\partial u_i}{\partial x_\alpha} = -\frac{\partial}{\partial x_i}\left(p + \frac{\mu}{8\pi}H^2\right) + \rho X_i + \frac{\mu}{4\pi}H_\alpha\frac{\partial H_i}{\partial x_\alpha}, \tag{1b}$$

$$u_\alpha\,\partial H_i/\partial x_\alpha = H_\alpha\,\partial u_i/\partial x_\alpha, \tag{2b}$$

and
$$u_\alpha\,\partial\rho/\partial x_\alpha = 0. \tag{4b}$$

The equations for streamlines are

$$\frac{dx_1}{u_1} = \frac{dx_2}{u_2} = \frac{dx_3}{u_3}, \tag{7}$$

On large-amplitude magnetohydrodynamics   263

the solutions of which are

$$\psi(x_1, x_2, x_3) = C \quad \text{and} \quad \chi(x_1, x_2, x_3) = C'. \tag{8}$$

The intersections of the two families of surfaces represented by (8) as each of C and C' takes on different values are the streamlines, which are therefore imbedded in the ψ-surfaces (on which $\psi = $ constant) and χ-surfaces. Since

$$\partial\psi/\partial x_i \quad (i = 1, 2 \text{ and } 3)$$

are the direction numbers for the normal to a ψ-surface,

$$u_\alpha(\partial\psi/\partial x_\alpha) = 0. \tag{9}$$

Similarly, $$u_\alpha(\partial\chi/\partial x_\alpha) = 0. \tag{10}$$

The velocity is then given by

$$\mathbf{v} = \operatorname{grad}\psi \times \operatorname{grad}\chi, \tag{11}$$

for more detailed developments, see Yih (1957). But the development of (11) is very old, and the present writer certainly does not claim priority in its discovery.

Since the streamlines and magnetic lines are coincident, the most general† relationship between u_i and H_i is‡

$$H_i = \lambda(\psi, \chi)\, u_i, \tag{12}$$

in which λ is an arbitrary function of ψ and χ. Note that $(2b)$ is then automatically satisfied, because both sides are equal to $\lambda u_\alpha(\partial u_i/\partial x_\alpha)$. The other terms on the right-hand side are $u_i u_\alpha(\partial\lambda/\partial x_\alpha)$ and these are zero as a result of (9) and (10). Equation $(1b)$ becomes, again by virtue of (9) and (10),

$$\left(\rho - \frac{\mu}{4\pi}\lambda^2\right) u_\alpha \frac{\partial u_i}{\partial x_\alpha} = -\frac{\partial}{\partial x_i}\left(p + \frac{\mu}{8\pi}H^2\right) + \rho X_i. \tag{1c}$$

Note in passing that from either $(1b)$ or $(1c)$ the Bernoulli equation *along a streamline*

$$\tfrac{1}{2}\rho u_\alpha u_\alpha - (\mu/8\pi)\,H^2 = -p - (\mu/8\pi)\,H^2 - \rho\Omega + C(\psi, \chi), \tag{13}$$

or $$\tfrac{1}{2}\rho u_\alpha u_\alpha + p + \rho\Omega = C(\psi, \chi), \tag{14}$$

can be derived, provided the body force has a potential Ω.

Up to this point the development is the same as that given by Grad§ (1960), who took (with a slight difference in notation)

$$\rho^* = \rho - \frac{\mu}{4\pi}\lambda^2 \quad \text{and} \quad p^* = p + \frac{\mu}{8\pi}H^2,$$

observed that $$u_\alpha(\partial\rho^*/\partial x_\alpha) = 0, \tag{4c}$$

and concluded that the resulting equations

$$\rho^* u_\alpha(\partial u_i/\partial x_\alpha) = -\partial p^*/\partial x_i \tag{1d}$$

† The dependence of λ only on ψ and χ is dictated by (5) and (6).

‡ This relationship was already recognized by Grad (1960), whose work will be discussed in the following paragraph. Goldsworthy (1961) also recognized it. But he took λ to be constant in further discussion.

§ I am indebted to my colleague W. W. Willmarth for calling my attention to Grad's paper after this work was done.

govern the flow of a non-homogeneous fluid in the absence of a magnetic field. However, the body force has been neglected in Grad's equation, or $(1d)$. If the term ρX_i is included in $(1d)$, his conclusion does not go through. Furthermore, if body force is indeed neglected, his conclusion does not go far enough. For we can define (Yih 1958)

$$u_i' = (\rho^*/\rho_0)^{\frac{1}{2}} u_i,$$

and by virtue of $(4c)$ write $(1d)$ and (5) as

$$\rho_0 u_\alpha'(\partial u_i'/\partial x_\alpha) = -\partial p^*/\partial x_i,$$

and

$$\partial u_\alpha'/\partial x_\alpha = 0,$$

thus reducing the equations to those governing the flow of an incompressible fluid of *homogeneous* density. The boundary conditions present no difficulty, as will be shown for the general case, in which body force is taken into account.

Now let

$$Q = 1 - \frac{\mu}{4\pi\rho}\lambda^2, \quad u_i' = |Q|^{\frac{1}{2}} u_i, \quad p' = \frac{Q}{|Q|}\left(p + \frac{\mu}{8\pi} H^2\right), \quad \Omega' = \frac{Q}{|Q|}\Omega. \tag{15}$$

If $Q = 0$, we take $Q/|Q|$ to be 1, although the value -1 will do as well. By virtue of (9) and (10), equations $(1c)$ can be written as

$$\rho u_\alpha' \frac{\partial u_1'}{\partial x_\alpha} = -\frac{\partial p'}{\partial x_i} - \rho\Omega'. \tag{16}$$

Furthermore, $\qquad\qquad\qquad\qquad \partial u_\alpha'/\partial x_\alpha = 0 \qquad\qquad\qquad\qquad\qquad$ (17)

holds by virtue of (5), (9) and (10), and

$$u_\alpha'(\partial\rho/\partial x_\alpha) = 0 \tag{18}$$

obviously holds by virtue of $(4b)$. But (16), (17) and (18) are the equations governing steady flows of an incompressible and inviscid fluid in the absence of a magnetic field.

The boundary conditions need to be considered. If solid boundaries are present, the kinematic conditions at these boundaries are identical for the original flow (u_i-field) as for the associated flow (u_i'-field). Dynamical boundary conditions in the original flow can always be translated into similar ones in the associated flow.

The change of sign of Q in the field does not present any difficulty. Consider a surface S separating a region of positive Q from a region of negative Q. On the surface, $Q = 0$, and

$$\{p + (\mu/8\pi) H^2\} + \rho\Omega = C, \tag{19}$$

corresponding to $\qquad\qquad\qquad\qquad p' + \rho\Omega' = C. \qquad\qquad\qquad\qquad\qquad$ (20)

The condition $Q = 0$ also corresponds to

$$u_\alpha' u_\alpha' = 0 \tag{21}$$

on S. Since the flow u_i' is not irrotational, (21) is not impossible. The two parts of the associated flow on opposite sides of S are all governed by (16), (17) and (18), and on S, (20) and (21) hold. The sign of C (though not its magnitude) changes abruptly. But this does not violate the equality of

$$p + (\mu/8\pi) H^2$$

at S and on both sides of S.

On large-amplitude magnetohydrodynamics   265

If λ and ρ are constant and Q is zero all over the field, so that

$$u_i = (\mu/4\pi\rho)^{\frac{1}{2}} H_i, \tag{22}$$

the equations of motion are automatically satisfied and the pressure p can be evaluated from (19).

3. Establishment of irrotational and current-free flows

Equation $(1a)$ indicates that if the magnetic field is current-free, irrotational flow is possible. If, further, the streamlines and magnetic lines are coincident, $(2a)$ indicates that the magnetic field is steady. The velocity field may be steady or not; both steady and unsteady irrotational flows are possible, so long as $\mathbf{v}$ is parallel to $\mathbf{H}$, and $\mathbf{j}$ is zero.

For convenience, flows for which streamlines and magnetic lines are coincident and both the velocity field and the magnetic field are irrotational will be called I^2-flows. Steady I^2-flows past cylindrical bodies have been studied by Sears & Resler (1959), who discussed not only such flows but also flows in which $\mathbf{v}$ is not parallel to $\mathbf{H}$ (see also Sears 1961). We are concerned here only with I^2-flows. Sears & Resler did not state how their steady I^2-flow was established, and Stewartson (1960), assuming† that establishment from an initial uniform field was implied in the work of Sears & Resler, showed that if U_0 is the velocity of the fluid and H_∞ the magnetic field strength at infinity and if

$$U_0(4\pi\rho/\mu)^{\frac{1}{2}} \ll H_\infty, \tag{23}$$

the final steady flow is a slug flow predicted with a simple development by Yih (1959) for an infinitely conducting fluid. We shall show here by a very simple argument that if H is intially uniform and has the single component $H_1 = H_\infty$, and if the fluid has only one component $u_1 = U(t)$ at infinity, which increases from zero to U_0, steady I^2-flows cannot be the final state. On the other hand, if a current-free magnetic field identical with the one in a steady I^2-flow is set up *before* $U(t)$ increases (or before the body moves), the final steady flow must be an I^2-flow. If the body is a sphere, such a field can be set up by superposing on the uniform magnetic field H_∞ a field due to a magnetic dipole at the centre of the sphere, with proper strength and the axis pointing to a direction opposite to that of H_∞. The dipole can of course be replaced by the sort of surface current Sears & Resler described. In the following we shall consider the motion *relative* to the body. It can be shown that the kinematical problem is quite the same, whether the absolute or the relative motion is considered, although this may not be immediately evident as in the non-magnetic case (see the discussion in the Appendix).

The discussion will not be limited to two-dimensional flows. First, note that flows governed by (1), (2), (4), (5) and (6) are all reversible. Suppose that in $-T \leqslant t \leqslant 0$ the flow is established as $U(t)$ increases from zero to U_0, and the velocity and magnetic fields are given by U_i and H_i. If $U(t)$ now decreases from U_0 to zero according to the reversed schedule

$$U(t) = -U(-t) \quad (t > 0), \tag{24}$$

---

† However, he was probably aware that an I^2-flow can be established from an initially streaming magnetic field. See also a further paper by him (1963).

then for $t > 0$, the governing equations are exactly satisfied if

$$u_i(t) = -u_i(-t), \quad H_i(t) = H_i(-t). \tag{25}$$

For the effect of the discontinuity in velocity implied in (25), see the Appendix.

Now consider the establishment of flow in the period $-T \leqslant t \leqslant 0$, with a streaming current-free magnetic field already at $t = -T$, and with $U(t)$ varying from zero at $t = -T$ to U_0 at $t = 0$. The flow is initially current-free. Hence the term $\mu \mathbf{j} \times \mathbf{H}$ in $(1a)$ is zero, and the initial motion will be irrotational, with the streamlines coinciding with the magnetic lines. Then $(2a)$ states that the magnetic field will be stationary, and therefore will continue to be current-free. Further increase of $U(t)$ will then not affect the flow pattern, and will give a fluid velocity at every point proportional to the velocity of the final steady flow, the coefficient of proportionality being $U(t)/U_0$. Thus the final I^2-flow will be reached through intermediate I^2-flows. Now if, starting from the steady flow so obtained, we reverse the flow according to (24), not only do we know that (25) will satisfy the governing equations, but exactly the same argument as just put forth will show that the original (at $t = -T$) quiescent state with a streaming current-free magnetic field, *and no other state*, will be reached at $t = T$. If it had been possible to establish the steady state of I^2-flow at $t = 0$ from an initial quiescent state with a uniform magnetic field $H_1 = H_\infty$, $H_2 = 0 = H_3$, it should have been possible to recover it according to (25) as $U(t)$ varies from U_0 to zero according to (24) in the interval $T \geqslant t \geqslant 0$, contrary to the result established above. Hence it is impossible to establish a steady I^2-flow from a quiescent state with a uniform magnetic field. Although it would be more realistic to consider real fluids of finite viscosity and conductivity, discussion of the question of establishment within the framework of inviscid and infinitely conducting fluids by the use of the simple idea of reversibility perhaps throws some light on the matter.

4. A current-induced jet

Long (1960) has studied the steady axisymmetric motion of an infinitely conducting fluid. Cylindrical co-ordinates r, θ, and z will be used. The velocity components in the directions of increasing r, θ, and z will be denoted by u, v, and w. The components of the magnetic field will be denoted by H_r, H_θ, and H_z. Following Long, we shall use

$$(f, g, h) = (\mu/4\pi\rho)^{\frac{1}{2}} (H_r, H_\theta, H_z). \tag{26}$$

From the equations of continuity for the flow and magnetic fields,

$$ur = -\psi_z, \quad wr = \psi_r, \tag{27}$$

$$fr = -\Lambda_z, \quad hr = \Lambda_r, \tag{28}$$

in which ψ is the Stokes stream function, Λ the corresponding function for the magnetic field, and subscripts denote partial differentiation. From $(2a)$, with the left-hand side equal to zero, Long was able to show that

$$\Lambda = \Lambda(\psi) \tag{29}$$

and

$$(g - \Lambda'v)/r = K(\psi), \tag{30}$$

On large-amplitude magnetohydrodynamics   267

with Λ' indicating $d\Lambda/d\psi$. Equation (29) shows that projections of the streamlines and magnetic lines coincide in the (r, z) plane. Furthermore, from the θ-equation in $(1\,a)$, again for steady flow, he was able to show

$$vr - \Lambda'gr = L(\psi).\tag{31}$$

Finally, from the other two equations of motion Long showed that

$$\psi_{zz} + \psi_{rr} - \frac{1}{r}\,\psi_r - \frac{\Lambda\Lambda}{1-\Lambda'^2}\,[(\psi_z)^2 + (\psi_r)^2] + \frac{A'}{2(1-\Lambda'^2)} + \frac{B'r^4}{2(1-\Lambda'^2)} = \frac{M(\psi)\,r^2}{1-\Lambda'^2},\tag{32}$$

in which
$$A = L^2/(1-\Lambda'^2), \quad B = K^2/(1-\Lambda'^2).\tag{33}$$

Now (29) indicates that, although the magnetic lines and streamlines do not necessarily coincide, their projections in the (r, z) plane do. Thus the flow is magnetically reinforced as far as the r and z components of the velocity and of the magnetic field are concerned. From the results obtained in §2, we expect that (32) can be considerably simplified by a transformation similar to the second equation in (15). Realizing that Λ' is really just the $(\mu/4\pi\rho)^{\frac{1}{2}}\lambda$ in (15), we make the transformation
$$d\Psi = (1-\Lambda'^2)^{\frac{1}{2}}\,d\psi,\tag{34}$$

which reduces (32), after it has been multiplied by $(1-\Lambda'^2)^{\frac{1}{2}}$, to

$$\Psi_{zz} + \Psi_{rr} - \frac{1}{r}\,\Psi_r + \frac{1}{2}\frac{dA}{d\Psi} + \frac{1}{2}\frac{dB}{d\Psi}\,r^4 = N(\Psi)\,r^2,\tag{35}$$

in which
$$N = M(1-\Lambda'^2)^{-\frac{1}{2}}.$$

That (35) is considerably simpler than (32) is quite evident.

Long gave two explicit linear cases of (32). The first is for the conditions $v_0 = 0$, $w_0 = \text{const.}$ $g_0 = 0$, $h_0 = \text{const.}$ at $z = \text{infinity}$. In this case (32) reduces to

$$\psi_{zz} + \psi_{rr} - (1/r)\,\psi_r = 0.$$

The second is for the same conditions at infinity except $v_0 = 0$, which is replaced by $v_0 = \omega r$ (solid rotation). In this case

$$\psi_{zz} + \psi_{rr} - \frac{1}{r}\,\psi_r + \sigma^2\psi = \tfrac{1}{2}\sigma^2 w_0 r^2, \quad \sigma = \frac{2\omega}{w_0[1 - (h_0/w_0)^2]}.\tag{36}$$

Long stated that other linear cases could be found by a procedure he used to deal with the vorticity equation for stratified flow in a gravitational field (Long 1958). But that procedure was quite labourious even for the equation to which it was applied, and will certainly be much more so if one attempts to apply it to (32). Furthermore, it cannot be used to find the linear cases exhaustively. We shall use the same approach as used by Yih (1960) for discovering the linear cases of steady stratified flows in a gravitational field. Starting with (35), the possible linear cases are simply the cases in which

$$\frac{1}{2}\frac{dA}{d\Psi} = a\Psi + b, \quad \frac{1}{2}\frac{dB}{d\Psi} = c\Psi + d, \quad N = m\Psi + n,\tag{37}$$

in which the lower-case letters are constants. Given *any* $\Lambda(\psi)$, the first two equations in (37) specify $L(\psi)$ and $K(\psi)$, and therefore v_0 and g_0. With (37) substituted in (35), the upstream condition is then determined by solving Ψ as a function of r far upstream. The function ψ is then also known as a function of r.

For instance, if $a = k^2, b = 0, c = 0, d = 0$, and $m = 0$ for any Λ', (35) becomes

$$\Psi_{zz} + \Psi_{rr} - (1/r)\,\Psi_r + k^2\Psi = nr^2, \tag{38}$$

which gives

$$\Psi_\infty = \beta r^2, \quad \beta = n/k^2. \tag{39}$$

If, further,

$$g = \Lambda'v, \tag{40}$$

then $B = 0$, and far upstream

$$L = (1 - \Lambda'^2)\,vr, \quad (1 - \Lambda'^2)\,v^2 r^2 = a\Psi^2 = (k\beta r^2)^2, \tag{41}$$

the latter of which specifies v_0 (at $z = $ infinity) if Λ' is specified, upon use of (39). The solution of (38) is of the form

$$\Psi = \beta r^2 + \sum_{n=1}^{\infty} A_n r J_1(k_n r) \exp\{\pm \sqrt{(k_n^2 - k^2)}\,z\}, \tag{42}$$

in which $J_1(k_n R) = 0$ if the flow is within a cylinder of radius R.

We shall present an interesting case of an axisymmetric flow in a cylinder of radius R into a point sink (of flow as well as electricity) at $z = 0$. Since the flow is symmetric with respect to the plane $z = 0$ it is sufficient to consider the *lower* half of the cylinder. The case described by

$$w = W, \quad h = h_0, \quad v = \omega r, \quad g = \gamma r = 2\pi j_0 (\mu/4\pi\rho)^{\frac{1}{2}} r \tag{43}$$

at $z = -\infty$ corresponds to a uniform flow, a uniform magnetic field, a solid rotation, and a uniform current density j_0 at $z = -\infty$. For definiteness, let

$$\Lambda' = h_0/W = \alpha < 1.$$

The conditions at infinity give $\psi = \frac{1}{2}Wr^2$ and $B = $ const. so that $B' = 0$. As to A,

$$vr - \Lambda'gr = (\omega - \alpha\gamma)\,r^2 = \frac{2(\omega - \alpha\gamma)}{W}\psi, \tag{44}$$

so that

$$A = 4\left(\frac{\omega - \alpha\gamma}{W}\right)^2 (1 - \alpha^2)^{-1}\psi^2. \tag{45}$$

Since $\Lambda' = $ const. we can use (32) directly, giving

$$\psi_{zz} + \psi_{rr} - \frac{1}{r}\psi_r + k^2\psi = \frac{k^2}{2}Wr^2, \tag{46}$$

in which the right-hand side has been determined from the upstream condition, and

$$k = 2(\omega - \alpha\gamma)/W(1 - \alpha^2). \tag{47}$$

The solution of (46) is

$$\psi = \frac{W}{2}r^2 + \sum_{n=1}^{\infty} A_n r J_1(k_n r) \exp(k_n^2 - k^2)^{\frac{1}{2}}z, \tag{48}$$

in which

$$J_1(k_n R) = 0, \quad A_n = \frac{W}{k_n J_0^2(k_n R)}. \tag{49}$$

The coefficients A_n are determined from the condition that $\psi = \frac{1}{2}WR^2$ at $z = 0$. The first eigenvalue $k_1 R$ is 3·831. If

$$k^2 R^2 < (3·831)^2, \tag{50}$$

the upstream condition is satisfied by (48). The solution is similar to the one obtained by Long (1956) for a rotating fluid. It is characterized by a jet more and more concentrated along the centreline as k^2R^2 increases toward $(3\cdot831)^2$, and by

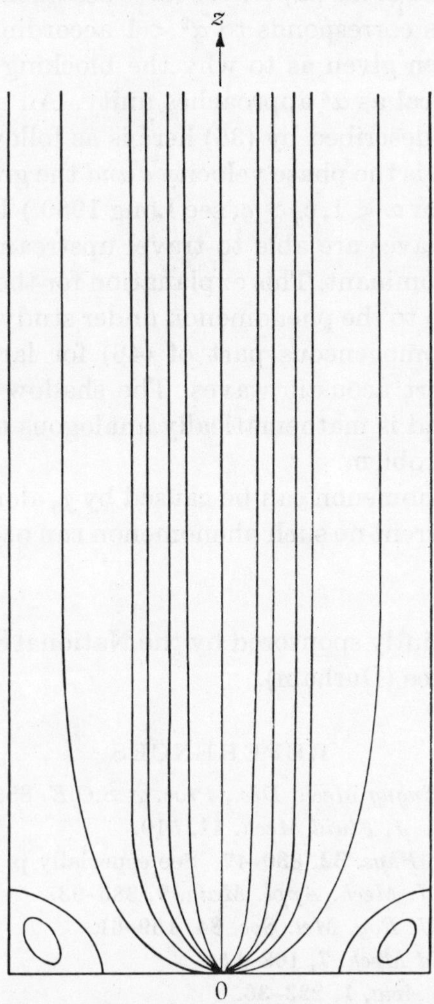

FIGURE 1. A sketch of the flow pattern for a current-induced jet. The plane $z = 0$ can either be a solid boundary or a plane of symmetry separating the flow shown from its mirror image described by (48).

a ring eddy on each side of the plane $z = 0$. The mirror image of the flow described by (48) is shown in figure 1. If

$$k^2R^2 > (3\cdot831)^2,\qquad(51)$$

the upstream condition is no longer satisfied by (48), and vortex sheets (and possibly current sheets) can be expected to occur, in analogy with stratified flow (see Debler 1959).

Now the form of k^2 given in (47) allows one to say that k^2 will be large if

(1) $\alpha\gamma R$ is large relative to W (strong current),

(2) ωR is large relative to W (strong rotation),

(3) α is near unity.

270 *Chia-Shun Yih*

It is interesting that between the limiting cases (1) and (2), the effects of rotation and current can be compensative, and the signs of $\alpha\gamma$ (or αj_0) and ω are all important in the intermediate range. Item (3) is pertinent to the discussion given by Long (1960) at the end of his paper. We have assumed the upstream condition to be undisturbed. This corresponds to $\alpha^2 < 1$ according to Long's conclusion. No explanation has been given as to why the blocking effect, which occurs at large k^2, should be critical as α^2 approaches unity. An explanation for the case discussed by Long and described by (36) here is as follows: As α^2 approaches 1, W approaches h_0, which is the phase velocity c *and* the group velocity c_g of waves at zero wavelength. (For $\alpha < 1, c_g > c$; see Long 1960.) Therefore as $\alpha^2 \to 1$ from below, *even* the short waves are able to travel upstream. The shadow effect or blocking effect is then dominant. This explanation for the phenomenon governed by (36) is applicable also to the phenomenon under study here, governed by (46). Mathematically, the homogeneous part of (46) for large k^2 is similar to the equation governing short acoustic waves. The shadow effect of high pitch in sound is well known, and is mathematically analogous to the blocking effect of high k^2 in the present problem.

Note that the jet phenomenon can be caused by j_0 alone, with $\omega = 0$, whereas without an electrical current no such phenomenon can occur without rotation, as indicated by (36).

This work has been jointly sponsored by the National Science Foundation and the Army Research Office (Durham).

REFERENCES

DEBLER, W. R. 1959 *J. Engng Mech. Div., Proc. A.S.C.E.* **85**, 51–65.

GOLDSWORTHY, F. A. 1961 *J. Fluid Mech.* **11**, 519.

GRAD, H. 1960 *Rev. Mod. Phys.* **32**, 830–47. See especially p. 836.

LONG, R. R. 1956 *Quart. J. Mech. Appl. Math.* **9**, 385–93.

LONG, R. R. 1958 *Quart. J. Roy. Met. Soc.* **84**, 159–61.

LONG, R. R. 1960 *J. Fluid Mech.* **7**, 108–114.

SEARS, W. R. 1961 *Astro. Acta,* **1**, 223–36.

SEARS, W. R. & RESLER, E. L. 1959 *J. Fluid Mech.* **5**, 257–73.

STEWARTSON, K. 1960 *J. Fluid Mech.* **8**, 82–96.

STEWARTSON, K. 1963 *Proc. Roy. Soc.* A, **275**, 70.

YIH, C.-S. 1959 *Quart. Appl. Math.* **16**, 409–15.

YIH, C.-S. 1960 *J. Fluid Mech.* **9**, 161–74.

YIH, C.-S. 1957 *La Houille Blanche,* no. 3, 439–50.

YIH, C.-S. 1958 On the flow of a stratified fluid. *Proc. Third U.S. National Congress of Appl. Mech.* pp. 857–61.

Appendix

The equivalence of the absolute motion and the motion relative to the body is based on (2) or (2 a). If u_i is the ith component of the velocity relative to the body, then the absolute velocity has the components

$$-U(t) + u_1, \quad u_2 \quad \text{and} \quad u_3,$$

On large-amplitude magnetohydrodynamics 271

in which $U(t)$ is the speed of the body, which moves in the direction of decreasing x_1. Now if u_i is proportional to H_i, $(2a)$ becomes, after utilization of (6),

$$\frac{\partial \mathbf{H}}{\partial t} - U \frac{\partial \mathbf{H}}{\partial x} = 0,$$

which states that the magnetic field moves with the body. If it is initially irrotational, it will continue to be. The irrotationality of the flow then follows from the fact that $\mathbf{j} = 0$, and the Helmholtz–Kelvin conservation theorems.

However, displacement current has so far not been considered, and my colleague, Dr J. D. Murray, has pointed out to me that the sudden reversal of velocity proposed in § 3 may result in infinite displacement currents. If displacement currents are to be included, $(1a)$ should be replaced by

$$4\pi\mathbf{j} = \operatorname{curl}\mathbf{H} - \frac{\partial(\epsilon\mathbf{E})}{\partial t}, \tag{A 1}$$

in which ϵ is the dielectric constant. The Ohm's law is still

$$\mathbf{j} = \sigma(\mathbf{E} + \mu\mathbf{v} \times \mathbf{H}), \tag{A 2}$$

in which σ is the electrical conductivity. The Maxwell equation

$$\mu \frac{\partial \mathbf{H}}{\partial t} = -\operatorname{curl}\mathbf{E} \tag{A 3}$$

is still valid. Eliminating $\mathbf{E}$ and $\mathbf{j}$ from the three preceding equations, we have

$$\frac{\partial \mathbf{H}}{\partial t} = \operatorname{curl}(\mathbf{v} \times \mathbf{H}) - \eta \operatorname{curl}\operatorname{curl}\mathbf{H} - \eta\epsilon\mu \frac{\partial^2 \mathbf{H}}{\partial t^2}, \tag{A 4}$$

if ϵ is assumed constant. Now for an infinitely conducting fluid, $\eta = 0$, and the last two terms vanish provided $\nabla^2 \mathbf{H}$ and $\partial^2 \mathbf{H}/\partial t^2$ are not infinite. Then $(2a)$ is recovered, and the argument in § 3 can again be applied to reach the conclusion of the persistence of the I^2-state.

To ensure that $\partial^2 \mathbf{H}/\partial t^2$ be not infinite, it is necessary to have a smooth reversal instead of the sudden reversal proposed in § 3, if displacement currents are taken into account. To do so, assume that an I^2-flow is established in any way whatsoever in the interval $-T < t < -t_1$, in which $U(t)$ increases from zero to U_0, and let $U(t)$ decrease smoothly but otherwise in any arbitrary manner from U_0 to zero in the interval $-t_1 < t < 0$. At $t = 0$ we have a quiescent fluid with a streaming irrotational magnetic field, according to the arguments in § 3. We then apply (25). On the one hand, the reversibility of the flow and the magnetic field demand that the initial $(t = -T)$ condition be retrieved at $t = T$. On the other hand, the I^2-state must persist from the moment $t = -t_1$, as argued in the preceding paragraph and in § 3. Hence a contradiction would be reached if the I^2-flow had been established from an initially uniform field at $t = -T$. Note that in this argument the smooth slowing down in $-t_1 < t < 0$ is introduced merely to remove the discontinuity which would be implied in (35) if t_1 were taken to be zero, as in § 3. The argument is quite unimpaired by extending the history of the motion to $t = 0$ before reversing it.

Chia-Shun Yih

On the Earnshaw Conjecture

In his Kinematics of Vorticity (p. 183), Truesdell [1] called attention to the Earnshaw conjecture [2] of 1837, which states that in a circulation-preserving motion, a particle once in complex-lamellar motion remains ever in complex-lamellar motion. Truesdell stated that he doubted the truth of this conjecture. A disproof of it, still lacking in the literature, is supplied in this brief note.

A complex-lamellar motion is one in which the velocity vector is everywhere perpendicular to the vorticity vector. Circulation is preserved in a barotropic fluid for which a relation

$$(1) \qquad \varrho = f(p, t)$$

exists between its density ϱ, pressure p, and the time t, provided the fluid is inviscid and the body force per unit mass possesses a potential Ω. For an inviscid barotropic fluid, the equations of motion are

$$(2) \qquad \frac{D u_i}{D t} = - \frac{\partial}{\partial x_i} \left(\int \frac{dp}{\varrho} + \Omega \right),$$

in which u_i is the velocity component in the direction of x_i, Cartesian coordinates (x_1, x_2, and x_3) being used. The integral $\int dp/\varrho$ is defined over the entire field of flow for any t which appears only as a parameter.

A fluid of constant density is a special case of a barotropic fluid. If Earnshaw's conjecture is true, it must be true for a fluid of constant ϱ. It is well known that for an inviscid fluid of constant ϱ one can deduce from (2) the vorticity equations

$$(3) \qquad \frac{D}{D t} \xi_i = \xi_\alpha \frac{\partial u_i}{\partial x_\alpha},$$

in which ξ_i is the i th component of the vorticity, and

$$\frac{D}{D t} = \frac{\partial}{\partial t} + u_\alpha \frac{\partial}{\partial x_\alpha},$$

as in (2). From (2) and (3), it follows that, for constant ϱ,

$$(4) \qquad \frac{D}{Dt} (u_\alpha \xi_\alpha) = - \xi_\alpha \frac{\partial}{\partial x_\alpha} \left(\frac{p}{\varrho} + \Omega - \frac{q^2}{2} \right),$$

in which $q^2 = u_\alpha u_\alpha$ is the speed squared.

Now for steady flows of an inviscid fluid of constant ϱ, (2) can be written as

$$(5) \qquad \boldsymbol{u} \times \boldsymbol{\xi} = \mathbf{grad}\, B,$$

in which

$$B = \frac{p}{\varrho} + \Omega + \frac{q^2}{2}$$

is the Bernoulli function. Thus for such flows B is constant along a streamline or a vortex line (or in any Lamb surface), as is well known. Thus

$$(6) \qquad \xi_\alpha \frac{\partial}{\partial x_\alpha} \left(\frac{p}{\varrho} + \Omega + \frac{q^2}{2} \right) = 0.$$

If Earnshaw's conjecture were true,

$$\frac{D}{D t} (u_\alpha \xi_\alpha) = 0,$$

Reprinted from *Z. A. M. M.* 46 (1966) 471−472.

and (4) and (6) would lead to the result that q^2 is constant along a vortex line. For two-dimensional and axisymmetric motion, this is evidently true. But counter examples can be easily constructed to show that for general three-dimensional motions Earnshaw's conjecture is not true.

One such counter example will be given. Consider a steady flow of an inviscid fluid of constant ϱ past a unit sphere with center at the origin. The velocity at infinity is in the x-direction and is

$$U = U_0 \left(1 + e^{-y^2} \right).$$

Cartesian coordinates x, y, and z are used. At $x = -\infty$ and $y = \varepsilon$, the vortex line is parallel to the z-axis, however small ε is. This vortex line will of course move with the fluid, as is well known. As its mid-point (at which $z = 0$) sweeps arbitrarily close to the stagnation point $(-1, 0, 0)$ on the sphere, where it will have an arbitrarily small speed, its far ends, being at infinity, will have the speed U_0. Thus q^2 will not be constant on a vortex line, whereas its constancy would be demanded by the Earnshaw conjecture if the latter were true. The latter is therefore not true for the example given, and therefore not generally true.

This work has been supported by the National Science Foundation.

References

1 C. Truesdell, Kinematics of Vorticity, Bloomington, Indiana, 1954, Indiana University Press.
2 S. Earnshaw, On fluid motion, so far as it is expressed by the equation of continuity, Trans. Cambr. Phil. Soc. 6, pp. 203−233 (1837).

Anschrift: Prof. Chia-Shun Yih, Department of Engineering Mechanics, The University of Michigan, Ann Arbor, Michigan 48104, U.S.A.

Peristaltic Transport[1]

Y. C. FUNG

Professor, Department AMES
(Bioengineering), University of
California—San Diego,
La Jolla, Calif.

C. S. YIH

Stephen P. Timoshenko University Professor,
Department of Engineering Mechanics,
University of Michigan,
Ann Arbor, Mich.

Peristaltic pumping (viscous fluid flow induced by a sinusoidal traveling wave motion of the walls of a tube) at moderate amplitudes of motion is analyzed in the two-dimensional case. The nonlinear convective acceleration is considered and the nonslip condition is applied on the wavy wall (rather than on the mean position) in order to account for the mean flow induced by the wall motion. In the case in which there is no other cause of flow, the mean flow induced by the peristaltic motion of the wall is proportional to the square of the amplitude ratio (wave amplitude/half width of channel). The velocity profile depends on the mean pressure gradient. In this paper only those cases in which the pressure gradient will produce a flow of the same order of magnitude as that induced by the peristaltic motion are considered. If the pressure gradient is positive and equal to a certain critical value, then the velocity is zero on the center line. Pumping against a positive pressure gradient greater than the critical value would induce a backward flow (reflux) in the core region of the stream. There will be no reflux if the pressure gradient is smaller than the critical value. The velocity profile and the value of the critical pressure gradient are presented in this paper.

Introduction

IN THIS paper, we shall consider an idealized, two-dimensional analogy of peristalsis.

The word peristalsis stems from the Greek word peristaltikos, which means clasping and compressing. In physiology, it may be described as a progressive wave of contraction seen in tubes provided with longitudinal and transverse muscular fibers. It consists in a narrowing and transverse shortening of a portion of the tube, which then relaxes, while a lower portion becomes shortened and narrowed. Some worms use peristaltic motion as a means of locomotion. The ureter passes urine from the kidney to the bladder by peristalsis. A number of biomedical instruments such as some heart-lung machines use peristaltic motion to pump blood or other fluids.

In the usual mode of operation of a peristaltic pump the amplitude of the traveling wave on the elastic wall is so large that at the narrowest point the walls press against each other. The action in a healthy ureter is the same. The ureter receives fluid from the kidney at the upper end, and passes it down to the bladder against a pressure gradient. It enters the bladder at the ureterovesical junction, which functions as a one-way valve. The following data about human ureter may be of interest (Bergman [1],[2] Boyarsky [2]). Normally, there are three or four waves along the entire length of the ureter, which is of the order of 30 cm. The amplitude of the wave is of the order of 5 mm. The contracted portion has practically zero lumen. On an X-ray film in pyelography the whole ureter appears as several "spindles"; the thinnest segments are almost invisible. The speed of travel of the waves is about 3 to 6 cm per sec. The frequency of contractions varies from one individual to another, and is about 1 to 8 per min. Each contraction lasts about 1.5 to 9 sec, the diastolic (dilating) phase is about twice as long as the systolic (contracting) phase. Pressure during the contraction varied from 2 to 8 mm Hg at the pelvis, 2 to 10 mm Hg

[1] This research was supported by the U. S. Air Force Office of Scientific Research through a Grant 1186-67 to the University of California, San Diego.

Contributed by the Applied Mechanics Division and presented at the Winter Annual Meeting, December 1–5, 1968, New York, N. Y., of THE AMERICAN SOCIETY OF MECHANICAL ENGINEERS.

Discussion of this paper should be addressed to the Editorial Department, ASME, United Engineering Center, 345 East 47th Street, New York, N. Y. 10017, and will be accepted until January 20, 1969. Discussion received after the closing date will be returned. Manuscript received by the ASME Applied Mechanics Division, October 3, 1967; final draft, June 10, 1968. Paper No. 68—WA/APM-11.

[2] Numbers in brackets indicate References at end of paper.

Nomenclature

Natural quantities are used before equation (8). Dimensionless variables are used after equation (8). Complex conjugates are indicated by an asterisk (*).

A, B = coefficients defined in equation (41)

a = amplitude of traveling waves (displacement of the wall)

C_1, C_2, C_3 = integration constants

c = wave speed

d = half of the mean spacing between the solid boundaries

D = constant defining boundary value of $\Phi_{20}(\pm 1)$, equation (45)

$F(y)$ = function defined in equation (47)

K = coefficient for steady flow, see (26)

p = pressure

$\dfrac{\overline{\partial p}}{\partial x}$ = the pressure gradient averaged over a period of time

$\left(\dfrac{\partial p}{\partial x}\right)_0$ = constant pressure gradient corresponding to the initial flow

$\left(\dfrac{\partial p}{\partial x}\right)_2$ = pressure gradient accompanying the peristaltic motion. See equations (7) (dimensional) or (13) (dimensionless)

R = Reynolds number = cd/ν

t = time

u, v, w = velocity components in x, y, z directions, respectively

$\bar{u}$ = mean flow, u averaged over time

x, y, z = rectangular Cartesian coordinates, see Fig. 1

α = wave number = $2\pi d/\lambda$

β = complex number defined in (38)

ϵ = amplitude ratio = a/d

λ = wavelength of the traveling motion of the wall

μ = viscosity

ν = kinematic viscosity

ρ = density of fluid

$\Phi_1, \Phi_{20}, \Phi_{22}$ = functions defining ψ_1, ψ_2. See equations (27) and (31)

ψ = stream function

ψ_0, ψ_1, ψ_2 = functions in the expansion of ψ. See equation (14), (27) and (31)

η = vertical displacement of the wall

in the upper segments of the ureter, and 2 to 14 mm Hg in the lower segment of the ureter (Weinberg [3], Orkin [4]).

From the point of view of fluid mechanics, the pumping action of the normal ureter is easy to understand. The fluid trapped between the contracted segments is sent downstream. However, there is another case, a pathologic one, that is not so clearly understood (Graves and Davidoff [5] Hutch [6, 7]). When there is some obstruction in the ureter, or in the ureter-bladder junction, the upstream ureter dilates. In such "hydroureter" cases, peristaltic motion becomes a traveling wave of relatively small amplitude over a cylindrical tube. It is evident that the efficiency of pumping is decreased in such cases. In fact, if the amplitude is so small that the motion is governed by a linear mathematical system, the fluid motion will be periodic, and one wonders whether peristaltic motion of small amplitude pumps at all. It is on this question that our attention is focused in the present article.

Our original interest in the problem of peristaltic pumping arose from yet another problem in physiology: in the vasomotion of the small blood vessels. The arterioles and venules in some preparations[3] are seen to change their diameters periodically. Although the spatial wave form of such a vasomotion has not been ascertained, it is conceivable that peristaltic pumping is involved. In this case, again, our interest is in wave motion of the wall of a circular cylindrical tube at a moderate amplitude.

In this paper we shall consider an idealized two-dimensional analogy of the real problem. A sinusoidal wave is assumed to travel down the walls of a two-dimensional channel of constant width and infinite length. The motion of a viscous fluid contained in the channel is to be determined.

The problem of peristaltic pumping in a two-dimensional flexible tube is solved by Shapiro ([19], 1967) under the conditions that (a) the appropriate Reynolds number is so small that the flow may be considered inertia-free, and (b) the length of the peristaltic wave is very long compared with the width of the tube. Under these assumptions the flow is steady in coordinates moving with the wave, and Shapiro obtains an exact solution which shows the well-known parabolic velocity profile of Poiseuille flow. In reference [11] (1966), Shapiro and Latham presented experiment findings which generally confirm the theory.

The present analysis is aimed at clarifying the role of the Reynolds number and the wavelength on the peristaltic pumping at moderate amplitudes of sinusoidal motion. The solution is based on expansion in power series of the amplitude-to-channel-width ratio; hence in practice it is valid only for small amplitudes. The nonlinearity of the equations of motion and the nonlinearity of the boundary conditions are both taken into account. In the limiting case of zero Reynolds number and small amplitude, our result is in agreement with Shapiro's.

Formulation of the Problem

We shall consider a two-dimensional channel of uniform thickness filled with a homogeneous Newtonian viscous fluid. The walls of the channel are flexible, on which are imposed traveling, sinusoidal waves of moderate amplitude. Certain conditions will be imposed on the pressures at the ends of the channel. The velocity distribution and the mean flow are sought.

The equations governing two-dimensional motion of a viscous fluid are the equations of motion

$$\frac{\partial u}{\partial t} + u \frac{\partial u}{\partial x} + v \frac{\partial u}{\partial y} = -\frac{1}{\rho} \frac{\partial p}{\partial x} + \nu \nabla^2 u, \tag{1a}$$

$$\frac{\partial v}{\partial t} + u \frac{\partial v}{\partial x} + v \frac{\partial v}{\partial y} = -\frac{1}{\rho} \frac{\partial p}{\partial y} + \nu \nabla^2 v, \tag{1b}$$

and the equation of continuity

$$\frac{\partial u}{\partial x} + \frac{\partial v}{\partial y} = 0. \tag{2}$$

In these equations, x and y are Cartesian coordinates, with x measured in the direction of wave propagation and y measured in the direction normal to the mean position of the membranes. The origin is located on the center line of the channel. The velocity components in the directions of increasing x and y, respectively, are denoted by u and v; t denotes the time, ρ the density of the fluid, p the pressure, and ν the kinematic viscosity.

Equation (2) allows the use of the stream function ψ, in terms of which

$$u = \frac{\partial \psi}{\partial y}, \qquad v = -\frac{\partial \psi}{\partial x}. \tag{3}$$

If p is eliminated between (1a) and (1b) and (3) is used, the resulting equation is

$$\frac{\partial}{\partial t} \nabla^2 \psi + \psi_y \nabla^2 \psi_x - \psi_x \nabla^2 \psi_y = \nu \nabla^2 \nabla^2 \psi, \tag{4}$$

in which

$$\nabla^2 = \frac{\partial^2}{\partial x^2} + \frac{\partial^2}{\partial y^2},$$

and subscripts indicate partial differentiation.

The fluid is subjected to boundary conditions imposed by the symmetric motion of the flexible walls. Let the vertical displacements of the upper and lower walls be η and $-\eta$, respectively, where

$$\eta = a \cos \frac{2\pi}{\lambda} (x - ct), \tag{5}$$

and a is the amplitude, λ the wavelength, and c the wave speed; see Fig. 1. The horizontal displacement will be assumed zero. Hence the velocity components of particles on the wall are $u = 0$, $v = \pm \partial \eta / \partial t$. Therefore, on the walls which are located at $y = \pm d \pm \eta$, the boundary conditions for the fluid are

$$\psi_y = 0, \qquad -\psi_x = \pm \frac{2\pi ac}{\lambda} \sin \frac{2\pi}{\lambda} (x - ct). \tag{6}$$

Finally, conditions at the ends of the tube must be specified. In the real problem of peristalsis of the ureter one end of which is joined to the kidney at the pelvis and the other end is joined to the bladder, the end conditions are hydroelastic in nature and nvolve feedback and control in a delicate way. To maintain pertinence to the real problem we shall consider an idealized tube of infinite length for which the pressure gradient is specified as a function of the amplitude of the peristaltic motion. We assume that the pressure gradient is of the form

$$\frac{\partial p}{\partial x} = \left(\frac{\partial p}{\partial x} \right)_0 + a \left(\frac{\partial p}{\partial x} \right)_1 + a^2 \left(\frac{\partial p}{\partial x} \right)_2 + \dots \tag{7}$$

The first term on the right corresponds to an imposed pressure gradient, whereas the higher-order terms correspond to the

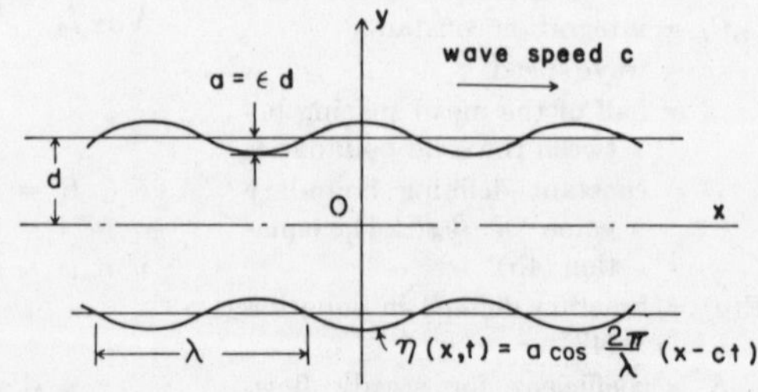

Fig. 1 Peristaltic motion of the walls

---

[3] For example, the bat's wing. See Nicoll [8, 9, 10].

peristaltic motion. It will be seen later that only the terms involving even powers of a can affect the pumping. We shall assume that the imposed pressure gradient $\left(\dfrac{\partial p}{\partial x}\right)_0$ is a constant, whereas $\left(\dfrac{\partial p}{\partial x}\right)_1$, $\left(\dfrac{\partial p}{\partial x}\right)_2$, etc., are functions of x, y, and t. The case $\left(\dfrac{\partial p}{\partial x}\right)_0 = 0$ shall be called *free pumping*, and will be given special attention later.

Equations (4) through (7) form the differential system governing the problem. It would be expedient to simplify these equations by introducing nondimensional variables. We have a characteristic velocity c and three characteristic lengths, a, λ, and d. Let us introduce the following nondimensional variables based on c and d:

$$x' = \frac{x}{d}, \qquad y' = \frac{y}{d}, \qquad u' = \frac{u}{c}, \qquad v' = \frac{v}{c},$$

$$\eta' = \frac{\eta}{d}, \qquad \psi' = \frac{\psi}{cd}, \qquad t' = \frac{ct}{d}, \qquad p' = \frac{p}{\rho c^2}. \tag{8}$$

The amplitude ratio ϵ, the wave number a, and the Reynolds number R are defined by

$$\epsilon = \frac{a}{d}, \qquad \alpha = \frac{2\pi d}{\lambda}, \qquad R = \frac{cd}{\nu}. \tag{9}$$

In terms of these, (4), (5), (6) and (7) become, *after* the accents are dropped,

$$\frac{\partial}{\partial t}\nabla^2\psi + \psi_y\nabla^2\psi_x - \psi_x\nabla^2\psi_y = \frac{1}{R}\nabla^2\nabla^2\psi, \tag{10}$$

$$\eta = \epsilon \cos \alpha(x - t), \tag{11}$$

$$\psi_u = 0, \qquad \psi_x = \mp \alpha\epsilon \sin \alpha(x - t), \qquad \text{at } y = \pm(1 + \eta), \tag{12}$$

and

$$\frac{\partial p}{\partial x} = \left(\frac{\partial p}{\partial x}\right)_0 + \epsilon\left(\frac{\partial p}{\partial x}\right)_1 + \epsilon^2\left(\frac{\partial p}{\partial x}\right)_2 + \ldots\ldots \tag{13}$$

A solution to this differential system is sought with particular attention to the mean flow.

Method of Solution

We shall seek a solution in the form of a series in the parameter ϵ:

$$\psi = \psi_0 + \epsilon\psi_1 + \epsilon^2\psi_2 + \epsilon^3\psi_3 + \ldots \tag{14}$$

On substituting (14) into (10), collecting terms according to powers of ζ and identifying the coefficients of like powers of ζ on both sides of the equation, we obtain:

$$\frac{1}{R}\nabla^2\nabla^2\psi_0 = \frac{\partial}{\partial t}\nabla^2\psi_0 + \psi_{0y}\nabla^2\psi_{0x} - \psi_{0x}\nabla^2\psi_{0y}, \tag{15}$$

$$\frac{1}{R}\nabla^2\nabla^2\psi_1 = \frac{\partial}{\partial t}\nabla^2\psi_1 + \psi_{0y}\nabla^2\psi_{1x} + \psi_{1y}\nabla^2\psi_{0x}$$
$$- \psi_{0x}\nabla^2\psi_{1y} - \psi_{1x}\nabla^2\psi_{0y}, \tag{16}$$

$$\frac{1}{R}\nabla^2\nabla^2\psi_2 = \frac{\partial}{\partial t}\nabla^2\psi_2 + \psi_{0y}\nabla^2\psi_{2x} + \psi_{1y}\nabla^2\psi_{1x} + \psi_{2y}\nabla^2\psi_{0x}$$
$$- \psi_{0x}\nabla^2\psi_{2y} - \psi_{1x}\nabla^2\psi_{1y} - \psi_{2x}\nabla^2\psi_{0y}, \tag{17}$$

etc.

The boundary conditions (12) may be first expanded in powers of η. Thus the first equation of (12) may be written[4]

$$\psi_y(\pm 1) \pm \eta\psi_{yy}(\pm 1) + \frac{\eta^2}{2}\psi_{yyy}(\pm 1) \pm \ldots = 0, \tag{18}$$

where η is given by (11). On substituting (14) and (11) into (18), and setting the coefficients of successive powers of ϵ to zero, we obtain the boundary conditions

$$\psi_{0y}(\pm 1) = 0, \tag{19}$$

$$\psi_{1y}(\pm 1) \pm \psi_{0yy}(\pm 1) \cos \alpha(x - t) = 0, \tag{20}$$

$$\psi_{2y}(\pm 1) \pm \psi_{1yy}(\pm 1) \cos \alpha(x - t)$$
$$+ \frac{1}{2}\psi_{0yyy}(\pm 1) \cos^2 \alpha(x - t) = 0. \tag{21}$$

Similarly, the second equation of (12) leads to

$$\psi_{0x}(\pm 1) = 0, \tag{22}$$

$$\psi_{1x}(\pm 1) + \psi_{0xy}(\pm 1) \cos \alpha(x - t) = \mp\alpha \sin \alpha(x - t), \tag{23}$$

$$\psi_{2x}(\pm 1) \pm \psi_{1xy}(\pm 1) \cos \alpha(x - t)$$
$$+ \frac{1}{2}\psi_{0xyy}(\pm 1) \cos^2 \alpha(x - t) = 0, \tag{24}$$

etc.

Equations (15), (19), and (22), together with the condition of symmetry and a uniform pressure gradient in the x-direction, $(\partial p/\partial x)_0 = $ constant, yield the classical Poiseuille flow:

$$\psi_0 = K\left(y - \frac{y^3}{3}\right), \tag{25}$$

$$K = -R\left(\frac{\partial p}{\partial x}\right)_0. \tag{26}$$

Equations (16), (20), and (23) can be satisfied by a solution of the form

$$2\psi_1 = \Phi_1(y)e^{i\alpha(x-t)} + \Phi_1^*(y)e^{-i\alpha(x-t)} \tag{27}$$

where the asterisk denotes the complex conjugate. A substitution into (16) yields the Orr-Sommerfeld equation

$$\left\{\frac{d^2}{dy^2} - \alpha^2 + i\alpha R[1 - K(1 - y^2)]\right\}$$
$$\times \left(\frac{d^2}{dy^2} - \alpha^2\right)\Phi_1 - i2K\alpha R\Phi_1 = 0. \tag{28}$$

The boundary conditions are, from (20) and (23),

$$\Phi_1'(\pm 1) - 2K = 0, \tag{29}$$

$$\Phi_1(\pm 1) = \pm 1. \tag{30}$$

The equations governing Φ_1^* are conjugate to (28)–(30) and and need not be considered.

Finally, equations (17), (21), and (24) can be satisfied by a solution of the form

$$2\psi_2 = \Phi_{20}(y) + \Phi_{22}(y)e^{i2\alpha(x-t)} + \Phi_{22}^*(y)e^{-i2\alpha(x-t)} \tag{31}$$

where again the asterisk denotes the complex conjugate. From (17) and (31), the equations governing Φ_{20} and Φ_{22} are

---

[4] Equation (18) is a shorthand for two equations

$$\psi_y(+1) + \eta\psi_{yy}(+1) + \frac{\eta^2}{2}\psi_{yyy}(+1) + \ldots\ldots = 0$$

$$\psi_y(-1) - \eta\psi_{yy}(-1) + \frac{\eta^2}{2}\psi_{yyy}(-1) \ldots\ldots = 0.$$

Thus either the upper signs are used throughout, or the lower signs are. This notation will be used throughout this paper.

$$\Phi_{20}'''' = -\frac{i\alpha R}{2}(\Phi_1\Phi_1^{*''} - \Phi_1^*\Phi_1'')', \qquad (32)$$

$$\left(\frac{d^2}{dy^2} - 4\alpha^2\right)\left[\frac{d^2}{dy^2} - (4\alpha^2 - 2i\alpha R)\right]\Phi_{22}$$

$$= i2\alpha RK(1 - y^2)\left(\frac{d^2}{dy^2} - 4\alpha^2\right)\Phi_{22}$$

$$+ i4\alpha RK\Phi_{22} + \frac{i\alpha R}{2}(\Phi_1'\Phi_1'' - \Phi_1\Phi_1'''). \quad (33)$$

The boundary conditions are, by virtue of (21), (24), and (27),

$$\Phi_{20}'(\pm1) - 2K \pm \frac{1}{2}[\Phi_1''(\pm1) + \Phi_1^{*''}(\pm1)] = 0 \quad (34)$$

$$\Phi_{22}'(\pm1) \pm \frac{1}{2}\Phi_1''(\pm1) - \frac{K}{2} = 0, \quad (35)$$

$$\Phi_{22}(\pm1) \pm \frac{1}{4}\Phi_1' = 0. \quad (36)$$

These equations are sufficient to determine the solution up to the second order in ϵ. It is seen that the structure of higher-order terms is the same. The solution requires handling of a fourth-order ordinary differential equation with variable coefficients of the type (28), which is well known in the theory of hydrodynamic stability, and has been treated by many hydrodynamicists. Aside from the epoch making papers of Sommerfeld [12] and Orr [13], reference is made to the bibliography contained in Lin's book [14], especially the very pertinent papers of Heisenberg [15], Goldstein [16], and Lin [17]. However, it should be pointed out that since the boundaries move in the present problem, the boundary conditions are not all homogeneous and the problem is not an eigenvalue problem as in all problems of hydrodynamic stability. It is clear that an extensive calculation is necessary. However, in the case of pumping of an originally stationary fluid, with a zero pressure gradient, $(\partial p/\partial x)_0 = 0$, the constant K vanishes and all the coefficients in the differential equations (28), (32), (33) become constants. For this important case a simple solution is possible, which will be presented next. On this solution the simple solution for Poiseuille flow can be superposed if $K = 0(\epsilon^2)$.

Free Pumping (Originally Stationary Fluid)

Let us consider the case in which the pressure gradient $(\partial p/\partial x)_0$ vanishes. In this case there will be no flow if the wall motion stops. Hence $K = \psi_0 = 0$. Then equation (28) becomes

$$\left(\frac{d^2}{dy^2} - \alpha^2\right)\left(\frac{d^2}{dy^2} - \beta^2\right)\Phi_1 = 0, \quad (37)$$

in which

$$\beta^2 = \alpha^2 - i\alpha R. \quad (38)$$

The boundary conditions are,

$$\Phi_1'(\pm1) = 0, \qquad \Phi_1(\pm1) = \pm1. \quad (39)$$

Clearly these boundary conditions demand that $\Phi_1(y)$ be odd in y or that the longitudinal velocity component be even in y. Hence the solution is

$$\Phi_1(y) = A \sinh \alpha y + B \sinh \beta y, \quad (40)$$

with A and B determined by equations (39) to be

$$A = \frac{-\beta \cosh \beta}{\alpha \cosh \alpha \sinh \beta - \beta \cosh \beta \sinh \alpha},$$
$$\qquad (41)$$
$$B = \frac{\alpha \cosh \alpha}{\alpha \cosh \alpha \sinh \beta - \beta \cosh \beta \sinh \alpha}.$$

Proceeding to the next term Φ_{20}, which alone concerns the mean flow so long as only terms of order ϵ^2 are concerned, we have from (32) and (34),

$$\Phi_{20}'''' = -\frac{i\alpha R}{2}(\Phi_1\Phi_1^{*''} - \Phi_1^*\Phi_1'')', \quad (42)$$

$$\Phi_{20}'(\pm1) \pm \frac{1}{2}[\Phi_1''(\pm1) + \Phi_1^{*''}(\pm1)] = 0. \quad (43)$$

It is clear that the right-hand side of (42) represents a steady inertial component due to the convective acceleration corresponding to Φ_1. The second term in (43) represents a steady velocity component at the mean position of the walls because the walls oscillate at finite amplitude in a nonuniform stream. On substituting $\Phi_1(y)$ from (40) and integrating once, we obtain

$$\Phi_{20}''' = \frac{\alpha^2 R^2}{2}[A^*B \sinh \alpha y \sinh \beta y + AB^* \sinh \alpha y \sinh \beta^* y$$

$$+ 2BB^* \sinh \beta y \sinh \beta^* y] + 2C_1, \quad (44)$$

$$\Phi_{20}'(\pm1) = \frac{1}{2}[(A + A^*)\alpha^2 \sinh \alpha + B\beta^2 \sinh \beta$$

$$+ B^*\beta^{*2} \sin \beta^*] \equiv D, \quad (45)$$

where C_1, D are constants. An integration of (44) yields the result

$$\Phi_{20}'(y) = F(y) + C_1 y^2 + C_2 y + C_3, \quad (46)$$

in which C_1, C_2, C_3 are integration constants, and

$$F(y) = \frac{\alpha^2 R^2}{2}\left\{\frac{A^*B}{2}\left[\frac{\cosh(\alpha + \beta)y}{(\alpha + \beta)^2} - \frac{\cosh(\alpha - \beta)y}{(\alpha - \beta)^2}\right]\right.$$

$$+ \frac{AB^*}{2}\left[\frac{\cosh(\alpha + \beta^*)y}{(\alpha + \beta^*)^2} - \frac{\cosh(\alpha - \beta^*)y}{(\alpha - \beta^*)^2}\right]$$

$$\left. + BB^*\left[\frac{\cosh(\beta + \beta^*)y}{(\beta + \beta^*)^2} - \frac{\cosh(\beta - \beta^*)y}{(\beta - \beta^*)^2}\right]\right\}. \quad (47)$$

The boundary conditions (45) then implies $C_2 = 0$ and

$$C_1 + C_3 = -F(1) + D, \quad (48)$$

Thus one constant, say C_1, remains arbitrary, which is proportional to the mean pressure gradient.[5] Returning to equation (1), we see that if every term is averaged over an interval of time equal to the period of oscillation, we obtain for our solution as given by (14), (27), (31), (40), and (46), the mean pressure gradient (in dimensionless form)

$$\overline{\frac{\partial p}{\partial x}} = \epsilon^2\overline{\left(\frac{\partial p}{\partial x}\right)_2} = \frac{\epsilon^2}{2R}\Phi_{20}''' + \frac{\epsilon^2}{4}i\alpha(\Phi_1\Phi_1^{*''} - \Phi_1^*\Phi_1'') + O(\epsilon^3)$$

$$= \frac{\epsilon^2}{R}C_1 + O(\epsilon^3), \quad (49)$$

i.e.,

$$\overline{\left(\frac{dp}{dx}\right)_2} = \frac{C_1}{R} \quad (50)$$

Thus C_1 is, apart from the factor $\frac{\epsilon^2}{R}$, the time average of the pressure gradient accompanying the peristaltic motion. Note that the time-averaged pressure gradient distribution $\overline{\left(\frac{dp}{dx}\right)_2}$ turns out to be uniform over the cross section; i.e., it is independent of the y-coordinate.

In practical applications the constant C_1 must be determined

---

[5] When we said the simple solution for Poiseuille flow can be superimposed if $K = O(\epsilon^2)$, we meant precisely that the terms $C_1 y^2 + C_3$ in (46) can be added to $F(y)$, with C_1 proportional to K, to form the complete solution.

from considerations of conditions at the ends of the channel. For example, in the ureter problem the end conditions are determined by the kidney and the ureterovesical junction with the bladder. With C_1 specified, our solution for the mean speed (average over time) of flow is:

$$\bar{u} = \frac{\epsilon^2}{2}\,\Phi'_{20} = \frac{\epsilon^2}{2}\,[F(y) - F(1) + D - C_1(1 - y^2)] \quad (51)$$

in which $F(y)$ is given by (47), and D is given by (45).

A few special cases may be mentioned:

(A) The second-order mean pressure gradient due to peristaltic motion vanishes. Then

$$C_1 = 0. \quad (52)$$

(B) The total flow vanishes over a period. Then

$$C_1 = \frac{3}{4}\int_{-1}^{1} F(y)\,dy - \frac{3}{2}F(1) + \frac{3}{2}D, \quad (53)$$

and the mean pressure gradient is given by equations (49) and (44). Note that the existence of C_1 means there is a Poiseuille flow accompanying the flow induced entirely by the peristaltic motion.

Thus the solution is completed up to the second order. Extension to higher orders, or to different end conditions is of course possible.

Numerical Results and Discussion

Numerical calculations show that the mean axial velocity distribution (averaged over time) due to peristaltic motion in the case of free pumping is dominated by the constant D and the parabolic distribution $-C_1(1 - y^2)$. The constant D, which defines the boundary value of Φ'_{20} in equation (45), has its origin in the radial gradient of the first-order axial velocity distribution, as can be seen in equation (43). In essence, this comes from the offset boundary conditions, i.e., to the second-order nonlinear effect of the fact that the nonslip condition applies to the wavy wall, and not to the mean position of the wall. The constant D is a function of the wave number α and the Reynolds number R; but its variation with α and R is slight. D has a numerical value about 3 for a wide range of α and R, see Table 1.

The parabolic mean-velocity distribution $-C_1(1 - y^2)$ is due to the second-order pressure gradient $\overline{\left(\dfrac{\partial p}{\partial x}\right)_2} = \dfrac{C_1}{R}$. It is negative for a positive pressure gradient, and vice versa.

In addition to the terms just mentioned, there is a perturbation term which varies across the channel. This is the term $F(y) - F(1)$ in equation (51). It turns out that $F(y) - F(1)$ is negative and essentially proportional to $\alpha^2 R^2$. If $F(y) - F(1)$ is divided by $\alpha^2 R^2$, then its values do not vary too much with α and R over a wide range, and are of the order of magnitude 10^{-2}. Therefore we define a function $\mathfrak{F}$

$$\mathfrak{F} = \frac{-200}{\alpha^2 R^2}\,[F(y) - F(1)] \quad (54)$$

and list its values in Table 1. A special case is plotted in Fig. 2.

The mean axial velocity (nondimensional) is, then

$$\bar{u}(y) = \frac{\epsilon^2}{2}\left[D - R\,\overline{\left(\frac{\partial p}{\partial x}\right)_2}(1 - y^2) - \frac{\alpha^2 R^2}{200}\,\mathfrak{F}(y)\right] \quad (55)$$

A few typical velocity-distribution curves are shown in Fig. 3, which is drawn for $\alpha R = 7$. The distance between the two vertical lines is $(D/2)\epsilon^2 c$ or approximately $(3/2)\epsilon^2 c$. The case (a) corresponds to a negative pressure gradient; (b), with a smaller pressure gradient than (a). The cases (c), (d), (e) are for zero or positive pressure gradients. It is seen that the mean

velocity profiles are quite different from the familiar Poiseuille profile. The difference is particularly evident in the cases of pumping against a positive pressure gradient, as shown in Fig. 3(d, e).

Let us define a critical reflux condition as one for which the mean velocity $\bar{u}(y)$ is equal to zero on the center line $y = 0$. Then according to equation (55) the critical reflux condition is reached when the time-averaged pressure gradient is

$$\overline{\frac{\partial p}{\partial x}}\Bigg|_{2\,\text{critical reflux}} = R\left[D - \frac{\alpha^2 R^2}{200}\,\mathfrak{F}(0)\right] \quad (56)$$

Use of this critical value yields the velocity distribution $\bar{u}(y)$ at the critical reflux condition, an example of which is plotted in Fig. 3(d). A reversal of velocity in the neighborhood of the

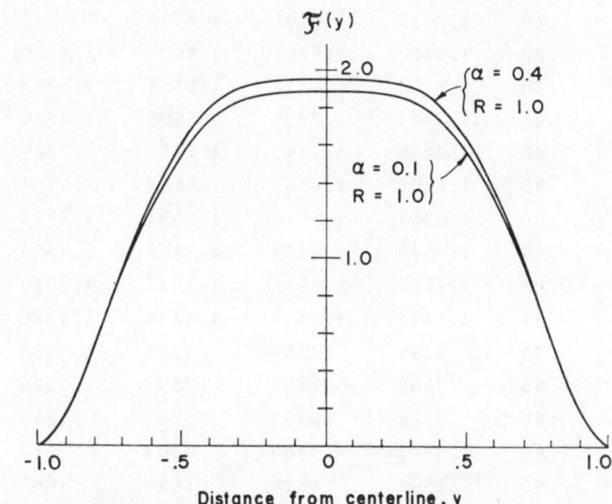

Fig. 2 The mean-velocity perturbation function $\mathfrak{F}(y)$

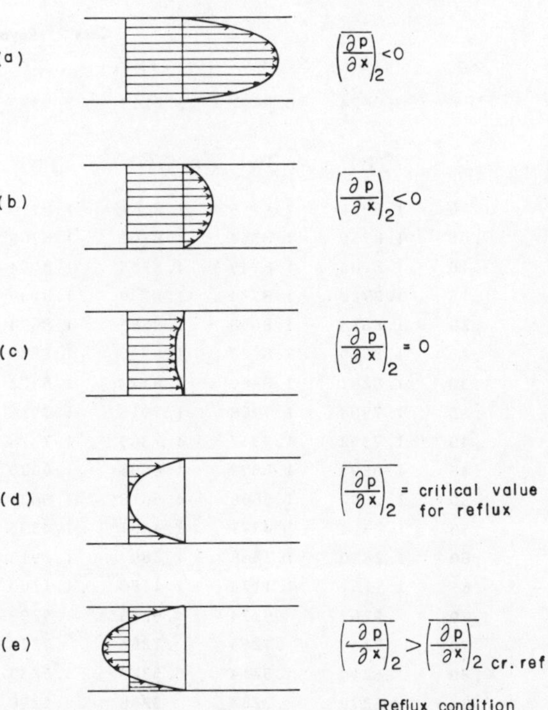

Fig. 3 Sketches of the variation of the time-averaged mean axial-velocity profile with pressure gradient. $\alpha R = 7$. The distance between the two vertical lines in this figure represents $(D/2)\epsilon^2 c$ or approximately $(3/2)\epsilon^2 c$.

Table 1 Perturbation of the mean-velocity profile as given by the function $\mathcal{F}(y)$

$$\mathcal{F}(y) = -\frac{400}{\epsilon^2\alpha^2R^2}\,(\bar{u})_{\text{pert}} = -\frac{200}{\alpha^2R^2}[F(y) - F(1)]$$

Case 1   Reynolds number R = 1

$\alpha =$	.05	.10	.15	.30	$\alpha =$	.25	.30	.35	.40
D =	3.0010	3.0041	3.0092	3.0163	D =	3.0256	3.0370	3.0506	3.0665

Y	$\mathcal{F}(y)$	$\mathcal{F}(y)$	$\mathcal{F}(y)$	$\mathcal{F}(y)$	Y	$\mathcal{F}(y)$	$\mathcal{F}(y)$	$\mathcal{F}(y)$	$\mathcal{F}(y)$
0	1.8920	1.8798	1.8859	1.8939	0	1.9045	1.9172	1.9321	1.9491
.05	1.8798	1.8791	1.8861	1.8940	.05	1.9044	1.9172	1.9321	1.9490
.10	1.8554	1.8798	1.8852	1.8935	.10	1.9038	1.9166	1.9315	1.9484
.15	1.8554	1.8775	1.8825	1.8908	.15	1.9013	1.9141	1.9289	1.9459
.20	1.8432	1.8707	1.8764	1.8842	.20	1.8946	1.9074	1.9222	1.9391
.25	1.8310	1.8562	1.8627	1.8705	.25	1.8810	1.8936	1.9084	1.9252
.30	1.8432	1.8333	1.8384	1.8465	.30	1.8568	1.8694	1.8840	1.9006
.35	1.7944	1.7936	1.8009	1.8086	.35	1.8187	1.8310	1.8453	1.8617
.40	1.7456	1.7395	1.7450	1.7529	.40	1.7627	1.7747	1.7887	1.8047
.45	1.6601	1.6647	1.6687	1.6764	.45	1.6858	1.6974	1.7109	1.7262
.50	1.5869	1.5647	1.5691	1.5763	.50	1.5853	1.5963	1.6091	1.6237
.55	1.4648	1.4404	1.4446	1.4514	.55	1.4597	1.4700	1.4819	1.4955
.60	1.2817	1.2916	1.2952	1.3016	.60	1.3091	1.3184	1.3293	1.3416
.65	1.1474	1.1199	1.1234	1.1286	.65	1.1353	1.1435	1.1530	1.1639
.70	.9399	.9284	.9325	.9368	.70	.9424	.9493	.9574	.9666
.75	.7568	.7263	.7295	.7329	.75	.7373	.7429	.7493	.7567
.80	.5126	.5233	.5247	.5269	.80	.5301	.5341	.5388	.5442
.85	.3417	.3280	.3303	.3318	.85	.3338	.3364	.3394	.3429
.90	.1586	.1617	.1638	.1646	.90	.1655	.1668	.1684	.1701
.95	.0366	.0465	.0457	.0458	.95	.0459	.0464	.0468	.0473
1.00	0	0	0	0	1.00	0	0	0	0

Case 2   Reynolds number R = 10

$\alpha =$	.05	.10	.15	.20	$\alpha =$	.25	.30	.35	.40
D =	3.0024	3.0097	3.0219	3.0390	D =	3.0611	3.0883	3.1205	3.1580

Y	$\mathcal{F}(y)$	$\mathcal{F}(y)$	$\mathcal{F}(y)$	$\mathcal{F}(y)$	Y	$\mathcal{F}(y)$	$\mathcal{F}(y)$	$\mathcal{F}(y)$	$\mathcal{F}(y)$
0	1.8751	1.8755	1.8761	1.8770	0	1.8780	1.8792	1.8804	1.8816
.05	1.8750	1.8754	1.8761	1.8769	.05	1.8780	1.8791	1.8804	1.8816
.10	1.8745	1.8749	1.8755	1.8764	.10	1.8774	1.8786	1.8798	1.8810
.15	1.8720	1.8724	1.8730	1.8739	.15	1.8749	1.8761	1.8773	1.8786
.20	1.8654	1.8658	1.8665	1.8674	.20	1.8684	1.8696	1.8709	1.8722
.25	1.8519	1.8523	1.8530	1.8539	.25	1.8550	1.8562	1.8576	1.8589
.30	1.8281	1.8285	1.8292	1.8302	.30	1.8314	1.8327	1.8341	1.8356
.35	1.7904	1.7908	1.7916	1.7926	.35	1.7939	1.7953	1.7969	1.7935
.40	1.7352	1.7357	1.7365	1.7376	.40	1.7390	1.7406	1.7424	1.7442
.45	1.6593	1.6599	1.6608	1.6620	.45	1.6635	1.6653	1.6672	1.6693
.50	1.5602	1.5608	1.5618	1.5631	.50	1.5648	1.5667	1.5689	1.5712
.55	1.4364	1.4371	1.4381	1.4395	.55	1.4413	1.4434	1.4458	1.4484
.60	1.2880	1.2886	1.2897	1.2912	.60	1.2931	1.2953	1.2979	1.3006
.65	1.1167	1.1174	1.1185	1.1200	.65	1.1219	1.1241	1.1267	1.1296
.70	.9267	.9274	.9284	.9299	.70	.9317	.9339	.9365	.9393
.75	.7249	.7255	.7264	.7278	.75	.7294	.7314	.7337	.7363
.80	.5210	.5214	.5222	.5233	.80	.5247	.5263	.5282	.5303
.85	.3279	.3283	.3288	.3296	.85	.3306	.3318	.3331	.3347
.90	.1625	.1627	.1630	.1635	.90	.1640	.1647	.1654	.1663
.95	.0451	.0452	.0453	.0454	.95	.0456	.0458	.0460	.0463
1.00	0	0	0	0	1.00	0	0	0	0

Table 2 The constant C_1 at the critical condition for reflux. The critical-reflux pressure gradient is $\overline{\left(\dfrac{\partial p}{\partial x}\right)}_{cr} = \dfrac{\epsilon^2}{R} C_1.$

α	$R = .01$	$R = .10$	$R = 1.0$	$R = 10.0$	$R = 100.0$
.1	3.0035	3.0040	3.0040	3.0003	2.7112
.2	3.0157	3.0161	3.0160	3.0015	2.2867
.3	3.0365	3.0365	3.0362	3.0037	2.0328
.4	3.0656	3.0656	3.0650	3.0075	1.9097
.5	3.1038	3.1039	3.1029	3.0135	1.8546
.6	3.1519	3.1519	3.1505	3.0228	1.8338
.7	3.2105	3.2106	3.2036	3.0363	1.8319
.8	3.2806	3.2806	3.2780	3.0556	1.8427
.9	3.3630	3.3630	3.3597	3.0820	1.8641
1.0	3.4587	3.4587	3.4545	3.1173	1.8959

center line occurs when the pressure gradient is greater than that at the critical reflux condition. The critical values of

$$R \frac{\overline{\partial p}}{\partial x_2}$$

are listed in Table 2 for several values of α and R.

Now, *vesicoureteral reflux* defined as the backward flow of urine from the bladder to the ureter, is an important pathological condition for human beings, although it seems to be normal with some other animals such as rabbits. See Graves and Davidoff [5], Hutch [6, 7], and Gruber [18]. Bacteria may pass from the bladder to the kidney or from one kidney to the other under reflux conditions. Diseases such as tuberculosis, interstitial cystitis, bladder stones, etc., are often complicated by reflux. Whether the mathematical reflux condition defined previously can be identified with the movement of bacteria or not remains to be seen. The real physiological problem is very complex, and a theoretical analysis as just presented can only serve as a model which may help understanding the physiology. From the point of view of mechanics, it is interesting to see how reflux can occur in opposition to the surrounding stream. The particle path in peristaltic pumping is discussed by Shapiro in [19] where the physiological problem is considered in greater details.

Conclusions

We have shown that the mean flow induced by peristaltic motion of the walls of a two-dimensional channel is proportional to the square of the amplitude ratio. The velocity profile depends on the mean pressure gradient. If the pressure gradient accompanying the peristaltic motion (also of the order of the amplitude ratio squared) is positive and equal to a critical reflux value, then the velocity is zero on the center line. Pumping against a positive pressure gradient greater than the critical value would result in a backward flow (reflux) in the central region of the stream. There will be no reflux if the pressure gradient is smaller than the critical value. The velocity and pressure profiles, and values of the critical pressure gradient, are presented in this paper.

The analysis is presented in detail only to the second order in the amplitude ratio ϵ. The results show that the expansion in ϵ is in fact an expansion in $\alpha R\epsilon$, (see equation (44) et seq), where α is the wave number, and R is the Reynolds number. The convergence will be poor if $\alpha R\epsilon$ is too large. On the other hand, the longer the wavelength (smaller α) and the smaller the Reynolds number, the more accurate is the second-order solution as presented here. If αR is small compared with unity the second-order solution presented here can be accurate and useful even if ϵ is not small. It would be interesting in the future to work out expansions in series of α or R, and to compare the results.

Acknowledgment

We present this work to our friend Prof. Jesse Ormandroyd of Ann Arbor as a token of respect. We thank Mrs. Yvonne Woo and Mr. Chin-Hsui Li for obtaining the numerical results. To Prof. A. H. Shapiro of M.I.T. we are grateful for comments which led to improvement of the paper.

References

1 Bergman, H., ed, *The Ureter*, Harpers & Row, New York 1967.

2 Boyarsky, S., ed, *Neurogenic Bladder*, Williams & Wilkins Co., Baltimore, 1967.

3 Weinberg, S. R., "Physiology of the Ureter," Bergman, ed., *The Ureter*, Harper & Row, 1967, pp 48–66.

4 Orkin, L. A., *Trauma In The Ureter: Pathogenesis and Management*, F. A. Davis Co., Philadelphia, Pa., 1964.

5 Graves, R. C., and Davidoff, L. M., "Studies on the Ureter and Bladder With Especial Reference to Regurgitation of Vesical Contents," *Journal of Urology*, Vol. 12, 1924, p. 93.

6 Hutch, John A.: *The Ureterovesical Junction*, Univ. of Calif. Press, 1958.

7 Hutch, John A, "Vesico-Ureteral Reflux," Bergman, ed. *The Ureter*, Harper & Row, 1967, pp. 465–507.

8 Nicoll, P. A., and Webb, R. L., "Blood Circulation in the Subcutaneous Tissue of the Living Bat's Wing," *Annals of the New York Academy of Science*, Vol. 46, 1956, pp. 697–711.

9 Nicoll, P. A., "The Anatomy and Behaviour of the Vascular Systems in Nereis Virens and Nereis Limbata," *Biological Bulletin*, Vol. 106, 1954, pp. 69–82.

10 Nicoll, P. A., "Structure and Function of Minute Vessels in Autoregulation," *Circulation Research, Suppl. I.*, Vols. 14 and 15, 1965, Chap. I, pp. 245–253.

11 Shapiro, A. H., and T. W. Latham, "On Peristaltic Pumping" (abstract), *Proc. Ann. Conf. on Engineering in Medicine and Biology*, San Francisco, Cal., Vol. 8, 1966, p. 147.

12 Sommerfeld, A., "Ein Beitrag zur hydrodynamischen Erklarung turbulenten Flussigkeitsbewegung," *Proc. 4th Int. Conf. Math.*, Rome, 1908, pp. 116–24.

13 Orr, W. McF., "The Stability or Instability of the Steady Motions of a Liquid," *Proc. Royal Irish Acad.*, A, 27, 1906–1907, pp. 9–27, 69–138.

14 Lin, C. C., "On the Stability of Two-Dimensional Parallel Flows," Parts I, II, III, *Quarterly of Applied Mathematics*, Vol. 3, 1945, pp. 117–142, 218–234, 277–301.

15 Heisenberg, W., "Über Stabilitat und Turbulenz von Flüssigkeitsströmen," *Annalen der Physik*, Lpz., 4, Vol. 74, 1924, pp. 577–627.

16 Goldstein, S., "The Stability of Viscous Fluid Flow Under Pressure Between Parallel Planes," *Proc. Roy. Soc.*, A, 145, 1936, pp. 40–54.

17 Lin, C. C., *The Theory of Hydrodynamic Stability*, Cambridge University Press, 1955.

18 Gruber, C. M., "A Comparative Study of the Intravesical Ureters in Man and in Experimental Animals," *Journal of Urology*, Vol. 21, 1929, p. 567.

19 Shapiro, A. H., "Pumping and Retrograde Diffusion in Peristaltic Waves," *Proceedings, Workshop on Ureteral Reflux in Children*, National Acad. of Science Natural Research Council, 1967, pp. 109–126.

Reprinted from

THE PHYSICS OF FLUIDS   VOLUME 11, NUMBER 3   MARCH 1968

Fluid Motion Induced by Surface-Tension Variation

CHIA-SHUN YIH

Department of Engineering Mechanics, The University of Michigan, Ann Arbor, Michigan
(Received 7 September 1967)

Fluid motion in a long straight channel induced by longitudinally varying surface tension has been discussed by Levich. This problem is re-examined and a different solution is given. In addition, the stability of laminar flows involving surface-tension variation is briefly discussed, and a correction of a previous result [C.-S. Yih, J. Fluid Mech. **28**, 493 (1967)] is made.

I. INTRODUCTION

It is now common knowledge that at the free surface of a liquid, the pressure at the liquid side of the surface depends on the local surface tension and the local curvature of the surface, and the shear stress depends on the local gradient of surface tension. If the surface tension is nonuniform, motion will be induced in the liquid.

Levich has written an impressive book with the title *Physicochemical Hydrodynamics*, in which fluid motion induced by surface tension has been discussed in some detail. A solution was given by Levich[1] for the motion of a thin and wide fluid film induced by surface-tension variation. Upon close examination of Levich's solution many inconsistencies are found. The correct solution of Levich's problem is presented here as a development resulting from the stimulation of his admirable work.

II. SOLUTION OF LEVICH'S PROBLEM

Levich's problem concerns the flow of a liquid layer induced by longitudinal variation of surface tension. The channel joining two reservoirs (Fig. 1) is supposed to be very much wider than the depth of the liquid supported by a horizontal bottom at $z = 0$. The reservoirs are supposed to be even wider, and the channel is supposed to be much longer than it is wide. Thus nonuniformities at the ends ($x = 0$ and $x = L$) of the channel can be neglected, and the flow can be assumed independent of the coordinate y measured in a direction across the channel. The flow is then two-dimensional. Since the depth is small compared with L, the flow is nearly, though not strictly, unidirectional. That is to say, it is nearly parallel to the x axis, but not quite, since the depth of the fluid, as will be seen, changes from one value of x to another.

The variation of surface tension is accomplished by the presence of surface-active material in the

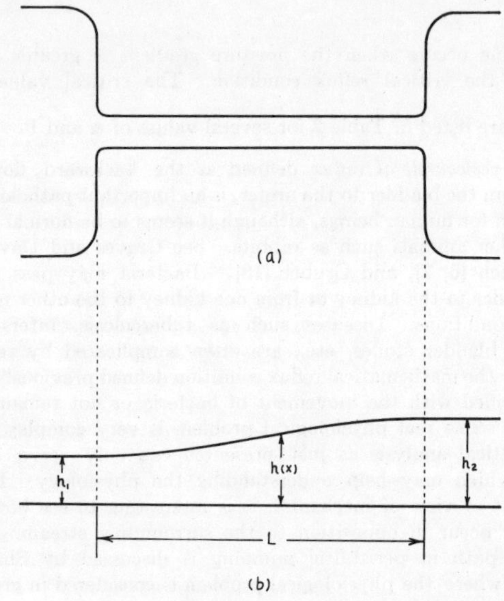

FIG. 1. Definition sketch. (a) Plan. (b) Vertical cross section along the longitudinal centerline. The vertical scale is exaggerated.

reservoir to the left of the position $x = 0$. If the surface concentration of that material is γ, the surface tension σ is a function of γ. For simplicity we shall assume $d\sigma/d\gamma$ to be constant. For steady flows the diffusion equation for the surface material can then be written as

$$\frac{\partial}{\partial x}(u\sigma) = \frac{d}{dx}\left(D\,\frac{d\sigma}{dx}\right), \qquad (1)$$

in which u is the velocity component in the x direction at the surface, and D is the diffusivity. Strictly speaking x should be replaced by a curvilinear distance in a direction along the curved free surface, and u should be the velocity in the same direction. We state without delay that the theory to be presented here is a shallow-water theory, that even though the depth changes, the vertical component of the velocity is much smaller than the horizontal component, and that all effects of the curvature of the free surface are neglected.

[1] V. G. Levich, *Physicochemical Hydrodynamics* (Prentice-Hall, Inc., Englewood Cliffs, New Jersey, 1962), 2nd ed. pp. 384–388.

Following Levich, we shall only treat cases in which the inertial effects are negligible. That is to say, we assume the Reynolds number VH/ν to be very small, in which H is the maximum depth of the liquid film, V is a representative velocity, and ν is the kinematic viscosity. [Note that the Péclét number VL/D, in which L is a representative horizontal scale, may not be small. In fact it may be so large that the diffusive term in Eq. (1) may be neglected.] The equations of steady motion are then

$$\frac{\partial p}{\partial x} = \mu \frac{\partial^2 u}{\partial z^2}, \qquad \frac{\partial p}{\partial z} = -\rho g, \qquad \text{(2a, b)}$$

in which p is the pressure, μ the viscosity, ρ the density, and g the gravitational acceleration. Both μ and ρ are assumed constant, and of the term $\nabla^2 u$ only the dominant term $\partial^2 u/\partial z^2$ is retained in (2a). Furthermore w (velocity component in the z direction) is small, so that the term $\mu\nabla^2 w$ is entirely neglected in (2b). The equation of continuity is

$$\frac{d}{dx} \int_0^h u\, dz = 0. \qquad \text{(3)}$$

The boundary condition at the bottom is simply

$$u = 0 \quad \text{at} \quad z = 0. \qquad \text{(4)}$$

The boundary conditions at the free surface are

$$\mu \frac{\partial u}{\partial z} = \frac{d\sigma}{dx} \quad \text{at} \quad z = h(x) \qquad \text{(5a)}$$

and

$$p = 0 \quad \text{at} \quad z = h(x), \qquad \text{(5b)}$$

$h(x)$ being the depth of the liquid film. Note that in (5) again the effect of curvature has been neglected. Suppose that we also specify the values of σ and of h at the two ends as follows:

$$\sigma = \sigma_1 \quad \text{and} \quad h = h_1 \quad \text{at} \quad x = 0, \qquad \text{(6)}$$

$$\sigma = \sigma_2 \quad \text{and} \quad h = h_2 \quad \text{at} \quad x = L. \qquad \text{(7)}$$

Equations (1), (2), and (3), and the boundary conditions (4)–(7) constitute the differential system to be solved.

At this time it is appropriate to mention the chief features of Levich's solution. He assumed

(a) that σ is linear with x,
(b) that h is constant,
(c) that there is a pressure gradient $\partial p/\partial x$, and
(d) that the net discharge across any section is zero.

Assumption (a) is made in Eq. (68.2) on p. 385 of his book[1], (b) on the first two lines on the same page (note the two uses of the word plane), (c) on pp. 385–387, and (d) in (68.7) on p. 386. We note that the diffusion equation (1) may not allow (a), that (b) and (c) are inconsistent, and (d) is a special case only. Levich never mentioned how his $\partial p/\partial x$ is to be evaluated. This may well be connected with his equation

$$\frac{\partial p}{\partial z} = 0,$$

which seems to indicate that the role of gravity was not recognized by him.

We shall satisfy (2a), (4), and (5a) by assuming

$$u = \frac{1}{\mu}\frac{d\sigma}{dx}z - \frac{1}{2\mu}\frac{\partial p}{\partial x}z(2h - z). \qquad \text{(8)}$$

This was obtained by Levich. On the surface

$$u = \frac{h}{\mu}\left(\frac{d\sigma}{dx} - \frac{h}{2}\frac{\partial p}{\partial x}\right). \qquad \text{(9)}$$

Equations (2b) and (5b) allow us to write

$$p = \rho g(h - y). \qquad \text{(10)}$$

Thus

$$\frac{\partial p}{\partial x} = \rho g \frac{dh}{dx}. \qquad \text{(11)}$$

Now we can use Eqs. (9) and (11), together with Eqs. (1) and (3), and forget about the boundary conditions (4) and (5) which have been satisfied. First, Eqs. (3), (8), and (11) yield

$$\frac{h^2}{6\mu}\left(3\frac{d\sigma}{dx} - 2g\rho h\frac{dh}{dx}\right) = Q, \qquad \text{(12)}$$

in which Q, a constant, is the discharge per unit width. With Eqs. (11) and (12), we can write Eq. (9) as

$$u = \frac{h}{4\mu}\left(\frac{d\sigma}{dx} + \frac{6\mu Q}{h^2}\right) \quad \text{at} \quad z = h. \qquad \text{(13)}$$

Equation (1) can be integrated to give

$$u\sigma = D\frac{d\sigma}{dx} + q, \qquad \text{(14)}$$

in which q is the (constant) discharge of σ per unit width. (Perhaps it is better to say that $q\, d\gamma/d\sigma$ is the discharge of the surface material per unit width.) We can, if we so choose, eliminate u and σ between Eqs. (12), (13), and (14), and obtain a differential equation in h alone. But this will only produce a highly nonlinear equation that in general cannot be solved analytically. For the general case, we prefer to resort to numerical integration in the following way. Substituting (13) into (14), we have

$$\left(\frac{h\sigma}{4\mu} - D\right)\frac{d\sigma}{dx} + \frac{3Q\sigma}{2h} = q. \tag{15}$$

Given h_1 and σ_1, we can assume Q and q and compute $d\sigma/dx$ at $x = 0$. Then compute dh/dx at $x = 0$ by (12). We then know σ and h at $x = \Delta x$, and can proceed further, until we come to $x = L$, where σ should be equal to σ_2 and h equal to h_2. These conditions are to be satisfied by the proper choice of Q and q. This is obviously a tedious calculation, and it may happen that the end values σ_1, σ_2, h_1, and h_2 cannot be satisfied by a steady flow. To proceed further and to bring out the possible lack of steady-state solutions, we shall consider the following special cases.

A. The Case of Zero Discharge

In case $Q = 0$, Eq. (12) can be immediately integrated to give

$$\sigma = \frac{\rho g}{3} h^2 + C_1, \tag{16}$$

and (15) can be integrated to produce

$$\frac{\rho g}{6\mu}\left(\frac{\rho g h^5}{15} + \frac{C_1 h^3}{3}\right) - \tfrac{1}{3} D\rho g h^2 = qx + C_2. \tag{17}$$

The constants are determined by Eqs. (6) and (7). Thus,

$$C_1 = \sigma_1 - \frac{\rho g}{3} h_1^2. \tag{18}$$

Due to the requirement that Q be zero, there is no freedom in choosing h_2 if σ_2 is given, since

$$\sigma_2 = \frac{\rho g}{3} h_2^2 + C_1. \tag{19}$$

We can now determine q and C_2 such that

$h = h_1$ at $x = 0$ and $h = h_2$ at $x = L$,

and the problem is solved.

But it is important to note the singular nature of the differential equation (15). Let us consider cases in which $\sigma_2 > \sigma_1$, $h_2 > h_1$. If

$$D > \frac{h_2 \sigma_2}{4\mu}, $$

q is negative according to Eq. (15), and by choosing a proper q we can satisfy the condition $\sigma = \sigma_2$ at $x = L$ on integrating Eq. (15) with the aid of Eqs. (16) and (18). Similarly, if

$$D < \frac{h_1 \sigma_1}{4\mu}, $$

a positive q can satisfy the condition for σ at $x = L$. But if

$$\frac{h_1 \sigma_1}{4\mu} < D < \frac{h_2 \sigma_2}{4\mu}, \tag{20}$$

for some intermediate value of x (15) is singular, and there will be a cusp there if the end conditions (6) and (7) are to be satisfied. Since cusps must be ruled out as physically inadmissible, for end values satisfying (20) steady-state solutions are impossible, and the flow will be transient until the liquid levels or the σ values at the ends have reached values for which steady flow is possible. When steady flow is possible, the profile is given by (17), and the surface-material discharge by $q\, d\gamma/d\sigma$.

B. The Case of Zero Surface Velocity

In this case the u in (9) is zero, so that

$$\frac{d\sigma}{dx} - \frac{h}{2}\frac{\partial p}{\partial x} = \frac{d\sigma}{dx} - \frac{\rho g h}{2}\frac{dh}{dx} = 0,$$

integration of which gives

$$\sigma = \frac{\rho g}{4} h^2 + C_3. \tag{21}$$

Since the u in (1) is zero, integration of (1) produces

$$\sigma = \sigma_1 + \frac{\sigma_2 - \sigma_1}{L} x. \tag{22}$$

Thus

$$\frac{\rho g}{4} h^2 = \sigma_1 + \frac{\sigma_2 - \sigma_1}{L} x - C_3. \tag{23}$$

The condition $h = h_1$ at $x = 0$ gives

$$C_3 = \sigma_1 - \frac{\rho g}{4} h_1^2. \tag{24}$$

But h_2 is no longer arbitrary. It is given by

$$\frac{\rho g}{4} h_2^2 = \sigma_2 - C_3. \tag{25}$$

The discharge of surface material per unit width is

$$q = D\frac{\sigma_2 - \sigma_1}{L}\frac{d\gamma}{d\sigma}. \tag{26}$$

One especially simple case of zero surface velocity and constant depth requires the bottom to be inclined. If the angle of inclination is β, and if we measure x along the inclined bottom and z in a direction normal to it, Eq. (1) remains valid but Eq. (2a) is replaced by

$$g\rho \sin\beta = \mu\frac{\partial^2 u}{\partial z^2} \tag{27}$$

480   CHIA-SHUN YIH

and Eq. (2b) by

$$\frac{\partial p}{\partial z} = -\rho g \cos \beta. \tag{28}$$

Equation (28) gives the pressure p, and is not needed if the depth is constant. The solution of (27) satisfying (4) and $u = 0$ at $z = \text{const } h$ is

$$u = \frac{g}{2\nu} (\sin \beta) z(z - h). \tag{29}$$

Since $u = 0$ at $z = h$, the solution of (1) is simply (22), and (5a) is satisfied if

$$\frac{\rho g h}{2} \sin \beta = \frac{d\sigma}{dx} , \tag{30}$$

which determines h for a given β, or β for a given h. Of course, if Eq. (30) is not satisfied the constant-depth solution does not exist, and a steady-state solution may not even exist.

III. STABILITY OF LAMINAR FLOWS DRIVEN BY SURFACE TENSION

As shown in Yih,[2] laminar flows driven by or affected by surface-tension variation can be unstable, especially with respect to long waves. It must be kept in mind that if instability with respect to long waves is considered, the longitudinal variation of the velocity must not be ignored. In the paper of Yih, the flow is strictly unidirectional.

I should like to avail myself of the opportunity to correct an omission kindly pointed out to me by A. Craik. Since the surface-diffusion equation must be applied on the free surface, the quantity u' should be replaced by $u' + \eta$ in Eq. (28) of Ref. 2. When this correction is made, and the anal-

---

[2] C.-S. Yih, J. Fluid Mech. 28, 493 (1967).

ysis is followed through, the correct criterion replacing the final formula in that paper is

$$\left(\frac{\alpha_0}{\omega} + 2\frac{\omega}{\alpha_0}\right) \Delta\alpha = \frac{i\omega^2 R}{60}\left\{-90 - 12\frac{\alpha_0}{\omega} - 3\left(\frac{\alpha_0}{\omega}\right)^2 \right.$$
$$\left. + \left(2 - \frac{9\alpha_0}{\omega}\right) F^{-2}\right\} - i2\omega^2\left(\frac{\bar{\gamma}}{\gamma_1 d}\frac{\alpha_0}{\omega} - \frac{1}{\text{Pé}}\frac{\alpha_0^2}{\omega^2}\right),$$
$$\tag{31}$$

in which

$$\frac{\alpha_0}{\omega} = 1 \pm \sqrt{3}, \tag{32}$$

the symbols being defined in Yih[2]. The interesting feature is that there are two modes, one traveling upstream and one traveling downstream. The former corresponds to the negative sign in (39), and for that mode instability corresponds to positive values of $\alpha_i(\Delta\alpha = i\alpha_i)$. The latter corresponds to the positive sign in (39), and for it instability corresponds to negative values of α_i, because of the form of the assumed exponential factor (for all perturbation quantities)

$$\exp i\left(\int \alpha \, dx - \omega\tau\right).$$

It turns out that both modes can be unstable! Note that the coefficient of $\Delta\alpha$ in (31) is simply $\pm 2\sqrt{3}$. A numerical verification can be given to show the actual possibility of instability, as was done in Yih[2]. The conclusion that there are realistic cases of instability remain valid.

ACKNOWLEDGMENT

This work has been jointly sponsored by the National Science Foundation and the Army Research Office (Durham).

Reprinted from

THE PHYSICS OF FLUIDS   VOLUME 12, NUMBER 10   OCTOBER 1969

Three-Dimensional Motion of a Liquid Film Induced by Surface-Tension Variation or Gravity

CHIA-SHUN YIH

Department of Engineering Mechanics
The University of Michigan, Ann Arbor, Michigan
(Received 7 February 1969)

Steady flows of a thin layer of viscous liquid on a horizontal plane induced by the nonuniformity of surface tension at its free surface are treated. If the film is very thin, surface-tension effects dominate gravity effects. Under that circumstance and away from vertical boundaries, a binomial of depth h of the liquid layer is a harmonic function of the Cartesian coordinates x and y in a horizontal plane, and the surface tension is a function of h. Near any vertical boundary there is a velocity boundary layer whose thickness is of the order of h. The velocity distribution in this boundary layer is given explicitly. The diffusion of the surface material affecting the surface tension is considered. Steady flows of a liquid film induced by gravity are also discussed. Simple solutions are possible if the film flows over a horizontal plane.

I. INTRODUCTION

Consider a thin liquid layer on a horizontal plane with a depth h at any point on that plane, very much smaller than any horizontal scale L defined by the spacing or size of vertical boundaries confining the liquid. Figure 1 shows an example of the horizontal geometry, the vertical boundaries being those of the circular cylinder and two plane vertical walls. Figure 2 shows a longitudinal cross section of the flow, which does not cut the cylinder.

If the surface tesnion at the free surface is not uniform, it will cause the fluid to move by surface traction. Only steady flows so induced will be considered, so that the depth h and the surface tension σ are both functions of the horizontal Cartesian coordinates x and y only, and independent of the time. The vertical coordinate is denoted by z.

We shall assume that, for a horizontal bottom and a thin film, the effect of surface tension dominates the effect of gravity. More specifically, this implies that

$$\Delta\sigma \gg \rho g h_0^2, \tag{1}$$

in which $\Delta\sigma$ is a characteristic variation in σ, ρ is the liquid density, g is the gravitational acceleration, and h_0 is a vertical scale, which can be taken to be the maximum of h. The analysis of this case will now be discussed in detail.

Steady flows of a liquid film induced solely by gravity will be treated in the last section of this paper.

II. ANALYSIS FOR FLOWS INDUCED BY SURFACE-TENSION VARIATION

In addition to the limitations stated in Sec. I, we assume the Reynolds number to be so small that the inertial terms can be neglected. The change in h is

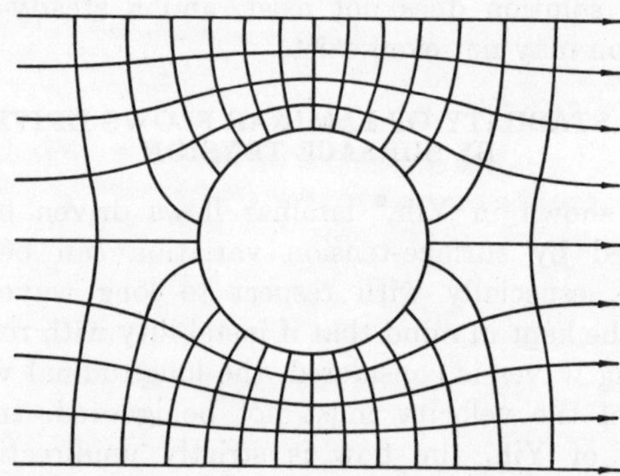

FIG. 1. A plan view of a typical flow pattern. Lines with arrow heads are streamlines. The other lines are lines of constant surface tension or constant depth.

assumed to be gradual, so that the curvature of the free surface is of the order of h/L^2, and the pressure caused by surface curvature is of the order of $\sigma h/L^2$. The shear stress caused by the nonuniformity of surface tension is of the order of $\Delta\sigma/L$. It is therefore clear, that under the assumption that L is much greater than h, the effect of the surface shear concomitant with the nonuniformity of surface tension dominates the effect of pressure induced by surface curvature. Aside from surface curvature and surface tension, the pressure is also affected by gravity; but if (1) holds, the gravity effect can be neglected. Under these assumptions the pressure gradient can be taken to be zero, and the pressure treated as constant throughout the liquid. The first two equations governing steady flows then become simply

$$0 = \mu\nabla^2 u, \qquad 0 = \mu\nabla^2 v, \tag{2}$$

in which ∇^2 is the Laplacian operator, and u and v are the velocity components in the directions of increasing x and y, respectively. The velocity component w, as well as $\partial w/\partial z$, is zero at the bottom, and hence w is of the order of $u(h/L)^2$ throughout.

If the values of u and v on the free surface are denoted by U and V, and steady flow is assumed, the equation governing the concentration γ of the surface material is, with κ denoting the diffusivity,

$$\frac{\partial}{\partial x}(U\gamma) + \frac{\partial}{\partial y}(V\gamma) = \kappa\left(\frac{\partial^2}{\partial x^2} + \frac{\partial^2}{\partial y^2}\right)\gamma, \qquad (3)$$

in which diffusion into the body of the liquid is neglected. This neglect is justified, provided the solubility of the surface material in the liquid is small, according to Levich[1] (first equation on page 420). [In a previous paper by this writer,[2] small solubility is implied in Eq. (1) of that paper, which is the one-dimensional counterpart of (3)]. The surface tension σ is dependent on γ. Within any small range the relationship between σ and γ, if not strictly linear, can always be replaced by a linear one

$$\sigma = \sigma_0 - k\gamma,$$

in which σ_0 and k are constants, and k is positive if σ decreases as γ increases. Thus, (3) can be written as

$$(\sigma - \sigma_0)\left(\frac{\partial U}{\partial x} + \frac{\partial V}{\partial y}\right) + U\frac{\partial\sigma}{\partial x} + V\frac{\partial\sigma}{\partial y}$$
$$= \kappa\left(\frac{\partial^2}{\partial x^2} + \frac{\partial^2}{\partial y^2}\right)\sigma. \qquad (4)$$

It should be noted that whereas the convective terms in the equations of motion have been neglected because the Reynolds number $U_0 h_0/\nu$ (U_0 is a representative velocity) is small, the convective terms in (3) and (4) are retained because the Péclet number $U_0 L/\kappa$ is not assumed small. For clarity, the analysis will now be divided into two parts.

III. THE CORE

Since h is very much smaller than L, it is clear that anywhere except very near the vertical boundaries delineating the flow region, the terms $\partial^2 u/\partial z^2$ and $\partial^2 v/\partial z^2$ dominate the other terms in the two equations contained in (2), so that these equations can simply be written

$$\frac{\partial^2 u}{\partial z^2} = 0, \qquad \frac{\partial^2 v}{\partial z^2} = 0. \qquad (5)$$

Thus, the velocity field is described by

$$u = Uz/h, \qquad v = Vz/h. \qquad (6)$$

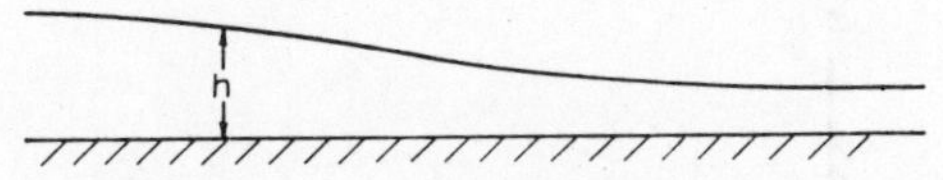

FIG. 2. A cross-sectional view of the flow.

The equation of continuity is

$$\frac{\partial}{\partial x}\int_0^h u\,dz + \frac{\partial}{\partial y}\int_0^h v\,dz = 0, \qquad (7)$$

or, by virtue of (6),

$$\frac{\partial}{\partial x}(hU) + \frac{\partial}{\partial y}(hV) = 0. \qquad (8)$$

The boundary conditions at the bottom, where $z = 0$, are satisfied by (6). The boundary conditions at the free surface are

$$\mu\frac{\partial u}{\partial z} = \frac{\partial\sigma}{\partial x}, \qquad \mu\frac{\partial v}{\partial z} = \frac{\partial\sigma}{\partial y},$$

or

$$\frac{\mu U}{h} = \frac{\partial\sigma}{\partial x}, \qquad \frac{\mu V}{h} = \frac{\partial\sigma}{\partial y}. \qquad (9)$$

Note that these equations would demand that $\sigma_{xx} + \sigma_{yy}$ vanish if w were strictly zero, which it is not. Only w_x and w_y are assumed small in comparison with u_z and v_z. It can also be shown that surface viscosities (both bulk and shear viscosities) contribute terms of negligible magnitude, so long as $h/L \ll 1$. The unknowns σ, U, V, and h are functions of x and y, and are governed by (4), (8), and (9), all of which are nonlinear. At first sight the situation seems rather hopeless. The solution, however, turns out to be very simple.

Substituting (9) in (8) and expanding, we have

$$\left(\frac{\partial^2}{\partial x^2} + \frac{\partial^2}{\partial y^2}\right)\sigma = -\frac{2\mu}{h^2}\left(U\frac{\partial h}{\partial x} + V\frac{\partial h}{\partial y}\right). \qquad (10)$$

Now, by virtue of (8), the left-hand side of (4) can be written as

$$U\frac{\partial\sigma}{\partial x} + V\frac{\partial\sigma}{\partial y} - \frac{\sigma - \sigma_0}{h}\left(U\frac{\partial h}{\partial x} + V\frac{\partial h}{\partial y}\right)$$
$$= h\left(U\frac{\partial}{\partial x}\frac{\sigma - \sigma_0}{h} + V\frac{\partial}{\partial y}\frac{\sigma - \sigma_0}{h}\right),$$

so that (4) can be written as

$$\kappa\left(\frac{\partial^2}{\partial x^2} + \frac{\partial^2}{\partial y^2}\right)\sigma = h\left(U\frac{\partial}{\partial x} + V\frac{\partial}{\partial y}\right)\frac{\sigma - \sigma_0}{h}. \qquad (4')$$

Comparison of (10) with (4') yields

$$\left(U\frac{\partial}{\partial x} + V\frac{\partial}{\partial y}\right)\left(\frac{\sigma - \sigma_0}{h} - \frac{\mu\kappa}{h^2}\right) = 0. \qquad (11)$$

[1] V. G. Levich, *Physicochemical Hydrodynamics* (Prentice–Hall, Inc., Englewood Cliffs, New Jersey, 1962).
[2] C.-S. Yih, Phys. Fluids **11**, 477 (1968).

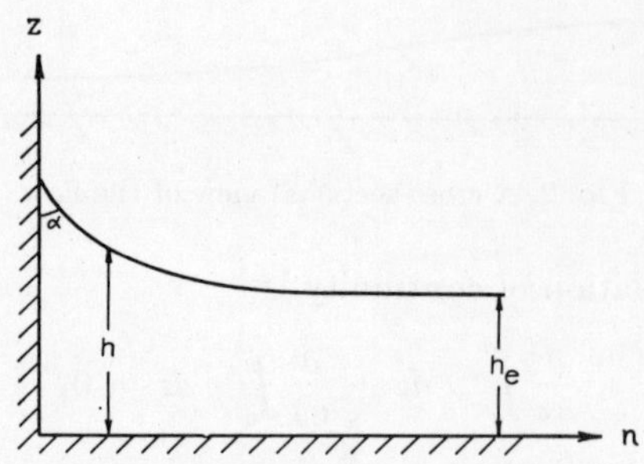

FIG. 3. The boundary-layer region.

Since (8) allows us to define a stream function ψ for the surface flow, in terms of which

$$U = \frac{1}{h}\frac{\partial \psi}{\partial y}, \qquad V = -\frac{1}{h}\frac{\partial \psi}{\partial x}.$$

From (9) it is evident that the constant-σ lines are orthogonal to the streamlines at the surface. From (11) it then follows that

$$\frac{\sigma - \sigma_0}{h} - \frac{\mu\kappa}{h^2} = f(\psi).$$

If along any one constant-depth line σ is also constant (for example, when the upstream flow is parallel),

$$\frac{\sigma - \sigma_0}{h} - \frac{\mu\kappa}{h^2} = C. \tag{12}$$

Equation (12) allows us to write (9) as

$$hU = \frac{\partial}{\partial x}\left(-\kappa h + \frac{C}{3\mu}h^3\right),$$
$$hV = \frac{\partial}{\partial y}\left(-\kappa h + \frac{C}{3\mu}h^3\right). \tag{13}$$

Substitution of (13) into (8) produces

$$\left(\frac{\partial^2}{\partial x^2} + \frac{\partial^2}{\partial y^2}\right)\left(-\kappa h + \frac{C}{3\mu}h^3\right) = 0. \tag{14}$$

Thus, the binomial

$$F(h) = -\kappa h + \frac{C}{3\mu}h^3$$

is a harmonic function of x and y, and for any specified boundary of the flow, (14) can be solved by any of the known methods for solving two-dimensional Laplace equations. Then, U and V are found by (13), and σ by (12), provided σ is known at some constant-h line. The core flow, therefore, can easily be determined. Figure 1 shows a well-known flow pattern merely for the sake of demonstration. The directed lines are streamlines issuing from an upstream reservoir into a downstream reservoir. For steady flow to be possible, the σ and h in the down-stream reservoir must be maintained to satisfy (12). with the C determined by conditions in the upstream reservoir.

IV. BOUNDARY LAYERS

Equations (13) show that

$$-\kappa \ln h + \frac{C}{2\mu}h^2$$

is a potential for the surface flow. At a vertical boundary the normal velocity component is zero, so that the normal component of the gradient of h must be zero. Since $F(h)$ is a harmonic function, the tangential component of the gradient of h at such a boundary cannot be zero without the trivial consequence of a constant h all over the field, according to a well-known result in potential theory. Thus, the tangential component of the velocity at any vertical boundary, as found by solving (14) and using (13) and (6), is not zero. However, the physical condition at such a boundary demands that the velocity on it be zero; hence, a boundary layer must exist. In that layer, the normal derivatives of the velocity are of the same order of magnitude as its vertical derivatives.

For clarity, we shall denote the horizontal distance along a vertical boundary by s, the velocity component in the direction of increasing s by q, and the distance normal to the wall by n. Then, in the boundary layer

$$\left(\frac{\partial^2}{\partial z^2} + \frac{\partial^2}{\partial n^2}\right)q = 0. \tag{15}$$

Outside of the boundary layer, q is equal to q_0, which is different from zero, and is given by (13), with h satisfying (14). We shall write

$$q_0 = \frac{Qz}{h_e}, \tag{16}$$

in which Q is the surface speed at the free surface and h_e the depth, both just outside of the boundary layer.

Due to surface tension, the free surface makes an angle α (Fig. 3) with the wall, which is less than $\pi/2$ if the liquid wets the wall, and more than $\pi/2$ if it does not. The value of α depends on the nature of the liquid and of the wall. Since the vertical acceleration is negligible under the assumptions made, the pressure distribution in the liquid is hydrostatic. This means that, for small $\cot \alpha$,

$$\sigma \frac{\partial^2 h}{\partial n^2} = \rho g h. \tag{17}$$

The solution of (17) is

$$h = A \exp\left[-\left(\frac{\rho g}{\sigma}\right)^{1/2} n\right] + h_e, \qquad (18)$$

in which

$$A\left(\frac{\rho g}{\sigma}\right)^{1/2} = \cot \alpha. \qquad (19)$$

Since within the boundary layer the component of velocity in the direction of n is of the order of h_0/L, as can be deduced from the equation of continuity in differential form in the usual way, σ must be constant at that part of the free surface which is within the boundary layer. Hence, the σ in (18) and (19) is that just outside the boundary layer. The region occupied by the wall is shown in Fig. 3.

If $\cot \alpha$ is not small, the free surface near the wall has to be obtained from the differential equation

$$\frac{\sigma h''}{(1 + h'^2)^{3/2}} = \rho g(h - h_e),$$

in which the accents indicate differentiations with respect to n. After multiplication by h', a first integration of this equation is

$$-2\sigma(1 + h'^2)^{-1/2} = \rho g(h - h_e)^2 - 2\sigma,$$

in which the constant of integration has been determined by the condition that $h = h_e$ when $h' = 0$. At the wall the value of h, denoted by h_w, is determined from

$$-2\sigma(1 + \cot^2\alpha)^{-1/2} = \rho g(h_w - h_e)^2 - 2\sigma.$$

A second integration gives

$$n = -\int_{h_w}^{h} \frac{1 - B(h - h_e)^2}{\{1 - [1 - B(h - h_e)^2]^2\}^{1/2}} \, dh,$$

in which $B = g\rho/2\sigma$. For any B and h_e, the integral can be carried out numerically if necessary. The fluid region near the wall can, therefore, be unambiguously determined for any α.

Equation (15) is to be solved for the region just described with the boundary conditions

$$(i) \qquad q = 0 \quad \text{at} \quad n = 0,$$

$$(ii) \qquad q = 0 \quad \text{at} \quad z = 0,$$

$$(iii) \qquad q \rightarrow q_0 \quad \text{at} \quad n \rightarrow \infty,$$

$$(iv) \quad \frac{\partial q}{\partial z} = \frac{Q}{h_e} \quad \text{at} \quad z = h.$$

Boundary condition (iii) is, of course, the usual simplified statement for $q \rightarrow q_0$ as n approaches the outer edge of the boundary layer, the "infinity" being used for convenience only. It is also evident that the effect of the boundary layer on the core is neglected.

The problem thus posed for the boundary-layer region is defined and solvable for any value of σ, ρg, and h by numerical methods, such as the method of relaxation. We shall not attempt to give an example of the numerical solution. Instead, we shall give an analytical solution for the special case $\alpha = \pi/2$. Since, in this case

$$\frac{\partial h}{\partial n} = 0, \qquad (20)$$

h is equal to h_e throughout, and for simplicity we shall drop the subscript e and consider h as constant throughout the boundary layer. The values of U, V, and hence Q, are also constant in the boundary layer. Although Q is not zero even at the intersection of the free surface with the vertical wall, this fact is not disturbing. The same situation is encountered at the intersection of a stationary and a moving boundary in contact with a viscous fluid.

We can now simply write the solution of (15)

$$q = \frac{Qz}{h} + \sum_{m=1}^{\infty} A_m \sin \frac{(2m - 1)\pi}{2h} z$$

$$\cdot \exp\left(-\frac{(2m - 1)\pi}{2h} n\right). \qquad (21)$$

The boundary conditions at the horizontal bottom, at the free surface, and just outside of the boundary layer are all exactly satisfied. It remains to determine A_m so that $q = 0$ at $n = 0$. This is accomplished by taking

$$A_m = \frac{2Q}{h} \int_0^h z \sin \frac{(2m - 1)\pi}{2h} z \, dz$$

$$= 8hQ(-1)^{m-1}[(2m - 1)\pi]^{-2}, \qquad (22)$$

in which Q and h are functions of s only. It should be noted that

(a) the boundary effect dies out exponentially, and the boundary-layer thickness is of the order of h,

(b) the velocity distribution in the boundary layer depends only on the local values of h and Q, and

(c) within the boundary layer the shear forces in horizontal planes are balanced by shear forces in vertical surfaces parallel to the wall.

The foregoing analysis can easily be extended for application to liquid films attached to curved surfaces.

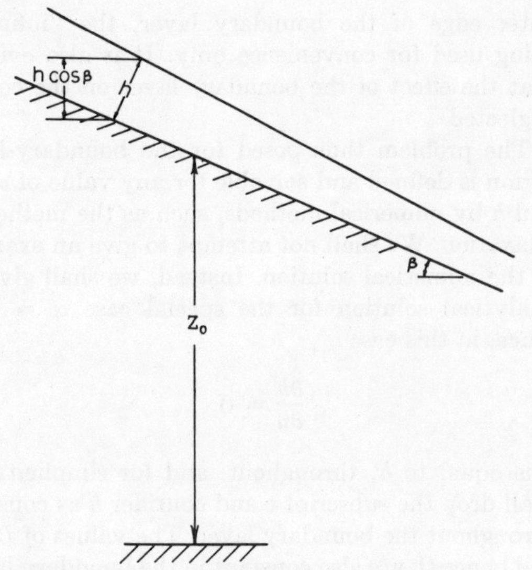

Fig. 4. Cross section in a vertical plane containing the line of steepest descent of the bottom.

V. FILM FLOW INDUCED BY GRAVITY

Consider a plane boundary described by

$$Z_0 = ax + by + c, \qquad (23)$$

in which Z_0 is the elevation of the plane, measured in the direction of the vertical, and x and y are Cartesian coordinates in the plane. The third Cartesian coordinate z is measured in the direction normal to the plane boundary, which we shall call the bottom. The angle of inclination of the bottom to the horizontal will be denoted by β. Boundaries normal to the bottom will be called walls. A liquid film on the bottom will flow under the action of gravity, provided there is a free surface. The depth of the film, measured in the direction of increasing z, is denoted by h. Equations governing the flow of the film under the combined action of gravity and surface-tension variation can be derived. However, they are so complicated that their analytical solutions are unlikely to be obtainable. For this reason we shall consider the effect of surface-tension variation and the effect of gravity separately. The former has been discussed in the foregoing sections. We now consider the effect of gravity alone.

The gravity potential is (Fig. 4)

$$\Omega = gZ = g(Z_0 + h \cos \beta)$$
$$= g(ax + by + c + h \cos \beta). \qquad (24)$$

As before, the velocity component w is negligible. The equations of motion are

$$0 = -\rho \frac{\partial \Omega}{\partial x} + \mu \frac{\partial^2 u}{\partial z^2}, \quad 0 = -\rho \frac{\partial \Omega}{\partial y} + \mu \frac{\partial^2 v}{\partial z^2}, \qquad (25)$$

and these are satisfied *in the core* by

$$u = \frac{1}{2\nu} \frac{\partial \Omega}{\partial x} z(2h - z), \quad v = \frac{1}{2\nu} \frac{\partial \Omega}{\partial y} z(2h - z), \qquad (26)$$

which also satisfy the zero-shear condition at the free surface. Thus,

$$\int_0^h u \, dz = \frac{1}{3\nu} \frac{\partial \Omega}{\partial x} h^3, \qquad \int_0^h v \, dz = \frac{1}{3\nu} \frac{\partial \Omega}{\partial y} h^3, \qquad (27)$$

and the equation of continuity in integral form is

$$\frac{\partial}{\partial x} \left[\left(a + \cos \beta \frac{\partial h}{\partial x} \right) h^3 \right] + \frac{\partial}{\partial y} \left[\left(b + \cos \beta \frac{\partial h}{\partial y} \right) h^3 \right] = 0. \qquad (28)$$

This partial differential equation is to be solved with the boundary condition

$$\frac{\partial \Omega}{\partial n} = 0 \quad \text{or} \quad \frac{\partial Z_0}{\partial n} + \cos \beta \frac{\partial h}{\partial n} = 0 \qquad (29)$$

at the walls, where n is measured in the direction normal to them. The differential system for the core is nonlinear. If a solution is obtained, the flow in the boundary layer is again governed by (15). The boundary-layer region is as shown in Fig. 3, except that the bottom has a slope.

We shall deal with the simpler case of the horizontal bottom, for which

$$a = b = \beta = 0.$$

The differential system governing the core is, from (28),

$$\left(\frac{\partial^2}{\partial x^2} + \frac{\partial^2}{\partial y^2} \right) h^4 = 0, \qquad (30)$$

and

$$\frac{\partial h}{\partial n} = 0 \qquad (31)$$

at the boundaries. Since the boundary conditions can be written as

$$\frac{\partial}{\partial n} h^4 = 0 \qquad (32)$$

at the boundaries, the differential system is linear in h^4, and all the available methods for solving potential-flow problems can be brought to bear.

After the flow in the core is determined, the flow in the boundary-layer region shown in Fig. 3 can be determined by solving (15). If $\alpha = \pi/2$, the solution is simple, since h is then constant throughout the boundary layer. Again using s to denote the distance measured along the boundary and q the velocity component in the direction of increasing s, we have, outside of the boundary layer,

$$q_0 = \frac{1}{2\nu} \frac{\partial \Omega}{\partial s} z(2h - z), \tag{33}$$

in which $\partial \Omega / \partial s$ is taken just outside of the boundary layer. The solution for q is

$$q = q_0 + \sum_{m=1}^{\infty} A_m \sin \frac{(2m-1)\pi z}{2h} \cdot \exp\left(-\frac{(2m-1)\pi n}{2h}\right), \tag{34}$$

in which

$$A_m = -2 \int_0^h q_0 \sin \frac{(2m-1)\pi z}{2h} \, dz$$

$$= -\frac{2}{\nu} \frac{\partial \Omega}{\partial s} \left(\frac{2h}{(2m-1)\pi}\right)^3. \tag{35}$$

All the comments in Sec. III regarding the nature of the boundary layer are still valid here.

ACKNOWLEDGMENT

This work has been jointly supported by the National Science Foundation and the Army Research Office (Durham).

THE HYDRAULIC ARCH*

By CHIA-SHUN YIH (*University of Michigan*)

Exact solutions for free surface flows are rare, especially if gravity is taken onto account. In this note an exact solution is given for a flow of which every streamline can be a free streamline.

As usual, u and v denote the velocity components in the directions of increasing x and y, respectively, x and y being Cartesian coordinates, with y increasing in the direction of the vertical. The gravitational acceleration, assumed constant in this note, will be denoted by g, and the density and the pressure will be denoted by ρ and p, respectively.

Effects of viscosity will be neglected. For steady flows, the equations of motion are then

$$uu_x + vu_y = -(1/\rho)p_x , \tag{1}$$

$$uv_x + vv_y = -(1/\rho)p_y - g. \tag{2}$$

The equation of continuity is, under the assumption of incompressibility,

$$u_x + v_y = 0. \tag{3}$$

The subscripts in the equations above indicate partial differentiation.

The simple solution

$$u = U \quad \text{(constant)}, \qquad v = -(gx/U) \tag{4}$$

satisfies (3). Substituting (4) into (1) and (2), we obtain

$$p_x = 0 = p_y , \tag{5}$$

whatever the value of ρ. Hence, for any density variation from streamline to streamline,

$$p = \text{constant} \tag{6}$$

throughout the whole field of flow, and in particular along any streamline.

The flow given by (4) is rotational, with vorticity equal to $-g/U$. The streamlines are given by

$$\psi/U = y + (g/2U^2)x^2, \tag{7}$$

where ψ is the stream function. They are parabolas with a vertical axis, obtainable from a single parabola by vertical displacement.

As a consequence of (6), the fluid above or below any streamline, or between any two streamlines, can be removed without affecting the rest of the flow. Furthermore, the density distribution, subjected to the sole restriction that ρ must be constant along

* Received September 4, 1972. This work has been supported by the Office of Naval Research.

CHIA-SHUN YIH

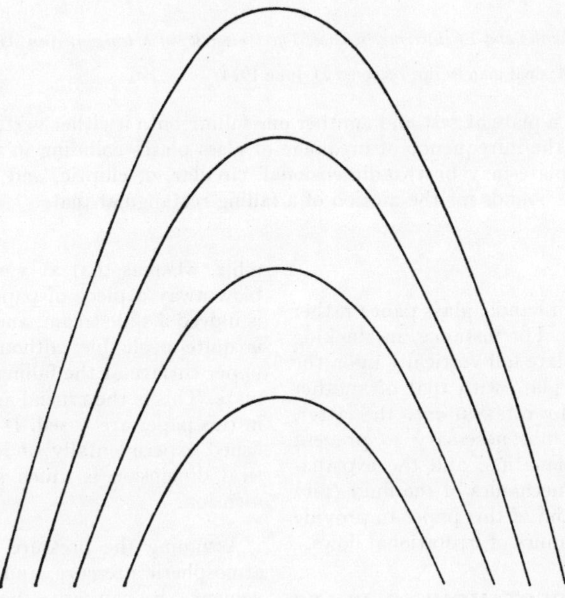

Fig. 1.

any streamline, may vary not only in any x-y plane, but with z (the third Cartesian coordinate) in any manner as well. Consequently, any portion of the fluid bounded by stream surfaces (in which streamlines are imbedded) can be removed without affecting the rest of the flow.

In particular, one can have a flow between two parabolas. This is a flow in a "hydraulic arch".

If the viscosity μ is constant, (4) still satisfies the Navier-Stokes equations, but the boundary conditions at the free surface (or free surfaces) are violated. However, if the Reynolds number (suitably defined) is large, the viscous effects will be concentrated in a thin layer (or in thin layers) at the free surface (or free surfaces).

Note also that if viscous effects are neglected the density along any streamline does not even need to be constant. If it is not constant the density will be unsteady, though the velocity field is steady.

Fluid mechanics of colliding plates

Chia-Shun Yih

Department of Applied Mechanics and Engineering Science, The University of Michigan, Ann Arbor, Michigan 48104

(Received 25 February 1974; final manuscript received 21 June 1974)

The flow of air between a plate at rest and another one falling onto it either vertically or by folding is studied, and the infrequency of breakage of glass plates colliding in this way is explained. The falling plate may be two-dimensional, circular, or elliptic, and the results for an elliptic plate give bounds for the motion of a falling rectangular plate.

I. INTRODUCTION

Glassmakers and glaziers often handle glass panes rather casually without breaking them. For instance, in stacking glass plates they either let one plate fall vertically upon the other, or line up one edge of a plate with that of another already in place, and let it fall by rotation onto the latter. In either case extreme care is not necessary to prevent breakage. This requires an explanation, and the explanation most surely resides in the mechanics of the fluid (air) separating the plates. It is the aim of this paper to provide such an explanation by the dynamics of irrotational flows.

II. VERTICALLY FALLING RECTANGULAR PLATE

Cartesian coordinates x and y will be used, with y measured vertically upward from the top surface of the plate at rest and x measured from the midpoint of this plate (Fig. 1). The width of the plates is $2b$, and the spacing

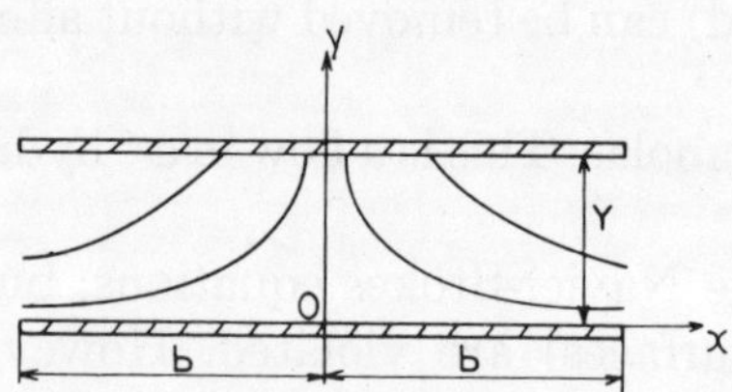

FIG. 1. Flow pattern and definition sketch for the vertically falling plate. (For the elliptic plate replace b by a.)

between the plates will be denoted by Y, which is a function of time. We shall use u and v to denote the velocity components in the directions of increasing x and y, respectively, ρ to denote the density of the fluid, and p to denote the pressure. Since we consider irrotational flow in this paper, the velocity potential exists. We shall denote it by ϕ, and the time by t.

Since the vertical velocity is zero on the plate at rest and is constant on the falling plate, the flow of the fluid between the plate, assumed irrotational, must be of the type

$$u = \beta x, \qquad v = -\beta y, \qquad \phi = \tfrac{1}{2}\beta(x^2 - y^2), \qquad (1)$$

in which β is a function of time.

Although at first sight one might assume that the flow *above* the falling plate would also be given by (1), closer examination shows that that would be unrealistic, and a simple experiment with a pad falling on the table shows that the horizontal velocity at $x = \pm b$ and $y > Y$ is negli-

gible, whereas that at $x = \pm b$ and $y < Y$ is sufficient to blow away a piece of paper. The wind issuing at $x = \pm b$ is indeed a slip stream, and the flow above the falling plate is quite negligible, although the vertical velocity at the upper surface of the falling plate is the same as that of the plate. This is the crucial assumption on which the analyses in this paper are based. It can be regarded as a fact established experimentally under the assumption that the vertical dimension is much smaller than any horizontal dimension.

Assuming the pressure at $x = \pm b$ to be equal to the atmospheric pressure, and taking that to be zero for convenience, we can write the Bernoulli equation for the flow, neglecting the effect of gravity on p, as

$$\tfrac{1}{2}\dot{\beta}(x^2 - Y^2) + \tfrac{1}{2}\beta^2(x^2 + Y^2) + \frac{p}{\rho} = \tfrac{1}{2}\dot{\beta}(b^2 - Y^2)$$
$$+ \tfrac{1}{2}\beta^2(b^2 + Y^2), \qquad (2)$$

between any point on the lower surface of the falling plate and the point (b, Y) or $(-b, Y)$. From (2) we obtain

$$p = \tfrac{1}{2}\rho(\beta^2 + \dot{\beta})(b^2 - x^2), \qquad (3)$$

where

$$\dot{\beta} = d\beta/dt. \qquad (4)$$

Thus, the vertical force on the plate is

$$2\int_0^b p\, dx = \tfrac{2}{3}\rho(\beta^2 + \dot{\beta})b^3. \qquad (5)$$

We now consider the dynamics of the falling plate. Let W be its weight and M be its mass, both per unit length in the direction normal to the x-y plane. Then,

$$W - \tfrac{2}{3}\rho(\beta^2 + \dot{\beta})b^3 = -M\ddot{Y}. \qquad (6)$$

Since v is given by (1), we have

$$v = \dot{Y} = -\beta Y \qquad (7)$$

on the falling plate. Thus, (6) can be written as

$$W - \frac{2\rho}{3}(2\dot{Y}^2/Y^2 - \ddot{Y}/Y)b^3 = -M\ddot{Y}, \qquad (8)$$

and it is immediately seen that for very small Y (compared with b) the right-hand side of (8) can be neglected. The

Copyright © 1975 American Institute of Physics   1936

situation at small Y is the most important, because it corresponds to the final stage of the fall. The negligibility of the right-hand side of (8) at small Y means that at that stage there is a virtual balance of forces on the falling plate.

Considering this stage, and returning to (6), we have

$$\dot{\beta} + \beta^2 - w^2 = 0, \tag{9}$$

where

$$w^2 = 3W/2\rho b^3 = \text{const.} \tag{10}$$

Integration of (9) gives

$$\beta + w = C(\beta - w)\exp(2wt),$$

or

$$\beta = w\,\frac{C\exp(2wt) + 1}{C\exp(2wt) - 1}, \tag{11}$$

where C is a constant of integration to be determined from the initial conditions (at $t = 0$). For instance, if β is zero at $t = 0$, $C = -1$. If β is positive at $t = 0$, $|C| > 1$. The initially rising plate, corresponding to initially negative β, will not be considered, for the flow at $x = \pm b$ is radically changed, and not a simple reversal of the flow for a falling plate.

As $t \to \infty$, $\beta \to w$, or, from (7),

$$\dot{Y} = -wY,$$

and

$$Y = C_1\exp(-wt), \qquad C_1 > 0, \tag{12}$$

where C_1 is determined from an initial condition. This means that $\dot{Y}$ will be smaller and smaller as time increases, and there is no danger of breakage of the glass plates. Of course, (12) contradicts common sense: It does not take infinite time for a plate to fall upon another. Nevertheless, (12) shows that the danger of large fall velocity when the plates meet is small. The reasons why (12) does not strictly apply and colliding plates sometime break may be

(a) No surface is perfectly smooth, and the plates meet when their protrusions do.
(b) The falling plate is not strictly horizontal in practice.
(c) Viscosity has so far not been taken into account.
(d) When Y is very small, the continuum theory fails.

Of these, (a) and (b) are probably the most important.

III. VERTICALLY FALLING CIRCULAR PLATE

If the plates are circular, then retaining the coordinate y but using x to denote the radial distance from the y axis, and u to denote the radial component of the velocity, we have, instead of (1),

$$u = \beta x, \qquad v = -2\beta y, \qquad \phi = \beta(x^2 - 2y^2)/2. \tag{13}$$

It is evident that u and v satisfy the equation of continuity

$$u_x + u/x + v_y = 0,$$

and ϕ satisfies the Laplace equation

$$\phi_{xx} + \phi_x/x + \phi_{yy} = 0.$$

If the radius of the plates is denoted by b, then at $x = b$ we again assume the pressure to be zero. The Bernoulli equation between a point on the lower side of the moving plate and the point (b, Y) is, with the effect of gravity neglected,

$$\tfrac{1}{2}\dot{\beta}(x^2 - 2Y^2) + \tfrac{1}{2}\beta^2(x^2 + 4Y^2) + p/\rho = \tfrac{1}{2}\dot{\beta}(b^2 - 2Y^2)$$
$$+ \tfrac{1}{2}\beta^2(b^2 + 4Y^2), \tag{14}$$

in which Y is the y on the lower surface of the falling plate. Thus,

$$p = \tfrac{1}{2}\rho(\beta^2 + \dot{\beta})(b^2 - x^2), \tag{15}$$

as in (3). The force on the moving plate is

$$2\pi\int_0^b pr\,dr = \tfrac{1}{4}\pi\rho(\beta^2 + \dot{\beta})b^4. \tag{16}$$

The equation of motion for the falling plate is

$$W - \tfrac{1}{4}\pi\rho(\beta^2 + \dot{\beta})b^4 = -M\ddot{Y}, \tag{17}$$

in which W is the weight and M is the mass of the falling plate. From the second equation of (13) we have

$$v = \dot{Y} = -2\beta Y \tag{18}$$

on the falling plate. Substituting (18) into (17), we see that, once again, the right-hand side of (17) can be neglected when Y is small. Considering small Y, and writing

$$w^2 = 4W/\pi\rho b^4, \tag{19}$$

we obtain from (17),

$$\dot{\beta} + \beta^2 - w^2 = 0.$$

The rest of the development is the same as that following (9), and using (18), we see that Y decays as $\exp(-2wt)$.

The case of the falling circular plate finds actual application in the case of falling records in phonographs with automatic changers.

IV. VERTICALLY FALLING ELLIPTIC PLATE

We have presented the case of the circular plate because of its special interest. Actually, the treatment can be generalized to deal with elliptic plates. We shall now give this generalization, and the results obtained will be used to estimate the speed of fall of rectangular plates.

Maintaining the y axis vertical, and using x and z as two horizontal Cartesian coordinates, we study the fall of the elliptic plate bounded by

$$x_e^2/a^2 + z_e^2/c^2 = 1, \tag{20}$$

where the subscript e denotes "edge." The appropriate velocity potential ϕ is now

$$\phi = \tfrac{1}{2}\beta[x^2 + Cz^2 - (1 + C)y^2], \tag{21}$$

in which β and C are functions of time. The velocity components derived from (21) are

$$u = \beta x, \qquad v = -\beta(1 + C)y, \qquad w = \beta Cz. \tag{22}$$

It is evident that the equation of continuity is satisfied.

The Bernoulli equation for unsteady irrotational flow is, since the pressure p is zero at $y = Y$ and on the ellipse (20),

$$\begin{aligned}
p/\rho &+ \tfrac{1}{2}\dot\beta[x^2 + Cz^2 - (1 + C)Y^2] + \tfrac{1}{2}\beta^2[x^2 + C^2z^2 \\
&+ (1 + C)^2Y^2] + \tfrac{1}{2}\beta\dot C(z^2 - Y^2) = \tfrac{1}{2}\dot\beta[x_e^2 + Cz_e^2 \\
&- (1 + C)Y^2] + \tfrac{1}{2}\beta^2[x_e^2 + C^2z_e^2 + (1 + C)^2Y^2] \\
&+ \tfrac{1}{2}\beta\dot C(z_e^2 - Y^2),
\end{aligned} \tag{23}$$

where Y is again the distance between the falling plate and the plate at rest. Now, since the pressure at any given point (x, z, Y) must be independent of x_e and z_e, we have

$$(\dot\beta + \beta^2)x_e^2 + (\dot\beta C + \beta\dot C + \beta^2 C^2)z_e^2 = \text{const.}$$

In view of (20), this is possible only if

$$\dot\beta C + \beta\dot C + \beta^2 C^2 = (a^2/c^2)(\dot\beta + \beta^2). \tag{24}$$

At first sight it seemed that we had to solve for C, and if so the subsequent calculation would be cumbersome. It turns out that for our purpose we need not know C explicitly, because substitution of (24) into (23) gives

$$p = (\rho/2)a^2(\dot\beta + \beta^2)(1 - x^2/a^2 - z^2/c^2). \tag{25}$$

The calculation of the pressure on the underside of the elliptic plate can be greatly simplified if we introduce the variable

$$m^2 = x^2/a^2 + z^2/c^2. \tag{26}$$

The area A_m within this ellipse is

$$A_m = \pi acm^2. \tag{27}$$

Then, the total hydrodynamic lift on the plate is

$$\begin{aligned}
\int_{m=0}^{m=1} p \, dA_m &= \tfrac{1}{2}\rho a^2(\dot\beta + \beta^2)\int_0^1 (1 - m^2)2\pi acm \, dm \\
&= \tfrac{1}{4}\rho\pi a^3 c(\dot\beta + \beta^2),
\end{aligned} \tag{28}$$

which reduces to (16) if $a = c = b$.

With

$$w^2 = 4W/\pi\rho a^3 c \tag{29}$$

instead of (19), the rest of the development is the same as in Secs. II and III. The exponential rate of decay is, ac-

cording to

$$v = \dot Y = -\beta(1 + C)Y,$$

equal to the value of $-\beta(1 + C)$ at $t = \infty$. The asymptotic value of β is, as before, equal to w; but we are now obliged to find the asymptotic value of C. The simplest way of finding $C(\infty)$ is by means of (24). First, if β decays to a constant value, C must also decay to a constant value, for otherwise the left-hand side of (24) would be a function of time whereas the right-hand side is a constant. Then, (24) gives

$$C(\infty) = a/c,$$

since the negative root must obviously be ruled out. Then, the asymptotic rate of exponential decay is

$$-\beta(\infty)[1 + C(\infty)] = -2(1/a + 1/c)(W/\rho\pi ac)^{1/2}.$$

We now say a few things about the fall of a rectangular plate. An exact development similar to that in Secs. II and III, and to the development for an elliptic plate is impossible. We can, however, estimate the exponential rate of decay by the following steps:

i. Construct the smallest circumscribed ellipse containing the four corners of the rectangle, and the greatest inscribed ellipse tangent to the four sides of the rectangle, and obtain the a and c for each ellipse. The axes of the ellipses are parallel to the sides of the rectangle.

ii. Obtain from (28) the w for the two ellipses.

iii. Then, the exponential rate of decay of the fall velocity of the rectangular plate must be between the two decay rates for the two ellipses.

Indeed, if we wish to obtain the history of motion of the rectangular plate, we can find the history of motion for each of the elliptic plate subjected to the same initial conditions, and estimate that the desired velocity–time curve must be between the two corresponding curves for the ellipses.

V. ROTATING RECTANGULAR PLATE

The appropriate solution for the fluid between the plates (Fig. 2) is still (1). The velocity component normal to the plate and toward the wedge space is

$$u_n = 2\beta xy/r = 2\beta r \cos\theta \sin\theta, \tag{30}$$

where r is the radial distance from the origin taken at the intersection of the plates and θ is the angle between the

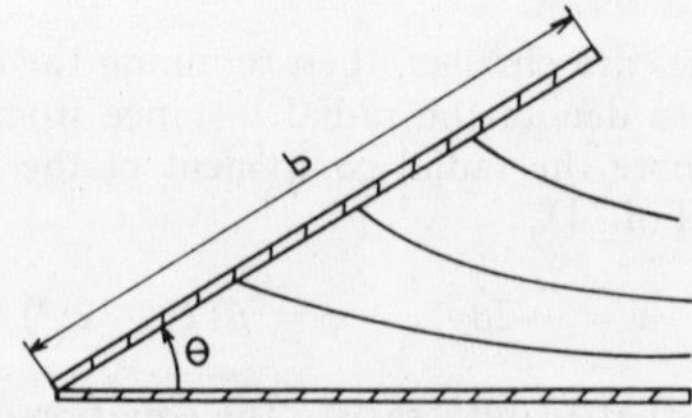

FIG. 2. Flow pattern and definition sketch for the rotating plate. (For the semielliptic plate replace b by a.)

plates; but u_n is equal to $-r\dot\theta$. Hence, (30) gives

$$\beta \sin2\theta = -\dot\theta, \tag{31}$$

which connects β and θ. The boundary conditions on both plates are now satisfied.

Again, we use zero for the value of the pressure at $r = b$ (b is now the full width of the plate) and at the angle θ of the moving plate, and for the pressure at the back of the plate. Applying the Bernoulli equation between this point and any point on the moving plate, we have as the pressure at the latter point

$$p = \tfrac{1}{2}\rho(\beta^2 + \dot\beta \cos2\theta)(b^2 - r^2),$$

and the moment about the origin of the force p is

$$\int_0^b pr\, dr = \tfrac{1}{8}\rho(\beta^2 + \dot\beta \cos2\theta)b^4. \tag{32}$$

If M is the mass and I is the moment of inertia (about the origin) of the moving plate, all per unit length perpendicular to the x-y plane, the equation governing the rotation of the plate is

$$\tfrac{1}{2}(Mgb)\cos\theta - \tfrac{1}{8}\rho(\beta^2 + \dot\beta \cos2\theta)b^4 = -I\ddot\theta, \tag{33}$$

which, together with (31), determines θ as a function of time. These equations are hopelessly nonlinear, and in any case, it is the final stage of the calculation (for small θ) that is important. We shall then consider small θ, for which (31) becomes

$$\beta = -\dot\theta/2\theta \tag{34}$$

and (33) becomes

$$Mgb/2 - (\rho b^4/8)(3\dot\theta^2/4\theta^2 - \ddot\theta/2\theta) = -I\ddot\theta. \tag{35}$$

Then, the right-hand side of (35) is obviously negligible for small θ, and we have the equation of moment balance from (33)

$$\dot\beta + \beta^2 - w^2 = 0, \tag{36}$$

where

$$w^2 = 4Mg/\rho b^3. \tag{37}$$

The rest of the analysis is the same as that following (9); and, we have

$$\theta = C_2 \exp(-2wt), \tag{38}$$

with w (positive) given by (37). Thus, again θ decreases with time, and there is no danger of breakage. The discussion of the infinite time needed for contact is the same as that given in Sec. III.

It has been observed that sometimes the rotating plate will rise at its axis of rotation and become afloat. It is therefore desirable to discuss the circumstances under which floating will occur.

The total hydrodynamic lift force per unit length of the plate is, from (32),

$$L = \int_0^b p \cos\theta\, dr = \tfrac{1}{3}(\rho b^3)(\beta^2 + \dot\beta \cos2\theta)\cos\theta. \tag{39}$$

The *downward* acceleration of the center of gravity of the plate is

$$a_p = \tfrac{1}{2}b(\dot\theta^2 \sin\theta + \ddot\theta \cos\theta). \tag{40}$$

With θ determined by (33) and the initial conditions, and β given by (31), we conclude that if

$$Mg - L = Ma_p, \tag{41}$$

then there is just zero upward force at the edge of the plate, about which it rotates. Thus, (39) to (41) together with (23) and the initial conditions, determine whether floating will occur, and, if it occurs, the time of occurrence. Obviously, the details of when floating will occur depend not only on M, g, ρ, and b, but also on the initial conditions. Note, however, that (39) and (41) give $-Mg/3$ as the asymptotic value for the right-hand side of (41), so that floating always occurs, and the fixed edge can be kept in place only if it is held down as well as in. (It needs to be held in because of the sidewise push of the hydrodynamic pressure.)

VI. ROTATING ELLIPTIC PLATE

In order to estimate the motion of a rectangular plate (of finite length) we shall consider the rotation of a semi-ellipse about an axis. To have a notation consistent with that used in Sec. V, we shall retain the meaning of x, y, and r, and consider the half of the elliptic plate bounded by

$$r_e^2/a^2 + z_e^2/c^2 = 1, \qquad r = 0, \tag{42}$$

where the subscript e again denotes the boundary of the elliptic plate. The appropriate solution for the fluid between the rotating semielliptic plate and the stationary plate at $y = 0$ is still (21), and the velocity components are still given by (22), but C will be different, for the pressure is now given by

$$\begin{aligned}
p/\rho + \tfrac{1}{2}\dot\beta[x^2 + Cz^2 - (1+C)y^2] + \tfrac{1}{2}\beta^2[x^2 + C^2z^2 \\
+ (1+C)^2y^2] + \tfrac{1}{2}\beta\dot C(z^2 - y^2) = \tfrac{1}{2}\dot\beta[x_e^2 + Cz_e^2 \\
- (1+C)y_e^2] + \tfrac{1}{2}\beta^2[x_e^2 + C^2z_e^2 + (1+C)^2y_e^2] \\
+ \tfrac{1}{2}\beta\dot C(z_e^2 - y_e^2),
\end{aligned} \tag{43}$$

and C must be such that the right-hand side of (43) is independent of x_e, y_e, and z_e, so that, given x, y, and z, p is uniquely determined. Since

$$x_e = r_e \cos\theta, \qquad y_e = r_e \sin\theta, \tag{44}$$

the right-hand side can be written, upon use of (44), as

$$\begin{aligned}
R = (r_e^2/2)\{(\dot\beta + \beta^2)\cos^2\theta - [\dot\beta(1+C) - \beta^2(1+C)^2 \\
+ \beta\dot C]\sin^2\theta\} + (z_e^2/2)(C\dot\beta + \beta\dot C + C^2\beta^2).
\end{aligned}$$

If this is to be a constant, comparison with (42) gives

$$R = \tfrac{1}{2}c^2(C\dot{\beta} + \beta\dot{C} + C^2\beta^2), \tag{45}$$

and

$$(\dot{\beta} + \beta^2)\cos^2\theta - [\dot{\beta}(1 + C) + \beta\dot{C} - \beta^2(1 + C)^2]\sin^2\theta$$
$$= (c^2/a^2)(C\dot{\beta} + \beta\dot{C} + C^2\beta^2). \tag{46}$$

Hence, (43) can be written as

$$p/\rho = R(1 - r^2/a^2 - z^2/c^2). \tag{47}$$

The moment of hydrodynamic forces (M_H) about the axis of rotation is, with A denoting the surface of the semi-elliptic plate,

$$M_H = \int_A pr\, dA = 4\rho Ra^2c/15.$$

The moment of the weight (M_w) of the semielliptic plate about the z axis is, with ρ_s denoting the density of the plate per unit *area*,

$$M_w = \rho_s g\cos\theta \int_A r\, dA = 2\rho_s ga^2c\cos\theta/3.$$

The moment of inertia of the plate about the z axis is

$$I = \rho_s \int_A r^2\, dA = \rho_s \pi a^3 c/8.$$

The equation of motion is then

$$M_w - M_H = -I\ddot{\theta}, \tag{48}$$

to be solved simultaneously with the kinematic equation

$$u_n = \beta(2 + C)r\cos\theta\sin\theta = -r\dot{\theta},$$

or

$$\beta(2 + C)\cos\theta\sin\theta = -\dot{\theta}. \tag{49}$$

For small values of θ, Eqs. (45) and (46) give

$$R = \tfrac{1}{2}a^2(\dot{\beta} + \beta^2). \tag{50}$$

Then, from (49) and (50) it is evident that again the term $-I\ddot{\theta}$ is negligible, and (48) becomes

$$\dot{\beta} + \beta^2 - w^2 = 0, \tag{51}$$

with

$$w^2 = 15M_w/2\rho a^4c = 5\rho_s g/\rho a^2. \tag{52}$$

From (49) it is evident that the exponential rate of decay is

$$-\beta(\infty)[2 + C(\infty)].$$

From (51) one again obtains

$$\beta(\infty) = w,$$

and from (46) one obtains

$$C(\infty) = c/a,$$

since $\theta = 0$ asymptotically. Hence, the exponential rate of decay is

$$-w(2 + c/a).$$

That this is no longer symmetric with respect to a and c is not surprising, since it is about the x axis that the plate rotates.

The phenomenon of floating for folding elliptic plates can be discussed as in Sec. V. We shall not elaborate further, except to say that floating can be expected to occur asymptotically at least, and possibly for smaller values of t, unless the fixed edge is held down (as it also needs to be held in).

For a rectangular plate we can again estimate its exponential rate of decay or its history of motion by replacing it, in turn, by a circumscribing semiellipse and an inscribing semiellipse, with one axis coinciding with the axis of rotation, thus establishing bounds for the motion of the rectangular plate, provided the initial conditions are the same for it and for the elliptic plates.

In conclusion, we permit ourselves to note that, under the assumption of small vertical dimension compared with any horizontal dimension, the analyses have gone very far in determining the motion of plates, two-dimensional, circular, or elliptic, falling vertically or by folding.

ACKNOWLEDGMENTS

The author wishes to express his appreciation to a referee of this paper for pointing out the phenomenon of floating and for suggesting the calculation for the elliptic plate. The answers to his suggestions have added to the weight and interest of this paper.

This work has been jointly sponsored by the National Science Foundation and the Office of Naval Research.

QUARTERLY OF APPLIED MATHEMATICS
JANUARY 1980

FLOWS WITH CONDENSATION*

By

CHIA-SHUN YIH

University of Michigan, Ann Arbor

Abstract. Some simple flows with condensation are considered and their solutions given. For the vapor phase, the nonlinearity of the equations of motion and of heat diffusion, and of the equation of state, and the dissipation due to shear and volume viscosities are taken into account. For the liquid phase the density is assumed constant. At the interface, where condensation takes place, the velocity, the stress, and the temperature gradient are all discontinuous. The same approach can be used for flows with evaporation.

1. Introduction. In the literature there are very few solutions of the Navier-Stokes equations for fluid flows with condensation. Studies of gas flows with evaporation at a wet boundary are much more common. But in these studies, with a few exceptions (notably the studies by Milton Plesset), the evaporating surface is treated at most as a source of vapor and a heat sink, and the concentration of vapor carried away by the flowing gas is considered to be a passive quantity with no effect on the flow except possibly through the action of gravity, since the Boussinesq approximation is invariably used. So far as I am aware, few attempts have been made to study the flow of the liquid phase and to match it with the flow of the vapor (or vapors) in contact with it, with the effects of the viscosities and the thermal diffusivity, the equation of state, and the condition of the vapor at the condensation surface all taken into account.

In this paper, a simple flow of the vapor of a pure substance downward toward a cooling porous plate will first be considered (Fig. 1). The cooling plate causes condensation and the liquid formed flows away through the pores of the plate. The solution of the Navier-Stokes and diffusion equations for this flow will be given. Then an inclined flow with condensation will be treated and flows with evaporation briefly discussed.

As will be seen presently, the solutions to be given have several novel features arising from the necessity of abandoning the many usual conditions of continuity at the vapor-liquid interface, such as the continuity of velocity, of stresses, and of heat flux.

2. Equations governing normal flow of a vapor against a cooling plate. Let y be measured in the direction opposite to that of the gravitational acceleration, and let the velocity component in the direction of increasing y be denoted by v. We consider steady downward flows of a vapor toward a cold plate. Far upstream, where y is taken to be (positive) infinite for convenience, the vapor has density ρ_0, velocity $-v_0$, temperature T_0, and pressure p_0. The position of the vapor-liquid interface will be taken to be the origin of y. At the plate, where the temperature is maintained at $T_0 - \Delta T$,

---

* Received February 26, 1979. The work leading to this paper has been supported by the Office of Naval Research.

CHIA-SHUN YIH

$$y = -d,$$

d being the thickness of the liquid above the plate, to be determined by calculation.

As usual, μ will denote the viscosity and λ the volume viscosity minus $2\mu/3$. The thermal conductivity, the specific heat at constant pressure, and the specific heat at constant volume will be denoted by k, c_p, and c_v, respectively, and will be assumed constant. The ratio c_p/c_v will be denoted by γ. The density will be denoted by ρ, the pressure by p, and the absolute temperature by T.

The surface representing the equation of state of a pure substance, say water or water vapor, is well known. There is a surface of zero curvature in the space of pressure, temperature and specific volume, on which, if the temperature is maintained constant, the pressure will remain constant as the specific volume ρ^{-1} changes. This is the region of condensation or evaporation, in which the liquid phase and the vapor of the substance coexist. This developable surface is bounded on the right by the vapor-saturation curve and on the left by the liquid-saturation curve, meeting at the critical point above which the liquid state and the vapor state are separated by a curve on which the two states merge and are indistinguishable. The pressure and the temperature at the critical point are called the critical pressure and the critical temperature. Condensation or evaporation can take place only when the pressure is lower than the critical pressure p_{cr} and the temperature is lower than the critical temperature T_{cr}. The change of state at a pressure higher than the critical pressure does not involve evaporation or condensation but takes place through a state of indistinguishable phases without the release or absorption of latent heat.

The temperature at the plate, of course, must be below T_{cr} for condensation to take place. The problem is to determine the temperature and velocity fields and the thickness d of the liquid phase.

Since the flow is vertically downward, v, the only non-zero velocity component, is

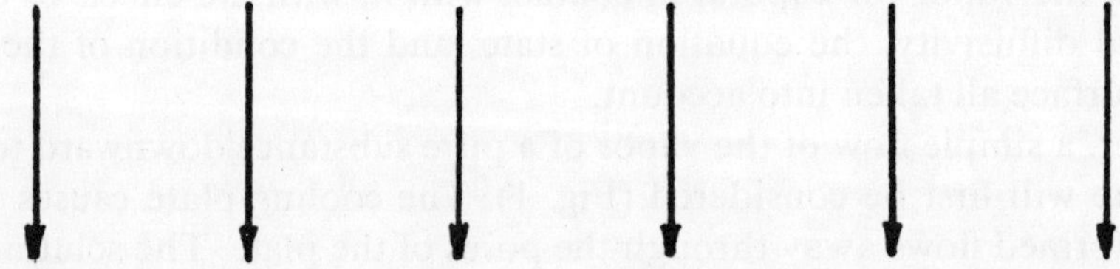

FIG. 1.   Sketch showing vapor flow downward toward a porous cooling plate, with an overlying liquid layer.

everywhere negative, including the liquid region. The flow considered being steady, y is the only independent variable, and the equation of motion is, with primes indicating d/dy,

$$\rho v v' = -g\rho - (p - \lambda v')' + (2\mu v')', \tag{1}$$

where g is the gravitational acceleration.

For the vapor phase we shall neglect the effect of gravity on the pressure and on the flow. This amounts to neglecting the variation in the hydrostatic pressure in comparison with the prevailing pressure, or neglecting the effect of the height of the apparatus, in any experiment done for the problem under study, on the pressure in the vapor. We continue to use $y = \infty$ for the position far upstream, with the understanding that y is very large compared with a length scale to be specified later. Hence for the vapor we have

$$\rho v v' = -p' + [(\lambda + 2\mu)v']'. \tag{2}$$

The heat equation is

$$\rho c_v T' + p v' = (kT')' + (\lambda + 2\mu)v'^2, \tag{3}$$

where the last term represents the effect of viscous dissipation.

The equation of continuity is

$$\rho v = -\rho_0 v_0 = m, \tag{4}$$

and the equation of state for the vapor will be taken to be that of the ideal gas:

$$p = R\rho T, \tag{5}$$

where R is the gas constant. This equation is not strictly satisfied near the vapor-saturation curve, but the latent heat for the evaporation of water calculated by the use of this equation, for instance, agrees very well with the measured values. Hence the use of (5) is expected to introduce very little error.

3. Preliminary integration of the equation of motion and of heat diffusion. For the vapor phase, then, (4) allows the left-hand side of (2) to be written as $-(mv)'$, and a first integration of (2) gives

$$-mv = -p + (\lambda + 2\mu)v' + C_1, \tag{6}$$

where

$$C_1 = p_0 + mv_0 = R\rho_0 T_0 + mv_0. \tag{7}$$

Eqs. (4) and (6) then reduce (3) to the simple form

$$-mc_v T' + mvv' = (kT')' - C_1 v'. \tag{8}$$

Assuming c_v to be constant, we can integrate (8) to

$$mc_v(T - T_0) + \frac{m}{2}v^2 = kT' - C_1 v + C_2, \tag{9}$$

where

$$C_2 = \frac{m}{2}v_0^2 - C_1 v_0 = -mRT_0 - \frac{m}{2}v_0^2, \tag{10}$$

since $T' = 0$ far upstream.

Eq. (6) can be written as

$$R\rho T = mv + (\lambda + 2\mu)v' + C_1,$$

or, by virtue of (4), as

$$-RmT = mv^2 + (\lambda + 2\mu)vv' + C_1 v. \tag{11}$$

Eqs. (9) and (11) govern the flow of vapor. After v and T are found, (4) gives ρ and (5) gives p.

It is desirable to put (9) and (11) in dimensionless forms. For this purpose we use the new variables

$$V = \frac{v}{v_0} + 1, \qquad \theta = \frac{T_0 - T}{T_0}, \qquad \eta = \frac{mc_v}{k} y, \tag{12}$$

so that V and θ vanish far upstream. Dividing (9) by mv_0^2, then multiplying the result by $\gamma(\gamma - 1)M^2$, we obtain

$$\theta + \frac{\gamma(\gamma - 1)}{2} M^2 V^2 = -\theta' - (\gamma - 1)V, \tag{13}$$

where

$$M = v_0/c_0, \qquad c_0^2 = \gamma R T_0, \tag{14}$$

c_0 being the speed of sound at temperature T_0, so that M is the Mach number far upstream. The prime in (13) now indicates differentiation with respect to η.

Eq. (11), upon division by mv_0^2 and then multiplication by γM^2, becomes

$$\theta = \gamma M^2 (V - 1)(V + \sigma V') + V, \tag{15}$$

where

$$\sigma = \frac{\lambda + 2\mu}{k} c_v \tag{16}$$

is a kind of Prandtl number. Eqs. (13) and (15) will be solved together with the equations governing liquid flow and the boundary and interfacial conditions. The vanishing of θ and V far upstream gives

$$\theta(\infty) = V(\infty) = 0. \tag{17}$$

The interfacial conditions will be given later.

4. The flow of the liquid.   We shall use the subscript l to indicate the properties of the liquid, and shall take ρ_l, the density of the liquid, to be constant. The v_l is also constant, for

$$\rho_l v_l = -m. \tag{18}$$

Therefore only the heat equation needs to be solved for the liquid. This equation is still (3), except that v there is now the constant v_l. The definition of θ is still given by (12), except that T is T_l, so that

$$\theta_l = (T_0 - T_l)/T_0.$$

Retaining the meaning of η defined in (13), we have

$$-\beta\theta_l' = \theta_l'', \tag{19}$$

where

$$\beta = \frac{k}{k_l}\frac{c_{vl}}{c_v}.$$

Since (19) is simple, we shall give its solution immediately. At the interface, where $\eta = 0$,

$$\theta_l = (T_0 - T_i)/T_0 = \theta_i$$

and

$$\theta_l = \Delta T/T_0 \equiv \alpha$$

on the plate, where

$$\eta = -\frac{mc_v}{k}d = -\delta. \tag{20}$$

Two integrations of (19) give

$$\theta_l = C_4 + C_3 \exp(-\beta\eta), \tag{21}$$

where the constants of integration are determined by the boundary conditions to be

$$C_3 = \frac{\alpha - \theta_i}{\exp(\beta\delta) - 1}, \qquad C_4 = \theta_i - C_3. \tag{22}$$

5. Interfacial conditions. On the vapor-saturation curve, with F standing for "function,"

$$T_i = F(\rho_i), \tag{23}$$

where and henceforth the subscript i denotes the interface, and this condition has to be satisfied by the density and temperature of the *vapor* at the interface. In a numerical calculation, (23) can be used without approximation. For an analytical solution, and perhaps even for a numerical one, it is better to approximate (23) with

$$T_i = \frac{A}{\rho_i} + B = -\frac{A}{m}v_i + B,$$

in which, for a typical substance (such as water), A is negative and B positive. In terms of θ and V, this can be written as

$$\theta_i = aV_i + b, \tag{24}$$

in which, for a typical substance (such as water), both a and b are negative. (Remember the definition of θ.) We can use (24) with a and b chosen to approximate (23) as closely as possible. Then, when θ is determined on the interface, we can go back to (23) to seek a pair of values of A and B for the tangent of the curve (23) for the temperature T_i determined. Then we use the new a and b corresponding to the new A and B, and so on. With the understanding that this iteration is always available, we shall assume a and b to be given and proceed with the calculation. We shall use h to denote the latent heat.

On the interface, where $\eta = 0$,

                                CHIA-SHUN YIH

$$\theta = \theta_l = \theta_i . \tag{25}$$

Furthermore, at the interface the heat-flux condition is

$$\theta'(0) - \frac{h}{c_v T_0} = \frac{k_l}{k} \theta_l'(0). \tag{26}$$

We note that the equation of state has been used in obtaining (8) and in going from (6) to (11). If p is found from (6) after v is determined and p_i is calculated, it will automatically satisfy the equation of state together with T_i and ρ_i .

6. Solution of the differential system governing the flow. Since the Mach number is expected to be small for most cases of interest, the forms of (15) and (16) suggest that the solution can be obtained by expausions of θ and V in power series of M^2. Thus we take

$$\theta = \theta_0 + M^2\theta_1 + M^4\theta_2 + \cdots , \tag{26}$$

$$V = V_0 + M^2 V_1 + M^4 V_2 + \cdots . \tag{27}$$

Furthermore, since d will change when terms of higher orders in M are taken into account, we shall expand δ in the power series

$$\delta = \delta_0 + M^2\delta_1 + M^4\delta_2 + \cdots . \tag{28}$$

Then from (13) and (15) we have

$$\theta_0 = -\theta_0' - (\gamma - 1)V_0 , \qquad \theta_0 = V_0 ,$$

the solution of which is

$$\theta_0 = V_0 = a_0 \exp(-\gamma\eta), \tag{29}$$

which satisfies (17).

The solution for θ_l is always given by (21). But C_3 and C_4 contain θ_i and δ. In particular,

$$C_3 = C_{30} + M^2 C_{31} + M^4 C_{32} + \cdots , \tag{30}$$

in which

$$C_{30} = \frac{\alpha - \theta_{0i}}{\exp(\beta\delta_0) - 1} ,$$

$$C_{31} = \frac{1}{\exp(\beta\delta_0) - 1}\left[\frac{\beta\delta_1}{\exp(\beta\delta_0 - 1)}(\theta_{0i} - \alpha) - \theta_{1i}\right],$$

etc.

Substituting (29) into (24), we have

$$a_0 = \frac{b}{1 - a} ,$$

which is negative since both a and b are negative. The interfacial heat-flux condition (26) then gives

$$-\gamma a_0 - \frac{h}{\gamma T_0} = -\frac{k_l}{k}\beta C_{30} ,$$

which determines the δ_0 in C_3.

Extracting terms of order M^2 in (13) and (15), and combining the two equations so obtained, we have

$$\theta_1' + \gamma\theta_1 = -2\gamma D \exp(-2\gamma\eta) + E \exp(-\gamma\eta), \tag{31}$$

where

$$D = \tfrac{1}{4}(\gamma - 1)(2\sigma\gamma - 1)a_0^{\,2}, \qquad E = \gamma(\gamma - 1)(\sigma\gamma - 1)a_0.$$

The solution of (31) is

$$\theta_1 = a_1 \exp(-\gamma\eta) + E\eta \exp(-\gamma\eta) + D \exp(-2\gamma\eta), \tag{32}$$

which satisfies (17). Then from the equation extracted from (15) by taking terms of $O(M^2)$, we have

$$V_1 = \left(a_1 - \frac{E}{\gamma - 1} + E\eta\right) \exp(-\gamma\eta) + G \exp(-2\gamma\eta), \tag{33}$$

in which

$$G = \tfrac{1}{4}[6\sigma\gamma^2 - (2\sigma + 5)\gamma + 1]a_0^{\,2}.$$

It is evident that V_1 satisfies (17).

The interfacial condition (24) demands

$$\theta_1(0) = aV_1(0),$$

so that

$$a_1 = \frac{1}{a - 1}\left(D + \frac{aE}{\gamma - 1} - aG\right). \tag{34}$$

The value of θ_1 at the interface is $a_1 + D$. The interfacial heat-flux condition is now

$$-a_1\gamma + E - 2\gamma D = (k_i/k) C_{31},$$

which determines the δ_1 in C_{31}.

Solutions for higher-order terms in the expansions (26), (27), and (28) proceed in the same way. But these are not necessary if the Mach number is less than $\tfrac{1}{4}$, say.

7. A special solution. If T_0 and ρ_0 already satisfy the relationship (23) for the evaporation or condensation curve, the solution is especially simple, for the solution of (15) and (13) is simply

$$\theta = 0 = V$$

for all values of y from the interface to positive infinity. The solution for θ_i being always (21), the condition (25) gives

$$\frac{k_i}{k} C_3 = -\frac{h}{c_v T_0},$$

and the δ in C_3 (negative) can be determined once for all, whatever the value of the Mach number M.

408   CHIA-SHUN YIH

For T_0 and ρ_0 that are not far from the T_i and ρ_i satisfying (23), V is nearly zero, and ignoring the nonlinear terms in (13) and (15), we can get the solutions once and for all, without using the Mach number expansions (26) to (28).

8. Discussion. Since (15) contains V', the procedure of solution by expansion in power series of M^2 reduces the order of the simultaneous differential equations (15) and (13), and this needs some clarification, which follows.

If one considers a flow in the neighborhood of the special solution just given, one can linearize (15) and (13) and obtain from them a linear second-order differential equation. This equation has two independent solutions, one of which becomes infinite at infinite y, and hence must be discarded. The useful one is the one produced by the expansion in power series in M.

We note also that use of the momentum equation between a section far upstream and the surface of the plate gives

$$p_0 + mv_0 + g\rho_i d = p_p + mv_i,$$

where p_p is the pressure at the plate. For steady flows to exist the pressure at the surface of the porous plate must be maintained at the p_p so determined. Otherwise the interface cannot remain stationary, or there will be a moving shock wave in the vapor phase.

It is interesting, but ultimately not very useful, that the two nonlinear differential equations (13) and (15) can be combined to give two first-order nonlinear differential equations that can be solved in sequence. The first equation is of the form

$$[\theta + f_1(V)]\,\frac{d\theta}{dV} = f_2(V)\theta + f_3(V),$$

and the second equation is just (15), which can be solved once θ is determined as a function of V from the above equation. Unfortunately a simple analytical solution is not possible, and in any numerical calculation one will encounter the difficulty of having to start at infinity. Hence the Mach-number expansion is still the best way to solve the problem.

9. Inclined flow of vapor toward a cold plate. If the velocity at infinite y is $(u_0, -v_0)$, u being the velocity in the (horizontal) direction of increasing x, the two velocity components are uncoupled: v is given by the solution given in the foregoing sections, and $u = u_0$ for the vapor. For the liquid

$$u_l = u_{li}\left(1 + \frac{y}{d}\right),$$

where u_{li} is the interfacial value of u_l. This interfacial value is determined by the equation for tangential momentum at the interface, i.e.,

$$\frac{u_l u_{li}}{d} = m(u_0 - u_{li}).$$

These results follow immediately from the equations of motion, which will not be presented in detail.

The streamlines start as inclined straight lines far upstream, become curvilinear as they approach the cold plate, suffer a discontinuity in their slope at the interface, and intersect the plate at right angles.

10. Flows with evaporation. We have discussed flows with condensation. If a porous plate is heated, and liquid approaches it normally or obliquely from below, the treatment is similar. We shall not give the details since all the points have been made in this paper.

We note that at the surface of the porous plate permitting the vapor to flow through, the normal stress must be specified to permit a solution. This normal stress is to be matched to that in the porous medium. The specification of the normal stress amounts to the specification of the velocity gradient, since the pressure is known once the temperature and the density (via the velocity) are specified.

Conical vortices: A class of exact solutions of the Navier–Stokes equations[a]

C.-S. Yih and F. Wu[b]
University of Michigan, Ann Arbor, Michigan 48103

A. K. Garg and S. Leibovich
Sibley School of Mechanical and Aerospace Engineering, Cornell University, Ithaca, New York 14853

(Received 23 February 1982; accepted 8 September 1982)

A two-parameter family of exact axially symmetric solutions of the Navier–Stokes equations for vortices contained within conical boundaries is found. The solutions depend upon the same similarity variable, equivalent to the polar angle ϕ measured from the symmetry axis, as flows previously discussed by Long and by Serrin, but are distinct from the cases they treated. The conical bounding stream surfaces of the present solution can be located at any angle $\phi = \phi_0$, where $0 < \phi_0 < \pi$. The flows in all of these cases, when solutions exist, are finite everywhere except at the cone vertex which is a source of axial momentum, but not of volume. Solutions are of three types, flow may be (a) towards the vertex on the axis and away from the vertex at the conical boundary, (b) towards the vertex both on the axis and at the cone, or (c) away from the vertex on the axis and towards it at the bounding cone. In the first and second case, strong shear layers form on the cone walls for high Reynolds numbers. In case (c), a region of strong axial shear and strong axial vorticity forms near the axis, even for low Reynolds numbers. The qualitative nature of the possible solutions is deduced, using methods of argument due to Serrin, and examples of flows are numerically computed for cone half-angles of $\pi/4$, $\pi/2$ (flows above the plane $z = 0$), and $3\pi/4$. Regions of the parameter space where solutions are proven not to exist are given for the cone half-angles given above, as well as regions where solutions are proven to exist.

I. INTRODUCTION

Known exact solutions of the Navier–Stokes equations representing steady axially symmetric flows with swirl fall into three classes. One class constitutes those solutions for which radial component u and the azimuthal component v of the velocity vector expressed in cylindrical (r,θ,z) coordinates are allowed to depend only upon r (time dependence may also be permitted). This class has been explored by Donaldson and Sullivan[1]; special cases had been discovered earlier by Burgers[2] and by Rott,[3] and has been further considered by Bellamy-Knights.[4,5] A second interesting class, not in similarity form, represents vortices with arbitrary stream surfaces for which the azimuthal velocity $v = \lambda r^{-1}\psi$, and the azimuthal vorticity $\zeta = \lambda v$, where λ is a constant and ψ is the Stokes stream function. The swirl components of these flows, which were discovered by Trkal[6] (cf. Berker[7]) decay like $\exp(-\nu\lambda^2\tau)$, where ν is the kinematic viscosity, and the asymptotic states are axially symmetric irrotational flows. The third class of exact solutions is that considered here, the "conical" vortices.

It is easy to show (see Sec. II) that solutions of the conical form are the only similarity solutions allowing the azimuthal velocity to vary along the axis of symmetry. This

class of flows is the generalization of the Landau–Squire[8–11] round jet to permit an azimuthal component of the velocity. The first work on conical vortices apparently can be traced to Loitsianskii[12] (in a boundary-layer approximation) and, independently, to Long.[13]

Many different flows are embraced by this conical form depending upon the conditions imposed on the solution of the similarity equations. Long[13] imposed the condition that the circulation, Γ, about the axis tend to a constant as $r \to \infty$, where r is the cylindrical radius. In addition, but without explicitly stating so, he imposed the condition that the flow be symmetric in z. This can be interpreted either as a symmetric flow with a sheet of sources of variable strength on the plane $z = 0$, or as a continuous flow with a porous wall at $z = 0$ with a prescribed variable normal velocity. The flow in either event is smooth in the upper half plane, and numerical solutions to a boundary-layer approximation of the governing equations have been given by Long[14] and by Burggraf and Foster.[15] These solutions are very interesting and represent vortices concentrated near the symmetry axis that closely resemble vortices observed in laboratory experiments.

Serrin[16] has given a complete mathematical treatment of a subclass of conical vortices representing flow above the plane $z = 0$. A special case of this subclass had earlier been discussed by Goldstik.[17] The no-slip condition was imposed on the plane, and $\Gamma \to$ const as $r \to 0$. Thus, this subclass represents the flow of a line vortex above a plane and a singularity is accepted on the axis $r = 0$.

In this paper, we consider the subclass of flows which are contained within a cone with vertex at the origin and axis

[a] This paper is an amalgamation of two independent efforts. The first, by Yih and Wu, dealt with flows above a plane surface, and was completed some months before the second, by Garg and Leibovich, which dealt with the same problem, but in the context of general conical boundaries. The methods used in the two papers were slightly different, but mathematically equivalent.

[b] Permanent address: Chinese Univ. of Science and Technology, Hofei, People's Republic of China.

© 1982 American Institute of Physics   2147

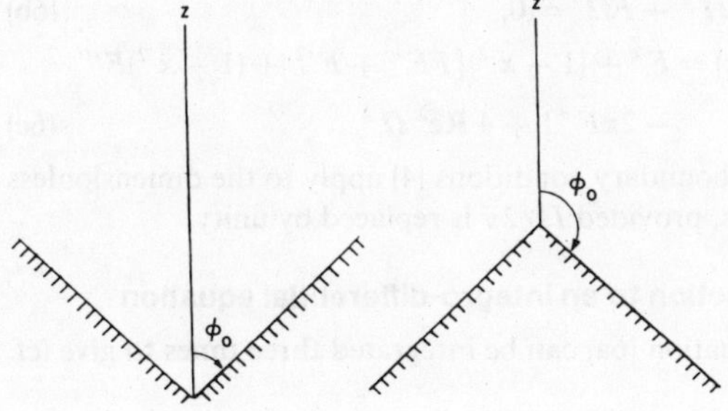

FIG. 1. Flow region.

the positive z axis, as shown in Fig. 1; the cone half-angle may exceed $\pi/2$. We require that solutions yield finite velocity except at the vertex of the cone, where a singularity is inevitable. In addition, we require the conical boundaries of the flow to be stream surfaces. The solutions are therefore distinct from those previously found. As in the various cases of the nonswirling exact axisymmetric solutions,[8–11] it is not possible to satisfy the no-slip condition on stream surfaces. This difficulty is discussed in the final section of the paper.

The solutions explored constitute a two parameter family, the parameters being a Reynolds number (defined as $\Gamma/4\pi\nu$, where Γ is a characteristic circulation about the symmetry axis), and a number representing the net momentum flux issuing from the vertex of the cone. The qualitative behavior and existence of this two-parameter family of solutions is explored using methods developed by Serrin,[16] Weyl,[18] together with modifications which appear to be necessary for this problem. Regions of the parameter space in which solutions exist, as well as regions in which solutions fail to exist, are delineated.

We then construct some examples of flows in this class by numerical integration of the governing equations, again following the lead of Serrin and of Weyl. Boundary layers can develop either on the axis or on the bounding conical stream surface, depending upon the choice of parameters. An interesting feature is that strong shear develops at low Reynolds number for some values of the second controlling parameter. Our numerical examples include a number of flows existing above the plane $z = 0$, and one each for flows within cones with half angles of $\pi/4$ and $3\pi/4$, respectively.

II. CONICAL SIMILARITY

In this section, we give a brief demonstration that conical vortices are, in fact, the only similarity form of the axially symmetric Navier–Stokes equations that yield both finite velocities at the axis and at arbitrarily great distances along the axis and perpendicular to it.

The steady axially symmetric Navier–Stokes equations in cylindrical coordinates (r,θ,z), with velocity components (u,v,w), may be written in the form

$$uK_r + wK_z = \nu D^2 K,$$

$$u\zeta_r + w\zeta_z - 2ur^{-1}\zeta - 2r^{-2}KK_z = \nu D^2\zeta,$$

$$\zeta = -D^2\psi, \quad w = r^{-1}\psi_r,$$

$$u = -r^{-1}\psi_z, \quad v = r^{-1}K,$$

$$D^2(\ ) = (\ )_{rr} - r^{-1}(\ )_r + (\ )_{zz}.$$

Here $2\pi K(r,z)$ is the circulation about the z axis, ζ is the azimuthal vorticity, and ν is the kinematic viscosity.

This set is invariant under the change of scale

$$r = ar', \quad z = bz', \quad \psi(r,z) = c\psi'(r',z'),$$

$$K(r,z) = \gamma K'(r',z')$$

in three cases

(I) $a = b, \quad \gamma = 1,$

(II) $\gamma_{zz} = K_{zz} = 0,$

(III) $r\dfrac{\partial}{\partial r}\dfrac{1}{r}\dfrac{\partial \psi}{\partial r} = r\dfrac{\partial}{\partial r}\dfrac{1}{r}\dfrac{\partial K}{\partial r} = 0.$

Case (II) admits solutions of the form

$$w = zw_1(r) + w_2(r), \quad u = u_1(r), \quad v = v_1(r),$$

which is a generalized form of the similarity assumed by Burgers,[2] Rott,[3] and Donaldson and Sullivan.[1] Case (II) can be further reduced to the problems considered by these authors, since the problem for $w_2(r)$ can be solved separately once $u_1(r)$, $v_1(r)$ and $w_1(r)$ are known.

In case (III), all solutions are of the form

$$w = w(z), \quad u = rw'(z) + u_2(z)/r, \quad v = r\omega(z) + v_2(z)/r.$$

With $u_2 = v_2 = 0$, the classical Kármán[19] or Bödewadt[20] forms for flow above a rigidly rotating plane or rigidly rotating flow above a stationary plane are obtained.

Case (I) leads to solutions of the form

$$K(r,z) = K(\eta), \quad \psi = zG(\eta), \quad \eta = r/z,$$

or

$$v = r^{-1}K(\eta), \quad u = -r^{-1}G(\eta), \quad w = z^{-1}G'(\eta).$$

The similarity variable is $\eta = r/z = \tan\phi$, where ϕ is the polar angle in spherical coordinates. There is, in addition, an unsteady version with this spatial symmetry. If time dependence is allowed, the functions K, and G depend upon $z^2/\nu\tau$ as well as η.

Case (I) admits solutions with the velocity field finite everywhere except for the origin $r = z = 0$. In cases (II) and (III), the velocities can be finite at the axis, but approach infinity as either r or z approaches infinity.

III. FORMULATION OF THE PROBLEM FOR CONICAL FLOWS

The equations of motion for conical similarity assume a more compact form when expressed in spherical coordinates, since the similarity variable is then simply the polar angle.

Thus, we adopt spherical coordinates (R,ϕ,θ), where R is the distance from the origin, ϕ is the polar angle, measured from the positive z axis, and θ is the azimuthal angle. Serrin[16] has presented the appropriate equations for the problem. Let the velocity vector be (v_R, v_ϕ, v_θ), then the similar solutions are in the form

$$v_R = \frac{\widetilde{F}'(x)}{R}, \quad v_\phi = \frac{\widetilde{F}(x)}{r}, \quad v_\theta = \frac{\widetilde{\Omega}(x)}{r}, \quad (1)$$

where

$$r = R \sin \phi$$

is the cylindrical radius, and

$$x = \cos \phi. \tag{2}$$

Continuity is satisfied by the form (1). In terms of x, $\widetilde{F}$ and $\widetilde{\Omega}$ must satisfy the pair of ordinary differential equations

$$\nu(1-x^2)\widetilde{F}^{iv} - 4\nu x\widetilde{F}''' + \widetilde{F}\widetilde{F}''' + 3\widetilde{F}'\widetilde{F}''$$
$$= -2\widetilde{\Omega}\widetilde{\Omega}'/(1-x^2), \tag{3a}$$
$$\nu(1-x^2)\widetilde{\Omega}'' + \widetilde{F}\widetilde{\Omega}' = 0. \tag{3b}$$

The pressure can be recovered, knowing $\widetilde{F}$ and $\widetilde{\Omega}$, from the relation

$$\frac{p}{\rho} = \frac{\widetilde{\Pi}(x)}{r^2} + \frac{p_\infty}{\rho}, \tag{3c}$$
$$-2\widetilde{\Pi} = \widetilde{F}^2 + \widetilde{\Omega}^2 + \{\widetilde{F}\widetilde{F}'' + \widetilde{F}'^2 + \nu[(1-x^2)\widetilde{F}'''$$
$$-2x\widetilde{F}'']\}(1-x^2), \tag{3d}$$

where p_∞ is the pressure at $r = \infty$.

The problem is therefore reduced to finding $\widetilde{F}$ and $\widetilde{\Omega}$ from (3) and appropriate boundary conditions.

A. Boundary conditions

Let the fluid be confined within an impenetrable cone with vertex at the origin and with the positive z axis $(x \equiv 1)$ as axis. The cone semi-angle may be larger than $\pi/2$, so the flow region may include the entire space, excluding the negative z axis, if desired. Let $x = x_0 \, (-1 < x_0 < 1)$ be the cone boundary. Then the boundary conditions are taken to be

$$2\pi\widetilde{\Omega}(x_0) = \Gamma, \tag{4a}$$
$$\widetilde{F}(x_0) = 0, \tag{4b}$$
$$\widetilde{F}(1) = 0, \tag{4c}$$
$$\lim_{x \to 1}(1-x^2)\widetilde{F}''(x) = 0, \tag{4d}$$
$$\widetilde{\Omega}(1) = 0. \tag{4e}$$

Condition (4a) establishes the existence and level of the swirl, and, without loss of generality, we take $\Gamma > 0$. Condition (4b) states that the normal velocity on the cone $x = x_0$ vanishes. Condition (4c) ensures that v_ϕ be finite and that the axis is not a source of mass. Condition (4d) ensures finite acceleration on any finite length needle of fluid on the z axis due to the viscous forces, and assures that the radial velocity [i.e., $F'(1)$] is finite as well. The limiting condition must be imposed due to the singularity at $x = 1$ associated with the coordinate system. Condition (4e) requires the azimuthal velocity to be finite at the axis.

If we now let

$$2\pi\widetilde{\Omega}(x) = \Gamma\Omega(x), \quad \widetilde{F} = \nu F, \quad \widetilde{\Pi} = \nu^2\Pi, \tag{5}$$

and define the Reynolds number

$$\mathrm{Re} = \Gamma/4\pi\nu,$$

then the system assumes the dimensionless form

$$(1-x^2)F^{iv} - 4xF''' + FF''' + 3F'F''$$
$$= 4\,\mathrm{Re}^2(-2\Omega\Omega'/1-x^2), \tag{6a}$$

$$(1-x^2)\Omega'' + F\Omega' = 0, \tag{6b}$$
$$-2\Pi(x) = F^2 + (1-x^2)\{FF'' + F'^2 + (1-x^2)F'''$$
$$-2xF''\} + 4\,\mathrm{Re}^2\,\Omega^2, \tag{6c}$$

and the boundary conditions (4) apply to the dimensionless variables, provided $\Gamma/2\pi$ is replaced by unity.

B. Reduction to an integro-differential equation

Equation (6a) can be integrated three times to give (cf. Ref. 16)

$$2(1-x^2)F' + 4xF + F^2 = 4\,\mathrm{Re}^2\,G(x), \tag{7a}$$

where

$$G(x) = -\int_{x_0}^x dt_2 \int_{x_0}^{t_2} dt_1 \int_{x_0}^{t_1} \frac{4\Omega\Omega'\,dt}{1-t^2} + Ax^2 + Bx + C. \tag{7b}$$

The boundary conditions (4c) and (4d) show that $G(1) = G'(1) = 0$. Application of these two conditions allows us to eliminate B and C in favor of A. Upon integration by parts and rearrangement, we can place G in the form

$$G(x) = 2(1-x)^2 \int_{x_0}^x \frac{t\Omega^2\,dt}{(1-t^2)^2}$$
$$+ 2x\int_x^1 \frac{\Omega^2\,dt}{(1+t)^2} + T(1-x)^2, \tag{8}$$

where

$$T = A + 1/(1-x_0^2),$$

and we adopt T as the basic parameter instead of A.

We will need to know the properties of $G(x)$; for later reference, we note that the first and second derivatives of G are

$$G'(x) = -4(1-x)\int_{x_0}^x \frac{t\Omega^2\,dt}{(1-t^2)^2}$$
$$+ 2\int_x^1 \frac{\Omega^2\,dt}{(1+t)^2} - 2T(1-x), \tag{9}$$

and

$$G''(x) = 4\int_{x_0}^x \frac{t\Omega^2\,dt}{(1-t^2)^2} - \frac{2\Omega^2(x)}{1-x^2} + 2T. \tag{10}$$

Thus, $G'(1) = 0$, and $G''(1)$ is finite provided $\Omega(x) = O(1-x)$ as $x \to 1$.

Using (9) and (10), one can reduce the pressure function $\Pi(x)$ in (6c) to the simpler form (cf. Ref. 16)

$$-2\Pi(x) = 4xF + 2F^2 - 4\,\mathrm{Re}^2\,xG'(x). \tag{11}$$

A similar formula allowed Serrin[16] to relate the parameter analogous to T to the pressure level on the wall. In our case, (11) evaluated at the cone $x = x_0$ gives

$$\Pi(x_0) = 4\,\mathrm{Re}^2\,x_0\left(\int_{x_0}^1 \frac{\Omega^2\,dt}{(1+t)^2} - T(1-x_0)\right). \tag{12}$$

On the axis, (11) reveals that

$$\Pi(1) = 0$$

so that the pressure on the axis equals p_∞. Thus T can be related to the wall pressure through (12) for $x_0 \neq 0$, but the connection is less direct than in Serrin's case.

The similarity relations (1) coupled with the boundary conditions (4b,4c) imply that the singular point at the origin is not a source of volume, but it is a source of axial momentum. The axial momentum flux issuing from the origin is

$$M = 2\pi\rho\nu^2 \int_{x_0}^{1} x F'^2 \, dx. \tag{13}$$

The nondimensionalized momentum flux $M/\rho\nu^2$ is a function of the parameters Re and T.

In the present case the integrand is everywhere finite. In Serrin's case, the integrand is infinite at $x = 1$, but it, too, is integrable.

We conclude this section by introducing the change of variable[16]

$$F(x) = 2(1 - x^2)f(x), \tag{14}$$

which puts (6a) and (6b) in the final form to be considered

$$f' + f^2 = \text{Re}^2[G(x)/(1 - x^2)^2], \tag{15}$$

$$\Omega'' + 2f\Omega' = 0, \tag{16}$$

subject to the conditions

$$\Omega(x_0) = 1, \quad f(x_0) = 0, \quad \Omega(1) = 0. \tag{17}$$

IV. QUALITATIVE BEHAVIOR OF SOLUTIONS

Equation (16) can be integrated, assuming f to exist and treating it as known; the result is

$$\Omega'(x) = \Omega'(x_0) \exp\left(- 2\int_{x_0}^{x} f\, dx\right). \tag{18}$$

Thus $\Omega'(x)$ is one-signed in $(x_0, 1)$, and $\Omega(x)$ is monotonic. Since $\Omega(1) = 0$ and $\Omega(x_0) = 1$, $\Omega'(x_0) < 0$.

Next, consider the behavior of the solution near $x = 1$. Since the argument above shows that

$$0 \leqslant \Omega(x) \leqslant 1,$$

we can derive upper and lower bounds on $G(x)$ by substituting either $\Omega = 0$ or $\Omega = 1$ in the integrals in (8). The choice of 0 or 1 depends upon which bound is being sought and, in considering that bound, whether the contribution of the terms involving integrals is positive or negative. For example, when calculating an upper bound for $x_0 < 0$, we set $\Omega = 0$ in both integrals of (8) when $x < 0$ and $\Omega = 1$ when $x > 0$. In this way, after minor manipulations, we arrive at the bounds

$$(1 - x)^2\left(T + \frac{xI(-x)I(-x_0)}{1 - x} - \frac{x_0^2 I(-x_0)}{1 - x_0^2}\right)$$
$$\leqslant G(x) \leqslant (1 - x)^2\left(T + \frac{xI(x)}{1 - x} - \frac{x_0^2 I(x_0)}{1 - x_0^2}\right), \tag{19}$$

where the function $I(x)$ is the unit function, $I(x) = 1$ for $x > 0$, $I(x) = 0$, $x \leqslant 0$.

Under similar conditions on G, Serrin[16] has proved that

$$f = O\{\ln[1/(1 - x)]\} \quad \text{as } x \to 1, \tag{20}$$

hence, from (18) $\Omega'(1)$ is finite, and his proof follows without change if G satisfies (19). Therefore

$$\Omega(x) = O(1 - x)$$

near $x = 1$, and this in turn shows that the functions

$$\int_{x_0}^{x} \frac{t\Omega^2}{(1 - t^2)^2} \, dt, \quad \frac{\Omega^2(x)}{(1 - x^2)}$$

are finite as $x \to 1$. Consequently

$$G(1) = G'(1) = 0, \quad G''(1) = 4\int_{x_0}^{1} \frac{t\Omega^2 \, dt}{(1 - t^2)^2} + 2T < \infty, \tag{21}$$

and we can consequently replace (19) by the stronger statement: the function

$$H(x) = \text{Re}^2[G(x)/(1 - x^2)^2] \tag{22}$$

is finite for all $x_0 < x < 1$. Furthermore, from (8) and (22), we observe that

$$\frac{d}{dx}[(1 + x)^2 H(x)] = 2\,\text{Re}^2\,\frac{(1 + x)}{(1 - x)^3}\int_{x}^{1}\frac{\Omega^2 \, dt}{(1 + t)^2}. \tag{23}$$

Since $\Omega = O(1 - x)$ near $x = 1$, the integral in (23) is finite for all x in the interval $I: \{x_0 \leqslant x \leqslant 1, x_0 > -1\}$. Thus,

$$\frac{d}{dx}[(1 + x)^2 H(x)] > 0 \tag{24}$$

in I. We infer from this that if $H(x)$ is positive at any point $x = x_1$, then it remains positive for all $x > x_1$. In particular, if $H(x_0) > 0$, then $H > 0$ throughout the interval I. If $H(x_0) < 0$, then $H(x)$ can change sign at most once. In this case, either

$H(x) < 0$ in I, or

$H(x) < 0$ for $x_0 \leqslant x < x_1 < 1$, and

$H(x) \geqslant 0$ for $x_1 \leqslant x \leqslant 1$.

Following Serrin[16] we write (15) in the easily verified form

$$f(x) = \int_{x_0}^{x} H(t)\exp\left(- \int_{t}^{x} f(u)du\right)dt, \tag{25}$$

where the boundary condition $f(x_0) = 0$ has been applied. In view of the properties of $H(x)$, (25) shows that $f > 0$ in I if $H(x_0) > 0$. Furthermore, if $H(x) < 0$ for $x_0 \leqslant x < x_1 \leqslant 1$, then either (i) $f < 0$, $f' < 0$ for all x in I, or (ii) $f \leqslant 0$ for $x_0 \leqslant x < x_2 \leqslant 1$, where $x_2 > x_1$, and $f > 0$ for $x_2 < x \leqslant 1$. Thus, if $H(x_0) < 0$, either f is negative everywhere in the cone, or it is negative in a sector near $x = x_0$, and positive in the remainder of the cone: it may pass through zero no more than once. We may immediately determine this behavior in some instances. The lower bound of (19) is non-negative when

$$T \geqslant \max[0, -x_0/(1 - x_0^2)], \tag{26}$$

and therefore $H(x) > 0$, $f(x) \geqslant 0$ for these values of T. Furthermore, $H(x_0) < 0$, implying $f(x) < 0$ in at least a sector near $x = x_0$, when

$$T < \min[0, -x_0/(1 - x_0^2)]. \tag{27}$$

Thus, for the case of a plane surface, $T = 0$ is the critical parameter dividing fully positive solutions from mixed or fully negative solutions. For other values of x_0, the specification of T does not completely resolve this issue *a priori*, since the critical value of T dividing fully positive solutions from mixed or negative ones lies in a gap between (26) and (27). In these cases we can only say, *a priori*, that there is a critical value of T, denoted T^*, where

$$\max[0, -x_0/(1 - x_0^2)] < T^* < \min(0, -x_0/(1 - x_0^2)], \tag{28}$$

such that fully positive solutions obtain when $T > T^*$ and mixed or fully negative solutions obtain for $T < T^*$.

A solution to the fluid-dynamical problem exists only if $(1 - x^2)f(x)$ is finite. Thus f must be finite for all $x_0 < x < 1$, but singularity in f with $f = O(1/1 - x)$ is permissible as $x \to 1$. Indeed, we have already cited Serrin's result (20) which shows that f, if it exists, can be no more singular than the logarithm. These arguments assume the existence of a solution, however, and it will be shown in the next section that there are no solutions to our problem for certain combinations of parameters, just as in Ref. 16. We may go one step further, if solutions exist: then we have already argued that f is integrable, thus, in view of (22), (23) shows that f is finite everywhere in the cone.

We may now summarize and sketch the general features of the flows. We have found that, if solutions exist:

(1) f is finite, and $\Omega' < 0$;

(2) (a) There is a number T^*, partially determined by (28) such that f is non-negative and (from (18)) $\Omega'' \geqslant 0$, for $T \geqslant T^*$, and

(3) (b) If $T < T^*$, then f will be negative and $\Omega'' < 0$ in an interval $x_0 < x < x_1 \leqslant 1$, and $f \geqslant 0$ and $\Omega'' \geqslant 0$ in $x_1 \leqslant x \leqslant 1$.

Since

$$Rv_R = 2[H(x)(1 - x^2) - (1 - x^2)f^2 - 2xf], \quad (29)$$

at the axis $x = 1$,

$$Rv_R = -4f(1), \quad (30)$$

and at $x = x_0$, $f(x_0) = 0$, and

$$Rv_R = 2H(x_0)(1 - x_0^2). \quad (31)$$

Case (a) above therefore has $v_R < 0$ on the axis, and $v_R > 0$ at the conical boundary [since this case corresponds to $H(x_0) \geqslant 0$]. In case (b), either $f \leqslant 0$ throughout, or $f < 0$ near $x = x_0$ and $f > 0$ near $x = 1$. In either event, $G(x)_0 < 0$, so $v_R < 0$ in the vicinity of the conical surface, and v_R may be either positive or negative near the axis. The possibilities are sketched in Fig. 2. Note that the structure of the flow can have one or two cells but no more than two cells is possible.

V. ACCESSIBLE AND NONACCESSIBLE REGIONS OF THE PARAMETER SPACE

In the last section, the structure of the flow was discussed under the assumption that solutions exist. Here we show that in this, as in Ref. 16 there are regions of the parameter space in which solutions fail to exist. Conversely, regions of the parameter space can be exhibited where the existence of solutions is expected.

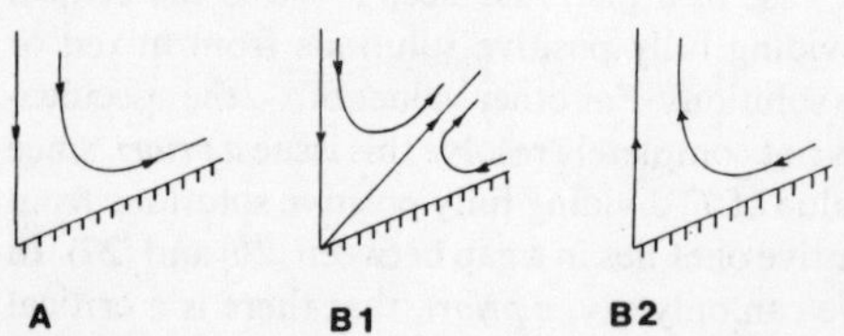

FIG. 2. Streamlines in the meridional plane illustrating the various possibilities for conical vortices.

We have used two equivalent methods to deal with these questions. Garg and Leibovich transformed Eq. (15) to its associated second-order linear equation and used Sturm's comparison theorems. Yih and Wu dealt directly with (15) and we describe their method.

Consider (15), written in the form

$$f' + f^2 = H(x), \quad (32)$$

for two functions $H_1(x)$ and $H_2(x)$, where the corresponding solutions $f_1(x)$ and $f_2(x)$ satisfy the initial condition

$$f_1(x_0) = f_2(x_0) = 0. \quad (33)$$

Then if $H_2(x) \leqslant H_1(x)$, a comparison theorem for equations of the form (32) due to Serrin[16] shows that

$$f_2(x) \leqslant f_1(x). \quad (34)$$

Let us assume that solutions exist, that is, that $f(x)$ is finite in I, and try to determine conditions under which the assumption is tenable or not. Assuming solutions exist, it follows from Sec. IV that $H(x)$ is finite.

A. An upper bound for the solution

Let $H(x)$ be positive in at least a part of the interval I, and suppose $f(x)$ does not approach $-\infty$ in I. Then the integral in (18) exists for all x in I, and $\Omega'(x_0)$ is neither zero nor infinite. That makes $\Omega'(1)$ finite and therefore $H(x)$ finite in I. It then must have a maximum in I. Let it be denoted by $H_{\max}$. Then

$$f < (H_{\max})^{1/2}, \quad (35)$$

and thus f has an upper bound.

For a proof of (35), let f_1 satisfy

$$f_1' + f_1^2 = H_{\max}. \quad (36)$$

The solution of this equation is

$$f_1 = (H_{\max})^{1/2} \tanh(H_{\max})^{1/2} x. \quad (37)$$

Now, since $H(x) \leqslant H_{\max}$, by virtue of the fundamental comparison theorem, $f \leqslant f_1$, and this, taken together with (37), proves (35).

Thus, the nonexistence or existence of the solution of (32) hinges on whether f does or does not become negatively infinite in I.

B. Region of existence of a solution

First, we recall that if $T \geqslant T^*$, then $H(x)$ is nonnegative throughout I. Thus, by virtue of the remarks made in Sec. VA, the existence of fully positive solutions is not contradicted, and we expect to be able to construct solutions for all $T \geqslant T^*$.

For $T < T^*$, f will be negative in the neighborhood of $x = x_0$, and if $|T - T^*|$ is sufficiently large for a given value of Re^2, f may become infinitely negative in I. We shall try to determine a curve in the $\beta - T$ space ($\beta = 0.5\,\pi/Re$) above which solutions exist.

For this purpose, we consider the lower bounds found in (19) for $G(x)$. This will give us a $G_1(x)$, and hence $H_1(x)$, smaller than their actual values.

From (19), we know that

$$H(x) \geqslant \frac{\text{Re}^2}{(1+x)^2} \left(T + \frac{xI(-x)I(-x_0)}{1-x} - \frac{x_0^2 I(-x_0)}{(1-x_0^2)} \right).$$

The large parentheses have a minimum value at $x = x_0$ when $x_0 < 0$, so

$$H(x) \geqslant \frac{\text{Re}^2}{(1+x)^2} \left(T + \frac{x_0 I(-x_0)}{1-x_0^2} \right). \tag{38}$$

We wish to simplify the calculation by considering a constant lower bound for $H(x)$, and, since we are interested only in those cases where the lower bound is negative, we may weaken (38) by taking

$$H(x) \geqslant H_1 \equiv \frac{\text{Re}^2}{(1+x_0)^2} \left(T + \frac{x_0 I(-x_0)}{1-x_0^2} \right) \tag{39}$$

and assuming that $H_1 < 0$. We now consider

$$f_1' + f_1^2 = H_1, \quad f_1(x_0) = 0, \tag{40}$$

and by the comparison theorem, $f > f_1$. Therefore if a finite solution to (40) exists, a solution to (15) exists. But the solution of (40) for negative H_1 is

$$f_1 = -(-H_1)^{1/2} \tan[(-H_1)^{1/2}(x-x_0)]. \tag{41}$$

This is finite in I if

$$(-H_1)^{1/2} < \pi/2(1-x_0), \tag{42}$$

or

$$\left(T + \frac{x_0 I(-x_0)}{1-x_0^2} \right)(1+x_0)^{-2} \geqslant -\frac{\beta^2}{(1-x_0)^2}. \tag{43}$$

C. Region of nonexistence of solutions

To show the nonexistence of solutions, we consider upper bounds for $H(x)$ as obtained from (19):

$$H(x) < H_2(x) = \frac{\text{Re}^2}{(1+x)^2} \left(T + \frac{xI(x)}{1-x} - \frac{x_0^2 I(x_0)}{1-x_0^2} \right). \tag{44}$$

Again, we only are concerned with values of $T < T^*$, since otherwise $H(x) > 0$ and existence of solutions is ensured.

Let $f_2(x)$ satisfy

$$f_2' + f_2^2 = H_2(x), \quad f_2(x_0) = 0. \tag{45}$$

We reiterate that solutions to (15) can fail to exist only if $f \to -\infty$ in I. Clearly $H_2(x) \to \infty$ as $x \to 1$, but our strategy is to select a value of $x = x_1 < 1$, and show that there are values of T and Re for which $f_2 \to -\infty$ in the interval $I_1(x_0 \leqslant x \leqslant x_1)$. By our comparison theorem $f_2 > f$ so $f \to -\infty$ in I as well, and nonexistence of solutions is established. Thus, let x_1 be chosen so that

$$H_2(x_1) = -A^2 < 0. \tag{46}$$

Then

$$f_2 = A \tan A (x - x_0),$$

and $f_2 \to -\infty$ in I, if

$$A(x_1 - x_0) \geqslant \pi/2, \tag{47}$$

or

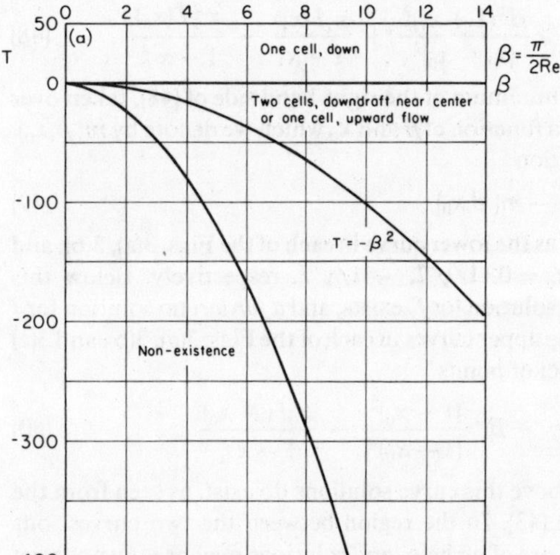

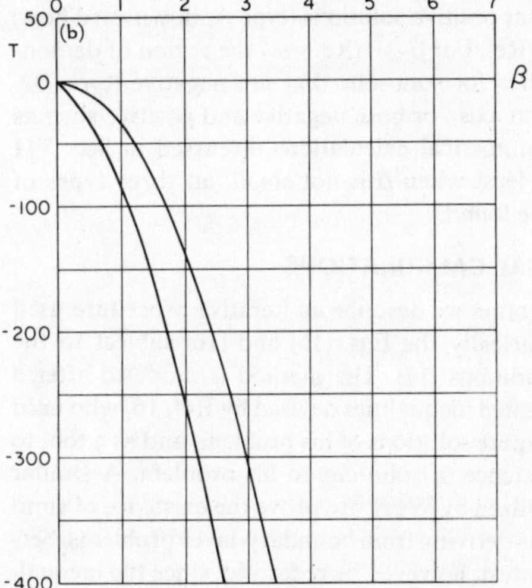

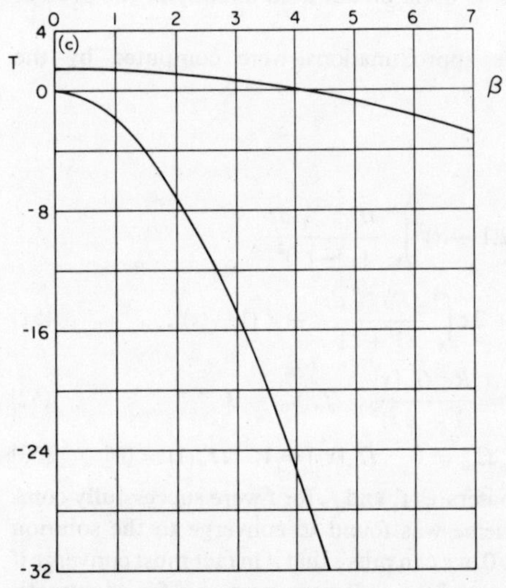

FIG. 3. Accessible and nonaccessible regions in the parameter space (T, Re); (a) when $\phi_0 = \pi/2 (x_0 = 0)$, (b) when $\phi_0 = \pi/4 (x_0 = 1/\sqrt{2})$, (c) when $\phi_0 = 3\pi/4 (x_0 = -1/\sqrt{2})$.

$$-T \geqslant \frac{\beta^2(1+x_1)^2}{(x_1-x_0)^2} + \frac{x_1 I(x_1)}{1-x_1} - \frac{x_0^2 I(x_0)}{1-x_0^2}. \tag{48}$$

The minimum of the right-hand side of (48), taken over x_1 in I, is a function of β and x_0 which we denote by $m(\beta,x_0)$. The equation

$$T = -m(\beta,x_0) \tag{49}$$

is plotted as the lower curve in each of the Figs. 3(a), 3(b), and 3(c) for $x_0 = 0$, $1/\sqrt{2}$, $-1/\sqrt{2}$, respectively. Below this curve, no solution for f_2 exists, and *a fortiori* no solution for f exists. The upper curves in each of the Figs. 3(a), 3(b), and 3(c) are the loci of points

$$T^* = -\beta^2 \frac{(1+x_0)^2}{(1-x_0)^2} - \frac{x_0 I(-x_0)}{1-x_0^2}. \tag{50}$$

On and above this curve solutions do exist, as seen from the condition (43). In the region between the two curves, our estimates are of no help, and solutions may or may not exist there.

Notice that positive solutions (type A, downward flow) exist for all β (Re). For $\beta \to 0$ (Re $\to \infty$) the region of demonstrated existence for solutions that are negative (type B2, upward flow on axis), or both negative and positive shrinks to zero. The numerical calculations discussed in Sec. VII show that, at least when β is not small, all three types of solution can be found.

VI. NUMERICAL CALCULATIONS

In this section we describe an iterative procedure used to solve numerically the Eqs. (15) and (16) subject to the boundary conditions (17). The method is modeled after a sequence of nested inequalities devised by Ref. 16, who used it both to compute solutions of his problem, and as a tool to prove the existence of solutions to his problem. A similar device was utilized by Weyl[18] to prove the existence of similarity solutions deriving from boundary-layer problems. Serrin's method must, however, be rederived, since the inequalities that he relies upon do not hold directly in the present problem.

Successive approximations were computed by the scheme

$$\Omega_0 \equiv 1,$$

and for $n \geqslant 1$,

$$G_n(x) = 2(1-x)^2 \int_{x_0}^{x} \frac{t\Omega_{n-1}^2 \, dt}{(1-t^2)^2}$$

$$+ 2x \int_{x}^{1} \frac{\Omega_{n-1}^2 \, dt}{(1+t)^2} + T(1-x)^2, \tag{51}$$

$$f_n' + f_n^2 = \frac{Re^2 G_n(x)}{(1-x^2)^2}, \quad f_n(x_0) = 0 \tag{52}$$

$$\Omega_n'' + 2f_n\Omega_n' = 0, \quad \Omega_n(x_0) = 1, \quad \Omega_n(1) = 0. \tag{53}$$

If the first two iterates f_1 and f_2 for f were successfully computed, the scheme was found to converge to the solution $(\bar{f},\bar{\Omega})$. For $x_0 \geqslant 0$, we can prove that it in fact must converge if the solution exists; for $x_0 < 0$, convergence is found numerically in some cases, but our method of proof does not hold.

First we define

$$\overline{G}(x) = 2(1-x)^2 \int_{x_0}^{x} \frac{t\overline{\Omega}^2 \, dt}{(1-t^2)^2}$$

$$+ 2x \int_{x}^{1} \frac{\overline{\Omega}^2 \, dt}{(1+t)^2} + T(1-x)^2,$$

and observe that since $\Omega_0 \geqslant \overline{\Omega}$,

$$G_1 > \overline{G},$$

and it follows from our fundamental comparison theorem that $f_1 \geqslant \bar{f}$.

The next step is to show that $\Omega_1 \leqslant \overline{\Omega}$. We have the equations

$$\Omega_1'' + 2f_1\Omega_1' = 0,$$

and

$$\overline{\Omega}'' + 2\bar{f}\,\overline{\Omega}' = 0,$$

with the corresponding boundary conditions,

$$\Omega_1(x_0) = 1, \quad \Omega_1(1) = 0,$$

and

$$\overline{\Omega}(x_0) = 1, \quad \overline{\Omega}(1) = 0.$$

Using the fact that both Ω_1' and $\overline{\Omega}'$ are negative we see that $h = \overline{\Omega} - \Omega_1$ must satisfy

$$h'' + 2\bar{f}h' \leqslant 0, \tag{54}$$

with the boundary conditions $h(x_0) = 0$ and $h(1) = 0$. Equation (54) can be written as

$$\left[h' \exp\left(\int_{x_0}^{x} 2\bar{f} \, dx \right) \right]' < 0. \tag{55}$$

Now suppose that $h(x)$ takes on negative values. Then it has a negative minimum at some point $x_m < 1$ where $h'(x_m) = 0$ and $h(x_m) < 0$. Integrating (55) from x_m to $x > x_m$ we obtain $h'(x) \leqslant 0$, which implies that $h(x) < h(x_m)$. This contradicts the boundary condition at $x = 1$ thus proving that $\overline{\Omega} > \Omega_1$.

Proceeding in the above manner we are led to the nested sequences $\{f_n\}$, $\{\Omega_n\}$ given by

$$f_1 \geqslant f_3 \geqslant \cdots \geqslant \bar{f} \geqslant \cdots \geqslant f_4 \geqslant f_2,$$

$$\Omega_0 \geqslant \Omega_2 \geqslant \cdots \geqslant \overline{\Omega} \geqslant \cdots \geqslant \Omega_3 \geqslant \Omega_1.$$

Thus, convergence is assured if a solution corresponding to the chosen values of the parameters Re and T exists and both f_1 and f_2 can be determined.

For some values of the parameters Re and T outside the nonaccessible region discussed in the preceding section, it was found that both f_1 and f_2 could not be computed. It may not, however, be concluded that the failure of the scheme necessarily implies nonexistence of a solution.

Adams predictor–corrector method was used to solve (52) while (53) was integrated by the finite-difference method. Simpson's rule was used for the integrations required to compute $G_n(x)$. Interpolations, wherever necessary, were done by cubic splines. Typically less than 20 iterations were necessary for obtaining the results presented in the next section.

VII. NUMERICAL RESULTS AND DISCUSSION

The method of successive approximations of the previous section was used to generate solutions for three values

TABLE I. The eight examples for which numerical solutions have been obtained.

Case No.	1	2	3	4	5	6	7	8
Re	2	3	100	3	$\sqrt{2}$	3	20	0.5
T	1	1	0	-0.57	-2.2	-0.15	0.1	0.5
x_0	0	0	0	0	0	0	$1/\sqrt{2}$	$-1/\sqrt{2}$

of x_0 corresponding, respectively, to flow over a flat surface, flow within a cone of semi-vertical angle $\pi/4$ and flow over a cone of semi-vertical angle $3\pi/4$. In the case of flow over a flat surface, the values of the parameters Re and T were selected such that all three possible flow patterns (A), (B1) and (B2) (cf. Fig. 2) were obtained.

We are especially interested in cases where $\widetilde{\Omega}$ is nearly constant (unity) except in a small region near the axis ($x = 1$) where it rapidly decreases to zero. When this condition exists, $|\widetilde{\Omega}'|$ and hence the axial vorticity component, is large near $x = 1$, we say that the flow exhibits boundary layer

behavior.

We discuss solutions for the eight cases of Table I. The functions $\widetilde{F}, \widetilde{F}'$, and $\widetilde{\Omega}$ are plotted (normalized by taking $\Gamma/2\pi$ equal to unity) in Figs. 4(a), 5(a), ... 11(a), and the corresponding stream surfaces are given in Figs. 4(b), 5(b), ... 11(b).

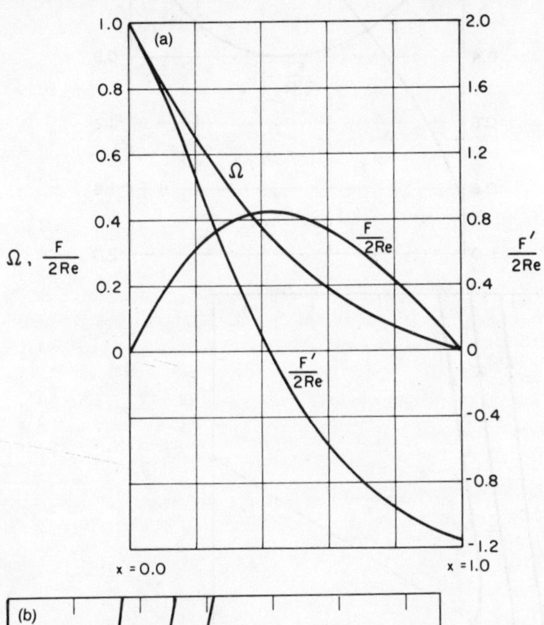

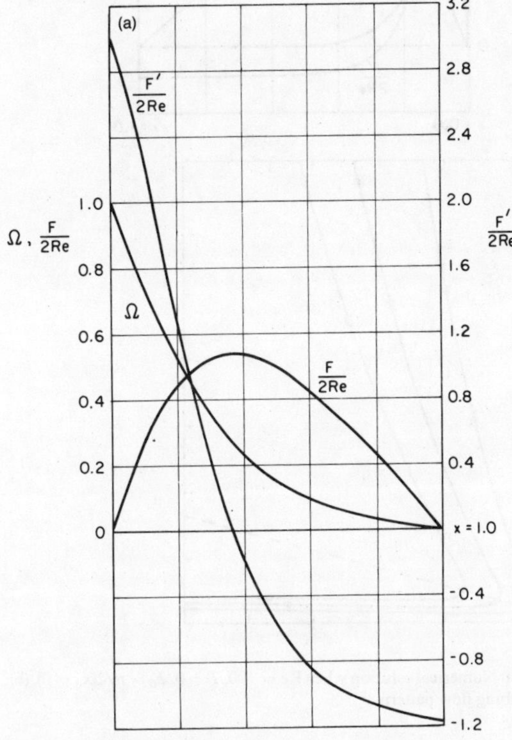

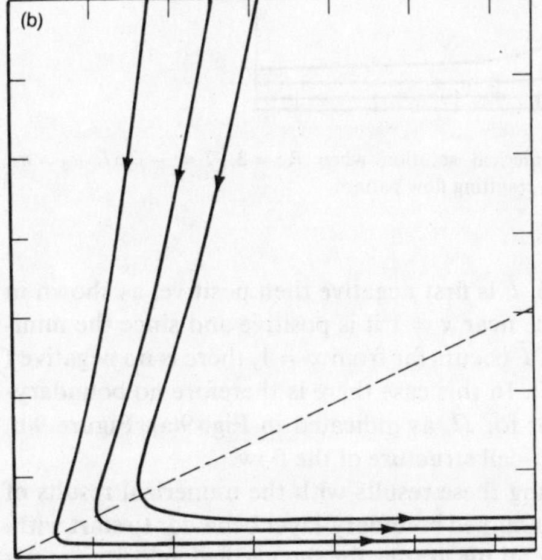

FIG. 4. (a) Numerical solution when Re = 2, $T = 1$, $\phi_0 = \pi/2(x_0 = 0)$. (b) The resulting flow pattern.

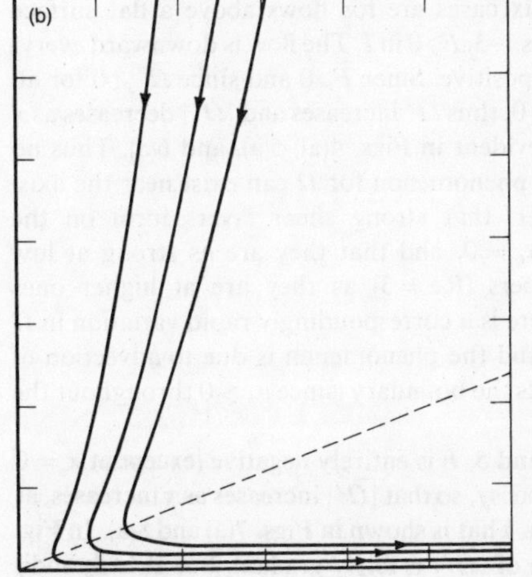

FIG. 5. (a) Numerical solution when Re = 3, $T = 1$, $\phi_0 = \pi/2(x_0 = 0)$. (b) The resulting flow pattern.

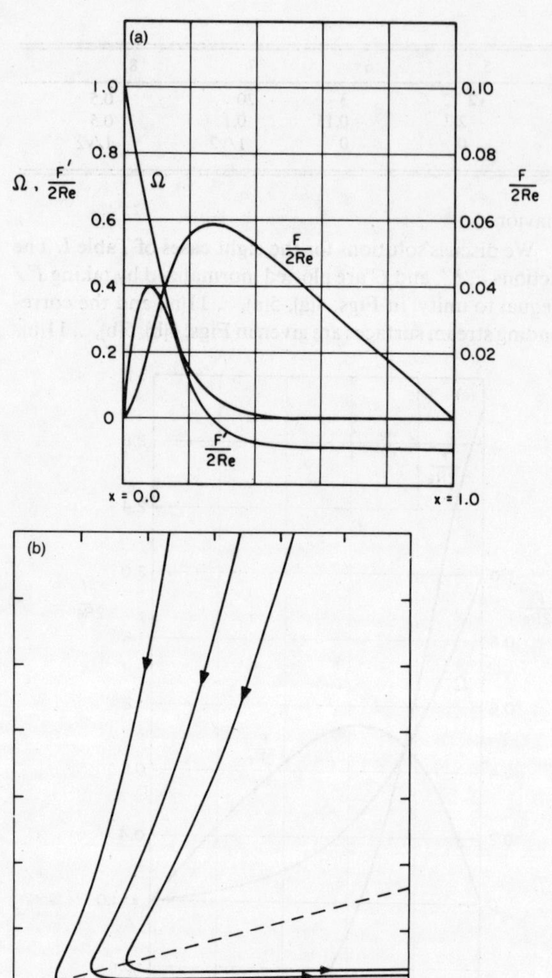

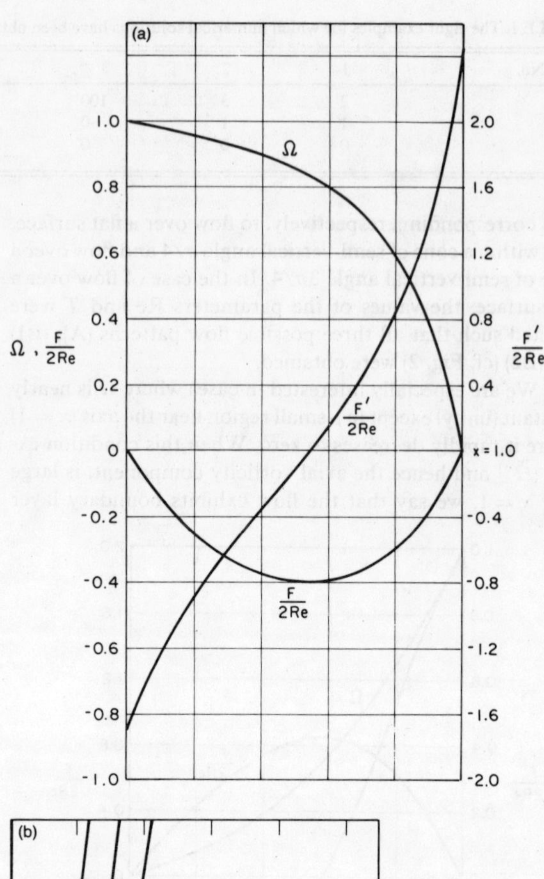

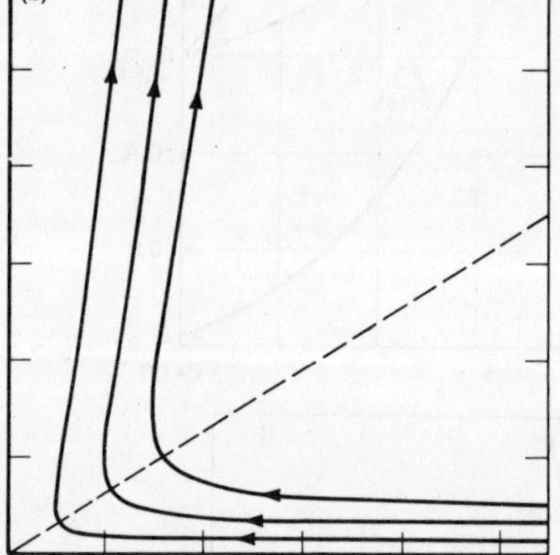

FIG. 6. (a) Numerical solution when Re = 100, $T = 0$, $\phi_0 = \pi/2(x_0 = 0)$. (b) The resulting flow pattern.

The first six cases are for flows above a flat surface $(x_0 = 0)$. In cases 1–3, $\widetilde{F} \geqslant 0$ in I. The flow is downward everywhere, with v_ϕ positive. Since $\widetilde{F} \geqslant 0$ and since $\widetilde{\Omega}' < 0$ for all our flows, $\widetilde{\Omega}'' > 0$: thus $\widetilde{\Omega}'$ increases and $|\widetilde{\Omega}'|$ decreases as x increases as is evident in Figs. 4(a), 5(a), and 6(a). Thus no boundary-layer phenomenon for $\widetilde{\Omega}$ can exist near the axis. Notice, however, that strong shear layers form on the boundary $x = x_0 = 0$, and that they are as strong at low Reynolds numbers (Re = 3) as they are at higher ones (Re = 100). There is a correspondingly rapid variation in $\widetilde{\Omega}$ in these cases, and the phenomenon is due to advection of vorticity towards the boundary (since $v_\phi > 0$ throughout the flow).

In cases 4 and 5, $\widetilde{F}$ is entirely negative (except at $x = 0$ and $x = 1$), and so is f, so that $|\widetilde{\Omega}'|$ increases as x increases, as indicated by (18). That is shown in Figs. 7(a) and 8(a). In Fig. 7(a) the increase of $|\widetilde{\Omega}'|$ is fairly gradual, but already indicates the possibility of boundary-layer behavior. In Fig. 8(a), boundary-layer behavior for $\widetilde{\Omega}$ is clearly manifested.

FIG. 7. (a) Numerical solution when Re = 3, $T = -0.57$, $\phi_0 = \pi/2(x_0 = 0)$. (b) The resulting flow pattern.

In case 6, $\widetilde{F}$ is first negative then positive, as shown in Fig. 9(a). Since near $x = 1$ it is positive and since the minimum value of $\widetilde{F}$ occurs far from $x = 1$, there is no negative f with large $|f|$. In this case there is therefore no boundary-layer behavior for Ω, as indicated in Fig. 9(a). Figure 9(b) shows the two-cell structure of the flow.

Comparing these results with the numerical results of Long,[14] who assumed boundary-layer behavior to start with, we see that in all his graphs for the vertical velocity w, w is either entirely positive (upward flow) or first negative (downdraft near the center) then positive. This is entirely in agree-

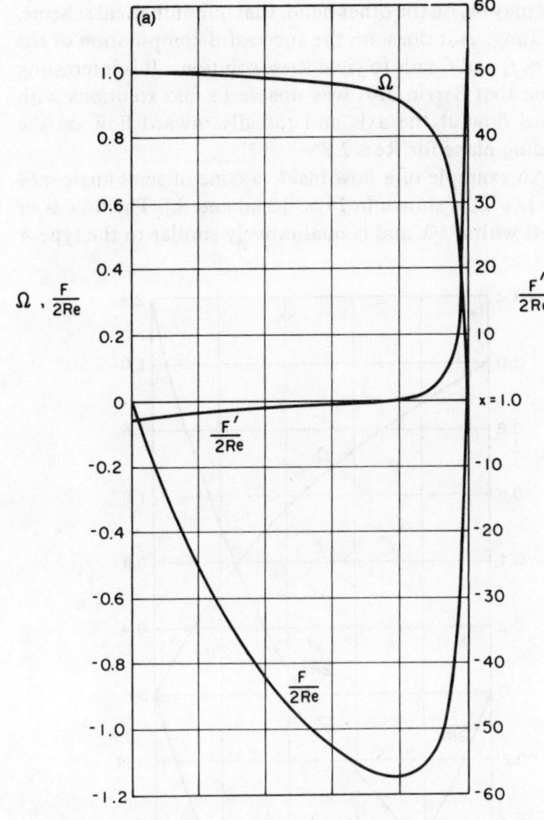

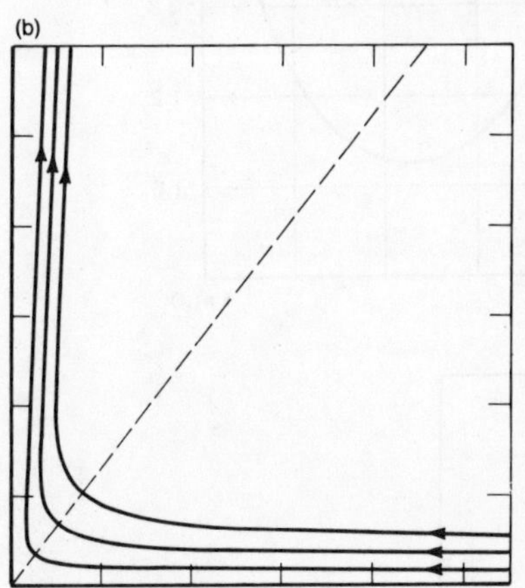

FIG. 8. (a) Numerical solution when $\mathrm{Re} = \sqrt{2}$, $T = -2.2$, $\phi_0 = \pi/2(x_0 = 0)$. (b) The resulting flow pattern.

ment with our deduction that boundary-layer behavior is impossible for positive $\widetilde{F}(x)$, which corresponds to completely downward flow. Physically, this is due to the fact that vorticity must be advected towards the axis to balance the outward viscous diffusion of vorticity away from the axis that must occur if a concentration of vorticity is to exist near the axis (i.e., if what we have called "boundary-layer behavior" obtains).

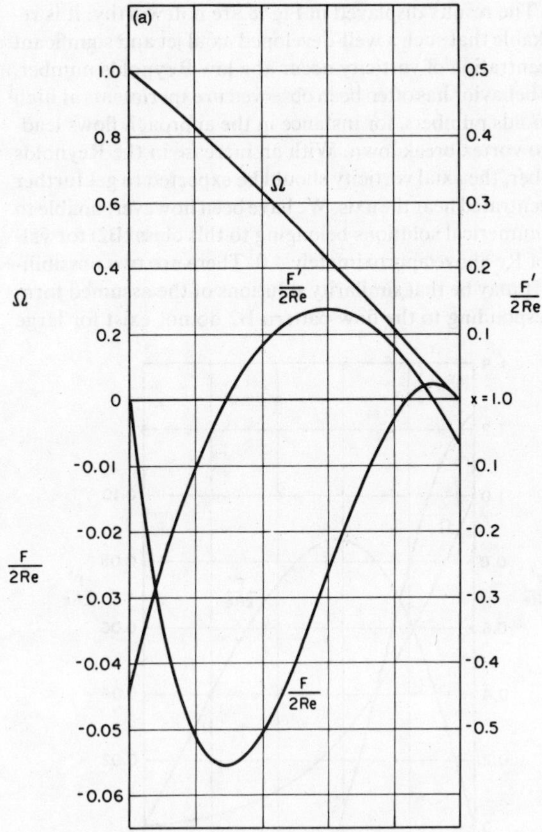

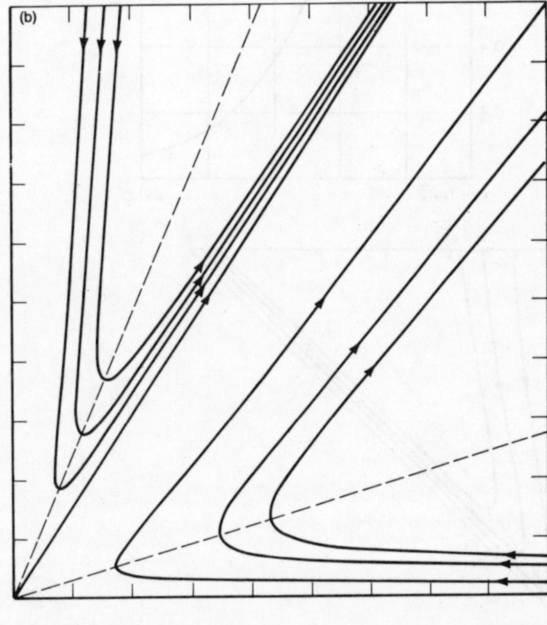

FIG. 9. (a) Numerical solution when $\mathrm{Re} = 3$, $T = -0.15$, $\phi_0 = \pi/2(x_0 = 0)$. (b) The resulting flow pattern.

The results displayed in Fig. 8 are noteworthy: it is remarkable that such a well-developed axial jet and significant concentration of vorticity occur at a low Reynolds number. This behavior has often been observed in experiments at high Reynolds numbers, for instance in the approach flows leading to vortex breakdown. With an increase in the Reynolds number, the axial vorticity should be expected to get further concentrated near the axis. We have been however, unable to find numerical solutions belonging to this class (B2) for values of Re above approximately 4.0. There are two possibilities. It may be that similarity solutions of the assumed form corresponding to the flow pattern B2 do not exist for large

Re. It may be, on the other hand, that our numerical scheme, depending, as it does, on the successful computation of the iterates f_1 and f_2 fails to yield these solutions. It is interesting to note that Serrin also was unable to find solutions with upward flow at the axis and radially inward flow on the bounding plane for Re > 2.86.

An example of a flow inside a cone of semi-angle $\pi/4$ $(x_0 = 1/\sqrt{2})$ is shown in Figs. 10 (a) and (b). The flow is of type A, with $\widetilde{F} > 0$, and is qualitatively similar to the type A

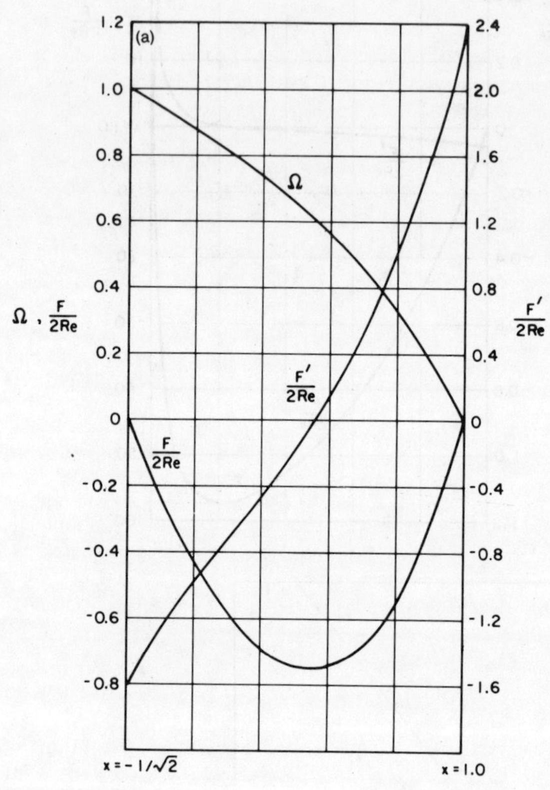

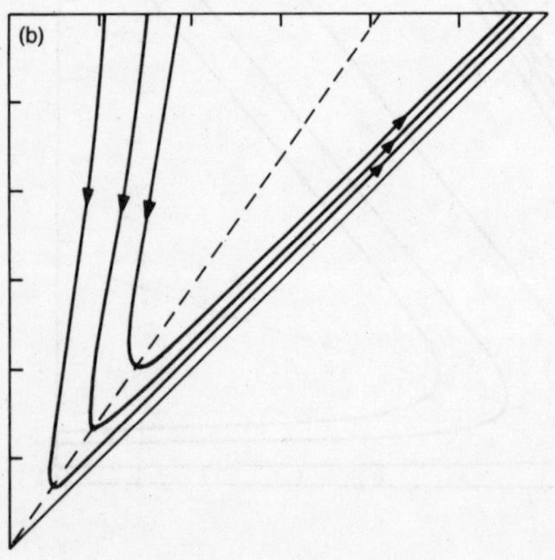

FIG. 10. (a) Numerical solution when Re = 20, $T = 0.1$, $\phi_0 = \pi/4 (x_0 = 1/\sqrt{2})$. (b) The resulting flow pattern.

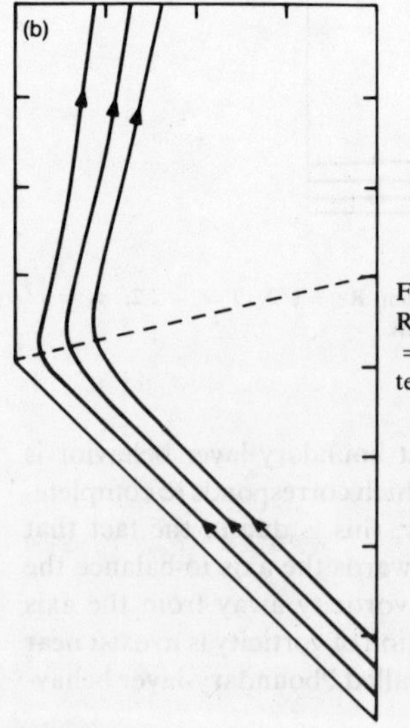

FIG. 11. (a) Numerical solution when Re = 0.5, $T = 0.5$, $\phi = 3\pi/4$ $(x_0 = -1/\sqrt{2})$. (b) The resulting flow pattern.

examples of above a flat surface. Flow *outside* a cone of the same semi-angle (so $\phi_0 = 3\pi/4$ and $x_0 = -1/\sqrt{2}$) is shown in Figs. 11 (a) and (b). The flow is upwards at the axis, or type B2. The Reynolds number is very low (0.5), and the concentration of vorticity near the axis, though in evidence, is weak.

As $x_0 \to -1$, the cone surface shrinks to a line vortex and the resulting flow may occupy the entire space excluding the negative z axis. In such a situation we have been able to show that $\widetilde{F} \sim (1+x)\ln(1+x)$ as $x \to -1$ and consequently the velocity along the line vortex must be infinite.

We turn next to the violation of the no-slip boundary condition inherent in these solutions. The inability to satisfy all boundary conditions in the presence of realistic (finite) boundaries capable of generating and constraining a viscous fluid motion is a problem that, to our knowledge, is shared by all but *one* known exact solution of the Navier–Stokes equations. (The exception is the trivial one, solid body rotation without relative motion of the fluid and its container: the rest case with zero rotation is a special case.) Exact self-similar solutions may or may not specify bounding surfaces but the region of space occupied by the fluid is always infinite. These solutions are always singular, with unbounded velocities either at a point, a line or at infinity. Each of these solutions represents a flow that can in principle be realized in a finite geometry that excludes the neighborhoods of any singular points provided a special distribution of velocity is arranged at the flow boundaries. Thus, the value of these solutions, so far as applications are concerned, lies in the extent to which portions of the exact solutions resemble flows in finite volumes generated by physically realizable velocity and pressure distributions.

The present solution is a direct generalization of the Squire[10] solution of the round jet. This jet solution improved (or extended) the earlier Landau–Squire[8–9] jet solution which has no boundaries (and, of course no swirl), and placed the flow within conical boundaries. Squire's improved solution, however, failed to satisfy the no-slip condition on the cone, and this condition cannot be remedied according to Squire,[10] Morgan,[21] and Potsch.[22] Schneider[23] has made an

attempt to show that this difficulty can be removed within the self-similar framework as Re$\to\infty$. It is our view that no-slip probably can be enforced on solutions such as these at high Reynolds numbers, but that this requires at least one of the basic symmetries of the similarity solution to be broken (i.e., it may be *unsteady*, but conical, or steady, but no longer conical). We suspect that higher-order approximations than Schneider's must break the conical similarity. This, however, must be the subject of a later paper.

ACKNOWLEDGMENT

The work of Yih and Wu was supported by the Office of Naval Research, and that of Garg and Leibovich was supported by the National Science Foundation under Grant No. CME 79-191817.

[1]C. duP. Donaldson and R. D. Sullivan, *Proceedings of the 1960 Heat Transfer Fluid Dynamics Institute* (Stanford U.P., Stanford, CA, 1960).
[2]J M. Burgers, Adv. Appl. Mech. **1**, 197 (1948).
[3]N. Rott, Z. Angew. Math. Phys. **9b**, 543 (1958).
[4]P. G. Bellamy-Knights, J. Fluid Mech. **41**, 673 (1970).
[5]P. G. Bellamy-Knights, J. Fluid Mech. **50**, 1 (1971).
[6]V. Trkal, Cas. Pst. Mat. **48**, 302 (1919).
[7]R. Berker, *Handbuch der Physik*, edited by S. Flügge (Springer-Verlag, Berlin, 1963), Vol. VIII/2.
[8]L. Landau, Dokl. Acad. Sci. U.R.S.S. **43**, 286 (1944).
[9]H. B. Squire, Q. J. Mech. Appl. Math. **4**, 321 (1951).
[10]H. B. Squire, Philos. Mag. **43**, 942 (1952)
[11]H. B. Squire, in *50 Jahre Grenz Schichtforschung*, edited by H. Gortler and W. Tollmien (Braunschweig, 1955).
[12]L. G. Loitsianskii, Prik. Mat. Mekh. **17**, 3 (1953).
[13]R. R. Long, J. Meteor. **15**, 108 (1958).
[14]R. R. Long, J. Fluid Mech. **11**, 611 (1961).
[15]O. R. Burggraf and M. R. Foster, J. Fluid Mech. **80**, 685 (1977).
[16]J. Serrin, Philos. Trans. R. Soc. London Ser. A **271**, 325 (1972).
[17]M. A. Goldstik, Prikl. Mat. Mekh. **24**, 610 (1960).
[18]H. Weyl, Ann. Math. **43**, 381 (1942).
[19]Th. V. Kármán, Z. Angew. Math. Mech. **1**, 233 (1921).
[20]U. T. Bödewadt, Z. Angew. Math. Mech. **20**, 241 (1940).
[21]A. J. A. Morgan, Aeronaut. Q. **7**, 225 (1956).
[22]K. Potsch, Z. Flugwiss. Weltraumforsch. **5**, 44 (1981).
[23]W. Schneider, J. Fluid Mech. **108**, 55 (1981).

J. Fluid Mech. (1985), *vol.* 152, *pp.* 163–172

New derivations of Darwin's theorem

By CHIA-SHUN YIH

The University of Michigan, Ann Arbor, Michigan

(Received 1 May 1984)

Two new derivations of Darwin's theorem on the equality of the added mass for translation of a body moving in an ideal fluid of infinite extent and the drift mass are given. The first is based on the idea of time lag, used by Rayleigh (1876), Ursell (1953), and Longuet-Higgins (1953) to study fluid drift. The second is truly elementary, relying only on the concept of continuity and Newton's second law of motion. A geometrical interpretation of the result in the first derivation is given, and a few examples are provided.

1. Introduction

Darwin's theorem (Darwin 1953) shows the equality of the added mass of a body in translation in an ideal fluid and the mass of the drift volume of the fluid at a section, as the body moves with constant velocity from the far right of the section to its far left. It is a beautiful theorem, for what it revealed was thitherto entirely unexpected and even today whoever encounters it for the first time still experiences the surprise and delight it affords.

In this paper two new derivations of Darwin's theorem are given. The first is based on the idea of time lag in steady irrotational flows, which allows Darwin's theorem to be obtained with simplicity and directness. At first I thought this idea was new, but it was pointed out to me that the idea originated with Lord Rayleigh (1876), who used it to study fluid drift in waves in a geometric way, but whose arguments (where he assumed two parallel streamlines near the bottom) are valid only for deep-water waves, as pointed out by Ursell (1953). It was Ursell (1953, p. 147) who first put Rayleigh's idea in analytical terms. Indeed (12) and (13) in this paper are quite reminiscent of Ursell's work. The idea of time lag was also used by Longuet-Higgins (1953) to steady fluid drift in space-periodic and solitary waves. However, neither Ursell nor Longuet-Higgins was concerned with Darwin's theorem, whereas this paper is.

The idea of time lag has also been quite explicitly used by Lighthill (1956). See, for instance, equation (46) on p. 42 of his article, which treated weak shear flows.

We shall derive Darwin's theorem for two-dimensional flows first. Then a geometrical interpretation will be given to the result obtained and a few examples provided. For the sake of completeness as well as to illustrate the usefulness of general stream functions, we shall derive Darwin's theorem for three-dimensional flows. Finally, an elementary proof of Darwin's theorem based on the concept of continuity and on Newton's second law will be given, without the explicit use of integral calculus, as well as an alternative form of Taylor's theorem (1928).

164   *C.-S. Yih*

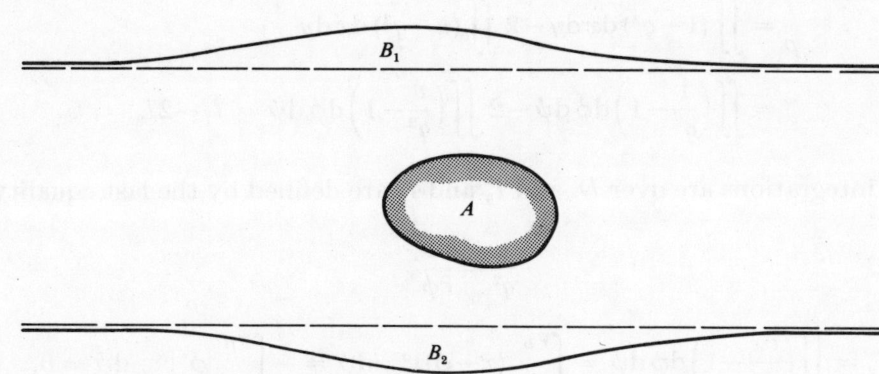

FIGURE 1. Sketch for the areas B_1, B_2, and A.

2. The two-dimensional case

As usual, the velocity potential ϕ' and the stream function ψ' of the irrotational flow caused by a body moving in an ideal fluid otherwise at rest are expressed in coordinates of a frame moving with the body. The velocity components in the directions of increasing x and y are, respectively,

$$u' = \phi'_x = \psi'_y, \quad v' = \phi'_y = -\psi'_x, \tag{1}$$

where subscripts indicate partial differentiation. The speed q' is defined by

$$q'^2 = u'^2 + v'^2. \tag{2}$$

Let the body move to the left (in the direction of decreasing x) with constant speed 1. Then the flow is steady with respect to the moving frame, and the velocity potential ϕ and the stream function ψ are given by

$$\phi = x + \phi', \quad \psi = y + \psi'. \tag{3}$$

The velocity components are

$$u = \phi_x = \psi_y = 1 + u', \quad v = \phi_y = -\psi_x = v' \tag{4}$$

and the speed q is given by $\qquad q^2 = u^2 + v^2. \tag{5}$

As is well known, the added mass of the body is given by

$$m_{\mathrm{a}} = \rho \iint q'^2 \, \mathrm{d}x \, \mathrm{d}y, \tag{6}$$

where ρ is the density of the fluid and the integral is over the (infinite) area outside the body. Now consider the integral

$$I = \rho \iint_D [(u-1)^2 + v^2] \, \mathrm{d}x \, \mathrm{d}y, \tag{7}$$

where D is a domain (figure 1) bounded by two streamlines $\psi = \psi_B$ and $\psi = \psi_{-B}$, one above the body and the other below it. As these streamlines recede to infinity above and below, respectively, I approaches m_{a}.

Now, since

$$q^2 = \frac{\partial(\phi, \psi)}{\partial(x, y)}, \tag{8}$$

we have

$$\frac{I}{\rho} = \iint (1-q^2)\,\mathrm{d}x\,\mathrm{d}y - 2\iint (u-q^2)\,\mathrm{d}x\,\mathrm{d}y$$

$$= \iint \left(\frac{1}{q^2}-1\right)\mathrm{d}\phi\,\mathrm{d}\psi - 2\iint \left(\frac{u}{q^2}-1\right)\mathrm{d}\phi\,\mathrm{d}\psi = I_1 - 2I_2, \tag{9}$$

where all integrations are over D, and I_1 and I_2 are defined by the last equality sign. But

$$\frac{u}{q^2} = \frac{\partial x}{\partial \phi},$$

so that

$$I_2 = \iint \left(\frac{\partial x}{\partial \phi}-1\right)\mathrm{d}\phi\,\mathrm{d}\psi = \int_{\psi_{-B}}^{\psi_B} (x-\phi)\,|_{-\infty}^{\infty}\,\mathrm{d}\psi = -\int_{\psi_{-B}}^{\psi_B} \phi'\,|_{-\infty}^{\infty}\,\mathrm{d}\psi = 0, \tag{10}$$

since $\phi' = 0$ at infinity for a body moving in infinite fluid. Therefore

$$I = \rho I_1. \tag{11}$$

In I_1,

$$\frac{\mathrm{d}\phi}{q} = \mathrm{d}s,$$

where $\mathrm{d}s$ is the distance along a streamline as ϕ changes by $\mathrm{d}\phi$. Thus

$$\frac{\mathrm{d}\phi}{q^2} = \mathrm{d}t, \tag{12}$$

where $\mathrm{d}t$ is the time required for a fluid particle to travel the distance $\mathrm{d}s$. The integral

$$I_3 = \int_{-\infty}^{\infty} \left(\frac{1}{q^2}-1\right)\mathrm{d}\phi \tag{13}$$

is then the difference between the time required by a fluid particle to go from $\phi = -\infty$ to $\phi = +\infty$ and the time required by a reference kinematic point moving with constant $u\,(=1)$ to do the same. That is, it is the drift distance for a particle moving along any particular streamline in the steady flow (ϕ, ψ). (If the particle requires more time, and eventually its velocity is 1, the same as that of the reference point, it will never catch up, and will lag behind the reference point by the distance equal to 1 times I_3. This distance is the drift distance.) Hence I_1, being

$$\int_{\psi_{-B}}^{\psi_B} I_3\,\mathrm{d}\psi,$$

is the drift area (or drift volume per unit distance normal to the x, y plane). Then in the limit, as $\psi_B \to \infty$ and $\psi_{-B} \to -\infty$,

$$m_{\mathrm{a}} = \lim \rho I_1. \tag{14}$$

That is, the drift mass is the added mass, per unit distance along the generatrix of the cylinder, which is the body under consideration. Thus Darwin's theorem is proved in a new, simple way.

166   *C.-S. Yih*

3. Geometrical significance of the integral I_1

Considering I_1 again, we see that

$$I_1 = D - S, \tag{15}$$

where

$$D = \text{area of domain } D = \iint \frac{1}{q^2}\,\mathrm{d}\phi\,\mathrm{d}\psi = \iint \mathrm{d}x\,\mathrm{d}y,$$

$$S = \iint \mathrm{d}\phi\,\mathrm{d}\psi.$$

Obviously S is the area of the infinite strip of width $\psi_B - \psi_{-B}$, including the cross-sectional area A of the body. Thus

$$D - S = B_1 + B_2 - A, \tag{16}$$

where B_1 is the area bounded by the streamline $\psi = \psi_B$ above and $y = \psi_B$ below, and B_2 is the area bounded by $\psi = \psi_{-B}$ below and $y = \psi_{-B}$ above. The bounding lines do not cross if ψ_B and $-\psi_{-B}$ are sufficiently large. Let

$$B = B_1 + B_2.$$

Then in the limit, as $\psi_B \to \infty$ and $\psi_{-B} \to -\infty$,

$$\rho B = m_{\mathrm{a}} + m, \tag{17}$$

where m is the mass of the fluid displaced by the body.

We do not have to go to the limit, however. From (16) we obtain that

$$\rho B = m_{\mathrm{d}} + m, \tag{18}$$

where m_{d} is the drift mass between the streamlines $\psi = \psi_B$ and $\psi = \psi_{-B}$. It is this generalization and the geometric relation (16) that lead us to the results presented in the section below.

4. Examples of fluid drift

Consider the classical solitary wave, the solution for which was first given by Rayleigh (1914) and refined by subsequent authors. No exact solution exists. But the result given below is exact, not depending on the particulars of the solution.

Take the steady-flow solution (ϕ, ψ) for the solitary wave, and take

$$\psi_{-B} = 0$$

and ψ_B to be the ψ on the free-streamline. The velocity scale is the speed c of the solitary wave. Upon use of this scale, everything developed in §§2 and 3 stands. In this case $A = 0$ exactly, because there is no solid body in the fluid, and $B_2 = 0$, because $\psi = 0$ and $y = 0$ coincide. Hence upon dividing (18) by ρ, we have

$$B = B_1 = \frac{m_{\mathrm{d}}}{\rho},$$

or the drift area is exactly equal to the area between the free surface and its horizontal asymptote, which is Ursell's result (1953), obtainable also by the consideration of continuity.

Internal solitary waves in two superposed fluid layers have been studied by Keulegan (1953), Long (1956), and Benjamin (1966). The wave may be one of elevation of the lower fluid (Case A), or one of depression of the lower fluid (Case B).

Upon application of (18), with $m = 0$, to the lower fluid in Case A, we see that again the drift area for the lower fluid is exactly equal to the area underneath the interface and above its horizontal asymptote. For the upper fluid the drift area is of exactly the same magnitude, but in the opposite direction (opposite to the direction of propagation of the solitary wave). The total drift area is then exactly zero. For Case B, the opposite is true. That is, the upper fluid drifts with the wave, and the lower fluid drifts in the opposite direction, the drift area for each layer being exactly equal to the area between the interface and its horizontal asymptote.

Obviously these results can be generalized to apply to solitary waves in a fluid system of many layers. But I shall refrain from doing so. Instead, I shall give some other examples.

Consider a circular cylinder of radius a moving with unit velocity to the left along the x-axis. As is well known, the stream function is given by

$$\psi = y - \frac{a^2 y}{x^2 + y^2}, \tag{19}$$

the origin of Cartesian coordinates x and y being at the centre of the cylinder. Area B_1 is given by

$$B_1 = \int_{-\infty}^{\infty} (y - \psi_B)\, \mathrm{d}x = a^2 \int_{-\infty}^{\infty} \frac{y}{x^2 + y^2}\, \mathrm{d}x, \tag{20}$$

in which y is a function of ψ_B and x, obtained by letting the ψ in (19) be ψ_B. As ψ_B increases indefinitely, we can replace the y in the second integral of (20) by ψ_B, committing thereby less and less error as ψ_B increases, and ultimately no error at all. Doing so, we obtain from (20) that

$$B_1 = \pi a^2.$$

Similarly $B_2 = \pi a^2$, so that

$$\rho B = \beta(B_1 + B_2) = 2\rho \pi a^2.$$

Since m, the mass of the fluid displaced by the body, is $\rho \pi a^2$, it follows from (17) that the added mass is

$$m_a = \rho \pi a^2.$$

By letting $\psi_B \to \infty$ and $\psi_{-B} \to -\infty$, we obtain from (18) the same value for the total drift mass m_d, as expected.

Another example is provided by the stream function

$$\psi = y' - \frac{a^2 y'}{x'^2 + y'^2},$$

where the flow in the x', y' plane is the flow past a circular cylinder. If the coordinates (x, y) and (x', y') are related by

$$y = y' - \frac{b^2 y'}{x'^2 + y'^2}, \qquad x = x' + \frac{b^2 x'}{x'^2 + y'^2},$$

we have the well-known result that the flow in the x, y plane is that past an elliptic cylinder with semi-major axis $a + b^2/a$ and semi-minor axis $a - b^2/a$. We have then

$$y - \psi = \frac{(a^2 - b^2)\, y'}{x'^2 + y'^2}.$$

If we replace y' by ψ_B and x' by x, and integrate with respect to x, in the limit, as ψ_B tends to ∞, we obtain without error

$$B_1 = \int_{-\infty}^{\infty} (y - \psi)\, \mathrm{d}x = (a^2 - b^2)\, \pi.$$

168   *C.-S. Yih*

Similarly B_2 has the same value, and

$$\rho B = \rho(B_1 + B_2) = 2\rho\pi(a^2 - b^2) = m_a + m = m_d + m.$$

But

$$m = \rho\pi\left(a + \frac{b^2}{a}\right)\left(a - \frac{b^2}{a}\right) = \rho\pi\left(a^2 - \frac{b^4}{a^2}\right).$$

Hence

$$m_a = m_d = \rho\pi\left(a - \frac{b^2}{a}\right)^2,$$

as is well known.

Note that Darwin proved this theorem (as I do here also) only for a fluid of infinite extent. It can be generalized to apply to a semi-infinite fluid bounded by a single plate to which the velocity of the immersed body is parallel. But it is not true for a restricted fluid, such as the fluid between two parallel plates, in which a body moves. In such cases the I_2 in (10) is not zero, and therefore Darwin's theorem does not hold, because ϕ' is not zero at infinity, as Ursell (1953) pointed out in the case of the solitary wave, and as can be shown easily in the case of the fluid bounded by two parallel plates. For such a case (9) needs to be carefully re-examined, for there is a subtle point involving the interpretation of the integral S in (15), which no longer represents the area of the infinite strip including the area A, as stated after (15), but contains an additional part that can be easily shown to be $-I_2$. Then, since B vanishes in this case, (9) becomes, upon use of (15),

$$I = -\rho A - \rho I_2, \quad \text{or} \quad -\rho I_2 = m_a + \rho A,$$

as can be shown independently by using a control volume and applying Newton's second law and Bernoulli's theorem (for unsteady flows with the body moving and the fluid at rest at infinity).

5. The three-dimensional case

We shall now return to a new proof of Darwin's theorem for three-dimensional flows, based on the idea of time lag. This proof has some incidental merit in demonstrating the usefulness of stream functions for three-dimensional flows (Yih 1957, 1979). Let these be denoted by ψ and χ. Then the velocity $\boldsymbol{u}$ is given by

$$\boldsymbol{u} = \operatorname{grad}\psi \times \operatorname{grad}\chi. \tag{21}$$

Thus

$$q^2 = u^2 + v^2 + w^2 = \frac{\partial(\phi, \psi, \chi)}{\partial(x, y, z)} = J, \tag{22}$$

$$\frac{u}{q^2} = \frac{1}{J}\frac{\partial(\psi, \chi)}{\partial(y, z)} = \frac{\partial x}{\partial\phi}, \tag{23}$$

in which u, v, and w are the velocity components in the directions of increasing x, y, and z, respectively, with the velocity *at infinity* being

$$u = 1, \quad v = 0, \quad w = 0.$$

We shall not assume any axial symmetry. But it is still useful to define

$$r = (y^2 + z^2)^{\frac{1}{2}}, \quad \theta = \tan^{-1}\frac{y}{z}, \tag{24}$$

because, at $x = \pm\infty$,

$$\psi = \tfrac{1}{2}r^2, \quad \chi = \theta. \tag{25}$$

Since the body is assumed to move with speed 1 (in the direction of decreasing x), the added mass is, as is well known,

$$m_a = \rho \iiint q'^2 \, dx \, dy \, dz, \tag{26}$$

q' being the speed of the fluid for the (unsteady) flow caused by the body in the fluid otherwise at rest. The integral in (26) is carried over the entire space occupied by the fluid. We now take D to be the domain between $\psi = 0$ and $\psi = \psi_0 = \frac{1}{2}r_0^2$, from $x = -\infty$ to $x = +\infty$, and consider the integral

$$I = \rho \iiint_D [(u-1)^2 + v^2 + w^2] \, dx \, dy \, dz.$$

Then the development is exactly as that following (7), and we obtain

$$\begin{aligned}
\frac{I}{\rho} &= \iiint (q^2 - 2u + 1) \, dx \, dy \, dz \\
&= \iiint \left(\frac{1}{q^2} - 1\right) d\phi \, d\psi \, d\chi - 2 \iiint \left(\frac{u}{q^2} - 1\right) d\phi \, d\psi \, d\chi \\
&= I_1 - 2I_2,
\end{aligned} \tag{27}$$

where I_1 and I_2 are defined by the last equality sign, and all integrations are over the domain D. Again, for an unrestricted fluid,

$$I_2 = \iiint \left(\frac{\partial x}{\partial \phi} - 1\right) d\phi \, d\psi \, d\chi = \iint_{(\psi, \chi)} (x - \phi)_{-\infty}^{\infty} \, d\psi \, d\chi = 0,$$

and we have

$$\frac{I}{\rho} = I_1.$$

In the limit,

$$\rho I_1 = m_a.$$

But, as before, I_1 is the drift volume. Hence we have given a new proof of Darwin's theorem for three-dimensional flows using the idea of time lag.

6. A proof of Darwin's theorem without calculation

Darwin showed in his paper (1953) that the drift volume V_D for three-dimensional flows (the formula for two-dimensional flows then follows directly) is given by

$$V_D = -\iiint \phi'_x \, dx \, dy \, dz, \tag{28}$$

where the integration is carried over the entire fluid domain, and where the sign convention of (1) regarding ϕ has been adopted. I have used a minus sign in (28) to make V_D positive, since in this paper the body is assumed to move toward the left (i.e. in the direction of decreasing x). It is evident that the integral is the total momentum of the fluid divided by ρ, and, if the body is moving with unit velocity to the left, the right-hand side of (28), with the minus sign included, is obviously the added mass divided by ρ, upon consideration of acceleration of the body. So the drift mass is the added mass, and this fact is the substance of Darwin's theorem.

Darwin's theorem is not only true; it is beautiful as well. Part of the reason for the delight it gives is its unexpectedness. And yet one could wonder whether it is a fortuitous truth stating a fortuitous equality, or whether the equality it states is

 C.-S. Yih

dictated by kinematics and dynamics in so simple and direct a way that it is obvious. Evidently if the latter is true it has hitherto not been recognized, for Darwin's theorem is widely regarded as difficult to grasp, and its unexpectedness (for this writer at least) seems to indicate that the equality of drift mass and added mass is fortuitous. But then how could such a general equality, regardless of shape of the body, be only fortuitously true? One could argue, of course, that any truth demonstrated mathematically is not fortuitous, that it has mathematical necessity. Yet mathematical necessity is not mechanical necessity, and, upon learning of Darwin's theorem, one is always left wondering why it must be true mechanically.

I shall now show, without the explicit use of integral calculus, that Darwin's theorem is to be expected on the basis of continuity and Newton's second law.

Consider the domain D shown in figure 1, bounded by two streamlines (or a stream surface if the flow is three-dimensional) and the body. For convenience, and convenience only, I shall treat the flow as two-dimensional. But every statement that follows can be made applicable to three-dimensional flows by the change of a word here and there (e.g. the word 'area' to 'volume'). The geometry of D will be called the 'pattern'. The pattern moves with the body, though the fluid at infinity is at rest.

Now, at $x = 0$ and $t = 0$, let the intersection of D with the y-axis (or the y, z plane in three-dimensional flows) be dyed blue, and let the streamlines shown in figure 1 be dyed red at $t = 0$. Furthermore, let the body move left from $x = \infty$. After the body has moved to the far left, the blue line will have drifted left, and the drift area is the area swept by the blue line from its initial position to its final position. The red lines (but not the particles on them) move with the body and are made of the same fluid particles.

Consider the fluid mass to the left of the blue line and bounded by the red lines and the body. There is no flow across either the blue lines or the red lines since they are material lines, and there is no flow at $x = -\infty$. The fluid area just described must then be constant and equal to the area initially to the left of the blue line (and bounded by the red lines), when the body was at $x = \infty$. Thus†

$$B - A = C, \tag{29}$$

where $B \equiv B_1 + B_2$, and C is the drift area between the red lines. (Recall the definitions of B_1, B_2, and A.)

Now consider the domain D at any time. As the body moves left, the centre of gravity of D moves also. There is no flow at infinity and the 'pattern' moves with the body, so that the area B and the area A (occupied by the body, which is a fluid hole) move with the body. Hence the amount of fluid moving with the same mean x-velocity as the body is $\rho(B - A) = \rho C$, which then must be the added mass, as the time-rate of change of the momentum of the fluid in D is equal to the force imparted it by the body when it accelerates, if the x-component of the force from integrating the pressure on the red lines is ignored‡ as it can be ignored when the red lines recede to $y = \pm \infty$. Thus the drift mass must be equal to the added mass upon consideration of continuity and Newton's second law, and Darwin's theorem can be expected on these principles.

It is regrettable that we can no longer ask Sir Charles what inspiration led him to his discovery. I think it was unlikely that the considerations I have just presented

---

† The same arguments can be applied to viscous fluids to obtain the same result, which can also be otherwise established.

‡ The force arising from pressure at the ends of D (where $x = \pm \infty$) is zero.

went through his mind. These considerations are mere hindsights, and his theorem stands as an interesting example of the essential inexplicability and intractability of inspiration of the human mind. However, my attempts here perhaps serve to make his theorem more graspable and therefore more satisfying to his readers.

7. Connection between Darwin's theorem and Taylor's theorem

Equation (17) is in effect Taylor's theorem (1928). To save space, I shall consider only two-dimensional flows here. The three-dimensional counterpart of the development can be established without difficulty.

It is clear that

$$B = B_1 + B_2 = \int_{-\infty}^{\infty} (y_1 - \psi_B)\, \mathrm{d}x + \int_{-\infty}^{\infty} (\psi_{-B} - y_2)\, \mathrm{d}x, \tag{30}$$

where y_1 is y on the streamline $\psi = \psi_B$ and y_2 is y on $\psi = \psi_{-B}$, the B's being defined in §3. Equation (30) can be written as

$$B = -\int_{-\infty}^{\infty} \psi'_B\, \mathrm{d}x + \int_{-\infty}^{\infty} \psi'_{-B}\, \mathrm{d}x. \tag{31}$$

As $\psi_B \to \infty$ and $\psi_{-B} \to -\infty$, we obtain from (17) and (31)

$$\rho \left[-\lim_{y \to \infty} \int_{-\infty}^{\infty} \psi'\, \mathrm{d}x + \lim_{y \to -\infty} \int_{-\infty}^{\infty} \psi'\, \mathrm{d}x \right] = m + m_a. \tag{32}$$

By taking an infinite strip bounded externally by

$$\phi = \phi_B \quad \text{and} \quad \phi = \phi_{-B} \tag{33}$$

and internally by the surface of the body, we can obtain (see Appendix)

$$\rho \left[\lim_{x \to \infty} \int_{-\infty}^{\infty} \phi'\, \mathrm{d}y - \lim_{x \to -\infty} \int_{-\infty}^{\infty} \phi'\, \mathrm{d}y \right] = m + m_a. \tag{34}$$

The left-hand side of (32) and (34) are an alternative expression of Taylor's expression obtained from the singularities inside the body. On the other hand (32) is (17), (34) is an alternative form of (17), and (17) is closely related to the proof of Darwin's theorem. Thus, although Darwin was thinking of drift mass and Taylor was not, the grounds they traversed, a quarter of a century apart, were not far from each other.

This work has been supported by the Fluid Mechanics Program of the Office of Naval Research.

Appendix

To show (34), consider the domain D' bounded by the curves (33) externally and by the body internally. Then

$$\frac{I}{\rho} = \iint_{D'} \left(\frac{1}{q^2} - \frac{u}{q^2} \right) \mathrm{d}\phi\, \mathrm{d}\psi - \iint_{D'} \left(\frac{u}{q^2} - 1 \right) \mathrm{d}\phi\, \mathrm{d}\psi$$

$$= \iint_{D'} \mathrm{d}x\, \mathrm{d}y - \iint_{D'} \mathrm{d}x\, \mathrm{d}\psi - \int_{-\infty}^{\infty} [(x_B - \phi_B) - (x_{-B} - \phi_{-B})]\, \mathrm{d}\psi. \tag{A 1}$$

The first integral on the right-hand side is the (infinite) area of D', the second integral

172   C.-S. Yih

is the area of the infinite strip bounded by (33), including the body of Area A. Hence their difference is $-A$, and upon multiplication by ρ, and recalling that $m = \rho A$ and $I \to m_a$ as $\phi_B \to \infty$ and $\phi_{-B} \to -\infty$, we have, in the limit, (34), since $\phi' = \phi - x$.

REFERENCES

BENJAMIN, T. B. 1966 Internal waves of finite amplitude and permanent form. *J. Fluid Mech.* **25**, 241–270.

DARWIN, C. G. 1953 Note on hydrodynamics. *Proc. Camb. Phil. Soc.* **49**, 342–354.

KEULEGAN, G. H. 1953 Characteristics of internal solitary waves. *J. Res. Nat. Bureau of Standards* **51**, 133.

LIGHTHILL, M. J. 1956 Drift. *J. Fluid Mech.* **1**, 31–53.

LONG, R. R. 1956 Solitary waves in one- and two-fluid systems. *Tellus* **8**, 460.

LONGUET-HIGGINS, M. S. 1953 On the decrease of velocity with depth in an irrotational water wave. *Proc. Camb. Phil. Soc.* **49**, 552–560.

RAYLEIGH, LORD 1876 On waves. *Phil. Mag.* **1** (5), 257–279.

RAYLEIGH, LORD 1914 On the theory of long waves and bores. *Proc. R. Soc. Lond.* A **90**, 324–328.

TAYLOR, G. I. 1928 The energy of a body moving in an infinite fluid, with an application to airships. *Proc. R. Soc. Lond.* A **120**, 13–21.

URSELL, F. 1953 Mass transport in gravity waves. *Proc. Camb. Phil. Soc.* **49**, 145–150.

YIH, C.-S. 1957 Stream functions in three-dimensional flows. *La Houille Blanche* **12**, 445–450.

YIH, C.-S. 1979 *Fluid Mechanics*, pp. 12–16. West River Press.

ARTICLES

Movement of liquid inclusions in soluble solids: An inverse Stokes' law

Chia-Shun Yih
*Department of Mechanical Engineering and Applied Mechanics, University of Michigan,
Ann Arbor, Michigan 48109*

(Received 25 February 1986; accepted 30 May 1986)

The temperature distribution in an ellipsoidal liquid inclusion in a soluble solid, with a
constant gradient far away from the liquid, and the movement of the liquid inclusion as a
whole, which results as a consequence, are investigated. Since the solid is soluble and its
concentration in solution is temperature dependent, any temperature variation in the liquid
induces a concentration variation, which will transfer mass by diffusion, eroding the wall
where the temperature is high and depositing solid material at the wall where the temperature
is lower. This erosion or deposition will cause the liquid inclusion to move, and will, through
absorption or release of latent heat, in turn affect the temperature distribution. From the result
obtained for the general ellipsoid, specific results for prolate and oblate ellipsoids of revolution,
the sphere, and circular and elliptic cylinders are obtained.

I. INTRODUCTION

Fluid inclusions in soluble solids are of interest not only
to geologists but also to manufacturers of artificial precious
stones such as emeralds. The manufacturers use a liquid
called flux to dissolve at high temperatures the substance of
the precious stone present in ores. When the substance cools,
it will form the stone. In manufactured stones as well as in
some natural precious stones, such as Columbian emerald,
there are usually some fluid inclusions.

Geologists have noted the movement of fluid inclusions
in soluble solids in the presence of a general temperature
gradient, but no mathematical analysis has been given for it.
This article provides such an analysis.

The temperature distribution in an ellipsoidal fluid inclusion and in the solid surrounding it will be found. In the
analysis, latent heat absorbed when solid material is dissolved in the liquid, or released when it is deposited at the
wall, is taken into account. From the result of the temperature distribution in the liquid, the speed of movement of the
fluid inclusion can be deduced. By specialization, specific
results for ellipsoids of revolution (prolate or oblate), the
sphere, and circular and elliptic cylinders are obtained.

The velocity of the fluid inclusion is generally very
small. Therefore the convective terms in the heat equation
are negligible. Their effect is briefly discussed in the case of
the sphere.

II. SOLUTION FOR THE GENERAL ELLIPSOID

Let the surface of the ellipsoid occupied by the liquid be
given by

$$x^2/a^2 + y^2/b^2 + z^2/c^2 = 1, \tag{1}$$

where (x,y,z) are Cartesian coordinates and a, b, and c the
semiaxes of the ellipsoid in the coordinate directions.

For simplicity, we shall assume that the temperature in
the solid far away from the liquid is

$$(T_s)_\infty = \alpha x + T_0, \tag{2}$$

and assume, for the moment, that the fluid does not move in
any direction. Then the temperature T_s in the solid and the

temperature T in the liquid satisfy

$$\nabla^2 T_s = 0, \quad \nabla^2 T = 0, \tag{3}$$

where

$$\nabla^2 = \frac{\partial^2}{\partial x^2} + \frac{\partial^2}{\partial y^2} + \frac{\partial^2}{\partial z^2}.$$

At infinity, T_s must approach $(T_s)_\infty$. Inside the liquid, T
must have no singularity. At the solid–liquid interface

$$T_s = T, \quad \frac{\partial T}{\partial n} = q \frac{\partial T_s}{\partial n}, \tag{4}$$

where n is the distance normal to the interface,

$$q = k_s/k, \tag{5}$$

k_s and k being the thermal conductivities of the solid and the
liquid, respectively. The differential system to be solved thus
consists of Eqs. (2)–(4).

Ellipsoidal coordinates (λ, μ, ν) are defined by the roots
of θ in the equation

$$\frac{x^2}{a^2 + \theta} + \frac{y^2}{b^2 + \theta} + \frac{z^2}{c^2 + \theta} = 1, \tag{6}$$

considered as a cubic in θ. We let λ lie between ∞ and $-c^2$,
μ between $-c^2$ and $-b^2$, and ν between $-b^2$ and $-a^2$.
Thus the surfaces $\lambda = $ const are ellipsoids, $\mu = $ const are hyperboloids of one sheet, and $\nu = $ const are hyperboloids of
two sheets. For $\theta = 0$, (6) becomes (1). Thus the surface
conditions are applied at $\theta = 0$, or $\lambda = 0$.

Let the functions (of λ, therefore of x, y, and z) A, B, and
C be defined by

$$A = \frac{abc}{2} \int_\lambda^\infty \frac{du}{(a^2 + u)\Delta}, \quad B = \frac{abc}{2} \int_\lambda^\infty \frac{du}{(b^2 + u)\Delta},$$

$$C = \frac{abc}{2} \int_\lambda^\infty \frac{du}{(c^2 + u)\Delta}, \tag{7}$$

where

$$\Delta = [(a^2 + u)(b^2 + u)(c^2 + u)]^{1/2}. \tag{8}$$

Then it can be shown that Ax, By, and Cz all satisfy the
Laplace equation. Furthermore, they tend to zero as λ ap-

© 1986 American Institute of Physics   2785

proaches infinity, that is, as the distance from the origin increases indefinitely.

One assumes, then, that the temperature in the solid is

$$T_s = \alpha x + \alpha_1 A x + T_0 \qquad (9)$$

and the temperature of the liquid is

$$T = \alpha' x + T_0. \qquad (10)$$

The Laplace equations (3), the asymptotic condition for T_s, and the requirement of regularity for T are all satisfied, and we turn to the conditions (4), which for $\lambda = 0$ are

$$\alpha + A_0 \alpha = \alpha', \qquad (11)$$

$$q[\alpha + (A_0 - 1)\alpha_1] = \alpha', \qquad (12)$$

where A_0 is the value of A at $\lambda = 0$. In obtaining (12), it has been necessary to use

$$(\lambda_x, \lambda_y, \lambda_z) = \frac{2}{P} \left(\frac{x}{a^2 + \lambda}, \frac{y}{b^2 + \lambda}, \frac{z}{c^2 + \lambda} \right), \qquad (13)$$

where

$$P = \frac{x^2}{(a^2 + \lambda)^2} + \frac{y^2}{(b^2 + \lambda)^2} + \frac{z^2}{(c^2 + \lambda)^2} \qquad (14)$$

and

$$\frac{\partial}{\partial n} (x, y, z) = P_0^{-1/2} \left(\frac{x}{a^2}, \frac{y}{b^2}, \frac{z}{c^2} \right), \qquad (15)$$

P_0 being the value of P at $\lambda = 0$.

The solution of (11) and (12) gives

$$\alpha_1 = \{(q - 1)/[q - (q - 1)A_0]\}\alpha, \qquad (16)$$

$$\alpha' = \{q/[q - (q - 1)A_0]\}\alpha. \qquad (17)$$

These results are already known (see Ref. 1, p. 427).

But if the solid is soluble, there will be a concentration c' (in units of mass per unit volume) in the liquid, and for the problem at hand, one can assume c' to be the saturation concentration, related to T by

$$c' = \epsilon(T - T_0) + c_0, \qquad (18)$$

where c_0 is the value of c' at the origin where $T = T_0$. If the mass diffusivity of the solute in solution is κ_c, its mass is transported in the direction opposite to the temperature gradient at a rate of $\kappa_c \, \partial c/\partial x$. The velocity with which the ellipsoidal boundary moves in the x direction, as a result of erosion and deposition, is then

$$u = \frac{\kappa_c}{\rho_s} \frac{\partial c'}{\partial x} = \frac{\kappa_c \epsilon \alpha'}{\rho_s}, \qquad (19)$$

ρ_s being the density of the solid. The same velocity is obtained if one calculates the speed of erosion or deposition by considering the component of concentration gradient normal to the wall. The assumption of a stationary fluid is now abandoned, and replaced by the assumption that it moves with a (very small) uniform velocity.

Erosion and deposition involve latent heat, which in turn will affect the temperature distribution. The values of α, and α' given by (16) and (17) must therefore be recalculated. The normal gradient of T is $\alpha' \, \partial x/\partial n$, so that the solute dissolved (or deposited) per unit time per unit area is $\kappa_c \alpha' \epsilon \, \partial x/\partial n$. The strength of the heat sink per unit area of the boundary is then $m\alpha' \, \partial x/\partial n$, where

$$m = L\kappa_c \epsilon, \qquad (20)$$

L being the latent heat per unit mass. Then (4) is replaced by

$$T_s = T, \quad k_s \frac{\partial T_s}{\partial n} = k \frac{\partial T}{\partial n} + m\alpha' \frac{\partial x}{\partial n}, \qquad (21)$$

and (11) and (12) are replaced by

$$\alpha + A_0 \alpha_1 = \alpha',$$
$$k_s[\alpha + (A_0 - 1)\alpha_1] = k\alpha' + m\alpha', \qquad (22)$$

the solution of which is

$$\alpha_1 = \{[q - (1 + mk^{-1})]/[q - (q - 1 - mk^{-1})A_0]\}\alpha, \qquad (23)$$

$$\alpha' = \{q/[q - (q - 1 - mk^{-1})A_0]\}\alpha. \qquad (24)$$

If the temperature gradient at infinity is in the y or z direction, the analysis is strictly similar, so that if

$$(T_s)_\infty = \alpha x + \beta y + \gamma z + T_0, \qquad (25)$$

the solution is

$$T_s = \alpha x + \beta y + \gamma z + \alpha_1 A x + \beta_1 B y + \gamma_1 C z + T_0, \qquad (26)$$

$$T = \alpha' x + \beta' y + \gamma' z + T_0, \qquad (27)$$

where α_1 and α' are given by (23) and (24), and

$$(\beta_1, \beta') = \{\beta/[q - (q - 1 - mk^{-1})B_0]\}$$
$$\times (q - 1 - mk^{-1}, q), \qquad (28)$$

$$(\gamma_1, \gamma') = \{\gamma/[q - (q - 1 - mk^{-1})C_0]\}$$
$$\times (q - 1 - mk^{-1}, q), \qquad (29)$$

B_0 and C_0 being the values of B and C at $\lambda = 0$, respectively. The velocity of the fluid inclusion is

$$(u, v, w) = (\kappa_c \epsilon/\rho_s)(\alpha', \beta', \gamma'), \qquad (30)$$

where u, v, and w are the velocity components in the directions of increasing x, y, and z, respectively. The speed is, in general, very small.

We now recall the assumption that the fluid moves with uniform velocity, i.e., as a solid. For this assumption not to be violated, the temperature in the fluid must be a function of height only. The cases in which this is true are:

Case 1: x-axis vertical, $\beta = 0 = \gamma$. In this case $v = 0 = w$.

Case 2: y-axis vertical, $\alpha = 0 = \gamma$. In this case $u = 0 = w$.

Case 3: z-axis vertical, $\alpha = 0 = \beta$. In this case $u = 0 = v$.

Case 4: $(\alpha', \beta', \gamma')$ are the direction numbers of the gravitational acceleration. The speed q of the fluid is, from (30),

$$(\kappa_c \epsilon/\rho_s)(\alpha'^2 + \beta'^2 + \gamma'^2)^{1/2}.$$

In all four cases the temperature gradient and the velocity of the fluid are uniform and vertical. Cases 1–3 may be considered special cases of Case 4, which is general.

We emphasize that these are all the possible cases if gravitational convection will not necessarily occur. Otherwise convection results, and the velocity of the fluid would not be uniform, and would be of much greater amplitude than that given by (30). While the problem of free convection and the problem of stability (involving double diffusion) are interesting in themselves, we exclude them from consideration in this paper.

III. EVALUATION OF A, B, AND C FOR SPECIAL FORMS OF THE ELLIPSOID

From solutions given for the general ellipsoid, solutions for its special forms can be obtained. For these forms, the functions A, B, and C can be evaluated directly, since the integrals defined by (7) are exactly integrable. From A, B, and C, one obtains A_0, B_0, and C_0 by putting λ equal to zero. The special cases are as follows:

Case (i). For a sphere of radius a,

$$A = B = C = (1/3a^3)(a^2 + \lambda)^{3/2}. \tag{31}$$

This result agrees with a direct calculation by the use of a heat doublet in addition to $(T_s)_\infty$ for T_s.

Case (ii). For a prolate ellipsoid, for which $a > b = c$,

$$A = \frac{1 - e_0^2}{e_0^3}\left(\frac{1}{2}\ln\frac{1 + e'}{1 - e'} - e'\right), \tag{32}$$

$$B = C = \frac{1 - e_0^2}{2e_0^3}\left(\frac{e'}{1 - e'^2} - \frac{1}{2}\ln\frac{1 + e'}{1 - e'}\right), \tag{33}$$

where e_0 is e' for $\lambda = 0$, and

$$e' = [(a^2 - b^2)/(a^2 + \lambda)]^{1/2}. \tag{34}$$

Case (iii). For an oblate ellipsoid, for which $a = b > c$,

$$A = B \frac{(1 - e_0^2)^{1/2}}{2e_0^3}\left(\cot^{-1}f - \frac{f}{f^2 + 1}\right), \tag{35}$$

$$C = \frac{(1 - e_0^2)^{1/2}}{e_0^3}\left(\frac{1}{f} - \cot^{-1}f\right), \tag{36}$$

where

$$f = \frac{c^2 + \lambda}{a^2 - c^2} = \frac{(1 - e'^2)^{1/2}}{e'}. \tag{37}$$

Case (iv). For a circular cylinder, with $a = \infty$, $b = c$,

$$A = 0, \tag{38}$$

$$B = C = [b^2/2(b^2 + \lambda)].$$

Case (v). For an elliptic cylinder, with $a = \infty$, $b > c$,

$$A = 0,$$

$$B = \frac{bc}{b^2 - c^2}\left[1 - \left(\frac{c^2 + \lambda}{b^2 + \lambda}\right)^{1/2}\right], \tag{39}$$

$$C = \frac{bc}{b^2 - c^2}\left[\left(\frac{b^2 + \lambda}{c^2 + \lambda}\right)^{1/2} - 1\right]. \tag{40}$$

The results (32)–(36) are given in Carslaw and Jaeger (Ref. 1, p. 427), and can be obtained by direct integration.

IV. REMARKS

It can be shown that the slow movement of the fluid introduces, apart from the complications of a moving boundary, a small positive constant on the right-hand side of the second part of Eq. (3). This is tantamount to a uniform (very weak) heat sink in the liquid. In the simple case of the sphere, this results (in the next approximation) in a (secondary) temperature increasing with radial distance from the origin. Two effects are produced. One is that the fluid is no longer in equilibrium, because of the change of its density with temperature, and a (very weak) convection will ensue. The other is that the (secondary) radial temperature field will erode the boundary through the dissolving action of the fluid, and the spherical cavity will be continually but very slowly enlarged. The liquid will continue to fill the cavity if the combined thermal expansion and expansion caused by pressure release are sufficient for it to do so without the pressure reaching the vapor pressure. When the vapor pressure is reached, evaporation will occur, and vapor will fill part of the cavity. Examination of geological specimens of salts indeed show fluid inclusions consisting of liquid as well as vapor. Migration of vapor–liquid inclusions in a solid in the presence of a temperature gradient was discussed by Anthony and Cline.[2]

Note that in this paper we have given a first approximation to the solution for the movement of liquid inclusions in a soluble solid, on the implicit assumption that the linear laws of thermal diffusion and mass diffusion hold. In all cases treated here the liquid inclusion moves in solid-body translation. An infinite number of possible shapes of the liquid inclusion is allowed, and the question of whether there is a unique shape of the inclusion does not arise.

Precise observations of the movement (or migration) of liquid inclusions in natural minerals are not available because the movement is extremely slow. Cline and Anthony[3] observed the shape of a liquid (water) inclusion in potassium chloride in an isothermal field. To obtain the asymptotic shape (nonspherical) it was necessary to wait seven years! The shape is influenced by the structure of the mineral, which has privileged crystalline surfaces. Thus these surfaces do strongly affect this shape, and seem to impose a unique shape to the inclusion after a very long time. Cline and Anthony[3] also calculated the shapes (which depend, among other things, on sizes) of liquid inclusions in the presence of a temperature gradient. But in their calculation the temperature distribution was not considered, whereas, as the calculation in this paper shows, it is very important. However, in the present calculation the effects of surface energy have been ignored. Thus the question of the asymptotic shape of a liquid inclusion, given its size, moving in a given soluble solid, including whether that shape is unique, must remain open. It seems that this rather new problem needs more attention of physicists and engineers.

ACKNOWLEDGMENT

This work has been supported by the Fluid Dynamics Program of the Office of Naval Research.

[1] H. S. Carslaw and J. C. Jaeger, *Conduction of Heat in Solids* (Clarendon, Oxford, 1959), pp. 425–426.
[2] T. R. Anthony and H. E. Cline, Acta Metall. **20**, 247 (1972).
[3] H. E. Cline and T. R. Anthony, J. Appl. Phys. **48**, 5096 (1977).

Reprinted from:
ADVANCES IN APPLIED MECHANICS, VOL. 16
© 1976
ACADEMIC PRESS, INC.
New York   San Francisco   London

Preface

This volume is dedicated to the memory of Sir Geoffrey Ingram Taylor (March 7, 1886–June 27, 1975), a great scientist and a wonderful man who was held in esteem and admiration by all who knew his work, and in affection by all who had the good fortune to enjoy his friendship.

Much has been written about him and his work since his death, and immediately following these few pages is an intimate sketch of G. I. (for it is thus that many of us refer to him) by Professor G. K. Batchelor, G. I.'s associate for 30 years, who is also writing a more complete biographical article of him for publication by the Royal Society of London. Here I shall only say a few things in remembrance of him.

His work was always marked by an originality of thought and a freshness of approach that continue to delight his readers, and a characteristic welding of analysis to experiment that is rarely attempted, let alone attained, by others. Since his collected works fill four large volumes, it is natural to wonder which of his works gave him the most satisfaction. In 1967, when he came to Ann Arbor to receive an honorary degree, I asked him that question, and he answered by singling out his work on the stability of Couette flows. At this, Professor A. M. Kuethe, who was walking with us, expressed some surprise, for he had thought G. I.'s statistical theory of turbulence occupied that position of honor. I suppose G. I.'s answer might well have been different if I had asked him which of his works he considered the most important. But I do not think that question would have been as congenial to him. He considered himself an amateur in science. It is therefore not surprising that the spirit of adventure is often evident in his work, for one who works out of curiosity and love of the subject is likely to explore where others dare not tread or, more often, do not think of treading. But if he called himself an amateur, the term was appropriate in the etymological sense only.

The spirit of adventure was evident in his life as well. He learned to fly an airplane and to parachute when aviation was young, he rode balloons,† he sailed all over Europe, he skied when bindings were primitive and skis were without steel edges, and he tried (unsuccessfully) to water-ski when he was eighty years old! On his holidays he was often accompanied by his wife (née Grace Stephanie F. Ravenhill), who shared his interests in travels and was an ideal companion. In 1929 they visited Borneo and then Japan, where they slept in picturesque ryokans (wayside inns). In 1933 and 1934 they visited Canada. The trip in 1934 was one on horseback through the Canadian Rockies, taken with two friends and a cook.

What he enjoyed most of his holidays was the beauty of nature and the feeling of solitude that it imparted. Once I showed him three volumes of old prints by Hiroshige, and the silent figures, the swaying willows, the blooming cherry trees, the temples, the bridges, and the waters gave him so much pleasure that he told Brooke Benjamin about them when he returned to England. The Japan G. I. knew was relatively unspoiled compared to the Japan of today, but the Japan Hiroshige depicted would have suited him even better.

His love of beauty might well be inherited from his father, who was an artist. In 1967, while we were looking at a book of Camille Pissaro's paintings, G. I. recalled a visit of the Pissaros (Camille and his son Lucien, who was also an artist) at his father's home in St. John's Wood in London. The Pissaros were in London in 1892 and 1897. Thus he was able to recall things that happened when he was six years or eleven years old. On Sunday afternoons at St. John's Wood, G. I.'s father would make pencil drawings of roses without using an eraser. G. I. gave me one of these drawings, of two sprigs of roses. The roses look soft and moist, as if the dew had just evaporated from them. In G. I.'s living room was an oil painting by his father, a purplish landscape of Wales with wet sand on the beach: not so wet as to give perfect reflection, just wet enough to give the feeling of wetness. G. I. seemed to have inherited his father's love of the beauty of Wales, for he had a cottage in Llanfair, Wales, where he kept his sailboat.

G. I.'s excellent health and adventurous spirit were only part of his gift for happiness; his capacity for enjoying the simple things in life and a natural

---

† He once described the hazards in landing balloons. One pulled the cord (to let gas escape) in order to descend, discarded sand bags to let it rise again when it descended too fast or toward the wrong place, and repeated the procedure over and over until one succeeded in landing. In one such maneuver, after some sand was discarded, "the sand rapidly dispersed and fell more slowly than the balloon so, relative to us, it went upwards. Then as our downward velocity stopped and reversed the sand caught up and filled the air all round us. It was like a sand storm."

detachment from the worldly aspirations that are a burden to less fortunate people were, I think, what gave his life the happiness that mere health and adventures could not have bestowed. His detachment arose not only from a natural simplicity but also from a desire to conserve time and energy to do what he wanted most to do. Indeed he received his numerous honors with a simple pleasure. But he never let these honors change him, and it is easy to believe that he could have been as happy without them.

I shall now quote two letters from him, because these are interesting, and because they will make the points I have made, only more eloquently. The first was written on July 28, 1969, and the second on October 30, 1969.

Many thanks for your letter and congratulations. I had just come back from Cape Breton Island when my O. M.† was announced. I had a beautifully quiet time there at my cousin's place which is on a dirt road 6 miles from the nearest paved highway: no noise from cars or planes—only the wind in the trees and the surf on the shore. One could safely drink out of any of the streams and I used to bathe in one close to where it ran into the sea. It has been so dry since I got back that I have been trying to keep the plants alive by watering them.

I had a very pleasant time (contrary to my expectations) when I was received by the Queen and given the O. M. insignia. I had expected officials all round, but I was introduced by an equerry who retired and shut the door, leaving me to talk with the Queen for a quarter of an hour. She is very easy to talk to and to listen to, and though nothing of any particular importance was said by either of us I thoroughly enjoyed the interview. I formed the impression that she is a very nice person whom one would much like to have as a friend under other circumstances.

I also have been looking at problems of interest, in particular what is the mechanism which drives sap up a tree and sugar down from the leaves? It is a very interesting problem but I doubt whether it has much hydrodynamic content.

I think that individualists like you and me should not feel the unimportance of what we do compared with the work of the thousands in the space programmes. Of course our works are minute by comparison; but as long as we enjoy doing them that is the thing.

Your writing of Gaspé reminds me of a holiday Stephanie and I took in 1933, sleeping in a barn which was, I think, then the nearest building to the lighthouse at Gaspé Point. I tried bathing but it was terribly cold. . . .

Although G. I. was never in China he did have one connection with it. Mary Boole, his mother's elder sister, married Howard Hinton. The Hintons' grandson William‡ and his wife were in China during the Sino-Japanese

---

† "This is a very illustrious order, confined to 24 people who make outstanding contributions of a non-political kind, and it is certainly the highest distinction which has been conferred on him. His close friend Adrian (whom you may remember as a former master of Trinity) is also a member of the Order of Merit. He will be able to wear a very fine medal and ribbon around his neck on dress-up occasions in the future." So wrote George Batchelor in a letter to me.

‡ William's sister Joan has been in China for many years and, like him, is very sympathetic to the Chinese people.

War, and stayed until many years after the Revolution of 1949. Indeed, at least one daughter was born to them in China. I once asked G. I. why the Hintons stayed so long in China, and he answered that they did so because they were idealistic.

The mechanics community has lost a leading light and a living example of excellence, goodness, and the possibility of happiness. His life and work will forever be an inspiration, but those of us who knew him shall always miss him.

CHIA-SHUN YIH

Sir Geoffrey I. Taylor, 1886–1975

Reprinted without change of pagination from the
Journal of Fluid Mechanics, *vol.* 17, *part* 1, *pp.* 154–160, 1963

REVIEWS

Handbook of Engineering Mechanics. Edited by W. FLÜGGE. New York: McGraw-Hill, 1962. 1632 pp. £10. 13*s*. 6*d*.

This formidable and well-printed book, in seven parts, contains eighty-eight chapters contributed by as many mathematicians and engineers, most of them well known in their own fields. Part 1, on mathematics, has twenty chapters. Five chapters on the mechanics of rigid bodies constitute Part 2, and forty-two chapters are devoted to the theory of structure (Part 3), elasticity (Part 4), plasticity and viscoelasticity (Part 5), and vibrations (Part 6). Fluid mechanics (Part 7) occupies the remaining twenty-one chapters.

Looking over the table of contents, one wonders immediately why this thick book had not been divided into three volumes, on mathematics, solid mechanics, and fluid mechanics, respectively, especially since a handbook of fluid mechanics has actually been published by the same publisher. As it stands, the extensive coverage makes the space devoted to each chapter so very small that one wonders to what extent the editor's first aim—to make the book useful to the expert in his work—is fulfilled. The other two aims of the editor, to stimulate the expert in one field by the thoughts, methods, and results in other fields and to provide a bazaar for window-shopping students of engineering mechanics, seem more assured of fulfilment.

The part on mathematics deals with a number of subjects ranging from the very elementary to the advanced. The effect of space on style is exemplified in the extreme by chapter 15 on special functions, which is more a collection of formulas than an exposition on the origin of special functions and their application to problems in engineering mechanics. The formulas are doubtless useful, but unlikely to be attractive to a window shopper. One notable omission in the chapter on ordinary differential equations is the Sturm–Liouville theory. Another is the theory of differential equations with a large parameter. However, the amount of information packed into the twenty thin chapters is really amazing, and represents a laudable achievement. The same is also true of the chapters on solid mechanics.

The part on fluid mechanics, with which this review is principally concerned, begins with a chapter on the basic concepts and equations. This is followed by a chapter of two pages on dimensionless parameters, in which, curiously enough, the concept of similarity is not even mentioned. The next two chapters deal with ideal-fluid flow, expertly written by Professors V. L. Streeter and I. Flügge-Lotz. Perhaps the only important criticism of the two chapters on ideal-fluid flow is that irrotational flows are introduced without a derivation of the theorem of persistence of circulation (and hence, in particular, of irrotationality). This practice has made it difficult for students to differentiate between potential flows and the flows of an inviscid fluid of constant density. Otherwise I find the two chapters perfectly readable and digestible.

In the attractively written chapter on airfoil theory by Dr A. Robinson more use of singular integral equations in the theory of thin airfoils would have been welcome, particularly since the section on singular integral equations in chapter 17 is quite sketchy.

The next eight chapters, two on thermodynamics and six on compressible-fluid flows, constitute the middle third of the part on fluid mechanics. The latter group progresses from subsonic through transonic and supersonic to hypersonic flow, and, after a brief interruption (the chapter on slender-body theory), ends in flutter (chapter 80). These are in general systematic, informative, and attractively written. It is, however, rather regrettable that there is no discussion of non-homentropic flows.

The rest of the chapters deal mainly with viscous fluids, with the exception of a chapter on surface waves and one on cavitation. The chapter on flow at low Reynolds numbers, particularly the second half of it, is a pleasure to read—in spite of the editor's warning that this book is not for readers. The next three chapters, on boundary layers and turbulence, cover more or less the familiar ground. On the first page of chapter 85 (on lubrication) there appears a footnote to the effect that Dr Poritsky's original manuscript has been greatly abridged. What a pity! It is regrettable, too, that we are not to benefit more from Professor T. Y. Wu's mathematical power and physical insight by having a longer chapter on surface waves, and that the chapter on cavitation is so short that it hardly reflects the amount of significant work done on cavitation at the California Institute of Technology. In the final chapter, on flow through porous media, one misses the modern results on instability, fingering, and the movement of fluid masses in another fluid (also flowing in the porous medium).

Looking at the contents as a whole, the most striking omission seems to be open-channel flow. Shallow-water theory, flood waves, back-water curves are completely absent, and even the old hydraulic jump has been moved out for being a bore, along with the instructive and important concept of subcritical and supercritical flows. Missing too is a chapter on water hammer. Has civil engineering become too old-fashioned to be represented? On the other end of the spectrum, a chapter on stability would be welcome; or one on geophysical fluid mechanics, which is having an increasing bearing on engineering. But surely it is easier to review a book than to edit one, and very much easier to criticize a thick book than to write a chapter in it. There is no doubt that this is a useful book.

CHIA-SHUN YIH

—BOOK REVIEW SECTION—

Stability of fluid motions, I (282 pp.) and II (274 pp.). By Daniel D. Joseph. Springer Verlag, Berlin, Heidelberg, New York. $39.80 each.*

It has been wellnigh one hundred years since Reynolds discovered turbulence in fluid flow, and although the increasingly extensive and intensive research on turbulence since the beginning of this century has provided much information on the *effects* of turbulence, it has not to this day really succeeded in illuminating our *understanding* of the phenomenon of turbulence. Efforts at understanding it have proceeded either along the avenue of statistical theories, with some success for homogeneous and isotropic turbulence but much less for shear flows, or along the road of the theory of hydrodynamic stability, in the hope of approaching turbulent flows from laminar ones through repeated bifurcations. It is this noble if distant aim that has attracted many able researchers to the field of hydrodynamic stability, among whom it is our good fortune to have Daniel D. Joseph, the author of the book under review.

There are few books on the same subject. One by C. C. Lin (1956) treats mainly the Orr-Sommerfeld equation and the intricacies of its solutions, although to a lesser extent it also deals with convective, inertial, and geophysical instabilities, and certain nonlinear aspects. An extensive book by S. Chandrasekhar (1961) deals exclusively with the linear theory of convective, inertial, and magnetohydrodynamic instabilities, especially those with geophysical and astrophysical applications. A more recent book by Betchov and Criminali (1971) is a computer-oriented treatment of the Orr-Sommerfeld equations. Against such a background, Joseph's book, in its reliance on the energy method and its insistence on taking the amplitude of the disturbance into account, is unique. It enriches our knowledge of hydrodynamic stability and is indispensable to university libraries and to serious researchers and students in the field.

The book consists of two volumes. Volume I contains seven chapters and five appendices. In Chapter I the basic ideas on global instability and well-known results on the uniqueness of the Navier-Stokes equations are presented. In Chapter II instability and bifurcation are discussed in a general way. These two chapters serve to orient the reader and to prepare him for things to come. In Chapters III and IV the author presents many interesting recent results on the stability of Poiseuille flow and of parallel flow through annular ducts. Chapter V discusses the global stability of Couette flows, and Chapters VI and VII treat spiral Couette-Poiseuille flows and flows between concentric rotating spheres. Appendices A, B, C, and D give useful mathematical results. Appendix E, on nearly parallel flows, could have constituted another chapter. It is curious that it is presented as an appendix.

Volume II contains five chapters dealing exclusively with gravitational convection, one of which concerns convection in porous media. One chapter treats viscoelastic fluids, and the final chapter is principally a study of the effect of surface tension on the stability of superposed fluids of different densities in a gravitational field.

Throughout the book the superbly-presented energy method runs like the warp of a loom. This method can be traced back to the work of Orr (1907), Hopf (1941), Thomas (1942), and Serrin (1959), and consists in expressing the Reynolds number, via the Navier-Stokes equations, as a ratio of two integrals, of which the integrands contain, quadratically, the unknown velocity (or temperature) of the disturbance, and in finding the maximum of this ratio as the unknown quantity is allowed to roam through a function space, subject only to the requirement of the equation of continuity and to the boundary conditions. Then if the actual Reynolds number is less than this maximum ratio, the flow is monotonically stable.

Since the finding of the maximum is by means of the Euler-Lagrange equation of the calculus of variations, which is linear, the method is finally a linear analysis emerging and arising from a baptism in the holy water of nonlinearity. The attending angel absolved linear analysis of its original sin, whispered in its ears one truth, then flew away, revealing no more secrets. The one truth enables it to provide a lower bound for the Reynolds number, below which the fluid is monotonically stable. Of course, since the function space in which the unknown roams is not very restricted, this bound is usually not very sharp. For Bénard cells, however, it coincides with the

---

* This book review was written during the tenure of a Senior Scientist Award given by the Alexander von Humboldt Foundation of the German Federal Republic, which enabled me to read the book at leisure at the University of Karlsruhe. To the Humboldt Foundation and my Karlsruhe hosts I wish to express my sincere appreciation.

upper bound (above which the fluid is unstable) provided by a linear analysis ab initio—a very satisfying fact.

If the energy method does not provide detailed description of fluid motion, and avoids direct confrontation with the difficulties of nonlinearity, the same cannot be said of the valiant attempts in determining the stability of perturbed flows (Chapter III and IV). For this purpose the Floquet theory is used, since the perturbed flows treated are periodic in time. The results obtained, taken together with the theorem (henceforth called Joseph's theorem in this review) given in Chapter II that flows with small subcritical disturbances are stable, are extremely interesting, exciting, and bewildering. I shall return to this point later. Here I only want to underline the importance of Joseph's theorem, and to point out one direct way of confronting nonlinearity admirably given in this book.

The simple and precise style of writing, emerging partly from the author's mathematical discipline, acquires, in the long run, an elegance. This fact emerges in spite of the occasionally unfortunate choice of mathematical symbols, and of one peculiar manner of presentation. Of the latter the reader should be warned. A theorem is often stated without promise of proof, and just when one, after mistaking it to be obvious and making a few vain attempts to prove it in his mind, is about to give up the effort, he finds the proof in the next paragraph or in the next three or five pages, in which he may repeat the experience at another level.

Since the game is, understandably, squeezing as much juice out of the lemon as one can, unnecessary insufficiencies are extremely rare in this book. I found only one, in Chapter V. In extending Synge's (1938) proof of the Rayleigh criterion for the stability of Couette flow against axisymmetric disturbances, the author imposed the unnecessary restriction that Ω_1 (angular velocity on the inner cylinder) be greater than Ω_2 (angular velocity on the outer cylinder), and, curiously enough, also attributes this restriction to Synge's proof for infinitesimal disturbances. Neither Rayleigh, Kármán, nor Synge ever needed this restriction, and upon close examination of Joseph's proof I found that he did not need it either. For (40.17) stands without it, $A + Br^{-2}$ will be positive if Rayleigh's criterion is satisfied, and all one needs to do to broaden the base of validity of (40.17) is to replace B by $|B|$ in the G_v defined on p. 150.

I now turn to a discussion of the consequences of Joseph's theorem and the neutral bifurcation solutions he has found for perturbed flows. Lest the reader, upon careful reading of Joseph's proof of his theorem, think there is a fatal flaw in it, I note first that there is an oversight in the proof, but in the end it does not matter. He states, in p. 47 and p. 51, that σ_v is positive. Actually it is positive only along the left branch of the neutral curve when it has two branches; along the right branch it is negative. However, when the sign of ν_ϵ is taken into account his theorem (pp. 47 and 51) stands intact. So the solid lines and dotted lines (indicating instability) in Fig. 34.1 on p. 111 are all properly drawn. As a consequence of his theorem, Joseph states that subcritical solutions are not observable.

But the host of questions they call forth, these dotted lines! First of all, comparing Fig. 34.1 with Fig. E1.6 in Appendix E, we find that most of Schubauer and Skramstad's experimental points lie in the subcritical region, and furthermore some points in the supercritical region are near the right branch, whereas according to Fig. 34.1 they should not be there at all. To be sure, Fig. E1.6 is only for nearly parallel flows. But I do not think that alone can explain the discrepancy.

On purely theoretical grounds, one might wonder what happens to unstable infinitesimal disturbances that fall within the loop of the neutral curve in Fig. 34.1. Do they all migrate downward when the amplitude ϵ is increased, to the region where supercritical disturbances can persist without growing or damping? That seems unlikely, since that region is so narrow. Even the application of the "principle of equi-conjecture" is not without risk. The author says that perhaps calculations to higher orders in ϵ might produce stable subcritical solutions, to which transient solutions might be attracted. This still leaves the going over from within the neutral loop at small ϵ to the surface representing stable subcritical solutions a cloudy affair. Furthermore, near 0 in Fig. 34.1, stable subcritical solutions should exist (by continuity) for small ϵ if they do for large ϵ. So why do the solid lines not continue beyond 0, if indeed stable subcritical solutions exist for some finite ϵ?

Joseph's theorem, together with his bifurcation solutions and their stability or instability, has led us to a point of the frontier separating conquered territory from terra incognita, on our way toward an understanding of the origin of turbulence. At this point of the frontier, we stand *verwirrt* if not quite *verirrt*. But it is a measure of Joseph's imaginativeness that the questions his work has raised not only do not detract from its value, but, on the contrary, bear testimony to the excitement it calls forth.

The two volumes contain a wealth of results and thought: interesting, stimulating, and often important. So if at this moment, soon after the appearance of the book, the author feels tempted to say "Verweile doch, du bist so schön!", we in our appreciation of his contribution rejoice with him. But before the last glass of champagne is poured, we already feel the urge to resume our journey, for we have "promises to keep, and miles to go."

CHIA-SHUN YIH

(*Ann Arbor*)

Curriculum Vitae

CHIA–SHUN YIH, Stephen P. Timoshenko Distinguished University Professor of Fluid Mechanics Emeritus, the University of Michigan, and Graduate Research Professor Emeritus, University of Florida.

Education:
B.S. (C.E.), National Central University, Chungking, China, 1942;
M.S. (Mechanics and Hydraulics), State University of Iowa, 1947;
Ph.D. (Mechanics and Hydraulics), State University of Iowa, 1948;
Brown University, summer of 1947.

Employment:
Academic:
Instructor, National University of Kweichow, Kweiyang, China, 1944–45;
Instructor in Mathematics, University of Wisconsin, 1948–49;
Lecturer in Mathematics, University of British Columbia, 1949–50;
Associate Professor, Colorado State University, 1950–51;
Attaché de Recherche (French Government Scholarship),
Mathematics, Université de Nancy, 1951–52;
Research Associate, State University of Iowa, 1952–54;
Associate Professor, State University of Iowa, 1954–56;
Associate Professor (Engineering Mechanics),
University of Michigan, 1956–58;
Professor of Fluid Mechanics, University of Michigan, 1958–68;
Stephen P. Timoshenko Distinguished University
Professor of Fluid Mechanics, University of Michigan, 1968–88.
Visiting Professor, Université de Paris and
Université de Grenoble; 1970–71.
Graduate Research Professor, the University of Florida, 1987–90.

Other Professional:
Research Assistant, National Hydraulic Laboratory, Quanshien, China;
Junior Engineer, National Bureau of Bridge Design,
Kweiyang, China; 1943–44;
Reviewer for Mathematical Reviews, Reviewer for various professional
journals;
Chairman, Executive Committee of the Fluid-Dynamics
Division of the American Physical Society, 1973–74.

Publications:
See Attached List.

Professional and
Honor Societies:
Sigma Xi, Pi Mu Epsilon, Tau Beta Pi, Phi Kappa Phi;
Fellow of the America Physical Society;
Member, International Association for Hydraulic Research,up to 1982;
Senior Fellow, Michigan Society of Fellows, 1971–73;
Member, Academia Sinica;
Member, U.S. National Academy of Engineering.
(Listed in Who's Who in America.)

Fellowships:
Senior Postdoctoral Fellow, National Science Foundation, 1959–60;
Guggenheim Fellow, awarded in 1959, used in 1964.

Editorial Duties:
On the editorial boards of the Physics of Fluids (1969–72),

the SIAM Journal of Applied Mathematics (1971–72), and the
Annual Reviews of Fluid Mechanics (First 4 volumes).
Editor of the Advances in Applied Mechanics (1970–82).

Honors:

1. 1968 Achievement Award, The Chinese Institute of Engineers, New York.
2. 1973 Achievement Award, Chinese Engineers and Scientists Association of Southern California.
3. Henry Ruseel Lecturer, 1974, The University of Michigan.
4. Alexander von Humboldt Senior Scientist Award, 1977–78.
5. Theodore von Kármaán medal, 1981, Am. Soc. Civil Eng.
6. Stephan S. Attwood Award, The University of Michigan, 1984.
7. Fluid-Dynamics Prize, American Physical Society (sponsored by the Office of Naval Research), 1985.
8. Otto Laporte Award, American Physical Society, 1989.

List of Chia-Shun Yih's Publications

1. Temperature Distribution in a Steady, Laminar, Preheated Air Jet, *J. Appl. Mech.* (1950) 381–382

2. An Extension of Dehn's Theorem on the Approximation of a Function by a Power Series, *Math. Stu. Indian Math. Soc.* **18** (1950) 117–122

3. Free Convection due to Point Source of Heat, *Proc. First U.S. Natl. Congr. Appl. Mech.* (1950) 941–947

4. Diffusion from a Line Source in Laminar Flow over a Wedge and in a Blasius Flow, *Proc. First U.S. Natl. Congr. Appl. Mech.* (1951) 797–800

5. On a Differential Equation of Atmospheric Diffusion, *Trans. Am. Geophys. Union* **33** (1952) 8–12

6. Similarity Solution of a Specialized Diffusion Equation, *Trans. Am. Geophys. Union* **33** (1952) 356–360

7. Gravitational Convection from a Boundary Source (jointly with Hunter Rouse and H. W. Humphreys), *Tellus* **4** (1952) 201–210

8. Laminar Free Convection due to a Line Source of Heat, *Trans. Am. Geophys. Union* **33** (1952) 669–672

9. On Tides in Estuaries and Around Small Islands, *Trans. Am. Geophys. Union* **34** (1953) 389–393

10. Free Convection due to Boundary Sources, *Symp. on the Use of Models in Geophysical Fluid Dynamics* (1953) 117–133

11. Temperature Distribution in Laminar Stagnation-Point Flow with Axisymmetry, *J. Aerospace Sci.* **21** (1954) 37–42

12. Stability of Parallel Laminar Flow with a Free Surface, *Proc. Second U.S. Natl. Congr. Appl. Mech.* (1954) 623–628

13. Applications of the Relaxation Technique in Fluid Mechanics (jointly with J. S. McNown and En-Yun Hsu), *Trans. A.S.C.E.* **120** (1955) 650–686

14. Stability of Two-Dimensional Parallel Flows for Three-Dimensional Disturbances, *Quart. Appl. Math.* **12** (1955) 434–435

15. Maximum Acceleration in Two-Dimensional Steady Flows of an Ideal Fluid, *Quart. Appl. Math.* **13** (1955) 202–203

16. Hydraulic Jump in a Fluid System of Two Layers (jointly with C. R. Guha), *Tellus* **7** (1955) 358–366

17. Solutions of the Hyper-Bessel Equation, *Quart. Appl. Math.* **13** (1956) 462–463

18. Forces, Moments, and Added Masses for Rankine Bodies (jointly with L. Landweber), *J. Fluid Mech.* **1** (1956) 319–336

19. On Stratified Flows in a Gravitational Field, *Tellus* **9** (1957) 220–228 (presented to Ninth Int'l Congr. Appl. Mech., 1956)

20. Laminar Convection of Heat from Two-Dimensional Bodies with Variable Wall Temperatures, *Proc. Fifth Midwestern Conference on Fluid Mech.* (1957) 29–40

21. Stream Functions in Three-Dimensional Flows, *La Houille Blanche* No.3 (1957) 445–450

22. Maximum Speed in Steady Subsonic Flows, *Quart. Appl. Math.* **16** (1958) 178–180

23. On the Flow of a Stratified Fluid, *Proc. Third U.S. Natl. Congr. Appl. Mech.* (1958) 857–861

24. Two Solutions for Inviscid Rotational Flow with Corner Eddies, *J. Fluid Mech.* **5** (1959) 36–40

25. Effects of Gravitational or Eletromagnetic Fields on Fluid Motion, *Quart. Appl. Math.* **16** (1959) 409–415

26. Thermal Instability of Viscous Fluids, *Quart. Appl. Math.* **17** (1959) 25–42

27. Ring Vortices Generated Eletromagnetically, *J. Fluid Mech.* **5** (1959) 436–444

28. Inhibition of Hydrodynamic Instability by an Electric Current, *Phys. Fluids* **2** (1959) 125–130

29. *Laminar Motion, Advanced Fluid Mechanics,* ed. H. Rouse (John Wiley and Sons, 1959), Chap. 5

30. Effect of Density Variation on Fluid Flow, *J. Geophys. Res.* **64** (1959) 2219–2223

31. Gravity Waves in a Stratified Fluid, *J. Fluid Mech.* **8** (1960) 481–508

32. Exact Solution for Steady Two-Dimensional Flow of a Stratified Fluid, *J. Fluid Mech.* **9** (1960) 161–174

33. A Transformation for Non-Homentropic Flows, with an Application to Large-Amplitude Motion in the Atmosphere, *J. Fluid Mech.* **9** (1960) 68– 80

34. Instability of a Rotating Liquid Film with a Free Surface, *Proc. Roy. Soc.* **A258** (1960) 63–86

35. Finite Two-Dimensional Cavities, *Proc. Roy. Soc.* **A258** (1960) 90–100

36. Flow of a Non-Homogeneous Fluid in Porous Medium, *J. Fluid Mech.* **10** (1961) 133-140

37. Dual Role of Viscosity in the Instability of Revolving Fluids of Variable Density, *Phys. Fluids* **4** (1961) 806–811

38. *Ideal-Fluid Flow, Handbook of Fluid Mechanics,* ed. V. L. Streeter (McGraw-Hill, 1961), Chap. 4

39. Prevention of Stagnation Zones in Flows of a Stratified or a Rotating Fluid (jointly with W. W. O'Dell and W. R. Debler), *Proc. Fourth U.S. Natl. Congr. Appl. Mech.* (1962) 1441–1453

40. Formation of Ring in a Liquid Film Attached to the Inside of a Rotating Cylinder (jointly with W. R. Debler), *J. Aerospace Sci.* **29** (1962) 364

41. On the Instability of Stock on a Fourdrinier Wire (jointly with W. R. Debler), *TAPPI* **45** (1962) 272–279

42. Stability of Liquid Flow Down an Inclined Plane, *Phys. Fluids* **6** (1963) 321–334

43. Velocity of Fluid Mass Imbedded in Another Fluid Flowing in a Porous Medium, *Phys. Fluids* **6** (1963) 1403–1407

44. A Transformation of Free-Surface Flow in Porous Media, *Phys. Fluids* **7** (1964) 20–24

45. Effect of Variation of Accleration on Free-Surface Instability (jointly with S. P. Lin), *TAPPI* **47** (1964) 88–94

46. Hydraulic Jump in a Rotating Fluid (jointly with H. E. Gascoigne and W. R. Debler), *Phys. Fluids* **7** (1964) 638–642

47. *Dynamics of Nonhomogeneous Fluids* (Macmillan Co., 1965)

48. Gravitational Instability of a Viscous Fluid in a Magnetic Field, *J. Fluid Mech.* **22** (1965) 579–586

49. Stability of a Non-Newtonian Liquid Film Flowing Down an Inclined Plane, *Phys. Fluids* **8** (1965) 1257-1262

50. Large-Amplitude Motion of a Nonhomogenous Fluid, General Lecture, *Transactions of Eleventh Congress, International Association of Hydraulic Research,* **VI** (1965) 189-215

51. On Large-Amplitude Magnetohydrodynamics, *J. Fluid Mech.* **23** (1965) 261–271

52. Note on Edge Waves in a Stratified Fluid, *J. Fluid Mech.* **24** (1966) 765–767

53. On the Earnshaw Conjecture, *Z.A.M.M.* **46** (1966) 471–472

54. Instability due to Viscosity Stratification, *J. Fluid Mech.* **27** (1967) 337–352

55. Instability of Laminar Flows due to a Film of Absorption, *J. Fluid Mech.* **28** (1967) 493–500

56. Equations Governing Steady Three-Dimensional Large-Amplitude Motion of a Stratified Fluid, *J. Fluid Mech.* **29** (1967) 539–544

57. Peristaltic Transport (jointly with Y. C. Fung), *J. Appl. Mech.* (1968) 669–675

58. Fluid Motion Induced by Surface-Tension Variation, *Phys. Fluids* **11** (1968) 477–480

59. Stability of a Horizontal Fluid Interface in a Periodic Vertical Electric Field, *Phys. Fluids* **11** (1968) 1447–1449

60. Instability of Unsteady Flows or Configurations. Part 1. Instability of a Horizontal Liquid Layer on an Oscillating Plane, *J. Fluid Mech.* **31** (1968) 737–751

61. A Class of Solutions for Steady Stratified Flows, *J. Fluid Mech.* **36** (1969) 75–85

62. Stratified Flows, *Ann. Rev. Fluid Mech.* **1** (1969) 73-110

63. Three-Dimensional Motion of a Liquid Film Induced by Surface-Tension Variation or Gravity, *Phys. Fluids* **31** (1969) 1982–1987

64. Note on Eigenvalue Bounds for the Orr-Sommerfeld Equation, *J. Fluid Mech.* **38** (1969) 273–278

65. *Fluid Mechanics, A Concise Introduction to the Theory* (McGraw-Hill Co., 1969) (West River Press, 1979,1988)

66. Some Results on the Nonoscillation of Salt Fingers, *Phys. Fluids* **13** (1970) 2907–2911

67. Stability of and Waves in Stratified Flows, *Proc. of the 8th Symposium of Naval Hydrodynamics* (1970) 219–237

68. Surface Waves in Flowing Water, *J. Fluid Mech.* **51** (1972) 209–220

69. Spectral Theory of Taylor Vortices. Part 1. Structure of Unstable Modes, *Archive of Rational Mechanics and Analysis* **46** (1972) 218–240

70. Spectral Theory of Taylor Vortices. Part 2. Proof of Nonoscillation, *Archive of Rational Mechanics and Analysis* **47** (1972) 288–300

71. Instability of Unsteady Flows or Configurations. Part 2. Convective Instabiliy (jointly with C.-H. Li), *J. Fluid Mech.* **54** (1972) 143–152

72. The Hydraulic Arch, *Quart. Appl. Math.* **37** (1973) 377–378

73. Wave Velocity in Parallel Flows of a Viscous Fluid, *J. Fluid Mech.* **58** (1973) 703–708

74. Wave Motion in Stratified Fluids, *Nonlinear Waves* (Cornell University Press, 1974) 263–290

75. Instability of Stratified Flows as a Result of Resonance, *Phys. Fluids* **17** (1974) 1483–1488

76. Progressive Waves of Permanent Form in Continuously Stratified Fluids, *Phys. Fluids* **17** (1974) 1489–1495

77. Fluid Mechanics of Colliding Plates, *Phys. Fluids* **17** (1974) 1936–1940

78. Vortices and Vortex Rings of Stratified Fluids, *SIAM J. Appl. Math.* **28** (1975) 899–912

79. Internal Waves in Pipes, *J. Hydraulic Res.* **13** (1975) 329–342

80. Internal Waves in a Circular Channel (jointly with W. H. Yang), *J. Fluid Mech.* **74** (1976) 183-192

81. Comparison Theorems for Gravity Waves in Basins of Variable Depth, *Quart. Appl. Math.* **33** (1976) 387–394

82. Instability of Surface and Internal Waves, *Adv. Appl. Mech.* **16** (1976) 369–419

83. Remembrance of G. I. Taylor,Preface, *Adv. Appl. Mech.* **16** (1976) viii–xii

84. Old China Remembered: 1. The Slate Court, 2. Crepuscule, 3. Mulberries, 4. Silk from Wild Cocoons, 5. Winter-Sweet, *The Ohio Rev.* **18** (1977) 67–77

85. Turbulent Buoyant Plumes, *Phys. Fluids* **20** (1977) 1234–1237

86. Stability of Time-Periodic Flows in a Circular Pipe (jointly with W. H. Yang), *J. Fluid Mech.* **82** (1977) 497–505

87. Buoyant Plumes in a Transverse Wind, *Proc. 12th Symposium on Naval Hydrodynamics* (1978) 607–617

88. Flows with Condensation, *Quart. Appl. Math.* **37** (1980) 401–409

89. Interplay and Competition of Forces in Stratified Flows, *Proc. Second International Symposium on Stratified Flows* (1980) 17–39

90. *Stratified Flows* (Academic Press,1980)

91. Similarity Solutions for Turbulent Jets and Plumes, *J. Eng. Mech. Div., Am. Soc. Civil Eng.,* **107** (1981) 455–478

92. Round Buoyant Plumes (jointly with Feng Wu), *Phys. Fluids* **24** (1981) 794–801

93. Similarity of Steady Stratified Flows, *J. Fluid Mech.* **108** (1981) 241–246

94. Plane Laminar and Turbulent Plumes (jointly with A. S. Gupta), *Brazilian J. Mech. Sci.* **3** (1981) 49–56

95. On the Nonexistence of Solution of a Differential System Governing Axisymmetric Flow of a Stratified Fluid, *Quart. Appl. Math.* **40** (1982) 101–104

96. Conical Vortices: A Class of Exact Solutions of the Navier-Stokes Equations (jointly with Feng Wu, A. K. Garg, and S. Leibovich), *Phys. Fluids* **25** (1982) 2147–2158

97. On Steady Stratified Flows in Porous Media, *Quart. Appl. Math.* **40** (1982) 219–230

98. Binnie Waves, *Proc. 14th Symposium of Naval Hydrodynamics* (1982) 89–102

99. Waves in Open Channels (jointly with Jinsung Shi), *J. Eng. Mech. Div., Am Soc. Civil Eng.,* **110** (1984) 847–870

100. Waves in Meandering Streams, *J. Fluid Mech.* **130** (1983) 109–121

101. Edge Waves Created by a Longshore Current and a Ridge in the Sea Bed, *Proc. 15th Symposium of Naval Hydrodynamics* (1984) 1–5

102. New Deriviations of Darwin's Theorem, *J. Fluid Mech.* **152** (1985) 163–172

103. Instability Resulting from Stratification in Thermal Conductivity, *Phys. Fluids* **29** (1986) 1769–1773

104. Movement of Liquid Inclusions in Soluble Solids: an Inverse Stokes' Law, *Phys. Fluids* **29** (1986) 2785–2787

105. Pattern of Gravity Waves Created by a Body Moving in a Stratified Ocean, *Tech. Rep. to the Office of Naval Research*, 1985

106. Stability of Time-Periodic Temperature Fields, *Quart. Appl. Math.* **55** (1987) 39–50

107. A Solitary Group of Two-Dimensional Deep-Water Waves, *Quart. Appl. Math.* **55** (1987) 177–183

108. Convective Instability of a Spherical Fluid Inclusion, *Phys. Fluids* **30** (1987) 36–44

109. Finite Groups of Gravity Waves, *Quart. Appl. Math.* **46** (1988) 737–750

110. Patterns of Ship Waves (jointly with Songping Zhu), *Quart. Appl. Math.* **47** (1989) 17–33

111. Patterns of Ship Waves. II. Gravity-Capillary Waves (jointly with Songping Zhu), *Quart. Appl. Math.* **47** (1989) 35–44

112. Nonlinear Gravity-Wave Groups, *Quart. Appl. Math.* **47** (1989) 167–184

113. Wave Formation on a Liquid Layer for De-Icing Airplane Wings, *J. Fluid Mech.* **212** (1990) 41–53

114. Nonlinear Groups of Gravity-Capillary Waves, *Quart. Appl. Math.* **47** (1990) 581–599

Books edited by C.-S. Yih, *Advnces in Applied Mechanics* (Academic Press, 1971–1982), **11–22.**

Book reviews by C.-S. Yih, *J. Fluid Mech.* **17** (1963) 154–155 and *Quart. Appl. Math.* **35** (1978) 199–200.

Corrigenda for papers not selected for this collection

Paper 8. The evaluation of many constants in this paper contains errors. The correct version is given in Paper 10.

Paper 44. The errors in this paper were corrected when the results were re-presented in Publication 90, which is a book.

Paper 70. The intuitive arguments used in this paper are not rigorous, and the conclusion is wrong for damped modes. In contrast, the results and arguments in Paper 69 are correct.

Paper 94. There are numerous truly typographical errors in this paper, due to the strange practice of the publisher of not sending proofs. These were corrected in a corrigenda published in a later issue of the same journal.

SELECTED PAPERS

by

Chia-Shun Yih

SELECTED PAPERS

by

Chia-Shun Yih

S. P. Timoshenko Dist. University Professor Emeritus
The University of Michigan

Editors

W. M. Lai
Columbia University

S.-P. Lin
Clarkson University

Volume I

Advanced Series on Fluid Mechanics

Published by

World Scientific Publishing Co. Pte. Ltd.

P O Box 128, Farrer Road, Singapore 9128

USA office: 687 Hartwell Street, Teaneck, NJ 07666

UK office: 73 Lynton Mead, Totteridge, London N20 8DH

SELECTED PAPERS BY CHIA-SHUN YIH, Vol. I

Copyright © 1991 by World Scientific Publishing Co. Pte. Ltd.

All rights reserved. This book, or parts thereof, may not be reproduced in any form or by any means, electronic or mechanical, including photocopying, recording or any information storage and retrieval system now known or to be invented, without written permission from the Publisher.

ISBN 981-02-0252-0
      981-02-0543-0 (Set)

Printed in Singapore by JBW Printers and Binders Pte. Ltd.

Acknowledgments

The author and the editors of these volumes gratefully acknowledge the gracious courtesy of:

1. The Cambridge University Press for permission to reprint the following papers published in
   <u>Journal of Fluid Mechanics</u>:
   A5, A6, A7, A8, A10, A11, A12, A19, A20, B3, B11, B13, B14, B16, B17, B18, B19, B22, B26,
   C2, C6, E4, E7, E12, E21, E24;

2. The American Mathematical society for permission to reprint the following papers published in
   the <u>Quarterly of Applied Mathematics</u>:
   A21, A22, B1, B2, B24, C3, C9, C10, C11, C12, C13, E2, E3, E6, E8, E17, E19, E25;

3. The American Physical Society for permission to reprint the following papers published in the
   <u>Physics of Fluids</u>:
   A16, B4, B6, B9, B12, B15, B20, B23, B25, D8, D11, E11, E15, E16, E18, E20, E22;

4. The Royal Society of London for permission to reprint the following papers published in its
   <u>Proceedings</u>:
   B5, E9;

5. The Office of Naval Research for permission to reprint the following papers published in the
   <u>Proceedings of Symposia on Naval Hydrodynamics</u>, which were organized under its aegis:
   A14, C4, C7, D9;

6. The U.S. Printing Office for permission to reprint the following paper published in the book
   <u>The Use of Models in Geophysical Fluid Mechanics</u>:
   D6;

7. The editor of <u>Tellus</u> for permission to reprint the following papers published in the journal:
   A1, A2, D5;

8. The editor of the <u>Journal of Geophysical Research</u> for permission to reprint the following papers
   published in that journal:
   A4, C1, D3, D4;

9. The editor of the <u>Journal of Hydraulic Research</u> for permission to reprint the following paper
   published in that journal:
   A18;

10. The editor of the <u>Annual Reviews of Fluid Mechanics</u> for permission to reprint a paper published in that series:
    A13;

11. Cornell University Press for permission to reprint an article published in the book <u>Nonlinear
    Waves</u>:
    A15;

12. The publisher of <u>Advances in Applied Mathematics</u> for permission to reprint the following articles published in that series:
    B12, E23;

13. The American Society of Mechanical Engineers for permission to reprint the following papers
    published in the <u>Journal of Applied Mechanics</u> or in <u>Proceedings of U.S. National Congresses</u>
    of Applied Mechanics:
    A3, A9, D1, D2, E14;

14. The American Society of Civil Engineers for permission to reprint the following papers published
    in the <u>Journal of Engineering Mechanics</u>:
    C5, D10, E1;

15. The American Institute of Aeronautics and Astronautics for permission to reprint the following articles published in its journals:
   B7, D7;

16. The Society of Industrial and Applied Mathematics for permission to reprint the following paper published in the Journal of Applied Mathematics:
   A17;

17. The Technical Association of Pulp and Paper Industries for permission to reprint the following papers published in TAPPI:
   B8, B10;

18. The Zeitschrift fuer Angewandte Mathematik und Mechanik for permission to reprint the following paper published in that journal:
   E13;

Article E5 was originally published in the journal La Houille Blanche, which no longer exists, and whose quondam editor, the eminent Pierre Danel, has long ago left this world. Were he alive today, he would have graciously and gladly given us his permission to reprint paper E5. His presence is sorely missed, and the author takes this opportunity to express once again his respect to and affection for his old friend Pierre Danel.

Finally, the author wishes to express his appreciation and gratitude to Mrs. Elaine Samson and Mrs. Aileen Zimmerman for typing the necessary papers for these volumes, and for cheerfully putting up with the many revisions the author had made.

Editors' Note

In 1985, a symposium in honor of Professor Chia-Shun Yih was held in Ann Arbor, Michigan. The present volumes are part of the outcome of that symposium, of which the organizing committee appointed us editors of these volumes. Several other former students of the author have also helped in our endeavor. In particular, the efforts of Professors Walter R. Debler and Timothy W. Kao are gratefully acknowledged.

Since Professor C. C. Lin introduced the author to the use of mathematics in the study of fluid mechanics in the summer of 1947 at Brown University, we have asked him to write the preface for these volumes. The preface is followed by three articles by the author's friends, on him and his work. Then, in each volume, after the corrigenda, prepared by the author himself for the papers contained therein, the selected papers are presented in the order indicated by the table of contents. At the end of Volume II we have included a curriculum vitae and a list of publications of the author, followed by the corrigenda for papers not included in these volumes.

Apart from the research papers, Yih also published the book *Dynamics of Nonhomogeneous Fluids*, Macmillan, New York, 1965, which was revised in 1980 and published under the title *Stratified Flows* by Academic Press. This book has been the standard reference book for researchers studying the behavior of stratified fluids. Yih's *Fluid Mechanics* was published by McGraw-Hill Company of New York in 1969, and was revised in 1979 and republished by West River Press of Ann Arbor. This book is often referred to, and is still used as a textbook in some American and European universities.

Looking over the titles of Yih's papers, one can hardly escape the impression that a great many of them deal with the dynamics of fluids stratified in density, entropy, viscosity, thermal conductivity, electrical conductivity, circulation, or else magnetic circulation. This bears testimony to his fascination with the effects of heterogeneity of all sorts in fluid flows, which provide a unifying thread through a great many, perhaps the majority, of his papers.

As a teacher, he is known generally, and especially among his thirty five research students, as a source of inspiration. His enthusiasm for fluid mechanics provides a contagious stimulation to his students. His presentation of some of the beautiful theories of fluid mechanics often took on a magician's touch, as when he gave the transformation with which a large-amplitude wave motion of a stratified fluid can under certain conditions be shown to be governed by a linear partial differential equation — or even when he presented the classical theorems of circulation and vorticity. His enthusiasm and his love of beauty in Nature and in science will be remembered by those of us who know him.

Sung-Piau Lin
W. Michael Lai

Preface

The editors of the present volumes have asked me to provide some comments on the significance of the contributions of Professor Chia-Shun Yih to the field of fluid mechanics. I am most happy to do so. Yih's contributions to the literature of fluid mechanics have been important and extensive. Besides some general comments, I shall also make some specific comments which are limited to a few salient points related to a small portion of his work.

In this volume, Yih's papers are collected into five parts:

A. Stratified Flows and Internal Waves,
B. Theory of Hydrodynamic Stability,
C. Gravity Waves,
D. Jets, Plumes and Diffusion,
E. General.

Of these, the first — stratified flows and internal waves — is clearly a field that Yih has made his own. But he is at heart a naturalist and an engineer, and his contribution to the literature of fluid mechanics have been quite broad, and span over a variety of physical phenomena and a wide area of applications. The diversity of his interest may be gleaned from Part E of his papers.

With his bountiful love for nature, it is not surprising that some of his most significant contributions deal with fluid flows that are ubiquitous in our environment. The field of stratified flows itself is rich in physical phenomena. This richness owes its origin to the interplay of the heterogeneity of the fluid medium and the gravitational field. This fact was noted by Yih in the preface to his book *Stratified Flows*, 1980, which first appeared in 1965 under the title *Dynamics of Nonhomogeneous Fluids*. This book, which is primarily based on Yih's original contributions to the field, has since become a classic reference for all serious students and researchers. The reader cannot but feel the author's enthusiasm for the subject, that he has indeed achieved an insight to the intricacies of the subject and that he is eager to share the fruits of his labor with the reader.

While much of Yih's success owes to his physical insight, it is perhaps equally true that he is always able to use precisely the right mathematical tool, especially for the purpose of enlarging our general perspectives. For example, in the paper *Gravity waves in a stratified fluid* (A5), he made use of Sturm's second comparsion theorem to obtain the result that the phase speed decreases as the wave number increases, in small-amplitude wave motion of a heterogeneous liquid with a free surface. He has also been very successful in introducing ingenious mathematical transformation of variables to enable certain general classes of difficult problems of wavy motions with finite amplitudes to be solved with relative simplicity. Such skillful use of mathematics has great impact on a number of scientific applications, including geophysics and water-quality engineering.

In view of the importance of these mathematical approaches, it is perhaps appropriate to describe some of them in some detail. In a series of papers starting with the 1958 paper (A3) on the flow of a stratified fluid, he demostrated the use of a transformation which enables one to cast the equation of two-dimensional steady flow of a stratified fluid into a form which can be rendered exactly linear from suitable choices of upstream conditions. He used a transformed stream function ψ' defined as

$$\rho^{\frac{1}{2}} u = \partial \psi'/\partial z , \quad \rho^{\frac{1}{2}} w = -\partial \psi'/\partial x ,$$

where (u, w) are the components of velocity in the (x, z) directions and ρ is the density. It can then be shown that the governing equation for the stream function ψ' is

$$\nabla^2 \psi' + (gz/\rho_0)d\rho/d\psi' = (1/\rho_0)dH/d\psi' ,$$

in which g is the acceleration of gravity, ρ_0 is a reference density and H is the total head, which is a constant along a streamline and therefore a function of ψ' only. The functions $d\rho/d\psi'$ and $dH/d\psi'$ are to be determined from upstream conditions and if these functions are linear in ψ' the solutions of the linear governing equation yield exact solutions to large-amplitude motions. As Yih noted in his book, "much can be achieved in this way." Similar transformations have also been given by him for a compressible fluid.

He was, in fact, able to solve several important classes of problems including those given in *Exact solutions for steady two-dimensional flow of a stratified fluid* (A6), and *A transformation for non-homentropic flows, with an application to large-amplitude motion in the atmosphere* (A7). Many of these solutions have important practical application in geophysics and water-quality engineering. In the paper *A class of solutions for steady stratified flows* (A12), the use of a more general form of transformation of variables led Yih to an elegant theorem in three-dimensional shallow-water theory. The theorem states that "so long as the shallow water theory is valid, a class of steady stratified flow with a free surface originated from rest can be found corresponding to each irrotational steady free-surface flow of a homogeneous fluid originated from rest." The mapping is by the use of the relationship $(u, v, w) = \lambda(\rho)(U, V, W)$ where (u, v, w) and (U, V, W) are the three components of velocity and $\lambda(\rho)$ is a function of the density ρ.

The subject of internal hydraulic jumps, of great importance to environmental and hydraulic problems, was first treated by Yih and Guha in 1955 (A1). That paper has been referred to in nearly every paper written on that subject ever since. The phenomenon of hydraulic jump in a rotating fluid was later treated by Yih and co-workers (E11).

Yih's work is not limited to the field of stratified flows and internal waves. In the field of hydro-dynamic stability, one is impressed by the span, in time and scope, of his work. The investigations include results that are applicable generally, such as *Stability of two-dimensional parallel flow for three-dimensional disturbances* (B1), *Stability of unsteady flows or configurations, Parts I and II* (B16, B18), and *Eigenvalue bounds for the Orr-Sommerfeld equation* (B17). He has also examined how specific fluid properties may affect the instability of the flows: for example, the instability of an electrically conducting fluid (B3, B4), the instability of a non-Newtonian fluid (B12), the effect of viscosity stratification (B13), and the effect of stratification in thermal conductivity (B23).

The solutions to many stability problems involved the utilization of new techniques or adapting those in other contexts. Thus, Yih's application of a perturbation technique for the problem of the stability of a liquid flowing down an inclined plane (B9) permitted a straightforward calculation to be made in a complex problem, a result that permitted others to adapt the methodology to other cases in which a long-wave solution would be informative. Also, the exploitation of the Floquet theory for periodic excitations allowed him to explore the instability of time-periodic temperature fields (B18) or time-periodic flows in a circular pipe (B22).

While Yih's work on hydrodynamic stability contains impressive components necessary for the academic development of the various subjects treated, much of his work was inspired by the needs in engineering problems. It is indeed the examination of the paper-making process that led him to the papers associated with Rayleigh-Taylor instability: *On the instability of stock on a Fourdrinier wire* (B8), and *Effect of variation of acceleration on free-surface instability* (B10). An inquiry from the Boeing aircraft company has been the reason for him to write the paper *Wave formation on a liquid layer for de-icing airplane wings* (B26).

As mentioned above, Yih has devoted much of his efforts to the study of stratified flows and internal waves. It is natural that he would also work on surface waves in fluids of homogeneous density. His work on waves in flowing water takes into account the effect of the velocity profile. He gave some comparison theorems for water waves in basins of variable depth in 1976 (C3), and studied waves in channels of various cross sections in 1984 (C5). Fascinated by the effect of geometry on water waves he also gave analytical results for Binnie waves (C4), waves in meandering streams (C6), and edge waves created by a long-shore current and a ridge in the sea bed (C7). In recent years, he turned his attention to classical problems in water-wave theory. Four papers (C8, C9, C12 and C13) are concerned with linear or nonlinear water-wave groups. The papers on nonlinear waves, in particular, give the effect of amplitude of the waves on the group velocity. His papers on patterns of ship waves (D10 and D11) give two formulae in closed form from which the patterns can be determined simply, be they of gravity waves, gravity-capillary waves, or internal waves. The theory is based on three things: (1) The relation between the local wave number and the local wave velocity, i.e., the elementary dispersion formula, (2) the principle of stationary phase, and (3) the requirement that the component of the ship velocity in a direction normal to the local wave front be equal to the local wave velocity, in other words, the requirement of steady pattern. From Yih's formulae, all the known results of Kelvin, Havelock, and others for all sorts of waves can be obtained readily, without the rather obscure reasoning initiated by Lord Kelvin. These formulae have brought the theory of ship waves within the reach of fourth-year undergraduates.

Yih's work on jets, plumes, and diffusion stems from his early work on convective plumes caused by a point source of heat. In this area, he rediscovered the transformations of Zel'dovich (1937) in 1948, while he was a graduate student at the University of Iowa, for laminar convection from a point or line source of heat, and he was able to give two exact solutions for the cases of Prandtl numbers 1 and 2 (D2 and D5). But, much more important for pratical applications are his contributions to turbulent jets and plumes, with or without a cross wind. The similarity solutions for straight turbulent jets were well-known in the nineteen thirties. Guided by a dimensional analysis, Yih worked with Hunter Rouse in 1947–48 on the experimental determination of the velocity and temperature distributions in a round turbulent plume caused by a point source of heat. But it was not until 1977 that Yih was able to give the eddy viscosity an expression on dimensional arguments and thus to give analytical solutions for both round and plane turbulent plumes for certain turbulent Prandtl numbers, including the number 1.1 for round plumes (D8), which is important because it is near 1. The eddy viscosity was assumed constant in any plane normal to the plume axis, (D9, D10). Yih was able to apply the same sort of analysis to jets and plumes in a transverse wind. One interesting analytical result is the double-helix structure of jets and plumes in a transverse wind, which one can observe in a chimney plume on a windy day.

Finally, it should be noted that Yih's contributions to fluid mechanics is not limited to his own work, which forms a significant segment of the literature on the mechanics of fluid flows. As a teacher, he has imparted his ideas to his students who carried them out and published papers under their own names. To appreciate Yih's contributions to fluid mechanics, one should include all these large quantities of results that he caused to appear by virtue of opening new areas of research and suggesting specific problems that needed attention.

C. C. Lin

Reminiscence by Friends of Chia-Shun Yih

Other Aspects of the Author

I met Chia-Shun in 1934, when we entered Soochow Senior High School. The oldest hall of the school, where we often took examinations, was called the "purple Sun Hall", in honor of Master Zhu Hsi, founder of neo-Confucianism in the Sung Dynasty. We were not sure whether Master Zhu actually lectured there, but the halo of tradition was real and palpable, and we were fortunate that the education we received at the school was worthy of the hallowed site.

We had excellent teachers. But we were very anxious to learn as much as we could, and supplemented their teaching by studying independently some English and American books that Chia-Shun brought back from Shanghai, which was a short ride from Soochow by train, after one spring vacation. These books, fortunately mostly well chosen, not only gave us additional instruction and information on mathematics, physics, and chemistry, but also formed our habit of reading scientific books in English rather early in our lives. Furthermore, among the books were literary works by English authors, such as Charles Dickens and Jane Austen. Chia-Shun has since become a devotee of Austen, has read nearly all of her works, and recalls with nostalgia the compact edition, with deep-blue covers, of Pride and Prejudice that he brought back from Shanghai.

The text books for English used in our school were edited by our own teachers. Looking back, we are impressed with their good judgment and taste in the selection of material for these books. The English authors represented were Shakespeare (Julius Caesar, The Merchant of Venice), Macauley, Dickens (A Tale of Two Cities), Jane Austen (Pride and Prejudice), George Eliot (The Mill on the Floss), among others, and curiously, also Lord Chesterfield (letters to his son). Among the American authors selected were Nathaniel Hawthorn (The Scarlet Letter) and Washington Irving (The Sketch Book). That this sort of education ill prepared us for ordering a meal or hailing a taxi when we came to America after the War was a minor inconvenience quickly overcome by the discipline of necessity; the influence of these masters of letters has remained with us ever since.

While we were in high school, the storm was gathering in China and in Europe. Japan had already occupied Manchuria since 1931, and had fought with our armed forces in Shanghai in 1932. Full-scale war between China and Japan finally broke out in 1937, soon after our graduation from high school. We managed to take the entrance examination of the National Central University, in Nanking, about two months before its fall. Our university was moved to Chungking far in the hinterland, by a quick and farsighted decision of Dr. Chia-Luen Lo, our president. While we were students in Chungking, war borke out in Europe in 1939, and the Japanese bombed Pearl Harbor in 1941. The Chinese people were no longer fighting alone.

Since Dr. Lo's wife and daughters were all Barber scholars at the University of Michigan at different times, it was natural that Chia-Shun should become a friend of the entire Lo family. To illustrate how thoroughly Western culture penetrated Chinese intellectuals one generation ahead of us, I shall repeat here a story about Dr. Lo that Chia-Shun likes to tell. Our university had an extensive library, many delicate instruments and various chemicals that were hard to come by, and much cattle (Holstein cows) of the Agriculture College. To move it from Nanking to Chungking it was necessary not only to crate and transport the books, records, instruments, and chemicals, but also to herd the cattle along the Yangtze River for a distance of some 1,500 miles. It took something like two years for the cows to arrive, and they were by then all shaggy and thin. Dr. Lo encountered them one day unexpectedly in the outskirts of Chungking. He told Chia-Shun that the words that immediately came to his mind were "Ah, du armes Kind, was hat man dir getan!" The warm humanity of the man! Goethe would have been pleased to have his words so applied. Dr. Lo was educated in Princeton and Berlin, and was a poet and a distinguished educator. Chia-Shun was very fond of him.

Our independent study of physics, chemistry, and mathematics stood us in good stead when we entered the university. We sailed through the first year without much effort. This gave Chia-Shun an opportunity to satisfy his thirst for Western literature. He was introduced to the romantic poets by Professor Yu Ta-Ying, and became very fond of John Keats' poetry. He also studied German literature with Professor Shang Dzang-Sun, who gave him, after graduation, a compact book of Goethe's "Die Leiden des jungen Werthers." Chia-Shun negotiated through the treacherous terrain of German grammar, and still managed to enjoy the beauty of the work. A few years later, while pursuing his doctorate at the University of Iowa, which demanded of its Ph.D. candidates proficiency in two foreign languages, Chia-Shun made good use of his German. But since English is not foreign in Iowa and Chinese is not foreign to Chia-Shun, he had to learn another Western language. He chose French, and many years later, while Visiting Professor at the University of Paris and the University of Grenoble, was able to lecture in that language. He was on rather friendly terms with the French nasal sounds and the u's and eu's so deadly to most Americans, and is fond of quoting Bernard Shaw's witticism that the French don't care what you say, so long so you pronounce it right. His interest in French finally enabled him to read Stendhal, Flaubert, Maupassant, and the part "Du Coté de chez Swann" of Proust's "Á la Recherche des Temps Perdus."

At our university Chia-Shun studied, among other things, mathematics and the theory and design of bridges, and I studied mathematics and the theory of airplane structures. Our college years were spent in make-shift classrooms and laboratories, classes at the crack of dawn to avoid air raids, long hours in the dugouts, military training, and an endless stream of exciting or sad news. One wintry day Japanese planes came and bombed out our simple shower hut, and for weeks afterwards some of us had to bathe in the emerald water of the near-by Chia-Ling River, beautiful but cold. Chia-Shun likes to say that the dominant sensation when one jumps into icy water is an immediate headache. "Afterwards, the shiver in the sun seemed almost pleasant by comparison."

After graduation Chia-Shun worked first in a hydraulics laboratory in Quanshien, and then for the National Bureau of Bridge Design in Kweiyang. I was then working for the Bureau of Airplane Design in Chengtu. At that stage we both intended to be practicing engineers. Then something changed our lives. By nationwide examinations, the ministry of Education chose forty-two scholars to study in the United States. We were among the forty-two, and after the War came to the United States via India. At Calcutta we boarded the American troop ship "General Hase," which took a month crossing the Red Sea, the Mediterranean, and the Atlantic before reaching New York City on December 28, 1945. I then went to Caltech, and Chia-Shun, after a very brief stay at Purdue University, went to the University of Iowa to study fluid mechanics with Hunter Rouse and John McNown, with whom he maintains a warm friendship to this day.

The story of his work after his graduate studies is best told by the papers included in these volumes. But I know enough of his work to say that Chia-Shun is a superb mathematician. Every paper of his contains some elegant mathematics that cuts through the complexity and clarifies the physics at the core. That is the feature of his work that has earned Chia-Shun the respect and admiration of his colleagues.

Yet Chia-Shun is much more than a mathematician. His human qualities, his generosity, and his sincerity touch every heart that comes in contact with him. His lively conversation at parties and dinners, his love of Nature, literature, and art (especially impressionist paintings), his knowledge of flowers and trees, and his eagerness to be helpful are well-known to his friends.

Memories are our most certain possessions. Yet we know they are also ephemeral, and will vanish with the inexorable passage of time. So let me indulge a little in my own remembrance of times past. One memorable trip we took in our high school days was a trip to Yi Shin, to see the stalactites and stalagmites in caves, and the underground running stream, in which one could row a boat for several kilometers. We used candles and kerosene lamps, which we could put out to experience a nearly total darkness in which fluorescent insects and mosses shone. In my recollection, that was the first time that we were truly impressed with our biosphere. Our "senior trip" was made on a small steamer along the Fu Chuen River near Hangchow. Fu Chuen! What a poetic name! Fu means "rich" or, in this context, "rich in", and Chuen means "spring". It was a limpid river bordered by tallish but not menacing mountains, and that night the moon shone bright. Chia-Shun loves that river. The other river he passionately loves is the Chia-Ling, which flows below where our university used to stand. Its emerald waters again and again found expression in the poems of

Li Shang-Yin (of the late Tang Dynasty), Chia-Shun's favorite poet. Chia-Shun's love of Nature, literature, and art is so essential a part of him that, without it, he would be greatly impoverished.

Every life has its sorrows. Most lives have some misfortunes. Chia-Shun's is no exception. But on the whole it seems that his is an enchanted life. I should like to quote a poem by Wang Wei (王維) to conclude this reminiscence:

安得捨塵網　　　拂衣辭世諠

悠然策藜杖　　　歸向桃花源

Paraphrased, it says: "Would that I could shake off the net that binds me to this dusty world, say good-bye to the hustle and bustle, and, swinging my bamboo stick leisurely, return to the Creek of Peach Blossoms."

People through the ages have searched for the legendary land of the Creek of Peach Blossoms. I think some of us are living in it.

Yuan-Cheng Fung
La Jolla, 1990

Chia-Shun Yih was the first Chinese fluid dynamicist I met, and naturally I assumed there were many others like him. I have not yet found one! Of all my friends, in any country, he is the most mercurial, the most emotional, and the most generous-spirited. It is unusual to find these qualities in a person with scientific interests, but in Chia-Shun they are combined happily. Given another life-time, one feels he might prefer to be a painter or a poet; but in his present incarnation he is outstanding as an applied mathematician, quick in perception, skilled in execution, and always on the look-out for a nice result which has both elegance and meat.

I first met Chia-Shun in the 1950's. We are near-contemporaries, and we both had the good fortune to 'grow up' in research during those exciting early post-war years when there seemed to be so much useful basic research in fluid mechanics to be done. Our areas of specialization were not the same, but we had a few common interests, for example in free convection and hydrodynamic stability. He made some short visits to Cambridge, and fell in love with the beautiful old College buildings, the academic atmosphere, and the old-world values, things which he greatly missed in USA. The idea of spending a whole academic year at Cambridge arose naturally between us, and a subsequent successful application to NSF for a visiting fellowship enabled him to live in Cambridge with his family during 1959–60. He was very interested in stratified fluid flow at the time, and this gave him common ground with a number of his Cambridge friends, especially Brooke Benjamin, Alfred Binnie, and Geoffrey Taylor. He was a marvelous visitor, he enjoyed everthing, even the weather, and was especially appreciative of opportunities to observe the Cambridge scene, to learn a little of its history, and to take part in the ceremonies of daily College life. He referred later to this as being the happiest year of his life. Speaking as one of the residents, I can testify that we felt the gain was entirely on our side. His capacity for human warmth and affection and his enthusiasm for research in fluid mechanics win him friends everywhere. May they continue to do so.

George Batchelor
Cambridge, August 1990

My advisor spent the academic year 1963–64 as Visiting Professor at M.I.T. and I as a "terminal" research assistant went along as a "visiting student." During that year Chia-Shun Yih gave an Applied Mathematics Colloquium on his now well-known transformation relating inviscid incompressible fluid flows to those of constant density via the mapping $\sqrt{\rho}\mathbf{v} \rightarrow \mathbf{v}$. I recall noting that there was something peculiar about this lecture, though it wasn't until the very end that I realized what it was. The speaker was really enjoying himself. He was enthused by his discovery and was not embarrassed to show it. This is one hallmark of Chia-Shun. He is a person of buoyant spirits and good cheer.

When I was put up for promotion and tenure at Johns Hopkins, Chia-Shun was asked to be a referee. He not only wrote a very positive letter on my behalf, but he sent a copy of it directly to me. This was a time of "cold war" within the department and my receipt of this letter greatly buoyed my spirits. This is another hallmark of Chia-Shun. He performs acts of kindness for his colleagues, acts that are beyond the call of duty.

Chia-Shun has been given two great honors by the American Physical Society, the Fluid Dynamics Prize and the Otto Laporte Award. On each occasion he was touched by the honor and obviously pleased by the action of his colleagues. One could, again, feel and share his joy.

Chia-Shun Yih is credited with several major discoveries. Instability driven by viscosity stratification, subharmonic instabilities in modulated viscous flows and the transformation $\sqrt{\rho}\mathbf{v} \rightarrow \mathbf{v}$ are some. His 1963 invention of long-wave analysis of free-surface instabilities has given birth to, perhaps, a thousand papers of others. But to me what is even more important is Chia-Shun's characteristics as a man. He is a gentleman, and I am proud and fortunate to know him.

Stephen H. Davis
Evanston, 1990

Contents

Volume I

Part A. Stratified Flows and Internal Waves

Part B. Theory of Hydrodynamic Stability

Volume II

Part C. Gravity Waves

Part D. Jets, Plumes and Diffusion

Part E. General

Corrigenda for Parts A and B

A14. In theorem 7, "If $(\bar{\rho}U')'$ is negative" should be "If $(\bar{\rho}U')'$ is positive".

A15. In theorem 2, $U' < 0$ should be $U' > 0$.

A16. On p. 1491:

    1. Line 6 of the right column, 2 should be 1.

    2. Delete comma in equation (24), and add to the right-hand side $-\exp(\beta\eta)(B_1' + B_2' \cos 2n\pi\eta + B_3 \sin 2n\pi\eta)\cos 2k\xi$,

    3. In (25), change period to comma, and add the following equations:

$$8B_1' = n^2\pi^2 - k^2 + \beta^2/4, \quad 32B_2' = 4n^2\pi^2 + 4k^2 - \beta^2 .$$

    On p. 1493:

    1. In (43), the right-hand side of the equation for $8T_2$ should be multiplied by $\sin k\xi$, and the right-hand side of the equation for T_3 should be multiplied by $\sin k\xi$ also.

    2. The integral on the left-hand side of (46) should be multiplied by 8.

    3. In lines 6 and 7 from the bottom of the right-hand column, $2s - 1$ should be $(2s - 1)\pi$, and $2s$ should be $2s\pi$.

    4. In (48), G_2 should be $8G_2$.

A20. 1. In line below equation (28), add "in the associated velocity field" after "circuit".

    2. Line above equation (29) should be changed to "Let $D'/D't$ stand for the substantial derivative in the associated velocity field, so that

$$\frac{D'}{D't}u_i' = u_\alpha'\frac{\partial u_i'}{\partial x_\alpha} .$$

    Then, using (25) and"

    3. Replace equation (29) by

$$(D'/D't)dx_i = du_i' , \tag{29}$$

    4. In equation (30), replace $\frac{D}{Dt}$ by $\frac{D'}{D't}$ and $u_\alpha u_\alpha$ by $u_\alpha' u_\alpha'$.

    5. Add "in the associated velocity field" after "constant" in the line below (30).

    6. Add "even in the associated velocity field" after "fluid" in the second line below (30).

    7. In the fourth line from the bottom of p. 244, add "in the associated velocity field" after "constant".

    8. In line 7, change "the constant part of the density" to "density variation".

    9. In (31), γ should be $1/\gamma$, and the slanted line indicating fraction should be deleted.

    10. In line above (36), delete "y,"

    11. In (39), γ should be $1/\gamma$, and ρ_c' should be ρ_c.

    12. In (43), the last term should be divided by ρ'.

    13. In (44) and the line below it, $D\Gamma'/Dt$ should be $D'\Gamma/D't$.

    14. In the fourth line below (44), "These" should be "There".

B1. In (6), s is not $\tan\beta$, as stated two lines below (6), but should be $\sin\beta$, and s' should be $\sin\beta'$, not $\tan\beta'$. This correction can also be verified by a detailed formulation of the stability problem for three-dimensional disturbances.

B2. Equation (27) should be

$$[\sigma - Pr(D^2 - b^2 - a^2)](D^2 - a^2)f = -RPrD\theta .$$

The second sentence following Eq. (27) should then be changed to: "Since Eqs. (26) and (27) would be identical to Eqs. (20) and (21) if $\sigma + \text{Prb}^2$ is replaced by σ, any variation of the flow with y will invariably make the flow more stable, if u_2 remains strictly zero, and the boundary conditions on f itself are not relaxed."

With the periodic variation in the y-direction provided, but with $a = 0$ and $u_2 = 0$, the boundary conditions on f itself can be relaxed, and the fluid may be more unstable. The greatest instability in fact corresponds to $b = 0$ and to the root zero of the characteristic equation

$$\tan R^{1/4} = \tanh R^{1/4}$$

given in the paper. The author is indebted to Mr. R. A. Wooding of Cavendish Laboratory of Cambridge for pointing out this most unstable mode.

B3. In the summary, $\geq$ J should be J $\geq$ in the second inequality. This correction has been made in this collection, but is mentioned here for completeness.

B4. In (5), $p^{-\lambda\theta'}$ should be $p - \lambda\theta'$.

B5. Add a minus sign before the first term on the left-hand side of (41). Consequently, change the two plus signs, just before the parentheses in the square brackets of (44) and (45), to minus signs.

B9. The details of the growth-rate contours in Figures 2–5 still await more extensive calculations for final definition.

B14. 1. In the second line above equation (3), "unsteady" should be "steady".

2. In (28) of this paper u' should be replaced by $u' + \eta$. When this correction is made, and the analysis is carried through, the correct criterion replacing the final formula in that paper is

$$\left(\frac{\alpha_0}{\omega} + 2\frac{\omega}{\alpha_0}\right)\Delta\alpha = \frac{i\omega^2 R}{60}\left\{-90 - 12\frac{\alpha_0}{\omega} - 3\left(\frac{\alpha_0}{\omega}\right)^2 + \left(2 - \frac{9\alpha_0}{\omega}\right)F^{-2}\right\}$$
$$- i2\omega^2\left(\frac{\bar{\gamma}}{\gamma_1 d}\frac{\alpha_0}{\omega} - \frac{1}{\text{Pé}}\frac{\alpha_0^2}{\omega^2}\right), \tag{1}$$

in which

$$\frac{\alpha_0}{\omega} = 1 \pm \sqrt{3}. \tag{2}$$

The interesting feature is that there are two modes, one travelling upstream and one travelling downstream. The former corresponds to the negative sign in (2), and for that mode instability corresponds to positive values of $\alpha_i(\Delta\alpha = i\alpha_i)$. The latter corresponds to the positive sign in (2), and for it instability corresponds to negative values of α_i, because of the form of the assumed exponential factor (for all perturbation quantities)

$$\exp i\left[\int \alpha dx - \omega\tau\right].$$

It turns out that both modes can be unstable! Note that the coefficient of $\Delta\alpha$ in (1) is simply $\pm 2\sqrt{3}$. A numerical verification can be given to show the actual possibility of instability. The conclusion that there are realistic cases of instability remains valid.

Part A
Stratified Flows and Internal Waves

Hydraulic Jump in a Fluid System of Two Layers

By CHIA-SHUN YIH and C. R. GUHA

Iowa Institute of Hydraulic Research

(Manuscript received October 1, 1954).

Abstract

The number of conjugate states for the flow of a fluid system of two layers is investigated by means of the momentum principle. The uniqueness of the conjugate state is proved for the cases in which the modified Froude number for either layer is predominantly large. Specific experimental results for three special cases demonstrate the uniqueness of the state downstream from the hydraulic jump, and show that, for a first approximation, the simple analysis provides a means for determining the downstream depths, with smaller errors for lower jumps.

Introduction

Although fluid motion in a stratified system was investigated more than a century ago by STOKES (1847), and not long afterwards by HELMHOLTZ (1868), WEBB (1884), GREENHILL (1887) and LOVE (1891), it is only during recent years that it has attracted the serious attention of oceanographers, meteorologists, and hydraulicians. As a result of the revived interest of the geophysicists, the subject is at present enjoying a period of intensive investigation. Among the recent contributors may be mentioned ROSSBY (1951), CRAYA (1951), KUELEGAN (1953), STOMMEL and FARMER (1952), TEPPER (1952), LONG (1953), and BENTON (1953).

In spite of the encouraging advancements of recent years, much is still to be learned about the subject and many questions at issue are yet to be settled. Among these the most important is the one concerning the determination of the state downstream from a hydraulic jump for a completely specified state upstream. It is with a view toward answering this question that an analysis based on simple assumptions was made for the case of two-layer flow and the relevant experiments were performed. The results obtained will be presented in the following sections of this paper.

Analysis

General Considerations

The system under study consists of two superposed layers of fluids flowing over a plane bottom. The upper surface is assumed to be free. For simplicity, the bottom is taken to be horizontal.

As indicated in Fig. 1, the density, the discharge per unit width, and the depths upstream and downstream from the hydraulic jump are respectively denoted by ϱ_1, q_1, h_1, and h_1' for the upper fluid, and by ϱ_2, q_2, h_2, and h_2' for the lower fluid. The gravitational acceleration is denoted by g. For fixed values of the densities, of the discharges, and of g, and for given upstream depths (h_1, h_2), the dynamically possible depths (h_1', h_2') downstream from the jump are said to be conjugate to (h_1, h_2), and the upstream and downstream states are conjugate by definition. A critical state is then defined as one which is conjugate

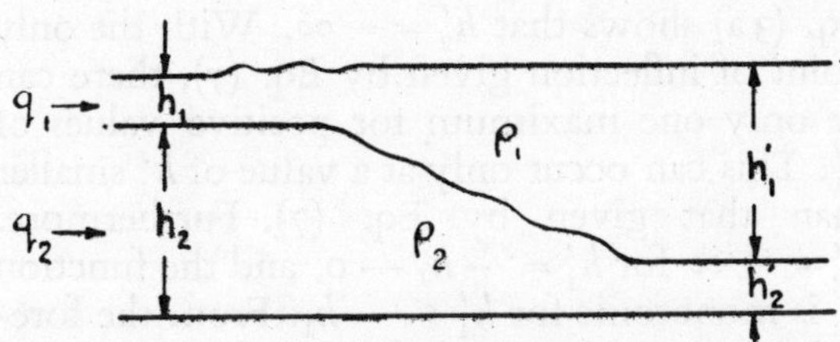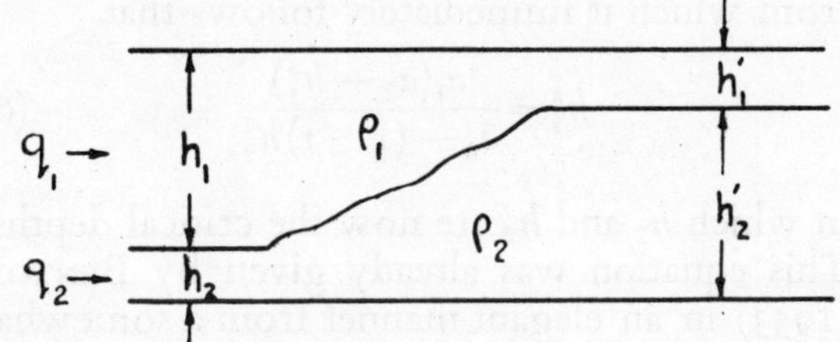

Fig. 1. Definition sketches (a) Normal jump (b) Inverted jump.

to itself, corresponding to an infinitesimal hydraulic jump. The number of conjugate states and the determination thereof will be the chief concern of the present analysis.

If a jump occurs in a fluid system of two layers, there is usually rather violent mixing at the interface. The interfacial shear is generally larger than the shear at the solid boundary, and cannot be neglected without introducing sizable error except under favorable conditions. Furthermore, due to the motion of the fluids the pressure distribution is no longer hydrostatic. As is well known, the distribution of the dynamic part of the pressure at the interface depends directly on the existence and location of the point of separation and therefore indirectly on the distribution of the interfacial shear. Since so little is known about the interfacial shear, it is evident that a rigorous theory cannot be achieved at present. However, if one is content with a first approximation, an *a priori* analysis can be constructed by neglecting the interfacial shear and assuming hydrostatic distribution for the pressure. This analysis will at least yield some conclusions of a qualitative nature which may be expected to hold even if interfacial shear is to be taken into account. Furthermore, for low jumps its conclusions may even be quantitatively correct. Thus, at the present stage of its development, the subject may well benefit from such an analysis.

Neglecting the shear, assuming hydrostatic distribution of pressure, and taking the mean head over the jump section as $\frac{1}{2}(h_1 + h_1')$, one has, by applying the momentum principle to the lower layer,

$$\varrho_2 q_2^2 \left(\frac{1}{h_2'} - \frac{1}{h_2} \right) = h_2 h_1 \varrho_1 g + \frac{1}{2} h_2^2 \varrho_2 g + \frac{1}{2}(h_1 + h_1') \cdot$$

$$\cdot (h_2' - h_2) \varrho_1 g - h_2' h_1' \varrho_1 g - \frac{1}{2} h_2'^2 \varrho_2 g \qquad (1)$$

This can be rewritten as

$$2a_2 (h_2 - h_2') = h_2 h_2' (h_2 + h_2') \left[r(h_1 - h_1') + (h_2 - h_2') \right] \qquad (2)$$

in which

$$a_2 = \frac{q_2^2}{g}, \quad r = \frac{\varrho_1}{\varrho_2}$$

Similarly, one obtains, for the upper layer,

$$2a_1 (h_1 - h_1') = h_1 h_1' (h_1 + h_1') \left[(h_1 - h_1') + (h_2 - h_2') \right] \qquad (3)$$

in which

$$a_1 = \frac{q_1^2}{g}$$

Given h_1 and h_2, one has to solve Eqs. (2) and (3) simultaneously for the conjugate depths h_1' and h_2'. Since these equations are all of the third degree in h_1' and h_2', there are in general nine solutions. One solution is obviously $h_1' = h_1$ and $h_2' = h_2$. Thus at first sight there may be as many as eight other solutions representing eight states conjugate to the given one. However, to have a physical meaning, the solutions must be real and positive. Therefore, the number of conjugate states is decided by that of the positive solutions of Eqs. (2) and (3), aside from the obvious one corresponding to the given state.

It may be noted that since the critical state is conjugate to itself by definition, the differences $h_1' - h_1$ and $h_2' - h_2$ are infinitesimal, and may be replaced by the differentials dh_1 and dh_2. Equations (2) and (3) then become the differential equations

$$\frac{dh_2}{dh_1} = \frac{r h_2^3}{a_2 - h_2^3} \qquad (4)$$

$$\frac{dh_1}{dh_2} = \frac{h_4^3}{a_1 - h_1^3} \qquad (5)$$

from which it immediately follows that

$$h_1^3 = \frac{a_1(a_2 - h_2^3)}{a_2 - (1-r)h_2^3} \qquad (6)$$

in which h_1 and h_2 are now the critical depths. This equation was already given by BENTON (1953) in an elegant manner from a somewhat different approach. Thus the present definition of a critical state is equivalent to that of Benton.

To investigate the number of conjugate states, one starts by tracing the graphs of Eqs. (3) and (2), using h_1' and h_2' as the variables. For this purpose these equations are rewritten as:

$$h_2' = \frac{2a_1(h_1' - h_1)}{h_1 h_1'(h_1 + h_1')} + h_2 - (h_1' - h_1) \qquad (3\,a)$$

$$h_1' = \frac{2a_2(h_2' - h_2)}{rh_2 h_2'(h_2 + h_2')} + h_1 - \frac{h_2' - h_2}{r} \qquad (2\,a)$$

From Eq. (3 a), it can be seen immediately that h_2' has a discontinuity at $h_1' = -h_1$ and $h_1' = 0$ in such a way that $h_2' = -\infty$ for $h_1' = -h_1 - 0$ and for $h_1' = +0$, and $h_2' = +\infty$ for $h_1' = -h_1 + 0$ and for $h_1' = -0$. Furthermore, for large values of $|h_1'|$, h_2' behaves like $-h_1'$.

Now if h_2' in Eq. (3 a) is differentiated twice and the result equated to zero, the following equation is obtained:

$$h_1'^3 - 3h_1'^2 - 3h_1' h_1^2 - h_1^3 = 0$$

the only real root of which is

$$h_1' = h_1(2^{1/3} - 1)^{-1} \qquad (7)$$

corresponding to a point of inflection of the graph of Eq. (3), located to the right of the h_2'-axis. Differentiating Eq. (3 a) once with respect to h_1' and setting the result to zero, one has

$$2a_1(h_1^2 + 2h_1 h_1' - h_1'^2) - h_1 h_1'^2(h_1 + h_1')^2 = 0 \qquad (8)$$

the roots of which correspond to the maxima and minima of h_2'. The left side of Eq. (8) is definitely negative for $h_1' < -h_1$, so that there can be no maxima or minima for such values of h_1'. Since $h_2' = +\infty$ for $h_1' = -0$ and $h_1' = -h_1 + 0$, and since there is no point of inflection for negative values of h_1', there is only one minimum of h_2' in the range $-h_1 < h_1' < 0$. For $h_1' = +0$ and $h_1' = +\infty$,

Eq. (3 a) shows that $h_2' = -\infty$. With the only point of inflection given by Eq. (7), there can be only one maximum for positive values of h_1'. This can occur only at a value of h_1' smaller than that given by Eq. (7). Furthermore, $h_2' = -\infty$ for $h_1' = -h_1 - 0$, and the function h_2' is monotonic for $h_1' < -h_1$. From the foregoing considerations, the graph of Eq. (3) or (3 a)—with branches I, II, and III—can be traced, and is shown in Fig. 2 in dimensionless terms.

Similarly the graph of Eq. (2) or (2 a) can be traced, as shown in Fig. 2 with branches IV, V, and VI. It is evident that I intersects IV and VI, VI intersects III, and the lower branch of VI intersects the left branch of III. The intersections will be denoted by A, B, C, and F. Furthermore, it should be noted that the left branch of III and the lower branch of VI have no point of inflection. These facts will prove useful in the investigation of the number of intersections of III and VI, which of all possible intersections, alone have positive coordinates and thus determine the number of conjugate states.

If one writes

$$\Delta h_2 = h_2' - h_2^3, \quad \Delta h_1 = h_1' - h_1 \qquad (9)$$

and equates the expressions for $\Delta h_2/\Delta h_1$ obtained from Eqs. (2) and (3), one has

$$\frac{2F_1}{x(x+1)} - 1 = r\left(\frac{2F_2}{2F_2 - y(y+1)} - 1\right) \qquad (10)$$

in which

$$F_1 = a_1/h_1^3, \quad F_2 = a_2/h_2^3, \quad x = h_1'/h_1, \quad y = h_2'/h_2 \qquad (11)$$

By a translation of coordinates Eq. (10) can be reduced to the symmetrical form

$$\left[\xi^2 - \left(\frac{1}{4} + 2F_1'^2\right)\right]\left[\eta^2 - \left(\frac{1}{4} + 2F_2'^2\right)\right] = \frac{4rF_1^2 F_2^2}{(1-r)^2} \qquad (12)$$

in which F_1' and F_2' are the modified Froude numbers defined by

$$F_1'^2 = F_1^2(1-r)^{-1}, \quad F_2'^2 = F_2^2(1-r)^{-1} \qquad (13)$$

and

$$\xi = x + \frac{1}{2}, \quad \eta = y + \frac{1}{2}$$

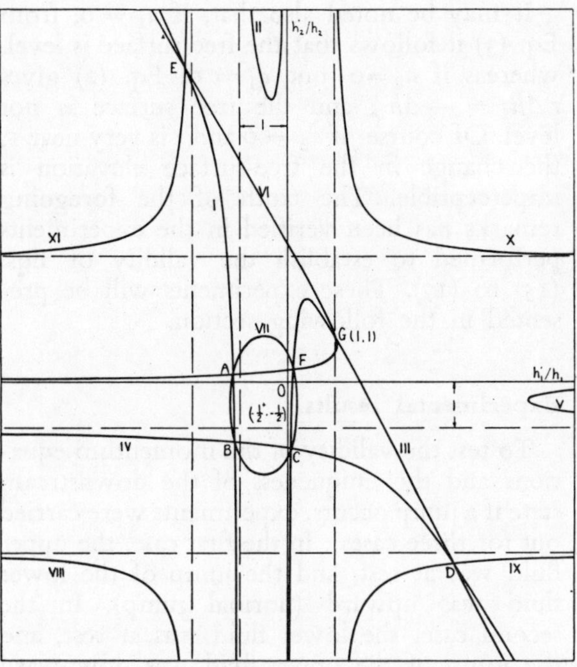

Fig. 2. Graphs of the momentum equations and of Eq. (10) or (12)

The solutions of Eqs. (2) and (3), except the one corresponding to the given state, are those of Eqs. (2) and (10), or those of Eqs. (3) and (10).

The graph of Eq. (10) can be easily traced, and is shown in Fig. 2—branches VII to XI. It is symmetrical with respect to the lines $x = -\frac{1}{2}$ and $y = -\frac{1}{2}$, and consists of one closed convex piece around the center $\left(-\frac{1}{2}, -\frac{1}{2}\right)$ and four branches of a hyperbolic shape with asymptotes

$$x = -\frac{1}{2} \pm \left(\frac{1}{4} + 2F_1'^2\right)^{1/2}$$

$$y = -\frac{1}{2} \pm \left(\frac{1}{4} + 2F_2'^2\right)^{1/2} \qquad (14)$$

It is immediately clear that IX must intersect III at a point D and XI must intersect VI at a point E. Since there are already five intersections A, B, C, D, and E which are not those of III and VI, these two branches can intersect in four points at most. That is, for a

given state, there can be at most three conjugate states.

Since there is no point of inflection on I, IV, the left branch of III, and the lower branch of VI, these can intersect VII (which is convex) only at A, B, C, and F, as shown in Fig. 2. It is then obvious that III, VI, and VII cannot intersect simultaneously at any point other than F. For otherwise the point, being on III, would lie to the right of F, and being on both VI and VII, would have an ordinate at once greater and smaller than that of F. Thus, if X does not meet III and VI, there can be only two points at which III intersects VI, namely, G (1, 1) and F, G representing the given state and F representing the unique conjugate state.

A few *sufficient* conditions for the uniqueness of the conjugate state can be easily obtained. From Eqs. (8) and (3 a) it is evident that the maximum ordinate on III depends on a_1, h_1, and h_2 only. But from Eq. (14) the horizontal asymptote of X can be so far above the x-axis for predominantly large values of F_2' that X and III, and consequently III and VI, do not intersect. Similarly if F_1' is predominantly large X and VII and consequently III and VII do not meet. Thus, under these conditions, the conjugate state is unique. It should be noted that whenever these conditions are satisfied, the conjugate depths are either both greater or both smaller than the corresponding depths of the given state—in other words, any jump that occurs cannot be primarily internal in character.

The results concerning the finiteness of the number of conjugate states in general and the uniqueness of the conjugate state under special conditions are in direct contrast to Benton's claim (BENTON, 1953) that, given a complete description of the upstream state, infinitely many downstream states are possible. It seems improbable that the present conclusions would be invalidated if shear were to be taken into account, since the process involved would still —perhaps *a fortiori*—have a deterministic nature.

If the conjugate state is unique, whether a hydraulic jump can occur is decided, as usual, from energy considerations. Otherwise several situations may present themselves. If the energy flux for the given state is less than that of each of the three conjugate states, a jump cannot occur, whereas if it is greater than that for one of the conjugate states only, a jump can occur and the downstream state is unique if it occurs. In all other situations a jump can occur but, if it occurs, the downstream state cannot be uniquely determined by momentum and energy considerations alone, and which of the two or three possible conjugate states will be realized after a jump depends primarily on the controls downstream.

Since the validity of the momentum equations and the uniqueness of the downstream state are to be tested for three cases of primarily internal jumps, specific results from Eqs. (2) and (3) will be given here for these cases. For the case in which the downstream velocities are the same for both layers, one has

$$\frac{q_1}{q_2} = \frac{h'_1}{h'_2} = \lambda$$

and Eq. (2) becomes

$$(1 + r\lambda)\left(\frac{h'_2}{h_2}\right)^3 + r\left(-\frac{h_1}{h_2} + \lambda\right)\left(\frac{h'_2}{h_2}\right) -$$

$$- \left(1 + r\frac{h_1}{h_2} + 2F_2^2\right)\left(\frac{h'_2}{h_2}\right) + 2F_2^2 = 0 \qquad (15)$$

This equation has two positive roots: one is $h'_2 = h_2$, corresponding to the given state, and the other corresponds to the conjugate state. If the upper layer is at rest, $a_1 = 0$, and from Eqs. (2) and (3) one obtains

$$\frac{h'_2}{h_2} = \frac{1}{2}\left(\sqrt{1 + 8F_2'^2} - 1\right) \qquad (16)$$

Similarly, if the lower layer is at rest, one has

$$\frac{h'_1}{h_1} = \frac{1}{2}\left(\sqrt{1 + 8F_1'^2} - 1\right) \qquad (17)$$

One notes in Eq. (16) that if h'_2 is greater than h_2 by a finite amount, F'_2 is definitely greater than 1. Physically, this means that the velocity q_2/h_2 must be greater than the celerity of the fastest long waves of infinitesimal amplitude in order to hold the finite jump in place, i.e., finite disturbances progress faster than infinitesimal ones. In this light, Eq. (16) can be considered as a formula giving the celerity of progression of disturbances of finite amplitudes. In fact, the greater the ratio $\Delta h_2/h_2$, the greater the celerity. The same remarks can be made in connection with Eq. (17).

It may be noted also that, if $a_1 = 0$, from Eq. (3) it follows that the free surface is level, whereas if $a_2 = 0$ but $a_1 \neq 0$, Eq. (2) gives $r\, \Delta h_1 = -\Delta h_2$, and the free surface is not level. Of course, if $a_2 = 0$ and r is very near 1, the change in the free-surface elevation is imperceptible. The truth of the foregoing remarks has been verified in the experiments performed to establish the validity of Eqs. (15) to (17). These experiments will be presented in the following section.

Experimental results

To test the validity of the momentum equations and the uniqueness of the downstream state if a jump occurs, experiments were carried out for three cases[1]. In the first case, the upper fluid was at rest, and the jump of the lower fluid was upward (normal jump). In the second case, the lower fluid was at rest, and the jump of the upper fluid was downward (inverted jump). In the third case, both fluids were in motion, but in such a way that the downstream velocities were the same for both layers. The limitation on the downstream condition for the third case was imposed by an experimental artifice which had to be adopted for the sake of expediency. Experimentally it would be rather difficult and expensive to enable the discharges to vary independently and to realize a stationary jump with two moving layers. Instead of attempting to have a stationary jump, one tried to obtain a surge by filling a channel sealed at the downstream end with the lighter fluid, and discharging the heavier fluid into it at the bottom. As the lower fluid reached the end of the channel, it rose in height to form a surge which moved upstream with a celerity depending on the actual discharge of the lower fluid and the upstream depths. On taking velocities relative to the surge, the situation of two moving layers was achieved, but with the restriction that the downstream velocities were necessarily the same for both layers.

Water was used for the moving fluid in het first two cases (stationary jumps), and for het

---

[1] The experiments for Cases 1 and 2 were performed by the second author for his M. S. Thesis at the Iowa Institute of Hydraulic Research. The first author is responsible for the rest of the material contained in this paper.

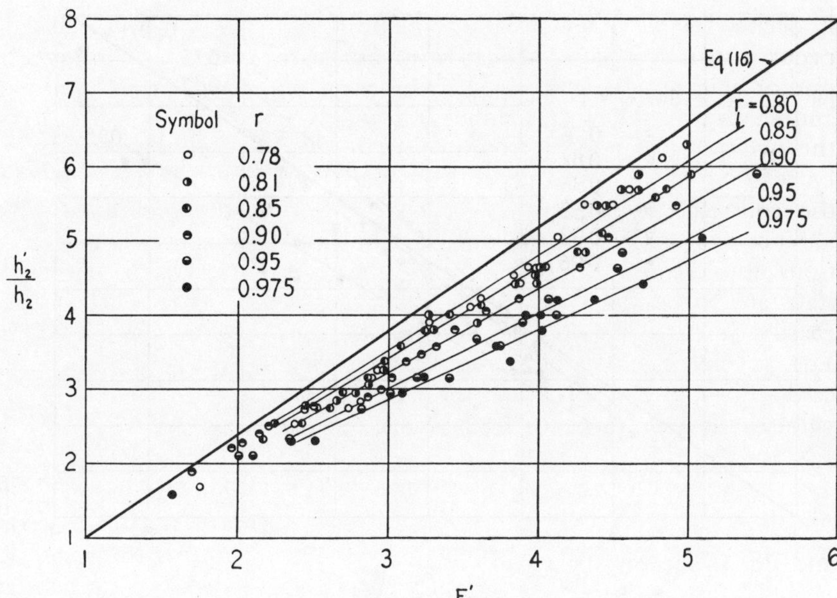

Fig. 3. Experimental results for the normal jump

lower fluid in the third case (surge). The other fluid used was either stanisol (an oil prepared by the Standard Oil Company, with specific gravity 0.777), or a mixture of stanisol and carbon tetrachloride (specific gravity 1.59). Since stanisol has a kinematic viscosity of about 3.4×10^{-5} ft²/sec, is not highly inflammable, and mixes well with carbon tetrachloride to form a homogeneous mixture, it was found to be quite suitable to use. For easy visualization of the interface, the oil or oil mixture was always dyed red.

The lucite flume used was 4 feet long, 6 inches wide, and 8 inches deep. For stationary jumps the depths were controlled by one upstream gate and one downstream gate. The upstream gate was designed to ensure parallel flow of the water into the channel, and the downstream gate was designed to reduce entrainment of oil. The discharge of water was controlled by a valve upstream and measured by a triangular weir downstream. A supply of oil was maintained to compensate for the loss due to entrainment. For the moving jump the total depth was controlled by horizontal slots on the side of the channel near the upstream end. As the water entered the sealed channel, the oil would spill over the lowest open slot, so that an approximately constant total depth was maintained at the upstream end. The depth of the water at entrance was not controlled, but was found to be about half an inch. With

the total depth at the entrance controlled by the slots, different combinations of (h_1, h_2) could be achieved. The discharge was again controlled by an upstream valve, and was measured through the celerity of the moving jump and the water depths upstream and downstream from the jump. All depths were measured either visually or photographically.

Before the experimental results are presented, it may be noted that the variables h_2' and h_2' depend on h_1, h_2, ϱ_1, ϱ_2, g, q_1, q_2, and the dynamic viscocities μ_1 and μ_2. If h_2' is taken as the dependent variable, a dimensional analysis shows that

$$\frac{h_2'}{h_2} = \left(\frac{h_1}{h_2}, \frac{q_1}{q_2}, \frac{\mu_1}{\mu_2}, r, F_2, R_2 \right) \qquad (18)$$

in which F_2 is the Froude number for the lower layer and $R_2 = q_2 \varrho_2 / \mu_2$ is the Reynolds number for the same layer. Equation (18) can be used to correlate the data obtained for Case 3 and Case 1 (for which $q_1/q_2 = 0$). For Case 2, a similar analysis yields

$$\frac{h_1'}{h_1} = F_1 \left(\frac{h_1}{h_2}, \frac{\mu_1}{\mu_2}, r, F_1, R_1 \right) \qquad (19)$$

in which F_1 and R_1 are respectively the Froude number and the Reynolds number for the upper layer. From Eq. (2) it follows that h_2'/h_2 does not depend on μ_1/μ_2 and R_2 according to the simple theory. Furthermore,

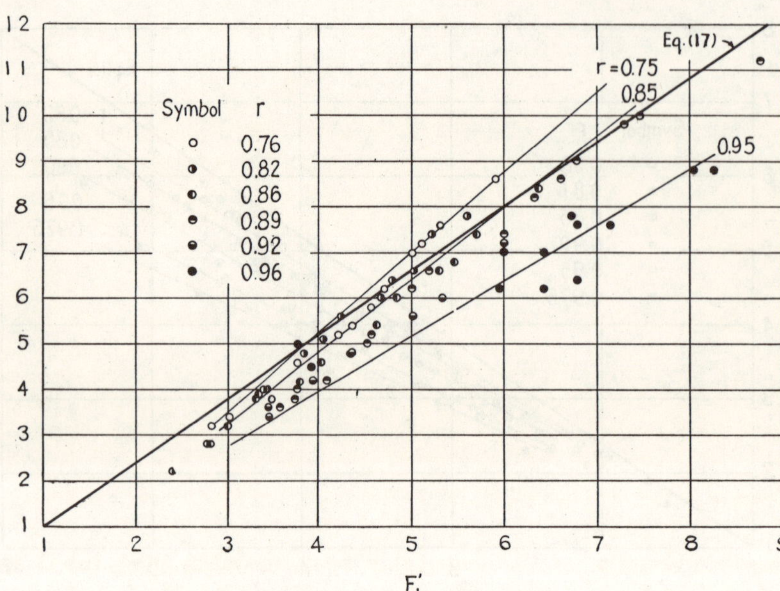

Fig. 4. Experimental results for the inverted jump

Eqs. (16) and (17) indicate that in Cases 1 and 2, respectively, the ratios h_2'/h_2 and h_1'/h_1 depends only on F_2 and F_1'. In other words, according to the simple theory, the parameters h_1/h_2, μ_1/μ_2, and R_2 or R_1 have no effect on h_2'/h_2 or h_2'/h_1, the effect of r and F_2 are embodied in F_2' in Case 1, and those of r and F_1 are embodied in F_1' in Case 2. To what extent the theoretical predictions are valid will be shown by the experimental results.

The results for the normal jump are shown in Fig. 3, from which it can be seen that the ratio h_2'/h_2 depends not only on the modified Froude number F_2', but also on the density ratio r. But F_2' and r seem to determine h_2'/h_2 uniquely in the range of experimentation. The points all lie below the theoretical curve, with increasing deviation for increasing r and F_2'. The results show that for increasing modified Froude number and density ratio, the effect of shear (chiefly interfacial shear) becomes increasingly important. The free surface was found to be level as expected.

Results for the inverted jump (Fig. 4) show similar trend, except that some points lie above the theoretical curve. The greater scatter is partly due to the difficulty of ascertaining the upstream depth h_1, since an undular jump occurred at the free surface. The free surface was observed to be definitely higher after the jump.

Figure 5 shows the result obtained for Case 3, the velocities being taken relative to the surge. The abscissa is the theoretical value of h_2'/h_2 computed from Eq. (15), and the ordinate is the experimental value of the same ratio. Here it can be seen that except for very high jumps the theoretical prediction is very well verified experimentally. Since h_1^3 was always large as compared with a_1, the free surface could be expected to be almost level according to Eq. (3). As can be seen from Plate 1, this expectation was well verified.

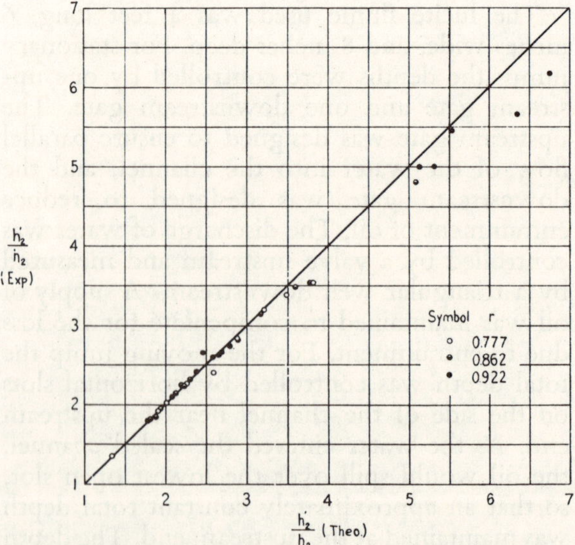

Fig. 5. Comparison of experimental results for the surge with theoretical predictions according to Eq. (15)

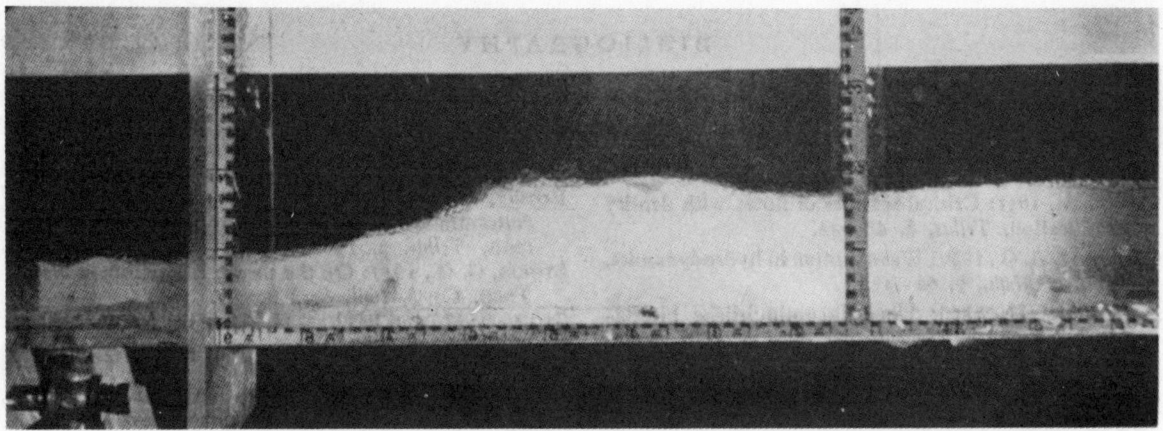

Plate 1. Photograph showing interfacial surge and the almost horizontal free surface between air and oil.

From the same plate it can be seen that the appearance of the surge was fairly smooth, and no violent interfacial mixing existed.

Because of the lack of violent interfacial mixing in Case 3 the neglecting of interfacial shear in the analysis is more nearly justified, and the agreement between theoretical and experimental results is consequently better than in Cases 1 and 2, in which rather violent mixing usually occurred at the interface. In this connection it may also be mentioned that because of the simplicity of the experimental technique employed in Case 3, the experimental limitations encountered in that case are much less severe than in the cases of steady jumps. Why the data for Cases 1 and 2 show a dispersion according to the density ratio whereas those for Case 3 does not, cannot be convincingly explained. This does not, however, prevent one from making the points in regard to the several questions at issue.

From the experiments it is evident that, for the special cases investigated, to a given upstream state there corresponds only one downstream state. Aside from this, it seems that the analysis previously presented provides a means for determining h_2'/h_2 or h_1'/h_1, at least to a first approximation, the absolute errors being small for small theoretical values of $\Delta h_2/h_2$ or $\Delta h_1/h_1$—which correspond to small values of $F_2'-1$ or $F_1'-1$ in Case 1 or 2.

Conclusions

From the foregoing investigation of the hydraulic jump in a fluid system of two layers, it can be concluded that:

1. According to a simple analysis based on the momentum principle and the neglecting of shear, there can be at most three states conjugate to a given one. These states can be determined from Eqs. (2) and (3). If the modified Froude number of either layer is predominantly large, there is only one conjugate state. If the conjugate state is unique, and if a jump can occur from the consideration of energy and does occur, the state downstream from the jump is completely determined. If there are more than one conjugate states, merely from momentum and energy considerations it may not be possible to determine uniquely the state downstream from a hydraulic jump.

2. Specific results of experiments performed on primarily internal hydraulic jumps for three special cases, shown in Figs. 3 to 5, demonstrate the uniqueness of the downstream state in these cases, which is expected from the analysis. Furthermore, these results show that the simple analysis provides means for determining the downstream depths to a first approximation, the absolute errors in h_1'/h_1 or h_2'/h_2 being small for small theoretical values of $\Delta h_1/h_1$ or $\Delta h_2/h_2$.

Acknowledgment

This work was sponsored jointly by the Iowa Institute of Hydraulic Research and the Office of Naval Research, under Contract No. N8onr—500. The writers wish to thank Dr Hunter Rouse, Director of the Institute, for his advice in regard to the experimental equipment.

SHIA-SHUN YIH AND C. R. GUHA

BIBLIOGRAPHY

BENTON, G. S., 1953: The occurrence of critical flow and hydraulic jumps in a multi-layered system, Tech. Rep. No. 1, The Johns Hopkins University, Dept. of Civil Eng.

CRAYA, A., 1951: Critical regimes of flows with density stratification, *Tellus*, **3**, 28—42.

GREENHILL, A. G., 1887: Wave motion in hydrodynamics, *Journ. of Math.*, **9**, 62—112.

HELMHOLTZ, H., 1868: Über discontinuirliche Flüssigkeitsbewegungen, *Monatberichte Akad. d. Wiss. Berlin*, 215—228.

KEULEGAN, G. H., 1953: Characteristics of internal solitary waves, Res. Paper 2442, *Journ. of Res. Nat. Bureau of Standards*.

LONG, R. R., 1953: Some aspects of the flow of stratified fluids, I. A theoretical investigation, Tech. Rep. No. 2, The Johns Hopkins University, Dept. of Civil Eng.

LOVE, A. E. H., 1891: Wave motion in a heterogeneous heavy liquid, *Proc. Lond. Math. Soc.*, **22**, 307.

ROSSBY, C.-G., 1951: On the vertical and horizontal concentration of momentum in air and ocean currents, *Tellus*, **3**, 15—27.

STOKES, G. G., 1847: On the theory of oscillatory waves, *Trans. Camb. Phil. Soc.*, **8**, 441.

STOMMEL, H., and FARMER, H. G., 1952: Abrupt changes in width in two-layer open channel flow, *J. Mar. Res.*, **11**, 205—214.

TEPPER, M., 1952: The application of the hydraulic analogy to certain atmospheric flow problems, Research Paper 35, U.S. Weather Bureau.

WEBB, R. R., 1884: Math. Tripos Papers.

On Stratified Flows in a Gravitational Field

By CHIA-SHUN YIH[1], Iowa Institute of Hydraulic Research, State University of Iowa

(Manuscript received July 5, 1956)

Abstract

This paper, which is restricted to the flow of inviscid fluids, is divided into three parts. In the first part existing formulas by A. R. Richardson, Hans Lewy, and K. N. Tong for constructing free-surface flows are identified with one another so that potential flows of one fluid in contact with a stagnant layer of another fluid can be constructed exclusively from one general formula, with proper modification of the gravitational acceleration. Further, a method for constructing potential flows of two fluids having a common interface (which may or may not be prescribed) is devised. It is hoped that this method will be of some use in the investigation of internal gravity waves. In the second part, it is shown that, for flows of a fluid system of discrete layers, Long's equation of motion for two-dimensional flow of an inhomogeneous fluid reduces to the Laplace equation for each layer (if the flow is irrotational) and the usual boundary conditions at the interfaces, so that flows with discontinuous density variations can be properly considered as limiting cases of flows with continuous ones. For the sake of completeness, equations of motion of an inhomogeneous fluid in axisymmetric motion in cylindrical and spherical coordinates are also given. In the third part the stability of a periodic disturbance present in a parallel flow with continuous density variation is discussed. Sufficient conditions for stability are found, and an upper bound for the amplification factor is given (if instability occurs) for a general class of flows.

I. Introduction

In the study of stratified flows, which have occupied the attention of many hydrodynamicists of the last century and a number of contemporary investigators, a fluid system of many distinct layers has often been considered, partly for the sake of simplicity, partly because essentially distinct layers do occur in nature. On the other hand, flows with continuous density variation have been treated by Love (1891) for small disturbances of a vertical stratification, by Rossby (1951) and Craya (1951), who used the momentum principle and the energy principle (respectively) to obtain the critical regime, and by Long (1953), who gave the equation for general two-dimensional motion of a heterogeneous inviscid fluid in terms of the stream function. There still appears to be some doubt (Benton 1953

and Long 1955) as to whether flows with continuous density variation can be approximated with those of descrete layers.

In this paper, a conformal-mapping method for generating potential flows of two distinct layers of fluid with a common interface (prescribed or unprescribed) will first be presented, after a brief discussion of the essential identity of existing methods for generating free-surface flows of a homogeneous fluid. Then it will be shown that for discontinuous stratification Long's equation reduces to the Laplace equation within each layer, and to boundary conditions on the interfaces according to the Bernoulli equation. Consequently, flows with discrete density variation can be properly considered as limiting cases of those with a continuous one. The reverse is very likely also true, though a rigorous demonstration is still lacking. The two modes of approach in the study of stratified flows are thus tied together, and at

---

[1] Now at the University of Michigan.

least a partial justification is provided for using discrete layers to approximate a continuous density variation. For the sake of completeness, equations of axisymmetric motion of an inhomogeneous fluid will be given in cylindrical and spherical coordinates, in terms of Stokes' stream function. Finally, the stability of parallel flows of a heterogeneous fluid will be discussed.

II. Potential Flows with an Interface in a Gravitational Field

Problems of potential flow of a single fluid with one or more free surfaces (on which the pressure is constant) are solved by demanding the velocity potential or the stream function to satisfy the Laplace equation and certain boundary conditions. Because the boundary condition on the free surfaces is a non-linear one, very few physically significant problems of this category have been solved exactly. Reversing the normal order of affairs, A. R. RICHARDSON (1920) devised a method for obtaining potential flows possessing a free surface, or for constructing one with a preassigned surface as the free surface. His method was later rediscovered by HANS LEWY (1951) and K. N. TONG (1954) and was described by these authors in formulas which differ more or less in form from Richardson's, but not in essence. In this section, the identity of the formulas of the three authors mentioned above will first be shown, and then Richardson's reverse method will be extended to apply to potential flows of two layers of immiscible liquids with a common interface, which may or may not be prescribed. Only two-dimensional flows will be considered.

1. *Identification of existing formulas for free-surface flows*

Richardson's first formula for constructing free-surface flows is

$$-\frac{dz}{dw} = [3gG(w)]^{-\frac{1}{3}}\{[1 - G'^2(w)]^{\frac{1}{2}} + iG'(w)\}$$

$$(1)$$

in which z is the complex variable $x + iy$ with y measured in a direction opposite to that of the gravitational force, w is the complex potential, g is the gravitational acceleration, primes denote differentiation with respect to w, and $G(w)$ is a function of w such that $G^{1/3}$, G', and $(1 - G'^2)^{1/2}$ are real and finite

on the free surface. His second formula is for constructing a free-surface flow for which the pressure on the free surface is a function of w, and has the form[1]

$$\frac{dz}{dw} = \left[\frac{1}{c^2 + 2gh - 2gF(w) - 2P(w)} - F'^2(w)\right]^{\frac{1}{2}} + iF'(w)$$

$$(2)$$

in which c and h are constants, F and P are functions of w, and F' and the square root of the bracket are real over the free surface.

It can be readily verified that the Bernoulli equation

$$\left|\frac{dw}{dz}\right|^2 + 2gy = \text{constant}$$

is satisfied on the free-surface by the flow given by Eq. (1), so that the pressure is constant on the free surface. With equal ease one can verify that on the free surface of the flow given by Eq. (2) one has

$$y = F(w), \qquad p = \varrho P(w)$$

except possibly for an additive constant. If the pressure on the free surface is constant, one can take

$$c^2 + 2gh - 2P = 0$$

and Eq. (2) reduces to

$$\frac{dz}{dw} = \left[-\frac{1}{2gF(w)} - F'^2(w)\right]^{\frac{1}{2}} + iF'(w) \quad (3)$$

Lewy's formula is, in the same notation and with g equal to 1,

$$z = \int\left[\frac{1}{2\lambda(w)} - \lambda'^2(w)\right]^{\frac{1}{2}}dw - i\lambda(w) \quad (4)$$

in which both $\lambda(w)$ and the integrand of the integral are real along the free surface, whereas Tong's formula is

$$\frac{dw}{dz} = [2c - 2gf(y)]^{\frac{1}{2}}\left[\frac{1 - if'(y)}{1 + if'(y)}\right]^{\frac{1}{2}} \quad (5)$$

in which y is a complex variable connected with z through the equation

$$z = y + if(y) \qquad (6)$$

---

[1] The multiplier 2 of the function P is added by the writer to make Richardson's statement about the pressure on the free surface correct.

in which both γ and $f(\gamma)$ are real on the free surface. It is a matter of straightforward calculation to show that the Bernoulli equation is satisfied on the free surface.

It will now be shown that Eqs. (1), (3), (4), and (5) are essentially identical. First, it is obvious that if Eq. (4) is differentiated with respect to w and $\lambda(w)$ is set equal to $-F(w)$ the resulting equation is identical with Eq. (3) if g is set equal to 1 (as Lewy did) in the latter. The condition of reality of the several quantities involved is not affected by the substitution of $-F$ for λ. Next, if one sets

$$F(w) = -(2g)^{-\frac{1}{3}} H(w)$$

in Eq. (3), and remembers that one is free to choose the sign of the square root therein, one has

$$-\frac{dz}{dw} = (2g)^{-\frac{1}{3}}\{[H^{-1}(w) - H'^2(w)]^{\frac{1}{2}} + iH'(w)\}$$

$$(7)$$

which is the same as Eq. (1) if one writes

$$H(w) = \left[3G(w)/2\right]^{2/3}$$

Thus Eqs. (1) and (3) are essentially the same. Finally, setting

$$f(\gamma) = -(2g)^{-\frac{1}{3}} H(w) + \frac{c}{g}$$

one can show, with the aid of Eq. (6) that Eqs. (5) and (7) are the same. Thus Eqs. (1), (3), (4), and (5) are essentially identical, and are equivalent to Eq. (7). Since among the five equations Eq. (7) is the simplest one that contains g explicitly, it will be used for further discussion.

Existing formulas for constructing free-surface potential flows are applicable to potential flows of one liquid in contact with a stagnant layer of another liquid. If γ_1 denotes the specific weight of the upper and stagnant layer, and γ_2 that of the moving layer, the Bernoulli equation for the moving layer at the interface is

$$\varrho_2 \left|\frac{dw}{dz}\right|^2 + 2(\gamma_2 - \gamma_1)\,\gamma = \text{constant} \qquad (8)$$

if ϱ_2 is the density of the moving fluid. Equation (14) can be written as

$$\left|\frac{dw}{dz}\right|^2 + 2g'\gamma = \text{constant}$$

if

$$g' = \frac{\gamma_2 - \gamma_1}{\varrho_2}$$

Thus all the existing formulas for constructing free-surface potential flows can be used to construct potential flows having an interface with a stagnant layer, if g is changed to g'. Since these formulas have been shown to be identical and replaceable by Eq. (7), one may use the formula

$$-\frac{dz}{dw} = (2g')^{-\frac{1}{3}}\{[H^{-1}(w) - H'^2(w)]^{\frac{1}{2}} + iH'(w)\}$$

$$(9)$$

exclusively for constructing potential flows having an interface with a stagnant layer.

2. *Steady potential flows of two layers with a common interface*

If w_1 denotes the complex potential of the upper layer and w_2 that of the lower layer, and if primes denote ordinary differentiation, the appropriate formulas for potential flows of two layers of fluid with a common interface are, with k as the density ratio ϱ_1/ϱ_2,

$$-\frac{dz}{dw_1} = \frac{1}{E}[(kF_1^{-1} - G_1'^2)^{\frac{1}{2}} + iG_1'] \quad (10)$$

and

$$-\frac{dz}{dw_2} = \frac{1}{E}\{[(F_1 + G_1)^{-1} - K_2'^2]^{\frac{1}{2}} + iK_2'\} \quad (11)$$

in which E is a constant to be determined, the argument of F_1 and G_1 is w_1, and that of K_2 is w_2. Integration of Eqs. (10) and (11) along a streamline on which the square roots and the multipliers of i in these equations are real yields the following relationships:

$$\gamma = -G_1/E, \qquad \gamma = -K_2/E \qquad (12)$$

$$kq_1^2 = E^2 F_1, \qquad q_2^2 = E^2(F_1 + G_1) \quad (13)$$

where q_1 is the magnitude of the velocity vector for the upper layer, and q_2 is that for the lower layer. In Eq. (12) the constants of integration have been absorbed in G_1 and K_2. If now E^3 is taken to be $2g'$, one has

$$\varrho_1 q_1^2 - \varrho_2 q_2^2 = 2g\,(\varrho_2 - \varrho_1)\,\gamma \qquad (14)$$

which is the condition of the continuity of pressure across the interface – the only condition aside from the one that the interface must be a streamline if steady flows are considered.

Geometrical compatibility requires, from Eq. (12), that

$$G_1(w_1) = K_2(w_2) \qquad (15)$$

and, from Eqs. (10) to (12), that

$$(kF_1^{-1} - G_1'^2)^{1/2} dw_1 = [(F_1 + G_1)^{-1} - K_2'^2]^{1/2} dw_2 \qquad (16)$$

on the interface. Thus if the functional forms G_1 and K_2 are known and w_1 is known on the surface, w_2 will be known on the surface as a function of w_1. Then by analytic continuation w_1 and w_2 are known for both layers. Under these circumstances, the function F_1 is not arbitrary. In fact, since

$$G_1' dw_1 = K_2' dw_2 \qquad (15)$$

one has, from Eq. (16)

$$kF_1^{-1} - G_1'^2 = [(F_1 + G_1)^{-1} - K_2'^2]G_1'^2/K_2'^2 =$$

$$= \frac{G_1'^2}{K_2'^2}(F_1 + G_1)^{-1} - G_1'^2$$

or

$$F_1 = \frac{kK_2'^2 G_1}{G_1'^2 - kK_2'^2} \qquad (17)$$

which determines F_1 on the interface since w_2 is a known function of w_1 there. By analytic continuation $F_1(w_1)$ is known throughout the upper layer, and $F_1[w_1(w_2)]$ known throughout the lower layer. The conformal mappings are thus complete.

If one wishes to construct two potential flows with a common interface given by

$$x = C(y) \qquad (18)$$

one can set

$$(kF_1^{-1} - G_1'^2)^{1/2}/G_1' = C'(-G_1/E) \qquad (19)$$

which, with the prime denoting ordinary differentiation, is the differential form of Eq. (18), as can be shown from Eq. (10). One can thus choose G_1 (to satisfy any other boundary condition if possible in practice), solve Eq. (19) for F_1 and Eq. (17) for K_2'. Thus from Eq. (15) dw_2/dw_1 (and hence w_2) is known as a function of w_1, and $K_2(w_2)$ is simply

$G_1[w_1(w_2)]$. The required conformal mappings are then given by Eqs. (10) and (11).

It is hoped that the method just achieved for constructing potential flows of two fluids with a common interface will be of some use in the investigation of many geophysical phenomena, the main features of which can be simulated by potential flows of two layers.

III. Equations of Motion of an Inhomogeneous Fluid

For the motion of a heterogeneous fluid considered to be inviscid, Euler's equations of motion do not yield the persistence of irrotationality as they do for that of a homogeneous inviscid fluid. For this reason, the customary procedure of substituting the Laplace equation (which is kinematic in nature) for the Euler equations (which are dynamic) cannot be used when the fluid is not homogeneous. What, then, is the equation governing the motion of an inviscid fluid with variable density? In the case of two-dimensional steady flows, this question has been answered by LONG (1953). In this section, the connection of Long's equation with the differential equation and boundary conditions at the interfaces governing the flow of distinct layers will be established, in order to provide a link between the two modes of study of stratified flows mentioned in the Introduction. Then the result of Long will be extended to axisymmetric steady flows, and the equations of motion of such flows will be given in cylindrical and spherical coordinates, in terms of Stokes' stream function.

1. *Discussion of Long's equation*

For two-dimensional steady flows of an inviscid and inhomogeneous fluid which is also incompressible and non-diffusive, Long obtained the equation of motion in terms of the stream function ψ:

$$\nabla^2 \psi + \frac{d\ln\varrho}{d\psi}\left(\frac{\psi_x^2 + \psi_y^2}{2} + gy\right) = F(\psi) \qquad (20)$$

in which ∇^2 is the Laplacian in two dimensions, ϱ is the density, which depends on ψ alone, x and y are Cartesian coodinates with y measured in the vertical direction, g is (as before) the gravitational acceleration, and subscripts denote partial differentiation.

For the flow of distinct layers, within each layer the density is constant, so that Eq. (20) reduces to

$$\nabla^2 \psi = F(\psi)$$

If the motion starts from rest or any irrotational state, the persistence of irrotationality demands that $F(\psi)$ vanish, and the equation of motion reduces to the usual Laplace equation:

$$\nabla^2 \psi = 0$$

At the interfaces not only the density but also the magnitude q of the velocity undergoes a sudden change, for there usually is slip at the interfaces because viscosity has been neglected. With this in mind, one may proceed from the equation of motion for a continuously stratified fluid and show that, at the interfaces of a discontinuous stratification, it reduces to the usual boundary condition. Since

$$q^2 = \psi_x^2 + \psi_y^2$$

Eq. (20) can be written in the form

$$\nabla^2 \psi + \frac{1}{\varrho} \frac{d\varrho}{d\psi} \left(\frac{q^2}{2} + gy \right) = F(\psi)$$

which becomes, after multiplication by $\varrho d\psi$,

$$\left(\frac{q^2}{2} + gy \right) d\varrho + \varrho \nabla^2 \psi d\psi = F(\psi) \varrho d\psi \quad (21)$$

But $-\nabla^2 \psi$ is the vorticity, so that

$$\nabla^2 \psi = \frac{\partial q}{\partial n} - \frac{\partial v_n}{\partial s}$$

in which s is measured along the interfacial streamline and n normal to it, v_n is the (zero) component of the velocity in the n-direction, and[1] $\partial v_n/\partial s$ is in general not zero even though v_n is zero. Since $d\psi$ is equal to qdn, Eq. (21) can be written as

$$\left(\frac{q^2}{2} + gy \right) d\varrho + \varrho q \frac{\partial q}{\partial n} dn + \varrho q \frac{\partial q}{\partial s} ds =$$

$$= \varrho \left[F(\psi) + \frac{\partial v_n}{\partial s} \right] \partial \psi + \varrho q \frac{\partial q}{\partial s} ds$$

---

[1] Strictly speaking, the absolute derivative of tensor calculus should be used. This point is not elaborated here because all one wants to say is that the quantity in question is finite.

or

$$d \left(\frac{\varrho q^2}{2} + \varrho gy \right) = \varrho \left[F(\psi) + \frac{\partial v_n}{\partial s} \right] d\psi + \varrho q \frac{\partial q}{\partial s} ds + \varrho g dy \quad (22)$$

The multipliers of the differentials on the right-hand side of Eq. (22) are all finite, even at the interface of a discontinuous stratification, since there is no discontinuity in the direction of s. The quantity in parentheses on the left-hand side, however, undergoes a jump at such an interface. Letting $d\psi$ and ds become small indefinitely, one has, at the interface of two distinct layers,

$$\triangle \left(\frac{\varrho q^2}{2} + \varrho gy \right) = 0 \quad (23)$$

or

$$\frac{\varrho_1 q_1^2}{2} + \varrho_1 gy = \frac{\varrho_2 q_2^2}{2} + \varrho_2 gy \quad (24)$$

if subscripts are used to distinguish two neighbouring layers. But Eq. (24) is nothing but the usual boundary condition at the interface in accordance with the Bernoulli equation.

Thus one has established a link between flows with continuous density variations and those with discontinuous ones, and shown that the latter can be properly considered as limiting cases of the former. In this manner one gains an insight into the structure of Long's equation. Although it is not possible to obtain Long's equation directly from the differential equation and interfacial conditions governing the flow of a fluid system of many layers, it must nevertheless be remembered that, since streamlines are isopcynic lines in Long's derivation, the resulting equation governs the flow of infinitely many homogeneous layers of infinitesimally small thickness. From this point of view flows with continuous density variation can be considered as limiting cases of flows of discrete layers. Thus one can hardly question the general validity of the approximation of continuously stratified flows by flows of distinct layers. The accuracy of the approximation depends, of course, on the number of layers used.

2. Equations of axisymmetric flows with continuous stratification

Long's equation will now be extended to steady axisymmetric flows, under the same assumptions in regard to the properties of the fluid. If subscripts indicate partial differentiation, the equation of continuity is, in cylindrical coordinates

$$(ru\varrho)_r + (rw\varrho)_z = 0 \qquad (25)$$

in which u is the velocity component in the r-direction, w is that in the z-direction, and ϱ is the density. But the persistence of ϱ along any path line, which is a consequence of the incompressibility and nondiffusiveness of the fluid, demands that

$$\frac{D\varrho}{Dt} = 0 \qquad (26)$$

in which t denotes time, and

$$\frac{D}{Dt} \equiv u \frac{\partial}{\partial r} + w \frac{\partial}{\partial z}$$

indicates the substantial differentiation. Since the motion is steady, path lines are streamlines, and the persistence of ϱ along any path line implies that along any streamline. With the aid of Eq. (26), Eq. (25) is now reduced to the simple form

$$(ru)_r + (rw)_z = 0 \qquad (27)$$

which permits the use of Stokes' stream function ψ such that

$$u = -\psi_z/r, \qquad w = \psi_r/r \qquad (28)$$

Euler's equations of motion are

$$\varrho \frac{Du}{Dt} = -p_r \qquad (29)$$

$$\varrho \frac{Dw}{Dt} = -p_z - g\varrho \qquad (30)$$

in which g is the gravitational acceleration in the negative z-direction, and p is the pressure.

Eliminating p from Eqs. (29) and (30) by cross differentiation, one has

$$\left(\varrho \frac{Du}{Dt} \right)_z - \left(\varrho \frac{Dw}{Dt} \right)_r = g\varrho_r$$

or

$$\varrho \frac{D(u_z - w_r)}{Dt} + \varrho(u_z - w_r)(u_r + w_z) +$$

$$+ \varrho_z \frac{Du}{Dt} - \varrho_r \frac{Dw}{Dt} - g\varrho_r = 0 \qquad (31)$$

But since ϱ is a function of ψ alone, one has, with the aid of Eq. (28),

$$\varrho_z \frac{Du}{Dt} - \varrho_r \frac{Dw}{Dt} - g\varrho_r =$$

$$= \frac{d\varrho}{d\psi} \left(\psi_z \frac{Du}{Dt} - \psi_r \frac{Dw}{Dt} - \psi_r g \right) =$$

$$= r \frac{d\varrho}{d\psi} \left(-u \frac{Du}{Dt} - w \frac{Dw}{Dt} - wg \right) =$$

$$= -r \frac{d\varrho}{d\psi} \frac{D}{Dt} \left(\frac{q^2}{2} + gz \right) \qquad (32)$$

in which

$$q^2 = u^2 + w^2$$

On the other hand

$$u_r + w_z = \psi_z/r^2 = -u/r \qquad (33)$$

$$u_z - w_r = -\frac{1}{r} \nabla'^2 \psi \qquad (34)$$

in which

$$\nabla'^2 \equiv \frac{\partial^2}{\partial r^2} - \frac{1}{r} \frac{\partial}{\partial r} + \frac{\partial^2}{\partial z^2}$$

is the Stokian operator.

If Eqs. (32) and (33) are substituted in Eq. (31), one obtains, after dividing through by r,

$$\frac{\varrho}{r} \frac{D(u_z - w_r)}{Dt} - \frac{\varrho u}{r^2}(u_z - w_r) -$$

$$- \frac{d\varrho}{d\psi} \frac{D}{Dt} \left(\frac{q^2}{2} + gz \right) = 0$$

or

$$\varrho \frac{D}{Dt} \frac{u_z - w_r}{r} - \frac{d\varrho}{d\psi} \frac{D}{Dt} \left(\frac{q^2}{2} + gz \right) = 0$$

Because the substantial derivatives of ϱ and ψ or of their functions are zero, one has

$$\frac{D}{Dt} \left[\varrho \left(\frac{u_z - w_r}{r} \right) - \frac{d\varrho}{d\psi} \left(\frac{q^2}{2} + gz \right) \right] = 0$$

or

$$\varrho \left(\frac{u_z - w_r}{r} \right) - \frac{d\varrho}{d\psi} \left(\frac{q^2}{2} + gz \right) = f(\psi) \qquad (35)$$

If Eqs. (28) and (34) are substituted into Eq. (35) and the result divided throughout by ϱ, it follows, finally, that

$$\frac{\nabla'^2 \psi}{r^2} + \frac{d \ln \varrho}{d\psi} \left(\frac{\psi_r^2 + \psi_z^2}{2 r^2} + gz \right) = F(\psi) \qquad (36)$$

which is the desired equation.

226   CHIA-SHUN YIH

The corresponding equation for spherical coordinates (r, Θ, φ) is

$$\frac{\nabla'^2 \psi}{r^2 \sin \Theta} + \frac{d \ln \varrho}{d\psi} \left(\frac{\psi_\Theta^2 + r^2 \psi_r^2}{2 r^4 \sin^2 \Theta} + gr \right) = F(\psi) \quad (37)$$

where now

$$\nabla'^2 \equiv \frac{\partial^2}{\partial r^2} - \frac{\cot \Theta}{r^2} \frac{\partial}{\partial \Theta} + \frac{1}{r^2} \frac{\partial^2}{\partial \Theta^2}$$

and ψ is Stokes' stream function in terms of which the velocity components u and v in the r- and Θ-directions are given, respectively, by

$$u = - \psi_\Theta / r^2 \sin \Theta, \qquad v = \psi_r / r \sin \Theta$$

It should be noted that gravitation is assumed to act in the negative r-direction, and the motion is assumed to be independent of the third coordinate φ.

IV. Stability of Flows with Continuous Stratification

In a well-known paper RAYLEIGH (1880) showed that two-dimensional flows of a homogeneous fluid are always neutrally stable if the effect of viscosity on the disturbance is neglected and if the curvature of the velocity-distribution curve for the primary flows is of the same sign throughout. In this section two-dimensional parallel flows with continuous density variation between two parallel fixed boundaries will be considered, and an upper bound for the amplification factor will be given, assuming that the flow is indeed unstable. The inequality giving this bound includes Rayleigh's theorem as a special case.

An early paper of SQUIRE (1933) contains the result that the stability or instability of a three-dimensional disturbance in two-dimensional flows of a homogeneous viscous fluid can be predicted   from   that of a two-dimensional one at a lower Reynolds number. The proof of this result was later considerably simplified by LIN (1952) who used a more physical approach. The extension of Squire's result to flows of a non-homogeneous fluid with a free surface and interfaces was given by YIH (1955), who applied Lin's approach. Because of this extension, only two-dimensional disturbances need be considered here.

If the direction of the primary flow is taken to be the x-direction, and the y-direction is taken opposite to that of gravitation, the velocity U, the density r, and the pressure P of the primary flow are functions of y only. Derivatives of these quantities with respect to y will be indicated by primes. The velocity components of the disturbance in the x- and y-directions will be denoted by u and v, respectively, and deviations of density and pressure (due to the disturbance) from the mean will be denoted simply by ϱ and p.

With this notation, Euler's equations of motion are

$$(r + \varrho) \left[u_t^* + (U + u) u_x + v(U' + u_y) \right] = - p_x \quad (38)$$

$$(r + \varrho) \left[v_t + (U + u) v_x + v v_y \right] = - P' - p_y -$$
$$- g(r + \varrho) = - p_y - g \varrho \quad (39)$$

since $P' = - gr$. The equation of continuity

$$u_x + v_y = 0$$

permits the use of the stream function ψ such that

$$u = - \psi_y, \qquad w = \psi_x \quad (40)$$

If Eqs. (40) are substituted in Eqs. (38) and (39), and only terms of the first order are taken, one has

$$r(- \psi_{yt} - U \psi_{xy} + U' \psi_x) = - p_x \quad (41)$$

$$r(\psi_{xt} + U \psi_{xx}) = - p_y - g \varrho \quad (42)$$

The persistence of the density along a path line is stated to the first order by the equation

$$\varrho_t + U \varrho_x + v r' = 0$$

or

$$\varrho_t + U \varrho_x + \psi_x r' = 0 \quad (43)$$

For a two-dimensional spatially periodic disturbance, one may take

$$\left. \begin{array}{l} \psi = f(y) \exp mi(x - ct) \\ \varrho = \Theta(y) \exp mi(x - ct) \end{array} \right\} \quad (44)$$

in which

$$c = c_r + i c_i$$

with c_r being the celerity of the disturbance, and c_i the amplification (or damping) factor. If c_i is not zero, a positive c_i is always associated with a negative one with the same magnitude. With the aid of Eqs. (43), Eq. (44) yields the relationship

$$\Theta = r'f/(c - U) \tag{45}$$

Now if p is eliminated from Eqs. (41) and (42) by cross differentiation, and Eqs. (44) and (45) are substituted into the result, one obtains, after simplification,

$$(rf')' + \left[\frac{(rU')'}{c - U} - m^2 r - \frac{gr'}{(c - U)^2}\right] f = 0 \tag{46}$$

which is associated with the boundary conditions

$$f(a) = 0, \qquad f(b) = 0 \tag{47}$$

in which a and b are the ordinates of the solid boundaries. The complex conjugate of Eq. (46) is (with the asterisk denoting complex conjugate)

$$(rf'^*)' + \left[\frac{(cU')'}{c^* - U} - m^2 r - \frac{gr'}{(c^* - U)^2}\right] f^* = 0 \tag{48}$$

with the corresponding boundary conditions

$$f^*(a) = 0, \qquad f^*(b) = 0 \tag{49}$$

If now Eq. (46) is multiplied by f^* and integrated from a to b, Eq. (47) is multiplied by f and integrated in the same interval, and the difference is taken, one has

$$\int_a^b (rf')'f^* \, d\gamma - \int_a^b (rf'^*)' f \, d\gamma =$$

$$= \int_a^b \left[(rU')'\left(\frac{1}{U - c} - \frac{1}{U - c^*}\right) + gr'\left(\frac{1}{(U - c)^2} - \frac{1}{(U - c^*)^2}\right)\right] ff^* \, d\gamma \tag{50}$$

The left-hand side of this equation can be shown to be zero by integration by parts and by utilization of the boundary conditions

given by Eqs. (47) and (49). After a straightforward calculation of the right-hand side and division by 2, Eq. (50) assumes the following form

$$c_i \int_a^b [(U - c_r)^2 + c_i^2]^{-2}\{(rU')'[(U - c_r)^2 + c_i^2] + 2(U - c_r)gr'\}ff^* \, d\gamma = 0 \tag{51}$$

From Eq. (51), one obtains the result that, if $(rU')'$ is of the same sign between a and b,

$$\text{Max} \left|\frac{gr'}{(rU')'}\right| \geqslant |c_i| \tag{52}$$

For if not, the integrand in Eq. (51) will be positive or negative definite depending on whether $(rU')'$ is positive or negative, and c_i will be zero, leading to a contradiction. The inequality (52) provides an upper bound for the amplification factor if instability occurs – under the restriction that $(rU')'$ does not change sign. If r is constant, one sees that it leads to neutral stability ($c_i = 0$) under the condition that U'' is of the same sign from a to b. Thus Rayleigh's theorem is an immediate consequence of (52).

From Eq. (51) two more deductions can be readily made. If $gr'/(rU')'$ is positive throughout the field of flow, a periodic disturbance travelling in the negative x-direction with a celerity exceeding the maximum value of U in that direction must necessarily be neutrally stable. Similarly, if the same quantity is negative throughout, the celerity of an unstable disturbance travelling in the positive direction of x cannot exceed the algebraic maximum of the mean velocity.

V. Acknowledgment

This work was jointly sponsored by the Iowa Institute of Hydraulic Research and the Office of Ordnance Research (Department of the Army) under Contract No. DA-11-022-ORD-1729.

BIBLIOGRAPHY

BENTON, G. S., 1953: The occurrence of critical flow and hydraulic jumps in a multi-layered system, Tech. Rep. No. 1, The Johns Hopkins Univ., Dept. of Civil Eng.

CRAYA, A., 1951: Critical regimes of flows with density stratification, *Tellus*, 3, pp. 28—42.

GREENHILL, A. G., 1887: Wave motion in hydrodynamics, *Journ. of Math.*, 9, pp. 62—112.

HELMHOLTZ, H., 1868: Über discontinuirliche Flüssigkeitsbewegungen, *Monatberichte Akad. d. Wiss. Berlin*, pp. 215—228.

KEULEGAN, G. H., 1953: Characteristics of internal solitary waves, Res. Paper 2442, *Journ. of Res. Nat. Bureau of Standards*.

LEWY, H., 1951: On steady free surface flow in a gravity field, Tech. Rep. 4, Applied Math. and Statistics Lab., Stanford Univ.

LIN, C. C., 1952: Hydrodynamic stability, *Proc. of Symposia in Applied Math., Am. Math. Soc.*, V, pp. 1—18.

LONG, R. R., 1953: Some aspects of the flow of stratified fluids, I. A theoretical investigation, Tech. Rep. No. 2, The Johns Hopkins Univ., Dept. of Civil Eng.

LONG, R. R., 1955: Some aspects of the flow of stratified fluids, III. Continuous density gradients, Tech. Rep. No. 6, The Johns Hopkins Univ., Dept. of Civil Eng.

LOVE, A. E. H., 1891: Wave motion in a heterogeneous heavy liquid, *Proc. Lond. Math. Soc.*, 22, p. 307.

RAYLEIGH, LORD, 1880: On the stability or instability of certain fluid motions, *Scientific Papers*, I, pp. 474—487, Cambridge Univ. Press.

RICHARDSON, A. R., 1920: Stationary waves in water, *Phil. Mag.* Series 6, 40, pp. 97—110.

ROSSBY, C.-G., 1951: On the vertical and horizontal concentration of momentum in air and ocean currents, *Tellus*, 3, pp. 15—27.

SQUIRE, H. B., 1933: On the stability for three-dimensional disturbances of viscous fluid flow between parallel walls, *Proc. Roy. Soc. London*, Ser. A, 142, pp. 621—628.

STOKES, G. G., 1847: On the theory of oscillatory waves, *Trans. Camb. Phil. Soc.*, 8, p. 441.

TONG, K. N., 1954: Two-dimensional potential flow in a gravitational field with a known free stream, *Proc. Second U.S. National Congress of Applied Mechanics*.

WEBB, R. R., 1884: Math. Tripos Papers.

YIH, C. S., and GUHA, C. R., 1955: Hydraulic jump in a fluid system of two layers, *Tellus*, 7, pp. 358—366.

YIH, C. S., 1955: Stability of two-dimensional parallel flows for three-dimensional disturbances, *Quart. Appl. Math.*, XII, pp. 434—435.

ON THE FLOW OF A STRATIFIED FLUID

This paper contains a discussion of the effect of inertia on steady stratified flows of an incompressible and inviscid fluid and an exact solution of the non-linear partial differential equations governing such flows. The latter is a solution for the steady two-dimensional flow of a stratified fluid in a channel toward a line sink, with constant density gradient in the vertical direction at infinity.

Chia-Shun Yih

University of Michigan

Introduction

In this paper the steady flows of an incompressible, inviscid, and stratified fluid are investigated. After a discussion of the effect o inertia, an exact solution of the non-linear partial differential equations governing such flows will be presented. This solution is for the steady two-dimensional flow of a stratified fluid in a channel toward a line sink, with constant density gradient at infinity.

The most important difference between stratified flows and the flows of a homogeneous inviscid fluid is that irrotationality persists in the latter but not in the former, even if the fluid is incompressible and inviscid. Furthermore, a quantity (corresponding to vorticity in the homogeneous case) the vanishing of which would persist in unsteady stratified flows has not been found, so that until now it has not been possible to specify other than arbitrarily the boundary condition at infinity for steady stratified flows in a channel, even if the motion is assumed to have started from rest. This difficulty can be overcome by considering the effect of inertia on steady flows.

Effect of Inertia on Steady Flows of a Stratified Fluid

The effect of density variation on fluid flow is twofold. On the one hand, in a gravitational field the variation of density corresponds to a variation of body force per unit volume, and engenders gravity effects which do not exist in the flow of a homogeneous fluid with fixed boundaries. On the other hand, density variation always has an effect on fluid flow, whether gravity is present or not, because the resistance per unit volume to accelerating forces is not constant. This effect is called the effect of inertia, and can be evaluated in a straightforward manner if the flow is steady.

To isolate the effect of inertia from gravity effects, the gravitational acceleration will be assumed to be zero. If (x, y, z) are Cartesian coordinates and (u, v, w) are the corresponding velocity components, ρ is the density,

p is the pressure, and partial derivatives are indicated by subscripts, the equations of steady motion of an inviscid fluid are

$$\rho \frac{D}{Dt}(u, v, w) = -(p_x, p_y, p_z), \tag{1}$$

in which

$$\frac{D}{Dt} \equiv u \frac{\partial}{\partial x} + v \frac{\partial}{\partial y} + w \frac{\partial}{\partial z}, \tag{2}$$

and letter subscripts denote partial differentiation. The equation of continuity is

$$(\rho u)_x + (\rho v)_y + (\rho w)_z = 0. \tag{3}$$

Since the fluid is incompressible,

$$\frac{D\rho}{Dt} = 0, \tag{4}$$

and (3) can be written

$$(\sqrt{\rho}\, u)_x + (\sqrt{\rho}\, v)_y + (\sqrt{\rho}\, w)_z = 0. \tag{5}$$

With the substitutions

$$(u', v', w') = \sqrt{\rho}\,(u, v, w), \tag{6}$$

the equations of motion become, by virtue of (4),

$$\left(u' \frac{\partial}{\partial x} + v' \frac{\partial}{\partial y} + w' \frac{\partial}{\partial z}\right)(u', v', w') = -(p_x, p_y, p_z), \tag{7}$$

and the continuity equation becomes

$$u'_x + v'_y + w'_z = 0. \tag{8}$$

But (7) and (8) are the equations governing the motion of a homogeneous inviscid fluid. If $(\Omega_1, \Omega_2, \Omega_3)$ denote the

Reprinted from *Proc. Third U. S. Natl. Congr. Appl. Mech.* (1958) 857–861.

vorticity components of the flow with velocity components (u', v', w'), and therefore

$$(\Omega_1)_x + (\Omega_2)_y + (\Omega_3)_z = 0, \qquad (9)$$

cross differentiation of (7) produces, by virtue of (8) and (9), the equations

$$\left(u'\frac{\partial}{\partial x} + v'\frac{\partial}{\partial y} + w'\frac{\partial}{\partial z}\right)(\Omega_1, \Omega_2, \Omega_3) =$$
$$\left(\Omega_1\frac{\partial}{\partial x} + \Omega_2\frac{\partial}{\partial y} + \Omega_3\frac{\partial}{\partial z}\right)(u', v', w'). \qquad (10)$$

Equations (10) state the persistence of irrotationality of the flow with velocity components (u', v', w'), which will henceforth be called the associated flow for brevity. Therefore, if the effect of gravity is neglected, and if the actual flow originates from a large reservoir where the velocity of the fluid is zero, then the associated flow is irrotational and can be obtained by solving the Laplace equation. From the associated flow the actual flow can be readily obtained from (4) and (6).

Of course, gravity effects can be neglected only if the streamlines are imbedded in horizontal planes. But horizontal flows need not be truly two-dimensional, for with stratification the velocity is not independent of the vertical distance. However, the associated flows, if irrotational, are truly two-dimensional. This fact will enable one to specify the boundary condition at infinity for the problem in the following section, in the solution of which the gravity effects are fully taken into account.

Stratified Flow Into a Horizontal Line Sink

If a closed canal terminates at a gate which is not fully closed, the slit that it leaves serves as a horizontal line sink, the strength of which may be considered as arbitrary because the flow is not assumed to be entirely due to gravity, e.g., it may be due to suction of the sink or the pressure upstream. The density of the fluid at a section far from the sink is assumed to have a stable linear distribution. Would as much of the lighter parts of the fluid enter the sink as the heavier parts? This question has direct bearing on the problem of partial separation of fresh water from sea water which has intruded into a fresh water reservoir, or of cool water (intended for cooling in thermo-electric plants) from the warm water which is discharged therefrom and finds its way back to the intake in the form of a warm wedge. Professor J. M. Burgers has informed the writer that the separation of fresh water from salt water is a problem of great importance to agriculture in Holland. Although a full answer to the question is not yet available, a maxi-

mum value for the Froude number based on total discharge has been found, above which fluid separation by changing the location of the line sink would be entirely futile.

The upstream density variation under consideration is

$$\rho = \rho_0 - \beta y, \quad \beta = \frac{\rho_0 - \rho_1}{d}, \qquad (11)$$

in which y is measured vertically from the horizontal bottom, d is the distance between the top and the bottom of the canal, ρ_0 is the density at the bottom, and ρ_1 is the density at the top. With x measured horizontally from the sink, the equations of motion are, for steady flows,

$$\rho u u_x + \rho v u_y = -p_x, \qquad (12)$$

$$\rho u v_x + \rho v v_y = -p_y - g\rho, \qquad (13)$$

in which g is the gravitational acceleration. The equation of persistence of density is now

$$u\rho_x + v\rho_y = 0 \qquad (14)$$

by virtue of which the continuity equation can be reduced to the usual form

$$u_x + v_y = 0. \qquad (15)$$

Equation (15) permits the use of the stream function ψ such that

$$u = -\psi_y, \quad v = \psi_x. \qquad (16)$$

From (12)–(15), Long [1] was able to derive the equation for the stream function:

$$\nabla^2\psi + \frac{1}{\rho}\frac{d\rho}{d\psi}\left(\frac{\psi_x^2 + \psi_y^2}{2} + gy\right) = H(\psi). \qquad (17)$$

If g were zero, the flow would be the kind discussed in Section 2, and the velocity distribution could be obtained from an associated irrotational flow as explained in that section. This suggests that the terms involving the squares of the derivatives of ψ can be eliminated if the new stream function ψ' is used:

$$\psi' = \int_0^\psi \rho^{1/2}\, d\psi. \qquad (18)$$

In fact, this transformation has been essentially discovered and utilized by Long [1, 2] in meteorological problems. With (18) and the fact that for steady flow streamlines are isopycnic lines (i.e., ρ is a function of ψ alone), (17) can be reduced to the simpler form

$$\nabla^2 \psi' + gy \frac{d\rho}{d\psi'} = H_1(\psi'),\qquad(19)$$

from which the squares of the derivatives of ψ have indeed disappeared. Equation (19) will be used instead of (17), which is Long's original equation.

The transformation defined by (18) is the same as that defined by (6). Therefore (19) is the equation for the stream function of the associated flow, though the effect of gravity is now fully taken into account. If the fluid is considered to originate from a large reservoir, where the velocity is zero, and to flow into the channel horizontally, the associated flow is irrotational far upstream from the line sink, according to the result of Section 2. Thus if ψ'_0 is the stream function for the associated flow far upstream,

$$\psi'_0 = -Ay,\qquad(20)$$

in which A is a positive constant. If $U(y)$ is the velocity of the actual flow far upstream,

$$\rho U^2 = A^2,\qquad(21)$$

which is an assumption made by Long [1, 2] without proof. With (11), (20), and (21), (19) becomes

$$\nabla^2 \psi' + \frac{g\beta}{A} y = H_1(\psi').\qquad(22)$$

Since far upstream ψ' is $-Ay$, from (20) and (22) it follows that

$$H_1(\psi') = -\frac{g\beta}{A^2}\psi'.$$

Thus (22) can be written

$$\nabla^2 \psi' + k\psi' = -Aky,\qquad(23)$$

in which

$$k = \frac{g\beta}{A^2}.$$

With the transformations

$$\Psi = \frac{\psi'}{Ad},\quad \xi = \frac{x}{d},\quad \eta = \frac{y}{d}.\qquad(24)$$

(23) becomes

$$\Psi_{\xi\xi} + \Psi_{\eta\eta} + F^{-2}\Psi = -F^{-2}\eta\qquad(25)$$

in which

$$F = A/d\sqrt{g\beta}\qquad(26)$$

is a Froude number. The boundary conditions are

$$\Psi = -1 \quad \text{at} \quad \eta = 1 \quad \text{and} \quad \xi = 0,$$
$$\Psi = 0 \quad \text{at} \quad \eta = 0,$$
$$\Psi = -\eta \quad \text{at} \quad \xi = -\infty.$$

If

$$\Psi = -\eta + f,\qquad(27)$$

then (25) becomes

$$f_{\xi\xi} + f_{\eta\eta} + F^{-2}f = 0,\qquad(28)$$

and the boundary conditions are

$$f = 0 \qquad \text{at} \quad \eta = 1,\qquad(29)$$
$$f = -1 + \eta \quad \text{at} \quad \xi = 0,\qquad(30)$$
$$f = 0 \qquad \text{at} \quad \eta = 0,\qquad(31)$$
$$f = 0 \qquad \text{at} \quad \xi = -\infty.\qquad(32)$$

Equations (28), (29), (31), and (32) are satisfied by

$$f = \sum_{n=1}^{\infty} B_n e^{a_n \xi} \sin n\pi\eta,\qquad(33)$$

in which

$$a_n^2 = n^2\pi^2 - F^{-2}.\qquad(34)$$

In order to satisfy (30), the B's must be chosen to be the Fourier coefficients of $\eta - 1$:

$$B_n = -\frac{2}{n\pi}.\qquad(35)$$

The solution has now been obtained, provided

$$F > F_{cr} = 1/\pi = 0.318,\qquad(36)$$

in which F_{cr} is the critical Froude number. Figures 1 to 4 show the flow patterns with

$$F = 0.32, 0.35, 0.5, \quad \text{and} \quad \infty.$$

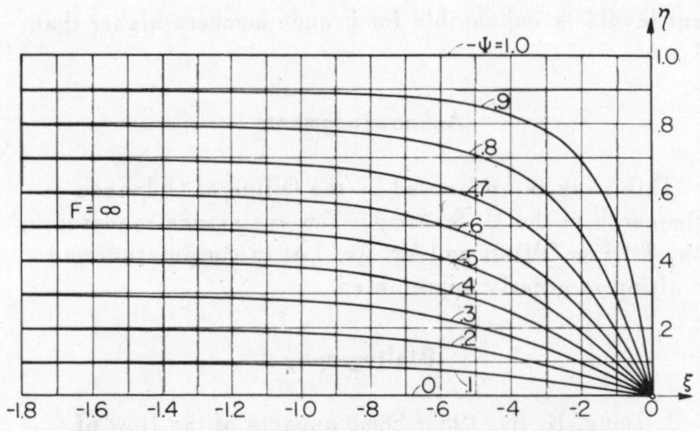

FIGURE 1. FLOW PATTERN FOR FROUDE NUMBER ∞.

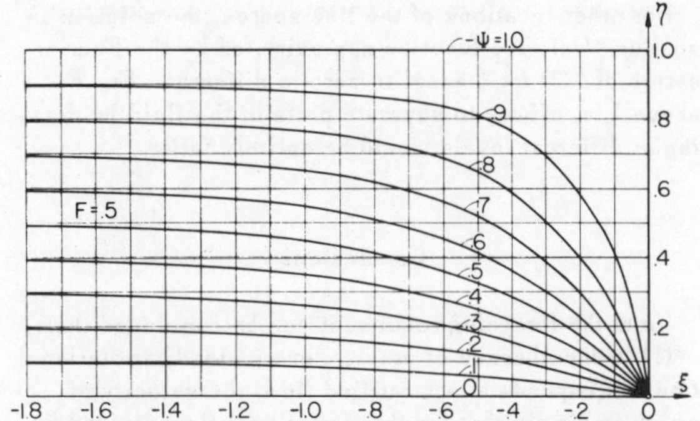

FIGURE 2. FLOW PATTERN FOR FROUDE NUMBER 0.5.

Computations for the case for F equal to 1 have also
been made. The resulting flow pattern does not differ
much from that for $F = \infty$. From Figs. 3 and 4 it can be
seen that the corner eddy becomes more and more pronounced as the critical Froude number is reached. For
F equal to or less than F_{cr}, the solution fails, and the
eddy will reach infinitely far upstream to invalidate the
boundary condition there, where the associated flow is
no longer irrotational[*] because of the presence of the
eddy which may introduce a vortex sheet in the fluid.
For F greater than F_{cr}, the solution is valid, and separation of parts of the fluid by drawing at the bottom is
impossible.

---

[*]The flow from the reservoir to the channel is no longer horizontal.

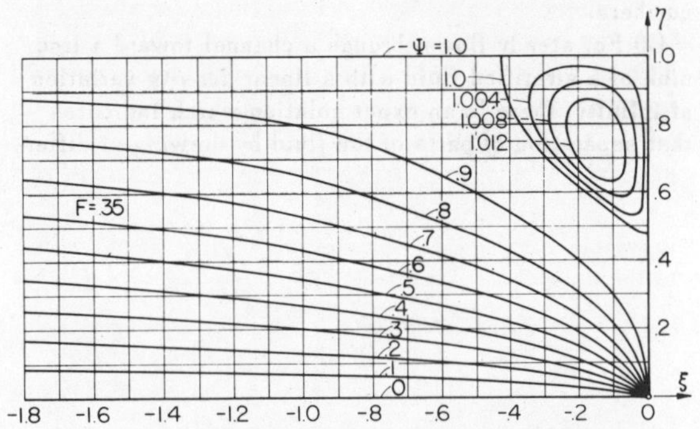

FIGURE 3. FLOW PATTERN FOR FROUDE NUMBER 0.35.

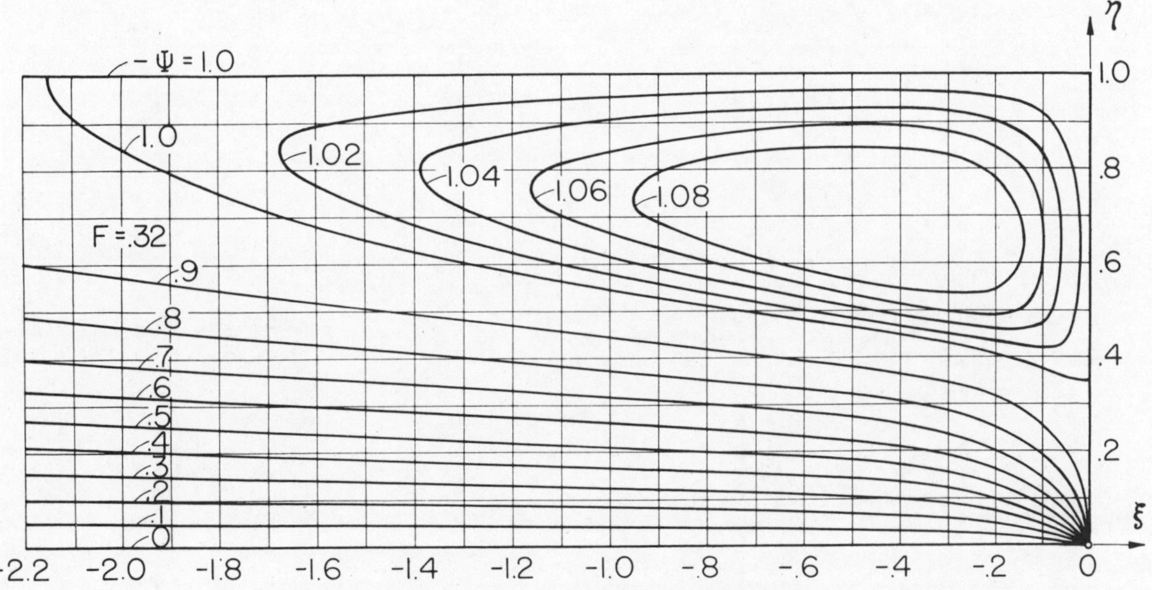

FIGURE 4. FLOW PATTERN FOR FROUDE NUMBER 0.32.

For other locations of the line source, the solution is similar. Only the function approximated by the Fourier series of (33) for ξ equal to zero is different. For F above $1/\pi$, efforts to separate parts of the fluid by drawing at different levels would be entirely futile.

Conclusions

From the foregoing results, it can be concluded that:

(1) In the absence of gravity, every steady irrotational flow corresponds to a stratified flow, the velocity of which is simply that for the irrotational flow divided by the square root of the density. Gravity effects can be neglected only for horizontal flows or for high Froude numbers.

(2) For steady flows through a channel toward a line sink of a stratified fluid with a linear density variation at infinity, there is an exact solution which indicates that separation of parts of the fluid by drawing at different levels is impossible for Froude numbers higher than $1/\pi$.

Acknowledgments

This work is sponsored by the Office of Ordnance Research of the U. S. Army. The assistance rendered by Mr. William O'Dell and Mr. Wei Lai in computation and drafting is greatly appreciated.

Bibliography

1. Long, R. R., 1953: Some aspects of the flow of stratified fluids, I. A theoretical investigation, Tech. Rep. No. 2, The Johns Hopkins Univ., Dept. of Civil Eng.

2. Long, R. R., 1955: Some aspects of the flow of stratified fluids, III. Continuous density gradients, Tech. Rep. No. 6, The Johns Hopkins Univ., Dept. of Civil Eng.

JOURNAL OF GEOPHYSICAL RESEARCH   VOLUME 64, No. 12   DECEMBER, 1959

Effect of Density Variation on Fluid Flow

CHIA-SHUN YIH

Department of Engineering Mechanics, University of Michigan
Ann Arbor, Michigan

Abstract—The effect of density variation on the flow of an incompressible and inviscid fluid is twofold. On the one hand, the inertia of the fluid changes in direct proportion to the density. On the other hand, the body force acting on a fluid element also changes in direct proportion to the density. Since body force is not the only force acting on the fluid, the inertia effect and the gravity effect of density variation do not cancel each other, and many interesting phenomena occur in the flow of a heterogeneous fluid that do not occur in the flow of a homogeneous fluid.

In this paper it is shown that the inertia effect can be simply evaluated for steady flows. If the velocity in the steady flow of a heterogeneous fluid in the absence of gravity is multiplied by the square root of the density, the result represents a dynamically possible flow of a homogeneous fluid. At the other extreme, when the gravitational effect dominates the flow, it has been shown both analytically and experimentally that the motion of a fluid is confined to the layer at which it originates. As usual, it is when the inertia effect and the gravity effect are comparable that the solutions of stratified flows become difficult, even if the flow is assumed to be steady and the fluid inviscid. From one series of such solutions and the supporting experiments one sees that, on the one hand, infinitely many modes of stationary internal waves of finite amplitude are dynamically possible (apart from the consideration of generation), and, on the other hand, physically significant solutions of stratified flows may involve velocity discontinuities.

Introduction—In the flow of an incompressible and inviscid fluid, inhomogeneity of the fluid affects the flow in two ways. First, a change of density always involves a proportional change of the inertia per unit volume of the fluid. Second, a density change always involves a change of body force per unit volume in a gravitational field. Although this body force is proportional to the density in a uniform gravitational field, it is unfortunately not the only force acting on the fluid. Thus the flow pattern of an inhomogeneous fluid may differ considerably from that of a homogeneous fluid even though the boundary conditions are the same.

In this paper it will be shown that the inertia effect of density change can be simply evaluated for steady flows, and that, when the flow is weak and therefore dominated by the gravitational effect, it is confined to the level at which the disturbance causing the motion is situated. A series of exact solutions for flow into a sink, in which both inertia and gravity effects are taken into account, will be given for all Froude numbers, however small. The results of supporting experiments will be cited to show that the ana-

lytical solutions for Froude numbers less than $1/\pi$ are not physically significant, and that the possibility for velocity discontinuities must sometimes be provided for in order to obtain a physically significant analytical solution.

Inertia effect in steady flows—Since the fluid is considered to be incompressible, the density ρ satisfies the equation

$$D\rho/Dt = 0 \qquad (1)$$

in which

$$\frac{D}{Dt} = \frac{\partial}{\partial t} + u_i \frac{\partial}{\partial x_i}$$

is the operator for substantial differentiation, with t denoting the time and u_i the velocity component in the direction of the cartesian coordinate x_i. The summation convention is adopted, so that

$$u_i \frac{\partial}{\partial x_i} = u_1 \frac{\partial}{\partial x_1} + u_2 \frac{\partial}{\partial x_2} + u_3 \frac{\partial}{\partial x_3}$$

The condition for continuity is

$$\frac{\partial \rho}{\partial t} + \frac{\partial(\rho u_i)}{\partial x_i} = 0 \qquad (2)$$

From equations 1 and 2 it follows that the continuity equation for an incompressible fluid (even of variable density) can be written

$$\partial u_i / \partial x_i = 0 \qquad (3)$$

Euler's equations of motion for an inviscid fluid are

$$\rho \frac{Du_i}{Dt} = -\frac{\partial p}{\partial x_i} + \rho g_i \qquad (i = 1, 2, 3) \qquad (4)$$

if g_i is the body force per unit mass in the x_i direction. If $(x_1, x_2, x_3) = (x, y, z)$, and the y axis is vertical, $(g_1, g_2, g_3) = (0, -g, 0)$.

Since the inertia effect exclusively is under examination, the term ρg_i in equation 4 can be omitted, and we have, for steady flows,

$$\rho u_i \frac{\partial u_i}{\partial x_i} = -\frac{\partial p}{\partial x_i} \qquad (5)$$

which, because of equation 1, can be written as [*Yih*, 1958]

$$\sqrt{\rho}\, u_i \frac{\partial \sqrt{\rho}\, u_i}{\partial x_i} = -\frac{\partial p}{\partial x_i} \qquad (6)$$

Furthermore, for steady flows the equation of continuity can be written as

$$\frac{\partial (\sqrt{\rho}\, u_i)}{\partial x_i} = 0 \qquad (7)$$

also by virtue of equation 1. Thus with

$$u_i' = \sqrt{\rho}\, u_i \qquad (8)$$

the governing equations become

$$u_i' \frac{\partial u_i'}{\partial x_i} = -\frac{\partial p}{\partial x_i} \qquad \frac{\partial u_i'}{\partial x_i} = 0 \qquad (9)$$

which are the equations governing the flow of a homogeneous fluid of density equal to unity. Hence, in the absence of a gravitational field, the general flow *pattern* of an inhomogeneous fluid is identical to that of homogeneous fluid under similar boundary conditions. Only the velocity is different. The velocity for the inhomogeneous fluid can be obtained from that for the homogeneous fluid through division of the latter by $\sqrt{\rho}$. **Furthermore, it can be shown from equation 9 that in the associated flow field u_i' irrotationality will persist, provided that gravity effect is negligible and the flow is steady. This is not true of the actual flow field u_i.**

In the presence of a gravitational field, the conclusions reached are true if the flow is entirely horizontal, or if the flow is so rapid that gravity effect, though present, is **negligible**.

Gravity effect—For very weak steady motions the situation is entirely different. Inertia effect is now negligible, and the motion is dominated by gravity effect. The equation of continuity can now be written, with (x, y, z) for (x_1, x_2, x_3) and (u, v, w) for (u_1, u_2, u_3),

$$v \frac{\partial \rho}{\partial y} = 0$$

Fig. 1—Apparatus for demonstrating the gravity effect of density stratification.

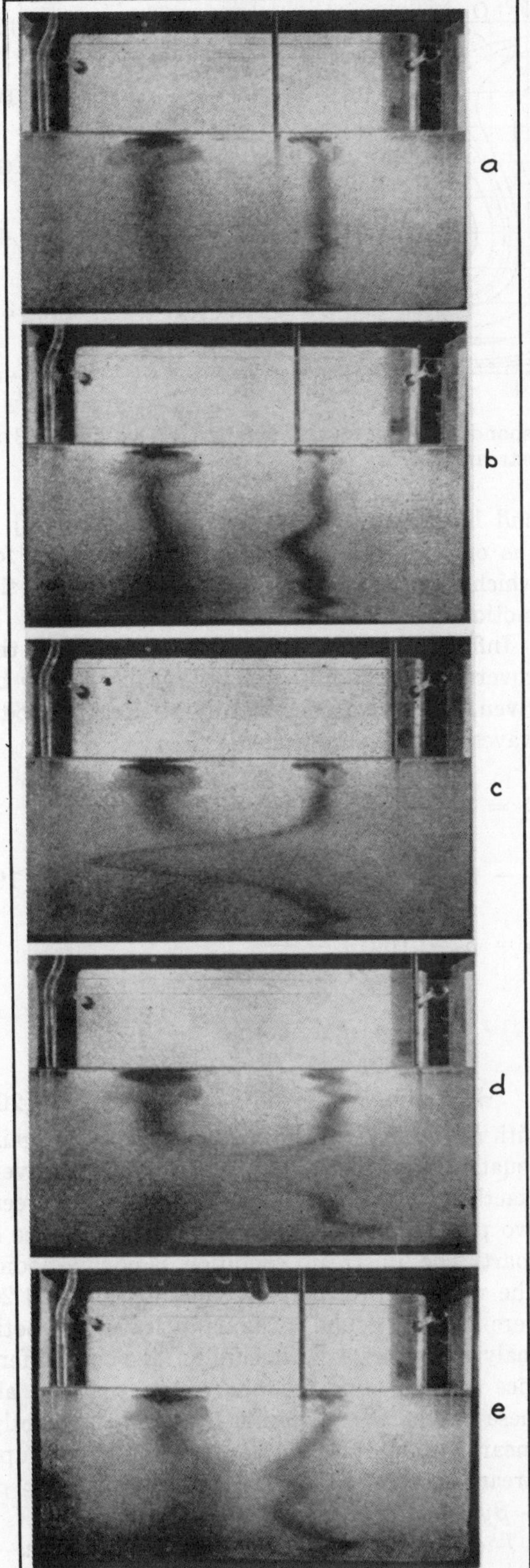

FIG. 2—Development of dye streaks, showing the confinement of the motion to the range of levels at which the paddle is situated.

from which it follows that

$$v = 0 \qquad (10)$$

since the fluid is stratified in the direction of y. Furthermore, from the equations of motion

$$\frac{\partial p}{\partial x} = 0 \qquad \frac{\partial p}{\partial y} = -gy \qquad \frac{\partial p}{\partial z} = 0$$

It follows that

$$\frac{\partial \rho}{\partial x} = 0 \qquad \frac{\partial \rho}{\partial z} = 0 \qquad (11)$$

Equations 10 and 11 state that for steady weak motions the effect of gravity is to inhibit vertical motion and horizontal density gradients completely.

If the motion is two-dimensional to start with, $w = 0$, and the motion is only in the x direction, with no change in u or ρ with respect to x. This result is directly similar to a result of *Proudman* [1916] for weak steady axisymmetric motions relative to a strong general rotation.

The conclusions of this section are generally supported by the results of a simple experiment. Figure 1 shows the apparatus used. The two partition walls do not extend the full length of the container, so that as the paddle moves the stratified fluid realized by layers of salt water of different density can circulate around. Figure 2a shows the vertical dye streaks, one in the inner channel, and the clearer one in one of the outer channels. Figures 2b to 2d show the development of streaks as the paddle was moved to the right. Finally, Figure 2e shows the return of the dyed particles as the paddle is moved back to a place near its original position. Aside from obvious viscous effects, the conclusions of this section are largely supported by the results of this simple experiment. The striking feature is that a little stratification is sufficient to make the effect of the moving paddle felt far upstream and downstream.

Stationary waves of finite amplitude—The equation governing steady two-dimensional flows of a stratified fluid can be derived from equations 1, 3, and 4, with u_3 equal to zero, and has been given by *Long* [1953]:

$$\nabla^2 \psi + \frac{1}{\rho} \frac{d\rho}{d\psi} \left(\frac{\psi_x^2 + \psi_v^2}{2} + gy \right) = H(\psi) \qquad (12)$$

in which

$$\nabla^2 = \frac{\partial^2}{\partial x^2} + \frac{\partial^2}{\partial y^2}$$

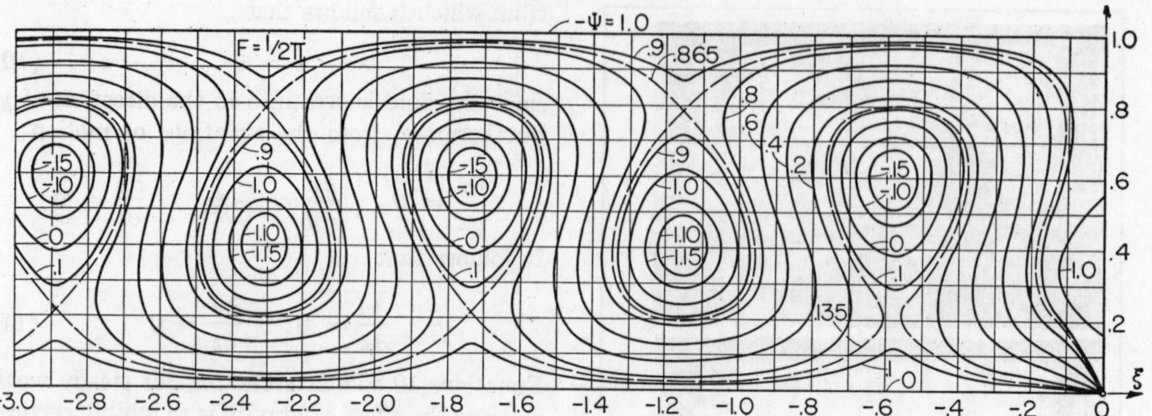

Fɪɢ. 3—Pattern of stratified flow into a sink, corresponding to a formal solution of equation 18 at $F = 3/4\pi$, with upstream waves.

ψ is the stream function, and subscripts indicate partial differentiation. Through the transformation [*Yih, 1958*]

$$\psi' = \int \sqrt{\rho}\, d\psi \qquad (13)$$

which is suggested by equation 8, Long's equation can be put in the simpler form

$$\nabla^2 \psi' + \frac{d\rho}{d\psi'}\, gy = H_1(\psi') \qquad (14)$$

in which the function $H_1(\psi')$ depends on upstream conditions.

For flows with an upstream velocity (horizontal) U such that $U^2\rho$ is constant (A^2, say) and with the linear density variation upstream

$$\rho = \rho_0 - \beta y \qquad (15)$$

equation 14 becomes

$$\nabla^2 \psi' + \frac{g\beta}{A^2}\, \psi' = -\frac{g\beta}{A}\, y \qquad (16)$$

If d is a representative length, the dimensionless variables

$$\Psi = \frac{\psi'}{Ad} \qquad \xi = \frac{x}{d} \qquad \eta = \frac{y}{d} \qquad (17)$$

can be used for convenience. Equation 16 then becomes

$$\Psi_{\xi\xi} + \Psi_{\eta\eta} + F^{-2}\Psi = -F^{-2}\eta, \qquad (18)$$

in which $F = A/d\sqrt{g\beta}$
is the Froude number. In his paper of 1953, Long stated: 'This [the case of constant $U^2\rho$

and linear variation of ρ with y upstream] is the only case I have been able to discover for which the differential equation governing the motion of a stratified fluid is exactly linear.'

Infinitely many other cases for which the governing equation is exactly linear will now be given. These correspond to stationary periodic waves of finite amplitude. If

$$\Psi = -\eta - \frac{2}{\pi} \sum_{n=1}^{N} \sin n\pi\eta\, [A_n \cos\, (F^{-2}$$
$$- n^2\pi^2)^{1/2}\xi + B_n \sin\, (F^{-2} - n^2\pi^2)^{1/2}\xi] \quad (19)$$

$$\rho = \rho_0 - (\beta d)\eta - \frac{2\beta d}{\pi}$$

$$\cdot \sum_1^N \sin n\pi\eta\, [A_n \cos\, (F^{-2} - n^2\pi^2)^{1/2}\xi$$

$$+ B_n \sin\, (F^{-2} - n^2\pi^2)^{1/2}\xi] \qquad (20)$$

with $F^{-1} > N\pi$, the governing equation is again equation 18, the solution of which is given exactly by equations 19 and 20 for flow between two parallel horizontal boundaries at distance d apart. The 'upstream condition' is now periodic. The waves represented by equations 19 and 20 were actually found by Long as lea waves both analytically and experimentally. The only difference is that Long did not realize that for all these waves the governing equation is exactly linear without the benefit of the stringent upstream conditions $U^2\rho = $ constant and $\rho = \rho_0 - \beta y$.

The occurrence of velocity discontinuities— From Figure 2 it has been seen that, but for the effect of viscosity, steady weak motions would

FIG. 4—Actual pattern of stratified flow into a sink when the Froude number F is below the critical number $1/\pi$. (Courtesy of Dr. W. R. Debler.)

develop velocity discontinuities (at the levels of the edges of the paddle). In a study of stratified flow between two horizontal boundaries into a sink [*Yih*, 1958], a solution for equation 18 was found for $F > 1/\pi$. For Froude numbers less than the critical value $1/\pi$, either waves would occur upstream or a velocity discontinuity would develop. For $F = 1/2\pi$, a solution[1] of equation

---

[1] The general solution (entirely formal) is

$$\Psi = -\eta - \frac{2}{\pi}$$

$$\cdot \left\{ \sum_{n=1}^{N} \frac{\sin n\pi\eta}{n} \left[\cos \left(F^{-2} - n^2\pi^2 \right)^{1/2} \xi \right. \right.$$

$$\left. + B_n \sin \left(F^{-2} - n^2\pi^2 \right)^{1/2} \xi \right]$$

$$\left. + \sum_{n=N+1}^{\infty} \frac{\sin n\pi\eta}{n} \exp \left(n^2\pi^2 - F^{-2} \right)^{1/2} \xi \right\}$$

$$\rho = \rho_0 - (\beta d)\eta - \frac{2\beta d}{\pi}$$

$$\cdot \left\{ \sum_{n=1}^{N} \frac{\sin n\pi\eta}{n} \left[\cos \left(F^{-2} - n^2\pi^2 \right)^{1/2} \xi \right. \right.$$

$$\left. + B_n \sin \left(F^{-2} - n^2\pi^2 \right)^{1/2} \xi \right]$$

$$\left. + \sum_{n=N+1}^{\infty} \frac{\sin n\pi\eta}{n} \exp \left(n^2\pi^2 - F^{-2} \right)^{1/2} \xi \right\}$$

18 with upstream waves gives the flow pattern in Figure 3, whereas the experiments of *Debler* [1959] showed that these waves do not occur upstream, that a velocity discontinuity occurs between a moving layer and an essentially stagnant layer (Fig. 4), and that the Froude number based on the thickness of the moving layer is approximately $1/\pi$. Hence, for an analytical solution to be physically significant, the possibility of the occurrence of velocity discontinuities may have to be provided for.

Acknowledgment—The work described in this paper has been sponsored by the Office of Ordnance Research, U. S. Army. The assistance of Mr. William O'Dell in producing Figure 3 is greatly appreciated.

REFERENCES

DEBLER, W. R., Stratified flow into a line sink, to be published in *Proc. Am. Soc. Civil Engrs.*, 1959.

LONG, R. R., Some aspects of the flow of stratified fluids. I. A theoretical investigation, *Dept. Civil Eng., Johns Hopkins Univ., Tech. Rept. 2*, 1953.

PROUDMAN, J., On the motion of solids in a liquid possessing vorticity, *Proc. Roy. Soc. London, A, 92*, 408–424, 1916.

YIH, C.-S., On the flow of a stratified fluid, *Proc. Third Natl. Congr. Appl. Mechanics*, pp. 857–861, 1958.

in which

$$(N + 1)\pi \geq F^{-1} \geq N\pi$$

and the B's are arbitrary.

Reprinted without change of pagination from the
Journal of Fluid Mechanics, *volume* 8, *part* 4, *pp.* 481–508, 1960

Gravity waves in a stratified fluid

By CHIA-SHUN YIH

Department of Engineering Mechanics, University of Michigan

(Received 18 December 1959)

A unified treatment of wave motion in a stratified fluid, with or without density discontinuities, is achieved by reducing the governing differential system to a Sturm–Liouville system. With the aid of Sturm's comparison theorem, it is found (without detailed calculations) that, for any stratification, the phase velocity increases as the wave-number decreases and that, for the same wave-number, the phase velocity increases as the density gradient is increased everywhere and decreases as the density is increased everywhere by a constant amount. Sturm's oscillation theorem provides upper and lower bounds for the phase velocity for a given stratification, a given wave-number, and a given number of zeros of the eigenfunction (or a given number of stationary surfaces in the fluid). The inequalities giving these bounds are used to explain the well-known tendency for surfaces of density discontinuities to behave as rigid boundaries when the stratification in each layer is slight. The rigid-boundary behaviour of interfaces in such cases enables one to obtain the approximate eigenvalue spectrum by superimposing the spectra of the individual layers (with the interfaces treated as rigid) on the spectrum of the interfacial (or free surface) waves, obtained by ignoring the slight continuous stratification in each layer. It is pointed out that the Ritz method can be used for calculating the eigenvalues even when the density is discontinuous, and examples are given to show the accuracy of the Ritz method. The nature of the spectrum when the depth is infinite is also clarified.

In the course of the development of the theory, the effects of compressibility and of three-dimensionality are determined and given explicitly, the rate of growth of unstable stratifications is related to the phase velocity of waves in stable ones, and equipartition of energy is proved. Motion due to a wavemaker is discussed in order to bring out the connexion between the type of the governing partial differential equation and the nature (local or not local) of the disturbances. The effect of surface tension and the stability of a stratified fluid under vertical oscillation are also discussed.

1. Introduction

The propagation of gravity waves in a system consisting of many distinct layers of fluids was investigated by Webb (1884) and Greenhill (1887) many years ago. Recently, Benton (1953) considered the propagation of long waves in a system of flowing layers, and by a limiting process generalized the result to apply to

482   *Chia-Shun Yih*

waves propagating in a flowing fluid with continuous stratification. His approach provides a desirable link between results for distinct layers and those for a continuously stratified fluid. However, a unified theory is still lacking, and a convenient method for determining the phase velocity remains to be adopted. In this paper, the approach is diametrically opposite to that of Benton. Instead of considering a continuous stratification as a limit of a discontinuous one, as Benton did, one deals with continuous stratifications directly and treats surfaces of density discontinuity as limits of regions of large density gradients. If the effect of viscosity is neglected, the governing differential system is a Sturm–Liouville system, and Sturm's theorems can be used for the prediction of the ranges in which the phase velocities for the various modes must lie, for comparing the phase velocity in one stratified fluid with that of the corresponding mode in another, and for explaining a well-known behaviour of the surfaces of density discontinuity. The theory of infinitesimal waves presented herein also includes a technique to obtain the phase velocity to any degree of accuracy, an example of wave motion generated by a simple wave-maker, and an investigation of stability under vertical vibration.

2. The governing differential system

The differential system governing the propagation of gravity waves in a continuously stratified fluid at rest is well known (Lamb 1945, p. 378). Since the effect of compressibility will be discussed later, it is desirable to derive the differential system for wave propagation in a stratified and compressible fluid at rest, on the assumption that the change of state for each material particle is isentropic (the entire fluid not necessarily having the same entropy). The equations for incompressible fluids can then be immediately obtained by letting the sound velocity approach infinity.

With x, y, and z denoting Cartesian co-ordinates, z being measured vertically upward, and u, v and w denoting the corresponding velocity components, the mean density $\overline{\rho}(z)$ and mean pressure $\overline{p}(z)$ are related by the hydrostatic condition

$$\overline{p}' = -g\overline{\rho}. \tag{1}$$

The linearized equation of continuity is

$$\frac{\partial \rho}{\partial t} + \overline{\rho}\left(\frac{\partial u}{\partial x} + \frac{\partial v}{\partial y} + \frac{\partial w}{\partial z}\right) + w\overline{\rho}' = 0, \tag{2}$$

in which ρ is the density fluctuation and the accent indicates differentiation with respect to z. Since the velocity and the density perturbation are assumed to be small, their products and products of their derivatives have been neglected in the equation of continuity, and will be neglected in all the equations to be presented in this section. The linearized equation of isentropy is

$$\frac{\partial p}{\partial t} + w\overline{p}' = \frac{\partial p}{\partial t} - g\overline{\rho}w = c_s^2\left(\frac{\partial \rho}{\partial t} + w\overline{\rho}'\right), \tag{3}$$

in which p is the pressure fluctuation and c_s the sound velocity, which can vary with z. The equations of motion are, for an inviscid fluid,

$$\bar{\rho}\frac{\partial}{\partial t}(u,v,w) = -\left(\frac{\partial}{\partial x},\frac{\partial}{\partial y},\frac{\partial}{\partial z}\right)p + (0,0,-g\rho). \tag{4}$$

From the first two of equations (4), it follows immediately upon cross-differentiation that

$$\frac{\partial}{\partial t}\left(\frac{\partial(\bar{\rho}u)}{\partial y}-\frac{\partial(\bar{\rho}v)}{\partial x}\right) = 0.$$

If the motion is started from rest, or if u and v (as well as other dependent variables) are assumed to have an exponential time factor,

$$\frac{\partial(\bar{\rho}u)}{\partial y}-\frac{\partial(\bar{\rho}v)}{\partial x} = 0,$$

and a potential ϕ exists for u and v

$$\bar{\rho}u = -\frac{\partial\phi}{\partial x}, \quad \bar{\rho}v = -\frac{\partial\phi}{\partial y}.$$

The motion is therefore irrotational when *viewed from above*, in much the same way that Hele–Shaw flows are irrotational when viewed in a direction perpendicular to the (closely spaced) plane boundaries. The equation of continuity then assumes the form

$$\nabla^2\phi = \bar{\rho}\frac{\partial w}{\partial z}+w\bar{\rho}'+\frac{\partial\rho}{\partial t}, \quad \left(\nabla^2 = \frac{\partial^2}{\partial x^2}+\frac{\partial^2}{\partial y^2}\right), \tag{2a}$$

and integration of the first two of equations (4) produces

$$\frac{\partial\phi}{\partial t} = p,$$

with the function of integration $F(z,t)$ absorbed in $\partial\phi/\partial t$. After differentiation with respect to t and utilization of equations (3) and ($2a$), this equation assumes the form

$$\frac{\partial^2\phi}{\partial t^2} = g\bar{\rho}w+c_s^2\left(\nabla^2\phi-\bar{\rho}\frac{\partial w}{\partial z}\right). \tag{5}$$

Substituting $\partial\phi/\partial t$ for p in the third of equations (4), one has

$$\frac{\partial}{\partial t}\left(\frac{\partial\phi}{\partial z}+\bar{\rho}w\right)+g\rho = 0. \tag{6}$$

From equations (6) and ($2a$), the equation

$$\frac{\partial^3\phi}{\partial t^2\partial z}+g\nabla^2\phi-g\frac{\partial}{\partial z}(\bar{\rho}w)+\frac{\partial^2}{\partial t^2}(\bar{\rho}w) = 0$$

is obtained, whereas differentiation of equation (5) produces

$$\frac{\partial^3\phi}{\partial t^2\partial z}-g\frac{\partial}{\partial z}(\bar{\rho}w)-\frac{\partial}{\partial z}(c_s^2\nabla^2\phi)+\frac{\partial}{\partial z}\left(\bar{\rho}c_s^2\frac{\partial w}{\partial z}\right) = 0.$$

484   *Chia-Shun Yih*

From these one obtains by subtraction

$$\nabla^2\left[g\phi+\frac{\partial}{\partial z}(c_s^2\phi)\right]+\frac{\partial^2}{\partial t^2}(\overline{\rho}w)-\frac{\partial}{\partial z}\left(\overline{\rho}c_s^2\frac{\partial w}{\partial z}\right)=0.$$

Equation (5) and the equation following (7) give

$$\frac{\partial^2}{\partial t^2}\left(g\phi+c_s^2\frac{\partial\phi}{\partial z}\right)-g^2\overline{\rho}w-c_s^2g\overline{\rho}'w+c_s^2\frac{\partial^2}{\partial t^2}(\overline{\rho}w)=0,$$

from which follows

$$-(c_s^2)'\frac{\partial^2}{\partial t^2}\nabla^2\phi=\frac{\partial^4}{\partial t^4}(\overline{\rho}w)-\frac{\partial^3}{\partial t^2\partial z}\left(\overline{\rho}c_s^2\frac{\partial w}{\partial z}\right)+(g^2\overline{\rho}+c_s^2g\overline{\rho}')\nabla^2w-c_s^2\overline{\rho}\frac{\partial^2}{\partial t^2}\nabla^2w. \quad (7)$$

In the problems treated in this paper, ϕ, w, p and ρ are assumed to have a common factor $S(x,y)$ which satisfies the equation

$$(\nabla^2+\alpha^2)S(x,y)=0. \tag{8}$$

If the time-dependence of ϕ and w is assumed to be contained in the exponential factor $e^{-i\sigma t}$, so that

$$(\phi,w)=e^{-i\sigma t}S(x,y)\,[\phi(z),w(z)],$$

elimination of ϕ from equations (5) and (7) with the aid of (8) produces, with w now indicating $w(z)$,

$$\left(\frac{\alpha^2c_s^2}{\sigma^2}-1\right)[\sigma^2c_s^2(\overline{\rho}w')'+(\sigma^4-\alpha^2g^2-c_s^2\alpha^2\sigma^2)\overline{\rho}w-c_s^2\alpha^2g\overline{\rho}'w]$$
$$+(c_s^2)'\overline{\rho}(\alpha^2gw-\sigma^2w')=0. \tag{9}$$

For three-dimensional sinusoidal waves, the appropriate form for $S(x,y)$ is $\exp i(kx+ly)$, so that, with $\sigma=kc$,

$$(u,v,w,p,\rho)=[u(z),v(z),w(z),p(z),\rho(z)]\exp i(kx+ly-kct).$$

If, for brevity, u is written for $u(z)$, etc., the relationships between the several unknowns are

$$c\overline{\rho}u=p,\quad lu=kv,\quad ikc\overline{\rho}w=c(\overline{\rho}u)'+g\rho,\quad -ikcp-g\overline{\rho}w=c_s^2(-ikc\rho+w\overline{\rho}'),$$

and

$$i\rho u=\frac{kc_s^2\overline{\rho}}{(k^2+l^2)c_s^2-k^2c^2}\left(\frac{gw}{c_s^2}-w'\right),$$

which are recorded here for general convenience. With $\alpha^2=k^2+l^2$ and $\sigma=kc$, equation (9) has the form

$$\left[\frac{(k^2+l^2)c_s^2}{k^2c^2}-1\right]\{k^2c^2c_s^2(\overline{\rho}w')'+(kc)^4\overline{\rho}w-(k^2+l^2)[(g^2+k^2c^2c_s^2)\overline{\rho}w-c_s^2g\overline{\rho}'w]\}$$
$$+(c_s^2)'\overline{\rho}[(k^2+l^2)gw-k^2c^2w']=0. \tag{9a}$$

If c_s is constant, equation (9a) assumes the simpler form

$$(\overline{\rho}w')'-\frac{k^2+l^2}{k^2}\left(k^2\overline{\rho}-\frac{g}{c^2}\overline{\rho}'\right)w+\frac{c^2}{c_s^2}\left(k^2-\frac{(k^2+l^2)g^2}{k^2c^4}\right)\overline{\rho}w=0. \tag{10}$$

If the fluid is bounded by two rigid barriers at $z = 0$ and $z = d$, the boundary conditions are

$$w(0) = 0, \quad w(d) = 0.$$

Boundary conditions at free surfaces and interfaces will be presented later.

For an incompressible fluid, $c_s = \infty$, and equation (10) reduces to

$$(\bar{\rho} w')' - \frac{k^2 + l^2}{k^2} \left(k^2 \bar{\rho} + \frac{g}{c^2} \bar{\rho}' \right) w = 0, \tag{11}$$

which for two-dimensional motion can be further reduced to the simple form

$$(\bar{\rho} w')' - \left(k^2 \bar{\rho} + \frac{g}{c^2} \bar{\rho}' \right) w = 0. \tag{12}$$

For two-dimensional motion of a compressible fluid with constant c_s, equation (10) has the form

$$(\bar{\rho} w')' - \left(k^2 \bar{\rho} + \frac{g}{c^2} \bar{\rho}' \right) w + \frac{c^2}{c_s^2} \left(k^2 - \frac{g^2}{c^4} \right) \bar{\rho} w = 0. \tag{13}$$

3. General considerations

Although equation (10) appears rather complex as it stands, for many problems its solution can be reduced to that of equation (12). First of all, the effect of three-dimensionality can be determined once and for all. From equation (9) it is seen that for a given stratification σ^2 is a function of α^2 (in this case $k^2 + l^2$) alone. (The sum $k^2 + l^2$ really is the square of the wave-number of a corresponding two-dimensional wave travelling in the direction with direction numbers k, l, and zero.) Thus, without any loss of generality, the problem of determining σ given k and l is reduced to the problem of determining σ for a two-dimensional wave motion with wave-number $k_2 = \alpha$, from equation (9). The rule of conversion, first enunciated and proved by Squire (1933) in connexion with a problem of hydrodynamic stability, is as follows. The σ for a three-dimensional disturbance of wave-numbers k and l is the same as that for a two-dimensional disturbance of wave-number $(k^2 + l^2)^{\frac{1}{2}}$, the actual phase velocity c (in the x-direction) is σ/k which is greater than the c for an actual two-dimensional disturbance of wave-number $(k^2 + l^2)^{\frac{1}{2}}$ by the factor $(k^2 + l^2)^{\frac{1}{2}}/k$.

Turning now to equation (13), one seeks to determine the effect of compressibility in a simple way, without any detailed calculations. In this connexion it must be remembered that the sound velocity is in general a function of location. For liquids it can without great error be taken to be constant, and at all events the effect of compressibility is small. For gases, c_s is constant only for an isothermal atmosphere. Under the assumption that c_s is constant, and with a fictitious wave-number k_i for a corresponding wave motion in incompressible fluid defined as

$$k_i^2 = k^2 + \frac{c^2}{c_s^2} \left(\frac{g^2}{c^4} - k^2 \right), \tag{14}$$

equation (13) is reduced to the form

$$(\bar{\rho} w')' - \left(k_i^2 \bar{\rho} + \frac{g}{c^2} \bar{\rho}' \right) w = 0.$$

486   *Chia-Shun Yih*

After c is determined from this equation for a chosen k_i, the actual k can then be calculated simply from equation (14). Of course, the assumed k_i should be greater than g/cc_s (in most cases) for a *wave* motion. Otherwise k^2 would be negative (since c is in most cases less than c_s) and the motion would not be a wave motion. With k found, σ is also known. This procedure evidently involves a process of trial and error if c is to be found for a given k, or k is to be found for a given σ, but it certainly is a convenient means of determining the effect of compressibility. Since g/k is the c^2 for free-surface waves in a semi-infinite fluid, and the c^2 for internal or interfacial waves is usually smaller, $k_i^2 > k^2$ in most cases of practical interest. In a subsequent paragraph it will be shown that the c^2 determined from equation (12) decreases with k^2. Thus, whenever c_s is constant and $g > kc^2$, the effect of compressibility is to *reduce* the phase velocity, and the amount of reduction can be simply determined in the manner described above.

Attention will then be focused on equation (12) in the major part of this paper. Since this corresponds to two-dimensional flows of an incompressible fluid, the stream function will be introduced for convenience

$$\psi = f(z)\exp ik(x-ct).$$

The velocity components being

$$u = -\frac{\partial\psi}{\partial z} = -f'(z)\exp ik(x-ct), \quad w = \frac{\partial\psi}{\partial x} = ikf(z)\exp ik(x-ct),$$

the function $w(z)$ in equation (12) can be replaced by $f(z)$

$$(\bar{\rho}f')' - \left(k^2\bar{\rho} + \frac{g\bar{\rho}'}{c^2}\right)f = 0. \tag{12a}$$

If, further, the new variable

$$\eta = \frac{z}{d}$$

is introduced, and accents are now used to denote differentiations with respect to η, equation (12a) becomes

$$(\bar{\rho}f')' - \left(m^2\bar{\rho} + \frac{gd}{c^2}\bar{\rho}'\right)f = 0, \tag{15}$$

in which $m = kd$ is the dimensionless wave-number.

The boundary conditions at the rigid boundaries are, in terms of η,

$$f(0) = 0, \quad f(1) = 0. \tag{16}$$

At a surface of density discontinuity the density below the surface will be denoted by $\bar{\rho}_l$ and that above by $\bar{\rho}_u$. The vertical velocity w at the interface is $\partial\zeta/\partial t$, in which ζ is the deviation of the interface from its mean position. With ζ expressed as $\zeta_0\exp ik(x-ct)$, the kinematic condition is

$$-c\zeta_0 = f, \tag{17}$$

to be applied at the interface. Apart from the exponential factor, the pressure at the interface is then, from equations (1), (17), and the first of equations (4),

$$\bar{\rho}_u\left(-cf' + \frac{g}{c}f\right)_u$$

for the upper fluid, and

$$\bar{\rho}_l\left(-cf'+\frac{g}{c}f\right)_l$$

for the lower. Continuity of the vertical velocity demands the continuity of the stream function:

$$f_u = f_l.$$

Hence the equality of pressures across the interface demands that

$$(\bar{\rho}f')_u - (\bar{\rho}f')_l + (\bar{\rho}_l - \bar{\rho}_u)\frac{gd}{c^2}f = 0, \tag{18}$$

in terms of η. Equation (18) has been obtained by a fairly complicated argument. But if $\bar{\rho}$ and f' in equation (15) are allowed to be discontinuous, and only the continuity of f is maintained, integration of that equation in the Stieltjes sense across the interface produces (18) immediately. There are then two possible approaches. One can consider the system of differential equations governing the motion in the various continuously stratified layers, together with the interfacial conditions derived above. Or one can consider the motion of the entire fluid to be governed by equation (15), and allow solutions with discontinuous f' at the interfaces. The former is the conventional approach, but the latter approach is adopted in this paper, and it appears to be the more powerful and fruitful.

By the use of the present approach the whole power of the Sturm–Liouville theory can be borrowed to achieve a unified treatment of wave motion in stratified fluids. Without detailed calculations, certain conclusions can be drawn in regard to the variation of the phase velocity with wave-length and with the density distribution, the range in which the phase velocity must lie can be predicted, and certain well-known effects of density discontinuities can be explained. Furthermore, the Ritz method can be applied for calculating the phase velocities even when the density has discontinuities. The unified treatment is the main contribution of this paper. Many of the results obtained as a consequence of this treatment are new, or have a greater generality than has previously been achieved.

In order to have a Sturm–Liouville system, the upper boundary is assumed to be always rigid, and a free surface is considered to be a liquid-gas interface covered by a fluid layer of small but non-zero* density which is bounded above by a rigid plane. The location of the upper boundary is, in the presence of a free surface, assumed to have little effect on the phase velocities. Thus the boundary condition at the upper boundary is always $f(1) = 0$, and the governing differential system is a Sturm–Liouville system consisting of equations (15) and (16) in the former of which $\bar{\rho}$ may have finite discontinuities. The integral form of equation (15) is

$$f(\eta) = \int_0^\eta \frac{1}{\bar{\rho}}\left[\bar{\rho}(0)f'(0) + \int_0^\eta (m^2\bar{\rho} + \lambda\bar{\rho}')f\,d\eta\right]d\eta, \tag{19}$$

---

* Dr F. Ursell has pointed out to the author that the assumption of non-zero density for the top layer, made here for convenience, is really not necessary, and the developments presented here can well be extended to include cases in which a free surface in the ordinary sense is present. In this connexion, see Sz.-Nagy (1947).

488   *Chia-Shun Yih*

in which $\lambda = gd/c^2$, and $\bar{\rho}$ is assumed to be greater than zero. In the presence of density discontinuities, the integration in equation (20) is in the Stieltjes sense, and the function $f(\eta)$ obtained (by step-wise integration, for instance) is continuous with discontinuous derivatives at the locations where the density is discontinuous. The boundary condition $f(0) = 0$ is automatically satisfied. Since $\bar{\rho}'$ is uniformly negative, it is easy to see that a sufficiently large λ will force f to be zero at $\eta = 1$, and that at least a first eigenvalue exists. The eigenfunction satisfies equation (15) everywhere except at the density discontinuities, where equation (18) is automatically satisfied.

To show that equations (19) and (16) possess infinitely many eigenvalues corresponding to eigenfunctions with the number of zeros increasing with the index of the eigenvalues, even when $\bar{\rho}$ is discontinuous, one may approximate the given stratification by an infinite sequence of continuous stratifications with increasingly greater density gradients near the discontinuities of the given stratification. For a specified number of zeros for f in the closed interval (0 to 1 inclusive), the eigenvalues (of λ) for the sequence must approach a limit* (by the Weierstrass–Bolzano theorem), which is the eigenvalue for the given stratification, for the specified number of zeros of f in the interval. That the limit is unique follows essentially from the fact that, for a specified number of zeros of f, the eigenvalue varies continuously with a continuous variation of the density distribution—a fact that can be proved easily. Consequently much of the Sturm–Liouville theory can be carried over to the case of discontinuous density. This fortunate situation is entirely due to the fact that the interfacial conditions (18) are implied in equation (15), and automatically satisfied by equation (19).

For a given density distribution and a given wave-number, the admissible values of c are determined by equations (15) and (16). These values are the phase velocities of waves propagating in the fluid (otherwise at rest). If c has an imaginary part, the waves will grow† in amplitude. It is easy to show that if $\bar{\rho}'$ is everywhere negative c is real, and if $\bar{\rho}'$ is everywhere positive c is purely imaginary. Thus, if equation (15) is multiplied by the complex conjugate of f and integrated between 0 and 1, and equations (16) are utilized, we have

$$-\int_0^1 \bar{\rho}\,|f'|^2\,d\eta - m^2 \int_0^1 \bar{\rho}\,|f|^2\,d\eta - \frac{gd}{c^2}\int_0^1 \bar{\rho}'\,|f|^2\,d\eta = 0, \tag{20}$$

which states that if $\bar{\rho}'$ is negative throughout, c^2 is positive and c is real, and that if $\bar{\rho}'$ is positive throughout, c is purely imaginary and the fluid is unstable. Clearly the same conclusion would have been reached if equation (11) for three-dimensional disturbances had been used instead of equation (15). If $\bar{\rho}'$ is partly negative and partly positive, equation (20) still demands that c^2 be real. It must also be negative, since it must be unstable on physical grounds. If $\bar{\rho}$ is discontinuous, the terms

$$-\frac{gd}{c^2}\sum_{i=1}^{M}(\Delta\bar{\rho})_i f_i^2$$

---

* That this limit exists can be proved by the aid of an easily constructed density distribution, which by Sturm's comparison theorem (for continuous $\bar{\rho}$) must have an eigenvalue (finite) greater than those for the sequence.

† The simplest way to see this is to note that k may be assigned negative values, so that whatever the sign of the imaginary part of c, the waves will grow.

must be added to the left-hand side of equation (20), and the conclusions are unchanged. In the above expression, i indicates the ith interface, $\Delta\bar{\rho}$ is the density jump (negative), and M is the total number of density discontinuities. The terms to be added arise from integration by parts and application of equation (18). Alternatively and preferably, the last integral in (20) can be considered to be in the Stieltjes sense. In this discussion, the density of the top layer can be taken to be zero without introducing any difficulty.

For an inversion of an originally stable stratification or, equivalently, for a reversal of the direction of gravity, equation (15) shows that the eigenvalue c^2 must change sign but retains its magnitude. Thus the fluid will be unstable, and the amplification factor $-ikc$ is exactly the same as the time frequency $\sigma\,(=kc)$ for the stable stratification. Calculations of phase velocities for given k's therefore also provides results for the amplification factor when the stratification is unstable. In the following sections, $\bar{\rho}'$ will be assumed to be negative throughout.

Without any detailed calculations, conclusions can be at once drawn from equations (15) and (16) that for the same stratification and the same mode* the smaller the wave-number m (hence the longer the wave-length), the greater the phase velocity c. This conclusion is the direct consequence of Sturm's fundamental theorem (Ince 1944, pp. 224–5) that the solutions of

$$\frac{d}{dx}\left(K\frac{df}{dx}\right) - Gf = 0 \tag{21}$$

oscillate more rapidly when K and G are diminished algebraically. In the present discussion K is $\bar{\rho}$, which is the same for all wave-lengths. The quantity G is

$$m^2\bar{\rho} + \frac{gd}{c^2}\bar{\rho}',$$

which certainly diminishes as m diminishes. Inspection of the proof of the theorem reveals that it is still valid for the specified K and G if $\bar{\rho}$ has finite discontinuities. For the greatest value of c, the boundary conditions call for exactly one oscillation in the interval $(0, 1)$. If for a certain m and c the boundary conditions are satisfied, for a smaller m and the same gd and c there would be one zero at $\eta = 0$ (as required) and one other between 0 and 1, but not at 1, since the new G would be uniformly smaller than the old. In order to satisfy the boundary condition at $\eta = 1$, c must be greater if gd is the same, since G increases uniformly with c. The fastest waves are therefore the longest waves. If the fluid is flowing at a uniform velocity U greater than the phase velocity of the longest waves of gravest mode, no infinitesimal disturbances can travel upstream. The flow is then supercritical and internal hydraulic jumps may occur under suitable downstream conditions. The reason for this is that finite disturbances travel faster than infinitesimal ones, and can travel with a speed equal to U to make a stationary jump possible. If U is less than the greatest possible c but larger than the greatest c for higher modes, internal hydraulic jumps may still occur.

From equations (15) and (16) it can be seen immediately that for a given $\bar{\rho}(\eta)$ and a given m, c is simply proportional to $\sqrt{(gd)}$. The values of gd/c^2 are deter-

---

* The mode of the wave is determined by the number of zeros of the function f.

mined by the governing differential system, and are the eigenvalues, the lowest of which corresponds to the greatest possible phase velocity. According to Sturm's main theorem of oscillation (Ince 1944, p. 233), the number of zeros in the open interval $0 < \eta < 1$ for the function $f(\eta)$ is greater by one as the index (arranged according to increasing magnitude) of the eigenvalue for $\lambda = gd/c^2$ is increased by one. (Since the end-points are always zeros by specification, the number of zeros in the closed interval $0 \leqslant \eta \leqslant 1$ also increases by one when the index of λ is increased by one.) If the first mode is associated with the first eigenvalue, etc., higher and higher modes correspond to more and more nodal planes of wave motion, and smaller and smaller phase velocities. In the following sections, the definition of 'mode' given above will be retained throughout, even in the presence of surfaces of density discontinuity. Whenever *distinguishable*, waves principally associated with surfaces of discontinuity are called interfacial waves in general or free-surface waves in particular (when the density on one side is very small), and waves principally associated with continuous stratifications are called internal waves.

Sturm's fundamental theorem is again useful for comparing the phase velocities for the same wave-number but different stratifications. According to the theorem, for the same m and gd/c^2, the number of zeros of $f(\eta)$ for a smaller $\bar{\rho}$ and a greater $|\bar{\rho}'|$ in the interval $(0, 1)$ is at least as great as that for a greater $\bar{\rho}$ and smaller $|\bar{\rho}'|$. This means that if the eigenvalues for $\bar{\rho}_1$ and $\bar{\rho}_2$ are λ_1 and λ_2, respectively, and if $\bar{\rho}_1 > \bar{\rho}_2$ and $|\bar{\rho}'_1| < |\bar{\rho}'_2|$, then $\lambda_2 < \lambda_1$ and $c_2 > c_1$. This is very understandable from a physical point of view. From a review of the derivation of equation (15), it is clear that $\bar{\rho}$ is associated with the role of density as a measure of inertia, whereas $g\bar{\rho}'$ is a measure of the restoring force responsible for the existence of wave motion. A smaller $\bar{\rho}$ and greater $|\bar{\rho}'|$ therefore correspond to a greater time frequency of oscillation and (for the same m) a greater phase velocity. If density discontinuities are present, the comparison theorem is useful only if they occur at the same locations for the two stratifications under comparison. In that case the inequality for $\bar{\rho}'$ must be supplemented by

$$|\Delta\bar{\rho}|_1 < |\Delta\bar{\rho}|_2$$

at all locations of density discontinuities.

With the aid of the Sturm–Liouville theory, the ranges in which phase velocities for the various modes must lie can be determined for the case of continuous density. If the lowest density is a and the highest density b, and if the algebraically least and greatest values of the density gradient are $-\beta$ and $-\beta + \epsilon$, then for the nth mode (with $n + 1$ zeros in the closed interval $0 \leqslant \eta \leqslant 1$)

$$\frac{g\,d\beta}{ac^2} - m^2 \geqslant n^2\pi^2, \qquad \frac{gd(\beta - \epsilon)}{bc^2} - m^2 \leqslant (n+1)^2\pi^2,$$

$$\text{or} \qquad \frac{g\,d\beta}{a(n^2\pi^2 + m^2)} \geqslant c^2 \geqslant \frac{gd(\beta - \epsilon)}{b[(n+1)^2\pi^2 + m^2]}. \tag{22}$$

Although these inequalities have been derived for continuous $\bar{\rho}$, they are still valid in the presence of density jumps, provided the $n + 1$ zeros all occur in one layer with continuous density. For small ϵ and small $b - a$, and for large n or m, the inequalities give a rather sharp estimate of c. These inequalities are obtained by comparing the zeros of the eigenfunctions with those of sine functions (which are solutions of a Sturm–Liouville system), and by applying Sturm's fundamental theorem (Ince 1944, p. 227.)

4. Surfaces of density discontinuity

It has been observed (Lamb 1945) that for two superposed layers of homogeneous fluids differing slightly in density and with a free surface on top, there are two distinct modes of gravity waves. For the one mode the phase velocity and the amplitude distribution with height are nearly the same as those of waves propagating on the free surface of a homogeneous fluid, the slight density difference of the two fluids producing only a slight correction. For the other mode the situation is entirely different. The free surface is now nearly horizontal, with negligible waviness, the greatest amplitude occurs at the interface, and the phase velocity is very much smaller. These conclusions follow from detailed calculations given in Lamb's book. What will happen in the general case of many interfaces (not excluding a free surface) separating many continuously but slightly stratified layers? Is it possible to reach similar conclusions? And, if so, is it possible to do so without detailed calculations? The answers to these questions are in the affirmative.

The simplest case of two continuously and slightly stratified layers with a single interface (which can be considered a free-surface if $\bar{\rho}_u$ is small) will be considered first. The first eigenvalue for $\lambda\,(=gd/c^2)$ calls for exactly two zeros situated at the end-points. Thus, the first mode corresponds essentially to interfacial waves only slightly affected by the slight continuous density variations. The subsequent modes are markedly different from the first one. For the next mode there is a zero of $f(\eta)$ between 0 and 1 (Sturm's oscillation theorem; see Ince (1944), p. 233). Since the continuous density gradient is small throughout, the inequalities (22) immediately show that $c^2 \sim \beta$ and is very small. Since f' is of the order* of 1, equation (18) shows that f is very small at the interface and of the order c^2. Equation (17) then shows that ζ_0 is of the order of c, and is therefore small. Thus the interface is almost horizontal, as if it were a rigid surface. For subsequent eigenvalues the number of zeros continually increases, and the same argument can be applied to reach the same conclusion. Furthermore, from the inequalities (22) it can be seen that, even if the density gradient is not very small, the phase velocity is still small (and hence the interface still behaves essentially as a rigid boundary) at large wave-numbers for any mode, and for high modes at the same wave-number.

The case next in complexity is that of three continuously stratified layers contained between two rigid boundaries and separated by two surfaces of density discontinuity. This includes the case of two layers with a free surface

---

* The function f can of course be multiplied by any constant. For convenience, its maximum value will be taken to be of order 1. For not too high a mode $f'(\eta)$ will then be of order 1. If the mode is high, f' may be considerably greater than 1, but then β is supposed to be very small, and the higher the mode, the smaller c^2 is for the same β. In fact, the product c^2f'/gd is of the order of β/n.

492   *Chia-Shun Yih*

on top, for the highest of the three layers can be considered to consist of a fluid of very small density. For the first mode, the only zeros of $f(\eta)$ occur at $\eta = 0$ and $\eta = 1$. By Sturm's oscillation theorem another zero must appear in the interval $(0, 1)$ for the second eigenvalue. In which layer will this zero appear? Depending on the thicknesses of the layers and the magnitude of the density gradient in each layer, this middle zero can occur in any of the three layers. However, for very small density gradients in the layers, it can be concluded that the middle zero must occur in the middle layer. For, with the density discontinuities at the interfaces kept constant, the density gradient in each layer can be made to approach zero. As these gradients become smaller and smaller, a stage will be reached when the middle zero will be situated in the middle layer and will stay there as the gradients are further reduced, since otherwise either the highest or the lowest layer would have two zeros, and, in the limiting case, with two zeros in a homogeneous fluid, there could be no wave motion. Only one mode of wave motion would then exist in the limiting case of three homogeneous layers of fluids, in contradiction to established facts.

If the continuous density gradients are not small, liberal sufficient conditions can be found under which the middle zero must be located in the middle layer. In the case of three layers of thicknesses d_1, d_2 and d_3, it can be shown that

$$\left[\frac{(-\bar{\rho}')_{\min}}{\bar{\rho}_{\max}}\right]_{\text{upper layers}} > \left(\frac{d_3}{d_1+d_2}\right)^2 \left[\frac{(-\bar{\rho}')_{\max}}{\bar{\rho}_{\min}}\right]_{\text{lowest layer}} \tag{23}$$

and

$$\left[\frac{(-\bar{\rho}')_{\min}}{\bar{\rho}_{\max}}\right]_{\text{lower layers}} > \left(\frac{d_1}{d_2+d_3}\right)^2 \left[\frac{(-\bar{\rho}')_{\max}}{\bar{\rho}_{\min}}\right]_{\text{top layer}} \tag{24}$$

are sufficient conditions for long waves. If there is indeed an additional zero in the lowest layer, then Sturm's oscillation theorem states that

$$\left[\frac{g(-\bar{\rho}')_{\max}}{c^2\bar{\rho}_{\min}}\right]_{\text{lowest layer}} > \frac{\pi^2}{d_3^2}. \tag{25}$$

From equation (23) it then follows that

$$\left[\frac{g(-\bar{\rho}')_{\min}}{c^2\bar{\rho}_{\max}}\right]_{\text{upper layers}} > \frac{\pi^2}{(d_1+d_2)^2}, \tag{26}$$

which is sufficient to guarantee an additional zero (other than the one at $\eta = 1$) in the upper two layers, in contradiction to hypothesis. Hence the middle zero must not occur in the bottom layer under the stated condition. The proof for the statement concerning equation (24) is entirely similar. For the general case of n layers of thicknesses $d_i\,(i = 1, \ldots, n)$, criteria similar to inequalities (25) and (26) can be used to determine the regions in which the additional zero or zeros must be located.

For the case of three layers, the next higher mode brings in a fourth zero. If the previous three zeros are in different layers, this fourth one must cause one of the layers to have two zeros. Then the inequalities (22) show that for small density gradients (small β) c^2 must indeed be very small. From the interfacial conditions stated by equation (18) it can be seen that the two interfaces now behave almost like rigid boundaries—a situation which is maintained in the subsequent modes. For the general case, it can be shown by reasoning similar to that employed in the preceding two paragraphs that, for very small density variation in each layer, zeros in addition to those at the end-points will appear one after the other as the modes are higher and higher, until each layer has one and only one zero. The next higher eigenvalue, bringing in another zero, corresponds to a mode with one of its layers having two nodal points (or zeros). The surfaces of density discontinuity will then behave like rigid boundaries, and will so behave for subsequent modes. The number of modes for which the surfaces of density discontinuity do not behave like rigid boundaries is $n-1$ for n layers of fluid— the same as the number of these surfaces. The phase velocities for these modes are, for small density variation in each layer, nearly the same as those for wave motion in n homogeneous fluid layers with the same depths and the same mean densities as the layers under consideration.

The conclusions reached in this section remain essentially valid if the effect of surface tension Γ is included in the interfacial boundary conditions, which then assume the form

$$(\overline{\rho}f')_u - (\overline{\rho}f')_l + \left[\frac{\Gamma m^2}{c^2 d} + (\overline{\rho}_l - \overline{\rho}_u)\frac{gd}{c^2}\right]f = 0. \tag{27}$$

If there is only one surface of density discontinuity and if the density gradient elsewhere is small, the effect of surface tension, as far as interfacial waves are concerned, is to increase g by the amount

$$\frac{\Gamma m^2}{(\overline{\rho}_l - \overline{\rho}_u)\,d^2} = \frac{\Gamma k^2}{\overline{\rho}_l - \overline{\rho}_u}.$$

If there are two or more surfaces of discontinuity, approximate phase velocities of the interfacial waves can be found by assuming the density in each layer to be constant and equal to the mean density (provided that the density variation in each layer is small), and by imposing the boundary conditions (27) instead of (18). For internal waves the effect of surface tension is to stiffen the interfaces further (as can also be seen from the fact that the coefficient of f in equation (27) is increased by surface tension), and if the interfaces behave like rigid barriers without surface tension, they will do so even more effectively with the aid of surface tension. Thus the phase velocities for truly internal waves are hardly affected by surface tension.

5. Equipartition of energy

Equation (20), used in a previous section to prove the reality of c, also contains the theorem of equipartition of energy. For isopycnic particles

$$(u, w, \zeta) = \left[-f'(z), ikf(z), -\frac{f(z)}{c}\right]\exp ik(x - ct).$$

Integration of u^2, w^2 and ζ^2 with respect to x over a wave-length produces the common factor $\frac{1}{2}$. With the multiplication of this common factor, equation (20) can be written, in dimensional terms

$$\frac{g}{2}\int_0^d \overline{\rho}'\zeta^2\,dz = \frac{1}{2}\left(\int_0^d \overline{\rho}f'^2\,dz + k^2\int_0^d \overline{\rho}f^2\,dz\right). \tag{28}$$

 Chia-Shun Yih

The left-hand side of this equation represents the excess of potential energy* per unit wave-length in the x-direction over that of the mean configuration, or the potential energy of wave motion. The right-hand side obviously represents the kinetic energy per unit length. The equation therefore states that there is equipartition of energy. Although the proof given is for progressive waves, a slight modification of the form of u, w and ζ will make it valid for standing waves also.

Equation (20) was derived for the case of rigid barriers at $z = 0$ and $z = d$, and for a continuous stratification. If there are density discontinuities, the integral on the left-hand side of equation (28) must be taken to be in the Stieltjes sense, but the equipartition of energy is unaffected. In this discussion, the density of the top layer can be taken to be zero without introducing any difficulty.

For the same wave-number m general wave motion in a stratified fluid may be composed of many modes, each of which corresponds to an eigenvalue of gd/c^2 (or of c). It will be shown that the kinetic and potential energies of the component modes are entirely separable. In other words there are no energy couplings between the component modes at all. The proof for the case of a continuously stratified fluid between rigid boundaries is straightforward. The differential system consisting of equations (15) and (16) is self-adjoint, and it is well known that for such a system the eigenfunctions are orthogonal. In the present instance this means that (with r and s indicating the modes)

$$\int_0^1 \bar{\rho}' f_r(\eta) f_s(\eta) \, d\eta = 0, \tag{29}$$

or that there is no coupling of the various modes as far as potential energy of the wave motion is concerned. To obtain the corresponding result for kinetic energy, equation (15) will be written in the form

$$(\bar{\rho} f_r')' - (m^2 \bar{\rho} + \lambda_r \bar{\rho}') f_r = 0. \tag{30}$$

If equation (30) is multiplied by f_s and integrated, and if equations (16) are utilized, the result

$$\int_0^1 \bar{\rho}(f_r' f_s' + m^2 f_r f_s) \, d\eta = 0 \tag{31}$$

is obtained, which states that there is also no coupling between the different modes in connexion with kinetic energy.

In the presence of surfaces of density discontinuity, the governing differential system is no longer self-adjoint in the ordinary sense, but the de-coupling of potential and kinetic energies can be proved with the aid of the boundary conditions (18). Cross-multiplication of equation (30) and the equation

$$(\bar{\rho} f_s')' - (m^2 \bar{\rho} + \lambda_s \bar{\rho}') f_s = 0 \tag{32}$$

---

* The factor $\frac{1}{2}$ can best be explained by considering the potential energy of water waves. The water in the troughs are raised to the crests, each element ζdx by the height ζ. Thus the total potential energy is proportional to the integral of ζ^2 over a half wave-length. Hence the factor $\frac{1}{2}$.

by f_s and f_r and integration of the difference of the results produces, after utilization of equation (20) at all the interfaces,

$$\sum_{i=1}^{M} (\Delta\bar{\rho} f_r f_s)_i + \sum_{j=1}^{n} \int_{\eta_{j-1}}^{\eta_j} \bar{\rho}' f_r f_s \, d\eta = 0, \tag{33}$$

which is the same as equation (29) if the latter is considered to be in the Stieltjes sense. From equations (30) and (33), equation (31) is again obtained. Thus the normality of the energy spectra is established even in the presence of density discontinuities, as indeed is to be expected.

So far the normality of the energy spectra has been established only for the same wave-number. It remains to mention that if the wave-numbers are different, the net coupling effect is finite over a distance in the x-direction however long, and is therefore zero per unit distance.

The conclusion of equipartition of energy is valid for three-dimensional waves also. The proof is entirely similar. One needs only to start with equation (11) instead of equation (15), and use $lu = kv$.

6. The case of infinite depth

As has been remarked by Lamb (1945) for incompressible fluids, and as can be easily verified from equation $(9a)$ for a semi-infinite fluid with any stratification (whether compressible or not), the system consisting of equation $(9a)$ (with $l = 0$ and w changed to f), the conditions at infinity

$$f(z) \to 0 \quad \text{as} \quad z \to -\infty, \tag{34}$$

and the *usual* free-surface condition

$$f'(0) - \frac{g}{c^2} f(0) = 0 \tag{35}$$

possess the solution $\qquad f(z) = e^{kz}, \quad c^2 = g/k. \tag{36}$

The fact that the solution is independent of the mean density distribution and that it corresponds to irrotational motion is certainly rather surprising. But the explanation is not far to seek. The solution is the same as the well-known solution for wave motion in a semi-infinite homogeneous fluid. If it is valid also for a non-homogeneous fluid, there must be something very special about it. The special feature is that in co-ordinates *moving with the waves* the streamlines of the (steady) flow corresponding to the solution are lines of constant pressure, as can be readily demonstrated. This situation is not affected if the density is a function of the stream function alone (which is the case for an incompressible fluid in steady motion) or for a compressible fluid with isentropic change of state along a streamline (hence p is a function of ρ alone along a streamline). The distribution of mean density or mean entropy in the vertical direction is quite immaterial, so long as the density or entropy does not change along a streamline in the moving frame of reference. For convenience only two-dimensional waves have been discussed. The essential features of the flow are, however, unchanged if the waves are three-dimensional.

Actually, though the solution given by equation (36) is the only one which is independent of density stratification, another interesting one exists if c_s is constant. Equation (13), with w changed to f, and the boundary conditions (34) and (35) are evidently satisfied by

$$f(z) = \exp\{(g/c_s^2)\,z\}, \quad c = c_s. \tag{37}$$

The motion represented by this solution, which is incidentally independent of the wave-number, is not irrotational. That it is independent of the density variation (so long as it is consistent with constant c_s or with an isothermal atmosphere) is again because streamlines in a frame moving with the waves are isobars. It has often been said that sound waves are longitudinal. The wave motion discovered here propagates with sound velocity, and is strongly affected by compressibility, and yet, since c_s is large and therefore $u \sim f'(z)$ is small, it is predominately transverse.

In the case of finite depth the eigenvalues are discrete and, if the stratification is continuous over any portion of the fluid, infinite in number. If the depth is infinite, the spectrum of the eigenvalues is continuous, with a number of discrete eigenvalues equal to the number of density discontinuities (or possibly greater than it if the fluid is compressible). For demonstration, a fluid with the density variation

$$\bar{\rho} = \rho_0 e^{-bz} \quad (b \text{ positive})$$

and with a free surface at $z = 0$ may be considered. For this particular density variation, the atmosphere is isothermal and the sound velocity constant, as can be seen by applying the hydrostatic equation $dp = -g\bar{\rho}\,dz$. Thus equation (13) can be solved exactly. (The free surface should, of course, be removed to $z = \infty$ to make the problem realistic.) However, the purpose of this section is to show the continuity of the spectrum of σ. Hence the fluid will be assumed to be incompressible for simplicity, and the fluid to extend to $z = -\infty$. Equation (12a) possesses the solution

$$f(z) = A\,e^{a_1 z} + B^{a_2 z}$$

in which
$$(a_1, a_2) = \frac{1}{2}\left[b \pm \sqrt{\left\{b^2 - 4k^2\left(\frac{gb}{\sigma^2} - 1\right)\right\}}\,\right] \quad (\sigma = kc). \tag{38}$$

If $gb < \sigma^2$, equation (34) demands that $B = 0$, and the surface condition (35) demands that

$$a_1 = \frac{gk^2}{\sigma^2} \quad \text{or} \quad c^2 = \frac{g}{k}.$$

The solution is therefore the one discussed before in the present section. However, if $gb > \sigma^2$, both a_1 and a_2 have a positive real part, so that the condition at $z = -\infty$ is automatically satisfied, and the surface condition assumes the form

$$A a_1 + B a_2 - (A + B)\frac{gk^2}{\sigma^2} = 0.$$

Given any k, b and σ, B can be solved in terms of A or vice versa. Thus any σ equal to or less than $\sqrt{(gb)}$ will do, and the spectrum of σ is continuous from zero to $\sqrt{(gb)}$. For any k the spectrum of c is then continuous from zero to $\sqrt{(gb)}/k$. For $k < b$, the value gk for σ^2 satisfies the requirement $gb/\sigma^2 \geqslant 1$. Thus the situation can be summarized as follows. (1) For any k, gk is an eigenvalue for σ^2. It corresponds to a motion identical to that of ordinary surface waves, and is an isolated mode if $k > b$. (2) Any σ^2 less than gb corresponds to a possible wave motion. For $k \leqslant b$, the eigenvalue (for σ^2) for the free-surface mode is imbedded in the continuous spectrum for σ^2.

The example just given is instructive in showing that free-surface waves are not necessarily faster than internal waves. In fact, even if the depth is finite, free-surface waves or interfacial waves (corresponding to discontinuous density changes) are not necessarily faster than internal waves that owe their existence to continuous stratifications. They are faster only if the gradients of the continuous density stratifications are small.

If the top of the fluid is covered with a rigid boundary, no solution is possible for $gb \leqslant \sigma^2$. The continuous spectrum is given by

$$\frac{gb}{\sigma^2} > 1, \quad \text{or} \quad \sigma^2 < gb.$$

These values of σ^2 all correspond to internal waves. The free-surface mode is removed with the removal of the free surface, as expected.

7. Calculation of phase velocities

The phase velocities of waves propagating in a stratified fluid can be calculated rapidly by the method of Ritz. The differential system determining $\lambda = gd/c^2$ for a given density variation and a given wave-number consists of equations (15) and (16) for the case of fixed boundaries. Equation (15) is a special case of the general equation

$$L(f) = \lambda G(\eta)f, \tag{39}$$

in which L is a linear operator. According to the Ritz method, a set of N linearly independent functions $\phi_r(\eta)$ satisfying the boundary conditions will be chosen. The quantities

$$A_{rs} = -\int_0^1 \phi_r(\eta)\, L[\phi_s(\eta)]\, d\eta \tag{40}$$

and

$$B_{rs} = -\int_0^1 G(\eta)\, \phi_r(\eta)\, \phi_s(\eta)\, d\eta \tag{41}$$

are symmetric in the sense that their values are unaffected as r and s are interchanged. This is obvious with B_{rs}. With A_{rs} symmetry is immediately clear upon integration by parts and utilization of the boundary conditions. The integrals in equations (40) and (41) are in the Stieltjes sense when applied to wave propagation in a stratified fluid with density jumps. (For a similar application, see Courant & Hilbert (1931, Vol. I. pp. 349–50). In fact, in case a free surface exists, it is not necessary to assume that there is a layer of light fluid with non-zero density over it. The choice of $\phi(\eta)$ can therefore be less restricted, see Courant (1926).) The eigenfunction is now approximated by a linear combination of the chosen functions

$$F(\eta) = \sum_{r=1}^N c_r \phi_r(\eta). \tag{42}$$

With f in equation (39) replaced by F, that equation is multiplied by F and integrated to yield

$$\int_0^1 FL(F)\, d\eta + \mu \int_0^1 \overline{\rho}'F^2\, d\eta = \sum_{r,\,s=1}^N (A_{rs} - \mu B_{rs})\, c_r c_s.$$

The right-hand side of this equation depends only on the c's. If the condition is imposed that it be stationary in value for variations in the c's, the N equations are obtained

$$\sum_{r=1}^{N} (A_{rs} - \mu B_{rs}) c_r = 0, \quad (s = 1, 2, \ldots, N).$$

Since the c's must not all vanish, it is necessary that

$$\begin{vmatrix} A_{11} - \mu B_{11} & A_{12} - \mu B_{12} & \ldots & A_{1N} - \mu B_{1N} \\ A_{21} - \mu B_{21} & A_{22} - \mu B_{22} & \ldots & A_{2N} - \mu B_{2N} \\ \ldots & \ldots & & \ldots \\ A_{N1} - \mu B_{N1} & A_{N2} - \mu B_{N2} & \ldots & A_{NN} - \mu B_{NN} \end{vmatrix} = 0. \tag{43}$$

Ritz has proved that the N roots (for μ) of this equation are near and slightly larger than the first N eigenvalues of λ. In general, if $N + M$ terms are taken for F in equation (42) the first N roots of the enlarged determinantal equation are nearer and nearer the first N eigenvalues as M becomes larger and larger. Thus, if only N terms are taken, the accuracy of the roots as eigenvalues increases in general from the Nth to the first root.

Two examples (for continuous density distribution) will be given to demonstrate the accuracy of the Ritz method. For the first, the density variation is assumed to be

$$\bar{\rho} = \rho_0 e^{-\beta \eta}.$$

Equation (15) can then be reduced to the form

$$f'' - \beta f' - \left(m^2 - \frac{\beta g d}{c^2}\right) f = 0. \tag{44}$$

With

$$(\alpha_1, \alpha_2) = \frac{1}{2}\left[\beta \pm \sqrt{\left\{\beta^2 - 4\left(\frac{\beta g d}{c^2} - m^2\right)\right\}}\right],$$

the solution satisfying the boundary condition at $\eta = 0$ is

$$f = A(e^{\alpha_1 \eta} - e^{\alpha_2 \eta}).$$

The condition $f(1) = 0$ then demands that

$$e^{\alpha_1} - e^{\alpha_2} = 0,$$

or

$$\alpha_1 - \alpha_2 = \sqrt{\{\beta^2 - 4(\beta\lambda - m^2)\}} = 2n\pi i \quad (n = 1, 2, \ldots).$$

Hence

$$4\beta\lambda = 4n^2\pi^2 + \beta^2 + 4m^2,$$

or, with

$$\lambda' = \beta\lambda,$$

$$\lambda' = n^2\pi^2 + m^2 + \tfrac{1}{4}\beta^2. \tag{45}$$

To use the Ritz method, it is better to write equation (44) in its original form, before the exponential factor was cancelled out

$$(e^{-\beta\eta} f')' - m^2 e^{-\beta\eta} f = -\lambda e^{-\beta\eta} f.$$

If $\phi_r(\eta) = \sin r\pi\eta$ and the first element of the determinant in equation (43) is equated to zero, the result (after cancelling a common factor) is obtained

$$2\pi^4 + m^2(2\pi^2 - \beta^2) = \mu_1(2\pi^2 - \beta^2),$$

or, for small β,

$$\mu_1 = \pi^2 + m^2 + \tfrac{1}{2}\beta^2.$$

This is greater than the first eigenvalue only by the amount $\frac{1}{4}\beta^2$. That roots of equation (43) are always greater than the first eigenvalue is well known, but it is important to remember that this is so only if the differential equation is written in the form of equation (15), i.e. in the self-adjoint form. Had equation (44) been used for the application of the Ritz method, the value $\pi^2 + m^2$ would have been obtained for μ_1, which is *smaller* than the first eigenvalue.

Had the true eigenfunctions $e^{\frac{1}{2}\beta\eta}\sin r\pi\eta$ been chosen to be $\phi_r(\eta)$, the true eigenvalues would of course be obtained. However, the purpose of this example is to demonstrate the power of Ritz's method in the general case, in which the form of the eigenfunctions is not known and cannot be easily guessed.

A second example is provided by the density variation

$$\bar\rho(\eta) = \rho_0\sqrt{(1-\beta\eta)}.$$

An exact solution exists in this case for long waves. Equation (15) can be written, for zero wave-number,

$$[\sqrt{(1-\beta\eta)}f']' + \frac{\beta\lambda}{2\sqrt{(1-\beta\eta)}}f = 0,$$

or

$$\frac{d^2f}{d\xi^2} + \frac{2\lambda}{\beta}\{1-\sqrt{(1-\beta)}\}^2 f = 0,$$

with

$$\xi = \frac{1-\sqrt{(1-\beta\eta)}}{1-\sqrt{(1-\beta)}}.$$

The boundary conditions are

$$f(\xi) = 0 \quad \text{at} \quad \xi = 0 \quad \text{and} \quad \xi = 1.$$

The eigenvalues for long waves are exactly

$$\lambda' = \beta\lambda = \frac{1}{2}\left[\frac{\beta n\pi}{1-\sqrt{(1-\beta)}}\right]^2.$$

Here again, if $\sin r\pi\xi$ were chosen to be $\phi_r(\eta)$ in the application of Ritz's method, the true eigenvalues would be obtained. This will not be done, for the same reason as stated before. Instead, we choose

$$\phi_r(\eta) = (1-\beta\eta)^{\frac{1}{4}}\sin r\pi\eta.$$

Then

$$B_{11} = \tfrac{1}{4},$$

$$A_{11} = \int_0^1 \left[\pi^2(1-\beta\eta)\cos^2\pi\eta - \frac{\beta\pi}{2}\sin\pi\eta\cos\pi\eta + \frac{\beta^2}{16}\frac{\sin^2\pi\eta}{1-\beta\eta}\right]d\eta$$

$$= \frac{\pi^2}{2} - \frac{\beta\pi^2}{4} + \frac{\beta^2}{32}\int_0^1 \frac{1-\cos 2\pi\eta}{1-\beta\eta}d\eta$$

$$= \frac{\pi^2}{2} - \frac{\beta\pi^2}{4} - \frac{\beta}{32}\ln(1-\beta) + O(\beta^4).$$

Therefore

$$\mu_1 = 2\pi^2 - \beta\pi^2 + \frac{\beta^2}{8} - \frac{\beta^3}{16} + O(\beta^4),$$

whereas

$$\lambda'_1 = 2\pi^2 - \beta\pi^2 - \frac{\beta^2\pi^2}{8} + \frac{3\pi^2}{32}\beta^3 + O(\beta^4),$$

showing that the error is again of the order of β^2. The two examples given demonstrate that the modified Froude number $c/\sqrt{(g'd)}$ (with g' equal to $(g/\bar{\rho})\,d\bar{\rho}/d\eta$) for a small and practically constant density gradient is approximately equal to π^{-1} for long waves—a fact of great importance for prediction of the existence of lee waves in the wake of a body advancing in a stratified fluid. The number π^{-1}, however, cannot be applied to fluids whose density gradient is not practically constant.

It has been shown that for n continuously stratified layers with $n-1$ or n surfaces of density discontinuity there are $n-1$ or n modes of motion corresponding to interfacial (or free-surface) waves. If the density gradient in each layer is small, approximations to the first $n-1$ or n eigenvalues corresponding to these modes can be found by Greenhill's formula on the assumption that the density in each layer is constant and equal to the mean of the actual density in that layer. Since it has been shown that for higher modes the surfaces of density discontinuity behave like solid barriers, the subsequent eigenvalues can be found without appreciable error by considering each layer to be bounded by solid planes, and by arranging the eigenvalues λ found separately for all the layers in ascending order of magnitude.

To test the validity of this statement, one may consider the case of two layers of depth d_1 and d_2, and with density variations given by

$$\bar{\rho}_1(\eta_1) = C_1 e^{-\beta_1 \eta_1}, \quad \bar{\rho}_2(\eta_2) = C_2 e^{-\beta_2 \eta_2},$$

in which
$$\eta_1 = \frac{z}{d_1}, \quad \eta_2 = \frac{z}{d_2},$$

the subscript 1 is for the upper layer, and the origin of z is taken at the interface. The differential equation governing the motion in each layer is equation (44), and the solutions satisfying the boundary conditions $f_1(1) = 0$ and $f_2(-1) = 0$ are

$$f_1(\eta_1) = A(e^{\alpha_1 \eta_1} - e^{(\alpha_2 - \alpha_1) + \alpha_2 \eta}),$$

$$f_2(\eta_2) = B(e^{\gamma_1 \eta_2} - e^{(\gamma_2 - \gamma_1) + \gamma_2 \eta}),$$

with
$$(\alpha_1, \alpha_2) = \frac{1}{2}\left[\beta_1 \pm \sqrt{\left\{\beta_1^2 - 4\left(\frac{\beta_1 g d_1}{c^2} - m^2\right)\right\}}\right],$$

$$(\gamma_1, \gamma_2) = \frac{1}{2}\left[\beta_2 \pm \sqrt{\left\{\beta_2^2 - 4\left(\frac{\beta_2 g d}{c^2} - m^2\right)\right\}}\right].$$

Imposing the interfacial conditions

$$f_1(0) = f_2(0) \quad \text{and} \quad \frac{C_1}{d_1} f_1'(0) - \frac{C_2}{d_2} f_2'(0) + (C_2 - C_1)\frac{g}{c^2} f_1(0) = 0,$$

one has

$$\frac{C_1}{d_1}(\alpha_1 - \alpha_2 e^{\alpha_2 - \alpha_1}) - \frac{C_2}{d_2}\frac{1 - e^{\alpha_2 - \alpha_1}}{1 - e^{\gamma_2 - \gamma_1}}(\gamma_1 - \gamma_2 e^{\gamma_2 - \gamma_1}) + (C_2 - C_1)\frac{g}{c^2}(1 - e^{\alpha_2 - \alpha_1}) = 0, \quad (46a)$$

or, alternatively,

$$\frac{C_1}{d_1}\frac{1 - e^{\gamma_2 - \gamma_1}}{1 - e^{\alpha_2 - \alpha_1}}(\alpha_1 - \alpha_2 e^{\alpha_2 - \alpha_1}) - \frac{C_2}{d_2}(\gamma_1 - \gamma_2 e^{\gamma_2 - \gamma_1}) + (C_2 - C_1)\frac{g}{c^2}(1 - e^{\gamma_2 - \gamma_1}) = 0. \quad (46b)$$

The question is now asked: what error will be committed if g/c^2 is calculated from equation (45) for each layer, on the assumption that the interface is rigid? For the upper layer

$$\frac{g}{c^2} = \frac{1}{\beta_1 d_1}(n^2\pi^2 + m^2 + \tfrac{1}{4}\beta_1^2) \tag{45a}$$

according to equation (45), which is large* for small β_1. The dominant term in equation (46) is therefore the last term, and one sequence of phase velocities is given approximately by
$$1 - e^{\alpha_2 - \alpha_1} = 0,$$

which is the condition that would be obtained for the upper layer if the interface were rigid. The error committed is the first term, and is of the magnitude $2n\pi C_1/d_1$ which can be annihilated by changing c^2 slightly (and therefore also making $1 - e^{\alpha_2 - \alpha_1}$ slightly different from zero). One may, in fact, multiply equation (46a) by $c^2/(C_2 - C_1)g$ and note that the error committed in calculating c^2/g by (45a) is of the order of $[2n\pi C_1/(C_2 - C_1)][\beta_1/(n^2\pi^2 + m^2)]$, which is small if β_1 is small or if n or m is large. For the lower layer, equation (46b) can be used for proving that little error is committed if equation (45) is used to calculate c, provided β_2 is small or n or m large. Thus the entire phase-velocity spectrum of internal waves (i.e. with the interfacial one excepted) is obtained by superimposing the phase-velocity spectrum of one layer on that of the other, both obtained on the supposition that the interfaces were rigid. Although the example is a specific one, the conclusion reached is evidently valid in general, in virtue of the results obtained in §4.

If, however, the density difference in each layer is not small compared with the mean density, phase velocities can only be obtained by solving the entire eigenvalue problem. This can be done either approximately, by the use of the Ritz method, or analytically, by solving the differential equation for the bottom layer with the restriction that $f(0) = 0$ and with $f'(0)$ arbitrary. In the analytical solution, when the first interface is reached the starting f for the next layer is made to be the same as the terminal f for the bottom layer, and the starting f' for the new layer is found from the first interfacial boundary condition. This procedure is continued until the upper boundary, free or rigid, is reached. The final boundary condition is imposed and the eigenvalues for λ are found from the final equation obtained.

8. Waves generated by a plane wave-maker

The motion generated in a stratified fluid contained between two rigid boundaries by an oscillating plane normal to these boundaries and extending all the way between them can be found by solving

$$(\bar{\rho}f')' - m^2\left(\bar{\rho} + \frac{g}{\sigma^2 d}\bar{\rho}'\right)f = 0, \tag{15a}$$

with σ now equal to 2π times the oscillation frequency of the wave-maker. The eigenvalues are now those of m^2 consistent with equations (16). If σ is sufficiently large, the quantity in the second parenthesis of equation (15a) is positive, and the

---

* Since interval waves are being discussed, c^2 is very small even according to the exact equations (46), as can be asserted by virtue of the inequalities (22). Therefore the statement that g/c^2 is large for small β_1 is not based on a circular argument.

eigenvalues will be negative. These correspond to imaginary m's and exponential (instead of sinusoidal) dependence of the disturbance on x. If σ is very small, the quantity referred to above is negative, and the eigenvalues for m^2 are positive. The m will be real and waves will propagate from the oscillating plane. For the intermediate case of medium σ, the quantity in the second parenthesis in equation $(15a)$ is positive for certain levels, and negative at others. In this case the eigenvalues of m^2 go from negative infinity (through discrete values) to positive infinity.

If the oscillating plane is situated at $x = 0$ and oscillates as $a \cos \sigma t$, and the fluid extends from there to $x = \infty$, the solution for the motion in general consists of a parallel-flow part, a part corresponding to the local disturbance, and a part corresponding to wave motion. The parallel-flow part is necessary in order to satisfy the demand of continuity and is given by

$$-a^2\sigma \left(\int_0^1 \frac{d\eta}{\bar{\rho}}\right)^{-1} \int_0^\eta \frac{d\eta}{\bar{\rho}},$$

which obviously satisfies equation $(15a)$, with m equal to zero (not an eigenvalue). The solution for the stream function is then, with Sommerfield's radiation condition at infinity,

$$\frac{\psi}{a^2\sigma} = -\cos \sigma t \left(\int_0^1 \frac{d\eta}{\bar{\rho}}\right)^{-1} \int_0^\eta \frac{d\eta}{\bar{\rho}} + \sum_{n=-\infty}^{n_1-1} A_n f_n(\eta)\, e^{-|m_n|x} \cos \sigma t$$

$$+ \sum_{n=n_1}^{\infty} A_n f_n(\eta) \cos(m_n x - \sigma t), \qquad (47)$$

in which n_1 is the index of the first positive eigenvalue for m^2, and the coefficients A are determined by the condition at the oscillating plane

$$-\eta = -\left(\int_0^1 \frac{d\eta}{\bar{\rho}}\right)^{-1} \int_0^\eta \frac{d\eta}{\bar{\rho}} + \sum_{n=-\infty}^{\infty} A_n f_n(\eta),$$

by the usual method, since the eigenfunctions f_n are orthogonal. Since the f's are eigenfunctions of a Sturm–Liouville system, and since the latter are known to be complete, the completeness of the f's is not in question. A similar solution can be obtained if density jumps are present, and if the wave-maker has any shape and any specified motion whatever.

The mean energy flux at infinity can be calculated either directly or by means of the group velocity for each wave component. (The formula for calculating group velocity from phase velocity is the usual one.) The mean rate of work done by the wave-maker is equal to this mean energy flux. If all the m's are imaginary, there is no wave motion and no mean energy flux at infinity. Hence the mean rate of work done by the oscillating plane is zero.

The sign of the second parenthesis, which decides whether the eigenvalues of m^2 are positive or negative, or partly positive and partly negative, is directly connected with the type of the partial differential equation governing the motion. For incompressible fluids in two-dimensional motion with a time dependence described by $e^{-i\sigma t}$, equation (8) assumes the form

$$(\sigma^2\bar{\rho} + g\bar{\rho}')\frac{\partial^2 w}{\partial x^2} + \sigma^2 \frac{\partial^2}{\partial z^2}\left(\bar{\rho}\frac{\partial w}{\partial z}\right) = 0.$$

If this is multiplied by $\bar{\rho}$ and the new variable

$$\xi = \int_0^z \frac{dz}{\bar{\rho}}$$

is used, the equation

$$\left(\sigma^2\bar{\rho}^2 + g\bar{\rho}\frac{d\bar{\rho}}{dz}\right)\frac{\partial^2 w}{\partial x^2} + \sigma^2\frac{\partial^2 w}{\partial \xi^2} = 0 \tag{48}$$

is obtained, which is elliptic or hyperbolic according as (Görtler 1954)

$$\sigma^2\bar{\rho} + g\frac{d\bar{\rho}}{dz}$$

is positive or negative. But this quantity is proportional to

$$\bar{\rho} + \frac{g}{\sigma^2 d}\frac{d\bar{\rho}}{d\eta}.$$

Consequently the sign of the second parenthesis in equation (15a) determines the type of equation (48). However, the type of the partial differential equation governing the motion of a stratified fluid, though of course relevant to the type of solution obtained (as shown in this section), does not play as significant a role as the type of the partial differential equation governing the homentropic flow of a compressible fluid. The reason is simply that for a given mode of wave motion corresponding to a $[\bar{\rho} + (g/\sigma^2 d)(d\bar{\rho}/d\eta)]$ with alternating signs, the particle velocities being small, the velocity in the steady flow relative to the waves is simply c everywhere, and the elliptic and hyperbolic regions do not in any sense correspond to subsonic and supersonic flows.

When equation (48) is hyperbolic, real characteristics exist, with slopes given by

$$\tan\gamma' = \frac{\sigma}{[-g\bar{\rho}(d\bar{\rho}/dz) - \sigma^2\bar{\rho}^2]^{\frac{1}{2}}}.$$

For very small σ, the characteristics are horizontal. This is in agreement with the finding (Yih 1959a) that steady, two-dimensional flows of an inviscid stratified fluid become one-dimensional when the motion is weak—a phenomenon that has been experimentally demonstrated (Yih 1959b).

9. Stability of stratified liquid under vertical vibration

The stability of a homogeneous liquid with a free surface when the container is accelerated periodically has been considered by Benjamin & Ursell (1954). The cause of instability is a kind of resonance, though not in the usual sense of a forced harmonic oscillation, and the frequency of free oscillation plays a role in the determination of stability or instability. For a stratified liquid the frequencies of free oscillation are infinite in number, and it can be expected that the resonance phenomenon has to be investigated for each mode of free oscillation, i.e. for each of the eigen-frequencies in the absence of the imposed vibration. That this is indeed the case can be seen from the following analysis.

The equations of motion *relative to the vibrating container* are

$$\bar{\rho}\frac{\partial}{\partial t}(u, v, w) = -\left(\frac{\partial}{\partial x}, \frac{\partial}{\partial y}, \frac{\partial}{\partial z}\right)p - \rho(0, 0, g - F\cos\omega t), \tag{49}$$

 Chia-Shun Yih

in which $F\cos\omega t$ is the acceleration of the container. Cross-differentiation of the first two of equations (49) again produces an equation which shows that $\bar{\rho}u$ and $\bar{\rho}v$ possess a potential ϕ, so that

$$\bar{\rho}(u,v) = -\left(\frac{\partial}{\partial x}, \frac{\partial}{\partial y}\right)\phi.$$

By the same procedure as that employed in §2, an equation similar to equation (6) is obtained

$$\frac{\partial}{\partial t}\left(\frac{\partial\phi}{\partial z} + \bar{\rho}w\right) + (g - F\cos\omega t)\rho = 0. \tag{50}$$

The equation of continuity now has the form

$$\bar{\rho}\frac{\partial w}{\partial z} = \nabla^2\phi,$$

and the equation of incompressibility is

$$\frac{\partial\rho}{\partial t} = -w\bar{\rho}',$$

with the prime indicating differentiation with respect to z. These equations are applicable even to gases if the effect of compressibility is small. Applying the Laplacian operator in x and y to equation (50), dividing throughout by $g - F\cos\omega t$, differentiating the result with respect to t, and utilizing the equations of continuity and of incompressibility, one has

$$\frac{\partial}{\partial t}\frac{\dfrac{\partial}{\partial t}\left[\dfrac{\partial}{\partial z}\left(\bar{\rho}\dfrac{\partial w}{\partial z}\right) + \bar{\rho}\nabla^2 w\right]}{g - F\cos\omega t} = \bar{\rho}'\nabla^2 w. \tag{51}$$

With equation (7) and

$$w = A(t)\,S(x,y)\,w(z),$$

equation (51) can be written, with w denoting $w(z)$ for simplicity,

$$\frac{\partial}{\partial t}\frac{(\partial/\partial t)\,A[(\bar{\rho}w')' - \alpha^2\bar{\rho}w]}{g - F\cos\omega t} = -\alpha^2\bar{\rho}'wA. \tag{52}$$

This shows that
$$(\bar{\rho}w')' - \alpha^2\bar{\rho}w = C\bar{\rho}'w \tag{53}$$

and
$$\frac{d}{dt}\left(\frac{dA/dt}{g - F\cos\omega t}\right) = -\frac{\alpha^2}{C}A. \tag{54}$$

For a continuously stratified fluid bounded by two horizontal planes of the container (at distance d apart), C must be $g\alpha^2/\sigma^2$ in which σ^2 is exactly the eigenvalue in equation (15 a), which is simply the dimensionless form (with w changed to f and for the special case of two-dimensional flow) of

$$(\bar{\rho}w')' - \alpha^2\left(\bar{\rho} + \frac{g\bar{\rho}'}{\sigma^2}\right)w = 0, \tag{55}$$

for only when C assumes such a value can the boundary conditions $w(0) = w(d) = 0$ be satisfied. Since surfaces of density discontinuity can be considered as limiting cases of regions of large density gradients, C must be equal to

$g\alpha^2/\sigma^2$ even in the presence of density discontinuities, so long as σ^2 is understood to be the eigenvalue of (55) for the given stratification, and so long as the effect of surface tension is neglected. Consequently, in the absence of surface tension, equation (54) has the form

$$\frac{d}{dt}\left(\frac{dA/dt}{g-F\cos\omega t}\right) = -\frac{\sigma^2}{g}A. \tag{56}$$

A more convenient equation than equation (56) for investigation of stability is the equation for the amplitude function $a(t)$ of the deflexion ζ of any material particle from its mean position. Since $w = \partial\zeta/\partial t$, we have $A = da/dt$, and integration of equation (56) yields

$$\frac{d^2a}{dt^2} = -\frac{\sigma^2}{g}(g-F\cos\omega t)\,a + C'. \tag{57}$$

Initially, u, v, w, p, ρ and ζ are all zero, so that a is zero and, from equation (49),

$$\frac{\partial w}{\partial t} = \frac{\partial^2\zeta}{\partial t^2} = 0$$

or

$$\frac{d^2a}{dt^2} = 0.$$

Consequently $C' = 0$, and, with $T = \frac{1}{2}\omega t$, equation (57) becomes

$$\frac{d^2a}{dT^2} + (p - 2q\cos 2T)\,a = 0, \tag{58}$$

in which (p not indicating pressure)

$$p = \frac{4\sigma^2}{\omega^2}, \quad q = \frac{2\sigma^2 F}{\omega^2 g}. \tag{59}$$

Equation (58) is Mathieu's equation in its standard form. If q vanishes, equation (58) shows that the frequency of oscillation is $\sigma/2\pi$, as expected. The quantity F/ω^2 is the linear amplitude of the vibration of the container. Hence $q = (2\sigma^2/g) \times$ (amplitude of vibration) (compare with Benjamin & Ursell 1954).

Whether the fluid is stable or not depends on whether $a(T)$ remains bounded as $T \to \infty$, and this in turn depends on p and q. The regions of stability and instability are shown in figure 1. Only the first quadrant of the diagram is shown because both p and q are positive. In fact, the complete diagram in McLachlan's book (1947, p. 41) shows that the diagram is symmetric about the p-axes. The unshaded regions are stable regions and the shaded ones unstable regions. Apart from an exponential factor $e^{\mu T}$ (μ depending on p and q) indicating the rate of growth, the solution for the unstable cases also possesses exact periodicities (see McLachlan 1947, pp. 40, 41, 77, 78). In the lowest shaded part of figure 1, the period for T is 2π, so that the period for ωt is 4π. This means that the frequency of fluid oscillation is only half the frequency of the container. In the next shaded region, the period for T is π, so that the oscillation of the fluid and that of the container are isochronous. The third shaded region is a region of half-frequency, etc. The stable regions would be regions of half-frequency or isochronous regions

 Chia-Shun Yih

but for a factor $e^{i\beta T}$, with β dependent on p and q. If β is irrational, the solution is not periodic at all.

Since

$$\frac{p}{q} = \frac{2g}{F},$$

the points in the p–q plane to be considered in each case are all on a straight line radiating from the origin. For *each** α there are infinitely many σ, and therefore infinitely many points on that straight line. Whereas some points may lie in regions of instability, others may lie in regions of stability. Since σ decreases

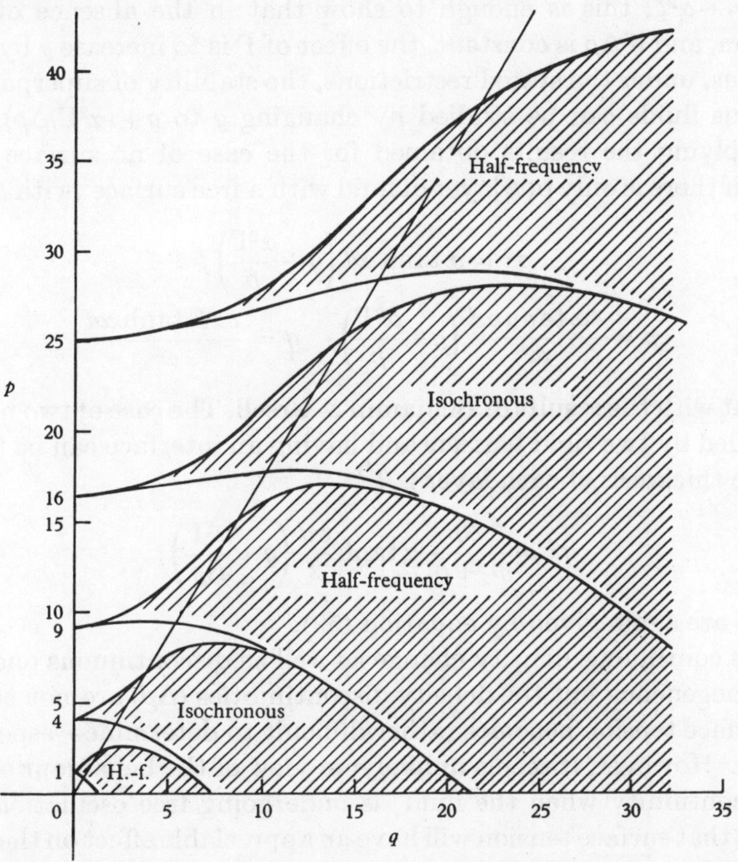

FIGURE 1. Chart for stability of fluid under vertical vibration. The acceleration of the container is $F\cos\omega t$, σ is the frequency (radians per second) of free oscillation, and $p = 4\sigma^2/\omega^2$, $q = 2\sigma^2 F/\omega^2 g$. The points for different modes lie on the line $p/q = 2g/F$.

toward zero as the index of the mode is higher and higher, the origin is a limit point of the (infinitely many) points in the p–q plane whose locations determine stability or instability. From figure 1 it is clear that there is a small region of stability around the origin, so that the fluid is stable for sufficiently high driving frequency, and against resonance with sufficiently high modes of free oscillation. Significant is the fact that no matter how small F is, there is always a region of instability, though the region is smaller and smaller as F becomes smaller and smaller.

* In the case treated by Benjamin & Ursell for each α there is only one σ.

So far surface tension has been omitted from the discussion. If the amount of density discontinuity ($\Delta\rho$) is constant, and if the fluid in each layer is homogeneous, the effect of surface tension can be taken into account in a very simple manner. The differential equation governing the flow in each layer is the Laplace equation, satisfied by the potential function $\phi(x, y, z)$. The boundary conditions at the interfaces are (compare with equation $(20a)$)

$$\left(\rho\frac{\partial\phi}{\partial t}\right)_l - \left(\rho\frac{\partial\phi}{\partial t}\right)_u - (g - F\cos\omega t)\Delta\rho\,\zeta + \Gamma\nabla^2\zeta = 0. \tag{60}$$

Since $\nabla^2\zeta = -\alpha^2\zeta$, this is enough to show that in the absence of continuous stratification, and if $\Delta\rho$ is constant, the effect of Γ is to increase g by the amount $\alpha^2\Gamma/\Delta\rho$. Thus, under the stated restrictions, the stability of superposed layers of homogeneous fluids can be studied by changing g to $g + (\alpha^2\Gamma/\Delta\rho)$, and subsequently applying the results obtained for the case of no surface tension. In particular, if there is only one layer of fluid with a free surface (with $\Delta\rho = \rho$)

$$\sigma^2 = \alpha\tanh\alpha d\left(g + \frac{\alpha^2\Gamma}{\rho}\right),$$

so that $\qquad p = \dfrac{4\alpha\tanh\alpha d}{\omega^2}\left(g + \dfrac{\alpha^2\Gamma}{\rho}\right), \quad q = \dfrac{2\alpha F\tanh\alpha d}{\omega^2},$

in agreement with the results of Benjamin & Ursell. The case of two homogeneous fluids bounded by two rigid barriers and having an interface can be treated similarly. If the thickness of each layer is $\frac{1}{2}d$

$$\sigma^2 = \frac{\Delta\rho}{\rho_1 + \rho_2}\alpha\tanh\frac{\alpha d}{2}\left(g + \frac{\alpha^2\Gamma}{\Delta\rho}\right),$$

and p and q are again given by equation (59).

If there is continuous density change as well as discontinuous ones, or if each layer is homogeneous but the density discontinuities ($\Delta\rho$) are not constant, the effect of surface tension becomes rather difficult to determine—especially in the former case. However, it seems unlikely, in view of the behaviour of surfaces of density discontinuity when the fluid is undergoing free oscillation with *small* frequencies, that surface tension will have an appreciable effect on the 'resonance' of the imposed acceleration with these free oscillations. In other words, for very small σ's, it is reasonable to expect that the stability or instability can be decided by ignoring surface tension entirely. Additional research in this direction is necessary before more definite and more general conclusions can be drawn as to the effect of surface tension on the kind of stability under discussion.

This work has been done during the tenure of a Senior Post-Doctoral Fellowship of the National Science Foundation, while the author has been at the Department of Applied Mathematics and Theoretical Physics, University of Cambridge. The author wishes to express his appreciation to the Foundation for the opportunity to pursue uninterrupted research. He is indebted to Dr G. K. Batchelor for stimulation, criticism, and several useful discussions, and to Dr. F. Ursell for a discussion that has led to an improvement of this paper. It is also a

508   *Chia-Shun Yih*

pleasure to acknowledge the support of fundamental research on stratified flows by the Office of Ordnance Research in the past several years, without which the present work would have taken much longer to accomplish.

REFERENCES

BENJAMIN, T. B. & URSELL, F. 1954 The stability of the plane free surface of a liquid in vertical periodic motion. *Proc. Roy. Soc.* A, **225**, 505–15.

BENTON, G. S. 1953 *A General Solution for the Celerity of Long Gravitational Waves in a Stratified Fluid*, pp. 149–62. Fluid Models in Geophysics, U.S. Government Printing Office.

COURANT, R. 1926 Über die Anwendung der Variationsrechnung.... *Acta Math.* vol. 49.

COURANT, R. & HILBERT, D. 1931 *Methoden der Mathematischen Physik*, Vol. I. Berlin: Julius Springer.

FJELDSTAD, J. E. 1933 Interne Wellen. *Geof. Publ.* Vol. x, no. 6, Oslo.

FJELDSTAD, J. E. 1952 Article in *Gravity Waves*, National Bureau of Standards Circular, **521**, 39–45.

GÖRTLER, H. 1954 Neuere Anwendungen der Charakteristikentheorie in der Hydrodynamik, Colloque Julius Massau des Mémoires des Sciences, Tom XXVIII.

GREENHILL, A. G. 1887 Wave motion in hydrodynamics. *J. Math.* **9**, 62–112.

INCE, E. L. 1944 *Ordinary Differential Equations*. New York: Dover Publications.

LAMB, H. 1945 *Hydrodynamics*. New York: Dover Publications.

MCLACHLAN, N. W. 1947 *Theory and Applications of Mathieu Functions*. Oxford.

SQUIRE, H. B. 1933 On the stability for three-dimensional disturbances of viscous fluid flow between parallel walls. *Proc. Roy. Soc.* A, **142**, 621–8.

SZ.-NAGY, B. 1947 Vibrations d'une corde non homogène. *Bull. Soc. Math. France*, vol. 75, pp. 193–208. See also, Riesz, F and Sz.-Nagy, B. 1956 *Functional Analysis*, §99. London and Glasgow: Blackie and Son.

WEBB, R. R. 1884. Math. Tripos Papers, Cambridge.

YIH, C.-S. 1959a Effects of gravitational or electromagnetic fields on fluid motion. *Quart. Appl. Math.* **16**, 409–15.

YIH, C.-S. 1959b Effects of density variation on fluid flow. *J. Geophys. Res.* **64**, 2219–23.

Reprinted without change of pagination from the
Journal of Fluid Mechanics, *volume 9, part 2, pp.* 161–174, 1960

Exact solutions for steady two-dimensional flow of a stratified fluid

By CHIA-SHUN YIH

Department of Engineering Mechanics, University of Michigan†

(Received 15 February 1960)

Three classes of exact solutions for steady two-dimensional flows of a stratified fluid are found. The flows which correspond to these solutions have arbitrary amplitude (however defined). Two of the three classes of solutions have close bearings on the lee-wave problem in meteorology. It is also shown that the amplitudes of the lee-wave components (if there is more than one component) depend not on the details of the shape of the barrier, but only on certain simple integral properties of the function for the singularity distribution generating the barrier.

1. The equation governing steady two-dimensional flow of a stratified fluid

This study is restricted to steady two-dimensional flows of a stratified fluid, assumed incompressible, inviscid, and non-diffusive. For such flows the Euler equations are

$$\rho\left(u\frac{\partial}{\partial x}+w\frac{\partial}{\partial z}\right)(u,w)=-\left(\frac{\partial}{\partial x},\frac{\partial}{\partial y}\right)p-(0,g\rho),\tag{1}$$

in which p and ρ are the pressure and the density, g is the gravitational acceleration, x and z are Cartesian co-ordinates, with z measured in the direction opposite to that of gravity, and u and w are the velocity components in the directions of increasing x and z, respectively. Since the fluid is incompressible and non-diffusive and the flow is steady,

$$\left(u\frac{\partial}{\partial x}+w\frac{\partial}{\partial z}\right)\rho=0.\tag{2}$$

This permits the equation of continuity to be written in the form

$$\frac{\partial u'}{\partial x}+\frac{\partial w'}{\partial z}=0,\tag{3}$$

and the equations of motion to be written as

$$\rho_0\left(u'\frac{\partial}{\partial x}+w'\frac{\partial}{\partial z}\right)(u',w')=-\left(\frac{\partial}{\partial x},\frac{\partial}{\partial z}\right)p-(0,g\rho),\tag{4}$$

in which $\qquad u'=u(\rho/\rho_0)^{\frac{1}{2}},\quad w'=w(\rho/\rho_0)^{\frac{1}{2}},\tag{5}$

† At Department of Applied Mathematics and Theoretical Physics, University of Cambridge, during 1959–60.

and ρ_0 is a reference density. With the pseudo-vorticity ω' defined by

$$\omega' = \frac{\partial w'}{\partial x} - \frac{\partial u'}{\partial z},$$

and ψ' the pseudo stream function, so that

$$u' = \frac{\partial \psi'}{\partial z}, \quad w' = -\frac{\partial \psi'}{\partial x}, \tag{6}$$

the equations of motion can be further simplified to

$$-\rho_0 \omega' \frac{\partial \psi'}{\partial x} = \frac{\partial}{\partial x}[p + \tfrac{1}{2}\rho_0(u'^2 + w'^2)], \tag{7}$$

$$-\rho_0 \omega' \frac{\partial \psi'}{\partial z} = \frac{\partial}{\partial z}[p + \tfrac{1}{2}\rho_0(u'^2 + w'^2)] + g\rho. \tag{8}$$

If (7) is multiplied by dx and (8) by dz, and the results added,

$$-\rho_0 \omega' \, d\psi = d[p + \tfrac{1}{2}\rho(u^2 + w^2)] + g\rho \, dz = dH - gz \, d\rho, \tag{9}$$

in which
$$H = p + \tfrac{1}{2}\rho(u^2 + w^2) + g\rho z$$

is the Bernoulli constant, which is constant along a streamline but may vary
from streamline to streamline, and is hence a function of ψ' alone. Since for
steady flows streamlines are path-lines, and for an incompressible and non-
diffusive fluid ρ is constant along a path-line, ρ is also a function of ψ' alone. Thus
(9) can be written as

$$\rho_0 \nabla^2 \psi' + gz \frac{d\rho}{d\psi'} = \frac{dH(\psi')}{d\psi'} = h(\psi'), \tag{10}$$

with $\nabla^2 \psi'$ replacing $-\omega'$. Equation (10) is the governing equation sought, and
is a modified form of an equation due to Long (1953), who did not relate the
arbitrary function of ψ' on the right-hand side of his equation to the Bernoulli
constant.

2. Types of exact solutions

To discover exact solutions of (10), it is natural to consider circumstances in
which the equation becomes linear in ψ. To this end, one may adopt two different
approaches. Since the function $h(\psi')$ is related to the upstream condition, one
may either try different upstream conditions and see whether these will make the
equation linear, or assume the equation to be linear to start with and inquire
what the corresponding upstream condition must be. The second approach is
evidently both exhaustive and more economical. Adopting the first approach,
Long said in his impressive paper (Long 1953) of the case in which ρu^2 is constant
far upstream where the flow is parallel: 'This is the only case I have been able to
discover for which the differential equation governing the motion of a stratified
fluid is exactly linear.' This is hardly surprising, because the equation originally
discovered by Long is in the form

$$\nabla^2 \psi + \frac{1}{\rho}\frac{d\rho}{d\psi}\left(\frac{\psi_x^2 + \psi_y^2}{2} + gz\right) = f(\psi), \tag{10a}$$

in which ψ is the usual stream function and subscripts indicate partial differentiation, and in this form it is quite unsuitable for discovering all the cases in which (10a) is exactly linear. The transformation (6) takes care of the inertia effect of density variation once and for all, removes the troublesome terms (representing the inertia effect) in Long's equation, and produces (10), which, while equivalent to Long's equation, is so much simpler that the second approach can now be applied. It will be shown by the second approach that there are three essentially distinct classes of flows for which (10) is exactly linear, each consisting of infinitely many flows. One of these three classes contains Long's case as a special (but very important) case. Thus the simple transformation (6) proves to be a very fruitful one.

For (10) to be linear in ψ, $d\rho/d\psi'$ and $h(\psi')$ must be linear in ψ'. The linear equation therefore has the general form

$$\nabla^2\psi' + gz(C + C_1\psi') = C_2 + C_3\psi'. \tag{11}$$

If $C_1 = C_3 = 0$, this equation has the form

$$\nabla^2\psi' + Cgz = C_2. \tag{11a}$$

If $C_1 = 0$ but $C_3 \neq 0$, ψ' can be changed by a constant, and (11) becomes

$$\nabla^2\psi' + Cgz = C_3\psi'. \tag{11b}$$

The class of flows governed by this equation includes Long's case as a special case. If $C_1 \neq 0$ but $C_3 = 0$, (11) becomes, after ψ' has been changed by a constant,

$$\nabla^2\psi' + C_1 gz\psi' = C_2. \tag{11c}$$

If C_1 and C_3 are both different from zero, the origin of z can be shifted so that the resulting equation is

$$\nabla^2\psi' + gz(C + C_1\psi') = C_0,$$

which, on changing ψ' by a constant, becomes identical in form with (11c).

If now the dimensionless parameters

$$\xi = x/d, \quad \eta = z/d, \quad \Psi = \psi'/Vd$$

are introduced, in which d is a reference length and V a reference velocity, (11a) to (11c) assume the form

$$\nabla^2\Psi + A\eta = B, \tag{12a}$$

$$\nabla^2\Psi + A\eta = B\Psi, \tag{12b}$$

$$\nabla^2\Psi + A\eta\Psi = B, \tag{12c}$$

in which A and B are dimensionless constants, and, now and henceforth,

$$\nabla^2 \equiv \frac{\partial^2}{\partial\xi^2} + \frac{\partial^2}{\partial\eta^2}.$$

3. Class (*a*): pseudo-potential flows

For class (*a*), the general solution is of the form

$$\Psi = \Psi_h - A\eta\begin{Bmatrix}\tfrac{1}{6}\eta^2\\\tfrac{1}{2}\xi^2\end{Bmatrix} + \tfrac{1}{2}B\begin{Bmatrix}\eta^2\\\xi^2\end{Bmatrix} + C\xi\eta + D\begin{Bmatrix}\eta\\\xi\end{Bmatrix}, \tag{13}$$

 Chia-Shun Yih

in which a fifth constant has been suppressed because Ψ can be changed by an arbitrary constant. Either member of the brackets in (13) can be used, or a linear combination of both members, except that for the first two brackets the linear combinations must be such that (12a) is satisfied. The first member on the right-hand side of (13) is a harmonic function satisfying the Laplace equation

$$\nabla^2 \Psi_h = 0. \tag{14}$$

A re-examination of (10), (11a) and (12a) reveals that

$$A = \frac{1}{\rho_0} \frac{d\rho}{d\Psi} \frac{gd}{V^2}, \tag{15}$$

so that, once Ψ is determined,

$$\rho = \frac{A\rho_0 V^2}{gd} \Psi + \text{constant} \tag{16}$$

is also known up to an additive constant. Furthermore, if ρ decreases with increasing η (stable stratification), and the flow is from left to right, $d\rho/d\Psi$ is negative, and the expression for A suggests that it is really the negative of the reciprocal of the square of a Froude number:

$$A = -F^{-2}. \tag{17}$$

A first example is furnished by a stratified flow between two horizontal boundaries, at $z = 0$ and $z = d$, into a line sink whose trace is situated at the origin. Since the flow is symmetric with respect to the z-axis, it is convenient to consider the flow to be separated by a plane vertical wall at $x = 0$ into two mirror images. The left one of these will be considered. If the flow at $x = -\infty$ is parallel and with the parabolic distribution for the velocity (as weighted by the factor $(\rho/\rho_0)^{\frac{1}{2}}$)

$$U(\eta) = 6U_m \eta(1 - \eta), \tag{18}$$

in which U_m is the mean of U, then with U_m as the representative velocity V,

$$A = 12, \quad B = 6, \quad C = D = 0$$

in (13), and

$$\Psi = \Psi_h - 2\eta^3 + 3\eta^2. \tag{19}$$

The boundary conditions are $\Psi = 0$ at $\eta = 0$, $\Psi = 1$ at $\eta = 1$, and at $\xi = 0$ $(0 < \eta \leqslant 1)$; $\Psi = 3\eta^2 - 2\eta^3$ at $\xi = -\infty$. In terms of Ψ_h, these are

$$\Psi_h = 0 \quad \text{at} \quad \eta = 0 \quad \text{and} \quad \eta = 1, \tag{20}$$

$$\Psi_h = 1 + 2\eta^3 - 3\eta^2 \quad \text{at} \quad \xi = 0 \quad (0 < \eta \leqslant 1), \tag{21}$$

$$\Psi_h = 0 \quad \text{at} \quad \xi = -\infty. \tag{22}$$

By the method of separation of variables the solution of (13) to (16) is found to be

$$\Psi_h = \Sigma A_n e^{n\pi\xi} \sin n\pi\eta, \tag{23}$$

in which

$$A_1 = \frac{2}{\pi}, \quad A_2 = \frac{1}{\pi}\left(1 + \frac{3}{\pi^2}\right), \quad A_3 = \frac{2}{3\pi}, \quad A_4 = \frac{1}{\pi}\left(\frac{1}{2} + \frac{3}{8\pi^2}\right), \quad A_5 = \frac{2}{5\pi}, \quad \text{etc.}$$

The final solution is

$$\psi' = U_m d(\Psi + 3\eta^2 - 2\eta^3), \tag{24}$$

and the density variation at infinity is

$$\rho = \rho_0 + (\rho_0 - \rho_1)(\Psi + 3\eta^2 - 2\eta^3), \tag{25}$$

in which ρ_0 is the density at the bottom plate and ρ_1 that at the top plate. The flow pattern can be expected to have an eddy at the corner bounded by the upper boundary and the vertical wall, extending to infinity.

For another example consider the case of stratified flow with $\Psi = -\tfrac{1}{6}A\eta^3$ at ∞. The lower boundary consists of a semicircle ($r = r_0$, $0 \leqslant \theta \leqslant \pi$) and the lines ($\theta = 0$, $\theta = \pi$, $r \geqslant r_0$). No upper boundary is imposed. After the solution is obtained, any streamline (and in particular the one on which ρ is zero) can be taken to be the upper boundary. Here $C = 0$ in (13), and the upper members in the brackets of (13) can be taken. For illustration, B and D will be taken to be zero. The general case in which B and D are not equal to zero can be solved similarly. The reference length is now the radius of the cylinder, r_0. For con-

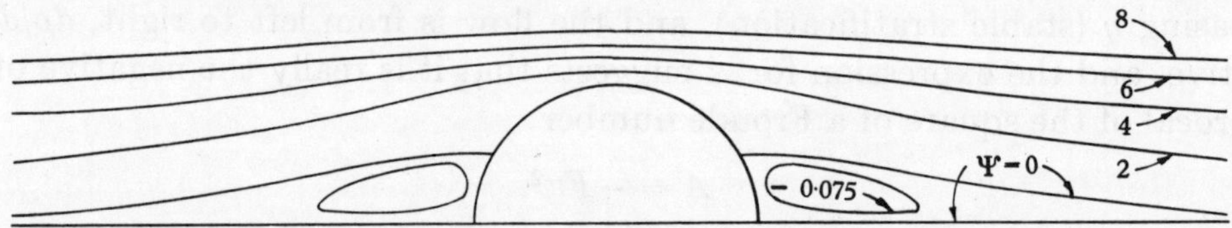

FIGURE 1. Pattern of a pseudo-potential flow of a stratified fluid over a semicircle.
$$\Psi = -\frac{24\psi'}{Cgr_0^3}, \qquad C = \frac{1}{\rho_0}\frac{d\rho}{d\psi'}, \qquad r_0 = \text{radius of semi-circle}, \qquad r_1 = r/r_0.$$

venience, let r/r_0 be denoted by r_1. The boundary conditions are (for $\Psi = -\tfrac{1}{6}A\eta^3$ at infinity): $\Psi_h = 0$ at $\eta = 0$ (at least for $r \geqslant 1$), $\Psi_h = 0$ at $r_1 = \infty$, $\Psi_h = \tfrac{1}{6}A\eta^3$ for $r_1 = 1$ ($\eta \geqslant 0$). The solution is

$$\psi' = \frac{Ar_0^3}{24}\left(\frac{3\sin\theta}{r_1} - \frac{\sin 3\theta}{r_1^3} - 4r_1^3\sin^3\theta\right)$$

$$= \frac{Ar_0^3}{24}\left[3\left(\frac{1}{r_1} - r_1^3\right)\sin\theta - \left(\frac{1}{r_1^3} - r_1^3\right)\sin 3\theta\right]. \tag{26}$$

The flow pattern is shown in figure 1. As can be readily calculated from (20), the stagnation points are the points:

$$(r, \theta) = (\infty, 0), \ (\infty, \pi), \ (r_0, 0), \ (r_0, \pi), \ (r_0, \tfrac{1}{6}\pi), \ (r_0, \tfrac{5}{6}\pi).$$

These form the corners of two roughly triangular eddies, symmetrically located over the horizontal boundary, as shown in the figure.

4. Class (*b*): waves of arbitrary amplitude, with application to flow over a barrier

The class of flows governed by (12*b*) can be applied to the atmosphere. If the flow is parallel, the corresponding stream function is governed by the equation

$$\frac{d^2\Psi_1}{d\eta^2} + A\eta = B\Psi_1, \tag{27}$$

which has the solution

$$\Psi_1 = \frac{A}{B}\eta + C \sinh \sqrt{B}\,\eta + D \cosh \sqrt{B}\,\eta. \tag{28}$$

If the solution of ($12b$) is written as the sum of two parts, i.e.

$$\Psi = \Psi_1 + \Psi_2, \tag{29}$$

then Ψ_2 satisfies
$$\nabla^2\Psi_2 - B\Psi_2 = 0, \tag{30}$$

the solution of which satisfying the boundary conditions† $\Psi_2 = 0$ at $\eta = 0$ and $\eta = 1$ is of the form

$$\Psi_2 = \sum_{n=1}^{\infty} A_n \exp \pm (B + n^2\pi^2)^{\frac{1}{2}} \xi \sin n\pi\eta. \tag{31}$$

The special case $C = D = 0$ has been considered by Long (1953). In this case, if Ψ and Ψ_1 are expressed in terms of Ud, with U denoting the *uniform* velocity (weighted by the factor $(\rho/\rho_0)^{\frac{1}{2}}$) far upstream, $\Psi = \Psi_1 = \eta$ far upstream, and $A = B$. Thus (17), (28), (29) and (31) produce the solution

$$\Psi = \eta + \sum_{n=1}^{\infty} A_n \exp\left\{\pm (n^2\pi^2 - F^{-2})^{\frac{1}{2}} \xi\right\} \sin n\pi\eta. \tag{32}$$

The solution by Long (1955) for stratified flow over barriers and the solution by Yih (1958) for stratified flow into a sink are of the form (32). These solutions can now be generalized to apply to the infinitely many upstream conditions described by (28). This gain in generality has been possible because (10) is substantially simpler than ($10a$). The actual modification of the solutions of Long and of Yih for application to the generalized upstream condition is straightforward and will not be presented here. Suffice it to say that (28) possesses so much latitude that an actual upstream wind condition can be much better approximated by (28) than by $\Psi_1 = \eta$, by appropriate choice of the constants A, B, C and D. Thus the meteorological significance of (27) is somewhat enhanced. Care must be taken, however, to ensure that Ψ (or Ψ_1, since Ψ_2 is assumed to vanish far upstream) be monotone in η, for otherwise (since $d\rho/d\Psi_1$ is constant) an unstable density distribution would be present in a part of the fluid in parallel flow.

If B is negative and greater in numerical value than $(N\pi)^2$ but less than $(N+1)^2\pi^2$, Ψ_2 in (31) will contain N terms periodic in ξ, representing wave motion. It is commonly assumed (and the assumption has been experimentally verified) that upstream waves do not occur. But if we do not inquire how the waves are made and only ask whether a periodic condition can be consistent with (27), we see immediately that the answer is in the affirmative, because

$$\Psi = \Psi_1 + \sum_{n=1}^{N} (B_n \cos |B + n^2\pi^2|^{\frac{1}{2}} \xi + C_n \sin |B + n^2\pi^2|^{\frac{1}{2}} \xi) \sin n\pi\eta \tag{33}$$

† The condition $\Psi_2 = 0$ at $\eta = 0$ is imposed to make $\eta = 0$ a streamline. This is desirable if the ground surface is flat or at least flat as $\xi \to \infty$ (since lee-waves, if they exist, will not die out as $\xi \to \infty$). If there is a barrier on the surface of which we demand $\Psi = 0$, then the streamline $\Psi = 0$ consists of the ground surface *and* the line $\eta = 0$ (which may constitute part of the ground surface), if the condition $\Psi_1(0) = 0$ is imposed. The boundary condition $\Psi_2 = 0$ at $\eta = 1$ follows from the requirement $\Psi = $ constant at $\eta = 1$. A discussion of the realism of this requirement when the theory is applied to the atmosphere will be given later in this paper.

is a solution of (27), with Ψ_1 given in (28). The corresponding density distribution given by

$$\frac{d\rho}{d\Psi} = \text{constant} \tag{34}$$

is not necessarily unstable, even though in certain regions the density increases upwards, because of the presence of acceleration toward the centre of curvature. The wave motion represented by (33) can have arbitrary amplitudes. For the particular case of $A = B$, $C = D = 0$,

$$\Psi = \eta + \sum_{n=1}^{N} (B_n \cos |F^{-2} - n^2\pi^2|^{\frac{1}{2}} \xi + C_n \sin |F^{-2} - n^2\pi^2|^{\frac{1}{2}} \xi) \sin n\pi\eta, \tag{35}$$

with

$$N\pi < F^{-1} < (N+1)\pi, \tag{36}$$

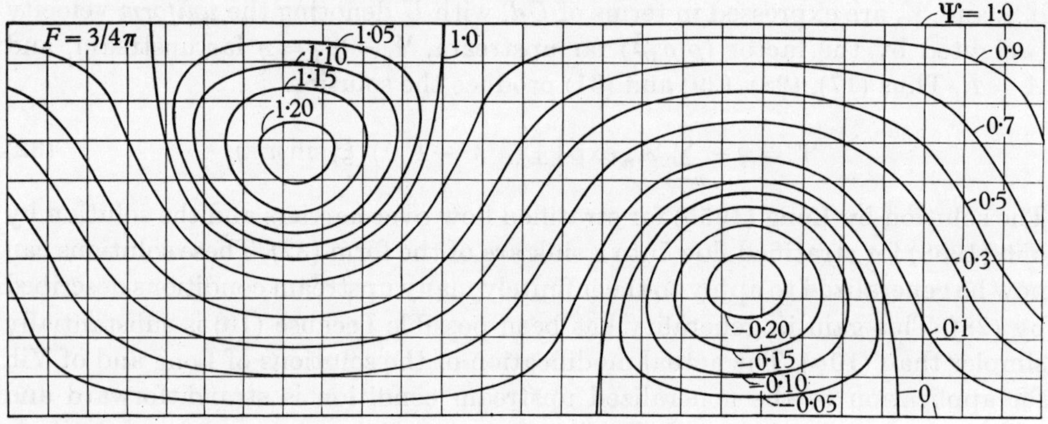

FIGURE 2. Stationary waves of arbitrary amplitude.

$$F = \frac{3}{4\pi}, \quad \Psi = -\frac{\psi'}{F^2 d^3 g C}, \quad C = \frac{1}{\rho_0} \frac{d\rho}{d\psi'}.$$

represents a period motion with N wave components. In spite of what Long himself said (as quoted in §2), the waves represented by (35)—but not those represented by (33)—can be considered to have been discovered by him, because they are identical with the lee-waves he studied. The flow pattern for

$$\Psi = \eta + \frac{2}{\pi} \cos (F^{-2} - \pi^2)^{\frac{1}{2}} \xi \sin n\pi\eta, \tag{37}$$

with $F = 3/4\pi$, is shown in figure 2. The term η in (35) and (37) represents only a pseudo-uniform velocity field, because Ψ is a stream function for the flow field (u', w'), and not for the flow (u, w). Therefore the parallel flow represented by η does not correspond to an actually uniform velocity, and it is not possible by a shifting of co-ordinate axes to remove the parallel flow altogether. However, if drift is allowed, the discharge relative to a moving frame of reference can be made to be zero. The speed c with which the frame moves is exactly the phase velocity of the wave pattern relative to the moving frame, which is quite different from the stationary wave pattern. This speed can be calculated readily, and will not be given explicitly here.

 Chia-Shun Yih

Use of vorticity distributions for generating stratified flows over a barrier

For the case $A = B$, $C = D = 0$, Long (1955) gave a method for generating the solution for flow over a barrier which is approximately the same as one with a prescribed form. We shall now give an alternate method, for generating solutions of (12b) for flow over a barrier of unspecified (except implicitly) form. This method has three advantages over Long's method. First, it is simpler. Secondly, the determination of the coefficients is exact, and does not involve the solution of infinitely many equations containing infinitely many unknowns. Thirdly, by means of it we can prove the very important fact† that the amplitudes of the various lee-wave components depend not on the *details* of the shape of the barrier, but only on certain integral properties of the singularities generating the barrier. On the other hand, the shape of the barrier is directly though only approximately accounted for by Long's method, whereas the alternative method to be presented is entirely an inverse method which does not attempt to generate a solution for a *prescribed* barrier even approximately, except indirectly.

The method will now be described. When

$$(N\pi)^2 < -B < (N+1)^2 \pi^2,$$

the solution of (12b) can be put in the form

$$\left.\begin{array}{l}
\Psi_- = \Psi_1 + \displaystyle\sum_{N+1}^{\infty} A_n e^{a_n \xi} \sin n\pi\eta \quad \text{(for } \xi \leqslant 0\text{)}, \\[3mm]
\Psi_+ = \Psi_1 + \displaystyle\sum_{n=1}^{N} (B_n \cos a_n \xi + C_n \sin a_n \xi) \sin n\pi\eta \\[3mm]
\qquad\qquad + \displaystyle\sum_{N+1}^{\infty} D_n e^{-a_n \xi} \sin n\pi\eta \quad \text{(for } \xi \geqslant 0\text{)},
\end{array}\right\} \tag{38}$$

in which Ψ_1 is given by (28) and

$$a_n = |B + n^2\pi^2|^{\frac{1}{2}}.$$

The coefficients A_n, B_n, C_n and D_n are determined by demanding

$$\Psi_- = \Psi_+ \quad \text{at} \quad \xi = 0, \tag{39}$$

$$\frac{\partial \Psi_-}{\partial \xi} - \frac{\partial \Psi_+}{\partial \xi} = f(\eta) \quad \text{at} \quad \xi = 0, \tag{40}$$

in which

$$f(\eta) = 0 \quad \text{for} \quad \eta \geqslant a \quad \text{and} \quad \eta = 0, \tag{41}$$

and is arbitrary elsewhere. Since Ψ_- and Ψ_+ satisfy (12b), (39) and (40) ensure that Ψ_+ is the analytic continuation of Ψ_-. There are no singularities in the domain outside of the barrier (which is determined *a posteriori*), and there are no upstream waves. The function $f(\eta)$ corresponds to a sheet of distributed vortices (with horizontal axes) of variable strength at $\xi = 0$, extending from $\eta = 0$ to $\eta = a$. It determines implicitly the shape of the barrier.

† The author is indebted to Dr G. K. Batchelor for pointing out the possibility of this fact.

It will now be seen that B_n and C_n depend not on the details of the function $f(\eta)$ but only on certain of its integral properties, or, more precisely, on certain of its Fourier coefficients associated with the functions $\sin n\pi\eta$. Indeed, (39) demands that

$$A_n = D_n \quad (n > N), \tag{42}$$

$$B_n = 0 \quad (n \leqslant N), \tag{43}$$

and (40) demands

$$a_n(A_n + D_n) = 2\int_0^1 f(\eta)\sin n\pi\eta\, d\eta \quad (n > N), \tag{44}$$

$$a_n C_n = -2\int_0^1 f(\eta)\sin n\pi\eta\, d\eta \quad (n \leqslant N). \tag{45}$$

Thus A_n and D_n are determined from (42) and (44), and C_n from (45).† But (45) is most significant. It states that the amplitudes of the N wave components are equal to the first N Fourier coefficients of the function divided by a_n (which depends only on B and n, and is quite independent of $f(\eta)$). Certainly there are infinitely many functions which satisfy (41), have the same first N Fourier coefficients, and yet are different. The barriers corresponding to all these different generating functions have lee-waves with the same wavelengths and the same amplitudes, provided B is the same for the upstream flow. The situation is even independent of the coefficients A, C, and D in (28), though the shapes of the resulting barriers are dependent upon them. Near the barrier, the flow depends also on A_n and D_n, and hence also on the rest of the Fourier components. In other words, near the barrier the flow depends on all the Fourier coefficients of or on the full details of $f(\eta)$, as is to be expected. Thus we have arrived at a sort of St Venant's principle in stratified flow.

Now that the alternative method has proved fruitful, it is desirable to improve the method, in order to obtain some flexibility for dealing with barriers of specified forms. The method outlined above is good for constructing flows over rather bluff barriers, and is not adequate if the barrier is elongated. To remedy this situation, the obvious thing to do is to achieve a freedom for displacing the vortices (represented by $f(\eta)$) in the x-direction. This can be done simply by using two or more vertical vortex sheets at different values of x or ξ. If (38) is rewritten as

$$\Psi = \Psi_1 + \Psi_2,$$

in which the expressions for Ψ_2 are different for $\xi > 0$ and for $\xi < 0$, we see that Ψ_2 is the stream function which owes its existence to the presence of the barrier or of the singularities generating this barrier. If an additional line of singularities is situated at $\xi = b$, with distribution function $f_1(\eta)$, and still another situated at $\xi = c$, with distribution function $f_2(\eta)$, the solution is of the form

$$\Psi = \Psi_1 + \Psi_2 + \Psi_3 + \Psi_4,$$

in which Ψ_3 and Ψ_4 are similar to Ψ_2 given in (38), except that the ξ in Ψ_2 should be changed to $\xi - b$ and $\xi - c$ for Ψ_3 and Ψ_4, respectively, and the coefficients are now determined from $f_1(\eta)$ for Ψ_3, and from $f_2(\eta)$ for Ψ_4. Generalization to

† If $B = -N^2\pi^2$, $a_N = 0$, and in order for the method to work the Nth Fourier coefficient of $f(\eta)$ must be zero.

170   *Chia-Shun Yih*

the case of more than three vortex sheets is obvious. If it is desirable to use isolated vortices, we can simply take $f(\eta)$ to be a Dirac delta-function located somewhere above $\eta = 0$.

Use of sources, sinks, and doublets for generating stratified flows over a barrier

Instead of demanding (39) and (40), we can demand

$$\Psi_- - \Psi_+ = f(\eta) \quad \text{at} \quad \xi = 0,$$

$$\frac{\partial \Psi_-}{\partial \xi} - \frac{\partial \Psi_+}{\partial \xi} = 0 \quad \text{at} \quad \xi = 0,$$

with

$$f(\eta) = 0 \quad \text{for} \quad \eta \geqslant a \quad \text{and} \quad \eta = 0,$$

and $f(\eta)$ arbitrary elsewhere. The function $f(\eta)$ now corresponds to a source distribution along a line element at $\xi = 0$. The solution is again in the form of (38), but the formulas for the coefficients are now

$$A_n = -D_n \quad (n > N), \quad C_n = 0 \quad (n \leqslant N),$$

$$A_n - D_n = 2 \int_0^1 f(\eta) \sin n\pi\eta \, d\eta \quad (n > N),$$

$$B_n = -2 \int_0^1 f(\eta) \sin n\pi\eta \, d\eta \quad (n \leqslant N).$$

If there is more than one line source, the generalization is the same as given in the last paragraph. The total algebraic sum of the sources must be zero in order that the barrier be closed.

Again, by taking $f(\eta)$ to be a Dirac delta-function, the solution corresponding to an isolated source or sink can be obtained. It can be readily shown that if a source is located at $\xi = -b$ and a sink of equal strength (m) is located at $\xi = b$ and at the same height h_s (dimensionless), the nth $(n \leqslant N)$ lee-wave is represented by

$$-4m \sin n\pi h_s \sin a_n b \sin a_n \xi \sin n\pi\eta.$$

If b is small, the amplitudes of the lee-waves are proportional to $2mb$, which is the negative of the moment of the source and sink. Thus, for a doublet of strength μ (equivalent to $-2mb$), the amplitude of the nth lee-wave is

$$2\mu a_n \sin n\pi h_s,$$

and, for a doublet distribution from $\eta = 0$ to $\eta = a$, the amplitude of the nth lee-wave is

$$2a_n \int_0^a \mu(\eta) \sin n\pi\eta \, d\eta.$$

If the doublet (isolated or distributed vertically) is not located at $\xi = 0$, *only* the *phase* of the pertaining lee-waves will be changed (by an amount equal to the ξ-coordinate of the doublet or doublet distribution).

An example, and a discussion of the effect of the upper boundary

Figure 3 shows a stratified flow (case (b)) over a barrier, with waves in the lee. The velocity distribution far upstream is given indirectly by (28), with $C = D = 0$ and $A = B = -9/16\pi^2$, so that u' is constant far upstream. The flow is analytically given by (38) and (42) to (45), with

$$-f(\eta) = 10\sin 5\pi\eta \quad \text{for} \quad 0 \leqslant \eta \leqslant 0\cdot 2,$$
$$= 0 \qquad\qquad \text{for} \quad 0\cdot 2 < \eta \leqslant 1.$$

There is a single lee-wave component, with wavelength $(6/\sqrt{7})\,d$, d being the depth from the (flat) upper boundary to the flat part of the lower boundary.

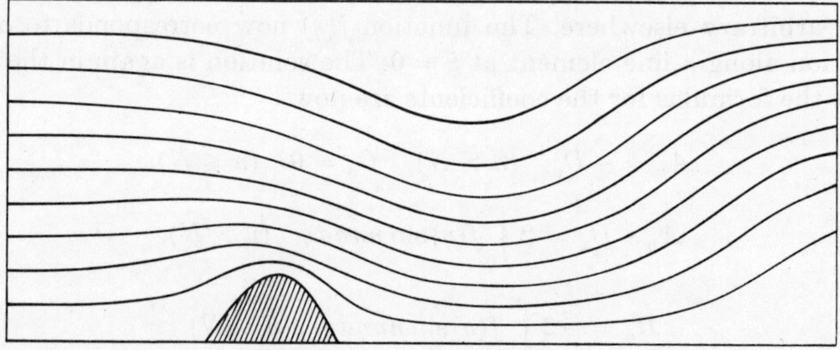

FIGURE 3. A stratified flow over a barrier, with waves in the lee.

Since the wave numbers of the lee-waves are a_n (for those n's that make $B + n^2\pi^2$ negative), the wavelengths must depend on B. In the example just given, $B = -F^{-2}$, with

$$F^2 = \frac{\rho_0 U'^2}{gd^2(d\rho/dz)},$$

U' being the (constant) velocity u' at $x = -\infty$, where $d\rho/dz$ is taken. Thus for a given U' and density distribution, the wavelengths depend on d. Consequently, the location of the upper boundary has in this case, as indeed it does in general, a profound influence on the flow pattern. This is not surprising, for as the depth increases the wave numbers for those lee-waves just able to stay stationary (i.e. to withstand the sweeping action of the parallel flow) must also increase, and vice versa, because the wave velocities increase with d and decrease with the wave-numbers (Yih 1960). However, the importance of the location of the imaginary upper boundary does raise the question of where to impose it in any given situation, and the question of the error committed by imposing it.

A partial answer to these questions can be obtained by considering two superposed layers of fluids. The lower layer has depth d, and is bounded below by a rigid plane boundary (the ground). The upper layer has depth d_u and is bounded above by an auxiliary rigid plane. This auxiliary boundary (not the one the effect of which is under discussion) is imposed only for convenience, and is not necessary, for the same conclusions can be reached on the assumption that the depth of the upper layer is infinite. The interface of the two layers is the place where the artificial rigid boundary under discussion is supposed to be imposed in the preceding analysis, and it is proposed to see under what conditions the presence of this boundary introduces only small errors. Let the density gradients in the two layers be constant but different, and the density be continuous at the interface. At $x = -\infty$, u' is supposed to be the same for both layers, and is denoted by U'. The equations governing fluid motion in the two layers are

$$\nabla^2 \Psi - F^{-2}\eta = -F^{-2}\Psi, \quad \nabla^2 \Psi_u - F_u^{-2}\eta = -F_u^{2}\Psi,$$

in which

$$F = -\frac{\rho_0 U'^2}{gd^2(d\rho/dz)}, \quad F_u = -\frac{\rho_0 U'^2}{gd^2(d\rho/dz)_u},$$

the density gradients being taken in the absence of waves. The parallel flow corresponds to

$$\Psi_1 = (\Psi_u)_1 = \eta,$$

and the wave motion is governed by (with the subscript 2 on the stream functions dropped for convenience)

$$\nabla^2 \Psi = -F^{-2}\Psi, \quad \nabla^2 \Psi_u = -F_u^{-2}\Psi_u.$$

These equations are to be solved with the boundary conditions

   (i) $\Psi = 0$ at $\eta = 0$;

   (ii) $\Psi_u = 0$ at $\eta = d_u/d$;

   (iii) that the displacement be the same for both layers at the interface;

   (iv) that the pressure (or, equivalently, the velocity) be continuous at the interface.

The solution of the eigenvalue problem so defined on the basis of a linearized analysis yields the secular equation

$$(F^{-2} - m^2)^{\frac{1}{2}} \cot (F^{-2} - m^2)^{\frac{1}{2}} = -(F_u^{-2} - m^2)^{\frac{1}{2}} \cot (F_u^{-2} - m^2)^{\frac{1}{2}} \left(\frac{d_u}{d} - 1\right)$$

for the determination of the eigenvalues for the wave-number m in the factor $\sin m\xi$ contained in Ψ and Ψ_u. Since in the atmosphere the gradient of the potential density in the stratosphere is greater than that in the troposphere,

$$F_u^{-2} = \alpha F^{-2} \quad (\alpha > 1).$$

Hence

$$\frac{F_u^{-2} - m^2}{F^{-2} - m^2} = \frac{(\alpha - 1) F^{-2}}{F^{-2} - m^2} + 1.$$

In the atmosphere, if d is taken to be the depth of the troposphere, $F^2 \ll 1$. Consequently, if m is large enough to make $F^{-2} - m^2$ much smaller than F^{-2}, the secular equation can be replaced by

$$\tan (F^{-2} - m^2)^{\frac{1}{2}} \cot (F_u^{-2} - m^2)^{\frac{1}{2}} \left(\frac{d_u}{d} - 1\right) = 0.$$

One set of solutions of this equation is

$$m = (F^{-2} - n^2\pi^2)^{\frac{1}{2}} = a_n,$$

so long as n is not so large an integer as to make m small. Another set of solutions is obtained by setting the other factor (in the approximate secular equation) equal to zero. The wave-numbers obtained are for waves in the upper layer when the interface is replaced by a rigid boundary. Thus, if we take d to be the depth of the troposphere and apply the analysis to meteorological problems, the situation is as follows:

(1) The exponential terms in (38), corresponding to local disturbances only, are least affected by the replacement of the tropopause by a rigid boundary, and, since d is rather large compared with the vertical dimension of a barrier, are practically independent of d.

(2) For small values of F, the shorter lee-waves predicted by the theory will exist in the atmosphere. The error committed by imposing the upper rigid boundary is small in connexion with the shorter lee-waves.

(3) For the longer lee-waves, the error may be large.

(4) The theory will furnish no information at all on lee-waves extending to the stratosphere.

Because of the situation stated in (3) and (4), further work is necessary to determine more accurately the effect of the upper boundary. In the absence of better information, d should be taken to be the depth of the troposphere when applying the theory presented here (which does have the advantage that the amplitude of the motion treated does not have to be small).

5. Class (c): another class of waves of arbitrary amplitude, with possible application to atmospheric flows

For convenience, the coefficient A in $(12c)$ will be denoted by α^2, so that α is imaginary if A is negative. The solution of $(12c)$ is of the form

$$\Psi = \Psi_1(\eta) + \Psi_2(\xi, \eta), \tag{46}$$

in which Ψ_1 satisfies the equation

$$\frac{d^2\Psi_1}{d\eta^2} + \alpha^2\eta\Psi_1 = B, \tag{47}$$

and Ψ_2 satisfies the equation

$$\nabla^2\Psi_2 + \alpha^2\eta\Psi_2 = 0. \tag{48}$$

The density variation now satisfies the equation $d\rho/d\Psi \propto \Psi$.

For $B = 0$ the solution of (47) is, aside from a constant factor,

$$\Psi_1(\eta) = \eta^{\frac{1}{2}}\{J_{\frac{1}{3}}(\tfrac{2}{3}\alpha\,\eta^{\frac{3}{2}}) + CN_{\frac{1}{3}}(\tfrac{2}{3}\alpha\,\eta^{\frac{3}{2}})\} \equiv f(\eta). \tag{49}$$

For $B \neq 0$ the substitution

$$\Psi_1 = f(\eta)\,\phi(\eta) + K_1 \tag{50}$$

leads to
$$\Psi_1 = f\left[\int_0^\eta \frac{B\int_0^\eta f\,d\eta - \alpha^2 K_1\int_0^\eta \eta f\,d\eta}{f^2}\,d\eta + K'\right] + K_1. \tag{51}$$

Since $f(0) = 0$, $\Psi_1 = K_1$ at $\eta = 0$. (It is no longer always permissible to take $\Psi = 0$ at $\eta = 0$, because in reaching $(11c)$ Ψ is already assumed to have been modified by an additive constant if necessary.) The constant K' in (51) ensures that Ψ_1 can be adjusted to take any value K_2 at $\eta = 1$ provided $J_{\frac{1}{3}}(\tfrac{2}{3}\alpha) \neq 0$.

174   *Chia-Shun Yih*

The solution of (48) is of the form

$$\Psi_2 = \sum_{n=1}^{\infty} A_n \exp\left[\pm (a_n \xi)\,\beta(\alpha, b_n, \eta)\right], \tag{52}$$

in which $b = -a^2/\alpha^{\frac{7}{3}}$, and

$$\beta(\alpha, b, \eta) = (\eta - b)^{\frac{1}{2}} \left\{ N_{\frac{1}{3}}\left[\tfrac{2}{3}\alpha(-b)^{\frac{3}{2}}\right] J_{\frac{1}{3}}\left[\tfrac{2}{3}\alpha(\eta - b)^{\frac{3}{2}}\right] - J_{\frac{1}{3}}\left[\tfrac{2}{3}\alpha(-b)^{\frac{3}{2}}\right] N_{\frac{1}{3}}\left[\tfrac{2}{3}\alpha(\eta - b)^{\frac{3}{2}}\right] \right\}, \tag{53}$$

and b_n are the eigenvalues satisfying

$$\beta(\alpha, b, 1) = 0. \tag{54}$$

If a_n^2 is negative, (52) corresponds to a wave motion with periodic components.

Solutions Ψ_1 and Ψ_2, given in (51) and (52), can be used for application of Long's method or the alternative method proposed in §4, in dealing with flow over a barrier. In fact, the entire development in §4 can be repeated in a strictly similar manner for the new forms of Ψ_1 and Ψ_2, and the problem of flow into a sink treated by Yih (1958) can again be solved if the upstream condition is described by (51) and $|A|$ is sufficiently small. We shall not work out the details, which are tedious but straightforward, and shall content ourselves by pointing out that (51) again represents infinitely many upstream conditions, corresponding to the infinitely many sets of values for A, B, K', and K_1, one of which may sometimes be a better approximation to the actual wind distribution than one represented by (28).

This work has been done during the tenure of a Senior Post-Doctoral Fellowship of the National Science Foundation at the University of Cambridge, and the author wishes to express his appreciation to the Foundation for the opportunity to pursue uninterrupted research. The author is indebted to Dr G. K. Batchelor, F.R.S., for stimulation, criticism, and several useful discussions. It is also a pleasure to acknowledge the support of fundamental research on stratified flows by the Office of Ordnance Research in the past several years, without which the present work would have taken much longer to accomplish.

Note added in proof. While this paper was in the proof stage, its contents were presented at a seminar of the Institute of Meteorology of the University of Stockholm. At that time Prof. G. Benton kindly informed the author that some of the results presented had already been published by Prof. R. R. Long in a brief note ('Tractable models of steady-state stratified flow with shear', *Quart. J. Roy. Met. Soc.* **84**, 1958, pp. 159–61). Upon examining that note, I found that equation (28) and the upstream condition corresponding to equation (12*c*) had already been obtained by Long by an entirely different approach.

REFERENCES

Long, R. R. 1953 Some aspects of the flow of stratified fluids. I. A theoretical investigation. *Tellus*, **5**, 42–57.

Long, R. R. 1955 Some aspects of the flow of stratified fluids. III. Continuous density gradients. *Tellus*, **7**, 342–57.

Yih, C.-S. 1958 On the flow of a stratified fluid. *Proc. Third U.S. Nat. Congr. Appl. Mech.* pp. 857–61.

Yih, C.-S. 1960 Gravity waves in a stratified fluid. *J. Fluid Mech.* **8**, 481–508.

Reprinted without change of pagination from the
Journal of Fluid Mechanics, *volume* 9, *part* 1, *pp.* 68–80, 1960

A transformation for non-homentropic flows, with an application to large-amplitude motion in the atmosphere

By CHIA-SHUN YIH

Department of Engineering Mechanics, University of Michigan*

(Received 23 March 1960)

A transformation has been found which reduces steady non-homentropic flows of a compressible fluid to homentropic flows, provided diffusive and gravity effects are negligible. With this transformation, the equation governing steady two-dimensional flows of a compressible fluid with variable entropy in a gravitational field is derived, which is then applied to the study of atmospheric waves in the lee of mountains. The corresponding equation governing swirling axisymmetric flows is also given.

1. Introduction

It is well known that the flow of gas behind a curved shock is non-homentropic. In the atmosphere, waves are sometimes formed in the lee of mountains as a result of the non-homentropy of air and of the action of gravity. But the equations governing non-homentropic flows are so complicated that no non-trivial exact solution exists. Therefore in existing literature on the formation of lee waves, the theory has always been based on perturbation methods, and is thus only valid if the amplitude of wave motion (i.e. the vertical displacement) is small.

In this paper a transformation will be presented which will render unnecessary the consideration of non-homentropy in steady flows of ideal gases, provided the effects of viscosity and of gravity are neglected, in the sense that every steady non-homentropic flow can be reduced thereby to a steady homentropic flow Gravity effects can certainly be neglected in the aerodynamics of aircraft or flying objects, though it is of primary importance in the study of waves in the atmosphere. Viscous effects can, as usual, be neglected outside of the boundary layer, and are certainly of secondary importance in atmospheric flows. Thus the transformation to be presented here is not without practical value.

In the study of lee waves in the atmosphere, the presence of gravity, which is now of paramount importance, prevents the above-mentioned transformation from absorbing the effects of non-homentropy altogether. Nevertheless, the use of this transformation leads to the derivation of a much simplified equation for steady two-dimensional flows, which, for an atmosphere slightly stratified in entropy and in specific energy, possesses four essentially different classes of

* At Department of Applied Mathematics and Theoretical Physics, University of Cambridge, during 1959–60.

solutions, provided the Mach number is everywhere small, so that the effect of *dynamic* compressibility on density variation can be neglected. (In the first 10 or 15 km of the atmosphere, where lee waves can conceivably be expected to occur, the Mach number of atmospheric flows is certainly everywhere small.) The solutions are exact in the sense that the displacements are not assumed to be small, but can have any arbitrary values of the same magnitude as the scale of the motion.

An equation governing steady axisymmetric flows with swirl has also been obtained, which may be helpful for the study of the Hirsch-tube phenomenon and of tornadoes.

2. The transformation

To bring out the full significance for ordinary aerodynamics of the transformation mentioned in the Introduction, body forces will be ignored for the time being. The equations of motion for steady flows are then

$$u_j \frac{\partial u_i}{\partial x_j} = -\frac{1}{\rho}\frac{\partial p}{\partial x_i}, \tag{1}$$

in which u_i is the velocity component in the direction of the Cartesian coordinate x_i ($i = 1, 2, 3$), ρ is the density, p is the pressure, and the summation convention has been adopted. The equation of continuity is, exactly,

$$\frac{\partial u_j}{\partial x_j} + \frac{1}{\rho} u_j \frac{\partial \rho}{\partial x_j} = 0. \tag{2}$$

If the flow is homentropic, and the fluid is a perfect gas,

$$p/\rho^\gamma = \text{constant}, \tag{3}$$

in which γ is the ratio of the specific heat* at constant pressure (c_p) to that at constant volume (c_v), and the flow is governed by equations (1) to (3). If the flow is not homentropic but diffusion is neglected, the entropy along a path line is constant. For steady flows this means that

$$u_j \frac{\partial}{\partial x_j}\left(\frac{p}{\rho^\gamma}\right) = 0, \tag{4}$$

which replaces equation (3), and states the constancy of entropy along a streamline in steady flows.

One of the great difficulties encountered in dealing with non-homentropic flows is that, since the gas is no longer barotropic (which is another way of saying that a single relationship between p and ρ does not exist), ρ cannot be absorbed into the pressure term in (1), and the motion, even started from rest, will not continue to be irrotational. The system consisting of equations (1), (2), and (4) is so complicated that at present no non-trivial solutions exist. However, the situation is not as bad as it appears at first sight, as the transformation now to be given will show.

---

* Both c_p and c_v are assumed to be constant.

In virtue of (4),

$$u_j \frac{\partial F(\lambda)}{\partial x_j} = 0, \tag{5}$$

in which $F(\lambda)$ is any arbitrary function of λ, defined by

$$\lambda = \frac{\rho}{\rho_0}\left(\frac{p_0}{p}\right)^{1/\gamma}, \tag{6}$$

with p_0 denoting a reference pressure and ρ_0 a reference density. Since the entropy S is connected with p, ρ, and c_v by

$$p/\rho^\gamma = \text{constant} \times e^{S/c_v}, \tag{7}$$

the quantity λ is connected with the entropy by

$$\lambda = \text{constant} \times e^{-S/c_p}, \tag{8}$$

and is to be determined *for each streamline* from the upstream conditions, by virtue of its constancy along a streamline in steady flows, as stated in (5). With the transformation

$$u_i' = \sqrt{\lambda}\, u_i, \quad \rho' = \rho/\lambda, \quad \text{and} \quad p' = p, \tag{9}$$

equations (1) and (2) become, in virtue of (5),

$$u_j' \frac{\partial u_i'}{\partial x_j} = -\frac{1}{\rho'}\frac{\partial p'}{\partial x_i} \tag{10}$$

and

$$\frac{\partial u_j'}{\partial x_j} + \frac{1}{\rho'} u_j' \frac{\partial \rho'}{\partial x_j} = 0. \tag{11}$$

Furthermore, the last two of equations (9) and equation (6) can be combined to give

$$\frac{p'}{\rho'^\gamma} = \frac{p}{\rho'^\gamma} = \frac{p_0}{\rho_0^\gamma} = \text{constant.} \tag{12}$$

Now equations (10), (11), and (12) are identical in form to (1), (2), and (3), and hence govern homentropic flows in terms of the primed quantities. But this means that to any solution of equations (10) to (12) representing a homentropic flow in terms of u_i', ρ', and p', there corresponds a non-homentropic flow in terms of u_i, ρ, and p, which are obtained from equations (9), and vice versa. Consideration of boundary conditions does not affect this conclusion. For convenience the flow in terms of the primed quantities will be called the associated flow.

The *associated* flow may not be irrotational. But if it originates from a big reservoir, where the fluid is at rest and therefore possesses no vorticity, irrotationality (in the u_i'-field) will persist downstream. This can be seen by eliminating p' from (10) by cross-differentiation, producing

$$u_j' \frac{\partial \xi_i'}{\partial x_j} = \xi_j' \frac{\partial u_i'}{\partial x_j} + \frac{\xi_i'}{\rho'} u_j' \frac{\partial \rho'}{\partial x_j}. \tag{13}$$

in which ξ_i' is the ith component of the vorticity in the u_i'-field. Equation (13) clearly indicates the persistence of irrotationality (or of the vanishing of ξ_i').

If $\xi_i' = 0$, integration of equations (10) in the usual way produces (with q' as the speed in the associated flow)

$$\tfrac{1}{2}q'^2 + \frac{\gamma}{\gamma-1}\frac{p'}{\rho'} = \tfrac{1}{2}q_{\max}'^2 = \text{constant}, \tag{14}$$

which is valid for the whole field of flow. This equation can also be written

$$\tfrac{1}{2}q^2 + \frac{\gamma}{\gamma-1}\frac{p}{\rho} = \frac{1}{2\lambda}q_{\max}'^2 = \text{constant} \times \frac{p^{1/\gamma}}{\rho}, \tag{15}$$

in which q is the speed of the actual flow. If $\xi_i' \neq 0$,

$$\tfrac{1}{2}q^2 + \frac{\gamma}{\gamma-1}\frac{p}{\rho} = f(S), \tag{16}$$

in which $f(S)$ is an arbitrary function of the entropy S.

Equation (14) is simply the ordinary Bernoulli equation. In fact, if gravity is not neglected the complete equation is (with z measured vertically upward)

$$\tfrac{1}{2}q^2 + gz + \frac{\gamma}{\gamma-1}\frac{p}{\rho} = f(S), \tag{17}$$

which is well known.

Since the transformation presented in this section may suggest a similarity in its underlying idea with Crocco's stream function, it is desirable to point out the essential differences between the two inventions. Crocco dealt with the homenergic (constant specific energy, or constant $f(S)$ in (17)) but non-homentropic flows behind a shock, and, utilizing the constancy of entropy along a streamline in steady flows, obtained the equation of continuity for two-dimensional flow* (in the usual notation)

$$\frac{\partial}{\partial x}\left[u(q_{\max}^2 - q^2)^{1/(\gamma-1)}\right] + \frac{\partial}{\partial y}\left[v(q_{\max}^2 - q^2)^{1/(\gamma-1)}\right] = 0, \tag{18}$$

which permits the use of a stream function ψ (Crocco's stream function), in serms of which the velocity components can be expressed

$$u = (q_{\max}^2 - q^2)^{-1/(\gamma-1)}\frac{\partial\psi}{\partial y}, \quad v = -(q_{\max}^2 - q^2)^{-1/(\gamma-1)}\frac{\partial\psi}{\partial x}. \tag{19}$$

Close examination of the factor

$$(q_{\max}^2 - q^2)^{1/(\gamma-1)}$$

shows that it is really just the density ρ multiplied by a function of the entropy. To this extent there is some similarity between the present transformation and Crocco's invention. But the similarity stops here. The important differences are: (*a*) Crocco's development is only for homenergic flows, whereas the present transformation deals with non-homenergic and non-homentropic flows; (*b*) Crocco's development is only for two-dimensional or axisymmetric flows, whereas the present transformation deals with general three-dimensional flows; (*c*) Crocco invented a new stream function but left the velocity unchanged, hence did not arrive at the transformation embodied in (9).

* The development for axisymmetric flows is similar.

We shall now take stock and see what conclusions can be drawn from the transformation embodied in (9). As is evident, the associated flow has the same *pattern* as the actual flow. It (the associated flow) is irrotational if the actual flow originates from a large reservoir where the gas is at rest, or, more generally, if the associated flow is irrotational far upstream. Whether the associated flow is irrotational or not, the third of equations (9) ensures that the drag and lift on any body placed in the gas stream will be the same as that calculated from the associated flow. If far upstream the actual flow* is unidirectional, with constant velocity but variable entropy, the associated flow will be rotational, and there will in general be lift on a body placed in the stream. This is an example illustrating how entropy stratification upstream can give rise to lift on a body moving with constant velocity in a quiescent but stratified gas.

The above conclusions, and indeed the transformation embodied in (9), are based on the conservation of entropy along each streamline. Therefore flows with shocks must be considered anew, if they are to be considered *as a whole* and not as a collection of separate regions. Looking at such flows in their entirety, we can draw some interesting conclusions in spite of the entropy change across the shock. Since three-dimensional shocks differ from two-dimensional ones only in complexity, not in principle, only two-dimensional shocks will be considered here. The pre-shock flow is assumed to be parallel to the x-axis, with velocity u_1 (which may vary with y), with the subscript 1 now referring to pre-shock flow and 2 to post-shock flow. The shock wave is in general curved and the post-shock flow in general non-parallel. With u and v denoting velocity components in the x- and y-directions, and β denoting the local angle of inclination of the shock wave, continuity demands (Liepmann & Puckett 1947, p. 51) that along the shock wave

$$\rho_1 u_1 \sin \beta = \rho_2 (u_2 \sin \beta - v_2 \cos \beta), \tag{20}$$

in which ρ is the density. The conservation of momentum normal to the shock wave demands that, along the shock wave,

$$p_1 + \rho_1 u_1^2 \sin^2 \beta = p_2 + \rho_2 (u_2 \sin \beta - v_2 \cos \beta)^2, \tag{21}$$

in which p is the pressure. The conservation of momentum parallel to the shock wave demands

$$p_1 u_1^2 \sin \beta \cos \beta = \rho_2 (u_2 \sin \beta - v_2 \cos \beta)(u_2 \cos \beta + v_2 \sin \beta), \tag{22}$$

and the energy equation remains

$$\tfrac{1}{2} u_1^2 + \frac{\gamma}{\gamma - 1} \frac{p_1}{\rho_1} = \tfrac{1}{2}(u_2^2 + v_2^2) + \frac{\gamma}{\gamma - 1} \frac{p_2}{\rho_2}. \tag{23}$$

Equations (20) to (23) contain five unknowns: u_2, v_2, ρ_2, p_2, and β. The variation of β from place to place along the shock wave can only be determined by the equations governing the flow before the shock, those governing post-shock flow, equations (20) to (23), and the conditions at the solid boundaries and at infinity, by a trial-and-error process.

* The flow is the steady flow equivalent to the flow caused by a body moving with constant velocity in a quiescent but stratified gas.

A transformation for non-homentropic flows

Whereas the transformation embodied in (9) does not obviate this tedious process, it does throw some light on shock waves ahead of which the fluid is already non-homentropic. With λ defined by (6) and determined for each streamline (even after it pierces through the shock wave) by the upstream or pre-shock condition, we insist on making the transformation represented by (9), in spite of the abrupt increase of entropy along each streamline as it crosses the shock wave. The associated flow is parallel and homentropic upstream, and is irrotational if λu_1^2 is constant throughout. Behind the shock even the associated flow is not homentropic, but is governed by the equations

$$\left(u'\frac{\partial}{\partial x}+v'\frac{\partial}{\partial y}\right)(u',v')=-\frac{1}{\rho'}\left(\frac{\partial}{\partial x},\frac{\partial}{\partial y}\right)p',$$

$$\frac{\partial u'}{\partial x}+\frac{\partial v'}{\partial y}+\frac{1}{\rho'}\left(u'\frac{\partial}{\partial x}+v'\frac{\partial}{\partial y}\right)\rho'=0,$$

$$\left(u'\frac{\partial}{\partial x}+v'\frac{\partial}{\partial y}\right)\left(\frac{p'}{\rho'^\gamma}\right)=0,$$

because λ is constant on each streamline by imposition. These equations, with the primes dropped, are identical with the equations governing post-shock flow. The transformation (9) achieves homentropy in the pre-shock region, but otherwise leaves the governing equations unchanged in form. At the shock wave, (20) to (23) are still valid if all the quantities (except, of course, β and γ) are primed. Thus, even when shock waves are present, to every flow with entropy stratification before the shock corresponds an associated flow of the *same pattern for the entire field of flow*, with homentropy (through not necessarily irrotationality) before the shock. The actual lift and drag on a body placed in the gas stream are the same as those calculated from the associated flow.

Although gravity has been neglected in this section, equations (9) are still helpful when gravity is taken into account, because they simplify the governing equations a great deal, as will be shown in the following sections.

3. Equation governing two-dimensional flows in a gravitational field

If (x_1, x_3) and (u_1, u_3) are now written as (x, z) and (u, w), the equations of motion for steady two-dimensional flows are, with the gravity included,

$$\rho\left(u\frac{\partial u}{\partial x}+w\frac{\partial u}{\partial z}\right)=-\frac{\partial p}{\partial x},$$

$$\rho\left(u\frac{\partial w}{\partial x}+w\frac{\partial w}{\partial z}\right)=-\frac{\partial \rho}{\partial z}-g\rho,$$

in which z is measured in a direction opposite to that of the gravitational acceleration g. With the transformation embodied in (7), the equations of motion become

$$u'\frac{\partial u'}{\partial x}+w'\frac{\partial u'}{\partial z}=-\frac{1}{\rho'}\frac{\partial p'}{\partial x}, \tag{24}$$

$$u'\frac{\partial w'}{\partial x}+w'\frac{\partial w'}{\partial z}=-\frac{1}{\rho'}\frac{\partial p'}{\partial z}-g\lambda. \tag{25}$$

The equation of continuity $\dfrac{\partial(\rho u)}{\partial x}+\dfrac{\partial(\rho w)}{\partial z}=0$

now has the form $\dfrac{\partial(\rho' u')}{\partial x}+\dfrac{\partial(\rho' w')}{\partial z}=0,$

which permits the use of the stream function ψ' such that

$$u'=\frac{1}{\rho'}\frac{\partial \psi'}{\partial z}, \quad w'=-\frac{1}{\rho'}\frac{\partial \psi'}{\partial x}.$$

With

$$q'^2=u'^2+w'^2, \quad I'=\frac{q'^2}{2}+\int\frac{dp'}{\rho'},$$

$$H'=\frac{q'^2}{2}+gz\lambda+\int\frac{dp'}{\rho'} \quad \text{and} \quad \eta'=\frac{\partial u'}{\partial z}-\frac{\partial w'}{\partial x}, \tag{26}$$

the equations of motion can be written

$$\frac{\eta'}{\rho'}\frac{\partial \psi'}{\partial x}=\frac{\partial I'}{\partial x}, \tag{27}$$

$$\frac{\eta'}{\rho'}\frac{\partial \psi'}{\partial z}=\frac{\partial I'}{\partial z}+g\lambda. \tag{28}$$

Multiplication of (27) by dx and (28) by dz and addition of the resulting equations produces

$$\frac{\eta'}{\rho'}d\psi'=dI'+g\lambda\,dz=dH'-gz\,d\lambda.$$

But since H and λ are functions of ψ' alone,

$$\frac{\eta'}{\rho'}+gz\frac{\partial \lambda}{\partial \psi'}=\frac{dH'}{d\psi'}=h(\psi'), \tag{29}$$

or, from equation (25) and the last of equations (26),

$$V^2\psi'-\frac{1}{\rho'}\left(\frac{\partial \rho'}{\partial x}\frac{\partial \psi'}{\partial x}+\frac{\partial \rho'}{\partial z}\frac{\partial \psi'}{\partial z}\right)+gz\rho'^2\frac{d\lambda}{d\psi'}=\rho'^2 h(\psi'), \tag{30}$$

which is the desired equation. The density ρ' has to be evaluated from the third of equations (26), in which $H'(\psi')$ and $\lambda(\psi')$ are determined from upstream conditions.

4. Swirling axisymmetric flows in a gravitational field

Cylindrical co-ordinates (r,θ,z) will be used. In these co-ordinates, the velocity components will be denoted by $u, v,$ and w, respectively. The equations of motion for steady axisymmetric flows are, with viscosity neglected,

$$u\frac{\partial u}{\partial r}+w\frac{\partial u}{\partial z}-\frac{v^2}{r}=-\frac{1}{\rho}\frac{\partial p}{\partial r}, \tag{31}$$

$$u\frac{\partial v}{\partial r}+w\frac{\partial v}{\partial z}+\frac{uv}{r}=0, \tag{32}$$

$$u\frac{\partial w}{\partial r}+w\frac{\partial w}{\partial z}=-\frac{1}{\rho}\frac{\partial p}{\partial z}-g, \tag{33}$$

 A transformation for non-homentropic flows

in which z is again measured in the direction opposite to that of the gravitational acceleration. The equation of continuity is

$$\frac{\partial(r\rho u)}{\partial r} + \frac{\partial(r\rho w)}{\partial z} = 0.$$

By the transformation indicated by equations (7), equations (31) to (33) become

$$u'\frac{\partial u'}{\partial r} + w'\frac{\partial u'}{\partial z} - \frac{v'^2}{r} = -\frac{1}{\rho'}\frac{\partial p'}{\partial r}, \tag{34}$$

$$u'\frac{\partial v'}{\partial r} + w'\frac{\partial v'}{\partial z} + \frac{u'v'}{r} = 0, \tag{35}$$

$$u'\frac{\partial w'}{\partial r} + w'\frac{\partial w'}{\partial z} = -\frac{1}{\rho'}\frac{\partial p'}{\partial z} - g\lambda, \tag{36}$$

and the equation of continuity becomes

$$\frac{\partial(r\rho' u')}{\partial r} + \frac{\partial(r\rho' w')}{\partial z} = 0. \tag{37}$$

Equation (37) permits the use of a stream function ψ' in terms of which the velocity components can be expressed:

$$u' = -\frac{1}{r\rho'}\frac{\partial\psi'}{\partial z}, \quad w' = \frac{1}{r\rho'}\frac{\partial\psi'}{\partial r}. \tag{38}$$

Equation (35) expresses the conservation of angular momentum for the same particle, because it can be written as

$$u'\frac{\partial(rv')}{\partial r} + w'\frac{\partial(rv')}{\partial z} = 0.$$

Consequently rv' is a function of ψ' alone. For convenience, we take

$$(rv')^2 = f(\psi'). \tag{39}$$

With $\quad q'^2 = u'^2 + v'^2 + w'^2, \quad J' = \dfrac{u'^2+w'^2}{2} + \displaystyle\int\frac{dp'}{\rho'}, \quad I' = \dfrac{q'^2}{2} + \displaystyle\int\frac{dp'}{\rho'},$

$$H' = \frac{q'^2}{2} + gz\lambda + \int\frac{dp'}{\rho'}, \quad \eta' = \frac{\partial u'}{\partial z} - \frac{\partial w'}{\partial r}, \tag{40}$$

equations (34) and (36) can be written, with the aid of (38) and (39)

$$\frac{\eta'}{r\rho'}\frac{\partial\psi'}{\partial r} - \frac{f(\psi')}{r^3} = -\frac{\partial J'}{\partial r},$$

$$\frac{\eta'}{r\rho'}\frac{\partial\psi'}{\partial z} = -\frac{\partial J'}{\partial z} - g\lambda,$$

or

$$\frac{\eta'}{r\rho'}\frac{\partial\psi'}{\partial r} - \frac{1}{2r^2}\frac{\partial}{\partial r}f(\psi') = -\frac{\partial I'}{\partial r}, \tag{41}$$

$$\frac{\eta'}{r\rho'}\frac{\partial\psi'}{\partial z} - \frac{1}{2r^2}\frac{\partial}{\partial z}f(\psi') = -\frac{\partial I'}{\partial z} - g\lambda. \tag{42}$$

Multiplication of (41) by $-dr$ and (42) by $-dz$ and addition of the results gives

$$-\frac{\eta'}{r\rho'}+\frac{1}{2r^2}\frac{df}{d\psi'}=\frac{dH'}{d\psi'}-gz\frac{d\lambda}{d\psi'}, \tag{43}$$

or, with the aid of (38) and the last of equations (40),

$$\left(\frac{\partial^2}{\partial r^2}-\frac{1}{r}\frac{\partial}{\partial r}+\frac{\partial^2}{\partial z^2}\right)\psi'-\frac{1}{\rho'}\left(\frac{\partial\rho'}{\partial r}\frac{\partial\psi'}{\partial r}+\frac{\partial\rho'}{\partial z}\frac{\partial\psi'}{\partial z}\right)+\frac{\rho'^2}{2}\frac{df}{d\psi'}+g\rho'^2 zr^2\frac{d\lambda}{d\psi'}=r^2\rho'^2\frac{dH'}{d\psi'}, \tag{44}$$

which is the equation governing swirling axisymmetric motion in a gravitational field. In many engineering applications (such as to the Hirsch tube), the term involving g can be neglected. Again, ρ' is to be calculated from the equation involving H' in (40), in which the functions $H'(\psi')$ and $\lambda(\psi')$ are again to be determined from upstream conditions. Equation (44) could serve as a starting point for the study of tornadoes.

5. Lee waves of large amplitude

The phenomenon of gravity waves in air (considered as a compressible fluid) in the lee of mountain ridges has been studied by Lyra, Queney, Corby, Scorer, and others, and recently by Crapper (1949). (For references, see Crapper's work.) Perturbation methods have been used by all of these authors, so that their results do not apply to large vertical displacements. Batchelor (1953) gave an equation governing homentropic flows in the atmosphere, obtained on the assumption of irrotationality (which is a consequence of homentropy if the motion has been started from rest) and small Mach number in the entire flow field. The effect of gravity is retained in Batchelor's equation, so that it applies to large vertical displacements under the assumptions stated. However, since wave motions in the atmosphere are essentially due to non-homentropy or non-homenergy, Batchelor's equation cannot be applied to a study of lee waves.

The exact equation governing steady two-dimensional non-homentropic flows is equation (30), which can be used to study lee waves. However, the equation is so very complicated that no solution can be obtained without some simplifying assumptions. With Batchelor, we shall assume that the Mach number is everywhere small, so that, *a fortiori*, the *variation* of the square of the speed is small compared with the square of the sound speed. Therefore the density variation due to the variation of speed is negligible, and any change in the density along the same streamline is due to change of elevation alone. Since isentropy along a streamline is the most important assumption underlying the derivation of (29), it might appear that the simplifying assumption on ρ (hence on ρ') implies that the pressure is a function of elevation alone for any streamline. Such an implication must not be inferred from the assumption on the density, because the pressure must be calculated from the equation containing H' in (26), with the term $\frac{1}{2}q'^2$ included. Indeed, if the pressure were only dependent on z on any one streamline, scarcely any non-trivial motion would be possible. The situation is not unlike that encountered in the study of free-convection problems, in which the fluid is assumed incompressible as far as continuity and the inertia of the fluid is concerned, but is considered to have a variable density as far as the important term representing body force is concerned. Another similar situation is encountered in the study of incompressible fluids. If entropy is assumed constant along a path line, surely there is some relation connecting the density to the pressure on such a line. But the assumption of constant density does not imply constant pressure, because the pressure can change a great deal for an infinitesimal change in the density of what is normally considered to be an incompressible fluid. In the present case, the assumption concerning ρ' affects only the first term in (29) or the first two groups of terms in (30), and is an assumption concerning essentially the continuity equation only. The inertia effect of density change has been absorbed once and for all in the transformation represented by equation (9). Gravity force is exactly represented by $gz(d\lambda/d\psi')$ and the force resulting from pressure gradient is represented by $dH'/d\psi'$ in (29), with H' given by the *full* expression in (26). The factor ρ'^2 in the last two terms of (30) appears from a common multiplication by that factor, and does not affect the physical reasoning given above.

If the variation of H' or of λ with ψ' is large, equation (30) is still too difficult to solve. Therefore we shall assume the variation of H' and λ to be small. As far as the calculation of ρ' is concerned, we shall ignore the variation of H' and λ altogether and justify the procedure by the same arguments as those presented in the last paragraph. For ρ', then, calculation from the third of (26), with the term $\frac{1}{2}q'^2$ neglected and λ equal to 1 (if the reference density and pressure are those at some point in the atmosphere under discussion), yields

$$\frac{\gamma}{\gamma-1}\frac{p_0}{\rho_0^\gamma}\rho'^{\gamma-1} = H' - gz, \tag{45}$$

or

$$\rho'^{\gamma-1} = \frac{H'-gz}{K}, \quad K = \frac{\gamma}{\gamma-1}\frac{p_0}{\rho_0^\gamma}. \tag{46}$$

With (46), equation (30) becomes

$$\nabla^2\psi' + \frac{1}{\gamma-1}\frac{g}{H'-gz}\frac{\partial\psi'}{\partial z} + gz\left(\frac{H'-gz}{K}\right)^{2/(\gamma-1)}\frac{d\lambda}{d\psi'} = \left(\frac{H'-gz}{K}\right)^{2/(\gamma-1)}h(\psi'), \tag{47}$$

in which, as in (45) and (46), H' is considered to be a constant except in connexion with $h(\psi')$. It must be remembered that whatever assumptions have been made on ρ', H', and λ, they do not limit the amplitude of the vertical displacement of the motion in any way, or the slope of the streamlines. Freedom from such limitations is the chief merit of the present theory. The functions $\lambda(\psi')$ and $h(\psi')$ are to be determined from upstream conditions.

Equation (47) is exactly linear if

$$\frac{d\lambda}{d\psi'} = a\psi' + b, \quad h(\psi') = m\psi' + n.$$

Since ψ' can be changed by a constant, there are seven different cases:

    (1) $a \neq 0, b = 0, m = n = 0,$ (5) $a = 0, b \neq 0, m = n = 0,$

    (2) $a \neq 0, b = 0, m = 0, n \neq 0,$ (6) $a = 0, b \neq 0, m = 0, n \neq 0,$

    (3) $a \neq 0, b = 0, m \neq 0, n = 0,$ (7) $a = 0, b \neq 0, m \neq 0, n = 0.$

    (4) $a \neq 0, b = 0, m \neq 0, n \neq 0,$

We have not included the cases in which $a = b = 0$, because they correspond to homentropic flows. If in addition $m = n = 0$, the flow is in fact irrotational. But if $m \neq 0$, wave motion is possible. This wave motion is not due to non-homentropy because the entropy is constant for $a = b = 0$, but is due to non-homenergy.

Since z can be changed by a constant, the seven cases can be reduced to four essentially different cases. Thus cases (3), (4), and (6) are not essentially different from cases (1), (2), and (5), respectively. The four essentially different cases, are therefore, (1), (2), (5), and (7).

If

$$\Psi = \psi'/\psi_0, \quad \xi = x/d, \quad \eta = z/d, \tag{48}$$

in which d is a reference length which can be taken either to be the depth of the troposphere or the depth below some very stable layer, and ψ_0 is a reference stream function, the linear cases are represented by

$$\left(\frac{\partial^2}{\partial \xi^2} + \frac{\partial^2}{\partial \eta^2}\right)\Psi + \frac{1}{\gamma - 1}\frac{1}{\alpha - \eta}\frac{\partial \Psi}{\partial \eta} + \eta(\alpha - \eta)^{2/(\gamma-1)}(A\Psi + B) = (\alpha - \eta)^{2/(\gamma-1)}(C\Psi + D), \tag{49}$$

in which

$$\alpha = H'/gd \tag{50}$$

is the ratio of the *equivalent* depth of the atmosphere, assumed completely homentropic (for defining this depth only), to the reference depth d. The value of α may vary over a range, but if d is taken to be $10\,\mathrm{km}$ (average depth for the troposphere) a representative value for α is $3\cdot5$.

In all the linear cases the solution can be put in the form

$$\Psi = \Psi_1(\eta) + \Psi_2(\xi, \eta), \tag{51}$$

in which both parts on the right-hand side satisfy (49). If we suppose that from $\eta = 1$ (or $z = d$) upwards the atmosphere is much more stable than the layer below, so that the vertical displacement at $\eta = 1$ is small compared with that prevailing in the layer $0 \leqslant \eta < 1$ (see Yih 1960a), a rigid plane may be imagined to be situated at $\eta = 1$. The boundary conditions for Ψ are then

$$\Psi_1(0) = 0, \quad \Psi_1(1) = E \text{ (a constant)}. \tag{52}$$

Solution of the differential equation (49), with Ψ_1 replacing Ψ therein, together with (52) then yield a $\Psi_1(\eta)$ corresponding to an upstream condition which makes (47) linear. Although the actual upstream condition may not give rise to the linearity of (47), suitable choices of the constants A, B, C, D, and E can produce infinitely many upstream conditions one of which may approximate the actual upstream condition rather closely, while the linearity of (47) is maintained throughout. The method of approach is therefore an inverse one, as is often the case in classical aerodynamics.

As to Ψ_2, the boundary conditions are, with the gas flowing from $\xi = -\infty$ to $\xi = +\infty$,

$$\Psi_2 \to 0 \quad \text{as} \quad \xi = -\infty, \tag{53a}$$

$$\Psi_2(\xi, 1) = 0, \tag{53b}$$

$$\Psi = \Psi_1 + \Psi_2 = 0 \quad \text{on the lower boundary (ground)}. \tag{53c}$$

No boundary condition is imposed at $\xi = +\infty$, because waves may exist in the lee of a barrier, and when they do not exist the condition far downstream is automatically the same as that far upstream. The condition (53a) is imposed on the assumption that the existence of a barrier, the effect of which is represented by Ψ_2, does not influence the condition far upstream. The (assumed) rigidity of the boundary at $\eta = 1$ demands (53b). The satisfaction of (53c) on the surface of a ground of given profile is difficult. But the inverse method given in another paper (Yih 1960b) can again be used. As described in that paper, the auxillary condition

$$\Psi_2(\xi, 0) = 0 \tag{53d}$$

is imposed to guarantee good behaviour of the solution far downstream, where the ground is assumed level and where the lee-wave components contained in Ψ_2 do not die out exponentially. The streamline $\Psi = 0$ therefore consists of two branches: the line $\eta = 0$ and the surface of the ground. As in the case of lee-wave formation in an incompressible fluid (Yih 1960b), the amplitudes of the lee-wave components depend only on certain integral properties of the barrier, and not on its detailed shape.

Although the calculation for the details of lee-waves governed by (49) involves the detailed calculations for the eigenfunctions, in case (7) at least, the number of lee-wave components can be predicted from the value of C without detailed calculations. Thus, the function Ψ_1 satisfies the equation (with $A = D = 0$ in case (7))

$$\Psi_1'' + \frac{1}{\gamma - 1}\frac{1}{\alpha - \eta}\Psi_1' + \eta(\alpha - \eta)^{2/(\gamma - 1)}B = (\alpha - \eta)^{2/(\gamma - 1)}C\Psi_1,$$

in which the primes indicate ordinary differentiation. The other part of the solution consists of terms of the form

$$\Psi_2 = \begin{Bmatrix} \sin k\xi \\ \cos k\xi \end{Bmatrix} f(\eta),$$

in which k may be imaginary, and f satisfies the equation

$$f'' + \frac{1}{\gamma - 1}\frac{1}{\alpha - \eta}f' - [C(\alpha - \eta)^{2/(\gamma - 1)} + k^2]f = 0. \tag{54}$$

With

$$\zeta = \frac{\gamma - 1}{\gamma}(\alpha - \eta)^{\gamma/(\gamma - 1)}, \tag{55}$$

equation (54) becomes

$$\frac{d^2 f}{d\zeta^2} - \left[C + k^2\left(\frac{\gamma}{\gamma - 1}\zeta\right)^{-2/\gamma}\right]f = 0. \tag{56}$$

The interval $0 \leqslant \eta \leqslant 1$ is now transformed to

$$\frac{\gamma - 1}{\gamma}(\alpha - 1)^{\gamma/(\gamma - 1)} \leqslant \zeta \leqslant \frac{\gamma - 1}{\gamma}\alpha^{\gamma/(\gamma - 1)}.$$

Let

$$l = \frac{\gamma - 1}{\gamma}[\alpha^{\gamma/(\gamma - 1)} - (\alpha - 1)^{\gamma/(\gamma - 1)}]. \tag{57}$$

By equating k to zero and computing the values for C which will enable f to satisfy the boundary conditions corresponding to (53b) and (53d), i.e.

$$f(0) = 0, \quad f(1) = 0,$$

we have
$$C_n = -(n\pi/l)^2.$$

If
$$(n\pi/l)^2 \leqslant -C < \{[(n+1)\pi]/l\}^2,$$

there are n non-negative eigenvalues for k^2, and hence n lee-wave components.

This work has been done during the tenure of a Senior Post-doctoral Fellowship granted by the National Science Foundation.

REFERENCES

BATCHELOR, G. K. 1953 The conditions for dynamic similarity of motions of a frictionless perfect-gas atmosphere. *Quant. J. Roy. Soc. Met.* **79**, 224–35.

CRAPPER, G. D. 1959 A three-dimensional solution for waves in the lee of mountains. *J. Fluid Mech.* **6**, 51–76.

LEIPMANN, H. W. & PUCKETT, A. E. 1947 *Introduction to Aerodynamics of a Compressible Fluid.* New York: Wiley and Sons.

YIH, C.-S. 1960a Gravity waves in a stratified fluid. *J. Fluid Mech.* **8**, 481–508.

YIH, C.-S. 1960b Exact solutions for steady two-dimensional flows of a stratified fluid. *J. Fluid Mech.* **9**, 161–174.

Reprinted without change of pagination from the
Journal of Fluid Mechanics, *volume* 10, *part* 1, *pp.* 133–140, 1961

Flow of a non-homogeneous fluid in a porous medium

By CHIA-SHUN YIH

Department of Engineering Mechanics, University of Michigan

(Received 27 September 1960)

If the viscosity and specific weight of a fluid are variable, the equations governing its flow in a porous medium are non-linear and in general very difficult to solve. It has been found, however, that steady flows of a fluid of variable viscosity but constant specific weight can be reduced to those of a homogeneous fluid by a remarkably simple transformation, which indicates that the flow patterns of the fluid are the same as those of a homogeneous fluid with the same boundary conditions, and that only the speed need be modified. The speed of the actual flow is obtained by dividing the speed of the homogeneous-fluid flow by a factor proportional to the actual viscosity. The transformation is also used to derive the equations governing steady two-dimensional flows and steady axisymmetric flows of a fluid of variable viscosity and specific weight. In a good many cases of practical importance these equations are exactly linear, in spite of the fact that the governing equations obtained without the use of the above-mentioned transformation are non-linear. An exact solution for a steady two-dimensional flow with prescribed boundary conditions is given. Two inverse methods for generating exact solutions for two-dimensional flows are presented, together with two illustrative examples. The theory also applies to Hele–Shaw flows, so that it can be easily verified in the laboratory.

1. Steady seepage flow of a fluid of variable viscosity

The generalized Darcy's law for steady flows of a non-homogeneous fluid in a porous medium is expressed by the equations

$$\frac{\mu}{k}u_i = -\frac{\partial p}{\partial x_i} + \rho X_i \quad (i = 1, 2, 3), \tag{1}$$

in which u_i is the (mean) velocity component in the direction of the Cartesian co-ordinate x_i, μ is the viscosity, k is the permeability (which may vary from place to place), p is the pressure, ρ is the density, and X_i is the body force per unit mass in the direction of increasing x_i. If the fluid is incompressible, the equation of continuity is

$$\frac{\partial u_i}{\partial x_i} = 0. \tag{2}$$

If μ and ρ are constant, equations (1) and (2) are linear. In particular, if (in addition) k is constant and X_i possesses a potential Ω so that

$$X_i = -\frac{\partial \Omega}{\partial x_i}, \tag{3}$$

then

$$\phi = \frac{k}{\mu}(p + \rho\Omega)$$

134   *Chia-Shun Yih*

is the potential for the velocity components and satisfies the Laplace equation, as can be seen from the three preceding equations. If ρ and μ are not constant, equations (1) are highly non-linear, and at first sight hopelessly complicated. The following development will show that the situation is actually not as hopeless as it appears to be.

For seepage flow with a macroscopic scale large compared with the dimension of the interstices, interstitial diffusion can be neglected† (Saffman 1959). Molecular diffusion can be neglected (Saffman 1960) if the Péclet number based on a macroscopic scale is large compared with 1. Thus in most practical cases diffusion can be neglected altogether, and for steady flows

$$u_\alpha \frac{\partial \mu}{\partial x_\alpha} = 0 \tag{4}$$

and

$$u_\alpha \frac{\partial \rho}{\partial x_\alpha} = 0. \tag{5}$$

In the absence of body forces, the effect of viscosity variation is simply and conclusively embodied in the transformation

$$u_i' = \frac{\mu}{\mu_0} u_i, \tag{6}$$

in which μ_0 is a reference viscosity and u_i' the velocity of an associated flow. To isolate the effect of viscosity variation, we shall assume ρ to be constant and the body force to be conservative. Equations (1) then become

$$\frac{\mu_0}{k} u_i' = -\frac{\partial}{\partial x_i}(p + \rho\Omega). \tag{7}$$

Furthermore, because of (4), equation (2) can be written

$$\frac{\partial u_i'}{\partial x_i} = 0. \tag{8}$$

Equations (7) and (8) are those governing the flow of a homogeneous fluid. Thus, by means of the transformation (6), the flow of a fluid of variable viscosity is related to that of a homogeneous fluid. In particular, if k is constant,

$$u_i' = -\frac{\partial \phi'}{\partial x_i}, \tag{9}$$

in which the potential

$$\phi' = \frac{k}{\mu_0}(p + \rho\Omega) \tag{10}$$

satisfies the Laplace equation

$$\nabla^2 \phi' = 0. \tag{11}$$

Consequently, if k and ρ are constant, the flow *pattern* is the same as that for a homogeneous fluid, provided the boundary conditions are unchanged.‡ The actual velocity u_i is obtained by means of (6) from the velocity u_i' of the irrotational flow

---

† The author owes this assurance to Dr P. G. Saffman.

‡ In this connexion, remember that the conditions at surfaces of density discontinuities are satisfied in the actual flow if they are satisfied in the associated flow (with density jumps).

Flow of a non-homogeneous fluid in a porous medium　　135

field determined by (11). Thus, in regions of constant u_i' (say $u_1' = U'$, $u_2' = u_3' = 0$), the actual speed u_1 is inversely proportional to the viscosity. This conclusion applies to regions of *horizontal* flow, even if ρ is not constant.

2. The equation governing steady two-dimensional flows of a non-homogeneous fluid

The effect of variation in specific weight (or of density in a gravitational field) will now be taken into account also. If (x, z) are used for (x_1, x_3), with z measured vertically upward, and (u, w) are used for (u_1, u_3), equations (1) can be written, for two-dimensional flows,

$$\frac{\mu}{k}u = -\frac{\partial p}{\partial x}, \quad \frac{\mu}{k}w = -\frac{\partial p}{\partial z} - g\rho, \tag{12}$$

or, with

$$(u', w') = \frac{\mu}{\mu_0}(u, w), \tag{13}$$

$$\frac{\mu_0}{k}u' = -\frac{\partial p}{\partial x}, \quad \frac{\mu_0}{k}w' = -\frac{\partial p}{\partial z} - g\rho. \tag{14}$$

The permeability k will be assumed constant in the subsequent development. If p is eliminated from equations (14), and, as a consequence of (5) and the steadiness of the motion, ρ is recognized to be a function of the stream function alone, the following equation is obtained:

$$\nabla^2\psi' = \frac{kg}{\mu_0}\frac{d\rho}{d\psi'}\frac{\partial\psi'}{\partial x}, \tag{15}$$

in which ψ' is the stream function (of Lagrange) for the velocity components u' and w':

$$u' = \frac{\partial\psi'}{\partial z}, \quad w' = -\frac{\partial\psi'}{\partial x}. \tag{16}$$

The quantity $d\rho/d\psi'$ is to be determined from the upstream condition.

3. The equation governing steady axisymmetric flows of a non-homogeneous fluid

For axisymmetric flows, the equations corresponding to (14) are, in cylindrical co-ordinates (with z measured vertically upward),

$$\frac{\mu_0}{k}u' = -\frac{\partial p}{\partial r}, \quad \frac{\mu_0}{k}w' = -\frac{\partial p}{\partial z} - g\rho, \tag{17}$$

in which u' and w' are again related to u and w by (13), except that now u is the radial and w the axial component of the velocity. The equation of continuity

$$\frac{\partial(ru)}{\partial r} + \frac{\partial(rw)}{\partial z} = 0 \tag{18}$$

can again be written as

$$\frac{\partial(ru')}{\partial r} + \frac{\partial(rw')}{\partial z} = 0, \tag{19}$$

because the substantial derivative of μ is zero. Equation (19) permits the use of Stokes's stream function ψ':

$$u' = -\frac{1}{r}\frac{\partial \psi'}{\partial z}, \quad w' = \frac{1}{r}\frac{\partial \psi'}{\partial r}. \tag{20}$$

Elimination of p from (17) by cross-differentiation and utilization of the fact that ρ is a function of ψ' alone produce the following equation governing steady axisymmetric flows:

$$-\left(\frac{\partial^2}{\partial r^2} - \frac{1}{r}\frac{\partial}{\partial r} + \frac{\partial^2}{\partial z^2}\right)\psi' = \frac{kgr}{\mu_0}\frac{dp}{d\psi'}\frac{\partial \psi'}{\partial r}, \tag{21}$$

in which $d\rho/d\psi'$ is to be determined from the upstream condition.

4. Exact solutions for two-dimensional flows

As a first example, the case of stratified seepage into a two-dimensional sink will be discussed. The fluid is assumed to be confined to the porous layer between two impermeable horizontal planes, one at $z = 0$ and the other at $z = d$. The sink is situated in the upper plane.

The point in the lower plane directly below the sink will be used as the origin for the co-ordinates (x, z) in the plane perpendicular to the direction of the length of the sink. Thus the co-ordinates for the trace of the sink in that plane are $(0, d)$. Since there is symmetry about the z-axis, only one half of the flow field need be considered. The flow at $x = -\infty$ is, as can be verified later, horizontal in direction. Hence (15) demands that, at $x = -\infty$,

$$\psi' = Cz \quad (C = \text{constant}),$$

where ψ' is taken to be zero at the lower boundary. If the upstream variation of μ with z is given, C is related to the actual discharge in a straightforward manner. With the dimensionless variables defined by

$$\xi = \frac{x}{d}, \quad \eta = \frac{z}{d}, \quad \Psi = \frac{\psi'}{Cd}, \quad \text{and} \quad B = -\frac{kg}{\mu_0 C}\frac{d\rho}{d\Psi}, \tag{22}$$

(15) becomes
$$\left(\frac{\partial^2}{\partial \xi^2} + \frac{\partial^2}{\partial \eta^2}\right)\Psi + B\frac{d\Psi}{d\xi} = 0. \tag{23}$$

The quantity B is in general a function of Ψ, to be determined from the upstream condition. But if ρ changes linearly with z far upstream, where the flow is parallel, it also changes linearly with Ψ and B is a constant. The constancy of B will be assumed in the examples given.

Equation (23) is to be solved with the boundary conditions

$$\Psi = 0 \quad \text{at} \quad \eta = 0 \quad \text{and} \quad \xi = 0 \quad (\eta < 1),$$
$$\Psi = 1 \quad \text{at} \quad \eta = 1,$$
$$\Psi = \eta \quad \text{at} \quad \xi = -\infty.$$

The solution, by the method of separation of variables, is

$$\Psi = \eta + \frac{2}{\pi}\sum_{n=1}^{\infty}\frac{(-1)^n}{n}\sin n\pi\eta \exp(\alpha\xi), \tag{24}$$

with
$$\alpha = \tfrac{1}{2}(-B + \sqrt{[B^2 + 4n^2\pi^2]}).$$

Flow of a non-homogeneous fluid in a porous medium — 137

The flow pattern for $B = 0$ is an irrotational flow pattern, familiar in hydro-dynamics, and will not be shown here. Those for $B = \pi$, 2π and 4π are shown in figures 1–3 respectively. The flow condition at $x = -\infty$ is entirely the same for

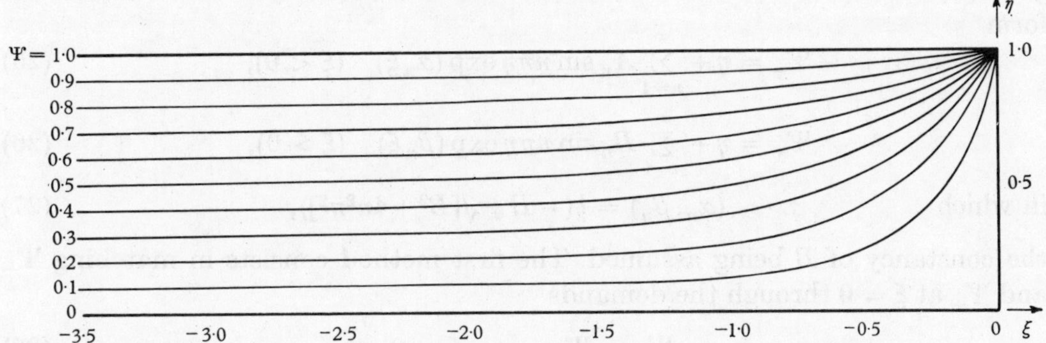

FIGURE 1. Two-dimensional flow of a stratified fluid in a porous medium into a sink, $B = \pi$.

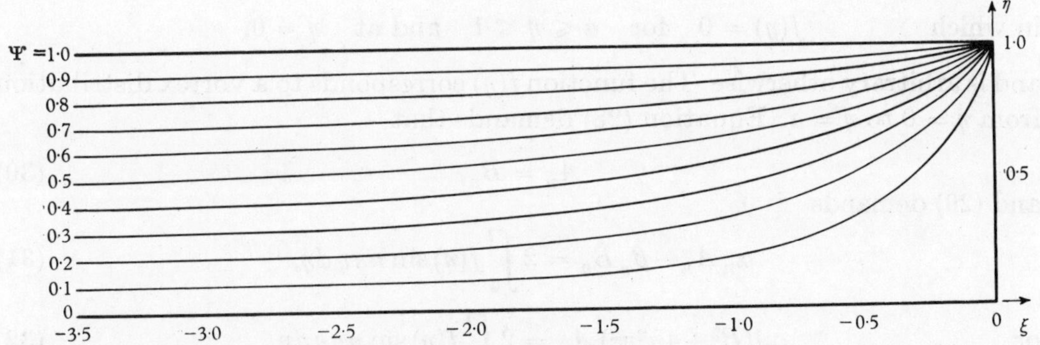

FIGURE 2. Two-dimensional flow of a stratified fluid in a porous medium into a sink, $B = 2\pi$.

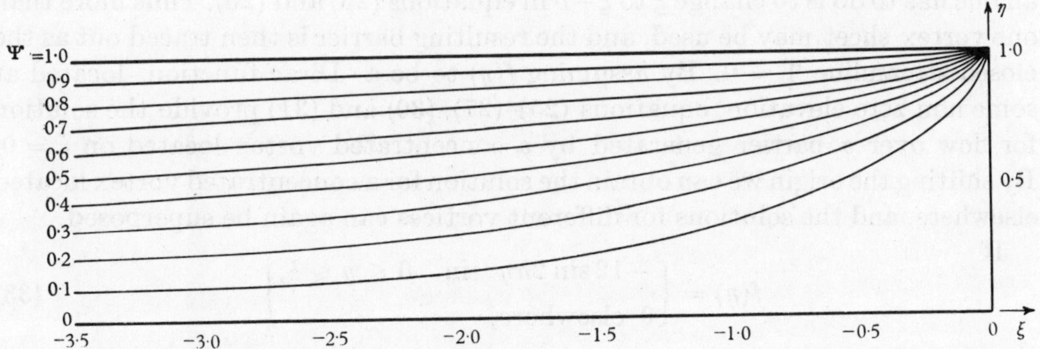

FIGURE 3. Two-dimensional flow of a stratified fluid in a porous medium into a sink, $B = 4\pi$.

any value of B (or of density variation), but the patterns show a concentration of streamlines near $\eta = 1$ for greater and greater values of B. The solution (24) and the corresponding one for axisymmetric flow may be useful for deciding whether the practice in the oil industry of forcing oil up for pumping by injecting water into the ground is an economical one.

 Chia-Shun Yih

For flows, confined between two impermeable planes $z = 0$ and $z = d$, from left to right past an impermeable barrier protruding from the lower plane (say), inverse methods can be advantageously used. Two inverse methods will now be given, which can be combined if desired. For either method the solution is of the form

$$\Psi_- = \eta + \sum_{n=1}^{\infty} A_n \sin n\pi\eta \exp(\alpha_n \xi) \quad (\xi < 0), \tag{25}$$

$$\Psi_+ = \eta + \sum_{n=1}^{\infty} B_n \sin n\pi\eta \exp(\beta_n \xi) \quad (\xi > 0), \tag{26}$$

in which
$$(\alpha_n, \beta_n) = \tfrac{1}{2}(-B \pm \sqrt{[B^2 + 4n^2\pi^2]}), \tag{27}$$

the constancy of B being assumed. The first method consists in matching Ψ_- and Ψ_+ at $\xi = 0$ through the demands

$$\Psi_- = \Psi_+ \quad \text{at} \quad \xi = 0, \tag{28}$$

$$\frac{\partial \Psi_-}{\partial \xi} - \frac{\partial \Psi_+}{\partial \xi} = f(\eta) \quad \text{at} \quad \xi = 0, \tag{29}$$

in which
$$f(\eta) = 0 \quad \text{for} \quad a \leqslant \eta \leqslant 1 \quad \text{and at} \quad \eta = 0,$$

and is arbitrary otherwise. The function $f(\eta)$ corresponds to a vortex distribution from $\eta = 0$ to $\eta = a$. Equation (28) demands that

$$A_n = B_n, \tag{30}$$

and (29) demands

$$\alpha_n A_n - \beta_n B_n = 2 \int_0^1 f(\eta) \sin n\pi\eta \, d\eta, \tag{31}$$

or
$$\sqrt{(B^2 + 4n^2\pi^2)} \, A_n = 2 \int_0^1 f(\eta) \sin n\pi\eta \, d\eta. \tag{32}$$

The vortex sheet does not have to be located at $\xi = 0$. If it is located at $\xi = b$, all one has to do is to change ξ to $\xi - b$ in equations (25) and (26). Thus more than one vortex sheet may be used, and the resulting barrier is then traced out as the closed streamline $\Psi = 0$. By assuming $f(\eta)$ to be a 'Dirac function' located at some non-zero elevation, equations (25)–(27), (30) and (31) provide the solution for flow over a barrier generated by a concentrated vortex located on $\xi = 0$. By shifting the origin we can obtain the solution for a concentrated vortex located elsewhere, and the solutions for different vortices can again be superposed.

If
$$f(\eta) = \begin{cases} -12 \sin 2\pi\eta & \text{in} \quad 0 \leqslant \eta \leqslant \tfrac{1}{2}, \\ 0 \text{ elsewhere,} \end{cases} \tag{33}$$

then
$$I_n \equiv 2 \int_0^1 f(\eta) \sin n\pi\eta \, d\eta = \begin{cases} 0 & \text{if} \quad n \text{ is even but} \neq 2, \\ -6 & \text{if} \quad n = 2, \\ \dfrac{48}{(n^2 - 4)\pi}(-1)^{\frac{1}{2}(n-1)} & \text{if } n \text{ is odd.} \end{cases} \tag{34}$$

The flow patterns for this choice of $f(n)$ are shown in figures 4 and 5, for $B = \pi$ and 2π respectively. From (25) and (26) it can be seen that the flow pattern is always unsymmetric about $\xi = 0$, even if the barrier itself is symmetric.

Flow of a non-homogeneous fluid in a porous medium 139

The second method consists in matching Ψ_- and Ψ_+ at $\xi = 0$ by demanding

$$\frac{\partial \Psi_-}{\partial \xi} - \frac{\partial \Psi_+}{\partial \xi} = 0 \quad \text{at} \quad \xi = 0, \tag{35}$$

$$\Psi_- - \Psi_+ = f(\eta) \quad \text{at} \quad \xi = 0, \tag{36}$$

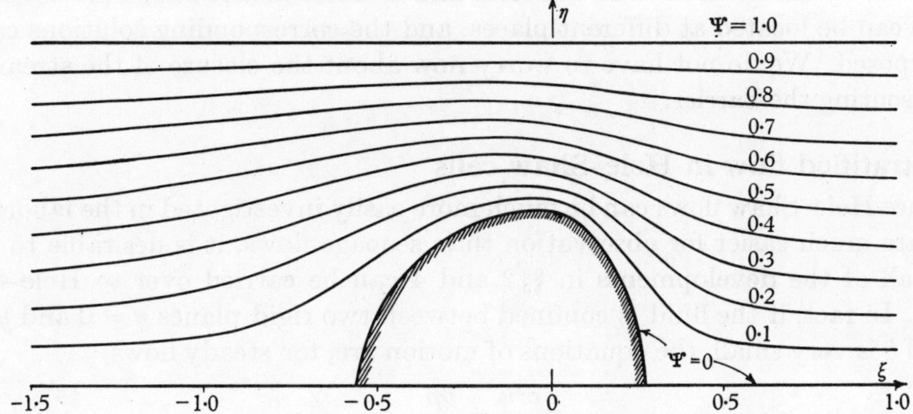

FIGURE 4. Two-dimensional flow of a stratified fluid in a porous medium over a barrier, $B = \pi$.

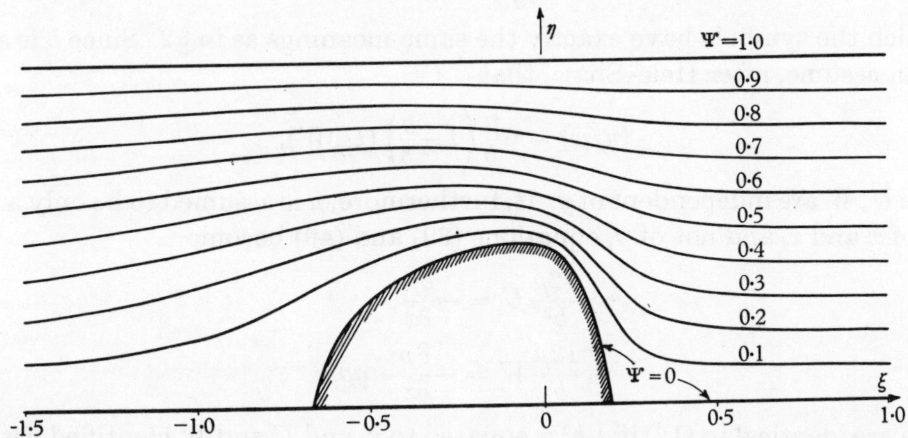

FIGURE 5. Two-dimensional flow of a stratified fluid in a porous medium over a barrier, $B = 2\pi$.

in which $f(\eta)$ is defined as in (29). The function $f(\eta)$ now corresponds to a source distribution. Equation (35) demands

$$\alpha_n A_n - \beta_n B_n = 0, \tag{37}$$

and (36) demands

$$\left(1 - \frac{\alpha_n}{\beta_n}\right) A_n = \left(2 + \frac{B}{n^2\pi^2}\beta_n\right) A_n = 2 \int_0^1 f(\eta) \sin n\pi\eta \, d\eta. \tag{38}$$

Again, the source distribution may be shifted to $\xi = b$. In that case the solution is given by equations (25)–(27), (37) and (38), with ξ changed to $\xi - b$. Solutions corresponding to concentrated sources located anywhere above $\eta = 0$ can be obtained by assuming $f(\eta)$ to be a 'Dirac function', and these can be superposed on those for source distributions to obtain a solution representing a flow over a barrier which is nearly the same in form as a prescribed one. In order that a closed

 Chia-Shun Yih

barrier be obtained, however, the total algebraic sum of the sources must be zero. In fact, from the solution corresponding to a concentrated source we can obtain that for a concentrated doublet, by differentiation of (25) and (26) with respect to ξ. The solution corresponding to a doublet distribution can then be obtained by integration. The doublets and doublet distributions (over vertical lines) can be located at different places, and the corresponding solutions can be superposed. We do not have to worry now about the closure of the streamline representing the barrier.

5. Stratified flow in Hele–Shaw cells

Since Hele–Shaw flows can be much more easily investigated in the laboratory and are much easier for observation than seepage flows, it is desirable to show that all of the developments in §§ 2 and 4 can be carried over to Hele–Shaw flows. In fact, if the fluid is confined between two rigid planes $y = 0$ and $y = b$, and if b is very small, the equations of motion are, for steady flows,

$$\mu \frac{\partial^2 u}{\partial y^2} = \frac{\partial p}{\partial x}, \tag{39}$$

$$\mu \frac{\partial^2 w}{\partial y^2} = \frac{\partial p}{\partial z} + g\rho, \tag{40}$$

in which the symbols have exactly the same meanings as in § 2. Since b is small, we can assume, after Hele–Shaw, that

$$(u, w) = 6 \frac{y}{b} \left(1 - \frac{y}{b} \right) (U, W),$$

where U, W are independent of y. If, furthermore, μ is assumed to be only a function of x and z, and not of y, equations (39) and (40) become

$$\frac{12\mu}{b^2} U = -\frac{\partial p}{\partial x}, \tag{41}$$

$$\frac{12\mu}{b^2} W = -\frac{\partial p}{\partial z} - g\rho, \tag{42}$$

which are identical to (12) if $\frac{1}{12}b^2$ is equated to k, and U and W identified with the u and w in (12). Since μ and ρ again do not change on a streamline in the x–z-plane, an equation identical to (15) can again be obtained, and all of the developments in § 4 can be carried over.

This work has been done at the University of Cambridge during the tenure of a Senior Post-doctoral Fellowship granted by the National Science Foundation. It is also a pleasure to acknowledge here the support of fundamental research in stratified flows by the Office of Ordnance Research in the past several years. The assistance of Mr Chintu Lai (supported by O.O.R.) in the production of the figures is much appreciated.

REFERENCES

SAFFMAN, P. G. 1959 A theory of dispersion in a porous medium. *J. Fluid Mech.* **6**, 321–49.

SAFFMAN, P. G. 1960 Dispersion due to molecular diffusion and macroscopic mixing in flow through a network of capillaries. *J. Fluid Mech.* **7**, 194–208.

Prevention of stagnation zones in flows of a stratified or a rotating fluid.

Chia-Shun Yih
W. O'Dell
W. R. Debler
The University of Michigan

1. Introduction

The solution for two-dimensional flow of a non-homogeneous inviscid fluid into a sink situated in a channel was given in 1958 at the preceding Congress by Yih [1]. Yih's solution is valid only for values of the modified Froude number F greater than $1/\pi$. Although formal solutions of the governing equation can be found for F less than $1/\pi$, which are characterized by upstream waves, the flow patterns (See Yih [2]) given by these solutions cannot be observed for $F < 1/\pi$, as shown by Debler's experiments [3], which indicated a zone of stagnant fluid when the Froude number is below 0.24 approximately. Two questions then present themselves. First, what is the proper mathematical solution of the problem for $F < 1/\pi$? Second, what can one do to prevent stagnation zones from forming in the fluid when F is less than 0.24? The answer to the first question turns out to be very difficult, and will be presented in a separate paper elsewhere. The second question will be answered in this paper.

The similar problem of axisymmetric flow of a swirling inviscid fluid into a sink situated in a cylinder was solved in 1956 by Long [4] for Rossby numbers greater than $1/\lambda_1$ (equal to 0.261) in which λ_1 is the first non-zero root of $J_1(\lambda) = 0$. For Rossby numbers less than that, formal solutions characterized by upstream waves can again be found. Experiments done by Long [4] and at The University of Michigan indicate that no upstream waves occur at low Rossby numbers, and that elongated

separation zones are formed. Thus, again, two questions present themselves: what is the proper solution for Rossby numbers less than 0.261 and what can one do to eliminate the separation zones (due to rotation of the fluid) at low Rossby numbers? Again, the answer to the first question will be presented in a later paper elsewhere, and only the second question will be answered in this paper.

For both problems, the prevention of separation zones is achieved by a structure near the sink, the form of which is obtained by making the mathematical singularity at the sink more complex in nature. With this idea, the first author carried out the entire analysis for the two problems. The rather extensive numerical calculation leading to the flow patterns and the figures depicting them are the work of the second author. The theoretical part of this paper was completed before the summer of 1959, but was not submitted for publication because the first two authors wished to have some supporting experimental evidence to go with their analytical work. The elaborate experiments were undertaken by the third author in 1961, and finished just before Christmas of that year.

2. Steady Flows of a Stratified Fluid Into a Sink

Steady two-dimensional flows of an incompressible and inviscid fluid of variable density are considered. The equation of incompressibility is

$$\frac{D\rho}{dt} \equiv \left(u \frac{\partial}{\partial x} + v \frac{\partial}{\partial y} \right) \rho = 0 \qquad (1)$$

Reprinted from *Proc. Fourth U. S. Natl. Congr. Appl. Mech.* (1962) 1441–1453.

in which t is the time, x and y are Cartesian coordinates, ρ is the density, and u and v are the velocity components in the directions of x and y. Equation (1) enables one to write the equation of continuity in the form

$$\frac{\partial u}{\partial x} + \frac{\partial v}{\partial y} = 0 , \tag{2}$$

or in the form

$$\frac{\partial u'}{\partial x} + \frac{\partial \dot{v}}{\partial y} = 0 , \tag{3}$$

in which

$$(u', v') = (\rho/\rho_0)^{\frac{1}{2}} (u, v). \tag{4}$$

If the direction of y is vertically upward, and p is the pressure, the equations of motion are

$$\rho \frac{D}{Dt}(u, v) = -\left(\frac{\partial}{\partial x}, \frac{\partial}{\partial y}\right) p + (0, -\rho g), \tag{5}$$

in which g is the gravitational acceleration. Equation (1) allows (5) to be written in the form

$$\rho_0 \left(u' \frac{\partial}{\partial x} + v' \frac{\partial}{\partial y}\right)(u', v') = -\left(\frac{\partial}{\partial x}, \frac{\partial}{\partial y}\right) p + (0, -\rho g) \tag{6}$$

and (3) permits the use of the stream function ψ':

$$u' = \frac{\partial \psi'}{\partial y} , \quad v' = -\frac{\partial \psi'}{\partial x} . \tag{7}$$

The modified stream function ψ' is connected with the ordinary stream function ψ by

$$\psi' = \int (\rho/\rho_0)^{\frac{1}{2}} d\psi . \tag{8}$$

If

$$q'^2 = u'^2 + v'^2 = (\rho/\rho_0)(u^2 + v^2)$$

and a modified vorticity is defined by

$$\omega' = \frac{\partial v'}{\partial x} - \frac{\partial u'}{\partial y} = -\nabla^2 \psi' , \tag{9}$$

the equations of motion can be written

$$\rho_0 \omega' \frac{\partial \psi'}{\partial x} = \frac{\partial}{\partial x}\left(p + \frac{q'^2}{2}\right) , \tag{10}$$

$$\rho_0 \omega' \frac{\partial \psi'}{\partial y} = \frac{\partial}{\partial y}\left(p + \frac{q'^2}{2}\right) + g\rho . \tag{11}$$

By multiplication of these two equations by dx and dy, respectively, and addition, the result is obtained:

$$\rho_0 \omega' d\psi' = d\left(p + \frac{q'^2}{2}\right) + g\rho \, dy = dH - g y \, d\rho , \tag{12}$$

in which

$$H = p + \frac{\rho(u^2 + v^2)}{2} + g\rho y$$

is the Bernoulli quantity, and is a function of ψ alone. Since the flow is steady and the fluid is incompressible, ρ is also a function of ψ, therefore of ψ' alone. Hence H is a function of ψ' alone. Equation (12) can then be written (See Yih [5])

$$\rho_0 \nabla^2 \psi' + g y \frac{d\rho}{d\psi'} = \frac{dH}{d\psi'} = H'(\psi') . \tag{13}$$

This equation is a modified form of Long's equation [1] (See Long [6])

$$\nabla^2 \psi + \frac{1}{\rho}\frac{d\rho}{d\psi}\left(\frac{u^2 + v^2}{2} + gy\right) = f(\psi) ,$$

but is in a much more convenient form.

Consider now a closed canal of depth d terminating at a gate which is not fully closed, so that the slit it leaves serves as a horizontal line sink (See Figs. 1 to 3). The density variation far upstream is assumed to follow the linear law

$$\rho = \rho_0 (1 - \beta y) , \quad \beta = (\rho_0 - \rho_1)/\rho_0 d , \tag{14}$$

ρ_1 and ρ_0 being the density at the top and at the bottom of the canal, respectively. With the trace of the line sink as the origin, x is measured horizontally to the right, and y vertically upward. If the fluid is assumed to issue horizontally from a large reservoir, far upstream in the canal one has

$$\frac{d}{dy}\left(\sqrt{\frac{\rho}{\rho_0}}\, U\right) = 0 ,$$

because the modified velocity is zero in the reservoir, and its vanishing persists as long as the flow is horizontal [1]. The symbol U is used to denote u far upstream. Thus

$$\frac{\rho U^2}{\rho_0} = \text{constant} = A^2 \text{ (say)},$$

or, if ψ_0' denotes the modified stream function ψ' far upstream,

$$\psi_0' = Ay. \tag{15}$$

Substitution of (15) into (13) yields

$$H'(\psi') = -\frac{\rho_0 g \beta}{A^2} \psi' \tag{16}$$

and

$$\nabla^2 \psi' + \frac{g\beta}{A^2}\psi' = \frac{g\beta}{A} y . \tag{17}$$

With the transformations

$$\Psi = \frac{\psi'}{Ad}, \quad \xi = \frac{x}{d}, \quad \eta = \frac{y}{d} , \tag{18}$$

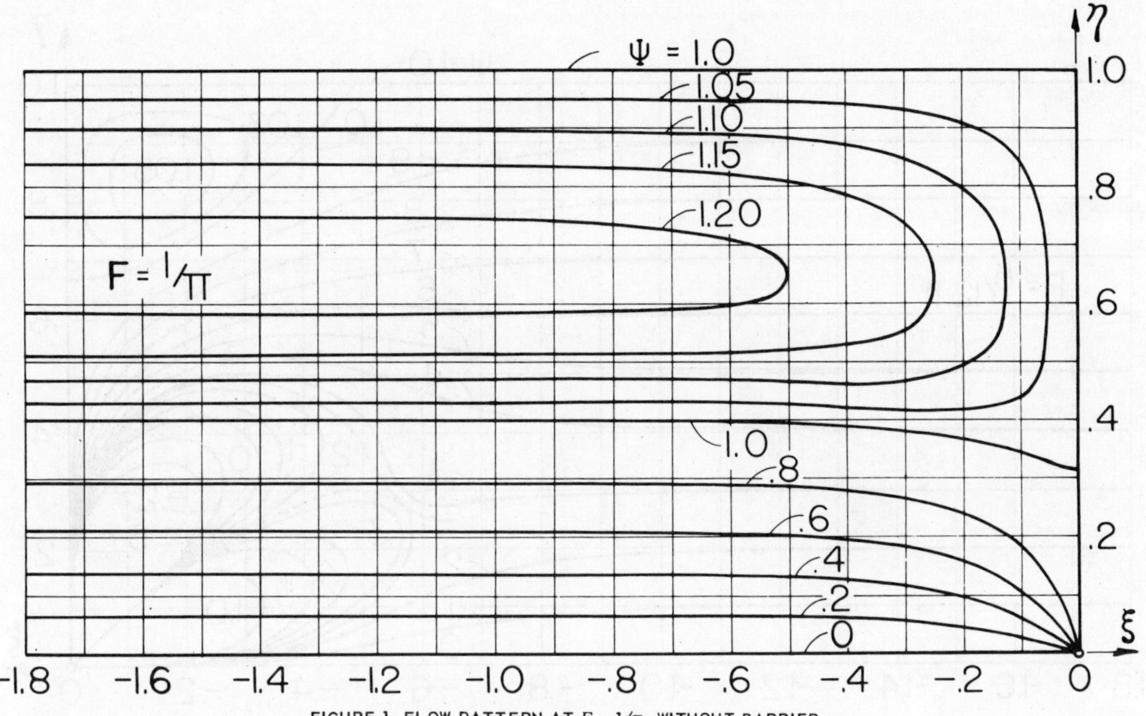

FIGURE 1. FLOW PATTERN AT $F = 1/\pi$, WITHOUT BARRIER.

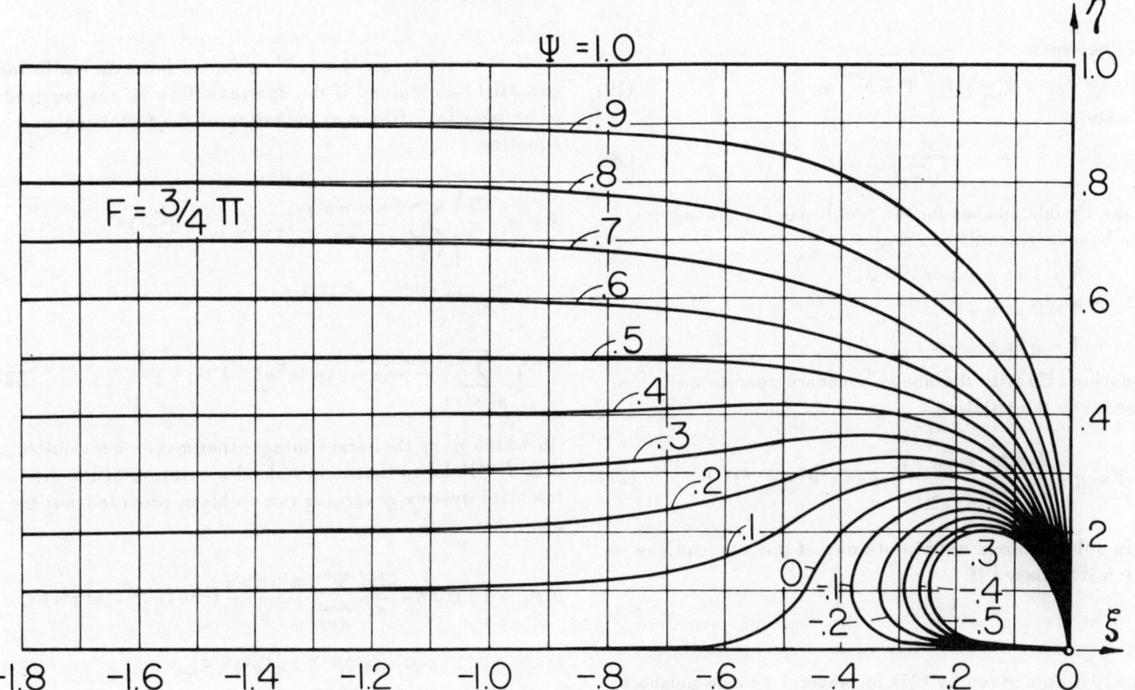

FIGURE 2. FLOW PATTERN AT $F = 3/4\pi$, WITH BARRIER.

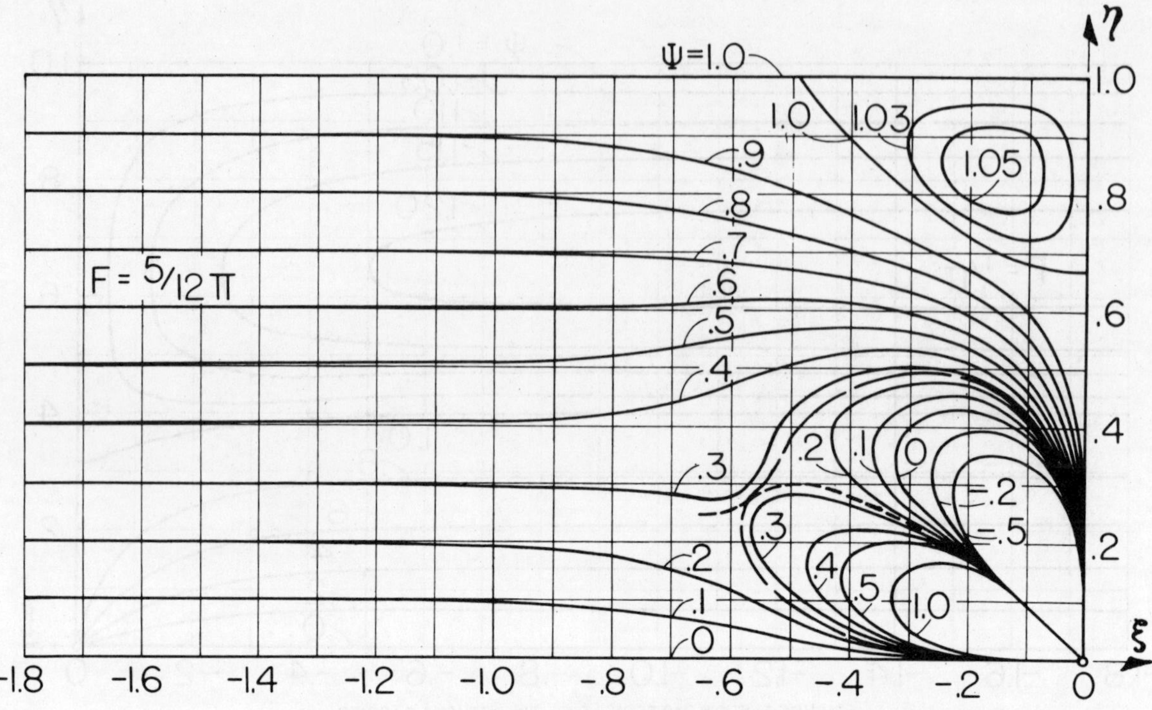

FIGURE 3. FLOW PATTERN AT $F = 5/12\pi$, WITH BARRIER.

(17) becomes

$$\Psi_{\xi\xi} + \Psi_{\eta\eta} + F^{-2}\Psi = F^{-2}\eta \tag{19}$$

in which

$$F = \frac{A}{d\sqrt{g\beta}} \tag{20}$$

is the Froude number for the problem under discussion. The boundary conditions are:

$$\Psi = 1 \text{ at } \eta = 1 \text{ or } \xi = 0,$$
$$\Psi = 0 \text{ at } \eta = 0,$$
$$\Psi = \eta \text{ at } \xi = -\infty.$$

Equation (19) with the above boundary conditions possesses the solution

$$\Psi = \eta + \frac{2}{\pi} \sum_{n=1}^{\infty} \frac{\sin n\pi\eta}{n} \exp (n^2\pi^2 - F^{-2})^{\frac{1}{2}} \xi. \tag{21}$$

This solution does not violate any of the assumptions on which it is based if

$$F > \frac{1}{\pi}.$$

Flow patterns given by (21) for several Froude numbers between ∞ and 0.32 are shown in a previous paper by Yih [1].

If F is not larger than π^{-1}, a formal but exact solution can still be obtained if the upstream flow is not required to be parallel. Close examination of the following equation

$$\Psi = \eta + \frac{2}{\pi}\left\{\sum_{n=1}^{n'} \frac{\sin n\pi\eta}{n} \left[\cos (F^{-2} - n^2\pi^2)^{\frac{1}{2}} \xi\right.\right.$$
$$\left. + B_n \sin (F^{-2} - n^2\pi^2)^{\frac{1}{2}} \xi\right]$$
$$\left. + \sum_{n=n'+1}^{\infty} \frac{\sin n\pi\eta}{n} \exp (n^2\pi^2 - F^{-2})^{\frac{1}{2}} \xi\right\} \tag{22}$$

(in which n' is the larger integer that makes $n\pi$ smaller than F^{-1}) shows that it is indeed a solution of the differential system governing the problem, provided that far upstream

$$\rho/\rho_0 = 1 - \beta d\eta - \frac{2\beta d}{\pi} \sum_{n=1}^{n'} \frac{\sin n\pi\eta}{n} \left[\cos (F^{-2} - n^2\pi^2)^{\frac{1}{2}} \xi\right.$$
$$\left. + B_n \sin (F^{-2} - n^2\pi^2)^{\frac{1}{2}} \xi\right]. \tag{23}$$

The quantity $d\rho/d\psi'$ is still equal to $-\rho_0\beta/A$ even though neither ρ nor ψ' varies linearly with y at $\xi = -\infty$ any more. The terms involving B_n in (22) and (23) correspond to "free oscillations" in wave motion and can and will be annulled without affecting the satisfaction of the differential system in any way. Figure 1 shows the flow pattern at $F = 1/\pi$. For F less than $1/\pi$, upstream waves are predicted by (22). (For the upstream flow pattern at $F = 3/4\pi$, see Yih [2].) However, Debler's experiments showed that for low Froude numbers there are no upstream waves or return flow to infinity. Instead, an essentially stagnation region (see plate) occurs on top. (Such a region would occur at the bottom at low Froude numbers if the sink were situated on top.) Therefore a proper solution of the problem for small F must allow the possibility for a vortex sheet to occur. Such a solution is not yet available. In this paper, a different question is asked: What can be done near the sink to force the flow to satisfy (15) upstream at small Froude numbers? The answer to this question is now provided.

Consider the case in which

$$\frac{1}{2\pi} < F < \frac{1}{\pi}.$$

If the opening of the sink is denoted by ϵ and if

$$k\epsilon = \pi,$$

the value of Ψ at $\xi = 0$ can be specified as follows:

$$\left.\begin{array}{ll} \Psi = 1 & \text{at } \xi = 0 \text{ for } \epsilon \leq \eta \leq 1, \\[2mm] \Psi = 1 - \dfrac{k^2}{\pi^3} \sin k\eta & \text{at } \xi = 0 \text{ for } 0 < \eta \leq \epsilon, \\[2mm] \Psi = 0 & \text{at } \xi = 0 \text{ and } \eta = 0. \end{array}\right\} \quad (24)$$

Since

$$\lim_{\epsilon \to 0} \int_0^\epsilon k^2 \sin k\eta \sin n\pi\eta \, d\eta = n\pi^2,$$

the solution for the limiting case (as $\epsilon \to 0$) with the new boundary conditions is

$$\Psi = \eta - \frac{2}{\pi} \sum_{n=1}^{\infty} \left(n - \frac{1}{n}\right) \sin n\pi\eta \exp(n^2\pi^2 - F^2)^{\frac{1}{2}} \xi, \quad (25)$$

which is free from the upstream waves predicted by (22). Although (25) is not convergent for ξ equal to zero, it is uniformly convergent in η for η between 0 and 1, for ξ equal to any negative number however small in magnitude, and the value of Ψ for $\xi = 0$ and $\eta > 0$ can be taken to be the limiting value of Ψ as given by (25), as ξ approaches zero. That the limit exists can be seen from Fig. 2, for $F = 3/4\pi$, in which the flow pattern is shown. If a bottom is built along the streamline $\Psi = 0$, the stratified fluid above will be forced to come down and the upstream condition (15) maintained. This result may have some engineering application if separation of part of a stratified

fluid from the rest at low rates of flow is to be prevented.

If the Froude number is lower than the next critical value $1/2\pi$, the singularity at the sink must be further modified to have a uniform velocity u' upstream. For

$$\frac{1}{3\pi} < F < \frac{1}{2\pi}, \quad k\epsilon = \pi,$$

the appropriate specification for ψ at $\xi = 0$ is the same as given by (24), except that

$$\Psi = 1 - Ak^2 \sin k\eta - Bk^4 (\sin k\eta + 2\sin 2k\eta)$$
$$\text{for } 0 < \eta \leq \epsilon.$$

The combination $(\sin k\eta + 2\sin 2k\eta)$ is necessary, for otherwise the two terms in (22) corresponding to upstream waves could not be eliminated. Since

$$\lim_{\epsilon \to 0} \int_0^\epsilon k^4 (\sin k\eta + 2k^2 \sin 2k\eta) \, d\eta = \frac{3n^3\pi^4}{4},$$

elimination of the said two terms requires that

$$2\left(n\pi^2 A + \frac{3n^3\pi^4}{4} B\right) = \frac{2}{n\pi} \text{ for } n = 1 \text{ and } 2.$$

Thus

$$A = \frac{5}{4\pi^3}, \quad B = -\frac{1}{3\pi^5}$$

and

$$\Psi = \eta - \frac{2}{\pi} \sum_{n=1}^{\infty} \left(\frac{5n}{4} - \frac{n^3}{4} - \frac{1}{n}\right) \sin n\pi\eta \exp\left(n^2\pi^2 - \frac{1}{F^2}\right)^{\frac{1}{2}} \xi,$$

concerning the convergence of which a remark similar to that on the convergence of (25) can be made. In Fig. 3, the flow pattern for $F = 5/12\pi$ is shown. The necessary bottom structure for uniform u' at infinity is provided now by the (long dashes) streamline $\Psi = 0.28$ (approximately). It is interesting to see that since now the barrier has to be very high to force the upper fluid to come down, a passage must be opened for the lower fluid, which cannot be expected to climb over the high hurdle.

3. Steady Flow of a Rotating Fluid Into a Point Sink

The equation governing steady motions of an inviscid rotating fluid has been derived by Long [5] on the assumption that far upstream the fluid is in solid-body rotation and is at the same time streaming longitudinally with a uniform velocity. Long's equation can be generalized by removing this assumption. The modification is simple. But since it is not convenient to present this modification without reproducing Long's original development, it is desirable to derive the more general equation *ab initio*.

In cylindrical co-ordinates (r, θ, z), the equations of motion for axisymmetric motion are

$$\frac{Du}{Dt} - \frac{v^2}{r} = -\frac{\partial}{\partial r}\left(\frac{p}{\rho} + \chi\right) , \qquad (26)$$

$$\frac{Dv}{Dt} + \frac{uv}{r} = 0 , \qquad (27)$$

$$\frac{Dw}{Dt} = -\frac{\partial}{\partial z}\left(\frac{p}{\rho} + \chi\right) , \qquad (28)$$

in which

$$\frac{D}{Dt} \equiv \frac{\partial}{\partial t} + u\frac{\partial}{\partial r} + w\frac{\partial}{\partial z} ,$$

(u, v, w) are the velocity components in the directions of (r, θ, z), respectively, and χ is the body-force potential. The equation continuity

$$\frac{\partial(ru)}{\partial r} + \frac{\partial(rw)}{\partial z} = 0 \qquad (29)$$

permits the use of Stokes' stream function ψ:

$$u = -\frac{1}{r}\frac{\partial\psi}{\partial z} , \quad w = \frac{1}{r}\frac{\partial\psi}{\partial r} . \qquad (30)$$

Equation (27) can be written as

$$\frac{D}{Dt}(vr) = 0 , \qquad (31)$$

which is true even for unsteady flow. For steady flows, pathlines are streamlines, and (31) can be written in the form

$$(vr)^2 = f(\psi) . \qquad (32)$$

For steady flows (26) and (28) become

$$w\left(\frac{\partial u}{\partial z} - \frac{\partial w}{\partial r}\right) - \frac{f(\psi)}{r^3} = -\frac{\partial}{\partial r}\left(\frac{p}{\rho} + \frac{u^2 + w^2}{2} + \chi\right) , \qquad (33)$$

$$u\left(\frac{\partial w}{\partial r} - \frac{\partial u}{\partial z}\right) = -\frac{\partial}{\partial z}\left(\frac{p}{\rho} + \frac{u^2 + w^2}{2} + \chi\right) . \qquad (34)$$

By cross differentiation and use of the continuity equation one obtains

$$\frac{D}{Dt}\frac{\zeta}{r} + \frac{1}{r^4}\frac{\partial f(\psi)}{\partial z} = 0 , \qquad (35)$$

in which

$$\zeta = \frac{\partial w}{\partial r} - \frac{\partial u}{\partial z} = \frac{1}{r}\left(\frac{\partial^2}{\partial r^2} - \frac{1}{r}\frac{\partial}{\partial r} + \frac{\partial^2}{\partial z^2}\right)\psi . \qquad (36)$$

But (35) can be written in the form

$$\frac{D}{Dt}\frac{\zeta}{r} - u\frac{f'(\psi)}{r^3} = \frac{D}{Dt}\left(\frac{\zeta}{r} + \frac{f'(\psi)}{2r^2}\right) = 0 , \qquad (37)$$

which yields

$$\left(\frac{\partial^2}{\partial r^2} - \frac{1}{r}\frac{\partial}{\partial r} + \frac{\partial^2}{\partial z^2}\right)\psi + \frac{f'(\psi)}{2} = r^2 h(\psi) . \qquad (38)$$

This is the generalized equation of Long. If (with Ω as the uniform angular speed and $-W$ as the velocity at infinity)

$$v = \Omega r , \quad \psi = -\frac{Wr^2}{2} \qquad (39)$$

at infinity, one has

$$f(\psi) = \Omega^2 r^4 = \frac{4\Omega^2}{W^2}\psi^2 , \text{ and } h(\psi) = -\frac{2\Omega^2}{W} , \qquad (40)$$

so that (38) becomes

$$\left(\frac{\partial^2}{\partial r^2} - \frac{1}{r}\frac{\partial}{\partial r} + \frac{\partial^2}{\partial z^2}\right)\psi + \frac{4\Omega^2}{W^2}\psi = -\frac{2\Omega^2}{W}r^2 , \qquad (41)$$

which is Long's equation. Long [7, p. 200] gave the general solution of (41), which however violates equations (39). In fact, in a later paper [4] Long published a solution for the flow of a rotating fluid into a sink, but did not attempt to use his general solution for small Rossby numbers, at which (39) would be violated.

Are (39) really necessary if one is concerned only with constructing solutions of the equations of motion? Take the case of the flow of a rotating fluid along a circular cylinder of radius b into a point sink situated at the center of a plate normal to the cylinder wall. With the origin at the sink, Long's solution [4] is

$$\psi = -\frac{Wr^2}{2} + r\sum_{n=1}^{\infty} A_n \exp\left[-(\lambda_n^2 - Ro^{-2})^{\frac{1}{2}}\left(\frac{z}{b}\right)\right]$$
$$\cdot J_1\left(\lambda_n\frac{r}{b}\right) , \qquad (42)$$

in which

$$Ro \text{ (Rossby number)} = \frac{W}{2\Omega b} , \qquad (43)$$

λ_n is the n-th zero of $J_1(\lambda)$, and

$$A_n = -\frac{Wb}{\lambda_n J_0^2(\lambda_n)} .$$

If Ro is greater than $1/\lambda_1$ (0.261), Long's solution does not violate (39). As soon as Ro is equal or less than 0.261, his solution ceases to be valid unless the conditions imposed by (39) are removed. If one relaxes the understanding of the quantities Ω and W, and re-defines them to be

Ωb = rotation speed at wall at z = infinity,

$\pi W b^2$ = discharge through the cylinder into the sink,

and if one assumes

$$(v\,r)^2 = f(\psi) = \frac{4\Omega^2}{W^2}\,\psi^2\ ,$$

then for any Rossby number one has as a general solution

$$\psi = -\frac{Wr^2}{2} + r\left\{\sum_{n=1}^{n_1} A_n \cos\left[(Ro^{-2}-\lambda_n^2)^{\frac{1}{2}}\left(\frac{z}{b}\right)\right] J_1\left(\lambda_n\frac{r}{b}\right)\right.$$
$$\left. + \sum_{n=n_1+1}^{\infty} A_n \exp\left[-(\lambda_n^2 - Ro^{-2})^{\frac{1}{2}}\left(\frac{z}{b}\right)\right] J_1\left(\lambda_n\frac{r}{b}\right)\right\},\ (46)$$

in which n_1 is the last integer that makes Ro less than $1/\lambda_n$. The velocity component v can simply be calculated from (45). The upstream waves corresponding to terms containing sines have again been suppressed without affecting the satisfaction of the differential system governing the problem.

But the solution given by (46) is a purely formal one only. Experiments done by Long [4,7] and at The University of Michigan in the summer of 1959 indicate that upstream waves do not occur. The solution only serves the useful purpose of suggesting the modification of boundary geometry near the sink that is necessary to prevent stagnation zones at small Rossby numbers. Consider, for instance, the case

$$\frac{1}{\lambda_2} < Ro < \frac{1}{\lambda_1}\quad.$$

With reference to Fig. 4, the following new boundary conditions at $z = 0$ can be imposed:

$$\psi = -\frac{Wb^2}{2}\ \text{for}\ \epsilon \leq r \leq b,$$
$$\psi = -\frac{Wb^2}{2} - \frac{Wb}{\lambda_1^4 J_0(\lambda_1)}\,k^3 r J_1\left(\frac{kr}{b}\right)\text{for}\ 0 < r \leq \epsilon,\ \Bigg\}\ (47)$$
$$\psi = 0\quad\text{for}\ r = 0$$

in which

$$\frac{k\epsilon}{b} = \lambda_1 = 3.8317\ ,$$

and ϵ will be made to approach zero. Since

$$\lim_{\epsilon\to 0}\int_0^{\epsilon} k^3 r J_1\left(\frac{kr}{b}\right) J_1\left(\frac{\lambda_n r}{b}\right) dr = -\frac{\lambda_1^2 \lambda_n J_0(\lambda_1)}{2}$$

and

$$\int_0^b r J_1^2\left(\lambda_n\frac{r}{b}\right) dr = \frac{J_0^2(\lambda_n)}{2}\ ,$$

the Fourier-Bessel expansion of the term involving k in (47) is

$$-\frac{Wb}{\lambda_1^4 J_0(\lambda_1)}\,k^3 r J_1\left(\frac{kr}{b}\right) = \frac{Wb}{\lambda_1^2}\sum_{n=1}^{\infty}\frac{\lambda_n}{J_0^2(\lambda_n)} J_1\left(\frac{\lambda_n r}{b}\right)$$
$$= \sum_{n=1}^{\infty} -\frac{\lambda_n^2}{\lambda_1^2} A_n J_1\left(\frac{\lambda_n r}{b}\right)\ .\qquad (48)$$

Thus the solution is

$$\psi = -\frac{Wr^2}{2} + r\sum_{n=2}^{\infty} A_n\left(1-\frac{\lambda_n^2}{\lambda_1^2}\right)\left[\exp-\ (\lambda_n^2 - Ro^{-1})^{\frac{1}{2}}\left(\frac{z}{b}\right)\right]$$
$$\cdot J_1\left(\lambda_n\frac{r}{b}\right)\ .\qquad (49)$$

Elimination of other wave components of the formal solution given by (46) when Ro decreases still further can be achieved by a procedure similar to that used in the preceding section for F less than $1/2\pi$. Again, at $z = 0$ the series in (49) does not converge. However, it converges for any positive z however small, and the limit (except near the origin) of the right-hand side of (49) as z approaches zero can be considered to be the value for ψ at $z = 0$. The flow patterns for Rossby numbers $1/5$ and $1/6$ (both between $1/\lambda_1$ and $1/\lambda_2$) are shown in Figs. 4 and 5. Insertion of the spindles corresponding to the stream surfaces $\psi = 0$ is what is necessary to prevent the annular zones of stagnation that would otherwise occur at low Rossby numbers, as observed in the summer of 1959 at The University of Michigan.

4. Experimentation

To support the analysis, an experiment was performed in the flume shown in Fig. 6 which has a channel section 1 foot wide, 1½ feet high, and 13½ feet long. During the course of the experiment there would be only discharge from the flume with the consequence that the free surface would be continually falling. To minimize this effect and thereby approach steady-state conditions, the large reservoir section (8 ft $\times$ 8 ft) was incorporated. In addition, there are separate mixing tanks which allow for an almost continuous preparation of the fluid which is to be admitted to the flume.

The flume was filled to a height of 14 in. with 15 separate additions of water, to which a prescribed amount of sodium chloride had been added. The densest solution was added first and subsequently lighter solutions were floated upon the previous ones. This filling operation was accomplished with an apparatus which is a modifi-

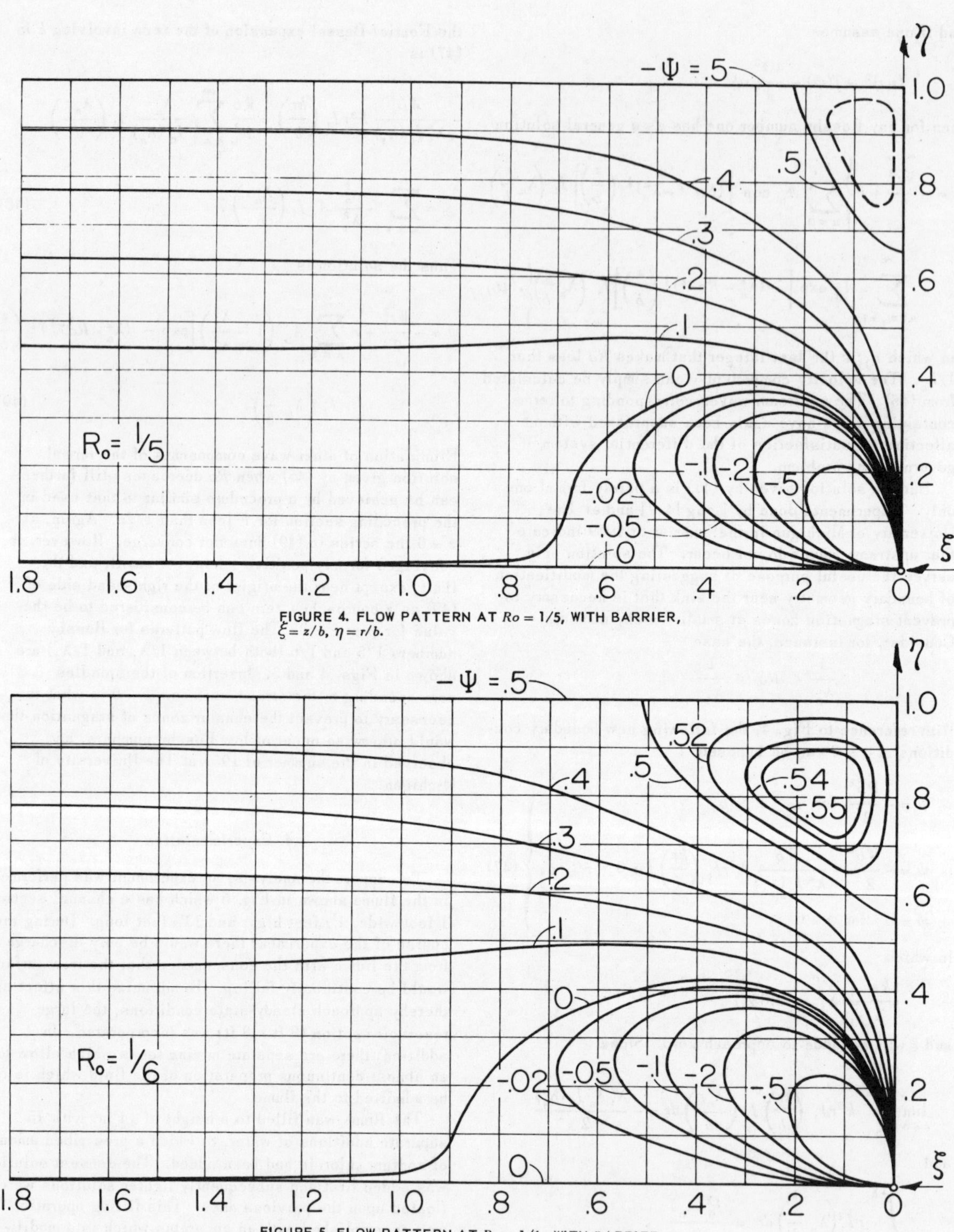

FIGURE 4. FLOW PATTERN AT $R_0 = 1/5$, WITH BARRIER,
$\xi = z/b, \ \eta = r/b$.

FIGURE 5. FLOW PATTERN AT $R_0 = 1/6$, WITH BARRIER,
$\xi = z/b, \ \eta = r/b$.

FIGURE 6. PICTURE OF THE APPARATUS.

cation of that developed by Dr. G. H. Keulegan and his co-workers at the National Bureau of Standards. Alternate layers received a very small quantity of Nigrosin dye which permitted the delineation of the layers. Upon waiting a period of about 18 hours after the completion of the filling process, the density variation, which is initially a staircase function, becomes linear through diffusion. The diffusion of the dye is apparently very much less because one can note from the photographs that the dye layers remain remarkably distinct.

The density gradient of the fluid in the flume is determined by first taking a sample of each solution as it is admitted into the flume and measuring its electrical conductivity. Since the percentage of salt in the solution is known, it is possible thereby to construct a calibration curve for the particular experiment. By extracting the fluid in the flume at half-inch intervals of the elevation, just prior to the beginning of the flow in the flume, one can measure the electrical conductivity of the samples and by comparing the results with the calibration curve determine the existing density gradient.

The discharge rate was measured with an orifice meter in the discharge line. During the tests described herein 0.32 pounds of sodium chloride were added per cubic foot of water for the bottom layer, so that the density variation from layer to layer is very small compared with the density of the fluid. As mentioned previously, the initial fluid depth was 14 inches.

The experiment consisted of discharging the fluid in the flume via a one-half inch high slot which ran the width of the flume and was located in the bottom corner of the downstream end of the flume. When there was no object in the flow, the flow pattern is as shown in Fig. 7 and shows the separation zone first noted in 1959 [3]. The Froude number (as defined in this paper) for this experiment was 0.157.

Upon examination of Fig. 2, one sees that the introduction of the quadruplet at the lower right hand corner has introduced a series of closed streamlines, the outermost of which can be conveniently taken as the boundary of a solid surface that would be located just upstream of the slot through which the flow is discharged. In order to simulate experimentally the flow presented in Fig. 2, a fiberglass barrier conforming to the dividing streamline was fabricated. (See Fig. 8). This body was located in the flume immediately upstream from the discharge slot, and a series of experiments was run with stratified fluid. For a Froude number of $3/4\pi$ (i.e. 0.238), the same value for which the streamlines are drawn in Fig. 2, the actual flow pattern obtained is shown in Fig. 9. Indeed, this flow pattern shows that there is no separation zone. Examination of other photographs shows that there is also a very small corner eddy directly above the discharge slot.

A number of experiments were run at Froude numbers different from 0.238, and one of these is shown in Fig. 10 for which the Froude number was 0.159. This experiment shows that the shape, while constructed to conform with the analysis for a specific Froude number, is efficient for eliminating the separation zone even for operational conditions different from those for which it was designed. A comparison of the flow patterns of Figs. 7 and 10 underscores this point.

The experiments show that the shape of the barrier selected as a result of the analysis presented herein for a Froude number of $3/4\pi$ does influence the flow markedly and effects a change in the flow pattern (i.e. elimination of separation regions) over a range of Froude numbers.

The tests also bear out the fact that the water solutions differ from the inviscid fluid treated in the analysis. For the experiments in which the barrier was placed in front of the discharge slot, a nearly uniform velocity distribution was observed far upstream. However, there was a definite boundary layer effect at the bottom surface of the flume. The effects of viscosity were also manifested in the experiments which were conducted without the barrier in place and for which

FIGURE 7. ACTUAL FLOW PATTERN AT $F = 0.157$, WITHOUT BARRIER.

separation was expected for Froude numbers which were sufficiently low. On examining the results of several experiments, one could see that, for Froude numbers near $3/4\pi$, separation indeed was incipient. However, the effects of viscous shear caused the separation zone to disappear. Where a separation zone existed it was possible to detect a velocity profile in the discharging section that was nearly parabolic. In these flows the viscosity was effective not only at the bottom of the flume, but also at the discontinuity plane. The discontinuity was accompanied by considerable waviness and mixing in the nearest dye layer.

5. Discussion of Experimental Results

Since the experiment showed that the barrier with a shape determined analytically for $F = 3/4\pi$ works not only for that Froude number, but for some other Froude numbers as well, the significance of the theoretically determined shapes may be questioned. First, why does a shape determined for a certain Froude number work also for some other Froude numbers? Second, if so, would not an arbitrarily prescribed shape do as well?

To answer these questions, it should be noted that the shape determined for any given Froude number has been obtained solely by modifying the nature of the singularity at the sink. When the barrier so shaped is placed in the flow at a different Froude number, singularities situated inside the barrier (and not merely at the sink) will make the boundary of the barrier a streamline. But this is not to say that this shape, or any shape, will work for all Froude numbers. There has not been time to run an experiment with the shape shown in Fig. 8 at very low Froude numbers, at which a stagnation zone near the

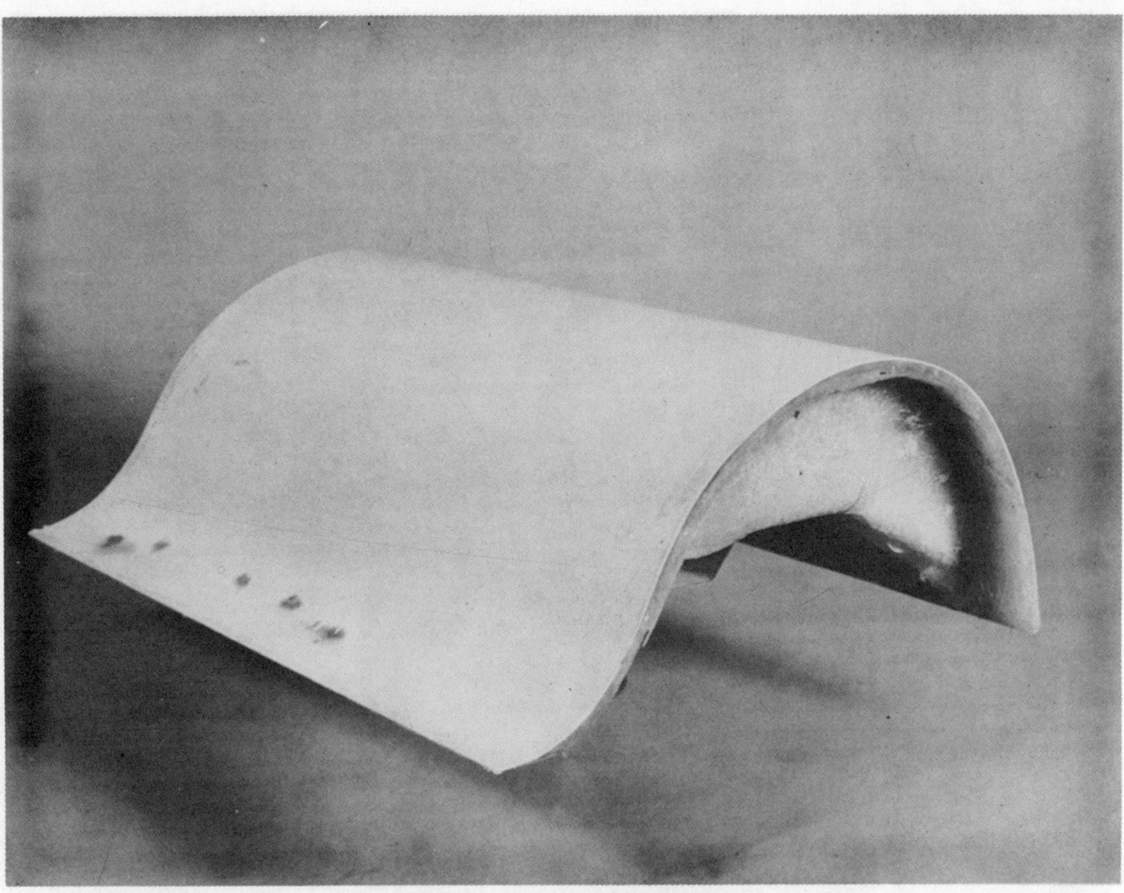

FIGURE 8. PICTURE OF THE BARRIER.

bottom can be expected. But three arguments can be given in support of the assertion that an arbitrary shape will not always do. First, surely a barrier can be constructed according to the analysis for a Froude number less than but very near $1/\pi$. This will be a very flat one, and cannot be expected to prevent separation near the top when the Froude number is too low. Second, a vertical wall erected near $x=0$ and leaving an opening at the top is an extreme form of a barrier installed to force the fluid at the top to flow. But this most certainly will cause the fluid at the bottom to stagnate. Third, from Fig. 3 it can be seen that as the Froude number decreases it will be necessary to have more than one access to the sink if stagnation is to be prevented everywhere. This seems reasonable, and appears to discredit the view that a barrier of any shape will always do the task of drawing the fluid at all layers.

To take stock, the value of the analysis is two-fold. For any given Froude number, it gives a shape which will work for Froude numbers not too different from the one for which the shape is designed. For these Froude numbers, the designed shape is one of the simplest that will work. Second, it indicates qualitatively what elaboration is needed for the shape of the barrier when the Froude number is decreased, if the barrier is to perform the assigned task.

Acknowledgment

Mr. William Huizenga constructed the flume and auxiliary equipment with great thoroughness and resourcefulness. His assistance and suggestions during the test program have been very valuable. The first author wishes to acknowledge a stimulating remark of his colleague Professor R. C. Bartels which led to the idea

FIGURE 9. ACTUAL FLOW PATTERN AT $F = 3/4\pi$, WITH BARRIER.

of modifying the nature of the singularity. The entire work has been supported by the Army Research Office (Durham), and recently also by the National Science Foundation.

References

1. Yih, C. S., "On the Flow of a Stratified Fluid," *Proc. 3rd U.S. National Congress Appl. Mech.*, 1958, pp. 857-61.

2. Yih, C. S., "Effects of Density Variation on Fluid Flow," *J. Geophys. Res.*, Vol. 64, 1959, pp. 2219-2223.

3. Debler, W. R., "Stratified Flow into a Line Sink," *Journal of the Engineering Mechanics Division, Proc. A.S.C.E.*, Vol. 85, 1959, pp. 51-65.

4. Long, R. R., "Sources and Sinks at the Axis of a Rotating Liquid," *Q.J.M.A.M.*, Vol. 9, 1956, pp. 385-93.

5. Yih, C. S., "Exact Solutions for Steady Two-Dimensional Flow of a Stratified Fluid," *J. Fluid Mech.*, Vol. 9, 1960, pp. 161-174.

6. Long, R. R., "Some Aspects of the Flow of Stratified Fluids, I. A Theoretical Investigation," *Tellus*, Vol. 5, 1953, pp. 42-57.

7. Long, R. R., "Steady Motion Around a Symmetrical Obstacle Moving Along the Axis of a Rotating Liquid," *J. Meteor.*, Vol. 10, 1953, p. 197.

FIGURE 10. ACTUAL FLOW PATTERN AT $F = 0.159$, WITH BARRIER.

J. Fluid Mech. (1966), *vol.* 24, *part* 4, *pp.* 765–767

Note on edge waves in a stratified fluid

By CHIA-SHUN YIH

Department of Engineering Mechanics, The University of Michigan

(Received 25 January 1965 and in revised form 4 October 1965)

The solution given by Gerstner for water waves of finite amplitude, which is valid for a semi-infinite liquid of arbitrary stratification, is reconsidered. By a transformation of co-ordinates, it is shown to represent edge waves propagating along a sloping shore.

---

1. Gerstner waves in a stratified liquid

Gerstner (1802; see Lamb 1945, p. 421) gave a particular solution for rotational waves of finite amplitude in a semi-infinite liquid of zero viscosity and constant density. It is well known that, in a frame of reference moving with Gerstner waves, the pressure on *any* streamline is a constant, and therefore any streamline can be considered as the trace of the free surface. This fact immediately suggests that Gerstner waves are possible in an inviscid liquid of any stratification in density, provided the depth is infinite as in Gerstner's case, and indeed the correctness of this conclusion has been fully established by Dubreil-Jacotin (1932, p. 819). The analysis occupying the remainder of this section, incorporating this extension of Gerstner's results and in essence following Dubreil-Jacotin's treatment, is presented as a convenient introduction for the new material in §2.

In terms of Lagrangian co-ordinates a_i $(i = 1, 2, 3)$, which are not necessarily the initial Cartesian co-ordinates, the equations of motion are

$$(\ddot{x}_\alpha - X_\alpha)\frac{\partial x_\alpha}{\partial a_i} + \frac{1}{\rho}\frac{\partial p}{\partial a_i} = 0 \quad (i = 1, 2, 3), \tag{1}$$

in which dots indicate differentiations with respect to the time t, x_i is the ith Cartesian co-ordinate of a fluid particle as it moves about, X_i is the ith component of the body force per unit mass, ρ is the density, and p is the pressure. The repeated indices α imply summation over 1, 2, and 3.

Gerstner considered a two-dimensional flow independent of a_3, and took the direction of increasing x_2 to be vertical, so that

$$X_1 = X_3 = 0, \quad X_2 = -g,$$

where g is the gravitational acceleration. Denoting x_1 and x_2 by x and y, and a_1 and a_2 by a and b, Gerstner showed that, for constant density, the solution consisting of

$$x = a + \frac{1}{k}e^{kb}\sin k(a - ct), \quad y = b - \frac{1}{k}e^{kb}\cos k(a - ct) \tag{2}$$

 Chia-Shun Yih

satisfies (1) and the Lagrangian equation of continuity, and represents waves of finite amplitude propagating in the x-direction with a speed c given by

$$c^2 = g/k, \tag{3}$$

in which k is a wave-number. The pressure is given by

$$P = p/\rho = C_0 - gb + \tfrac{1}{2}c^2 e^{2kb}, \tag{4}$$

in which C_0 is a constant.

For clarity in exposition we shall consider Gerstner's solution for a homogeneous liquid to be a solution satisfying

$$(\ddot{x} - X_\alpha)\frac{\partial x_\alpha}{\partial a_i} + \frac{\partial}{\partial a_i}P = 0 \quad (i = 1, 2), \tag{5}$$

with α ranging over 1 and 2. Now, if ρ is variable, the corresponding two equations in (1) are satisfied if

$$\frac{1}{\rho}\frac{\partial p}{\partial a_i} = \frac{\partial P}{\partial a_i}, \tag{6}$$

or

$$p = f(P), \quad \rho = f'(P), \tag{7}$$

with the accent indicating differentiation with respect to the argument of the arbitrary function f. Since P is a function of b only, this means that the velocity field obtained by Gerstner is dynamically possible even if ρ is not constant, but is a function of b, and that the isopycnic surfaces are isobaric surfaces in Gerstner's flow. The density stratification is entirely arbitrary, and any constant-density surface can be taken to be a free surface.

Equations (6) permit one to write

$$p = \int \rho \, dP. \tag{8}$$

With P given in (4), this becomes

$$p = g\int_0^b \rho(e^{2kb} - 1)\,db = I(b), \tag{9}$$

in which the lower limit of the integral has been chosen so that $p = 0$ for $b = 0$.

2. Edge waves in a stratified fluid

If a co-ordinate system as shown in figure 1 is adopted, in which the direction of x (or x_1) is normal to the plane of the figure, and x_2 and x_3 are designated y and z, the body-force components are

$$X_1 = 0, \quad X_2 = -g\sin\beta = -g_2, \quad X_3 = -g\cos\beta = -g_3. \tag{10}$$

If Gerstner's velocity field is retained, the two equations in (1) for $i = 1$ and 2 are satisfied if

$$\frac{1}{\rho}\frac{\partial p}{\partial a_i} = \frac{\partial}{\partial a_i}(P - g_3 z), \tag{11}$$

with $z = a_3$, and g replaced by g_2 in the expressions for c and P in (3) and (4). The third equation in (1) merely states that p is hydrostatic in the direction of z. But (11) implies that

$$p = f(P - g_3 z), \quad \rho = f'(P - g_3 z). \tag{12}$$

Thus again the isopycnic surfaces are isobaric surfaces, any of which can be taken to be the free surface. The density stratification is again arbitrary. With ρ or p fixed, $P \to \infty$ as $z \to \infty$. Since according to (2) and (4), with g in (4) identified with the present g_2, we have

$$P \sim -g_2 y + \text{const.}, \tag{13}$$

so that $y \to -\infty$ as $P \to \infty$. Thus the surfaces of constant ρ or p are asymptotically normal to the body force $\mathbf{g} = (0, -g_2, -g_3)$, as is to be expected from the vanishing of the acceleration under this limit, that is, as $z' \to \infty$ in figure 1.

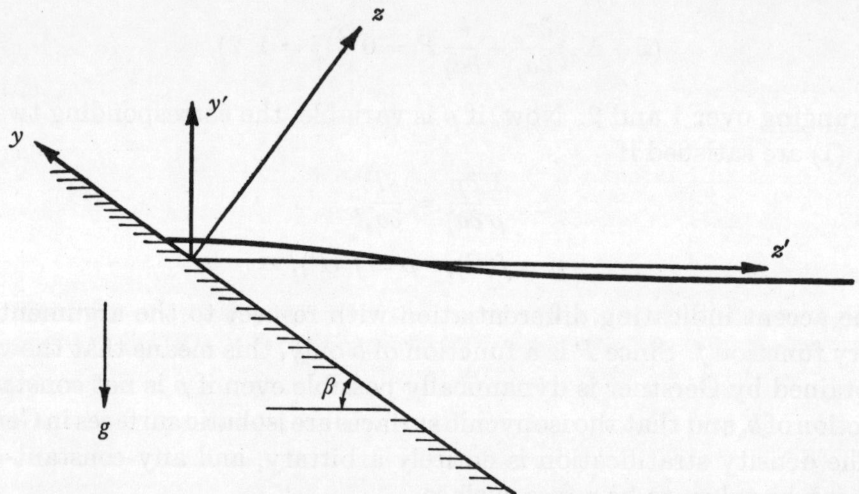

FIGURE 1. Sketch of a cross-section of edge waves of finite amplitude.

That there is no velocity normal to the sloping shore (inclined at an angle β with the horizontal) is obvious, because Gerstner's velocity field is plane, and without any component in the direction of z. It remains to mention that, since g_2 now corresponds to the g in Gerstner's original solution, it follows without further ado that the phase velocity of edge waves is given by

$$c^2 = g \sin \beta / k. \tag{14}$$

This work has been supported by the National Science Foundation and the Army Research Office (Durham). The author wishes to thank the referee of this paper for his helpful criticisms, and Dr T. Brooke Benjamin for directing his attention to the article by Dubreil-Jacotin.

REFERENCES

DUBREIL-JACOTIN, M. L. 1932 Sur les ondes de type permanent dans les liquides hétérogènes. *Atti Accad. Lincei, Rend. Cl. Sci. Fis. Mat. Nat.* (6), **15**, 814–819.

LAMB, H. 1945 *Hydrodynamics*, 6th ed. New York: Dover.

J. Fluid Mech. (1967), *vol.* 29, *part* 3, *pp.* 539–544

Equations governing steady three-dimensional large-amplitude motion of a stratified fluid

By CHIA-SHUN YIH

Department of Engineering Mechanics, The University of Michigan

(Received 22 November 1966)

The exact equations governing three-dimensional motion of an inviscid non-diffusive incompressible fluid stratified in density or of an inviscid non-diffusive gas stratified in entropy are given and briefly discussed.

1. Introduction

Since the Reynolds number and the Péclet number for most flows occurring in the atmosphere are extremely large, the study of the flows of an inviscid and non-diffusive fluid is relevant to the understanding of many atmospheric phenomena. In this paper inviscidness and non-diffusiveness are assumed throughout for the fluids considered. The equations governing steady two-dimensional flows were given by Madame Dubreil-Jacotin for an incompressible fluid of variable density (1935, p. 345, equation (B)) and for an ideal gas of variable entropy (1935, p. 346, equation (*b*)). These equations were later rediscovered by Prof. Long (1953 *a*, *b*), and have been effectively and fruitfully utilized by him in his excellent studies of atmospheric waves. Simplified versions of these equations were given by Yih (1958, 1960 *a*, *b*), who used modified stream functions to remove the non-linear terms arising from the convective terms in the Eulerian expression of the acceleration in the equations of motion.

For three-dimensional motion the corresponding equations are not available to this day. Of course we always have the Euler equations of motion, the equation of continuity, and the equation of conservation of density or of entropy. But these basic equations, four of which non-linear, do not give much promise. Before their solution can be attempted, their number need to be reduced by some sort of elimination, in the same way that such a reduction is effected to produce the final single equation of Dubreil-Jacotin for either an incompressible fluid or a gas. In this paper we shall present the three-dimensional counterparts of the equations of Madame Dubreil-Jacotin.

2. Some preliminaries

It is very helpful to visualize the very pronounced properties of stratified flows of inviscid and non-diffusive fluids before we attempt to derive the equations sought. If we assume the motion to be steady, the conservation equations are

$$(\mathbf{v}.\mathrm{grad})\rho = 0 \quad \text{or} \quad (\mathbf{v}.\mathrm{grad})S = 0, \tag{1}$$

540 *Chia-Shun Yih*

in which $\mathbf{v}$ is the velocity vector, ρ the density, and S the entropy. These equations show that in steady flows the velocity vector must lie in isopycnic surfaces or surfaces of constant entropy. Since the circulation along any circuit lying entirely in an isopycnic surface or a surface of constant entropy is preserved, this circulation must be zero if the flow is supposed to have been established from rest. Hence for such a flow the vorticity vector must also lie in an isopycnic surface or a surface of constant entropy. (See Yih 1965, p. 14.) Then for the case of an incompressible fluid

$$\mathbf{v} = \operatorname{grad} a \times \operatorname{grad} \rho, \quad \boldsymbol{\omega} = \operatorname{grad} b \times \operatorname{grad} \rho, \qquad (2\,a, b)$$

in which $\boldsymbol{\omega}$ is the vorticity vector, a is a stream function (Yih 1957), the other stream function being ρ, and b a vorticity function of Clebsch (Lamb 1945, p. 248), the other vorticity function being ρ. Of course $\mathbf{v}$ and $\boldsymbol{\omega}$ are related by

$$\boldsymbol{\omega} = \operatorname{curl} \mathbf{v}. \qquad (3)$$

For a compressible fluid $(2\,a)$ and $(2\,b)$ are to be replaced by

$$\rho\mathbf{v} = \operatorname{grad} a \times \operatorname{grad} S \quad \text{and} \quad \boldsymbol{\omega} = \operatorname{grad} b \times \operatorname{grad} S. \qquad (4\,a, b)$$

3. Derivation of the equations for an incompressible fluid

The equations of steady motion are

$$(\rho\mathbf{v}\,.\,\operatorname{grad})\,\mathbf{v} = -\operatorname{grad} p + \rho\mathbf{F}, \qquad (5)$$

in which p is the pressure and $\mathbf{F}$ the body force per unit mass given by

$$\mathbf{F} = -\operatorname{grad} gz,$$

z being the Cartesian co-ordinate measured in the direction of the vertical. If we assume (Yih 1958)

$$\mathbf{v}' = (\rho/\rho_0)^{\frac{1}{2}}\mathbf{v}, \quad \boldsymbol{\omega}' = \operatorname{curl} \mathbf{v}', \qquad (6)$$

(4) can be written as

$$(\rho_0\mathbf{v}'\,.\,\nabla)\,\mathbf{v}' = -\operatorname{grad} p + \rho\mathbf{F}, \qquad (5a)$$

which can further be written as

$$-\rho_0\mathbf{v}' \times \boldsymbol{\omega}' = -\operatorname{grad} \chi + \rho\mathbf{F}, \qquad (7)$$

with

$$\chi = p + \tfrac{1}{2}\rho(u^2 + v^2 + w^2),$$

u, v, and w being the components of $\mathbf{v}$ in the directions of increasing Cartesian co-ordinates x, y, and z respectively, and ρ_0 being a reference density.

Now since $\mathbf{v}'$ and $\boldsymbol{\omega}'$ are still solenoidal, we can write

$$\mathbf{v}' = \operatorname{grad} \alpha \times \operatorname{grad} \rho, \quad \boldsymbol{\omega}' = \operatorname{grad} \beta \times \operatorname{grad} \rho. \qquad (8\,a, b)$$

Then a simple calculation shows that

$$\mathbf{v}' \times \boldsymbol{\omega}' = -(\mathbf{v}'\,.\,\operatorname{grad} \beta)\operatorname{grad} \rho = (\boldsymbol{\omega}'\,.\,\operatorname{grad} \alpha)\operatorname{grad} \rho. \qquad (9)$$

This is as it should be, since both the velocity vector and the vorticity vector lie in a surface of constant ρ, and thus their vector product must be parallel to $\operatorname{grad} \rho$. Substituting (9) in (7), separating the result into three equations, multiplying these respectively by dx, dy and dz, and adding, we obtain, after an obvious simplification,

$$\rho_0 \, \boldsymbol{\omega}' . \operatorname{grad} \alpha = (dH/d\rho) - gz, \tag{10}$$

in which

$$H = \chi + \rho gz \tag{11}$$

is a function of ρ only, since the Bernoulli function is constant in an isopycnic surface for steady flows. Now since $\boldsymbol{\omega}'$ is in an isopycnic surface,

$$\boldsymbol{\omega}' . \operatorname{grad} \rho = 0. \tag{12}$$

We shall now use the second equation in (6) and (8 a) to obtain

$$\left.\begin{aligned}
\xi' &= (\rho_{yy} + \rho_{zz})\,\alpha_x - \rho_{xy}\,\alpha_y - \rho_{xz}\,\alpha_z - (\alpha_{yy} + \alpha_{zz})\,\rho_x + \alpha_{xy}\,\rho_y + \alpha_{xz}\,\rho_z, \\
\eta' &= (\rho_{zz} + \rho_{xx})\,\alpha_y - \rho_{yx}\,\alpha_x - \rho_{yz}\,\alpha_z - (\alpha_{zz} + \alpha_{xx})\,\rho_y + \alpha_{yx}\,\rho_x + \alpha_{yz}\,\rho_z, \\
\zeta' &= (\rho_{xx} + \rho_{yy})\,\alpha_z - \rho_{zx}\,\alpha_x - \rho_{zy}\,\alpha_y - (\alpha_{xx} + \alpha_{yy})\,\rho_z + \alpha_{zx}\,\rho_x + \alpha_{zy}\,\rho_y,
\end{aligned}\right\} \tag{13}$$

in which ξ', η' and ζ' are the three components of $\boldsymbol{\omega}'$. With (13) introduced in (10) and (12), we obtain two equations of the two unknowns α and ρ, which are the equations sought. For two-dimensional flows in the (x, z)-plane, $\boldsymbol{\omega}'$ has only the component η' and $\operatorname{grad} \rho$ in the (x, z)-plane. Hence (12) is automatically satisfied. Furthermore, if we keep the dimensions correct and write

$$\alpha = (Vd/\rho_0)\,y,$$

in which V is a reference velocity, d a reference length, and ρ_0 a reference density, we have

$$\rho_{xx} + \rho_{zz} = \frac{\rho_0}{(Vd)^2}\left(\frac{dH}{d\rho} - gz\right). \tag{14}$$

With

$$\xi = \frac{x}{d}, \quad \zeta = \frac{z}{d}, \quad r = \frac{\rho}{\rho_0}, \quad h = \frac{H}{\rho_0 V^2}, \quad F^2 = \frac{V^2}{gd},$$

(14) becomes

$$r_{\xi\xi} + r_{\zeta\zeta} = (dh/dr) - F^{-2}\zeta. \tag{15}$$

We can also recover Yih's form of the equation of Dubreil-Jacotin if we put

$$\alpha = (d\psi'/d\rho)\,y,$$

in which ψ' is the modified stream function used by Yih and

$$u' = \psi'_z, \quad w' = -\psi'_x.$$

Since neither ψ' nor ρ depends on y, the result is

$$\psi'_{xx} + \psi'_{zz} = \frac{1}{\rho_0}\frac{dH}{d\psi'} - \frac{gz}{\rho_0}\frac{d\rho}{d\psi'}, \tag{16}$$

which is the equation of Dubreil-Jacotin in Yih's form.

Equations (10) and (12), with $\boldsymbol{\omega}'$ given by (13), are integrated forms of the equations of motion. That (10) results from integration is obvious from its derivation. Even (12) results from an integration—the integration along any closed circuit in an isopycnic line to obtain the circulation, which is zero if the motion started from rest. Thus (10) and (12) are several steps in advance of the Euler equations of motion. The equation of continuity is automatically satisfied

Chia-Shun Yih

by $(2a)$ or $(8a)$. The first equation in (1), which has been used to obtain $(5a)$, is also automatically satisfied by $(2a)$, or $(8a)$ taken together with the definition of v' in (6).

The left-hand side of (10) is linear in ρ, and the left-hand side of (12) is linear in α. In this sense the left-hand sides of (10) and (12) are quasi-linear. If $dH/d\rho$ is linear in ρ, (10) and (12) are quasi-linear, and a calculation can be performed by first assuming a plausible form for α, solving (10) for ρ, using the result in (12) and solving it for α, and repeating the process.

4. Derivation of the equations for a compressible fluid

For a compressible fluid in steady motion the basic equations are still (5). The equation of continuity

$$\operatorname{div}(\rho \mathbf{v}) = 0 \tag{17}$$

is automatically satisfied by $(4a)$. We shall again use the variable λ defined by

$$\lambda = \frac{\rho}{\rho_0}\left(\frac{p_0}{p}\right)^{1/\gamma} = \text{constant} \times e^{-S/c_p}, \tag{18}$$

in which ρ_0 is a reference density and p_0 a reference pressure, and γ is the ratio of the specific heat c_p at constant pressure to the specific heat c_v at constant volume. With the substitutions (Yih 1960b)

$$\mathbf{v}' = \sqrt{\lambda}\,\mathbf{v}, \quad \rho' = \rho/\lambda, \quad p' = p, \tag{19}$$

the basic equations of motion can be written as

$$(\rho'\mathbf{v}'.\nabla)\,\mathbf{v}' = -\operatorname{grad} p' + \rho'\lambda \mathbf{F}, \tag{20}$$

in which

$$\rho'/(p')^{1/\gamma} = \text{constant}. \tag{21}$$

Equation (20) can be written as

$$-\mathbf{v}' \times \boldsymbol{\omega}' = -\operatorname{grad}\chi + \lambda \mathbf{F}, \tag{22}$$

in which

$$\chi = \int \frac{dp'}{\rho'} + \frac{q'^2}{2}, \tag{23}$$

q' being the magnitude of $\mathbf{v}'$. The equation of continuity in terms of ρ' and $\mathbf{v}'$ is, in virtue of the second equation in (1),

$$\operatorname{div}(\rho'\mathbf{v}') = 0,$$

which is automatically satisfied by

$$\rho'\mathbf{v}' = \operatorname{grad}\alpha \times \operatorname{grad}\lambda. \tag{24}$$

We use this form not only because the satisfaction of the equation of continuity is assured, but also because the velocity vectors must lie in surfaces of constant S or λ. Similarly, since the vorticity vector $\boldsymbol{\omega}$ (and hence $\boldsymbol{\omega}'$) must also lie in surfaces of constant λ,

$$\boldsymbol{\omega}' = \operatorname{grad}\beta \times \operatorname{grad}\lambda. \tag{25}$$

A simple calculation shows that

$$\rho'\mathbf{v}' \times \boldsymbol{\omega}' = -(\rho'\mathbf{v}'.\operatorname{grad}\beta)\operatorname{grad}\lambda = (\boldsymbol{\omega}'.\operatorname{grad}\alpha)\operatorname{grad}\lambda. \tag{26}$$

Substituting this in (22), multiplying it by $d\mathbf{x}$, and integrating, we obtain

$$\frac{1}{\rho'}\,\boldsymbol{\omega}'\,.\,\mathrm{grad}\,\alpha = \frac{dH}{d\lambda} - gz, \tag{27}$$

in which
$$H = \chi + gz\lambda. \tag{28}$$

The other equation is

$$\boldsymbol{\omega}'\,.\,\mathrm{grad}\,\lambda = 0. \tag{29}$$

The expression for $\boldsymbol{\omega}'$ is now a little more complicated. It is

$$\boldsymbol{\omega}' = \mathrm{curl}\,\mathbf{v}' = \mathrm{curl}\,[(1/\rho')\,\mathrm{grad}\,\alpha \times \mathrm{grad}\,\lambda]. \tag{30}$$

We shall not expand it in full. Equations (27) and (28), with $\boldsymbol{\omega}'$ given by (30), are the equations sought. The quantity ρ' can be expressed in terms of H, q' and λ by the use of (28).

For two-dimensional flows,
$$\alpha = \rho_0\,Vdy,$$

and (27) becomes

$$\left(\frac{\rho_0\,Vd}{\rho'}\right)^2\left[(\lambda_{xx}+\lambda_{zz}) - \frac{1}{\rho'}(\lambda_x\rho'_x + \lambda_z\rho'_z)\right] = \frac{dH}{d\lambda} - qz. \tag{31}$$

If we put
$$\alpha = (d\psi'/d\lambda)\,y, \tag{32}$$

we obtain Yih's form of the equation of Dubreil-Jacotin

$$\nabla^2\psi' - \frac{1}{\rho'}(\psi'_x\rho'_x + \psi'_z\rho'_z) - gz\rho'^2\frac{d\lambda}{d\psi'} = \rho'^2\frac{dH}{d\psi'}, \tag{33}$$

in which
$$\nabla^2 = \frac{\partial^2}{\partial x^2} + \frac{\partial^2}{\partial z^2}.$$

Equations (27) and (28) are a few steps in advance of the basic equations of motion because they have been obtained from the latter equations by integration.

5. Discussion

Actually, (10) and (12) governing the motion of a stratified incompressible fluid are also the equations governing steady vortex motion of a homogeneous incompressible fluid. Isopycnic surfaces would of course have no definite meaning, but we can replace ρ by L, which is constant on a Lamb surface with streamlines and vorticity lines imbedded in it. Since ρ is now constant, the last term in (10) drops out for vortex motion, which is then governed by

$$\rho\boldsymbol{\omega}\,.\,\mathrm{grad}\,\alpha = \frac{dH}{dL} \quad \text{and} \quad \boldsymbol{\omega}\,.\,\mathrm{grad}\,L = 0, \tag{34}$$

with $\boldsymbol{\omega}$ given by (13), in which ρ is replaced by L, and the accents on ξ', η' and ζ' are removed. Of course, the motion is now not assumed to have started from rest. It would be irrotational in that case.

544   *Chia-Shun Yih*

For a homentropic gas in steady vortex motion, the governing equations are

$$\frac{1}{\rho}\,\boldsymbol{\omega}\cdot\operatorname{grad}\alpha = \frac{dH}{dL} \quad\text{and}\quad \boldsymbol{\omega}\cdot\operatorname{grad}L = 0, \tag{35}$$

in which $\qquad\qquad \boldsymbol{\omega} = \operatorname{curl}\mathbf{v} = \operatorname{curl}\left[(1/\rho)\operatorname{grad}\alpha \times \operatorname{grad}L\right].$ $\qquad$ (36)

Equations (34) and (35) are the results of first integrations of the vorticity equations. It is a little surprising that they have not been found before.

Finally, we remark that the solution of (10) and (12), or (27) and (29), or (34), or (35), is not unique. For if α is a solution so is $\alpha + F(\rho)$, or $\alpha + F(\lambda)$, or $\alpha + F(L)$, as the case may be, but the velocity field is uniquely determined.

This work has been jointly sponsored by the National Science Foundation and the Army Research Office (Durham).

REFERENCES

DUBREIL-JACOTIN, M. L. 1935 Complément à une note antérieure sur les ondes de type permanent dans les liquides héterogènes. *Atti Accad. Lincei, Rend. Cl. Sci. Fis. Mat. Nat.* (6), **21**, 344–346.

LAMB, H. 1945 *Hydrodynamics*. New York: Dover.

LONG, R. R. 1953a Some aspect of the flow of stratified fluids. I. A theoretical investigation. *Tellus* 5, 42–57.

LONG, R. R. 1953b Models of small-scale atmospheric phenomena involving density stratification, article in *Fluid Models in Geophysics*, pp. 135–147. Published by U.S. Government Printing Office in 1956.

YIH, C.-S. 1957 Stream functions in three-dimensional flows. *La Houille Blanche*, no. 3, pp. 439–450.

YIH, C.-S. 1958 On the flow of a stratified fluid. *Proc. 3rd U.S. Nat'l Congr. Appl. Mech.* 857–861.

YIH, C.-S. 1960a Exact solutions for steady two-dimensional flows of a stratified fluid. *J. Fluid Mech.* **9**, 161–174.

YIH, C.-S. 1960b A transformation for non-homentropic flows, with an application to large-amplitude motion in the atmosphere. *J. Fluid Mech.* **9**, 68–80.

YIH, C.-S. 1965 *Dynamics of Nonhomogeneous Fluids*. New York: MacMillan.

J. Fluid Mech. (1969), *vol.* 36, *part* 1, *pp.* 75–85

A class of solutions for steady stratified flows

By CHIA-SHUN YIH

Department of Engineering Mechanics,
The University of Michigan

(Received 13 June 1967 and in revised form 8 September 1968)

Under the assumption that the horizontal scales of the flow of a stratified fluid are much greater than the vertical scale, it can be shown that the pressure distribution in the fluid is nearly hydrostatic and that the solution for steady flows can be reduced to the solution of a non-linear partial differential equation with only horizontal co-ordinates as the space variables. The theory built on the basic assumption is the shallow-water theory for stratified fluids. Transformations are explicitly given with which a class of solutions for steady three-dimensional flows of a fluid of arbitrary stratification, continuous or discontinuous, issuing from a large reservoir can be found from a corresponding solution for a homogeneous fluid, provided a free surface is present and the shallow-water theory is applicable. A few examples of exact solutions according to the shallow-water theory are given and the parallel flow in a horizontal canal issuing from a large reservoir with the same horizontal bottom, which has some bearing on previous works on stratified flows, is discussed. But it is emphasized that the class is a very special one and that there are other solutions not belonging to this class. The conditions under which a solution belonging to this class is valid are discussed.

1. Introduction

The equations governing large-amplitude three-dimensional steady flows of a stratified fluid have been presented in a previous paper (Yih 1967). Due to the non-linearity and complexity of these equations not a single solution for a truly three-dimensional case is known. If, however, the vertical scale of a stratified liquid is small compared with a representative horizontal scale, the pressure distribution at any section is essentially hydrostatic. As a consequence the number of the spatial variables can be reduced from three to two, although the flow treated is still truly three-dimensional. The theory built on the basic assumption of small vertical scale is the so-called shallow-water theory. In this paper we shall show that, whenever the shallow-water theory assumption is valid, a class of exact solutions exists for steady flows of a stratified fluid. The principal result is that to any solution by the shallow-water theory for a steady flow of a homogeneous fluid there corresponds a solution for a steady flow of a stratified fluid with arbitrary stratification, the velocity field for the latter being obtained from that for the former by a transformation explicitly dependent on the density stratification, and that steady stratified flows issuing from a large reservoir enjoy

                              Chia-Shun Yih

this correspondence, provided the assumptions underlying the shallow-water theory are satisfied and the downstream conditions allow it.

2. The basic assumptions and their principal consequence

We restrict our attention to the case of an incompressible, inviscid and non-diffusive fluid of variable density. For such a fluid the equations of motion are

$$\rho \frac{Du}{Dt} = -\frac{\partial p}{\partial x}, \tag{1}$$

$$\rho \frac{Dv}{Dt} = -\frac{\partial p}{\partial y}, \tag{2}$$

$$\rho \frac{Dw}{Dt} = -\frac{\partial p}{\partial z} - g\rho. \tag{3}$$

In these equations x, y and z are Cartesian co-ordinates; u, v and w are velocity components in the directions of increasing x, y and z, respectively; p is the pressure, ρ the density, g the gravitational acceleration, which is in the direction of decreasing z, and

$$\frac{D}{Dt} = \frac{\partial}{\partial t} + u\frac{\partial}{\partial x} + v\frac{\partial}{\partial y} + w\frac{\partial}{\partial z}.$$

The equation of continuity is

$$\frac{D\rho}{Dt} + \rho\left(\frac{\partial u}{\partial x} + \frac{\partial v}{\partial y} + \frac{\partial w}{\partial z}\right) = 0$$

and the equation of incompressibility is

$$D\rho/Dt = 0, \tag{4}$$

in virtue of which the equation of continuity can be written as

$$\frac{\partial u}{\partial x} + \frac{\partial v}{\partial y} + \frac{\partial w}{\partial z} = 0. \tag{5}$$

We shall consider flows of which u and v are of the order of a representative velocity V_0, and the representative horizontal length is L. Furthermore, for unsteady flows, if

$$f = O(E) \quad \text{and} \quad \partial f/\partial t = O(\omega E),$$

in which f as well as E is any variable, we shall say that $\partial/\partial t$ is of the order of ω, for convenience.

If we denote by ζ the vertical displacement of a fluid particle from its upstream elevation or mean elevation, then

$$\frac{\partial \zeta}{\partial t} + u\frac{\partial \zeta}{\partial x} + v\frac{\partial \zeta}{\partial y} = w. \tag{6}$$

The basic assumption of the shallow-water theory is

$$\text{(i)} \quad (h/L)^2 = \epsilon^2 \ll 1,$$

in which h is the depth of the fluid and a function of x, y and t. Since $\zeta < h$, (i) implies that $(\zeta/L)^2 < \epsilon^2 \ll 1$. We shall assume that the bottom is flat and situated at $z = 0$. Integration of (5) with respect to z then produces the result

$$w = O(\epsilon V_0), \tag{7}$$

in which V_0 is a representative velocity. Now the second and third terms in (6) are also $O(\epsilon V_0)$; hence

$$\partial \zeta/\partial t = O(\epsilon V_0) \quad \text{and} \quad \partial/\partial t = O(V_0/L).$$

Substituting (7) into (3) and ignoring quantities of order ϵ or of higher order in ϵ, we then obtain

$$\frac{\partial p}{\partial z} = -g\rho \quad \text{or} \quad p = \int_z^h g\rho \, dz, \tag{8}$$

if the free surface is present and given by

$$z = h(x, y, t). \tag{9}$$

In this paper we assume that a free surface is present. Equation (8) is the principal consequence of (i). Subsequent developments will be for steady flows only.

3. Shallow-water theory for stratified liquids in steady flow

For the development of the shallow-water theory for stratified fluids in steady flow, a presentation of the shallow-water theory for a homogeneous liquid is essential. Consider a homogeneous fluid with a free surface flowing above a horizontal bed. The depth will be denoted by h. If we assume the upstream flow to be irrotational, or, more generally, the flow to have been started from rest, then the whole flow is irrotational, since the fluid is inviscid and the density constant. Since (7) is still valid under the basic assumption (i), the equations of irrotationality are, if U and V denote u and v for homogeneous fluids,

$$\frac{\partial V}{\partial z} = 0, \quad \frac{\partial U}{\partial z} = 0, \quad \frac{\partial V}{\partial x} - \frac{\partial U}{\partial y} = 0, \tag{10}$$

if quantities of order ϵ are neglected. The first two equations in (10) state simply that U and V are independent of z and the third allows the use of a velocity potential Φ in terms of which

$$U = \partial \Phi/\partial x, \quad V = \partial \Phi/\partial y. \tag{11}$$

The equation of continuity is then, as can be shown in the usual way by taking as the control surface the surface formed by the bottom, the free surface and the lateral surface of a vertical prism of cross-section $dx\,dy$,

$$\frac{\partial (Uh)}{\partial x} + \frac{\partial (Vh)}{\partial y} = 0. \tag{12}$$

The Bernoulli equation is, with h_0 denoting the depth at a stagnation point or in a large reservoir,

$$U^2 + V^2 + 2gh = 2gh_0, \tag{13}$$

78   *Chia-Shun Yih*

since the neglected term w^2 is of the order of ϵ^2. Instead of the equations of motion, we can simply use (13), which can be derived from them. Substitution of (13) into (12) produces

$$(c^2 - U^2)\, U_x - UV\,(U_y + V_x) + (c^2 - V^2)\, V_y = 0, \tag{14}$$

in which
$$c^2 = gh. \tag{15}$$

In virtue of (11), (14) can be written as

$$(c^2 - \Phi_x^2)\, \Phi_{xx} - 2\Phi_x \Phi_y \Phi_{xy} + (c^2 - \Phi_y^2)\, \Phi_{yy} = 0, \tag{16}$$

in which subscripts indicate partial differentiation. The c^2 in (14) and (16) can be expressed in terms of U and V by the use of (13), or in terms of Φ in the further use of (11). It was Riabouchinsky (1932) who first pointed out the analogy between (16) and the equation governing the velocity potential of two-dimensional irrotational flows of a homentropic inviscid gas. Equation (16) is, as Riabouchinsky pointed out, identical to the equation governing two-dimensional irrotational motion of a homentropic gas obeying the law for isentropic change of state
$$p/\rho^\gamma = \text{constant}, \quad \text{with} \quad \gamma = 2.$$

The equation in gas dynamics corresponding to (16) has been studied by Molenbroek (1890) and more fruitfully by Chaplygin (1904), both of whom used hodographic variables as independent variables.

Now, for the motion of a stratified liquid started from rest, vorticity will be created. But the vortex lines will lie in surfaces of constant density, so that the vorticity component normal to a surface of constant density is zero, as a direct consequence of the Kelvin theorem (see Yih 1965, pp. 13–14). Remembering the assumption (i), this means that, with terms of order ϵ neglected, the third equation in (10) still stands. Thus we have irrotationality in a constant-density surface, when the motion is viewed from above. This does not save (11) for the whole field of flow, but does save it for a constant-density surface. As to the first two equations in (10), they are certainly no longer valid.

We shall now show that, if the shallow-water assumption is satisfied, steady flow of a stratified fluid with a free surface issuing from a large reservoir can, although it does not necessarily, have a flow pattern exactly like that of a homogeneous fluid with a free surface, issuing from the same reservoir into the same channel. Since a flow having such a pattern is far from the only kind of flow a stratified fluid can have, it is sufficient to show that such a flow is dynamically permissible, i.e. it is consistent with the only two equations governing the flow: the equation of continuity and the Bernoulli equation.

We shall, then, assume that for every constant-density surface

$$\zeta/h = \zeta_0/h_0, \tag{17}$$

in which h_0 is the depth far upstream (in the reservoir), ζ_0 is the reservoir elevation of the constant-density surface, which has the elevation $\zeta(x, y)$ at other places, and $h(x, y)$ the depth at any (x, y). The pressure at any point is, under the shallow-water assumption,

$$p = g\int_z^h \rho(z')\,dz'. \tag{18}$$

A class of solutions for steady stratified flows 79

At any *fixed* values of x and y, z' can be identified with ζ and dz' with $d\zeta$, and a change in the value in ζ involves a change in the value of ρ. Hence (18) can be written as

$$p = g \int_z^h \rho(\zeta)\,d\zeta = \frac{gh}{h_0} \int_{z_0}^{h_0} \rho_0(\zeta_0)\,d\zeta_0 = \frac{gh}{h_0} \int_{z_0}^{h_0} \rho_0(z_0')\,dz_0', \tag{19}$$

in which the validity of the second equality sign depends on (17).

Whether or not (17) is assumed, the Bernoulli equation written for any point (x, y, z) and a point far upstream on the same constant-density surface is

$$u^2 + v^2 + 2g\left(z + \frac{1}{\rho(z)} \int_z^h \rho(z')\,dz'\right) = C(\rho), \tag{20}$$

in which
$$C(\rho) = 2g\left(z_0 + \frac{1}{\rho_0(z_0)} \int_{z_0}^{h_0} \rho_0(z_0')\,dz_0'\right). \tag{21}$$

If (17) is assumed, (20) and (21) permit (22) to be written as

$$u^2 + v^2 + 2ghB(\rho) = 2gh_0 B(\rho), \tag{22}$$

in which
$$B(\rho) = C(\rho)/2gh_0. \tag{23}$$

If we now write
$$(u, v) = \lambda(\rho)\,(U, V), \quad \lambda^2 = B(\rho), \tag{24}$$

(22) becomes
$$U^2 + V^2 + 2gh = 2gh_0, \tag{25}$$

the same as (13). That is, if the Bernoulli equation is satisfied by the flow of a homogeneous fluid, it is also satisfied by a stratified flow with the same flow pattern and a velocity distribution given by (24).

Note that, for steady flows, (6) gives

$$W = U\frac{\partial \zeta}{\partial x} + V\frac{\partial \zeta}{\partial y} \tag{26}$$

for a homogeneous fluid and
$$w = u\frac{\partial \zeta}{\partial x} + v\frac{\partial \zeta}{\partial y} \tag{27}$$

for a stratified fluid. Hence (24) also implies

$$w = \lambda(\rho)\,W. \tag{28}$$

Then, in virtue of (4), (5) is satisfied if

$$\frac{\partial U}{\partial x} + \frac{\partial V}{\partial y} + \frac{\partial W}{\partial z} = 0 \tag{29}$$

is satisfied, provided the velocity distribution in the stratified fluid is given by (24). The consistency of (17) and (24) with the equation of continuity and with the dynamical equations is thus established, and we state the

Theorem: So long as the shallow-water theory is valid, a class of steady stratified flows with a free surface originated from rest can be found corresponding to each irrotational steady free-surface flows of a homogeneous fluid originated from rest. The mapping is by the use of (24).

Note that even in the presence of a stagnant layer of fluid the *flowing part* of the stream can still obey the theorem. In other words, the theorem is true

80   *Chia-Shun Yih*

wherever the basic assumptions of the shallow-water theory are fulfilled and a free surface or stagnant upper layer is present. We shall now present a few examples. Examples 3 and 4 illustrate flows with a stagnant layer.

Example 1. Gravity jets of a stratified fluid

With reference to figure 1, the water level (A) behind the vertical wall far from the opening is higher than the water level in front of the vertical wall, which is flat except in the jet issuing from the opening. The curved free surface of the jet

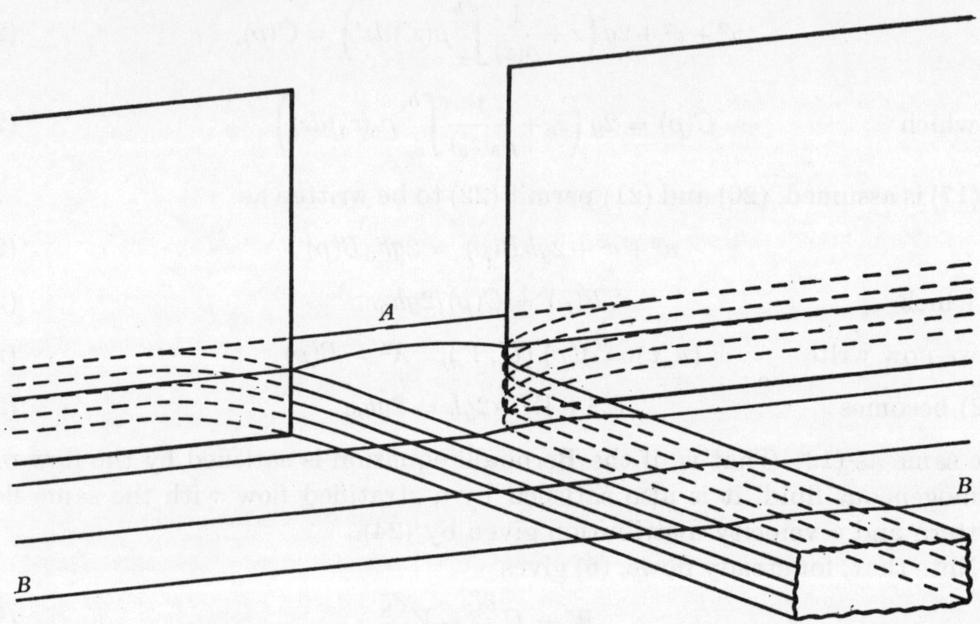

FIGURE 1. A perspective view of the gravity jet. The line A indicates the level of the free surface far upstream. The flat part of the intersection B–B of the free surface with a vertical plane is on the surface of the stagnant liquid surrounding the jet. There are three other lines like B–B in the figure. Their flat parts are at the same level as the flat part of B–B. The fluid may be homogeneous or stratified.

is higher than the flat level (straight part of B–B) of the dead water surrounding it, but approaches that level very far downstream. The bottom is horizontal throughout and the depth of water is assumed to be small compared with the opening in the wall. The problem for a homentropic gas was solved by Chaplygin (1904), and Ferguson & Lighthill (1947) calculated the coefficient of contraction for $\gamma = 1.4$. In the shallow-water case $\gamma = 2$, whereas for the classical Kirchhoff jet $\gamma = \infty$. The coefficient of contraction C_c is the ratio of the asymptotic width of the jet to the opening of the wall. For the Kirchhoff jet

$$C_c = \frac{\pi}{\pi + 2} = 0.611.$$

For the Chaplygin jet Ferguson & Lighthill (1947) gave C_c for $\gamma = 1.4$ and various values of

$$\tau_1 = \frac{q^2}{q_{\max}^2}, \tag{30}$$

q being the speed along the boundary of the jet and q_{max} the maximum speed attainable by the gas. In our case $\gamma = 2$ and q_{max} is now the maximum speed attainable by the liquid.

A calculation by Mr C. H. Li gives, for $\gamma = 2$,

τ_1	0	0·02	0·04	0·06	0·08	0·10	0·12	0·14	—
C_c	$\pi/(\pi+2)$	0·6156	0·6205	0·6255	0·6307	0·6362	0·6419	0·6479	—
τ_1	0·16	0·20	0·22	0·24	0·26	0·28	0·30	0·32	$\frac{1}{3}$
C_c	0·6542	0·6677	0·6749	0·6825	0·6904	0·6987	0·7075	0·7167	0·7230

The maximum value of τ_1 for subcritical flow is $(\gamma-1)/(\gamma+1) = \frac{1}{3}$ for $\gamma = 2$.

For a stratified fluid with any stratification, we need (24) to obtain the velocity distribution. But the coefficient of contraction is the same if the flow pattern remains unchanged. It is tacitly assumed that, if the density far upstream is given by $\rho = f(z)$, that in the stagnant liquid surrounding the jet is given by $\rho = f(rz)$, with r equal to the ratio of the upstream depth to the depth far downstream, if the flow pattern is to remain the same as for a homogeneous liquid. This can be achieved by having two large basins divided by the wall, filling them while keeping the sluice gate open, then closing the gate and enlarging in any way the area of the downstream basin, thus lowering the levels of the constant-density surfaces proportionally. When the gate is then opened, the condition at the edge of the jet is just what is needed for the solution to be physically relevant.

Example 2. *Stratified flow in a channel expansion*

Figure 2 (a, b) shows the plan and elevation (at the centre plane) views of a homogeneous liquid flowing through a channel supercritically, i.e. with the velocity everywhere greater than the local speed of long waves of the gravest mode. Equation (16) is now entirely hyperbolic and the solution by the use of the method of characteristics is well known. For a stratified liquid with any stratification, again (24) provided the corresponding solution.

Example 3. *Gravity jets with an overlying stagnant layer*

In figure 3, if the flowing layer is homogeneous and has the constant density ρ_t, the gravity jet will be identical to the gravity jet without an overlying layer in every respect, except that the velocity is reduced by the factor $(\rho_t - \rho')/\rho_t$, ρ' being the density of the overlying layer. This can be easily seen, since the Bernoulli equation is now

$$U'^2 + V'^2 + 2g'h = 2g'h_0, \tag{31}$$

in which

$$g' = \frac{\rho_t - \rho'}{\rho_t} g, \tag{32}$$

and the primes on U and V are to indicate the presence of the overlying layer, for the sake of distinction.

If the flowing layer is stratified, the velocity distribution in a dynamically possible flow with the same flow pattern is given by

$$u = \lambda'(\rho) U', \quad v = \lambda'(\rho) V', \tag{33}$$

in which ρ now varies from one surface to another and the prime on λ does not

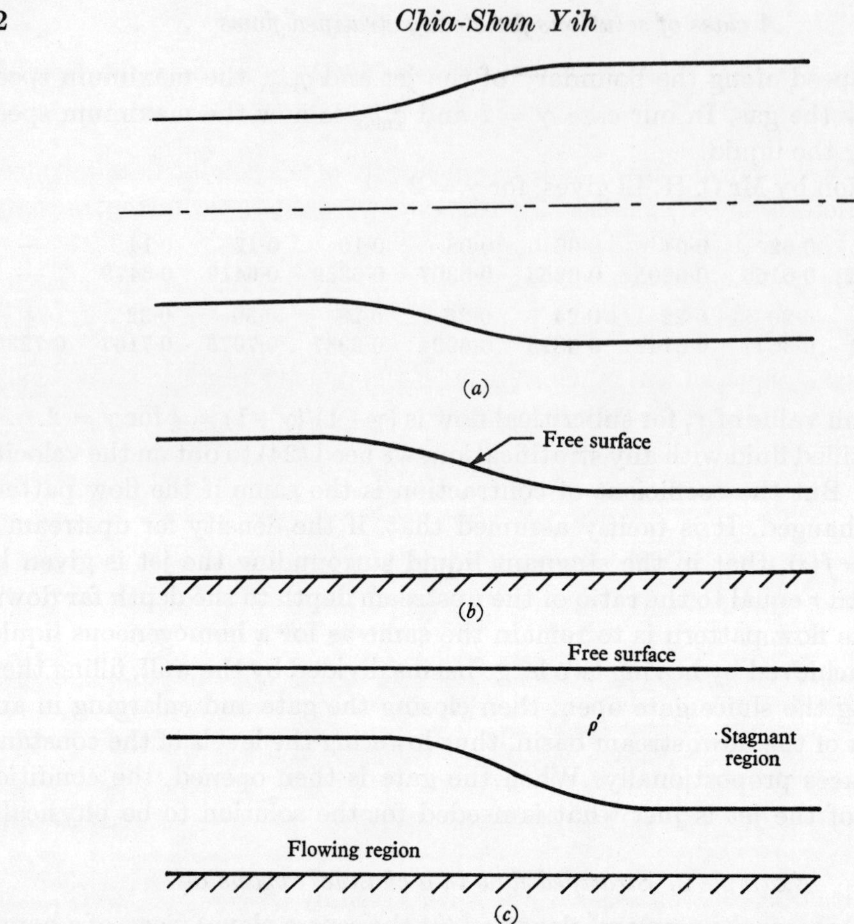

FIGURE 2. (*a*) The plan view of a channel contraction. (*b*) The elevation view of the cross-section along the centre plane. The fluid may be homogeneous or stratified. (*c*) The elevation view of the same cross-section, with an overlying stagnant layer present. The flowing fluid may be homogeneous or stratified.

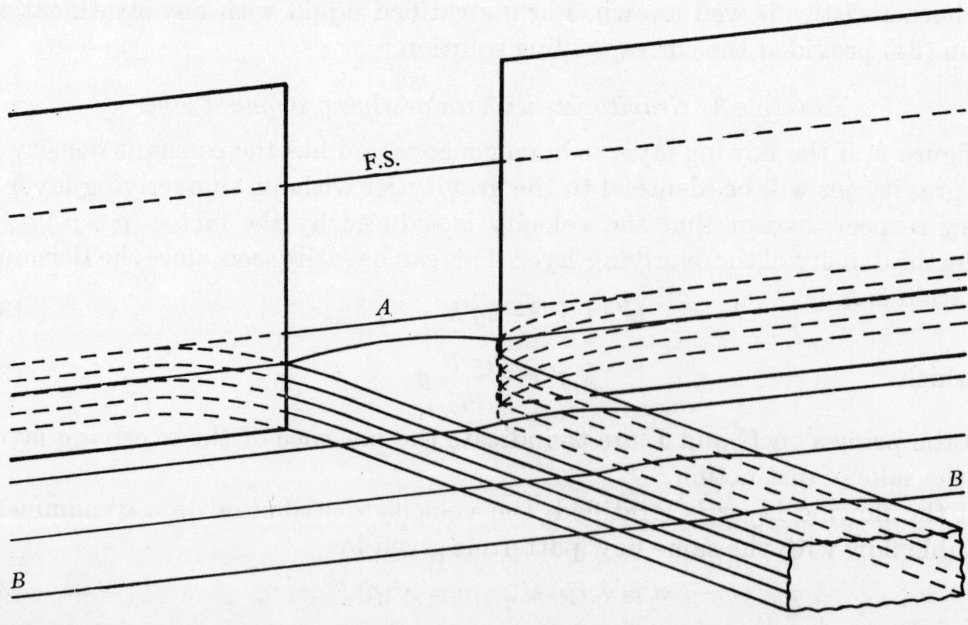

FIGURE 3. A perspective view of the gravity jet with an overlying stagnant layer. Line *A* again marks the elevation of the flowing fluid far upstream. The fluid may be homogeneous or stratified. F.S. is the free surface.

A class of solutions for steady stratified flows 83

indicate differentiation. It is important to note that $\lambda'(\rho)$ is not proportional to $\lambda(\rho)$ by the factor

$$(\rho_t - \rho')/\rho_t,$$

where ρ_t is now the density at the top stream surface of the flowing liquid. Indeed, we have to determine $\lambda'(\rho)$ anew. To this end we need to write the Bernoulli equation for the stratified fluid, which is

$$u^2 + v^2 + 2g\left[z + \frac{1}{\rho}\int_z^h \rho(z')\,dz' - \frac{\rho'}{\rho}h\right] = C(\rho), \tag{34}$$

if h is again the depth of the flowing layer, ρ the density in a constant-density surface and, from the upstream conditions,

$$C(\rho) = 2gh_0 B'(\rho),$$

in which
$$B'(\rho) = \left[\frac{z_0}{h_0} + \int_{z_0}^{h_0} \frac{\rho_0}{\rho_0(z_0)}\frac{dz_0}{h_0} - \frac{\rho'}{\rho_0(z_0)}\right]. \tag{35}$$

Note that $\rho_0(z_0) = \rho(z)$. Again it can be shown that the assumption is dynamically permissible and that, with it, the Bernoulli equation becomes

$$u^2 + v^2 + 2ghB'(\rho) = 2gh_0 B'(\rho), \tag{36}$$

or
$$u^2 + v^2 + 2g'h\frac{\rho_t}{\rho_t - \rho'}B'(\rho) = 2g'h_0\frac{\rho_t}{\rho_t - \rho'}B'(\rho). \tag{37}$$

Thus
$$[\lambda'(\rho)]^2 = \frac{\rho_t}{\rho_t - \rho'}B'(\rho). \tag{38}$$

Since $B'(\rho)$ is not a constant multiple of $B(\rho)$ given by (23) and (21), $\lambda'(\rho)$ is not proportional to $\lambda(\rho)$ given by (24). With $\lambda'(\rho)$ given by (38), (33) gives u and v, with

$$(U', V') = \frac{\rho_t - \rho'}{\rho_t}(U, V). \tag{39}$$

Of course we do not have to use the flow (U', V') parametrically and could have related u and v to U and V by inspection of (36). We have used the flow (U', V') chiefly to show more clearly that it is dangerous to apply (24) indiscriminately. Such an indiscriminate application would have given the wrong results

$$u = \lambda(\rho)\,U', \quad v = \lambda(\rho)\,V',$$

with $\lambda(\rho)$ given by (24). Again, it is tacitly assumed that the density far upstream in the flowing layer is obtainable from that in the stagnant liquid surrounding the jet by a stretching of the vertical length scale. This situation can be achieved as explained under example 1, although the overlying fluid must be made level throughout by addition to the lower basin.

Example 4. Flow through a channel expansion, with an overlying stagnant layer

Figure 2 (a, c) shows the plan and elevation (through the centre plane) views of a homogeneous liquid of density ρ_t flowing through a channel. The density of the stagnant layer is again ρ'. The flow is supposed to be supercritical in the sense that the speed q is everywhere greater than $(g'h)^{\frac{1}{2}}$, with g' given by (32). Again the velocity distribution is given by (33) and (38).

84   *Chia-Shun Yih*

Example 5. Flow from a reservoir into a channel

In a previous paper (Yih 1958) it was shown that, if a stratified liquid flows horizontally from an infinitely large reservoir into an adjoining channel with the same horizontal bottom and the same horizontal cover, the velocity distribution in the channel, where the velocity becomes unidirectional, is given by

$$\sqrt{\rho}\, u = \text{constant}. \tag{40}$$

For convenience of reference, we shall call (40) solution A, which is an inertial solution. In other words, it is true only if the acceleration is achieved by very low pressure downstream and gravity plays no role. That is to say, if we define the local Froude number as

$$V_0/\sqrt{(g'h_0)},$$

in which

$$g' = \frac{gh_0}{\rho}\frac{\partial\rho}{\partial z},$$

then the higher the minimum of the Froude number, the more nearly is the velocity distribution given by (40). At low Froude numbers (40), though dynamically possible, is not likely to describe what actually happens, since the flow is then strongly affected by gravity. With a free surface, acceleration is caused by descent of the fluid, and the velocity distribution in a channel joining a reservoir from which the fluid issues is determined by (24), provided the downstream conditions allow such a flow. There is no contradiction of the two results. It matters a great deal whether there is a free surface, and when there is no free surface it matters a great deal how high the Froude number is.

If the upper surface is free, the velocity distribution of a homogeneous fluid issuing *subcritically* from the reservoir into the channel will be free from waves, since no real characteristics exist for (16), according to the shallow-water theory. The velocity distribution far downstream from the contraction will then be uniform. That is, U will be constant. For a stratified fluid, downstream conditions allowing, the asymptotic velocity distribution is given by (24). For convenience we shall call this velocity distribution solution B. We know also that it is possible to have a flowing layer of a homogeneous liquid under a stagnant layer of lighter density. If we use (33) and (38) to determine u, with $U' = \text{constant}$, we obtain a flow of a stratified fluid, with an upper part of it stagnant from the reservoir into the channel. Since the upper layer is stagnant, it indeed does not matter whether the upper surface is covered or free. This solution, called solution C, is different from solutions A and B, even granted the same upstream density distribution. But solution C is valid only if blocking has occurred, due to some obstacle downstream. The theorem is still true for the flowing region.

In concluding this section, we remark that there is a weakness in the gravity-jet examples. For the Kirchhoff jets the radius of curvature of the free streamline at the starting-point (as it leaves the wall) is zero. The same is also true for the case of $\gamma = 2$. Professor M. J. Lighthill suggested to the writer in London that the sharp corner at the corresponding point in the hodograph plane guarantees that the curvature at the point in question is infinite. And this turns out to be generally true. Whereas an infinite curvature is no weakness in the Kirchhoff and Chaplygin jets, it is a weakness for the gravity jets discussed here, for at a point with infinite curvature the shallow-water assumption is violated.

In all examples the flow is supposed to have originated from a large reservoir, where the fluid is at rest.

4. Discussion

The flows discussed so far belong to a special class. Because of their very special nature it is possible to go far in the description of their detailed features. But the downstream conditions must be consistent with any particular flow belonging to this special class before it can be expected to occur, as we have described, for instance, in example 1. It is certainly desirable to discuss the situation that will prevail for a given density distribution in the upstream reservoir and one in the downstream reservoir connected with the upstream reservoir by an open channel. This will serve to show that other flows than the class just discussed can occur.

If the free surface in the downstream reservoir is sufficiently lower than the free surface upstream, and the velocity determined by (24) is so fast that no internal waves, even of finite amplitude, can travel upstream, then the flows described by (24) will actually happen. This is true even if there are obstacles in the channel, before the obstacles are reached. The fastest speed of internal waves is of the order of the square root of the density gradient if the density gradient is continuous, or of the square root of the density difference $\Delta\rho$ divided by the main density ρ_m if there is a density discontinuity. If the density gradient and $\Delta\rho/\rho_m$ (if an interface is present) are all very small and the velocity (U, V) determined from the free-surface drop not small, then the solution (24) is valid. If a stagnant layer is present, the solution given by (33) and (39) is valid under the same conditions. Obviously, if the free-surface drop is very small, internal waves can travel upstream, and the downstream stratification will have a far-reaching influence on the flow, which then cannot in general be described by (24), or by (33) and (39).

This work has been jointly sponsored by the National Science Foundation and the Army Research Office (Durham). I am grateful to a referee of this paper for his criticisms, which have contributed to the improvement of this paper.

REFERENCES

CHAPLYGIN, S. A. 1904 On gas jets. *Sci. Mem. Moscow Univ. Math. Phys. Soc.* **21**, 1–121. (Translation: *NACA* Tech. Mem. 1063, 1944.)

FERGUSON, D. F. & LIGHTHILL, M. J. 1947 The hodograph transformation in trans-sonic flow, IV. Tables. *Proc. Roy. Soc.* A **192**, 35–42.

MOLENBROEK, P. 1890 Ueber einige Bewegungen eines Gases bei Annahme eines Geschwindigkeitspotentials. *Arch. Math. Phys.* **9**, 157–195.

RIABOUCHINSKY, D. 1932 Sur l'analogie hydraulique des mouvements d'un fluide compressible. *Acad. Sci., Comptes Rendus,* **195**, 998–9.

YIH, C-S. 1958 On the flow of a stratified fluid. *Proc. 3rd U.S. Nat. Cong. Appl. Mech.* 857–61.

YIH, C-S. 1965 *Dynamics of Nonhomogeneous Fluids.* New York: MacMillan.

YIH, C-S. 1967 Equations governing steady three-dimensional large-amplitude motion of a stratified fluid. *J. Fluid Mech.* **29**, 539–44.

Reprinted from *Ann. Rev. Fluid Mech.* **1** (1969) 73–110.

STRATIFIED FLOWS

By Chia-Shun Yih

Department of Engineering Mechanics, The University of Michigan,
Ann Arbor, Michigan

Part I. General Considerations

1. Introduction.—The intrusion of salt wedges into estuaries and the behavior of sediment-laden currents in clear water have long been of interest to hydraulic engineers. It is now known that the density of water in oceans varies significantly in a layer called the thermocline, and that their behavior, such as manifested in the Gulf Current and the Kuroshio Current, is intimately related to this layer as well as to the rotation of the Earth. The occurrence of cold currents in the atmosphere, the stagnation of air in the neighborhood of a mountain range whenever there is a strong inversion, and the formation of atmospheric waves in the lee of mountains are now well known. In certain regions some of these phenomena are even a matter of daily experience. Aside from the Earth's rotation, which plays an important part in large-scale motion of the oceans and the atmosphere, all of the aforementioned phenomena are characterized by the nonhomogeneity in density or entropy of the fluid and by the important role played by gravity. Such a fluid is called a stratified fluid, and its flows are called stratified flows.

In this survey, because of the limitation of space, the effect of the Earth's rotation will not be discussed. Since the use of the potential temperature and the potential density (which are the temperature and the density of a parcel of air brought isentropically to a standard pressure) to a large measure, though of course not completely, reduces the dynamics of a nonhomentropic gas to that of a liquid of variable density, the discussion will be limited to the behavior of an incompressible fluid in the presence of gravity. The effect of viscosity will be touched upon wherever its discussion is profitable. But this survey primarily concerns inviscid fluids or, more precisely, flows of a fluid of variable density for which an adequately formed Reynolds number is large.

2. The governing equations.—If x_1, x_2, and x_3 are Cartesian coordinates and u_1, u_2, and u_3 the corresponding velocity components, the equation of continuity is

$$\frac{\partial \rho}{\partial t} + \frac{\partial(\rho u_\alpha)}{\partial x_\alpha} = 0 \qquad\qquad 1.$$

in which t is the time, ρ is the density, and the repeated indices indicate summation, so that

$$\frac{\partial(\rho u_\alpha)}{\partial x_\alpha} = \frac{\partial(\rho u_1)}{\partial x_1} + \frac{\partial(\rho u_2)}{\partial x_2} + \frac{\partial(\rho u_3)}{\partial x_3}$$

74 YIH

The equation of incompressibility is

$$\frac{D\rho}{Dt} = 0 \qquad\qquad 2$$

in which

$$\frac{D}{Dt} = \frac{\partial}{\partial t} + u_\alpha \frac{\partial}{\partial x_\alpha}$$

is the symbol for substantial differentiation. From Equations 1 and 2 it follows that

$$\frac{\partial u_\alpha}{\partial x_\alpha} = 0 \qquad\qquad 3.$$

since ρ is never zero. Equation 3 is the form of the equation of continuity to be used in the following.

The dynamical equations are the Euler equations of motion

$$\rho\left(\frac{\partial u_i}{\partial t} + u_\alpha \frac{\partial u_i}{\partial x_\alpha}\right) = -\frac{\partial p}{\partial x_i} + \rho X_i \qquad (i = 1, 2, 3) \qquad\qquad 4.$$

in which p is the pressure and X_i is the ith component of the body force per unit mass of the fluid. We observe immediately that in Equation 4 the density is associated with the acceleration and with the body force of gravity. Heterogeneity in density can therefore be expected to have two effects: the inertial effect because heterogeneity in density always implies heterogeneity in the capacity of the fluid, per unit volume, to resist acceleration; and the gravity effect because heterogeneity in density implies heterogeneity in body force per unit volume in the presence of the Earth's gravitational field. The ratio of a representative acceleration to the gravitational acceleration g determines whether the inertial effect and the gravity effect are equally important, or one of them predominates.

If the flow is steady the acceleration has the components $u_\alpha \partial u_i/\partial x_\alpha$, and the aforementioned ratio is V^2/gd, in which V is a representative velocity and d a representative length. One expects that the inertial effect or the gravity effect predominates accordingly as the ordinary Froude number $V/\sqrt{gd}$ is large or small. However, in stratified flows one is often concerned with internal motion of a slightly stratified fluid for which the density variation is small compared with the mean density. For such a fluid we can write

$$\rho = \rho_m + \rho_1 \qquad\qquad 5.$$

in which ρ_m is constant, and ρ_1/ρ_m is uniformly small. Substitution of Equation 5 into Equation 4 produces

$$\rho\left(\frac{\partial u_i}{\partial t} + u_\alpha \frac{\partial u_i}{\partial x_\alpha}\right) = -\frac{\partial \Delta p}{\partial x_i} + \rho_1 X_i \qquad\qquad 6.$$

in which

$$\Delta p = p + \rho_m \Omega$$

and Ω is the body-force potential (presumed to exist) defined by

$$X_i = - \frac{\partial \Omega}{\partial x_i} \qquad 7.$$

Inspection of Equation 6 shows that for steady flows it is the ratio $\rho V^2/\rho_1 gd$, instead of V^2/gd, that is significant. If ρ_1 is replaced by a representative density difference $\Delta\rho$, the F defined by

$$F^2 = \frac{V^2}{(\Delta\rho/\rho_m)gd} \qquad 8.$$

called variously the internal Froude number or the modified Froude number, is indicative of the relative importance of inertial and gravity effects in internal motions of a slightly stratified fluid. It will be called simply the Froude number here. Note that F governs only internal motions of a stratified fluid. If a free surface is present and the motion involves significant deflection of the free surface, the motion is not primarily internal, and the stratification, if it is slight, will only cause a small deviation from the flow of a homogeneous fluid. Whether or not $\Delta\rho/\rho_m$ is small, the distribution of ρ/ρ_m at an upstream section is an important factor affecting the flow. If $\Delta\rho/\rho_m$ is small, the effect of ρ/ρ_m is felt mainly through the last term in (4), and very little through the first term. Thus Boussinesq (7), in treating the flow of slightly stratified fluids, simply replaced the first ρ in Equation 4 by ρ_m. This procedure is now called the Boussinesq approximation.

    3. The inertial effect of density variation.—The inertial and gravity effects of density variation are simultaneous, and cannot be separately ascertained. Nevertheless, it is instructive to study the extreme cases in which one of these effects dominates the other. In studying the inertial effect, we shall assume g to be zero. This amounts to saying that F is extremely large. Even after this assumption it is impossible to ascertain the effect of density variation in a general and simple way without specifying steadiness of the flow.

    If gravity effects are neglected and the flow assumed steady, Equations 2 and 4 become

$$u_\alpha \frac{\partial \rho}{\partial x_\alpha} = 0 \qquad 9.$$

and

$$\rho u_\alpha \frac{\partial u_i}{\partial x_\alpha} = - \frac{\partial p}{\partial x_i} \qquad 10.$$

Then the transformation [Yih (49)]

$$u_i' = \sqrt{\frac{\rho}{\rho_0}} \, u_i, \qquad p' = p \qquad 11.$$

in which u_i' is the ith component of a fictitious velocity, transforms Equations 3 and 10 to

76 YIH

$$\frac{\partial u_\alpha'}{\partial x_\alpha} = 0$$

and

$$\rho_0 u_\alpha' \frac{\partial u_i'}{\partial x_\alpha} = -\frac{\partial p'}{\partial x_i} \qquad 12.$$

upon two utilizations of Equation 9. Thus the equations governing the flow of a nonhomogeneous fluid are reduced to those governing the flow of a homogeneous fluid, which we shall call the associated flow. For every associated flow there are infinitely many stratified flows, with arbitrary density variation and with the velocity (u_i) given by the first equation in 11 in terms of u_i'. Thus the inertial effect of density variation in steady flows is ascertained in a general and simple way.

If the effects of gravity are unimportant, that is, if F is very high, and if the flow is steady, we can use Equation 12 instead of Equation 4. Then irrotationality of the associated flow will persist, as is well known. Hence if Equation 12 can be used and if the flow originates in a large reservoir where u_i' is zero, the associated flow will be irrotational, i.e., curl u' will be zero. Such an associated flow will be governed by the Laplace equation, and after the solution is found u_i can be determined from the first of Equation 11.

4. The gravity effect of density variation.—To isolate the gravity effect of density variation for discussion, we consider a steady flow with so small a Froude number that the inertial effect can be neglected. The equations of motion are then

$$0 = \frac{\partial p}{\partial x}, \qquad 0 = \frac{\partial p}{\partial y}, \qquad 0 = \frac{\partial p}{\partial z} + g\rho \qquad \text{13a. 13b. 13c.}$$

if x, y, and z are used instead of x_1, x_2, and x_3, and if z is measured in the direction of the vertical. The equation of incompressibility is

$$u \frac{\partial \rho}{\partial x} + v \frac{\partial \rho}{\partial y} + w \frac{\partial \rho}{\partial z} = 0 \qquad 14.$$

in which u, v, and w are the velocity components in the directions of increasing x, y, and z, respectively. Upon differentiation of Equation 13 with respect to x and y and using Equations 13a and 13b respectively, we find that

$$\frac{\partial \rho}{\partial x} = 0 = \frac{\partial \rho}{\partial y} \qquad 15.$$

which makes

$$w = 0 \qquad 16.$$

if we consider a continuously stratified fluid for which $\partial \rho/\partial z$ never vanishes. Thus the vertical component of the velocity is zero, and isopynic surfaces are horizontal. For a somewhat less crude derivation of this result see Yih (55, pp. 9–10).

If the motion is, in addition to being steady and weak, also two-dimensional, so that it is independent of y, then Equation 16 and

$$\frac{\partial u}{\partial x} + \frac{\partial v}{\partial y} + \frac{\partial w}{\partial z} = 0 \qquad\qquad 17.$$

become

$$\frac{\partial u}{\partial x} = 0 \qquad\qquad 18.$$

which states that if a solid cylinder is dragged slowly and steadily through a stratified fluid in the horizontal direction, the fluid before and behind it will be pushed and dragged as if solid [Yih (50)]. This conclusion has been verified qualitatively by Yih (51), who towed a plane strip broadside-on in a salt solution of variable concentration. Of course viscosity, whose effects have been ignored in the derivation, will act to destroy the strict validity of the conclusion. The velocity in the entrained fluid will not be uniform, and there will not be a vortex sheet at the two horizontal planes touching the top and bottom ridges of the moving solid cylinder. But in the main, the prediction of a long entrainment of fluid in front and behind has been verified experimentally.

The phenomenon just discussed is called blocking, and is the same phenomenon as the stagnancy of a highly stable atmosphere before a mountain range. We shall return to the question of blocking later.

5. *The creation of vorticity and circulation by density variation.*—We shall define the vorticity vector ξ by

$$\xi = \mathbf{curl}\ u$$

in which u is the velocity vector, and denote its components by ξ_1, ξ_2, and ξ_3. For instance

$$\xi_3 = \frac{\partial u_2}{\partial x_1} - \frac{\partial u_1}{\partial x_2}$$

Elimination of p in the first two equations contained in Equation 4 produces

$$\frac{D\xi_3}{Dt} + \xi_3 \frac{\partial u_\alpha}{\partial x_\alpha} = \xi_\alpha \frac{\partial u_3}{\partial x_\alpha} - \left(\frac{\partial \rho^{-1}}{\partial x_1}\frac{\partial p}{\partial x_2} - \frac{\partial \rho^{-1}}{\partial x_2}\frac{\partial p}{\partial x_1}\right) \qquad 19.$$

Since Equation 1 can be written as

$$\frac{\partial u_\alpha}{\partial x_\alpha} = -\frac{1}{\rho}\frac{D\rho}{Dt}$$

Equation 19 can be written as

$$\frac{D}{Dt}\left(\frac{\xi_3}{\rho}\right) = \frac{\xi_\alpha}{\rho}\frac{\partial u_3}{\partial x_\alpha} + \frac{1}{\rho^3}\left(\frac{\partial \rho}{\partial x_1}\frac{\partial p}{\partial x_2} - \frac{\partial \rho}{\partial x_2}\frac{\partial p}{\partial x_1}\right) \qquad 20.$$

Thus the vector form of the vorticity equations is

$$\frac{D}{Dt}\frac{\xi}{\rho} = \left(\frac{\xi}{\rho}\cdot\mathbf{grad}\right)u + \frac{1}{\rho^3}\left(\mathbf{grad}\,\rho \times \mathbf{grad}\,p\right) \qquad 21.$$

78   YIH

For an incompressible fluid Equation 2 allows 21 to be written as

$$\frac{D}{Dt}\xi = (\xi \cdot \mathbf{grad})u + \frac{1}{\rho^2}(\mathbf{grad}\,\rho \times \mathbf{grad}\,p) \qquad 22.$$

One recognizes that, apart from the last term, this equation is just the vorticity equation for an inviscid fluid of constant density. The first term is the rate of change of vorticity of a fluid particle, the second term represents the contribution to that rate by stretching and turning of the vortex lines, as is well known. The last term represents the contribution to that rate by the density variation, or the rate of creation of vorticity. The significance of the last term can be qualitatively understood in an intuitive way. That component of **grad** p that is parallel to **grad** ρ does not create vorticity. To understand this intuitively, we can consider a stratified fluid being accelerated vertically as a solid body. There is no relative motion and therefore no vorticity. That the component of **grad** p that is normal to **grad** ρ will create vorticity can be understood if we consider the acceleration of the fluid slightly above and slightly below a constant-density surface. Above it the fluid is less dense and below denser. Hence the fluid above has to accelerate more under the same pressure gradient along the constant-density surface than the fluid below. Thus vorticity is created.

If the density variation creates vorticity it must also create circulation. Consider a closed curve C, along which s is measured. Let the distance along C between two neighboring points on it be denoted by ds, with components dx_1, dx_2, and dx_3, and the difference in u_i at any instant between these points be denoted by du_i. If we follow the particles on C, dx_i $(i = 1, 2, 3)$ is a function of time, and the purely kinematic relation

$$du_i = \frac{D}{Dt}dx_i \qquad 23.$$

holds. Multiplication of Equation 4 by dx_i/ρ and integration along C produce

$$\int_C \frac{Du_i}{Dt}dx_i = \int_C X_i dx_i - \int_C \frac{1}{\rho}\frac{\partial p}{\partial x_i}dx_i \qquad 24.$$

which, by virtue of Equation 23, can be written as

$$\frac{D}{Dt}\int_C u_i dx_i = \int_C (X_i dx_i + u_i du_i) - \int_C \frac{1}{\rho}\frac{\partial p}{\partial x_i}dx_i \qquad 25.$$

If we assume the body force to have a potential Ω, and Ω and u_i to be single-valued, Equation 25 can be written as

$$\frac{D}{Dt}\Gamma = -\int_C \frac{1}{\rho}\frac{\partial p}{\partial x_i}dx_i \qquad 26.$$

in which

$$\Gamma = \int_C u_i dx_i \qquad 27.$$

is the circulation along C. If the surface S is bounded by C, and $d\mathbf{A}$ is an element of area on S, considered as a vector with its direction normal to S (that is, as the vector product of two line elements on S), then by Stokes' theorem

$$\int_C \frac{1}{\rho} \frac{\partial p}{\partial x_i}\, dx_i = \int\int_S \operatorname{curl}\left(\frac{1}{\rho}\operatorname{grad} p\right)\cdot dA$$

$$= \int\int_S \left(\operatorname{grad}\frac{1}{\rho} \times \operatorname{grad} p\right)\cdot dA$$

because **curl grad** $p = 0$. Hence

$$\frac{D\Gamma}{Dt} = \int\int_S \frac{1}{\rho^2}(\operatorname{grad}\rho \times \operatorname{grad} p)\cdot dA \qquad\qquad 28.$$

This is to be expected, for the second term in Equation 22, though contributing to the rate of change of vorticity, does not contribute to any change in Γ, as is well known. We have stated that the last term in Equation 22 contributes to the creation of vorticity. This statement is further verified here. The integrand in Equation 28 is precisely the third term in Equation 22, and we know that the circulation Γ is the integral of $\xi\cdot dA$ over S (Stokes' circulation theorem). Therefore Equation 28 states clearly that the third term in Equation 22 represents the rate of creation of vorticity.

Equation 28 is the theorem of V. Bjerknes (5). The creation of vorticity and circulation by density variation is the root of the difference between stratified flows and the flows of a homogeneous fluid. This difference can sometimes be rather dramatic. For instance the "train effect" discussed in Section 4 is related to the creation of vortex sheets (albeit only within the framework of a theory for inviscid fluids) in horizontal planes touching the cylinder.

6. *Imbedment of the vorticity lines.*—If the surface S indicated in Equation 28 is a constant-density surface, the integrand vanishes on S, and Equation 28 becomes

$$\frac{D}{Dt}\Gamma = 0 \qquad\qquad 28a.$$

with Γ taken along C which now must lie in a constant-density surface. If the motion has started from rest, Γ will then remain zero along any such circuit. Stokes' circulation theorem then states that the vorticity component normal to a constant-density surface must be zero. That is to say, vortex lines in the flow of an inviscid incompressible fluid of variable density must be imbedded in the constant-density surfaces, provided the flow has started from rest. The flow is therefore layer-wise irrotational.

The creation of streamwise vorticity was discussed by Marris (30), but the role of gravity has not yet been properly taken into account.

7. *The Bernoulli equation in steady flow.*—The Euler equations for steady flows can be written as

$$-u \times \xi = -\frac{1}{\rho}\operatorname{grad} p - \operatorname{grad}\left(\frac{q^2}{2} + \Omega\right) \qquad\qquad 29.$$

as can be easily verified. Since for steady flows path lines are streamlines, along which ρ is therefore constant, from Equation 29 it is immediately clear that along a streamline the Bernoulli quantity

$$\frac{q^2}{2} + \frac{p}{\rho} + \Omega$$

is invariant, in which q is the speed. As we have just seen, vortex lines are imbedded in constant-density surfaces, if the flow has started from rest. Therefore, along a vortex line the Bernoulli quantity just defined is also a constant. In fact if we consider the surface formed by vortex lines intersecting a streamline, or by streamlines intersecting a vortex line, along such a surface the Bernoulli quantity must be invariant, by virtue of its invariance along a streamline and a vortex line in steady flows established from rest. Such a surface is called a Lamb surface, and in the present circumstances is obviously just a surface of constant density. Hence we can write

$$\frac{q^2}{2} + \frac{p}{\rho} + \Omega = F(\rho) \qquad\qquad 30.$$

for steady flows established from rest. [Note that even if u and ξ coincide in direction in any part of the fluid the conclusion still stands. But Beltrami flows (for which $u \times \xi = 0$) of stratified flows are not dynamically possible over any finite three-dimensional region of the fluid domain. Otherwise we could take the dot product of Equation 28 and dx, and integrate over a curve C in that region. Since $\frac{1}{2}q^2 + \Omega$ is single-valued, the result would demand that dp/ρ be an exact differential in that region, which it is not, since ρ is neither constant nor a function of p alone.]

We have seen that vortex lines are imbedded in constant-density surfaces in flows of an inviscid stratified fluid started from rest, whether the flow is steady or unsteady, and that therefore such flows are layer-wise irrotational. Then a potential $\phi(x, t, \rho)$ can be introduced for each constant-density surface, of which the velocity component in that surface is the gradient. Then in that surface

$$\frac{\partial}{\partial t} \operatorname{grad} \phi = -\frac{1}{\rho} \operatorname{grad} p - \operatorname{grad}\left(\frac{q^2}{2} + \Omega\right) \qquad\qquad 31.$$

Since $\rho = $ constant in such a surface, integration gives

$$\frac{\partial \phi}{\partial t} + \frac{p}{\rho} + \frac{q^2}{2} + \Omega = \text{function of } \rho \qquad\qquad 32.$$

which is the Bernoulli equation for unsteady flows. But it is only useful after ϕ is already determined.

PART II. WAVES OF VERY SMALL AMPLITUDE

1. The governing differential system.—With x, y, and z defined as in Section 4 of Part I, and assuming that the mean density $\bar{\rho}$ and the components U and V of the wind velocity are functions of z only, we shall derive the equation governing waves of small amplitude. For simplicity we shall use u, v, and w to denote the components of the velocity perturbation, and p and ρ to denote the perturbations in pressure and density, respectively. Thus the density is $\bar{\rho}(z)+\rho$, for instance. The mean pressure $\bar{p}$ and the mean density $\bar{\rho}$ satisfy the hydrostatic condition

$$\frac{d\bar{p}}{dz} = -g\bar{\rho} \qquad\qquad 1.$$

If products of the perturbation quantities are neglected, the linearized equations of motion are

$$\frac{D}{Dt}(\bar{\rho}u) + \bar{\rho}U'w = -\frac{\partial p}{\partial x}, \qquad\qquad 2.$$

$$\frac{D}{Dt}(\bar{\rho}v) + \bar{\rho}V'w = -\frac{\partial p}{\partial y}, \qquad\qquad 3.$$

$$\frac{D}{Dt}(\bar{\rho}w) = -\frac{\partial p}{\partial z} - g\rho \qquad\qquad 4.$$

in which

$$\frac{D}{Dt} = \frac{\partial}{\partial t} + U\frac{\partial}{\partial x} + V\frac{\partial}{\partial y}, \qquad U' = \frac{dU}{dz}, \qquad V' = \frac{dV}{dz} \qquad 5.$$

Note that Equation 1 has been used to obtain Equation 4 from the original equation of motion. The linearized equation of incompressibility is

$$\frac{D}{Dt}\rho + w\frac{d}{dz}\bar{\rho} = 0 \qquad\qquad 6.$$

and the equation of continuity is Equation 17 in Part I.

Differentiation of Equations 2 and 3 with respect to x and y, respectively, and addition of the results produce, with the use of Equation I.17,

$$-\frac{D}{Dt}\left(\bar{\rho}\frac{\partial w}{\partial z}\right) + \bar{\rho}\left(U'\frac{\partial}{\partial x} + V'\frac{\partial}{\partial y}\right)w = -\nabla_2^2 p \qquad 7.$$

in which

$$\nabla_2^2 = \frac{\partial^2}{\partial x^2} + \frac{\partial^2}{\partial y^2} \qquad\qquad 8.$$

Applying the operator $\nabla_2^2 D/Dt$ to Equation 4, and using Equations 6 and 7, we obtain

$$\bar{\rho}\left(\frac{D}{Dt}\right)^2\nabla_2^2 w = \frac{D}{Dt}\frac{\partial}{\partial z}\left\{-\frac{D}{Dt}\left(\bar{\rho}\frac{\partial w}{\partial z}\right) + \bar{\rho}\left(U'\frac{\partial}{\partial x} + V'\frac{\partial}{\partial y}\right)w\right\} + g\frac{d\bar{\rho}}{dz}\nabla_2^2 w \qquad 9.$$

which, after simplification, becomes

$$\bar{\rho}\left(\frac{D}{Dt}\right)^2\nabla_2^2 w = -\left(\frac{D}{Dt}\right)^2\frac{\partial}{\partial z}\left(\bar{\rho}\frac{\partial w}{\partial z}\right) + \frac{D}{Dt}$$
$$\cdot\left\{(\bar{\rho}U')'\frac{\partial w}{\partial x} + (\bar{\rho}V')'\frac{\partial w}{\partial y}\right\} + g\bar{\rho}'\nabla_2^2 w \qquad 10.$$

in which the accents indicate differentiation with respect to z. This is the fundamental equation governing waves of small amplitude in a stratified incompressible fluid with wind shear. Before going on to more detailed discussions, we note that the boundary condition for Equation 10 at any rigid horizontal boundary is simply

$$w = 0 \qquad\qquad 11.$$

The free-surface condition is

$$\left[\frac{\partial}{\partial t} + (U + u)\frac{\partial}{\partial x} + (V + v)\frac{\partial}{\partial y} + w\frac{\partial}{\partial z}\right](\bar{p} + p) = 0 \qquad\qquad 12.$$

the linearized form of which is, upon utilization of Equation 1,

$$\frac{D}{Dt}p = g\bar{\rho}w \qquad\qquad 13.$$

Applying the operator $\nabla_2{}^2$ to this equation, and using Equation 7, we obtain finally, after canceling a factor $\bar{\rho}$,

$$\left(\frac{D}{Dt}\right)^2\frac{\partial w}{\partial z} - \frac{D}{Dt}\left\{\left(U'\frac{\partial}{\partial x} + v'\frac{\partial}{\partial y}\right)w\right\} = g\nabla_2{}^2 w \qquad\qquad 14.$$

as the boundary condition at the free surface.

 2. *Wave motion in a fluid otherwise at rest.*—The form of Equation 10 allows w to have an exponential time factor $e^{-i\sigma t}$. For the case $U = 0 = V$ Equation 10 becomes then, after division by σ^2,

$$\frac{\partial}{\partial z}\left(\bar{\rho}\,\frac{\partial w}{\partial z}\right) + \left(\bar{\rho} + \frac{g}{\sigma^2}\frac{d\bar{\rho}}{dz}\right)\nabla_2{}^2 w = 0 \qquad\qquad 15.$$

It is immediately clear that if [Görtler (14)]

$$\sigma^2 > \left(-\frac{g}{\bar{\rho}}\frac{d\bar{\rho}}{dz}\right)_{\max} \qquad\qquad 16.$$

in which $d\bar{\rho}/dz$ is negative since the fluid is tacitly assumed to be statically stable, Equation 15 is elliptic in type, and, in the absence of density discontinuities, i.e., of a free surface and interfaces, wave motion is impossible. The marginal frequency

$$N = \left(-\frac{g}{\bar{\rho}}\frac{d\bar{\rho}}{dz}\right)^{1/2}_{\max} \qquad\qquad 17.$$

is the upper limit of the possible frequencies (with the factor $1/2\pi$ omitted for simplicity) that wave motion can have in a stratified fluid. Note that if there is any discontinuity in density there will be no maximum of the possible frequencies. That N is indeed the maximum possible frequency is so obvious that it is not surprising that many people have found its significance independently, and that it is therefore variously named after Väisälä, Brunt, and others. It has been proposed that it be called the intrinsic frequency. But that would be a misnomer, because the fluid certainly does not intrinsically have N as the frequency of its oscillatory motion. In fact N is at the border of realizable frequencies. It is only as the upper limit of all possible frequencies that it is intrinsic with the fluid. Perhaps "limiting frequency" is a good term. If a solid body oscillates in a stratified fluid without density discontinuities (and therefore without a free surface, in particular) with a frequency higher than N, no wave motion is possible, and the disturbance will be local.

If we assume that the dependence of w (and of any other perturbation) on x and y is of the form

$$w = e^{-i\sigma t}S(x, y)w(z) \qquad 18.$$

in which $S(x, y)$ satisfies

$$(\nabla_2{}^2 + \alpha^2)S(x, y) = 0 \qquad 19.$$

and if $U = 0 = V$, then Equation 10 becomes, with accents indicating differentiation with respect to z,

$$(\bar{\rho}w')' - \alpha^2 \left(\bar{\rho} + \frac{g\bar{\rho}'}{\sigma^2} \right) w = 0 \qquad 20.$$

which was first obtained by Love (28), and the free-surface boundary condition, Equation 14, becomes

$$\sigma^2 w' = g\alpha^2 w \qquad 21.$$

w' and w to be evaluated at the mean position of the free surface. The boundary condition at the bottom, where $z = 0$, is $w(0) = 0$. The boundary condition at the upper surface is either Equation 11 or 21, depending on whether the surface is rigid or free. Whether the upper surface is rigid or free, Equations 20, 11, and 21 define an eigenvalue problem, the solution of which yields the functional dependence of σ^2 on α^2. The relation between σ^2 and α^2 is called the dispersion equation, and the waves are dispersive in the sense that waves of different values of α (which will be called the wavenumber) will have different frequencies, and unless confined, will disperse, so that wave trains with different wavenumbers will eventually separate.

If there are density discontinuities in the fluid, so that $\bar{\rho}$ has finite jumps at certain positions of z, the interfacial condition at each location of discontinuity can be derived by demanding the pressure to be continuous across the interface. The derivation is similar to that of Equation 21, and the result is

$$(\bar{\rho}w')_u - (\bar{\rho}w')_l + \frac{\alpha^2}{\sigma^2} g\Delta\bar{\rho}w = 0 \qquad 22.$$

in which the subscripts indicate, respectively, the upper and lower fluid at the interface, and

$$\Delta\bar{\rho} = \bar{\rho}_l - \bar{\rho}_u \qquad 23.$$

The interfacial condition, Equation 22, can also be obtained simply by integrating Equation 20 across the interface over a vanishing interval. Since $\bar{\rho}$ is discontinuous $\bar{\rho}w'$ must also be, according to Equation 20. Integration in such an interval in the Stieltjes sense produces Equation 22. If there are density discontinuities, Equation 20 is solved in each of the regions of continuous $\bar{\rho}$, and the solutions are required to satisfy the boundary conditions and the interfacial conditions. The result is again a relationship between σ^2 and α^2.

If we consider the motion of a continuously stratified fluid confined between two rigid planes due to a body oscillating at a frequency σ, then if σ exceeds N, the parenthesis before w in Equation 20 is positive. Hence w is non-oscillatory if α is real, as is well known through the Sturm-Liouville theory, and wave motion is impossible because the boundary conditions cannot be satisfied. However there are negative eigenvalues of α^2 for the assigned σ^2. Hence disturbances of a local nature, similar to those in potential flows, do exist. All these confirm the discussion of Equation 15 concerning the limiting frequency N.

The forms of Equations 20, 11, and 21 indicate clearly that whether the waves are two-dimensional or three-dimensional, the mathematical problem is quite the same. As far as normal modes are concerned, we can therefore concentrate on two-dimensional waves. From another point of view, three-dimensional waves with diamond patterns can always be obtained by super-position of two two-dimensional wave trains propagating in two different directions, and again we can concentrate on two-dimensional waves, as far as normal modes are concerned.

3. *Two-dimensional wave motion.*—For two-dimensional wave motion the factor $S(x, y)e^{-i\sigma t}$ can be replaced by $\exp ik(x-ct)$, in which k is the wave-number and replaces α, c is the wave velocity, and $kc=\sigma$. Equation 20 then assumes the form

$$(\bar{\rho}w')' - \left(k^2\bar{\rho} + \frac{g\bar{\rho}'}{c^2}\right)w = 0 \qquad 24.$$

and Equations 21 and 22 become

$$w' = \frac{g}{c^2}w \qquad 25.$$

and

$$(\bar{\rho}w')_u - (\bar{\rho}w')_l + \frac{g}{c^2}\Delta\bar{\rho}w = 0 \qquad 26.$$

respectively. At a rigid surface the boundary condition is still Equation 11.

For a given positive k^2, the nature of the eigenvalues of c^2 can be ascertained by multiplying Equation 24 by w^*, the complex conjugate of w, and integrating over the depth. For illustration, we shall consider the case of finite depth d and no density discontinuities, the upper surface being rigid as a consequence. Such an integration produces, after a change of sign,

$$\int_0^d \bar{\rho}\,|w'|^2dz + k^2\int_0^d \bar{\rho}\,|w|^2dz + \frac{g}{c^2}\int\bar{\rho}'\,|w|^2dz = 0 \qquad 27.$$

since $w(0)$ and $w(d)$ are both zero. If $\bar{\rho}'$ is positive throughout, c^2 must then be negative, which means that the fluid is unstable, since w has the factor $\exp(-ikct)$, k is real, and one of the c's will make w grow with time. If $\bar{\rho}'$ is negative throughout, c^2 is positive, and wave motion is possible. If $\bar{\rho}'$ is partly positive and partly negative, then according to the Sturm-Liouville theory both positive and negative eigenvalues of c^2 exist, and the fluid is unstable, though wave motion is also possible. We shall assume that $\bar{\rho}'$ is negative throughout.

If there are density discontinuities, Equations 25 and 26 must be used in addition to 11. But an equation like 27 can be readily obtained, which allows us to draw the same conclusion.

However, the demonstration of the nature of c^2 does not prove the existence of eigenvalues of c^2. This existence is guaranteed by the Sturm-Liouville theory for a continuously stratified fluid between rigid boundaries, as noted by Groen (16) and independently by Yih (52). If a free surface is present, the proof of existence is more difficult, since Equation 25 involves c^2. However, this has been achieved by Bôcher (6). Bôcher's proof has been extended by Yih (54; 55, pp. 48–52) to the general case of an arbitrary number of density jumps in an otherwise continuously stratified fluid. For lack of space we shall not go into the details of the proofs here, but shall state some of the results concerning c^2 as follows:

(a) For a given k^2 and a finite depth d, there are a denumerably infinite number of eigenvalues for c^2. Let these be arranged in descending order as $c_1{}^2$, $c_2{}^2$, $c_3{}^2$, ... The greatest, $c_1{}^2$, is less than N^2/k^2, N being the limiting frequency, and zero is the limit point of these eigenvalues. If the upper surface is rigid, the eigenfunction f_1 corresponding to $c_1{}^2$ has one zero in the interval $0 < z \leq d$ (two in the closed interval), and f_n (corresponding to $c_n{}^2$) has n zeros in the same interval. If the upper surface is free, then f_1 has no zeros and f_n has $n-1$ zeros in the same interval. For the same k^2, c_n and f_n are the eigenvalue and eigenfunction of the nth mode.

(b) For the same mode, c^2 decreases as k^2 increases. This means that for any mode the longest waves propagate the fastest. This result for the general case including density discontinuities was proved by Yih (54; 55, pp. 48–52) and by variational methods by Yanowitch (48). Since the group velocity is given by

$$c_g = \frac{d\sigma}{dk} = c + k\frac{dc}{dk} \qquad 28.$$

this also means that the group velocity of normal modes is always less than the phase velocity, since c can be taken as positive for this discussion without loss of generality. Of course, the effect of surface tension at a free surface or interface, if any, has been neglected, so that this statement is true only for gravity waves.

(c) For a given k^2 and a specified mode, c^2 increases if $\bar{\rho}$ decreases in such a way that $\bar{\rho}'$ is nowhere decreased, or if $\bar{\rho}'$ increases in such a way that $\bar{\rho}$ is nowhere increased, and c^2 decreases if $\bar{p}$ increases without increasing $\bar{p}'$ anywhere, or $\bar{p}'$ decreases without decreasing $\bar{p}$ anywhere. This result is useful chiefly in comparing the wave speeds in different stratified fluids.

　　4. *Propagation of disturbance in three dimensions.*—Although normal modes of three-dimensional waves propagating in two horizontal dimensions can be obtained from normal modes of two-dimensional waves propagating in one dimension, knowledge concerning such waves does not illuminate the propagation of arbitrary disturbances in three dimensions, which will be briefly discussed here.

　　To achieve the greatest degree of simplicity, we shall consider the mean-density distribution

$$\bar{\rho} = \rho_0 e^{-2\beta z} \qquad\qquad 29.$$

Then N^2 is just $2\beta g$, since that is the constant value of $-g\bar{\rho}'/\bar{\rho}$. Suppose that the fluid is set in motion by a body oscillating with frequency σ. If there is no mean flow, so that $U = 0 = V$, Equation 10 becomes

$$\left(\frac{\partial^2}{\partial t^2} + N^2\right)\nabla_2{}^2 w + \frac{\partial^2}{\partial t^2}\left(\frac{\partial^2 w}{\partial z^2} - 2\beta\,\frac{\partial w}{\partial z}\right) = 0 \qquad\qquad 30.$$

the solution of which with the frequency σ is [Wu (46)]

$$w(x, y, z, t) = f(z)\exp\left[i(k_x x + k_y y - \sigma t)\right] \qquad\qquad 31.$$

in which

$$f(z) = e^{\beta z}\left[A e^{ik_z z} + B e^{-ik_z z}\right] \qquad\qquad 32.$$

$$k_z = \left[\left(\frac{N^2}{\sigma^2} - 1\right)k_r{}^2 - \beta^2\right]^{1/2}, \qquad k_r{}^2 = k_x{}^2 + k_y{}^2 \qquad\qquad 33.$$

Hence $k_z{}^2$ is positive or negative accordingly as

$$\sigma \underset{>}{\overset{<}{=}} \sigma_c = \frac{N}{\sqrt{1 + (\beta/k_r)^2}} \qquad\qquad 34.$$

Equation 33 can be rewritten as

$$\frac{\sigma}{N} = \frac{k_r}{(k_r{}^2 + k_z{}^2 + \beta^2)^{1/2}} \qquad\qquad 35.$$

If $k_z{}^2$ is positive, so that the motion is oscillatory in all three directions, the phase velocity is defined by the kinematic relation

$$c = \frac{\sigma}{k}\,n \qquad\qquad 36.$$

in which

$$k = |\mathbf{k}|, \qquad \mathbf{k} = (k_x, k_y, k_z), \quad \text{and} \quad \mathbf{n} = \mathbf{k}/k \qquad\qquad 37.$$

Then[1]

---

[1] Note that this definition of c is not the same as the definition of c as σ/k_x, which has been found useful in the reduction of three-dimensional normal modes to two-dimensional ones. See Yih (55, pp. 23–26), where c' is the c here.

STRATIFIED FLOWS 87

$$c = |c| = \frac{\sigma}{k} = \frac{Nk_r}{k(k^2 + \beta^2)^{1/2}} \tag{38}$$

Equations 35 and 38 show that for a given k, waves propagate the fastest in the horizontal direction. Note that if real k_x and k_y are prescribed, and the fluid extends from $z=0$ to $z=d$, then the boundary conditions determine the eigenvalues of k_z and hence of σ. Then the mode is the normal mode of three-dimensional waves propagating in two dimensions. However, if we regard the disturbance to be arbitrary and σ as given, Equation 33 merely gives a relationship between k_z and k_r, and the solution, Equation 31, does not represent a normal mode propagating in two dimensions, but stands for a rather more general disturbance which is dynamically possible.

The group velocity c_g, defined by

$$c_g = \left(\frac{\partial \sigma}{\partial k_x}, \quad \frac{\partial \sigma}{\partial k_y}, \quad \frac{\partial \sigma}{\partial k_z} \right) \tag{39}$$

is given by

$$(c_{gx}, c_{gy}) = \frac{A}{k_r} \frac{k_z^2 + \beta^2}{k^2 + \beta^2} (k_x, k_y), \qquad c_{gz} = -\frac{A k_r k_z}{k^2 + \beta^2} \tag{40}$$

Wu (46) noted that $c_{gy}/c_{gx} = c_y/c_x$, and hence c and c_g are in the same vertical plane. For a disturbance with a specified σ,

$$\left(\frac{\beta}{k} \right)^2 = M^2 \sin^2 \theta - \cos^2 \theta \tag{41}$$

where

$$M^2 = \left(\frac{N}{\sigma} \right)^2 - 1, \qquad \theta = \tan^{-1}(k_r/k_z)$$

then

$$\theta_M \leq \theta \leq \pi - \theta_M, \qquad \theta_M = \cot^{-1} M \tag{42}$$

which was found by Görtler (14) by consideration of the characteristics. Wu (46) noted that, from Equations 40 and 35,

$$\frac{c_{gz}}{c_{gr}} = -\frac{k_r k_z}{k_z^2 + \beta^2} = -\frac{1}{M^2} \cot \theta \tag{43}$$

so that disturbances are bounded away from the vertical cone $r = \pm Mz$, and can only reach the region outside of it, confirming Equation 42 by group-velocity arguments.

Mowbray & Rarity (33) investigated the propagation in the x-z plane, and confirmed Equation 42, for $k_y = 0$, both analytically and experimentally. Experimental verification of Equation 42 for wave motion in the x-z plane, however, was carried out first by Görtler (14).

Mowbray & Rarity (33) discussed the case of short waves, for which the $k_z^2 + \beta^2$ in Equation 40 can be replaced by k_z, and found the interesting result that for such waves c is perpendicular to c_g. Since c is normal to the crests of the waves, this means that c_g is along them, a most intriguing situation. Energy is thus propagated from the source of disturbance along the crest of waves in the permissible region specified by Equation 42. If the disturbance is created by a vertical plate oscillating vertically, the sources of disturbance are the edges of the plate.

The group velocity defined by Equation 39 has kinematic and dynamic significances. After the waves of all wavenumbers have sufficiently dispersed, so that

$$\frac{\partial k}{\partial t} + \text{grad}\,\sigma = 0 \qquad 44.$$

is valid, it can be shown that c_g defined by Equation 39 is the velocity with which wavenumbers are propagated, or the velocity with which a point with a given k moves in space, provided N is constant. If N varies, σ is a function not only of k but also of z, and the wavenumber is no longer conserved on a point moving with the group velocity. Waves are then reflected internally and may well be trapped in regions of limited vertical extent, as shown by Mowbray & Rarity (33). From a dynamical point of view, if N is constant, as it is in their case, the demonstration of Broer (7a) by the method of stationary phase applies, and the group velocity is the velocity of energy propagation. It should, however, be remembered that here also it is tacitly assumed that the different wave components have been sufficiently dispersed for Equation 44 to be valid. Otherwise there would arise the question of for what wavenumber the group velocity is evaluated. Also, since the method of stationary phase is used, the shorter the waves the more exact the conclusion of Broer.

A few words are necessary to explain why, for the normal modes of two-dimensional waves propagating horizontally, the group velocity is in the same direction as the phase velocity, whereas for propagation in the x-z plane this is not so, and for $\beta^2 < <k_z^2$ the two velocities can even be perpendicular. The former is in fact the result of superposition of infinitely many disturbances continually reflected at both the upper and lower boundaries. Although the energy of each reflected disturbance is propagated along the crests, the resultant propagation of the interwoven, roughly diamond-shaped disturbances is in the x direction. The diamond pattern cannot be seen any more, because it is obscured by the continual reflections of the original disturbances, which furthermore are continuous to start with.

It is appropriate to mention here the study of Wu & Mei (47) of the two-dimensional waves created in a stratified fluid by a line source moving horizontally in a direction normal to its length. The two-dimensional motion due to a line disturbance moving arbitrarily has been studied by Rarity (36), and the three-dimensional motion produced by a point disturbance moving arbitrarily has been studied by Wu (46).

5. *Geophysical applications.*—Since the atmosphere and the oceans are stratified, it is to be expected that the dynamical equations for stratified flow

have many geophysical applications. Space does not allow a detailed account of these, and we shall merely mention a few representative works. The theories of Lyra (29), Queney (34, 35), and Scorer (38) on two-dimensional waves in the lee of mountain ranges all involve, after separation of variables, an ordinary differential equation of constant coefficients. Lyra treated a polytropic atmosphere, and used a Green's function ensuring the absence of upstream waves. Queney treated an isothermal atmosphere and used the Fourier transform to obtain the solution, the boundary condition on the ground being linearized. Scorer used a two-layer model which possesses discrete waves. Compressibility was taken into account by these authors. Lee waves of finite amplitude will be mentioned in Part III of this article.

The response of an ocean to stationary or moving wind-systems was studied by Rossby (37), Charney (8), Veronis & Stommel (45), and Veronis (44), who found that if the time-scale of the disturbance exceeds about one day, most of the energy in the response resides in quasi-geostrophic motions, i.e., motions in which the pressure gradient is nearly hydrostatic in the direction of the vertical, and nearly balances the Coriolis force in horizontal directions, the effect of the centrifugal acceleration being negligible. These motions are in the form of oscillations having a period of at least several days, as a consequence of the variation of the vertical component of the Earth's rotation (the so-called β-effect). The response of a stratified ocean to a sinusoidally distributed wind stress was studied by Veronis & Stommel (45). For a homogeneous ocean, the special case of the "tweak," for which the wind-stress is a delta function of time and space, was investigated numerically by Veronis (45a) for horizontally nondivergent flows, and analytically by Longuet-Higgins (27) who used the Fourier transform and the method of stationary phase to evaluate his integrals, and considered horizontally divergent flows. He also investigated the disturbance by a depression moving horizontally in a straight line. The waves are planetary in nature, and the wave pattern for the "tweak" is similar to the Kelvin-wave pattern. Longuet-Higgins (27) generalized his results to a two-layer system.

6. *Stability*.—The stability of one-dimensional stratified flows with $V=0$ and w given by Equations 18 and 19 can be obtained directly from Equation 10, and is

$$(\bar{\rho}w')' + \left[\frac{(\bar{\rho}U')'}{c-U} - k^2\bar{\rho} - \frac{g\bar{\rho}'}{(c-U)^2}\right]w = 0 \qquad 45.$$

in which the w is the $w(z)$ in Equation 18, $c=c_r+ic_i$ is defined by $\sigma=kc$, k is the wavenumber and replaces α in Equation 19, and accents indicate differentiation with respect to z. Replacing w by $ik(U-c)F(z)$, we can write Equation 45 as

$$[\bar{\rho}(U-c)^2F']' - [\bar{\rho}'g + k^2\bar{\rho}(U-c)^2]F = 0 \qquad 46.$$

Howard (18) set $W=U-c$ and $G=W^{1/2}F$, and transformed Equation 46 to

$$(\bar{\rho}WG')' - [\tfrac{1}{2}(\bar{\rho}U')' + k^2\bar{\rho}W + \bar{\rho}W^{-1}(\tfrac{1}{4}U'^2 - g\beta)]G = 0 \qquad 47.$$

90   YIH

where $\beta = -\bar{\rho}'/\bar{\rho}$. (This β is twice the β in Equation 29.) The stability or instability of flow corresponds to $c_i = 0$ or $c_i \neq 0$, respectively. If $c_i \neq 0$, then multiplication of (47) by G^*, the complex conjugate of G, and integration between the boundaries, assumed fixed, yield the result

$$\int_0^d \bar{\rho}(|G'|^2 + k^2|G|^2)dz + \int_0^d \bar{\rho}(g\beta - \tfrac{1}{4}U'^2)|G/W|^2dz = 0 \qquad 48.$$

which proves that if $g\beta \geq \tfrac{1}{4}U'^2$ then c_i must be zero—a result due to Miles (31). The elegant proof reproduced here is Howard's (18).

By working with Equation 46 Howard (18) also showed that

$$[c_r - \tfrac{1}{2}(a+b)]^2 + c_i^2 \leq [\tfrac{1}{2}(a-b)]^2 \qquad 49.$$

in which a is $U_{\max}$ and b is $U_{\min}$. This is Howard's semi-circle theorem, the beauty of which is much appreciated by this writer. Howard (18) found the following bound for the growth rate kc_i:

$$k^2c_i^2 \leq \max(\tfrac{1}{4}U'^2 - g\bar{\rho}) \qquad 50.$$

The stability of two layers of fluid flowing between inclined planes was investigated by Graebel (15), Sangster (41), and Kao (20). The stability of a continuously stratified inviscid liquid has been studied by Drazin (9), Drazin & Howard (11), and by Howard (18) for long waves. Drazin (10) also studied the stability of a fluid with variable density and viscosity. The instability of viscosity discontinuities resulting in the formation of long waves has been demonstrated by Yih (56).

Finally, the experimental works on the behavior of a fluid in a rotating annulus, heated at the outer rim and cooled at the inner one, by Fultz (13) and Hide (17), definitely have geophysical bearings. The flow patterns they obtained showed regular azimuthal variations. The phenomenon was analyzed quite successfully by Kuo (22).

Part III. Steady Flows of Finite Amplitude

1. Equations governing steady three-dimensional motion.—Although the basic equations governing the motion of an inviscid, incompressible, and nondiffusive fluid of variable density have been presented in Section 2 of Part I, these equations need to be integrated in order to arrive at simpler equations which offer a little more promise for their solution. For unsteady flows the task of integration has yet to be performed, but for steady flows the results are known [Yih (58)].

For steady flows the equation of incompressibility is

$$(\mathbf{u}\cdot\mathbf{grad})\,\rho = 0 \qquad 1.$$

which clearly shows that streamlines are imbedded in surfaces of constant density. As mentioned in Section 5 of Part I, vorticity lines are also imbedded in surfaces of constant density, provided, as we shall assume here, that the flow has started from rest. Since $\mathbf{u}$ and the vorticity vector $\boldsymbol{\xi}$ are both solenoidal, they can both be expressed as the vector product of two scalar functions, one of which is simply ρ since in a surface of constant density both the streamlines and the vorticity lines are imbedded. Thus

$$u = \operatorname{grad} a \times \operatorname{grad} \rho, \qquad \text{2a.}$$
$$\xi = \operatorname{grad} b \times \operatorname{grad} \rho \qquad \text{2b.}$$

in which

$$\xi = \operatorname{curl} u \qquad 3.$$

The vector equation of motion

$$(\rho u \cdot \operatorname{grad})u = -\operatorname{grad} p - \rho \operatorname{grad} \Omega \qquad 4.$$

can be transformed by

$$u' = (\rho/\rho_0)^{1/2} u \qquad 5.$$

into

$$(\rho_0 u' \cdot \operatorname{grad})u' = -\operatorname{grad} p - \rho \operatorname{grad} \Omega \qquad 6.$$

which can be further written as

$$-\rho_0 u' \times \xi' = -\operatorname{grad} \chi - \rho \operatorname{grad} \Omega \qquad 7.$$

in which

$$\xi' = \operatorname{curl} u', \qquad \chi = p + \tfrac{1}{2}\rho q^2 \qquad 8.$$

q being the speed. Since u' and ξ' are still solenoidal, and since $\xi' \cdot \operatorname{grad} \rho$ vanishes if $\xi \cdot \operatorname{grad} \rho$ does, we can write

$$u' = \operatorname{grad} \alpha \times \operatorname{grad} \rho, \qquad \xi' = \operatorname{grad} \beta \times \operatorname{grad} \rho \qquad 9.$$

and therefrom

$$u' \times \xi' = -(u' \cdot \operatorname{grad} \beta)\operatorname{grad} \rho = (\xi' \cdot \operatorname{grad} \alpha)\operatorname{grad} \rho \qquad 10.$$

If this is substituted into Equation 7 and the result integrated after multiplication by dx, the equation becomes

$$\rho_0 \xi' \cdot \operatorname{grad} \alpha = \frac{dH}{d\rho} - \Omega = \frac{dH}{d\rho} - gz \qquad 11.$$

in which

$$H = \chi + \rho gz \qquad 12.$$

and ξ' is evaluated as $\operatorname{curl} u'$ in terms of α and ρ. The other equation is simply

$$\xi' \cdot \operatorname{grad} \rho = 0 \qquad 13.$$

in which ξ' is again in terms of α and ρ. Equations 11 and 12 are the final equations governing steady three-dimensional motions. Note that Equation 2b is already an equation obtained by considering the circulation along a constant-density surface, and therefore a result obtained through an integration. See Section 5, Part I. In addition Equation 11 has been obtained from Equation 7 by integration.

2. *Equation governing steady two-dimensional flow.*—For two-dimensional flows Equation 13 is always satisfied, and if we use ψ' for the stream function, so that

92   **YIH**

$$u' = \psi'_z, \qquad w' = -\psi'_x \qquad\qquad 14.$$

and take

$$\alpha = (d\psi'/d\rho)y \qquad\qquad 15.$$

Equation 11 becomes, since neither ρ nor ψ' depends on y,

$$\psi'_{xx} + \psi'_{zz} + \frac{g}{\rho_0} z \frac{d\rho}{d\psi'} = \frac{1}{\rho_0} \frac{dH}{d\psi'} \qquad\qquad 16.$$

which is the simplified form [Yih (49, 53)] of

$$\psi_{xx} + \psi_{zz} + \frac{1}{\rho} \frac{d\rho}{d\psi} \left(\frac{\psi_x^2 + \psi_z^2}{2} + gz \right) = f(\psi) \qquad\qquad 17.$$

which is the equation of Madame Dubreil-Jacotin (12b), rediscovered by Long (23).

We note in passing that equations similar to 11 and 13 governing steady flows of an inviscid nondiffusive compressible fluid can be derived in a similar way, and that from these equations an equation for two-dimensional flows, similar to Equation 15, can be obtained for a compressible fluid.

Equation 16 is linear if ρ and H are polynomials of at most the second degree in ψ'. The many linear cases were discussed by Long (23, 24) and Yih (49, 53), the former starting with Equation 17 and the latter starting with Equation 16. In the following sections, a few examples of the linear cases will be chosen for discussion.

3. Two-dimensional stratified flow into a sink.—Consider an infinite channel of depth d, with a line sink situated across the bottom at $x=0=z$. The width of the channel is arbitrary, and for convenience let the upper surface be bounded by a rigid plane. The results are not seriously affected if the upper surface is free. Since the flow is symmetric about the plane $x=0$, we shall consider the flow in the domain

$$0 \geq x > -\infty, \qquad 0 \leq z \leq d$$

Let U' be the value of u' at infinity, assumed constant, and

$$\rho = \rho_0 - (\rho_0 - \rho_1)\eta \qquad\qquad 18.$$

Then with

$$\xi = \frac{x}{d}, \qquad \eta = \frac{z}{d}, \qquad \Psi = \frac{\psi'}{U'd}$$

the condition at infinity is given by

$$\Psi = \eta, \qquad \nabla^2\Psi = 0, \qquad \frac{d\rho}{d\psi'} = \frac{\rho_0 - \rho_1}{U'd}$$

and the function $dH/d\psi'$ can be determined. The resulting equation is

$$\left(\frac{\partial^2}{\partial \xi^2} + \frac{\partial^2}{\partial \eta^2} \right) \Psi - F^{-2}\eta = -F^{-2}\Psi \qquad\qquad 19.$$

where

$$F^2 = \frac{U'^2}{g'd}, \qquad g' = \frac{\rho_0 - \rho_1}{\rho_0} \qquad\qquad 20.$$

The boundary conditions are

$$\Psi = 0 \quad \text{at} \quad \eta = 0$$
$$\Psi = 1 \quad \text{at} \quad \eta = 1 \quad \text{and at} \quad \xi = 0, \qquad 0 < \eta \leq 1$$
$$\Psi = \eta \quad \text{at} \quad \xi = -\infty$$

and the solution satisfying these boundary conditions, obtained by the method of separation of variables, is

$$\Psi = \eta + \frac{2}{\pi} \sum_{n=1}^{\infty} \frac{1}{n} \exp\left[(n^2\pi^2 - F^{-2})^{1/2}\xi\right] \sin n\pi\eta \qquad\qquad 21.$$

This solution is not valid for $F < 1/\pi$, for then the condition $\Psi = \eta$ at $\xi = -\infty$, so crucial in the derivation of Equation 19, is violated.

The patterns of streamlines were given by Yih (49; or 55, pp. 84–85) for $F = \infty$, 0.5, 0.35, 0.32, and will not be given here again. Suffice it to say that for $F = \infty$ the pattern is identical with the pattern of irrotational flow for the same boundaries, and that as F decreases, the streamlines with the same values of Ψ generally sink a little, while an eddy gradually develops near the upper corner (where $\xi = 0$, $\eta = 1$), until at $F = 0.32$ the eddy is quite long (about two times d). The stratification in the upper half of an eddy is statically unstable, and if the eddy is elongated may actually be unstable to small disturbances. In such a case, perhaps a region of nearly stagnant fluid will develop, extending from the upper corner, and the solution may still be valid qualitatively in the flowing region. If $F < 1/\pi$, however, it is highly likely that separation will result. In fact it may occur when F is near but not less than $1/\pi$. The critical F for separation is therefore near $1/\pi$, or $1/3$. This is of some physical significance, since selective withdrawal is a problem in civil engineering. What happens when F is low will be the subject for discussion in the following section.

4. *Two-dimensional flow into a sink at low Froude numbers.*—To see what happens at low Froude numbers to the sink flow just discussed, Debler (8b) conducted a series of experiments with saline water with a linear density stratification at infinity. His experiments showed (Fig. 1) that at low Froude numbers there is a stagnant layer on top of a layer flowing into the sink, and that the Froude number F_1 based on the discharge, the depth of the flowing layer $d_1(<d)$, and the density gradient at infinity is about 0.24, and nearly constant for all discharges.

That F_1 should remain constant for all discharges after separation is not fortuitous. In Figure 2 the density ρ_w in the wedge region can be assumed to be the same as ρ_A, the density along the dividing streamline. If we assume U' to be still constant in the flowing region, and use d_1 as the length scale and U' the velocity scale, so that

$$\xi = \frac{x}{d_1}, \qquad \eta = \frac{y}{d_1}, \qquad \Psi = \frac{\psi'}{U'd_1}, \qquad \text{and} \quad F_1^2 = \frac{U'^2}{g'd_1}$$

FIG. 1. Two-dimensional flow of a stratified fluid into a sink at a low Froude number, showing a stagnation region [Debler (8b)].

the differential equation governing the flow is

$$\left(\frac{\partial^2}{\partial \xi^2} + \frac{\partial^2}{\partial \eta^2}\right)\Psi - F_1^{-2}\eta = -F_1^{-2}\Psi \qquad 22.$$

with the boundary conditions $\Psi = 0$ at $\eta = 0$, $\Psi = 1$ at $\xi = 0$, $\eta \neq 0$, and $(\partial\Psi/\partial\xi)^2 + (\partial\Psi/\partial y)^2 = 1$ along the dividing streamline, where $\Psi = 1$. The last condition is simply the consequence of the Bernoulli equation and the hydrostatic condition along the dividing streamline. The solution of this differential system determines a value of F_1, which should be unique.

Kao (19) started from this idea and obtained an approximate solution for which $F = 0.345$, or $F_1 = 0.675$, for a ρ_w slightly different from ρ_A. The

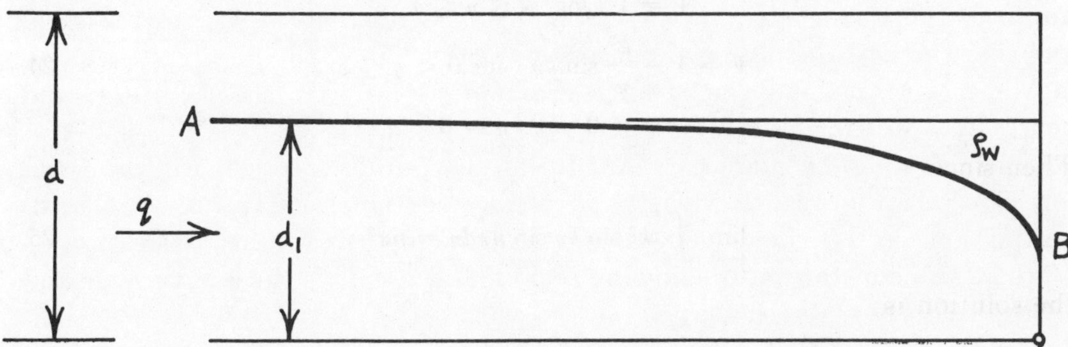

FIG. 2. Sketch of flow with stagnation zone.

value of F_1 appears too high.[2] It is not clear whether the solution is sensitive to numerical errors. But there is the deeper question of whether a flow dynamically possible in its terminal state is dynamically establishable. One example of this is the flow into the sink when there is no stratification. The correct solution is simply Equation 21 with $F = \infty$. But if we insist on solving Equation 22 with the boundary conditions specified for it, we can do so easily in that case, by the use of the hodograph and the Schwarz-Christoffel transformation. The flow so obtained is, however, unrealistic because for a strictly inviscid fluid its establishment involves the creation of a vortex sheet, and the separation pattern is not what a flow with large Reynolds number should have. It appears, however, that the F_1 should be and can be made unique for a stratified fluid, and if an accurate determination gives it a value somewhat above $1/\pi$, it is then a realistic value.

It is appropriate here to mention the nice work of Koh (21), who obtained a solution for the flow of a linearly stratified fluid of infinite extent into a sink, and considered both viscosity and diffusivity in his solution. Koh's solution does not merge into a solution for the inviscid and nondiffusive case. As the viscosity or diffusivity decreases toward zero, the region of validity of his solution recedes from the sink toward infinity, so that what happens near the sink for a fluid at large Reynolds numbers (based on an appropriate length) is not given by his solution.

5. *Prevention of separation at low Froude numbers.*—Since the separation just discussed, variously called blocking or the formation of upstream wake, is of theoretical as well as practical interest, we shall describe a method to prevent separation at low Froude numbers [Yih, O'Dell & Debler (59)]. Let

$$\frac{1}{2\pi} < F < \frac{1}{\pi}$$

and let

$$k\epsilon = \pi, \quad \text{and} \quad \epsilon \to 0 \qquad 23.$$

where ϵ is the height of the opening of the gate at $\xi = 0$. We can demand the sink to be a simple sink plus a quadrupole by specifying for the Ψ in Equation 19 the boundary conditions

$$\Psi = 1 \quad \text{for} \quad \epsilon \leq \eta \leq 1$$

$$\Psi = 1 - \frac{k^2}{\pi^3} \sin k\eta \quad \text{for } 0 < \eta \leq \epsilon \qquad 24.$$

$$\Psi = 0 \quad \text{at} \quad \eta = 0$$

Then since

$$\lim_{\epsilon \to 0} \int_0^\epsilon k^2 \sin k\eta \, \sin n\pi d\eta = n\pi^2 \qquad 25.$$

the solution is

---

[2] In Kao's work and on pp. 107–108 of Yih's book (55) the value 0.345 was erroneously given to F_1.

$$\Psi = \eta - \frac{2}{\pi} \sum_{n=1}^{\infty} \left(n - \frac{1}{n} \right) \sin n\pi\eta \, \exp \, (n^2\pi^2 - F^{-2})^{1/2}\xi \qquad 26.$$

Note that the term for $n=1$ vanishes, and gives no trouble at $\xi = -\infty$. As the streamlines are traced out (Fig. 3) it appears that the streamline $\Psi = 0$, rising from the bottom, can be replaced by a rigid boundary. When this was done and an experiment was carried out to see how the fluid would behave, a flow pattern (Fig. 4) very similar to the theoretical one was obtained. Hence it is possible to eliminate blocking at low Froude numbers. (As F decreases below $1/2\pi$, a similar analysis produces a more elaborate structure. One may conjecture that as F decreases indefinitely, the structure needed to prevent separation would be more and more like vanes guiding the flow into the sink.)

6. *Flow over a barrier and lee waves.*—Of all the linear forms that Equation 16 can take, the one that has the form of Equation 19 when non-dimensionalized is the simplest. This equation corresponds to a constant U' (which is u' at infinity) and the density distribution of Equation 18. Long (23) first used it to obtain solutions for the flow of a stratified fluid over a barrier for various values of the Froude number. For $F < 1/\pi$ Equation 19 has solutions periodic in ξ. These correspond to waves in the lee, since experiments and the analysis of Crapper (8a) for linear waves indicate the absence of upstream waves.

The particular solution of (19) is $\Psi = \eta$, and the complementary solution of Equation 19 by the method of separation of variables is of the form

$$\exp \left\{ (n^2\pi^2 - F^{-2})^{1/2}\xi \right\} \sin n\pi\xi \qquad 27.$$

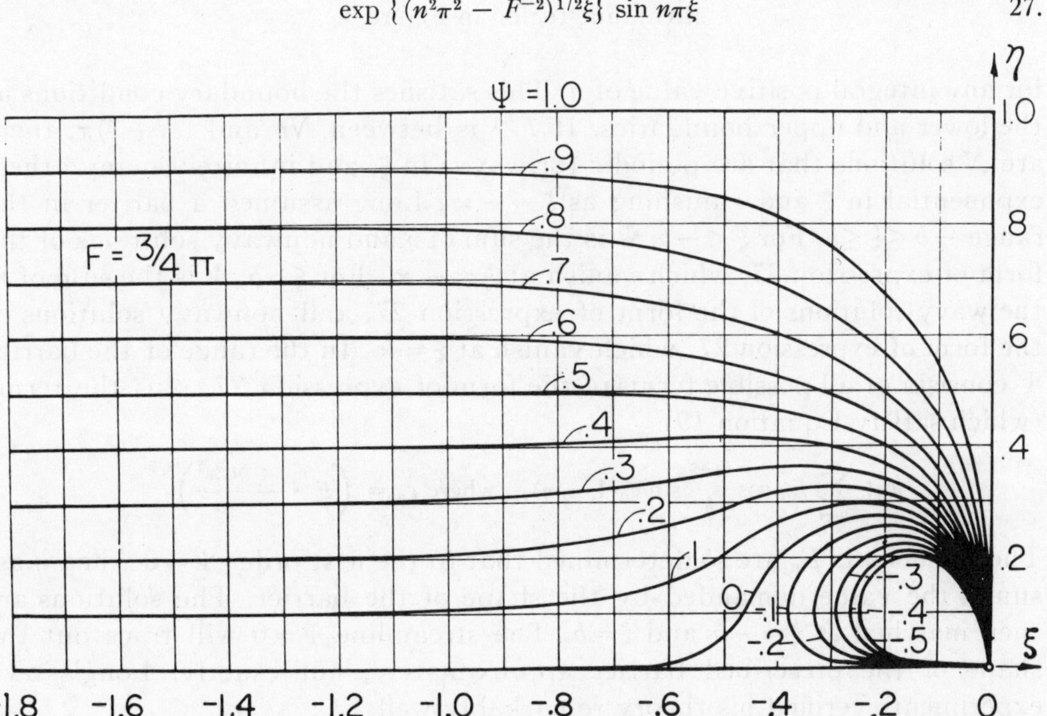

FIG. 3. Two-dimensional flow of a stratified fluid into a sink at which a quadrupole is also situated, at $F = 3/4\pi$, showing the lack of a stagnation zone.

FIG. 4. Actual flow pattern at $F = 3/4\pi$, with a structure simulating the closed-streamline region in Figure 3.

for any integral positive value of n. This satisfies the boundary conditions at the lower and upper boundaries. If F^{-1} is between $N\pi$ and $(N+1)\pi$, there are N solutions that are periodic (or wavy) in ξ, and infinitely many others exponential in ξ and vanishing as $\xi \to -\infty$. Long assumed a barrier in the range $-b \leq \xi \leq b$. For $\xi < -b$, Ψ is the sum of η and nonwavy solutions of the form of expression 27, which vanish at $\xi = -\infty$. For $\xi > b$, Ψ is the sum of η, the wavy solutions of the form of expression 27, and nonwavy solutions of the form of expression 27, which vanish at $\xi = \infty$. In the range of the barrier Ψ consists of all possible terms of the form of expression 27, plus the terms (which satisfy Equation 19)

$$\eta + \sum_{n=1}^{\infty} E_n \cos \frac{n\pi\xi}{b} \sin c_n(1 - \eta), \quad \text{where } c_n = \left(F^{-2} - \frac{n^2\pi^2}{b^2}\right)^{1/2}$$

The coefficients E_n are so determined that to the first order $\Psi = 0$ when η assumes the value demanded by the shape of the barrier. The solutions are then matched at $\xi = -b$ and $\xi = b$. The streamline $\Psi = 0$ will trace out the shape of the prescribed barrier approximately, not exactly. Long's own experiments verified his theory remarkably well.

Long's solution is appropriate for low barriers only. Yih (53) gave a method for obtaining solutions of Equation 19 corresponding to flow over barriers of arbitrary height, which consists in the use of singularities in the flow. A solution of Equation 19 which is the sum of η and nonwavy solutions of the type of expression 27 vanishing far upstream is matched at $\xi = 0$ to a downstream solution which is the sum of η and wavy and nonwavy terms of the form of expression 27 but with the nonwavy terms vanishing far downstream. At $\xi = 0$ the Ψ and $\partial\Psi/\partial\xi$ are continuous only over a part of the depth. Along the rest of the depth at $\xi = 0$, either Ψ or $\partial\Psi/\partial\xi$ has prescribed discontinuities, which produces the barrier. It was shown that when $F < /\pi$, the amplitudes or strengths of the lee-wave components depend only on certain integral properties of the singularity distribution, and hence not on the complete details of the shape of the barrier.

Neither Long (23) nor Yih (53) attempted to solve Equation 19 for a barrier of arbitrary height and prescribed shape and for ξ extending from minus infinity to plus infinity. Drazin & Moore (12) and Miles (32) considered flow in a channel of finite depth d over a vertical wall of height less than d. In their works, an integral equation has to be solved. This was done approximately by these authors. Drazin & Moore found that a solution is possible however high the barrier (not necessarily the vertical wall). But their solutions for low values of F and high barriers showed very complicated flow patterns in the lee of the wall. Miles stayed on the safe side and ruled out any solution with closed streamlines. The physical relevance of the solutions of Drazin & Moore for low F and high barriers will be discussed further in the next section. We note here that had the hodograph methods been applicable and a free-streamline theory been available for stratified fluids as for homogeneous fluids, the problem of flow over a vertical wall would have been treated differently and more satisfactorily, since separation is bound to occur in the flow at the sharp edge of the wall. Drazin & Moore also obtained a solution for a horizontal dipole in the stream governed by Equation 19. The solution is a special case of the solution by singularities.

7. *Blocking.*—The preceding four sections have been presented not only for their practical interest, especially to civil engineers concerned with the problem of selective withdrawal and to meteorologists interested in lee waves, but also because they bear upon the important phenomenon of blocking at low Froude numbers, which has been already indicated in Section 3 of Part I.

There has been a lot of interest in and discussion of the phenomenon of blocking, and there has been a good deal of confusion about what constitutes blocking. Many workers in the field, and the related fields of rotating fluids and magnetohydrodynamics, consider the phenomenon of blocking identical with the phenomenon of upstream wakes, and as a consequence consider blocking unavoidable as soon as the flow becomes so slow as to permit waves to propagate upstream.

For clarity we shall define blocking as the phenomenon of stagnation of a layer of the fluid leading from an obstacle upstream to infinity. So defined, blocking or the lack of blocking is not synonymous with the presence or absence of the upstream influence of an obstacle. To see this in the simplest way, consider a layer of homogeneous liquid of depth d flowing in a straight channel with a level bottom at a speed U greater than $\sqrt{(gd)}$. If now a low obstacle is put in the stream, it will flow over it without changing the condition upstream. If the height of the obstacle is gradually increased, a hydraulic jump will finally appear, which will be stationary somewhere over the obstacle. The discharge over the obstacle as well as the condition far upstream will remain the same. As the height of the obstacle becomes near the conjugate depth of the supercritical stream, the hydraulic jump can no longer be stationary, because the height of water over the obstacle is insufficient for the fluid to have the same discharge as upstream. The hydraulic jump will then travel upstream and the influence of the obstacle will eventually be felt far upstream. But there still is no blocking. As the height of the obstacle becomes much more than the conjugate depth of the original supercritical stream, not only will the hydraulic jump travel upstream but there will eventually be no flow. Blocking has then occurred.

If the stream is subcritical, so that U is less than $\sqrt{(gd)}$, then any obstacle, however low, will affect the condition far upstream. There will be no hydraulic jump for any obstacle. As the obstacle becomes higher and higher, the water level far upstream will rise, but the discharge will decrease. Finally, as the obstacle becomes as high as the total head of the original stream, there is no flow over the obstacle, and blocking has occurred.

From this discussion it is evident that an obstacle can have an influence far upstream even in a supercritical stream, provided it is sufficiently high, that it always has an influence far upstream in a subcritical stream, that in any case it can block the fluid, but does not do so unless it is sufficiently high. If now the fluid is supposed to be stratified, similar conclusions can be expected, except that now it is possible for part of the fluid (near the bottom) to be blocked, while the top part still flows. Although here the discharge over the obstacle is controlled by gravity, whereas in the flow into the sink or over a barrier in a closed channel, as discussed in Sections 3 through 6, the discharge is prescribed and maintained by suction at the sink or downstream, there is much similarity between the two situations.

A rigorous treatment of the problem of blocking in a stratified fluid is not yet possible. But the foregoing discussion allows us to make the following qualitative assertions concerning the problem of blocking in a stratified fluid with some confidence.

(*a*) If the stream is supercritical with respect to internal waves, that is, if no infinitesimal waves can travel upstream (this means $F > 1/\pi$ in Equation 19), then low barriers will have no upstream influence, and therefore no blocking. If the barrier is high, the original upstream condition may be affected, and partial blocking is possible.

(*b*) If the stream is subcritical with respect to internal waves, any barrier will have an upstream influence, but low barriers may not cause blocking. The change of upstream conditions when blocking is absent is obscured when we merely assume the final upstream conditions and seek a solution, as in Section 8. Such upstream conditions can be considered to be the result of putting the barrier in an initial stream with somewhat different velocity and density distributions. Upstream influence is then not denied, merely bypassed. The same can be said of an originally supercritical stream when a high barrier is introduced into it, producing change upstream but not blocking. If the barrier is high in an originally subcritical stream, blocking will occur. One important conclusion to be drawn from this consideration is that solutions of Equation 19 for $F < 1/\pi$ and for a low barrier are not spurious.

We now turn in particular to a discussion of the results described in Sections 3 through 6, in the light of the possibility of blocking. The solution, Equation 21, shows that [Yih (49, Fig. 4) or Yih (55, Fig. 9)] for $F = 0.32 > 1/\pi$ there is an elongated eddy in which the fluid is unstable, indicating that blocking of the fluid must have occurred at a Froude number near $1/\pi$ for such an extremely high barrier, whose height is very near d. It is likely that the initial velocity and density distributions are affected by the vertical wall. But as we mentioned before, we are concerned only with the terminal distributions in the flowing region. For $F < 1/\pi$ there must then be blocking unless a structure is built, as mentioned in Section 5. The flow without such a structure is the one described in Section 4 and indicated by Debler's experiments (8b). But with the structure shown in Figure 4, blocking does not occur even for $F < 1/\pi$ and a very high barrier, indicating that the shape of the boundary has a lot to do with the occurrence or absence of blocking. The results of Drazin & Moore (12) showed, in the present notation, patterns of flow over a vertical wall for $F^{-1} = 1.5, 2.5, 3.5$, and the height of the barrier equal to $d/4$ and $d/2$ ($d =$ depth of channel). The cases for $d/2$ and especially the cases for $F^{-1} = 3.5$ and 4.5 and barrier height $d/4$ have very complicated flow patterns. These are not likely to have the physical relevance of those obtained by Long (23) for low barriers, even though Long's flow patterns also have eddies, which are verified by his experiments. The patterns can be realized, of course, if the regions of closed streamlines are replaced by solid structures. Miles (32) ruled out any solution with closed streamlines, even though Long's patterns have been experimentally verified. Thus, in ignoring the possibility of blocking and insisting on a formal solution with prescribed upstream conditions, Drazin & Moore may have pushed the limit of validity of their solutions too far, and Miles, in ruling that the appearance of eddies immediately invalidates the solution, may be too much on the safe side.

The question can only be settled convincingly by a study of the establishment of flow. Such a study would be extremely difficult. Trustrum (43) did what can possibly be done at this time and used the Oseen approximation for such a study. Although the Oseen approximation is very much violated at the sink (which she considered) and far upstream as soon as blocking occurs, her conclusions are quite reasonable and in agreement with the qualitative assertions made here.

8. Gerstner waves in a stratified fluid.—It was Madame Dubreil-Jacotin (12a) who discovered that the well-known Gerstner waves are still possible for an incompressible fluid of any stratification. This remarkable fact is due to a very special character of the Gerstner waves, namely that in a frame of reference moving with the waves, the streamlines are also lines of constant pressure. Thus the stratification of the fluid, which makes the density different from streamline to streamline, but the same on the same streamline, does not disturb the satisfaction of the dynamical equations. Later, Yih (56) discovered that the very special property of Gerstner waves allows them to be interpreted, by a rotating of coordinate axes, as edge waves.

9. Periodic waves of finite amplitude.—Waves created in a quiet stratified fluid are governed by Equations 16 or 17, in a reference frame moving with the waves. For special cases these equations are linear, and if then they admit periodic solutions the amplitude is quite arbitrary. If, however, the waves are produced by a body moving in otherwise quiet fluid, Equations 16 or 17 will not be linear, and solutions for waves of finite amplitude can only be obtained by iteration, starting with the solution for linear waves. For an exponentially distributed density the calculation has been done by this writer (unpublished). The results are rather lengthy, but the general features of the waves are quite similar to those of gravity waves of finite amplitude in a stratified fluid, for which Equation 16 is linear.

Standing internal waves of finite amplitude have been studied in an excellent paper by Thorpe (42), who also presented beautiful photographs to support his theory.

10. Internal solitary and cnoidal waves.—In a paper remarkable for its elegance and originality, Benjamin (1) gave results for solitary and cnoidal waves of finite amplitude and permanent form in a stratified incompressible fluid. The idea is rather simple, and can be simply represented. He started by defining the quantity (ψ = stream function)

$$\int_A^B (p\,dz + \rho u\,d\psi) \qquad\qquad 28.$$

between two points A and B, which is independent of the path, provided the flow is steady and there is no singularity between any two different paths, this independence being a consequence of the momentum principle. If we perform the integration at a vertical section between the bottom, where $z = 0$, and the upper boundary, where $z = h$, and evaluate p in terms of H given by Equations 12 and 8, we can write the integral as

$$S = \int_0^h \{H + \tfrac{1}{2}\rho(\psi_z{}^2 - \psi_x{}^2) - g\rho z\}dz \qquad\qquad 29.$$

If we adopt a coordinate system traveling with the wave or waves to the left, the flow is steady with respect to that system. In the case of the solitary wave the flow far upstream is parallel. In the case of cnoidal waves we can consider them to have been created by a moving barrier of special shape, far downstream of which the cnoidal waves are in their pure form and far upstream of which the flow is parallel. In the parallel part of the flow the height of a particle will be denoted by η. (Note that this definition of η is different from that of the η in Equation 19.) The elevation z of the same particle at other places will then depend on x. Thus for any particle

$$z = z(x, \eta) \qquad 30.$$

The velocity $W(\eta)$ far upstream is $U(\eta)+c$, if $U(\eta)$ is the velocity with respect to fixed coordinates and c the wave speed. Obviously

$$\frac{d\psi}{d\eta} = W(\eta) \qquad 31.$$

and

$$u = \psi_y = W(\eta)/z_\eta, \qquad v = -\psi_x = W(\eta)\frac{z_x}{z_\eta} \qquad 32.$$

since ψ is a function of η only, and $\partial\eta/\partial x$ for constant z is $-z_x/z_\eta$. Then, with Q denoting ρW^2,

$$S = \int_0^{h_0} \left\{ H + \frac{1}{2} Q \left(\frac{1 - z_x^2}{z_\eta^2} \right) - g\rho z \right\} z_\eta d\eta \qquad 33.$$

and far upstream

$$S_0 = \int_0^{h_0} \left\{ H + \tfrac{1}{2}Q - g\rho\eta \right\} d\eta \qquad 34.$$

When wave motion is present we can write

$$z = \eta + \epsilon\zeta(x, \eta) \qquad 35.$$

in which ϵ is a small finite number. If we now evaluate $S - S_0$ in powers of ϵ, we have, to the first power,

$$S - S_0 = \epsilon \int_0^{h_0} \left\{ (H - \tfrac{1}{2}Q - g\rho\eta)\zeta_\eta - g\rho\zeta \right\} d\eta$$

$$= \epsilon \int_0^{h_0} (p_0\zeta_\eta - g\rho\zeta)d\eta = \epsilon\left[p_0\zeta \right]_0^{h_0} \qquad 36.$$

since $dp_0/d\eta = -g\rho$. Since $\zeta = 0$ at the bottom and either $p_0 = 0$ or $\zeta = 0$ at the upper surface, $S - S_0$ vanishes to the first order in ϵ.

The Bernoulli equation at the free surface is

$$H(h_0) = \frac{1}{2}Q + g\rho h_0 = \frac{1}{2}Q\left(\frac{1 + z_x^2}{z_\eta^2} \right) + g\rho z \qquad 37.$$

Using Equations 35 and 37, and linearizing in ϵ, we obtain

$$Q\zeta_\eta = g\rho\zeta \quad \text{at} \quad \eta = h_0 \qquad 38.$$

as the free-surface condition for infinitesimal waves. With this condition, we are ready to calculate $S - S_0$ to the second order in ϵ. To $O(\epsilon^2)$, Equations 33 and 34 give

$$S - S_0 = \epsilon^2 \int_0^{h_0} \{ \tfrac{1}{2} Q(\zeta_\eta^2 - \zeta_x^2) - g\rho\zeta\zeta_\eta \} d\eta$$

$$= - \tfrac{1}{2}\epsilon^2 \int_0^{h_0} \{ Q\zeta_x^2 + (Q\zeta_\eta)_\eta \zeta - g\rho_\eta\zeta^2 \} d\eta$$

39.

an integrated term

$$\tfrac{1}{2}\epsilon^2 \{ \zeta(Q\zeta_\eta - g\rho\zeta) \}_0^{h_0}$$

having been dropped because it vanishes by virtue of the boundary conditions, whether the upper surface is rigid or free.

For solitary waves $S = S_0$. For periodic waves S is different from S_0 but is independent of x, since the bottom is flat in the part of the fluid where waves have been established. Differentiating Equation 39 with respect to x, we have then, in any case,

$$0 = - \epsilon^2 \int_0^{h_0} \zeta_x \{ Q\zeta_{xx} + (Q\zeta_\eta)_\eta - g\rho_\eta\zeta \} d\eta \qquad 40.$$

for all values of x in the region occupied by waves. Since ζ_x is not zero for all x, this suggests that

$$Q\zeta_{xx} + (Q\zeta_\eta)_\eta - g\rho_\eta\zeta = 0 \qquad 41.$$

which is the equation governing infinitesimal two-dimensional waves. With this it can be shown that $S - S_0$, which is the wave resistance on the body creating the waves, is

$$S - S_0 = \tfrac{1}{2}\epsilon^2 \int_0^{h_0} Q(\zeta_x^2 - \zeta\zeta_{xx}) d\eta \qquad 42.$$

It is immediately evident that for periodic waves the wave resistance is always positive. It is also evident that if ζ_η and $\zeta_{\eta\eta}$ are of the order $O(1)$, and for long waves ζ_{xx} is of the order $O(\epsilon)$, then $S - S_0$ is $O(\epsilon^3)$.

To the order $O(\epsilon)$,

$$\zeta(x, \eta) = \phi(\eta) \sin(\alpha x + \nu) \qquad 43.$$

where, for long waves,

$$\frac{d}{d\eta}\left(Q \frac{d\phi}{d\eta} \right) - \left(Q\alpha^2 + g \frac{d\rho}{d\eta} \right) \phi = 0 \qquad 44.$$

with boundary conditions

$$\phi(0) = 0 \qquad 45.$$

and

$$\phi(h_0) = 0 \quad \text{or} \quad Q\frac{d\phi}{d\eta} = g\rho\phi \quad \text{at} \quad \eta = h_0 \qquad 46.$$

according as the upper surface is fixed or free. The eigenvalues $c_1, c_2, \ldots$ for this system are assumed to exist. (However, if U is not constant, there can be only a finite number of them, possibly none.) The corresponding values for Q will be denoted by Q_1, Q_2, etc., which are still functions of η.

Benjamin (1) used the new space variable $X = \epsilon^{1/2}x$, so that

 YIH

$$\zeta_x^2 = \epsilon \zeta_x^2 \qquad 47.$$

where ζ_x^2 is $O(1)$ for long waves. Furthermore, if the amplitude is no longer infinitesimal, Q should deviate from Q_n somewhat. Benjamin took

$$Q = Q_n + \epsilon \gamma_n \qquad 48$$

where γ_n is a function of η, and $\gamma_n > O$ for waves of finite amplitude.

Equations 42 and 47 indicate that

$$S_0 - S = \epsilon^3 s \qquad 49.$$

where s is $O(1)$. Benjamin even included a little loss of energy, and assumed that

$$\int_0^{h_0} (H_0 - H) d\eta = \epsilon^3 r \qquad 50.$$

where $r = O(1)$. This done, one can get from Equations 33 and 34 the equation

$$2\epsilon^3(r - s) = \int_0^{h_0} \{ \epsilon^2 (Q\zeta_\eta^2 - 2g\rho\zeta\zeta_\eta) - \epsilon^3 Q(\zeta_x^2 + \zeta_\eta^3) d\eta$$

$$51.$$

$$= \epsilon^2 [\zeta(Q\zeta_\eta - g\rho\zeta)]_0^{h_0} - \int_0^{h_0} [\epsilon^2 \{ (Q\zeta_\eta)_\eta - g\rho_\eta\zeta \}\zeta + \epsilon^3 Q(\zeta_x^2 + \zeta_\eta^3)] d\eta$$

Introducing Equation 48 and

$$\zeta = f(X)\phi_n(\eta) \qquad 52.$$

and noting that $\phi_n(\eta)$ satisfies the boundary conditions at the lower and upper surface, Benjamin obtained

$$2(r - s) = f^2 \left[\gamma_n \phi_n \frac{d\phi_n}{d\eta} \right]_0^{h_0} - f^2 \int_0^{h_0} \phi_n \frac{d}{d\eta} \left(\gamma_n \frac{d\phi_n}{d\eta} \right) d\eta$$

$$53.$$

$$- f_x^2 \int_0^{h_0} Q\phi_n^2 d\eta - f^3 \int_0^{h_0} Q_n \left(\frac{d\phi_n}{d\eta} \right)^2 d\eta$$

which, after integrating by parts the second term on the right-hand side, becomes

$$If_x^2 = Jf^2 - Kf^3 + 2(s - r) \qquad 54.$$

where

$$I = \int_0^{h_0} Q\phi_n^2 d\eta, \qquad J = \int_0^{h_0} \gamma_n \left(\frac{d\phi_n}{d\eta} \right)^2 d\eta, \qquad K = \int_0^{h_0} Q_n \left(\frac{d\phi_n}{d\eta} \right)^3 d\eta \qquad 55.$$

Equation 54 is the Korteweg-DeVries equation, from which solutions for solitary and cnoidal waves can be obtained for all values of n, that is, for all modes of these waves. This finishes the structural description of Benjamin's theory.

Benjamin noted that K is $O(1)$ when $n = 0$, but $O(\beta^2)$ for $n = 1$, β being a measure of the density gradient. [The demonstration that K is $O(\beta^2)$ for $n = 1$ is a little involved. We refer the reader to the appendix of Benjamin's paper(1).] The approximation to the order ϵ^3 is valid only if

$$K \gg \epsilon L, \quad \text{where} \quad L = \int_0^{h_0} Q_n \left(\frac{d\phi_n}{d\eta}\right)^4 d\eta = O(1) \qquad 56.$$

Thus it appears at first sight that for internal modes the theory is adequate only if $\beta^2 \gg \epsilon$, which would impose a severe restriction on the usefulness of the theory. Benjamin suggested the "simple expedient" of using $\phi_n(y) = \phi_n(\eta + \epsilon\zeta)$ in Equations 52 through 55, which removes the restriction. That $\phi_n(y)$ is more suitable than $\phi_n(\eta)$ is perhaps acceptable on intuitive grounds, for the eigenfunctions should reflect the local conditions more than the conditions far upstream. Nevertheless the expedient of using $\phi_n(y)$ instead of $\phi_n(\eta)$ lacks the quality of inevitability, and a formal justification would have been welcome.

Since the determination of γ_n is left unspecified, it is desirable to see how a solution can be obtained without first determining it. Take the case of the solitary wave in a homogeneous fluid with $U=0$, for which $s=0$, since no obstacle is needed to create the wave and the constant S is just the S_0 far upstream. If energy loss is neglected $r=0$, and a solution for the solitary wave exists for $J>0$:

$$f = a \operatorname{sech}^2 \kappa X, \qquad a = J/K, \qquad \kappa = \tfrac{1}{2}(J/I)^{1/2} \qquad 57.$$

Hence

$$z - \eta = \epsilon\zeta = \frac{\epsilon J \phi_n}{K} \operatorname{sech}^2 \left\{ \frac{x}{2} \left(\frac{\epsilon J}{I}\right)^{1/2} \right\} \qquad 58.$$

Here $\phi_0 = \eta$, and

$$I = \tfrac{1}{3}\rho c^2 h_0{}^3, \qquad \epsilon J = \rho(c^2 - c_0{}^2)h_0, \qquad K = \rho c_0{}^2 h_0 \qquad 59.$$

in which ρ is the constant density, $c_0{}^2 = g h_0$ ($c_0 =$ speed of infinitesimal waves), and c is the speed of the solitary wave. Equation 58 can be written as

$$z - \eta = \eta \left(\frac{c^2}{c_0{}^2} - 1\right) \operatorname{sech}^2 \left\{ \frac{(3c^2 - 3c_0{}^2)^{1/2}x}{2ch_0} \right\} \qquad 60.$$

For $\eta = 1$ (top streamline)

$$z(h_0) - h_0 = \Delta \operatorname{sech}^2 \left\{ \left(\frac{3\Delta}{h_0 + \Delta}\right)^{1/2} \frac{x}{h_0} \right\} \qquad 61.$$

in which $c^2 = g(h_0 + \Delta)$. Thus c^2, or J, or γ_0, is related to the amplitude of the solitary wave, as well as its shape.

Solitary waves in an incompressible fluid with an exponentially distributed density have been investigated by Long (25), who found that the relative magnitudes of three small parameters are very important. These parameters are the amplitude, the reciprocal of the effective length of the wave, and the density gradient. The explicit examples given by Long indicate the danger of using the Boussinesq approximation when other small parameters (than the density variation) exist. His conclusion is supported by Benjamin's work (1).

It is appropriate to add here that time-dependent equations for the development of weakly nonlinear waves in a stratified shear flow have been derived by Benney (4), who also gave solutions of these equations. Solitary waves in a compressible, stratified fluid confined between two rigid boundaries and flowing with uniform velocity at infinity have been studied by Long & Morton (26). Shen (39) studied solitary waves in a compressible stratified fluid of infinite height and with arbitrary wind and density profiles, and later (40) gave results for long waves (solitary and conidal) of finite amplitude in an atmosphere with crosswind. However, in both of his papers Shen assumed that the pressure depends on the density alone, in the entire fluid of flow. His solutions therefore do not apply to nonhomentropic atmospheres, for which p/ρ^γ varies from streamline to streamline in a steady flow, γ being the ratio of specific heats.

It is also pertinent to mention here the work of Benjamin (2) on internal long waves of permanent form in a stratified fluid layer with an overlying or underlying homogeneous fluid of infinite depth. The crucial point is that while the waves are long with respect to the stratified layer they are of course not long with respect to the fluid of infinite depth, and the usual analysis for long waves has to be modified in such a way that the long-wave solution and the solution for the homogeneous fluid can be matched at the interface (where Benjamin assumed no density discontinuity). Benjamin started by noting that for linear waves in two layers of homogeneous fluids of depths h_1 and h_2, the dispersion equations for long waves are radically different for the two cases $h_2 =$ finite and $h_2 =$ infinite, if h_1 is kept finite, and based the subsequent work on this observation. Space does not allow us to dwell long here, except to mention that solitary waves of the form

$$\text{vertical displacement of the interface} = \frac{a\lambda^2}{x^2 + \lambda^2}$$

are obtained, where a and λ are constants depending on the amplitude and the depth of the stratified layer.

11. Gravity currents.—A gravity current is a current of a fluid progressing in a body of another fluid which is of a different density, under the action of gravity. Figure 5 shows a heavier fluid progressing in a lighter one, and Figure 6 shows a gravity current in nature. von Kármán (45b) considered the lighter fluid to be infinite in extent, and derived the speed U of the current by using the Bernoulli equation between points A and B:

$$p_A = p_B + g\rho_1 d + \frac{\rho_1}{2} U^2 \qquad\qquad 62.$$

the flow being steady in a frame moving with the current. Since the current is at rest with respect to this frame,

$$p_A = p_B + g\rho_2 d \qquad\qquad 63.$$

so that

$$U = \left\{ \frac{2g(\rho_2 - \rho_1)d}{\rho_1} \right\}^{1/2} \qquad\qquad 64.$$

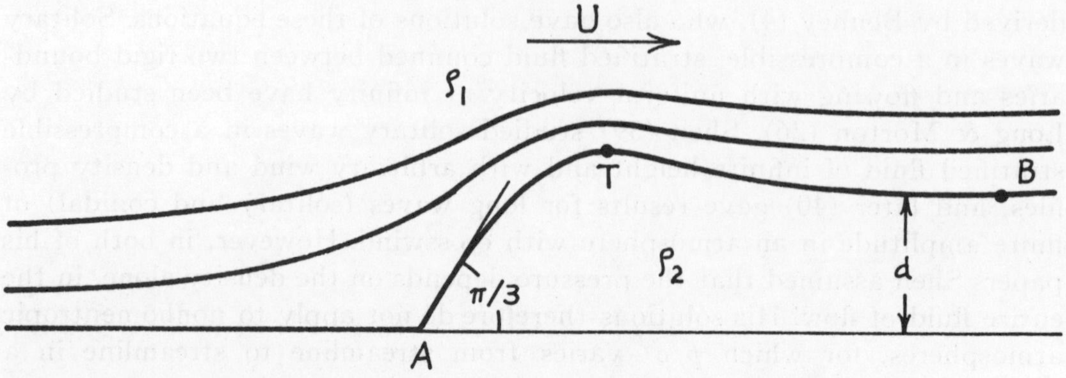

FIG. 5. Sketch of a gravity current.

It was implied in von Kármán's work that one can find a solution for potential flow over the current, the surface of which is a streamline on which the pressure is the hydrostatic pressure in the heavier fluid. Benjamin (3) pointed out that this is quite impossible if U is constant, since the hydrodynamic pressure (excluding the hydrostatic part) on the interface has a resultant of zero, and the hydrostatic forces on the interface cannot alone balance the hydrostatic pressure in the current at a cross section at B, say. Benjamin concluded there must be some separation and some turbulence near point T, giving rise to some hydrodynamic drag. He is no doubt right. But so long as p_B does not differ much from the pressure at point B' at the same eleva-

FIG. 6. A gravity current in nature.

tion far upstream—and it certainly does not—writing the Bernoulli equation between B′ and A and using Equation 63 still gives Equation 64. Thus von Kármán's formula, Equation 64, is still correct, in spite of his oversight, which is worth mentioning but quite unimportant so long as one does not try to determine the actual shape of the interface, and is interested only in determining U. The same conclusion can be drawn if the upper fluid is not infinite in extent.

Acknowledgment

The major part of this review was written during the month when the author was a visiting professor at the Mathematics Research Center of the University of Wisconsin. It was finished in Ann Arbor under the joint sponsorship of the National Science Foundation and the Army Research Office (Durham). To all three sponsoring agencies the author wishes to express his sincere appreciation.

LITERATURE CITED

1. Benjamin, T. Brooke, *J. Fluid Mech.*, **25**, 241–70 (1966)

2. Benjamin, T. Brooke, *J. Fluid Mech.*, **29**, 559–92 (1967)

3. Benjamin, T. Brooke, *J. Fluid Mech.*, **31**, 209–48 (1968)

4. Benney, D. J., *J. Math. & Phys.*, **55**, 52–63 (1966)

5. Bjerknes, V., *Vid-Selsk. Skrifter* (Kristiania, 1918)

6. Bôcher, M., *Leçons sur les Méthodes de Sturm dans la Théorie des Équations Differentielles Linéaires et leur Développements Modernes* (Gauthier Villars, Paris, 1917)

7. Boussinesq, J., *Théorie Analytique de la Chaleur*, 2 (Gauthier Villars, Paris, 1903)

7a. Broer, L. J. F., *Appl. Sci. Res.*, **A2**, 329–44 (1950)

8. Charney, J. G., *J. Marine Res.*, **14**, 477–98 (1955)

8a. Crapper, G. D., *J. Fluid Mech.*, **6**, 51–76 (1959)

8b. Debler, W. R., *J. Eng. Mech. Div., Proc. ASCE.*, **85**, 51–65 (1959)

9. Drazin, P., *J. Fluid Mech.*, **4**, 214–24 (1958)

10. Drazin, P., *Proc. Cambridge Phil. Soc.*, **58**, 646–61 (1962)

11. Drazin, P., Howard, L. N., *J. Eng. Mech. Div. Am. Soc. Civil Engrs.*, **87**, 101–16 (1961)

12. Drazin, P. G., Moore, D. W., *J. Fluid Mech.*, **28**, 353–83 (1967)

12a. Dubreil-Jacotin, M. L., *Atti Accad. Lincei, Rend. Cl. Sci. Fis. Mat. Nat. (6)*, **15**, 814–19 (1932)

12b. Dubreil-Jacotin, M. L., *Atti. Accad. Lincei, Rend. Cl. Sci. Fis. Mat. Nat. (6)*, **21**, 344–46 (1935)

13. Fultz, D., *Fluids Models in Geophysics*, 27–63 (U.S. Govt. Printing Office, Washington, 1956)

14. Görtler, H., *Z, Angew. Math. Mech.*, **23**, 65–71 (1943)

15. Graebel, W. P., *J. Fluid Mech.*, **8**, 321–36 (1960)

16. Groen, P., *Mededelingen en Verhandlingen*, Serie B Deel II, No. II (Koninklijk Nederlands Meteorologisch Instituut de Bilt, 1958)

17. Hide, R., *Fluids Model in Geophysics*, 101–16 (U.S. Govt. Printing Office, Washington, 1956)

18. Howard, L. N., *J. Fluid Mech.*, **10**, 509–12 (1961)

19. Kao, T. W., *J. Fluid Mech.*, **21**, 535–44 (1965)

20. Kao, T. W., *Phys. Fluids*, **12**, 2190–94 (1965)

21. Koh, R. C. Y., *J. Fluid Mech.*, **24**, 555–76 (1966)

22. Kuo, H. L., *Fluids Model in Geophysics*, 65–72 (U. S. Govt. Printing Office, Washington, 1956)

23. Long, R. R., *Tellus*, **5**, 42–57 (1953)

24. Long, R. R., *Quart. J. Roy. Meteorol. Soc.*, **84**, 159–61 (1958)

25. Long, R. R., *Tellus*, **17**, 46–52 (1965)

26. Long, R. R., Morton, J. B., *Tellus*, **18**, 79–85 (1965)

27. Longuet-Higgins, M. S., *Deep-Sea Res.*, **12**, 923–73 (1965)

28. Love, A. E. H., *Proc. London Math. Soc.*, **22**, 307 (1891)

29. Lyra, G., *Z. Angew. Math. Mech.*, **23**, 1–28 (1943)

30. Marris, A. W., *J. Fluid Mech.*, **20**, 177–81 (1964)

31. Miles, J. W., *J. Fluid Mech.*, **10**, 496–508 (1961)

32. Miles, J. W., *J. Fluid Mech.*, **32**, 549–68 (1968)

33. Mowbray, D. E., Rarity, B. S. H., *J. Fluid Mech.*, **28**, 1–16 (1967)

34. Queney, P., *Misc. Rept. 23* (Dept. Meteorol., Univ. Chicago, 1947)

35. Queney, P., *Bull. Am. Meteorol. Soc.*, **29**, 16 (1948)

36. Rarity, B. S. H., *J. Fluid Mech.*, **30**, 329–36 (1967)

37. Rossby, C. G., *J. Marine Res.*, **7**, 74–99 (1938)

38. Scorer, R. S., *Quart. J. Roy. Meteorol. Soc.*, **76**, 41–56 (1949)

39. Shen, M. C., *Phys. Fluids*, **9**, 1944–50 (1966)

40. Shen, M. C., *J. Fluid Mech.*, **28**, 481–92 (1967)

41. Sangster, W., *Stability of Free-surface Flow down an Inclined Plane* (Doctoral thesis, State Univ. Iowa, 1961)

42. Thorpe, S. A., *J. Fluid Mech.*, **32**, 489–528 (1968)

43. Trustrum, K., *J. Fluid Mech.*, **19**, 415–32 (1964)

44. Veronis, G., *Deep-Sea Res.*, **3**, 157–77 (1956)

45. Veronis, G., Stommel, H., *J. Marine Res.*, **15**, 43–75 (1956)

45a. Veronis, G. *J. Oceanog. Soc. Japan*, **14**, 3–5 (1958)

45b. von Kármán, Th., *Bull. Am. Math. Soc.*, **46**, 615–83 (1940)

46. Wu, T. Y. T. *Radiation and Dispersion*

of Internal Waves (Paper presented to Intern. Conf. Stratified Fluids, Ann Arbor, April 11–14, 1967)

47. Wu, T. Y. T., Mei, C. C., *Phys. Fluids*, **10**, 482–86 (1967)

48. Yanowitch, M., *Comm. Pure Appl. Math.*, **15**, 45–61 (1962)

49. Yih, C.-S., *Proc. 3rd U.S. Congr. Appl. Mech.*, 857–61 (1958)

50. Yih, C.-S., *Quart. Appl. Math.*, **16**, 409–15 (1959)

51. Yih, C.-S., *J. Geophys. Res.*, **64**, 2219–23 (1959)

52. Yih, C.-S., *J. Fluid Mech.*, **8**, 481–508 (1960)

53. Yih, C.-S., *J. Fluid Mech.*, **9**, 161–74 (1960)

54. Yih, C.-S. *Some Results on Gravity Waves in a Stratified Fluid* (Paper presented to Conf. Fluid Dynam., Boulder, Colo., September, 1962)

55. Yih, C.-S., *Dynamics of Nonhomogeneous Fluids* (Macmillan, New York, 1965)

56. Yih, C.-S., *J. Fluid Mech.*, **24**, 765–67 (1966)

57. Yih, C.-S., *J. Fluid Mech.*, **27**, 337–52 (1967)

58. Yih, C.-S., *J. Fluid Mech.*, **29**, 539–44 (1967)

59. Yih, C.-S., O'Dell, W., Debler, W. R., *Proc. 4th U. S. Congr. Appl. Mech.*, 1441–53 (1962) (For a more complete bibliography, see Yih 1965.)

STABILITY OF AND WAVES IN STRATIFIED FLOWS

Chia-Shun Yih
*University of Michigan
Ann Arbor, Michigan*

ABSTRACT

A theorem giving sufficient conditions for stability
of stratified flows, which is a natural generalization
of Rayleigh's theorem for shear flows of a homogeneous
fluid, is given. Sufficient conditions for the existence
of singular neutral modes, and consequently of unstable
modes, are also presented, and in the development the
possibility of multi-valued wave number for neutral
stability of the same flow is explained. Finally, neutral
waves with a wave velocity outside of the range of the
velocity of flow (non-singular modes) are studied, and
results concerning the possibility of these waves are
given. In addition, Miles' theorem [1961] on the stability
of stratified flows for which the Richardson number is
nowhere less than 1/4, and Howard's semi-circle theorem
[1961] are extended to fluids with density discontinuities.

I. INTRODUCTION

The stability of stratified flows of an inviscid fluid has been
studied in a general way, i.e., without specifying the actual density
and velocity distributions, by Synge [1933], Yih [1957], Drazin
[1958], Miles [1961, 1963], Howard [1961], and others. Of these,
Miles has made particularly substantial contributions to the subject.
However, many questions still remain open. Among these are the
following:

(i)   Miles [1961] showed that if the Richardson number is
        nowhere less than 1/4, the flow must be stable. This
        is a sufficient condition for stability. What can one say
        regarding the stability of the flow when the Richardson
        number is less than 1/4 in part or all of the fluid? Are
        there then some sufficient conditions for stability not

219

Reprinted from *Proc. Eighth Symposium of Naval Hydrodynamics* (1970) 219–237.

covered by Miles' criterion? What, in fact, is the
natural generalization of Rayleigh's theorem on the
sufficient condition for stability of a homogeneous
fluid in shear flow?

(ii)   Are there some sufficient conditions for instability?

(iii)   Miles [1963] has shown that the wave number at neutral
stability can be multi-valued for the same flow, in an
actual calculation for a special density distribution and
a special velocity distribution. Is there an explanation
for this, even if not completely general?

(iv)   Do internal waves with a wave velocity outside the
range of the velocity of flow exist? How many modes
are there? What is the character of each mode?

In this paper the questions posed above will be answered in as
general a way as possible. By "general" I mean "without numerical
computation." Although special calculations for special flows,
involving the use of computers, are important because they often
give us insight into and understanding of the subject, and sometimes
are of practical interest, results obtained in a general way are often
more useful. The question naturally arises: Can general results be
continually improved and sharpened, albeit with increasing cost in
labor, but without the use of computers? The answer to this question
necessarily reveals the attitude of the respondent more than anything
else. My answer to it is in the affirmative, and the results contained
in this paper, aside from whatever interest or merit they may have
for those cultivating the subject, are given to substantiate my faith.

In addition, some straightforward extensions of Miles' theorem
mentioned in (i) above, and of Howard's semi-circle theorem [1961],
are made to make these theorems applicable to fluids with discontinuities in addition to continuous stratification in density.

II. DIFFERENTIAL SYSTEM GOVERNING STABILITY

If U and $\bar{\rho}$ denote the velocity (in the x-direction) and the
density, respectively, of the primary flow in the absence of disturbances, and u and v denote the components of the perturbation in
velocity in the directions of increasing x and y, the linearized
equations of motion are

$$\bar{\rho}(u_t + Uu_x + U'v) = - p_x , \qquad (1)$$

$$\bar{\rho}(v_t + Uv_x) = - p_y - g\rho , \qquad (2)$$

in which subscripts indicate partial differentiation, t denotes time,

Stability of and Waves in Stratified Flows

p is the <u>deviation</u> of the pressure from the hydrostatic pressure in the primary flow, ρ is the density <u>perturbation</u>, g is the gravitational acceleration, and

$$U' = \frac{dU}{dy} .$$

The equation of continuity

$$u_x + v_y = 0$$

permits the use of a stream function ψ, in terms of which the velocity components can be expressed:

$$u = \psi_y, \qquad v = -\psi_x. \tag{3}$$

The linearized form of the equation of incompressibility is

$$\rho_t + U\rho_x + v\overline{\rho}' = 0, \tag{4}$$

in which

$$\overline{\rho}' = \frac{d\overline{\rho}}{dy} .$$

If η is the vertical displacement of a line of constant density from its mean position, the kinematic relationship

$$\eta_t + U\eta_x = v = -\psi_x \tag{5}$$

holds. All perturbation quantities will be assumed to be periodic in x and have the exponential factor $\exp ik(x-ct)$, so that from (5) and (3) we have

$$\psi = -(U-c)\eta, \qquad u = -[(U-c)\eta]', \qquad v = ik(U-c)\eta. \tag{6}$$

Then (1) and (4) give

$$p = \overline{\rho}(U-c)^2\eta' \qquad \text{and} \qquad \rho = -\overline{\rho}'\eta. \tag{7}$$

Writing

$$\eta(x,y,t) = F(y)e^{ik(x-ct)} \tag{8}$$

and substituting (6) and (7) into (2), we have, with β denoting $-\overline{\rho}'/\overline{\rho}$,

$$[\overline{\rho}(U-c)^2 F']' + \overline{\rho}[\beta g - k^2(U-c)^2]F = 0, \tag{9}$$

which is the equation used by Miles [1961] and Howard [1961] to study the stability of stratified flows.

Miles [1961] assumed U to be monotonic and U and $\overline{\rho}$ to be analytic in his studies. Howard [1961] was able to prove Miles' theorem (on a sufficient condition for stability) and to obtain his own semi-circle theorem without these hypotheses. But both of them assumed $\overline{\rho}$ to be continuous, and considered the upper boundary to be fixed as well as the lower one. We shall now show that the theorems of Miles and Howard can be generalized to allow density discontinuities. The mean velocity U (though not necessarily U') will be assumed continuous.

Let there be n surfaces of density discontinuity, and let the free surface, if there is one, be the first of such surfaces. The densities above and below the i-th surface of density discontinuity will be denoted by $(\overline{\rho}_u)_i$ and $(\overline{\rho}_\ell)_i$, respectively, and we shall define $(\Delta\overline{\rho})_i$ by

$$(\Delta\overline{\rho})_i = (\overline{\rho}_\ell - \overline{\rho}_u)_i. \tag{10}$$

The interfacial condition can be obtained by integrating (9) in the Stieltjes sense in an arbitrarily small interval containing the discontinuity under consideration, and is, with the accent indicating differentiation with respect to y,

$$[\overline{\rho}(U-c)^2 F']_u - [\overline{\rho}(U-c)^2 F']_\ell = -g\Delta\overline{\rho}F, \tag{11}$$

to be applied at any surface of discontinuity. At a free surface $\overline{\rho}_u$ vanishes, and (11) becomes

$$(U-c)^2 F' = gF, \tag{12}$$

which is the free-surface condition, to be applied at $y = d$, d being the depth. If the upper surface is fixed instead of free, the condition there is

$$F(d) = 0. \tag{12a}$$

The boundary condition at the bottom, where $y = 0$, is

$$F(0) = 0. \tag{13}$$

Stability of and Waves in Stratified Flows

III. EXTENSION OF MILES' THEOREM

Following Howard [1961], we set

$$G = W^{1/2} F,$$

where $W = U - c$. Then (9) can be written as

$$(\overline{\rho}WG')' - [(\overline{\rho}U')'/2 + k^2\overline{\rho}W + \overline{\rho}W^{-1}(U'^2/4 - g\beta]\,G = 0. \tag{14}$$

The boundary condition at the bottom is

$$G(0) = 0. \tag{15}$$

The interfacial conditions (11) become

$$\overline{\rho}_\ell(WG' - U'G/2)_\ell - \overline{\rho}_u(WG' - U'G/2)_u = g\Delta\overline{\rho}W^{-1}G, \tag{16}$$

to be applied at the surfaces of density discontinuity, and in particular the upper-surface condition becomes

$$WG' - U'G/2 = gW^{-1}G, \qquad \text{or} \qquad G(d) = 0, \tag{17}$$

depending on whether the upper surface is free or fixed.

Multiplying (14) by G^*, where the asterisk indicates the complex conjugate, and integrating from the bottom to the first surface of density discontinuity and then from discontinuity to discontinuity throughout the fluid domain, and utilizing (15), (16), and (17), we have

$$\int \overline{\rho}W[\,|G'|^2 + k^2|G|^2\,] + \int (\overline{\rho}U')'|G|^2/2 + \int \overline{\rho}[\,U'^2/4 - g\beta]\,W^*|G/W|^2$$

$$- \sum_i g\Delta_i\overline{\rho}W^*|G/W|^2 - \sum_i [(\overline{\rho}U')_\ell - (\overline{\rho}U')_u]\,|G|^2/2 = 0, \tag{18}$$

in which each of the integrals is over the entire fluid domain exclusive of the surfaces of density discontinuity (i.e., it is a summation of integrals over the layers of continuous density distributions), and the summation is over the discontinuities, including the free surface if there is one. If the flow is unstable, $c_i > 0$, and the imaginary part of (18) is

$$\int \overline{\rho}[\,|G'|^2 + k^2|G|^2\,] + \int \overline{\rho}[\,g\beta - U'^2/4]\,|G/W|^2 + \sum_i g\Delta_i\overline{\rho}|G/W|^2 = 0, \tag{19}$$

from which it is again evident that if

$$g\beta \geq U'^2/4$$

everywhere in the fluid exclusive of the interfaces and the free surface (if there is one), the flow must be stable.

IV. EXTENSION OF HOWARD'S SEMI-CIRCLE THEOREM

Equation (9) can be written as

$$(\overline{\rho}W^2 F')' + \overline{\rho}(\beta g - k^2 W^2) F = 0.$$

Multiplying this equation by F^*, the complex conjugate of F, integrating throughout the fluid domain and using the boundary or interfacial conditions (11), (12), and (13), we have

$$\int \overline{\rho}W^2[|F'|^2 + k^2|F|^2] - \int \overline{\rho}g\beta|F|^2 - \sum_i g\Delta_i\overline{\rho}|F|^2 = 0, \qquad (20)$$

in which the summation is over the surfaces of density discontinuity, and the integrals extend throughout the fluid exclusive of the surface of discontinuity in density. The real and imaginary parts of (20) are

$$\int \overline{\rho}[(U - c_r)^2 - c_i^2][|F'|^2 + k^2|F|^2] - \int \overline{\rho}g\beta|F|^2 - \sum_i g\Delta_i\overline{\rho}|F|^2 = 0, \qquad (21)$$

$$2c_i\int \overline{\rho}(U - c_r)[|F'|^2 + k^2|F|^2] = 0. \qquad (22)$$

Writing

$$Q = \overline{\rho}[|F'|^2 + k^2|F|^2],$$

we obtain from (22)

$$\int UQ = c_r\int Q, \qquad (23)$$

then from this and from (21) we obtain

$$\int U^2 Q = (c_r^2 + c_i^2)\int Q + \int g\rho\beta|F|^2 + \sum_i g\Delta_i\overline{\rho}|F|^2. \qquad (24)$$

If a and b are respectively the minimum and the maximum of U,

Stability of and Waves in Stratified Flows

so that $a \leq U \leq b$, we have

$$0 \geq \int (U - a)(U - b)Q = \int U^2 Q - (a + b)\int UQ + ab\int Q$$

$$= [\, c_r^{\,2} + c_i^{\,2} - (a + b)c_r + ab\,]\int Q + \int g\bar{\rho}B|F|^2 + \sum_i g\Delta_i\bar{\rho}|F|^2,$$

after using (23). This means that

$$[\, c_r - (a + b)/2\,]^2 + c_i^{\,2} \leq [\,(b - a)/2\,]^2, \tag{25}$$

that is, the complex wave velocity c for any unstable mode must lie
inside the semi-circle in the upper half-plane, which has the range of
U for diameter. Thus Howard's semi-circle theorem is recovered.

From (19) and noting that $|W|^{-2} \leq c_i^{\,-2}$, we deduce that

$$k^2 c_i^{\,2} \leq \max (\, U'^2/4 - g\beta) \tag{26}$$

remains valid even if there are surfaces of discontinuity in density.
In (26) we <u>exclude</u> these surfaces in the evaluation of β. It is easy
to see that (26) contains Miles' theorem.

V. SUFFICIENT CONDITIONS FOR STABILITY

Miles' theorem gives a sufficient condition for stability. But
it certainly does not guarantee instability if the local Richardson
number $J(y)$ defined by

$$J(y) = \frac{g\beta}{U'^2} \tag{27}$$

is less than 1/4 in part of the fluid or even all of the fluid. We shall
sharpen Miles' sufficient condition for stability by deriving two
theorems which constitute, **more** than anything hitherto known, the
natural generalization of Rayleigh's theorem for the stability of a
homogeneous inviscid fluid.

For the discussion in this section it is more convenient to use
the stream function

$$\psi = f(y)e^{ik(x-ct)}. \tag{28}$$

Comparison with (6) and (8) shows that

225

$$f(y) = (c - U)\,F(y). \tag{29}$$

In terms of $f(y)$, the governing equation (9) becomes

$$\left(\overline{\rho}f'\right)' + \left[\frac{(\overline{\rho}U')'}{c - U} - k^2\overline{\rho} - \frac{g\overline{\rho}'}{(c - U)^2}\right] f = 0. \tag{30}$$

Equation (30) can be made dimensionless by the use of the new variables

$$\hat{f} = \frac{f}{V}, \quad \hat{\overline{\rho}} = \frac{\overline{\rho}}{\rho_0}, \quad \hat{y} = \frac{y}{d}, \quad \hat{U} = \frac{U}{V}, \quad \hat{c} = \frac{c}{V}, \tag{31}$$

where ρ_0 is a reference density and V a reference velocity. Then (30) becomes, after the circumflexes are dropped,

$$\left(\overline{\rho}f'\right)' + \left[\frac{(\overline{\rho}U')'}{c - U} - \alpha^2\overline{\rho} - \frac{N\overline{\rho}'}{(c - U)^2}\right] f = 0, \tag{32}$$

in which everything is now dimensionless, the accents indicate differentiation with respect to the dimensionless y,

$$\alpha = kd \tag{33}$$

is the dimensionless wave number, and

$$N = gd/V^2 \tag{34}$$

is actually the reciprocal of the square of a Froude number. The appearance of N does not necessarily signify the importance of surface waves, since it appears even if the upper boundary is fixed. The fact that it is associated by multiplication to $\overline{\rho}'$ indicates that the entire term represents the effect of gravity in a stratified fluid in shear flow.

Henceforth in this paper we shall consider rigid boundaries only, for which the boundary conditions are

$$f(0) = 0 \quad \text{and} \quad f(1) = 0, \tag{35a,b}$$

to be imposed on the function f in (32).

It is then clear that the system consisting of (32) and (35a,b) gives, for a non-trivial solution, a relationship

$$F_1(\alpha, N, c) = 0. \tag{36}$$

Since c is complex, (36) has a real part and an imaginary part. When c_i is set to zero and c_r eliminated from the two component equations, a relationship

$$F_2(\alpha, N) = 0, \tag{37}$$

if one such exists, gives the neutral-stability curve. It is possible, however, that c is real for all values of α and N, in which case $c_i = 0$ in the entire $N - \alpha$ plane, and then of course there is no neutral-stability curve because one component equation of (36) is $c_i = 0$, and the other is simply (36) itself, with the c therein real.

In this section, we shall assume $\bar{\rho}$ and U to be continuous, analytic, and monotonic. Furthermore, we assume $\bar{\rho}' < 0$ throughout. We now recall the following known results:

(i)   If $J(y)$ is not less than $1/4$ for the entire fluid domain, then the flow is stable [Miles 1961],

(ii)   If $c_i \neq 0$ then c_r must be equal to U at some point in the flow, as a consequence of the semi-circle theorem of Howard [1961], and

(iii)   If an eigenfunction exists for (c_0, α_0, N_0), then near that point c is a continuous function of α and N, [Miles 1963 and Lin 1945].

Under the assumptions we have made on $\bar{\rho}$ and U, and in view of the known results just cited, we conclude that the non-existence of any singular neutral mode, which is a mode with a real c equal to U at some point in the flow, implies the non-existence of unstable modes. The reason is as follows. In the $N - \alpha$ plane there is always a region of stability. For we can imagine g and hence $J(y)$ to increase indefinitely, until $J(y)$ is everywhere greater than $1/4$, which is attainable since β is nowhere zero. Thus there is a region of large N for which the flow is stable. If unstable modes exist there must then be a stability boundary dividing the region of stability from the region of instability, and hence a neutral-stability curve. As we approach that curve from the region of instability, c_r being within the range of U so long as $c_i \neq 0$ and continuous in α and N so long as c is an eigenvalue, according to (iii) above, in the limit, when $c_i = 0$, c_r must be within the range of U, i.e., the limiting mode must be a singular neutral mode. Hence the non-existence of a singular neutral mode implies the non-existence of unstable modes.

In fact even the existence of special singular neutral modes for which
c equals the maximum or minimum of U does not imply the existence
of contiguous unstable modes, as a consequence of the semi-circle
theorem of Howard. Hence we need not be concerned with these
special border cases. In demonstrating the non-existence of unstable
modes it is sufficient to demonstrate the non-existence of singular
neutral modes with a < c < b, where a is the minimum and b the
maximum of U.

Miles [1961, p. 507] has shown that singular neutral modes
are impossible for monotonic U if $J(y) > 1/4$ everywhere. In his
demonstration he actually showed that a singular neutral mode with
a $J(y_c) > 1/4$ at the place $y = y_c$ where U = c is impossible. Hence
we need only consider the case $J(y_c) \leq 1/4$ in our search for the non-
existence of singular neutral modes. For $J(y_c) = 1/4$, one solution
of (32) is

$$f_1 = (y - y_c)^{1/2} w_1 \tag{38}$$

where

$$w_1 = 1 + A(y - y_c) + \cdots \tag{39}$$

with

$$A = \left[(1 + J) \frac{(\overline{\rho} U')'}{\overline{\rho} U'} - \frac{J \overline{\rho}''}{\overline{\rho}'} + \gamma (\ln \overline{\rho})' \right]_c, \quad (\gamma = \tfrac{1}{2}) \tag{40}$$

provided U' does not vanish at $y = y_c$. [We shall consider monotonic U only. Hence this restriction on U' does not affect our
results in this paper.] The other solution is found by assuming it
to be of the form $f_1 h$, substituting it into (32), and solving for h.
The result, after division by a constant (which is $\overline{\rho}_c$ or ρ at y_c),
is

$$f_2 = f_1 \ln (y - y_c) - \left[2A + (\ln \overline{\rho})_c' \right] (y - y_c)^{3/2} \left[1 + B(y - y_c) + \cdots \right], \tag{41}$$

where B is a constant. Now the Reynolds stress defined by

$$\tau = - \overline{\rho} \, \overline{uv}, \tag{42}$$

where the bar over uv means time or space average, can be expressed in terms of f as

$$\tau = \frac{\rho_0 V^2}{2} \alpha (f' f^*)_i \, e^{2\alpha c_i t}, \tag{43}$$

Stability of and Waves in Stratified Flows

in which the asterisk denotes the complex conjugate, and the t, now
in terms of d/V, is dimensionless, as is f. Considering the singular neutral case, for which $c_i = 0$, it is easy to see from (40) and
(41) that $f'f^*$ is real for $y > y_c$ and equal to $-i\pi$ for $y < y_c$. Hence
$(f'f^*)_i$ suffers a jump at y_c. Since $f'f^*$ is zero at both rigid
boundaries, it cannot afford this jump. [If $\alpha \neq 0$, this jump corresponds to a jump in the Reynolds stress. But we do not have to
consider the jump in τ, and can consider merely the jump in $(f'f^*)_i$.]
Consequently a singular neutral mode with $J(y_c)$ equal to 1/4 is impossible. And we can henceforth concentrate on the case $J(y_c) < 1/4$.

For $J(y_c) < 1/4$ Miles [1961] gave the solutions of (32):

$$f_{\pm}(y) = (y - y_c)^{(1 \pm \nu)/2} w_{\pm} \tag{44}$$

in which

$$w_{\pm} = 1 + A(y - y_c)/(1 \pm \nu) + \ldots, \tag{45}$$

with A given by (40) [but with $\gamma = (1 \pm \nu)/2$ therein] and

$$\nu = (1 - 4J_c)^{1/2} , \quad J_c = J(y_c). \tag{46}$$

We can use (44) and (45) with all terms therein considered dimensionless. Miles [1961, pp. 506-507] showed that for $J_c < 1/4$ the solution, if one exists, must be either f_+ or f_-. We can demonstrate
our point by considering f_+ as the solution. The demonstration for
the other case is strictly similar.

The study of the eigenvalue problem defined by (32) and (35a,b)
naturally leads to a study of the zeros of f. Since f is given by
(44), it leads to the study of the zeros of w_+. This in turn leads us
to consider the differential equation for w (from which the subscripts
are removed for convenience). Denoting w_+ or w_- by w, we can
easily obtain that equation:

$$(\bar\rho z^{2\gamma} w')' + z^{2\gamma} \left[-J_c \bar\rho z^{-2} + \gamma \bar\rho' z^{-1} + \frac{(\bar\rho U')'}{c - U} - \alpha^2 \bar\rho - \frac{N\bar\rho'}{(c - U)^2} \right] w = 0, \tag{47}$$

with $z = y - y_c$, and $\gamma = (1 \pm \nu)/2$.

We are now in a position to present

Theorem 1. If $\bar\rho$ and U are continuous and analytic, with $\bar\rho' < 0$
and $U' > 0$, and if $(\bar\rho U')'$ and $(\ln \bar\rho)''$ are positive throughout, then
singular neutral modes are impossible.

Proof. We have shown that it is necessary only to consider the case $J(y_c) < 1/4$. We may consider f_+ only, since the proof for f_- is the same, and since the solution is either f_+ or f_-. Now at $y = y_c$ we have $f_+ = 0$. Near y_c we have

$$Q \equiv - \frac{N\bar{\rho}'}{(U-c)^2} - \frac{J_c\bar{\rho}}{z^2} = \frac{\bar{\rho}_c J_c}{z^2} \left[\left\{ \bar{\rho}(\ln\bar{\rho})''/\bar{\rho}' - \frac{U''}{U'} \right\} z + \dots \right] . \tag{48}$$

Since $\bar{\rho}'$ is negative and U' and $(\bar{\rho}U')'$ are positive, U'' is positive. Thus $U-c$ is greater than $U_c'z$ for $z > 0$. On the other hand $-\bar{\rho}'/\bar{\rho}$ is less than $(-\bar{\rho}'/\bar{\rho})_c$ for $y > y_c$, since $(\ln\bar{\rho})''$ is positive. We know that for small positive z Q is negative, as can be seen from (48). Hence for any $z > 0$ the term

$$- \frac{N\bar{\rho}'}{(U-c)^2}$$

is less than $\bar{\rho}J_c/z^2$ and Q is negative. Equation (48) exhibits the behavior of Q near y_c. Let the bracket in (47) be denoted by $-G$. Then since Q is negative and $U-c$ is positive for $y > y_c$, and since $\bar{\rho}'$ is negative and $(\bar{\rho}U')'$ positive, G must be positive for $y > y_c$. Multiplying (47) by w and integrating between y_c and 1, we have

$$(\rho z^2 \gamma w w')_1 - \int_{y_c}^1 z^2 \gamma (\bar{\rho} w'^2 + G w^2) \, dy = 0, \tag{49}$$

where the subscript 1 indicates that the parenthesis is evaluated at $y = 1$. Note that the integral in (49) is convergent in spite of the simple pole in two terms contained in G -- one of which in Q, as indicated by (48). Equation (49) clearly shows that $w(1)$ cannot be zero. Hence the theorem.

Another theorem is

Theorem 2. If $\bar{\rho}$ and U are continuous and analytic, with $\bar{\rho}'$ negative and U' positive, and if U'' and $(\ln\bar{\rho})''$ are negative throughout, then singular neutral modes are impossible.

The proof for this theorem is similar to that for Theorem 1. The only modification demanded for clarity is that instead of (44) we should write

$$f_{\pm}(y) = z^{(1\pm\nu)/2} w_{\pm}(z)$$

with z now defined as $y_c - y$. The equation corresponding to (47) is now

Stability of and Waves in Stratified Flows

$$\frac{d}{dz}\left[\bar{\rho}z^2\gamma\frac{d}{dz}\,w\right] + z^2\gamma\left[-J_c\bar{\rho}z^{-2} + \gamma\bar{\rho}'z^{-1} + \frac{(\bar{\rho}U')'}{c-U} - \alpha^2\bar{\rho} - \frac{N\bar{\rho}'}{(c-U)^2}\right]w = 0,$$

$$(50)$$

in which, it must be emphasized, all accents indicate differentiation with respect to y, not z. The rest is strictly similar to the proof for Theorem 1, except the range of integration is between $z = 0$ and $z = y_c$ (or between $y = y_c$ and $y = 0$), and we want to show $w \neq 0$ at $y = 0$. Note also that $U'' < 0$ now guarantees $(\bar{\rho}U')' < 0$.

Since the non-existence of singular neutral modes implies the non-existence of unstable modes, we have also

Theorem 3. *If $\bar{\rho}$ and U are continuous and analytic, with $\bar{\rho}'$ negative and U' positive, and if either $(\bar{\rho}U')'$ and $(\ln\bar{\rho})''$ are both positive throughout, or U'' and $(\ln\bar{\rho})''$ are negative throughout, the flow is stable.*

This theorem is the natural generalization of Rayleigh's theorem for inviscid homogeneous fluids in shear flow. Previous attempts at this generalization [Synge 1933, Yih 1957, Drazin 1958] have produced the result that there must be stability if (in dimensional terms)

$$\frac{2\beta g(U-c_r)}{|U-c|^2} - \frac{(\bar{\rho}U')'}{\bar{\rho}}$$

does not change sign. This criterion is not useful because it involves not only c_r but also c_i.

VI. SUFFICIENT CONDITIONS FOR INSTABILITY

Sufficient conditions for instability have seldom been given in studies of hydrodynamic stability. In giving some such conditions, we shall also be able to explain why the α can be multi-valued for the same N, at neutral stability.

We assume that $\bar{\rho}$ and U are analytic, that $\bar{\rho}' \leq 0$, and that at a point where $\bar{\rho}' = 0$, U'' is also zero. The value of U at that point will be denoted by U_c, for we shall consider the possibility of having c equal to U at that point. We demand that at any other point where $U = U_c$, $\bar{\rho}' = 0 = U''$ must be satisfied. If U is monotonic, of course there is only one point at which $U = U_c$.

Under the assumptions made, $\bar{\rho}''$ must be zero at y_c, since $\bar{\rho}'$ is never positive, and near y_c

$$\overline{\rho}' = \overline{\rho}_c''(y - y_c).$$

If $\overline{\rho}_c''$ were not zero $\overline{\rho}'$ would be positive for y slightly larger than y_c. With this realization, it is immediately clear that the bracket in (32) has no singularity at y_c. Let us denote the bracket in (32) by the sumbol B, which is a function of y, α, and N. Then if m is the minimum of $B/\overline{\rho}$ between two points y_1 and y_2, with $0 \le y_1 < y_2 \le 1$, for $\alpha = 0$, and if

$$m \ge \frac{(n\pi)^2}{(y_2 - y_1)^2}, \qquad n = \text{a positive integer}, \qquad (51)$$

by the use of Sturm's first comparison theorem we know that there must be at least n zeros of f between y_1 and y_2, whatever the value of $f(0)$ and $f'(0)$. (Note that the $\overline{\rho}$ in m or in (32) is dimensionless.) We can always choose $f(0) = 0$. If (51) is satisfied then there must be at least n internal zeros of f. We can increase α so that, again by Sturm's first comparison theorem

$$f(1) = 0$$

for

$$\alpha = \alpha_1, \ \alpha_2, \ \alpha_3, \ \ldots, \ \alpha_n,$$

where

$$\alpha_1 < \alpha_2 < \alpha_3 < \ldots < \alpha_n.$$

It is evident that for $\alpha = \alpha_i$ there are at least $n - i$ internal zeros.

Hence we have

Theorem 4. Under the assumptions stated in the second paragraph of this section, if (51) is satisfied there are at least n modes with $c = U_c$ and $\alpha = \alpha_i$ $(i = 1, 2, \ldots, n)$, and with α_i increasing with i. For the i-th mode there are at least $n - i$ internal zeros.

It is easy to show, by exactly the same approach used by Lin [1955, pp. 122-123], which we shall not repeat here, that by varying α^2 slightly (now not necessarily by decreasing it, as is in Lin's case), c will become complex. Hence we have

Theorem 5. Near the neutral modes stated in Theorem 4, there are contiguous unstable modes.

Stability of and Waves in Stratified Flows

Theorem 4 explains why for the same N, given $\bar{\rho}$ and U, there can be many values for α on the neutral-stability curve (or curves), which has been observed by Miles [1963] for a special $\bar{\rho}$ and a special U.

We can sharpen Theorems 4 and 5 by defining M to be the maximum of $B/\bar{\rho}$ in (y_1, y_2) for $\alpha = 0$. Then if (51) holds and

$$M \leq \frac{(n+1)^2 \pi^2}{(y_2 - y_1)^2}, \tag{52}$$

the words "at least" in Theorem 4 can be replaced by the word "exactly."

We note that the analyticity of $\bar{\rho}$ and U is needed only near y_c, and that, as a consequence of Theorem 5, a layer of homogeneous fluid containing a point of zero U'' and adjoining a stratified layer with uniformly large $J(y)$ is always unstable.

VII. NON-SINGULAR MODES

It remains to study neutral waves with a (real) c outside of the range of U, whose minimum and maximum will continue to be denoted by a and b. We assume $\bar{\rho}$ and U to be continuous, and that their derivatives as appear in (32) exist. Then if m and M retain their definitions as given by (51) and (52), except that $c = a - \epsilon$, we have

Theorem 6. Under the assumptions on $\bar{\rho}$ and U stated above, if (51) holds there are at least n modes with $c = a - \epsilon$, $\alpha = \alpha_i$ ($i = 1, 2, \ldots, n$), and α_i increasing with i. For the i-th mode there are at least $n - i$ internal zeros. If (52) holds in addition, then there are exactly n such modes, the i-th of which has exactly $n - i$ internal zeros. If $(\bar{\rho}U')'$ is negative, then n can only increase as the arbitrary positive constant ϵ decreases.

The proof of this theorem is by a straightforward application of the first comparison theorem of Sturm. Similarly, if m and M are defined by (51) and (52), except that $c = b + \epsilon$, where ϵ is an arbitrary positive constant, we have

Theorem 7. Under the assumptions on $\bar{\rho}$ and U stated above, if (51) holds there are at least n modes with $c = b + \epsilon$, $\alpha = \alpha_i$ ($i = 1, 2, \ldots, n$), and α_i increasing with i. For the i-th mode there are at least $n - i$ internal zeros. If (52) holds in addition, then there are exactly n such modes, the i-th of which has exactly $n - i$ internal zeros. If $(\bar{\rho}U')'$ is negative, then n can only increase as ϵ decreases.

Yih

If for $c = a - \epsilon$ or $c = b + \epsilon$, and any $\epsilon \geqq 0$, M is less than $\pi^2/(y_2 - y_1)^2$ for all y_1 and y_2 between zero and 1, then there can be no waves propagating with c equal to a or b, or outside of the range of U. On the other hand, if $U'' = 0$ at the point of maximum or minimum U, and, a fortiori, if there is a region of constant U where U = a or b, it can be easily shown that waves of any finite wave length and any finite number of internal zeros n can propagate with c < a or c > b. All this is in contrast with waves propagating in a layer of homogeneous fluid with a free surface and in shear flow. In that case [Yih 1970], if U is monotonically increasing with y, waves of all wave lengths can propagate with c greater than b, and only sufficiently long waves can propagate with c less than b.

ACKNOWLEDGMENT

This work has been supported by the National Science Foundation.

REFERENCES

Drazin, P. G., "On the Dynamics of a Fluid of Variable Density," Ph.D. Thesis, Cambridge University, 1958.

Howard, L. N., "Note on a Paper of John W. Miles," J. Fluid Mech., Vol. 10, pp. 509-512, 1961.

Lin, C. C., "On the Stability of Two-dimensional Parallel Flows, Part II," Quart. Appl. Math., pp. 218-234, 1945.

Lin, C. C., The Theory of Hydrodynamic Stability, Cambridge University Press, 1955.

Miles, J. W., "On the Stability of Heterogeneous Shear Flows," J. Fluid Mech., Vol. 10, pp. 496-508, 1961.

Miles, J. W., "On the Stability of Heterogeneous Shear Flows, Part 2," J. Fluid Mech., Vol. 16, pp. 209-227, 1963.

Synge, J. I., "The Stability of Heterogeneous Liquids," Trans. Roy. Soc. Can., Vol. 27, pp. 1-18, 1933.

Yih, C.-S., "On Stratified Flows in a Gravitational Field," Tellus, Vol. 9, pp. 220-227, 1957.

Yih, C.-S., "Surface Waves in Flowing Water," to be published in J. Fluid Mech. in 1971.

Stability of and Waves in Stratified Flows

DISCUSSION

L. van Wijngaarden
Twente Institute of Technology
Enschede, The Netherlands

The flow with a free surface of a fluid, homogeneous in density, but with inhomogeneous velocity distribution, is a special case of your class of stratified fluids. Burns [1953] considered this case and I guess his results are comprised in yours. When viscosity is allowed for, the problem becomes much more complicated. It may be of interest to note that Velthuizen and I [1969a, 1969b] studied this problem taking viscosity into account. We obtained results essentially different from Burn's results, which is due to viscous effects.

At large Reynolds number the flow can be divided in an inviscid region and viscous regions at the critical layer and at the bottom. At the outer edge of the viscous layer at the wall the Reynolds stress cannot be put equal to zero a priori because a stress may build up in the wall layer.

REFERENCES

Burns, J. C., "Long Waves in Running Waters," Proc. Camb. Phil. Soc. 49, 695, 1953.

Velthuizen, H. G. M. and L. v. Wijngaarden, J. Fluid Mech. 39, 4, 817, 1969a.

Velthuizen, H. G. M. and L. v. Wijngaarden, IUTAM Symposium on Instability of Continuous Systems, Herrenalb, Sept. 1969.

* * * * *

REPLY TO DISCUSSION

Chia-Shun Yih
*University of Michigan
Ann Arbor, Michigan*

It is well known that Rayleigh's sufficient condition for stability of inviscid fluids flowing between rigid boundaries is satisfied by a parabolic velocity profile, whereas plane Poiseuille flow, which has this profile, has been found by Heisenberg and Lin to be unstable at sufficiently large Reynolds numbers, when viscous effects are taken into account. Since the present paper is a study of the stability of inviscid fluids, and, in particular, Rayleigh's criterion for stability is generalized in it, Professor van Wijngaarden's position that the consideration of viscosity may force us to modify some of the conclusions in the paper is easily acceptable.

In considering viscous effects, however, it is not entirely self-consistent to assume a horizontal mean flow with a free surface, as Velthuizen and Professor van Wijngaarden have done [1969a,b], since such a flow obviously cannot be maintained, and must in time attenuate to a state of rest. This is not to say that any conclusion of instability reached by them is without significance, for instability of a transient nature may well occur, with the disturbances growing for a short duration of time. In this regard the results of Benjamin [1957] and Yih [1963] for surface waves in a fluid layer flowing down an inclined plane are relevant. They found that the speed c_r of long surface waves, be they unstable, neutral, or stable, exceeds the maximum speed of flow. The absence of long waves propagating upstream supports Professor van Wijngaarden's claim in connection with Burn's result, which is supported by a study [Yih 1971] of waves in a flowing inviscid liquid. But the nonexistence of a critical layer renders rather less cogent the argument given in Professor van Wijngaarden's discussion. On the other hand, this nonexistence substantiates the conclusion made in Yih [1971] (and similarly in this paper) regarding the nonexistence of singular neutral modes, since the velocity U in laminar flow of a viscous fluid down an inclined plane is parabolic, with a constant U''.

We also recall that Tollmien's sufficient condition for <u>instability</u> [1935] of an inviscid fluid is not much affected by the consideration of viscosity, at least when the Reynolds number is large, and hope that the same is true with the sufficient conditions for instability presented in this paper.

Stability of and Waves in Stratified Flows

REFERENCES

Benjamin, T. B., "Wave formation in laminar flow down an inclined plane," J. Fluid Mech., 2, pp. 554-574, 1957.

Tollmien, W., "Ein allgemeines kriterium der instabilität laminarer geschwindigkeitsverteilungen," Nachr. Ges. Wiss. Göttingen, Math. Phys. Kl., Fachgruppe 1, 1, pp. 79-114, 1935.

Yih, C.-S., "Stability of liquid flow down an inclined plane," Phys. of Fluids, 6, pp. 321-334, 1963.

(The other references are given either in the paper itself or in Professor van Wijngaarden's discussion.)

* * * * *

CHAPTER X

Wave Motion in Stratified Fluids

Chia-Shun Yih

If an incompressible fluid at rest has variable density, with the density decreasing with height, or if a compressible fluid has variable entropy, with the entropy increasing with height, a particle of the fluid, when displaced from its original position, will experience a gravitational force that acts to restore it to its original position. This restoring force makes wave motion possible in such a stratified fluid.

Waves can be made not only by an oscillating wave maker or by an obstacle placed in a stream but also as the result of instability. This chapter describes waves in a stratified incompressible fluid at rest, waves created by obstacles in a stratified stream, and waves arising from instability of stratified flows.

1. Waves of Small Amplitude

If x, y, and z are cartesian coordinates, with z measured in the direction of the vertical, the mean density $\bar{\rho}$ (in the absence of waves) of a stratified fluid at rest is a function of z only. The mean pressure $\bar{p}$ is related to $\bar{\rho}$ by the hydrostatic equation

$$\bar{p}_z = -g\bar{\rho}, \tag{1}$$

in which g is the gravitational acceleration. Since three-dimensional infinitesimal waves can be obtained by superposition of two two-

The writing of this chapter, as well as part of the research, has been sponsored by the Office of Naval Research through Grant NRO62-448 to the University of Michigan.

dimensional wavetrains, it is sufficient to consider two-dimensional motion.

Using u and w to denote the velocity components in the x and z directions, respectively, we obtain the linearized equations of motion

$$\bar{\rho} u_t = -p'_x \tag{2}$$

and

$$\bar{\rho} w_t = -p'_z - g\rho', \tag{3}$$

in which t indicates time, and p' and ρ' are the perturbations in pressure and density, respectively. In arriving at (3), the terms involving $\bar{p}$ and $\bar{\rho}$ have been eliminated by the use of (1). The equation of continuity is

$$\rho_t + (\rho u)_x + (\rho w)_z = 0, \tag{4}$$

in which

$$\rho = \bar{\rho} + \rho'$$

is the total density. The equation of incompressibility is

$$\frac{D\rho}{Dt} = 0, \tag{5}$$

in which

$$\frac{D}{Dt} = \frac{\partial}{\partial t} + u\frac{\partial}{\partial x} + w\frac{\partial}{\partial z}.$$

From (4) and (6) we obtain

$$u_x + w_z = 0 \tag{6}$$

as an alternative (and simpler) form of the equation of continuity. Since $\bar{\rho}$ is a function of z only, (5) can be written as

$$\rho'_t + w\bar{\rho}_z = 0, \tag{7}$$

if quadratic terms in the perturbation quantities are neglected. Equations (2), (3), (6), and (7) are the equations on which a linear theory for infinitesimal waves in a stratified incompressible fluid is based.

Equation (6) allows the use of a stream function ψ, in terms of which u and w can be expressed as follows:

$$u = \psi_z, \qquad w = -\psi_x. \tag{8}$$

To study wave motion, we assume ψ to have the factor $\exp(-i\omega t)$, where ω is the "circular frequency" of wave motion, or 2π times the frequency. Elimination of p' and ρ' among (2), (3), and (7) and use of (8) produce

$$(\omega^2\bar{\rho} + g\bar{\rho}')\frac{\partial^2\psi}{\partial x^2} + \omega^2\frac{\partial}{\partial z}\left(\bar{\rho}\frac{\partial\psi}{\partial z}\right) = 0, \tag{9}$$

in which

$$\bar{\rho}' = \frac{d\bar{\rho}}{dz}.$$

It is evident that at any point (9) is of the elliptic or hyperbolic type according as

$$\omega^2 > -\frac{g\bar{\rho}'}{\bar{\rho}} \quad \text{or} \quad \omega^2 < \frac{-g\bar{\rho}'}{\bar{\rho}}. \tag{10}$$

If

$$\omega^2 > g\left(-\frac{\bar{\rho}'}{\bar{\rho}}\right)_{\max}, \tag{11}$$

then (9) is elliptic everywhere and wave motion is impossible. The square root of the righthand side of (11) is called the Brunt-Väisälä frequency. If a body oscillates in a stratified fluid with a frequency higher than the Brunt-Väisälä frequency, it creates no waves in the fluid, which oscillates with the body in much the same way as a homogeneous fluid without a free surface. If the second of the two inequalities in (10) holds, (9) possesses two characteristic lines passing through the point in question, and wave motion is possible there. Of course the first inequality in (10) may hold in certain regions of the fluid, and the second inequality holds elsewhere. In that case (9) is of the mixed type, and its solution is in general difficult. (See Görtler, 1943, and the more recent work of Mowbray and Rarity, 1967, for further information in this connection.)

1a. The Differential Equation for Normal Modes

For the two-dimensional waves propagating in the x direction, we may assume

$$\psi = f(z)\exp[ik(x-ct)], \tag{12}$$

in which k is the wavenumber defined by

$$k = \frac{2\pi}{\lambda},$$

λ being the wavelength, and c is the phase velocity.

Equations (8) and (12) give

$$u = f'(z) \exp [ik(x - ct)], \tag{13}$$

$$w = -ikf(z) \exp [ik(x - ct)], \tag{14}$$

in which $f'(z) = df(z)/dz$. It is understood that the real parts of the right-hand sides of (13) and (14) are to be used. Examination of (7) shows that ρ' has the same exponential factor as ψ; hence,

$$ikc\rho' = w \frac{d\bar{\rho}}{dz} . \tag{15}$$

Equations (13) to (15) show how to obtain u, w, and ρ' from $f(z)$. To obtain the equation governing f, we can substitute (13) and (15) into (2) and (3) and eliminate p', or, what amounts to the same thing, we can substitute (12) into (9). The result is

$$(\bar{\rho}f')' - \left(k^2\bar{\rho} + \frac{g\bar{\rho}'}{c^2} \right) f = 0 \tag{16}$$

or

$$(\bar{\rho}f')' - k^2 \left(\bar{\rho} + \frac{g\bar{\rho}'}{\omega^2} \right) f = 0, \tag{17}$$

where the primes indicate differentiation with respect to z.

1b. Boundary Conditions

Let the depth of the fluid be d. If the lower and upper boundaries are rigid planes, w must vanish at these boundaries, and the boundary conditions are

$$f(0) = 0 \quad \text{and} \quad f(d) = 0. \tag{18}$$

If there is a discontinuity in density $\bar{\rho}$ at some value of z, at which the density $\bar{\rho}$ jumps from $\bar{\rho}_l$ to $\bar{\rho}_u$ ($< \bar{\rho}_l$), the interfacial condition at this discontinuity can be obtained by integrating (16) in the Stieltjes sense (allowing infinite values of the integrand) across the discontinuity. Inspection of (16) shows that there is a jump in $\rho f'$ because there is one in $\bar{\rho}'$, since f is continuous. Thus integration across the discontinuity (from $z_0 - \epsilon$ to $z_0 + \epsilon$, z_0 being the point of density discontinuity) gives

$$(\bar{\rho} f')_u - (\bar{\rho} f')_l + \frac{g}{c^2}(\bar{\rho}_l - \bar{\rho}_u)f = 0, \tag{19}$$

which is the interfacial condition. Note that while f is continuous at $z = z_0, f'$ may not be and in fact is not. At a free surface (if there is one), $\bar{\rho}_u = 0$. Therefore, if the lower boundary is a rigid plane and the upper surface of the fluid is free, the boundary conditions are

$$f(0) = 0 \quad \text{and} \quad f'(d) = \frac{g}{c^2} f(d), \tag{20}$$

the second of which follows from (19).

From (17) we can also see the implication of the inequality (11). For (11) to hold, $\bar{\rho}$ must not have any discontinuity, and, in particular, the fluid must not have a free surface. The boundary conditions are then given by (18). Multiplying (17) by f and integrating, using (18) whenever necessary, we obtain

$$-\int_0^d \bar{\rho} f'^2 \, dz - k^2 \int_0^d \left(\bar{\rho} + \frac{g\bar{\rho}'}{\omega^2}\right) f^2 \, dz = 0,$$

which is quite impossible if $k^2 \geq 0$ and (11) holds. Hence wave motion is impossible if the frequency is greater than the Brunt-Väisälä frequency, as we have seen already from the viewpoint of the type of (9).

1c. Proof that ω^2 is Real

Whether $\bar{\rho}'$ is positive, negative, or partly positive and partly negative, whether there are discontinuities in $\bar{\rho}$ or not, ω^2 is real. To show this we note that, with (12) substituted into (9), we obtain

$$\omega^2 [(\bar{\rho} f')' - k^2 \bar{\rho} f] - k^2 g \bar{\rho}' f = 0. \tag{21}$$

We note first of all that ω cannot be zero, for otherwise (21) would show that $f = 0$, since $\bar{\rho}'$ is not identically equal to zero. It was only after division of this result by ω^2 that we obtained (17). We prefer to use (21) for the proof of the reality of ω^2.

To show that ω^2 is real for the case of no density discontinuities, multiply (21) by f^*, the complex conjugate of f, and integrate, using (18) whenever necessary, to obtain

$$\omega^2 \int_0^d [\bar{\rho}|f'|^2 + k^2\bar{\rho}|f|^2]\, dz + k^2 g \int_0^d \bar{\rho}'|f|^2\, dz = 0. \tag{22}$$

Equation (22) shows that ω^2 is real even if $\bar{\rho}'$ changes sign in $0 \le z \le d$. If the upper surface is free, the term

$$\bar{\rho}(d)\,\omega^2\,\frac{g}{c^2}|f|^2 = \bar{\rho}(d)\,k^2 g\,|f|^2$$

is subtracted from the lefthand side of (22). It is clear that if there are density discontinuities (including the free surface, if there is one), upon the use of (19) (and (20) if there is a free surface) one need only consider the last integral in (22) to be in the Stieltjes sense. That is to say, if there are N continuously stratified layers, one need only replace the last integral in (22) by

$$\sum_{n=1}^{N} \int \bar{\rho}'|f|^2\, dy - \sum_{n=1}^{M} (\Delta\bar{\rho}|f|^2)_n,$$

in which the integrals are performed over the N layers, exclusive of the discontinuities, $\Delta\bar{\rho}$ is the jump in the mean density $\bar{\rho}$, and the subscript n means the value is taken at the nth discontinuity. The value of M is N if there is a free surface and $N - 1$ if there is not. By exactly the same argument as that for the case of no density discontinuities, we conclude that ω^2 is real.

Whether there are density discontinuities or not, if the density always decreases as z increases (and $\bar{\rho}_l > \bar{\rho}_u$ at every discontinuity if there are density discontinuities), ω^2 must be positive as can be seen from (22), in which the last integral is in the Stieltjes sense if there are density discontinuities. If the density always increases with height, with $\bar{\rho}_u > \bar{\rho}_l$ at all density discontinuities if any, then (22) shows that ω^2 is negative. A negative ω^2 means two imaginary values of ω, one of which makes $\exp(-i\omega t)$ an exponentially increasing function of time, so that the fluid is unstable. If $\bar{\rho}$ increases with height in part of the fluid and decreases with height elsewhere, ω^2 can be positive or negative.

1d. *Existence of Eigenvalues*

If there are no internal density discontinuities, the Sturm-Liouville theory as extended by Bôcher (1917) guarantees the existence of eigenvalues of ω^2 whether or not the upper surface is free. Indeed, the following oscillation theorem of Sturm not only states this existence but also says something important about the eigenfunctions (Bôcher, 1917, pages 66-67):

THE STURM-BÔCHER THEOREM. *Consider the system*

$$\left.\begin{array}{c} \dfrac{d}{dz}(Kf') - Gf = 0, \\[2mm] \alpha'f(a) - \alpha f'(a) = 0, \\[1mm] \beta'f(b) + \beta f'(b) = 0, \end{array}\right\}$$

in which K is always positive, and K and G are functions of z and the parameter λ, which do not increase as λ increases from Λ_1 to Λ_2 ($>\Lambda_1$), and α, α', β, and β' are functions of λ. If $\beta = 0$, or $\beta \neq 0$ and $K(b)\beta'/\beta$ is a decreasing function of λ, and if, in addition,

$$\lim_{\lambda \to \Lambda_2} \left(\frac{-\max G}{\max K} \right) = +\infty$$

and

$$\lim_{\lambda \to \Lambda_1} \left(\frac{-\min G}{\min K} \right) = -\infty,$$

then the system has an infinite number of eigenvalues λ_0, λ_1, ..., between Λ_1 and Λ_2, in ascending order of magnitude. Each of the eigenfunctions f_0, f_1, ..., which are solutions of the system for $\lambda = \lambda_0$, λ_1, ..., has a number of zeros in $a < z < b$ exactly equal to its respective index.

We note that the system consisting of (16) and (18) or (20), or of (17) and (18) or (20), satisfies every requirement of the Sturm-Liouville system stated in the theorem above if we identify λ with c^{-2} or ω^{-2}. Note also that if the boundary conditions are given by (18), then there are $n + 2$ zeros in $0 \leq z \leq d$ for $\lambda = \lambda_n$. (Here $a = 0$ and $b = d$.) If the boundary conditions are given by (20), then there are $n + 1$ zeros in $0 \leq z \leq d$

for $\lambda = \lambda_n$. If $\bar{\rho}'$ is negative throughout, it can be readily verified that, with $\lambda = c^{-2}$, for (16) $\Lambda_2 = +\infty$ ($c^2 = +0$) and $\Lambda_1 = -\infty$ ($c^2 = -0$). Similarly, with $\lambda = \omega^{-2}$ in (17), $\Lambda_2 = +\infty$ ($\omega^2 = +0$) and $\Lambda_1 = -\infty$ ($\omega^2 = -0$). Since we know that if $\bar{\rho}'$ is negative throughout, c^2 and ω^2 are both real and positive, and for any k^2 the value of ω^2 (and also of c^2) is bounded, all the eigenvalues of λ are between some positive value and $+\infty$ —that is, all the eigenvalues of ω^2 or c^2 are between zero and some finite, positive, upper bound.

If $\bar{\rho}'$ is uniformly negative where $\bar{\rho}$ is continuous, and at all density discontinuities $\bar{\rho}_u < \bar{\rho}_l$, the eigenvalues for c^2 (or ω^2) have been shown to exist (see Yih, 1965, pages 48-52). The part of the Sturm-Bôcher theorem that relates the index of the eigenvalues to the zeros of the eigenfunctions is still true even if $\bar{\rho}$ has discontinuities. This can be seen in the following way. First let the upper surface be rigid. For $\lambda = 0$ (or $c^2 = \infty$), obviously $f(z)$ increases with z as can be seen from (16) or (17) if $f'(0)$ is positive. Hence $f(d)$ is not zero. (If $f'(0)$ is negative, then $f(z)$ decreases as z increases, and we have the same result.) Since $c^2 = \infty$, this is true whether or not there are discontinuities in $\bar{\rho}$, as a glance at the interfacial conditions (19) will make clear. As we increase λ (or decrease c^2), $f(d)$ will vanish when the first eigenvalue λ_0 for fixed upper surface is reached. The existence of this λ_0 is known (Yih, 1965, pages 48-52). As subsequent eigenvalues λ_1, λ_2, ... are passed, the number of internal zeros is increased by 1 at each such passing. For otherwise there are two possibilities:

(i) Zeros can be created or destroyed internally.

(ii) The passing of λ_m (for any integral m) does not increase the number of internal zeros by 1.

If (i) were possible, there would be a stage at which two (or more) zeros coalesce at $z = z_a$, for instance, since the positions of the zeros are continuous functions of λ for given $\bar{\rho}$ and k^2. But a double zero for $f(z)$ at $z = z_a$ would mean the vanishing of $f(z)$ identically everywhere, and therefore (i) cannot happen. If (ii) were possible, $f(d)$ would have a double zero at $\lambda = \lambda_m$ (for otherwise $f(d)$ would change sign as λ_m is crossed), and it can be shown that double eigenvalues are not possible. If the upper surface is free, it can be shown that $f'(d)/f(d)$ decreases from a positive value to negative infinity as λ increases from zero toward λ_0 (the first eigenvalue for λ for the case of rigid upper surface) so that at some $\lambda < \lambda_0$ the free-surface condition (20) is satisfied. Similarly, if λ_{n-1} denotes the nth eigenvalue of λ for the rigid-upper-surface case, as λ varies from λ_{n-1} to λ_n, $f'(d)/f(d)$ decreases from positive infinity to negative infinity, so that (20) is satisfied at some λ between λ_{n-1} and λ_n. Furthermore, since zeros of the eigenfunction can be neither created nor destroyed internally, and as each λ_m is passed the internal zeros are increased by 1, that part of the Sturm-Bôcher theorem concerning the index of eigenvalues and the internal zeros of eigenfunctions remains true even if there are internal discontinuities in $\bar{\rho}$ and a free surface.

It is evident that if $\bar{\rho}'$ is everywhere positive and $\bar{\rho}_l < \bar{\rho}_u$ at every density discontinuity (if any), the existence of the eigenvalues of c^2, necessarily negative, and the relationship between the index of the eigenvalue and the internal zeros of the eigenfunction as stated by the Sturm-Bôcher theorem follow immediately from that theorem and the discussion in the preceding paragraph if we simply take $\lambda = -c^{-2}$. To each eigenvalue of c^2 at constant k^2 corresponds an eigenvalue of ω^2, of course; hence we need not discuss the existence of the eigenvalues of ω^2 independently.

If $\bar{\rho}'$ is positive in part of the fluid and negative elsewhere, by the use of the comparison theorems of Sturm to be presented in the next section we can show that there are two infinite series of eigenvalues of c^2, one positive and one negative, both tending to zero as a limit point, and for each series f_n $(n = 0, 1, \ldots)$ corresponding to λ_n has exactly n internal zeros. This situation is unchanged when there are density discontinuities, for some of which $\bar{\rho}_l < \bar{\rho}_u$, and for others of which $\bar{\rho}_u < \bar{\rho}_l$.

1e. The Variation of ω^2 and c^2 with k^2

Like gravity waves in a homogeneous fluid, gravity waves in a stratified fluid are also dispersive. That is to say, their velocity is a function of k. That this must be so can be seen from (16) or (17) and their boundary conditions. Without detailed calculations, which are in any case impossible unless $\bar{\rho}$ is specified, we can show that c^2 always decreases and ω^2 always increases as k^2 increases. For this purpose we need the comparison theorems of Sturm.

Consider the two systems (Bôcher, 1917, pp. 58-63)

$$(K_1 f'_1)' - G_1 f_1 = 0, \qquad f(a) = \alpha_1, \quad f'(a) = \alpha'_1,$$

and

$$(K_2 f'_2)' - G_2 f_2 = 0, \qquad f(a) = \alpha_2, \quad f'(a) = \alpha'_2,$$

where K_1, K_2, G_1, and G_2 are functions of z (and possibly of a parameter also), and

$$K_1 \geq K_2 > 0, \qquad G_1 \geq G_2.$$

It is assumed that

$$|\alpha_1| + |\alpha'_1| \neq 0, \qquad |\alpha_2| + |\alpha'_2| \neq 0,$$

that the equalities $K_1 = K_2$ and $G_1 = G_2$ do not hold in any part of the interval $[a, b]$, and that $G_1 = 0 = G_2$ does not hold in any part of the interval. Furthermore, if $\alpha_1 \neq 0$, it is assumed that $\alpha_2 \neq 0$ and

$$\frac{K_1(a)\alpha'_1}{\alpha_1} \geq \frac{K_2(a)\alpha'_2}{\alpha_2}.$$

If $\alpha_1 = 0$, no supplementary assumption need be made. Under the preceding assumptions, we have the following comparison theorems of Sturm:

STURM'S FIRST COMPARISON THEOREM. *If f_1 has a certain number of zeros in the interval $a < z \leq b$, f_2 must have at least as many zeros in this interval, and if $z_1, z_2, z_3, \ldots$ are the zeros of f_1 in ascending order, and $z'_1, z'_2, z'_3, \ldots$ are those of f_2, then*

$$z'_i < z_i$$

for all values of i corresponding to a zero of f_1 and f_2.

STURM'S SECOND COMPARISON THEOREM. *If, in addition to the assumptions stated in this paragraph, it is assumed that $f_1(b) \neq 0$ and $f_2(b) \neq 0$, then*

$$\frac{K_1(b)f'_1(b)}{f_1(b)} > \frac{K_2(b)f'_2(b)}{f_2(b)},$$

provided that f_1 and f_2 have the same number of zeros in $a < z \leq b$.

We are now in a position to see how c^2 or ω^2 varies with k^2. Consider first a stably stratified fluid with no internal density discontinuities. If the upper boundary is fixed, we can conclude from Sturm's first comparison theorem that for the same mode—that is, for a fixed number of zeros of the eigenfunction in $0 < z \leq d$—c^2 decreases as k^2 increases. For if $k_1{}^2 > k_2{}^2$ and $c_1{}^2$ and $c_1{}^2 \geq c_2{}^2$,

$$G_1 \equiv k_1{}^2 \bar{\rho} + \frac{g\bar{\rho}'}{c_1{}^2} > k_2{}^2 \bar{\rho} + \frac{g\bar{\rho}'}{c_2{}^2} \equiv G_2 \,,$$

and if $z = d$ is the nth zero of f_1, it cannot be the nth zero of f_2, which must occur at $z < d$. Hence, either f_2 does not vanish at $z = d$, violating the boundary condition there, or f_2 has at least one more zero than f_1 in $0 < z \leq d$. Hence, if $k_1{}^2 > k_2{}^2$, we must have $c_1{}^2 < c_2{}^2$. This result was first obtained by Groen (1948).

If the upper surface is free, use of Sturm's second comparison theorem leads to the same result. (See Yih, 1965, pages 32-33.)

If there are density discontinuities but the density never increases continuously or discontinuously as z increases, the same result can be used upon repeated applications of the comparison theorems of Sturm. But this application is tedious and inconvenient for exposition. Hence we shall present a new and more elegant proof of the theorem that c^2 decreases as k^2 increases, particularly since it can be used to show that ω^2 *increases* with k^2. Consider (16) with (18) and (19) or with (19) and (20). Let k^2 increase by dk^2 and c^2 by dc^2, and let the corresponding variation in f be ϵ. Then ϵ satisfies

$$(\bar{\rho}\epsilon')' - \left(k^2\bar{\rho} + \frac{g\bar{\rho}'}{c^2}\right)\epsilon = (dk^2)\bar{\rho}f - \frac{g\bar{\rho}'}{c^4}(dc^2)f. \tag{23}$$

The boundary condition for ϵ is $\epsilon = 0$ at a rigid surface, and

$$\epsilon' = \frac{g}{c^2}\epsilon - \frac{g(dc^2)}{c^4}f$$

at a free surface. The conditions on ϵ at an internal surface of density discontinuity can be similarly obtained. We can now multiply (16) by ϵ and (23) by f, integrate (layer by layer if there are density discontinuities) between zero and d, and apply the boundary and interfacial conditions on f and ϵ. The difference of the two equations so obtained is, with the last integral understood in the Stieltjes sense if there are any density discontinuities,

$$0 = (dk^2) \int_0^d \bar{\rho} f^2 \, dz - \frac{g(dc^2)}{c^4} \int_0^{d+} \bar{\rho}' f^2 \, dz. \tag{24}$$

Since the first integral in (24) is positive and the second negative, (24) means that

$$\frac{dk^2}{dc^2} < 0. \tag{25}$$

Note that since we have obtained (25) by perturbation, which does not change the mode, (25) is automatically for the same mode only. Here lies the simplicity of this approach.

We can also show that for the same mode

$$\frac{d\omega^2}{dk^2} > 0. \tag{26}$$

All that is necessary is to replace (16) by (17), (23) by

$$(\bar{\rho}\epsilon')' - k^2 \left(\bar{\rho} + \frac{g\bar{\rho}'}{\omega^2} \right) \epsilon = (dk^2) \left(\bar{\rho} + \frac{g\bar{\rho}'}{\omega^2} \right) f - \frac{k^2 g\bar{\rho}'}{\omega^4} (d\omega^2) f,$$

and to note that multiplication of (17) by f and integration shows that

$$\int_0^d \left(\bar{\rho} + \frac{g\bar{\rho}'}{\omega^2} \right) f^2 \, dz < 0.$$

The rest follows as before, and (26) results.

We can choose k and c to be positive. Then ω is positive, and (25) and (26) can be replaced by

$$\frac{dc}{dk} < 0, \tag{27}$$

$$\frac{d\omega}{dk} > 0. \tag{28}$$

Since $d\omega/dk$ is the group velocity C, (28) shows that C is in the same direction as c, and (27) shows that

$$C = \frac{d\omega}{dk} = \frac{d(kc)}{dk} = c + k \frac{dk}{dc} < c.$$

For gravity waves of a homogeneous liquid, $C < c$ has the significance that there are no upstream waves ahead of an obstacle placed in a stream of uniform velocity or moving in a stratified fluid at rest.

We have just discussed the propagation of normal modes in the x direction. The direction of group velocity in a two-dimensional wave motion propagating in the x-z plane (not merely in the x direction) can have some peculiar and strange behavior. (See Mowbray and Rarity, 1967, and the brief discussion in Yih, 1969b.)

2. Waves of Finite Amplitude

We shall first consider two-dimensional gravity waves created by an obstacle placed in a stratified fluid in steady flow. The equations of motion for steady two-dimensional flows are

$$\rho(uu_x + wu_z) = -p_x, \tag{29}$$

and

$$\rho(uw_x + ww_z) = -p_z - g\rho, \tag{30}$$

in which ρ is the density and p the pressure, the other symbols retaining their meanings given in Section 1. The equation of incompressibility is

$$u\rho_x + w\rho_z = 0 \tag{31}$$

by virtue of which the equation of continuity has the form (6). If we define (Yih, 1958)

$$(u', w') = \sqrt{\frac{\rho}{\rho_0}}\,(u, w),$$

in which ρ_0 is a constant reference density, because of (31), the equations (29), (30), and (6) can be written as

$$\rho_0(u'u'_x + w'u'_z) = -p_x, \tag{32}$$

$$\rho_0(u'w'_x + w'w'_z) = -p_z - g\rho, \tag{33}$$

and

$$u'_x + w'_z = 0. \tag{34}$$

Equations (32) and (33) are simpler than (29) and (30) because ρ_0 is constant, whereas the ρ on the lefthand sides of (29) and (30) is variable. We shall therefore work with (32), (33), and (34).

Equation (34) allows the use of the stream function ψ', in terms of which

$$u' = \psi'_z, \qquad w' = -\psi'_x,$$

and the y component of the vorticity of the associated flow (with velocity components u' and w') is

$$\eta' = u'_z - w'_x = \nabla^2 \psi',$$

where ∇^2 is the two-dimensional Laplacian. We can write (32) and (33) as

$$\rho_0 \eta' \, \psi'_x = \left[p + \frac{\rho_0(u'^2 + w'^2)}{2} \right]_x, \tag{35}$$

$$\rho_0 \eta' \, \psi'_z = \left[p + \frac{\rho_0(u'^2 + w'^2)}{2} \right]_z + g\rho. \tag{36}$$

Multiplying (35) by dx and (36) by dz and adding the results, we obtain

$$\rho_0 \eta' \, d\psi' = d\left[p + \frac{\rho(u^2 + w^2)}{2} \right] + g\rho \, dz = dH - gz \, d\rho, \tag{37}$$

in which

$$H = p + \frac{\rho(u^2 + w^2)}{2} + g\rho z$$

is the Bernoulli function, which does not vary along a streamline and therefore, like ρ, is a function of ψ' alone. Equation (37) can thus be written as

$$\nabla^2 \psi' + \frac{gz}{\rho_0} \frac{d\rho}{d\psi'} = \frac{1}{\rho_0} \frac{dH}{d\psi'} = h(\psi'), \tag{38}$$

(Yih, 1958) which is a simpler form of the corresponding equation in terms of Ψ' [stream function for the actual flow related to u and w by (8)] obtained first by Madame Dubreil-Jacotin (1935) and then independently by Long (1953):

$$\nabla^2 \psi + \frac{1}{\rho} \frac{d\rho}{d\psi} \left(\frac{\psi_x{}^2 + \psi_z{}^2}{2} \right) + gz = f(\psi). \tag{39}$$

Because of its simplicity, we shall use (38) instead of (39).

It is appropriate to note here that the analogous equations governing steady three-dimensional finite-amplitude motion of a stratified fluid are also known (Yih, 1967) but are difficult to solve.

2a. Lee Waves in a Stratified Stream

Given a density and a velocity distribution upstream, ρ and H in (38) can be evaluated as functions of ψ'. Thus (38) is in general nonlinear. Linear forms of (38) can, however, be obtained simply by demanding $d\rho/d\psi'$ and $h(\psi')$ to be linear in ψ'. One can then determine the corresponding upstream conditions. Fortunately, the classes of upstream conditions so obtained are sufficiently realistic, numerous, and adjustable to approximate actual conditions far upstream. We shall limit our discussion to lee waves created by an obstacle placed in a stratified stream for which (38) has a particularly simple linear form. Note that a linear form for (38) does not result from a linearization and does not require that the disturbances be small.

Consider a flow in the region $-\infty \le x \le 0$, $0 \le z \le d$, with

$$u' = U' = const. \quad \text{and} \quad \rho = \rho_0 - \frac{\rho_0 - \rho_1}{d} z \text{ at } x = -\infty. \tag{40}$$

If we use the dimensionless variables

$$\xi = \frac{x}{d}, \qquad \eta = \frac{z}{d}, \qquad \Psi = \frac{\psi'}{U'd},$$

then at $x = -\infty$ we have

$$\Psi = \eta, \qquad \nabla^2 \Psi = 0, \quad \text{and} \quad \frac{d\rho}{d\psi'} = \frac{\rho_1 - \rho_0}{U'd},$$

and we find $h(\psi')$ to be proportional to ψ' or Ψ, and (38) to have the form

$$\Psi_{\xi\xi} + \Psi_{\eta\eta} - F^{-2}\eta = -F^{-2}\Psi, \tag{41}$$

where

$$F^2 = \frac{U'^2}{g'd}, \qquad g' = g\frac{\rho_0 - \rho_1}{\rho_0}.$$

If there is a barrier in the stream, it will disturb that stream, and if the Froude number F is sufficiently low, there will be waves in the lee of the barrier. To represent a barrier, we shall use the method of singularities described below.

Let a line of singularities be situated at $x = 0$. We shall find the solution of (41) for $x < 0$, which we call Ψ_-, and the solution of (41) for $x > 0$, which we call Ψ_+. Then we shall match Ψ_- to Ψ_+ at $x = 0$, taking into account the presence of the singularities. The resulting solution then describes the flow past the barrier created by the line of singularities. As we shall see, we can use more than one line of singularities.

Taking into account the experimentally observed absence of waves upstream from the barrier (which can be explained in the case of infinitesimal waves but will be assumed here), we have (Yih, 1960)

$$\Psi_- = \eta + \sum_{N+1}^{\infty} A_n e^{a_n \xi} \sin n\pi\eta \qquad \text{for } \xi < 0,$$

$$\Psi_+ = \eta + \sum_{1}^{N} (B_n \cos a_n\xi + C_n \sin a_n\xi) \sin n\pi\eta \qquad (42)$$

$$+ \sum_{N+1}^{\infty} D_n e^{-a_n \xi} \sin n\pi\eta \qquad \text{for } \xi > 0,$$

in which

$$a_n = | n^2\pi^2 - F^{-2} |^{1/2} \qquad (43)$$

and N is defined by

$$N^2\pi^2 < F^{-2} < (N+1)^2\pi^2. \qquad (44)$$

Note that each term in (42) is a solution of (41), that the term η corresponds to the undisturbed flow, and that the solution for Ψ_- contains no wave terms. The number of lee-wave components is determined by (44), and the wavelengths are determined by (43).

We can demand that

$$\Psi_- = \Psi_+ \qquad \text{at } \xi = 0, \qquad (45)$$

$$\frac{\partial \Psi_-}{\partial \xi} - \frac{\partial \Psi_+}{\partial \xi} = f(\eta) \qquad \text{at } \xi = 0, \qquad (46)$$

where

$$f(\eta) = 0 \qquad \text{for } d > \eta > a$$

and $f(\eta)$ is specified for $\eta \le a$. Equation (45) means that there are no sources and sinks along the line $\xi = 0$, and (46) means that there is a

Wave Motion in Stratified Fluids **279**

vortex sheet at $\xi = 0$ for $\eta \le a$. Condition (45) demands that $A_n = D_n$ for $n > N$, and $B_n = 0$ for $n \le N$, and (39) demands that

$$a_n(A_n + D_n) = 2 \int_0^1 f(\eta) \sin n\pi\eta \, d\eta \qquad \text{for } n > N$$

and

$$a_n C_n = -2 \int_0^1 f(\eta) \sin n\pi\eta \, d\eta \quad \text{for } n \le N. \qquad (47)$$

Thus, once $f(\eta)$ is specified, all the coefficients in (42) are known. Equation (47) is especially significant, for it states that the C_n's, which are the amplitudes of the lee-wave components, depend on only the first N Fourier coefficients of $f(\eta)$ and not on the rest of them. That is to say, they do not depend on the complete details of $f(\eta)$, hence do not depend on the complete details of the barrier. Also, the form of Ψ_+ in (42) shows that there are N lee-wave components, since $B_n = 0$.

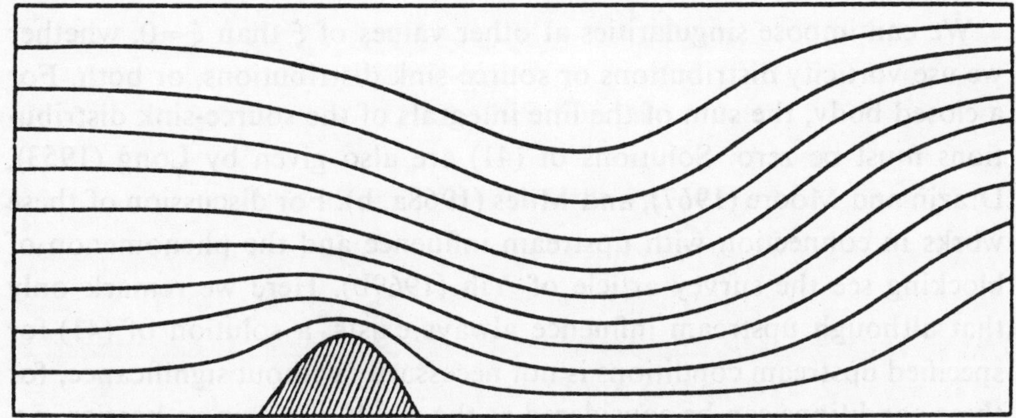

X.1. Pattern of a stratified flow with waves in the lee of a barrier. One lee-wave component.

Figure X.1 shows the flow pattern at $F = 3/4\pi$, with a barrier created by the singularity distribution

$$\begin{aligned} f(\eta) &= -10 \sin 5\pi\eta \qquad && \text{for } 0 \le \eta \le 0.2, \\ f(\eta) &= 0 && \text{for } 0.2 \le \eta \le 1. \end{aligned}$$

There is only one lee-wave component.

                                                              Chia-Shun Yih

Instead of demanding (45) and (46), we can demand

$$\Psi_- - \Psi_+ = f(\eta) \qquad \text{at } \xi = 0$$

and

$$\frac{\partial \Psi_-}{\partial \xi} = \frac{\partial \Psi_+}{\partial \xi} \qquad \text{at } \xi = 0.$$

The line singularity is then a distribution of sources and sinks. For a closed barrier, the integral of $f(\eta)$ from zero to a must be zero. The coefficients in (42) are then given by

$$A_n = -D_n \qquad \text{for } n > N,$$
$$C_n = 0 \qquad \text{for } n \leq N,$$
$$A_n - D_n = 2 \int_0^1 f(\eta) \sin n\pi\eta \, d\eta \qquad \text{for } n > N,$$

and

$$B_n = -2 \int_0^1 f(\eta) \sin n\pi\eta \, d\eta \qquad \text{for } n \leq N.$$

We can impose singularities at other values of ξ than $\xi = 0$, whether we use vorticity distributions or source-sink distributions, or both. For a closed body, the sum of the line integrals of the source-sink distributions must be zero. Solutions of (41) are also given by Long (1953), Drazin and Moore (1967), and Miles (1968a, b). For discussion of these works in connection with upstream influence and the phenomenon of blocking see the survey article of Yih (1969b). Here we remark only that although upstream influence always exists, a solution of (41) for specified upstream conditions is not necessarily without significance, for these conditions can be considered as the result of placing a barrier in a flow originally different from the upstream flow that results. Solutions for high barriers at low Froude numbers and with very complicated flow patterns and regions of closed streamlines may not be realistic, however, since blocking can occur in those cases to change the upstream conditions from those assumed in the solutions.

We conclude this section by noting that other classes of finite-amplitude wave motions are known for stratified fluids.

Solitary waves in an incompressible fluid with an exponential distribution in density were studied by Long (1965), and solitary and cnoidal waves in a stratified incompressible fluid by Benjamin (1966). In these studies, the amplitude of motion in the vertical direction is taken to be that for periodic waves of long wavelength, and a stretching (or rather contraction) of the horizontal coordinate in the direction of wave propagation gives the equation that determines the waveform after the dynamical equations have been satisfied at the required order of approximation.

A class of solutions according to the shallow-water theory for gravity waves in a stratified fluid is known (Yih, 1969a). In addition, Gerstner's solution for finite-amplitude waves, found to remain valid for a stratified fluid by Madame Dubreil-Jacotin (1932), has been discovered to represent edge waves in a stratified fluid also (Yih, 1966).

3. Stability

Since waves may be generated by instability of stratified flows, it is appropriate to discuss the question of stability. But we shall limit our discussion to general results.

Since the stability or instability of three-dimensional disturbances in a stratified flow can be deduced from the stability or instability of two-dimensional disturbances in a flow with reduced mean velocity (Yih, 1955), we shall study two-dimensional disturbances only.

For convenience we shall henceforth use y for the vertical coordinate instead of z, and v for the vertical component of the velocity instead of w. If the mean velocity in the x direction denoted by U is a continuous function of y, u and v denote the components of the perturbation velocity in the directions of increasing x and y, respectively, and $\bar{\rho}$ still denotes the mean density, the linearized equations of motion are

$$\bar{\rho}(u_t + U u_x + U' v) = -p_x \tag{48}$$

and

$$\bar{\rho}(v_t + U v_x) = -p_y - g\rho, \tag{49}$$

in which p is now the pressure perturbation and ρ the density perturbation and the prime denotes differentiation with respect to y. The equation of continuity

$$u_x + v_y = 0$$

again permits the use of the stream function ψ in terms of which

$$u = \psi_y, \qquad v = -\psi_x. \tag{50}$$

The linearized equation of incompressibility is

$$\rho_t + U\rho_x + v\bar{\rho}' = 0. \tag{51}$$

If η is the vertical displacement of a line of constant density from its mean position, the kinematic equation for that line is

$$\eta_t + U\eta_x = v = -\psi_x. \tag{52}$$

All perturbation quantities are assumed to have the factor $\exp ik(x - ct)$, which completely represents their dependence on x and t. Hence (52) and (50) give

$$\psi = -(U - c)\eta, \qquad u = -[(U - c)\eta]' \, v = ik(U - c)\eta, \tag{53}$$

and (48) and (51) give

$$p = \bar{\rho}(U - c)^2\eta' \quad \text{and} \quad \rho = -\bar{\rho}'\eta. \tag{54}$$

If $F(y)$ is the amplitude of η—that is, if

$$\eta(x, y, t) = F(y) \exp ik(x - ct)$$

—substitution of (53) and (54) into (49) produces

$$[\bar{\rho}(U - c)^2 F']' + \bar{\rho}[\beta g - k^2(U - c)^2]F = 0, \tag{55}$$

where

$$\beta = -\frac{\bar{\rho}'}{\bar{\rho}} > 0.$$

Equation (55) and the boundary conditions constitute the system governing stability. The eigenvalue c may be complex. Let $c = c_r + ic_i$. If c_i is positive, the flow is unstable. It can be easily verified that the boundary conditions (whether the upper surface is free or not, and whether internal density discontinuities exist), like (55), do not involve the imaginary number i explicitly. Hence, if c is an eigenvalue, so is its complex conjugate c^*. Hence, if c is complex, there is an eigenvalue of c with positive c_i, and the flow is unstable.

Instead of using (55), which is an equation for η, we can obtain an equation for ψ by writing

$$\psi = f(y) \exp ik(x - ct) \tag{56}$$

and working with (50), (48), and (49). Elimination of p between (48) and (49) gives

$$(\bar{\rho}f')' + \left[\frac{(\bar{\rho}U')'}{c - U} - k^2\bar{\rho} - \frac{g\bar{\rho}'}{(c - U)^2}\right]f = 0. \tag{57}$$

Of course, we can also use (56) and the first equation of (53) to obtain

$$f(y) = -(U - c)F(y)$$

and substitute this in (55) to obtain (57).

If the upper surface is fixed, the boundary conditions for $F(y)$ and $f(y)$ are, respectively,

$$F(0) = 0 = F(d), \tag{58}$$
$$f(0) = 0 = f(d).$$

3a. Miles' Theorem

Miles (1961) obtained the theorem that if

$$g\beta > \frac{1}{4} U'^2 \quad \text{or} \quad J(y) \equiv \frac{g\beta}{U'^2} > \frac{1}{4} \tag{59}$$

everywhere in the flow, then the flow is stable, or $c_i = 0$. Here J is called the Richardson number. The following elegant proof of Miles' theorem was given by Howard (1961).

Writing

$$W = U - c \quad \text{and} \quad G = W^{1/2}F,$$

one transforms (55) into

$$(\bar{\rho}WG')' - [\tfrac{1}{2}(\bar{\rho}U')' + k^2\bar{\rho}W + \bar{\rho}W^{-1}(\tfrac{1}{4}U'^2 - g\beta)]G = 0. \tag{60}$$

If the boundaries are fixed,

$$G(0) = 0 = G(d).$$

284   **Chia-Shun Yih**

Multiplying (60) by G^*, integrating, and using the boundary conditions, Howard obtained

$$\int_0^d \left[\bar{\rho} W(|G'|^2 + k^2 |G|^2) + \frac{1}{2}(\rho U')' |G|^2 + \bar{\rho}\left(\frac{1}{4}U'^2 - g\beta\right)\left|\frac{G}{W}\right|^2 \right] dy = 0.$$

(61)

If $c_i \neq 0$, the imaginary part of (61) is

$$\int_0^d \bar{\rho}(|G'|^2 + k^2 |G|^2)\, dy + \int_0^d \bar{\rho}\left(g\beta - \frac{1}{4}U'^2\right)\left|\frac{G}{W}\right|^2 dy = 0,$$

from which the truth of Miles' theorem is evident. Realizing that $|W|^{-2} \leq c_i^2$, Howard also obtained from the preceding equation the result

$$k^2 \int_0^d \bar{\rho}|G|^2\, dy < \frac{1}{c_i^2} \max\left(\frac{1}{4}U'^2 - g\beta\right) \int_0^d \bar{\rho}|G|^2\, dy$$

or

$$k^2 c_i^2 < \max\left(\frac{1}{4}U'^2 - g\beta\right),$$

(62)

if $c_i \neq 0$. Inequality (62) gives an upper bound for c_i^2. It also contains Miles' theorem.

3b. Howard's Semicircle Theorem

Working with (55) and (58), Howard (1961) succeeded also in showing that, if $c_i \neq 0$,

$$[c_r - \tfrac{1}{2}(a + b)]^2 + c_i^2 < \tfrac{1}{4}(b - a)^2,$$

(63)

in which a is the minimum and b the maximum of U. This is Howard's semicircle theorem, which states that if $c_i > 0$, then c must lie within the semicircle in the upper half of the complex-c plane with the range of U as diameter.

We note that if $\bar{\rho}$ has discontinuities, including the one at the free surface if the upper surface is free, Miles' theorem and Howard's semicircle theorem remain true, provided U remains continuous. All one needs to do is to consider $\bar{\rho}'$ and $[\bar{\rho}(U - c)^2 F']'$ as generalized functions and regard the integrals in (61) and other equations as integrals in the Stieltjes sense.

3c. Sufficient Conditions for Stability

In terms of the dimensionless variables

$$\hat{f}=\frac{f}{Vd}, \quad \hat{\bar{\rho}}=\frac{\bar{\rho}}{\rho_0}, \quad \hat{y}=\frac{y}{d}, \quad \hat{U}=\frac{U}{V}, \quad \hat{c}=\frac{c}{V}, \quad \alpha=kd,$$

in which V is a reference velocity and ρ_0 a reference density, equation (57) becomes, after the circumflexes are dropped,

$$(\bar{\rho}f')' + \left(\frac{(\bar{\rho}U')'}{c-U} - \alpha^2\bar{\rho} - \frac{N\bar{\rho}'}{(c-U)^2}\right)f = 0, \tag{64}$$

in which the primes indicate differentiations with respect to the dimensionless y, and $N=gd/V^2$. We now specify that $\bar{\rho}$ is continuous and the upper surface is fixed. Hence the boundary conditions are

$$f(0)=0=f(1). \tag{65}$$

The system consisting of (64) and (65) gives rise to the (complex) secular equation

$$F_1(\alpha, N, c)=0. \tag{66}$$

When c_i is set to zero and c_r is eliminated from the two real equations contained in (66), we have

$$F_2(\alpha, N)=0,$$

which gives the neutral stability curve, if one exists. It is possible, however, that c is real for all values of α and N, in which case there is no neutral stability curve or stability boundary in the α-N plane.

In this subsection we shall assume $\bar{\rho}$ and U to be continuous and analytic, and $\bar{\rho}' < 0$ throughout. First, we note that given $\bar{\rho}$, U, and α, the flow is stable for a sufficiently large N according to Miles' theorem, since a large enough N can always be found to make (59) hold. If for some N the flow is unstable, as N is increased there will be one N for which c_i first becomes zero. At this N the c (or c_r) must be within the range of U, since as it is approached through unstable states c_r must be within the range of U according to Howard's semicircle theorem. At the stability boundary (where c first becomes real), (57) is then singular, and we call the mode a singular neutral mode (SNM). The discussion in this paragraph shows that the flow cannot be unstable if singular neutral modes do not exist. To find sufficient conditions for stability, it is then sufficient to find conditions under which singular neutral modes do not exist.

We shall assume U to be monotonic in this subsection. Miles (1961) has shown that singular neutral modes are impossible if the Richardson number $J(y)$ is everywhere greater than $\frac{1}{4}$. In his proof he actually showed that an SNM with a $J(y_c) > \frac{1}{4}$ at $y = y_c$ where $U = c$ is impossible. It can be shown (Yih, 1970) that a SNM with $J(y_c) = \frac{1}{4}$ is also impossible. In that case the two roots of the indicial equation of (57), which has a "regular" singularity at $y = y_c$, are equal, and all that is necessary to construct a proof is to use the solutions, one of which contains a term with the factor $\ln(y - y_c)$, in such an exceptional case. If this latter solution is present, the jump of the Reynolds stress makes the SNM impossible. If it is absent, the proof for $J(y_c) < \frac{1}{4}$ applies. We shall not give the details of the proof here but instead shall concentrate on the case $J(y_c) < \frac{1}{4}$.

For $J(y_c) < \frac{1}{4}$ Miles (1961) gave the solutions of (64) to be

$$f_{\pm}(y) = (y - y_c)^{(1 \pm \kappa)/2} w_{\pm}, \tag{67}$$

in which $w = 1 + A(y - y_c)/(1 \pm \nu) + \cdots$, with

$$\kappa = (1 - 4J_c)^{1/2},$$

$$J_c = J(y_c),$$

$$A = \left[(1 + J) \frac{(\bar{\rho} U')'}{\bar{\rho} U'} - \frac{J \bar{\rho}''}{\bar{\rho}'} + \gamma (\ln \bar{\rho})' \right]_{y_c},$$

$$\gamma = \frac{1 + \kappa}{2}.$$

Miles also showed that for $J_c < \frac{1}{4}$ the solution for an SNM, if one exists, must be either f_+ or f_-. We can demonstrate our point by showing the impossibility of the solution f_+. The demonstration of the impossibility of f_- is similar.

We note first of all that for an SNM which is a stability boundary c (or c_r), being the limit of c_r as $c_i \to 0$, must be bounded away from a or b, since c_r for a nonzero c_i, however small, is bounded away from a or b because (63) is a strict inequality, never an equality. Hence, for our purpose of finding sufficient conditions for stability, it is sufficient to consider the impossibility of an SNM with y_c in $0 < y_c < 1$, with the end-points zero and 1 ruled out for y_c. The satisfaction of the boundary conditions then demands that $w_\pm$ be zero at $y = 0$ and $y = 1$. The possibility or impossibility of an SNM hinges on the zeros of w_+, which will be denoted by w for brevity. This leads us to consider the differential equation for w, which can be obtained from (64) and (67):

$$(\bar\rho z^{2\gamma} w')' + z^{2\gamma} \left[-J_c \bar\rho z^{-2} + \gamma \bar\rho' z^{-1} + \frac{(\bar\rho U')'}{c - U} - \alpha^2 \bar\rho - \frac{N\bar\rho'}{(c - U)^2} \right] w = 0,$$

(68)

in which $z = y - y_c$, $\gamma = (1 + \kappa)/2$, and

$$J_c = \left(-\frac{\bar\rho'}{\bar\rho U'^2} \right)_c N,$$

(69)

with $\bar\rho$ and U now dimensionless.

We define Q by

$$Q = -\frac{N\bar\rho'}{(U - c)^2} - \frac{J_c \bar\rho}{z^2},$$

and assume U', $(\bar\rho U')'$, and $(\ln \bar\rho)''$ to be positive. Since $\bar\rho' < 0$ and U' and $(\rho U')'$ are positive, U'' is positive. Thus $U - c$ is greater than $U_c z$ for $z > 0$. On the other hand $-\bar\rho'/\bar\rho$ is less than $(-\bar\rho'/\bar\rho)_c$ for $z > 0$, since $(\ln \bar\rho)'' > 0$. Thus Q is negative above any point with $y_p > y_c$ if it is negative at $y = y_p$. But for small z

$$Q = \frac{\bar\rho_c J_c}{z^2} \left\{ \left[\frac{\bar\rho}{\bar\rho'} (\ln \bar\rho)'' - \frac{U''}{U'} \right]_{y_c} z + \cdots \right\},$$

(70)

which is negative for small positive z, hence Q is and, a fortiori, the bracket in (68) is negative above y_c. Integrating (68) between y_c and 1, we have

$$(\bar\rho z^{2\gamma} w w')_1 - \int_{y_c}^1 z^{2\gamma} (\bar\rho w'^{2\gamma} + G w^2) \, dy = 0,$$

(71)

in which $-G$ is the bracket in (69), so that G is positive in the interval of integration. Equation (71) shows clearly that $w(1)$ cannot vanish. Note that the integral in (71) is convergent in spite of the simple pole at $z=0$ in G, one of which is in Q, as can be seen from (70). Hence we have (Yih, 1970):

THEOREM 1. *If $\bar{\rho}$ and U are continuous and analytic, $\bar{\rho}' < 0$, $U' > 0$, and $(\bar{\rho}U')'$ and $(\ln \bar{\rho})''$ are positive throughout, then singular neutral modes are impossible, and the flow is stable.*

In a similar way, we can prove

THEOREM 2. *If $\bar{\rho}$ and U are continuous and analytic, $\bar{\rho}' < 0$ and $U' < 0$, and U'' and $(\ln \bar{\rho})''$ are negative throughout, then singular neutral modes are impossible, and the flow is stable.*

To prove Theorem 2, it is necessary only to define z as $y_c - y$ and integrate the equation for w corresponding to (68) from zero to y_c.

Theorems 1 and 2 constitute the natural generalization of the well-known Rayleigh theorem for homogeneous fluids.

It remains to note that normal modes may not be adequate for studying stability. But nobody has yet shown a case of instability not described by normal modes, except the obviously unstable case when $\bar{\rho}$ increases upward for a horizontal flow.

3d. Sufficient Conditions for Instability

Let B be the coefficient of f in (64), m be the minimum and M the maximum of $B/\bar{\rho}$ between y_1 and y_2, with $0 < y_1 < y_2 < 1$. For convenience of exposition, we state three conditions, or assumptions, some or all of which will be met or made:

(a) $\bar{\rho}$ and U are continuous and analytic, $\bar{\rho}' \leq 0$, and at any point where $\bar{\rho}'$ vanishes U'' also vanishes, and $U = U_c = $ constant,

(b) $m \geq \dfrac{(n\pi)^2}{(y_2 - y_1)^2}$, $n = $ an integer,

(c) $M \leq \dfrac{(n+1)^2\pi^2}{(y_2 - y_1)^2}$, $n = $ an integer.

Note that if assumption (a) is satisfied, then $\bar{\rho}''$ must vanish where $\bar{\rho}'$ does, for $\bar{\rho}$ cannot increase with z since $\bar{\rho}' \leq 0$. Furthermore, with (a) satisfied, (64) is not singular if $c = U_c$, and we can apply the Sturm-Liouville theory. Applying that theory, we readily obtain two theorems (Yih, 1970):

THEOREM 3. *If assumptions (a) and (b) are satisfied, there are at least n modes with $c = U_c$ and $\alpha = \alpha_i$ ($i = 1, 2, \ldots, n$), and with α_i increasing with i. For the i-th mode there are at least $n - i$ internal zeros of the eigenfunction f.*

THEOREM 4. *If assumptions (a), (b), and (c) are satisfied, there are exactly n modes with $c = U_c$ and $\alpha = \alpha_i$ ($i = 1, 2, \ldots, n$), and with α_i increasing with i. For the i-th mode there are exactly $n - i$ internal zeros of the eigenfunction f.*

It can be shown, by an argument similar to that used by Lin (1955), that if we vary α^2 slightly from any of the $\alpha_1, \alpha_2, \ldots, \alpha_n$ mentioned in Theorems 3 and 4, c will become complex. We then have

THEOREM 5. *Near the neutral modes stated in Theorem 3, there are contiguous unstable modes. That is to say, if conditions (a) and (b) are satisfied, the flow is unstable.*

Incidentally, Theorems 3 and 4 explain why the stability boundary in the α-N plane may be multivalued in α for the same N, as found by Miles (1963).

3e. Nonsingular Modes

It remains to study waves with a real c outside of the range of U, whose minimum and maximum will continue to be denoted by a and b. We now replace assumption (a) with

(d) $\bar{\rho}$ and U are continuous and analytic, $\bar{\rho}' \leq 0$,

and we recall that m and M defined in Subsection 3d depend on c. Since for c outside of the range of U (64) is nonsingular, we can again apply the Sturm-Liouville theory. Doing so, we obtain the following two theorems (Yih, 1970):

                                                              Chia-Shun Yih

THEOREM 6. *If* (d) *and* (b) *are satisfied for* $c = a - \epsilon$, *then there are at least n nonsingular modes with* $c = a - \epsilon$, $\alpha = \alpha_i$ $(i = 1, 2, \ldots, n)$, *and* α_i *increasing with i. For the n-th mode there are at least* $n - i$ *internal zeros for f. If* (c) *holds in addition, there are exactly n such modes, the i-th of which has exactly* $n - i$ *interval zeros of f. If* $(\bar{\rho} U')'$ *is negative, then n can only increase as the arbitrary constant* ϵ *decreases.*

THEOREM 7. *Theorem 6 remains true if we replace* $c = a - \epsilon$ *with* $c = b + \epsilon$, *and the word "negative" with the word "positive."**

* This theorem, as given in Yih (1970), contains a misprint; the word "negative" there should be changed to "positive."

Progressive waves of permanent form in continuously stratified fluids

Chia-Shun Yih

Department of Applied Mechanics and Engineering Science, The University of Michigan, Ann Arbor, Michigan 48104

(Received 21 February 1974)

A theory for internal progressive waves of permanent form in any continuously stratified fluid is presented, and a calculation for the flow and the wave velocity is carried out for an exponential stratified fluid. The most important conclusion from this calculation, also valid for other weak stratifications, is that the wave velocity always *decreases* with the amplitude, provided the density gradient is weak and the wavelength is not too short. This conclusion is significant because it entails the existence or nonexistence of solitary waves in weakly stratified fluids. The validity of the Boussinesq approximation and the significance of the well-known exactly linear cases are also discussed.

I. INTRODUCTION

Waves of permanent form progressing in a stratified fluid otherwise at rest can be studied most conveniently by adopting a frame of reference moving with the waves and thereby making the flow independent of time. The equation governing steady two-dimensional flows of a continuously stratified incompressible fluid was given in 1932 by Dubreil-Jacotin[1] and independently by long.[2] If Cartesian coordinates x and y are used, and if ρ denotes the density and ψ denotes the stream function, this equation is

$$\psi_{xx} + \psi_{yy} + \frac{1}{\rho}\frac{d\rho}{d\psi}\left(\frac{\psi_x{}^2 + \psi_y{}^2}{2} + gy\right) = h(\psi),\qquad(1)$$

where g is the gravitational acceleration and

$$h(\psi) = \frac{1}{\rho}H'(\psi),\qquad H \equiv p + \frac{\rho}{2}q^2 + \rho gy,$$

with p denoting the pressure and q denoting the speed. It is well known that both ρ and H are functions of ψ alone if the flow is steady and viscous and diffusive effects are neglected. Long was able to find a set of upstream conditions for which (1) is exactly linear, and he successfully used the linear equation to study finite-amplitude waves in the lee of two-dimensional obstacles in the flow. His solution was subsequently elaborated by other workers.

The equation of Dubreil–Jacotin and Long was considerably simplified by Yih[3] who used the transformation

$$\psi' = \int \left(\frac{\rho}{\rho_0}\right)^{1/2} d\psi,\qquad(2)$$

ρ_0 being a constant reference density, and obtained the equation

$$\psi_{xx}' + \psi_{yy}' + \frac{gy}{\rho_0}\frac{d\rho}{d\psi'} = h(\psi'),\qquad(3)$$

in which

$$h(\psi') = \frac{1}{\rho_0}\frac{dH}{d\psi'}.$$

It is immediately obvious that all the linear cases of (1) and of (3) can be obtained by simply letting $d\rho/d\psi'$ and $h(\psi')$ be linear functions of ψ'. Soon after the paper[3] bearing (3) was presented, Long[4] gave a set of upstream conditions for which (1) is exactly linear. This linear form is different from the linear form[2] which he had found previously, but is one of the linear forms readily obtained from (3) and discussed in some detail by Yih[5] sometime later.

Whenever (1) or (3) is exactly linear and admits solutions representing waves, such solutions are for waves of any amplitude in a continuously stratified fluid. However, there is some artificiality associated with the upstream conditions permitting (1) or (3) to be exactly linear: There is always a *nonuniform* velocity distribution of a parallel flow to which the solutions for waves are superposed, and this nonuniformity is always there no matter how small the amplitude of the waves. In other words, a current of nonuniform velocity must always be present for (1) or (3) to be exactly linear. For waves propagating in an otherwise quiescent fluid, it is well known that the solution for the flow in the frame of reference moving with the waves must consist of a flow with uniform velocity and a flow representing the waves, provided the amplitude of the waves is very small. Consequently, the exactly linear cases cannot correspond to progressive infinitesimal waves, and by extension cannot correspond to waves of finite amplitude (which are adjacent to infinitesimal waves) progressing in an otherwise quiescent fluid.

In this paper we wish to investigate waves of permanent form progressing in an otherwise quiescent fluid. Since the differential equation (1) or (3) is bound to be nonlinear for such waves, there is no advantage in using (3). The problem then is first to determine the functions $d\rho/d\psi$ and $h(\psi)$ in (1). This is now not as simple a task as in the study of lee waves, since the waves extend from minus infinity to infinity in the x direction, and there is no parallel flow far upstream. We shall use a series expansion in powers of the amplitude, and show how the differential equation can be determined at each stage of the approximation, as well as the eigenfunctions and eigenvalues (for the wave velocity). In arriving at the mathematical solution of the problem, we are also able to assess the degree of validity of the Boussinesq approximation, which has been used so very extensively. Our solution is for any wavenumber, any stratification, and any mode of the internal wave for a given wave number. (The precise meaning of the density stratification will be discussed in the following section. The need for such a discussion arises from the lack of a section far upstream where the flow is parallel.) Special attention will be given to the important and realistic cases of weak density gradients.

Before formulating and solving our problem in the following section we note that this problem has already been studied by Thorpe[6] in an extensive paper. However, in Thorpe's work the Boussinesq approximation has been used and the effect of amplitude on the wave velocity has not been determined, and indeed there is no indication how that effect can be determined. Furthermore, in all previous work on waves in a continuously stratified fluid, Thorpe's included, it has never been pointed out that it is necessary to determine or specify the density distribution in the fluid when it is allowed to quiet down, so that we know for what fluid the problem is solved. This will be an important aspect of our solution to be presented in the next section.

We note that the method of determining the eigenvalue of the wave velocity at each stage of the approximation involves the requirement that the inhomogeneous part $g(y, \Delta\lambda)$ of the equation

$$L_\lambda f(y) = g(y, \Delta\lambda), \tag{4}$$

be orthogonal to the eigenfunction $f_0(y)$ satisfying

$$L_\lambda f_0(y) = 0$$

and the boundary conditions, L_λ being a linear operator containing the eigenvalue λ, and $\Delta\lambda$ being the correction to λ that is necessary at any particular stage of the approximation under consideration. This technique was used by Yih[7] to study the stability of film flow, is indispensible here, and is, in general, a powerful tool in the study of linear eigenvalue problems.

II. FORMULATION

The problem is to study the flow due to waves progressing in a continuously stratified fluid otherwise at rest. The fluid is specified by its density distribution when waves are absent, and this same fluid is always under consideration when waves are present.

The first task is to specify the general form of (1) that applies to our problem, whatever the density distribution of the fluid. To this end we recognize that that form must satisfy the following requirements: When the amplitude of the waves is very small, it must reduce to the well-known linear equation (for the moving frame of reference) governing infinitesimal waves, and as a consequence it must allow a parallel flow of uniform velocity (equal to the wave velocity) when the amplitude of the waves is reduced to zero. Keeping this velocity-distribution requirement in mind we see that the form sought is

$$\psi_{xx} + \psi_{yy} + \frac{1}{\rho}\frac{d\rho}{d\psi}\left(\frac{\psi_x^2 + \psi_y^2}{2} + gy\right) = \frac{1}{\rho}\frac{d\rho}{d\psi}\left(\frac{g}{c}\psi + \frac{c^2}{2}\right), \tag{5}$$

where c is the wave velocity. Indeed, this equation has already been given by Davis and Acrivos.[8] A flow of uniform

velocity c in the direction of increasing x has been superposed on waves progressing in the opposite direction to make the flow steady. Note that

$$\psi = cy \tag{6}$$

is always a possible solution, with no waves present at all, and that when the amplitude is small (5) indeed reduces to the wave equation for infinitesimal waves, upon replacing ψ in $d\rho/d\psi$ by cy. Note, however, that $d\rho/d\psi$ for finite-amplitude waves is not known and cannot be specified a priori. Indeed, it has to be determined and re-determined at succeeding stages of approximation, with the density-distribution requirement in mind.

We shall consider two-dimensional internal waves bounded by the horizontal boundaries $y = 0$ and $y = d$, so that

$$\psi = a \text{ const at } y = 0 \quad \text{and} \quad y = d. \tag{7}$$

Equations (5) and (7) constitute the eigenvalue problem, with c as the eigenvalue and ψ as the eigenfunction. Note that we do not demand that ψ be zero at $y = 0$ or at $y = d$.

It will be convenient to use the following dimensionless variables:

$$\Psi = \psi/cd, \quad \xi = x/d, \quad \eta = y/d, \quad F^2 = c^2/gd, \quad \hat{\rho} = \rho/\rho_0, \tag{8}$$

where ρ_0 is the density at $\eta = 0$, and F is the Froude number. In terms of these dimensionless variables, Eq. (5) becomes, after the circumflex on $\hat{\rho}$ has been dropped,

$$\Psi_{\xi\xi} + \Psi_{\eta\eta} + \frac{1}{\rho}\frac{d\rho}{d\Psi}\left(\frac{\Psi_\xi^2 + \Psi_\eta^2}{2} + F^{-2}\eta\right)$$

$$= \frac{1}{\rho}\frac{d\rho}{d\Psi}\left(F^{-2}\Psi + \tfrac{1}{2}\right). \tag{9}$$

The boundary conditions become

$$\Psi = \text{const} \quad \text{at } \eta = 0 \text{ and at } \eta = 1. \tag{10}$$

In what follows we shall consider a fluid which, when at *rest*, has the dimensionless-density distribution

$$\rho = \exp(-\beta\bar{\eta}) \tag{11}$$

where $\bar{\eta}$ is η when no waves are present. The theory developed for the particular distribution applies to any general density distribution when the necessary changes are made to account for the density distribution specified. The "densimetric" or "internal" Froude number F_i is defined by

$$\beta F_i^2 = F^2. \tag{12}$$

III. THE SOLUTION

We shall expand Ψ and F_i^2 in the series (A = amplitude)

$$\Psi = \Psi_0 + A\Psi_1 + A^2\Psi_2 + \cdots, \tag{13a}$$

$$F_i^{-2} = G_0 + AG_1 + A^2G_2 + \cdots. \tag{13b}$$

It is obvious that

$$\Psi_0 = \eta, \tag{14}$$

which satisfies (9) and (11) exactly. At this stage of approximation η is $\bar{\eta}$. Hence, from Eqs. (11) and (14) we have

$$\frac{1}{\rho}\frac{d\rho}{d\Psi} = \frac{1}{\rho}\frac{d\rho}{d\Psi_0} = -\beta, \tag{15}$$

and (9) becomes, upon collecting terms of the power A,

$$(\Psi_1)_{\xi\xi} + (\Psi_1)_{\eta\eta} - \beta(\Psi_1)_\eta = -G_0\Psi_1, \tag{16}$$

which is the equation governing infinitesimal waves. The solution of (16) with the boundary conditions (10), in which Ψ_1 is used for Ψ, gives

$$\Psi_1 = \exp(\beta\eta/2)\,\sin n\pi\eta\,\sin k\xi \tag{17}$$

and

$$G_0 = n^2\pi^2 + k^2 + (\beta^2/4), \tag{18}$$

where k is the wavenumber and n is an integer indicating the mode. For any given k there are infinitely many modes corresponding to positive integral values of n. The larger n is, the "higher" the mode.

At this stage it is necessary to re-evaluate $d\rho/d\Psi$, to see whether a new evaluation should be used for the next approximation. For this purpose we take two terms on the right-hand side of (13a), and rewrite it as

$$\eta = \Psi - A\,\exp(\beta\eta/2)\,\sin n\pi\eta\,\sin k\xi. \tag{19}$$

Upon successive iterations we obtain, from (19), the result

$$\begin{aligned}
\eta = {} &\Psi - A\,\exp(\beta\Psi/2)\,\sin n\pi\Psi\,\sin k\xi \\
&+ \tfrac{1}{4}A^2\,\exp(\beta\Psi)\,(n\pi\,\sin 2n\pi\Psi + \beta\,\sin^2 n\pi\Psi) \\
&\times (1 - \cos 2k\xi) + O(A^3),
\end{aligned} \tag{20}$$

which, upon averaging with respect to ξ, gives

$$\begin{aligned}
\bar{\eta} = {} &\Psi + \tfrac{1}{4}A^2\,\exp(\beta\Psi)\,(\beta - \beta\cos 2n\pi\Psi + 2n\pi \\
&\times \sin 2n\pi\Psi) + O(A^4),
\end{aligned} \tag{21}$$

because the average value of the terms of $O(A^3)$ is zero. Note that the averaging is not an inexact process, for the definition of $\bar{\eta}$ demands exactly such an averaging process.

If we write

$$\frac{1}{\rho}\frac{d\rho}{d\Psi} = \frac{1}{\rho}\frac{d\rho}{d\bar{\eta}}\frac{d\bar{\eta}}{d\Psi} = -\beta\frac{d\bar{\eta}}{d\Psi},$$

and substitute this into (9), we have

$$\Psi_{\xi\xi} + \Psi_{\eta\eta} - \beta\frac{d\bar{\eta}}{d\Psi}\left(\frac{\Psi_\xi^2 + \Psi_\eta^2}{2} + F^{-2}\eta\right)$$

$$= -\beta\frac{d\bar{\eta}}{d\Psi}\,(F^{-2}\Psi + \tfrac{1}{2}). \tag{22}$$

Using (21) in (22), we find that the terms of $O(A^2)$ in Eq. (21) introduce only terms of $O(A^3)$ in Eq. (22). Therefore, while we are determining the terms of $O(A^2)$ in Ψ, we need not yet make the correction for $d\rho/d\Psi$.

Keeping

$$\frac{1}{\rho}\frac{d\rho}{d\Psi} = -\beta,$$

then, we can proceed with the determination of Ψ_2. Using Eqs. (13a), (13b), and (14) and gathering terms of $O(A^2)$ in (9), we obtain

$$\nabla^2\Psi_2 - \beta(\Psi_2)_\eta + G_0\Psi_2 = \beta S - G_1\Psi_1, \tag{23}$$

where

$$\nabla^2 = \frac{\partial^2}{\partial\xi^2} + \frac{\partial^2}{\partial\eta^2}$$

and, after some reductions,

$$S = \exp(\beta\eta)\,(B_1 + B_2\cos 2n\pi\eta + B_3\sin 2n\pi\eta)$$
$$- \exp(\beta\eta)\,(B_1' + B_2'\cos 2n\pi\eta + B_3\sin 2n\pi\eta)\cos 2k\xi. \tag{24}$$

where

$$8B_1 = G_0, \quad 32B_2 = 4n^2\pi^2 - 4k^2 - \beta^2, \quad 8B_3 = n\pi\beta. \tag{25}$$
$$8B_1' = n^2\pi^2 - k^2 + \beta^2/4, \quad 32B_2' = 4n^2\pi^2 + 4k^2 - \beta^2.$$

Solving (23) with the boundary conditions (10), we find that

$$G_1 = 0, \tag{26}$$

and

$$\begin{aligned}
\Psi_2 = \beta\{ &B_1 f_1(\eta) + B_2 f_2(\eta) + B_3 f_3(\eta) \\
&- [B_1' f_4(\eta) + B_2' f_5(\eta) + B_3 f_6(\eta)]\cos 2k\xi\},
\end{aligned} \tag{27}$$

where

$$f_1(\eta) = G_0^{-1}\exp(\beta\eta),$$
$$\begin{aligned}
f_2(\eta) = {} &(1/M)\exp(\beta\eta)[(G_0 - 4n^2\pi^2) \\
&\times \cos 2n\pi\eta + 2n\pi\beta\,\sin 2n\pi\eta],
\end{aligned}$$
$$\begin{aligned}
f_3(\eta) = {} &(1/M)\exp(\beta\eta)[(G_0 - 4n^2\pi^2) \\
&\times \sin 2n\pi\eta - 2n\pi\beta\,\cos 2n\pi\eta],
\end{aligned}$$
$$\begin{aligned}
f_4(\eta) = {} &(G_0 - 4k^2)^{-1}\exp(\beta\eta/2)[\exp(\beta\eta/2) \\
&- \cos\gamma\eta - a\,\sin\gamma\eta],
\end{aligned} \tag{28}$$
$$\begin{aligned}
f_5(\eta) = {} &(1/N)\exp(\beta\eta/2)\{-P[\exp(\beta\eta/2)\cos 2n\pi\eta \\
&- \cos\gamma\eta - a\,\sin\gamma\eta] + 2n\pi\beta\,\exp(\beta\eta/2)\,\sin 2n\pi\eta\},
\end{aligned}$$
$$\begin{aligned}
f_6(\eta) = {} &(1/N)\exp(\beta\eta/2)\{-P\,\exp(\beta\eta/2)\,\sin 2n\pi\eta \\
&- 2n\pi\beta[\exp(\beta\eta/2)\cos 2n\pi\eta - \cos\gamma\eta - a\,\sin\gamma\eta]\},
\end{aligned}$$

with

$$M = (G_0 - 4n^2\pi^2)^2 + 4n^2\pi^2\beta^2, \quad P = 4n^2\pi^2 + 4k^2 - G_0,$$
$$N = P^2 + 4n^2\pi^2\beta^2, \tag{29}$$

and

$$\gamma = \left(G_0 - 4k^2 - \frac{\beta^2}{4}\right)^{1/2},$$

$$a = (\exp(\beta/2) - \cos\gamma)(\sin\gamma)^{-1}. \tag{30}$$

The result (26) is obtained because the term βS does not contain the factor $\sin k\xi$ or $\cos k\xi$, and if G_1 did not vanish there would be no solution for Ψ_2. This has already been mentioned in Sec. I, in connection with (4). Indeed, since Ψ_1 contains $\sin k\xi$, the particular solution of (23) to account for the term $-G_1\Psi_1$ must also contain it. Then, denoting that particular solution by $p_1(\eta)\sin k\xi$, we have $p_1(0) = 0 = p_1(1)$ and

$$Lp_1 = -G_1 \exp(\beta\eta/2) \sin n\pi\eta, \tag{31}$$

where

$$L = \frac{d^2}{d\eta^2} - \beta\frac{d}{d\eta} + G_0 - k^2. \tag{32}$$

On the other hand, (16) can be written as

$$L \exp(\beta\eta/2) \sin n\pi\eta = 0. \tag{33}$$

Multiplying (31) by $\exp(-\beta\eta/2) \sin n\pi\eta$ and (33) by $\exp(-\beta\eta)p_1$, integrating between zero and 1, using the boundary conditions for p_1, and taking the difference of the two integrated equations, we have (26).

The functions f_4, f_5, and f_6 need a discussion because the γ defined in (30) may be zero or equal to $m\pi$, with m equal to an integer and less than n. In either case $\sin\gamma$ vanishes and the number a in (30) is infinite. The case $\gamma = 0$ is not really troublesome because the complimentary solutions $\exp(\beta\eta/2)\cos\gamma\eta$ and $\exp(\beta\eta/2)\sin\gamma\eta$ in f_4, f_5, and f_6 can be replaced by $\exp(\beta\eta/2)$ and $\eta \exp(\beta\eta/2)$, respectively, and with the constant a replaced by $\exp(\beta/2) - 1$. The case $\gamma = m\pi$, with $m = $ a nonzero integer less than n is much more significant. In this case

$$G_0 = n^2\pi^2 + k^2 + \frac{\beta^2}{4} = m^2\pi^2 + 4k^2 + \frac{\beta^2}{4} \tag{34}$$

and a look at (16) shows that whenever (34) holds the nth mode of internal waves with wavenumber k has the same wave velocity as the mth mode with wavenumber $2k$. In such a case it is necessary (in order to have internal waves of permanent form) to have first-order solutions in addition to Ψ_1 given by (17). These are solutions of (16) but with wavenumbers zero and $2k$, respectively, and are

$$\chi_1 = A \exp(\beta\eta/2)(a_1 \sin\mu\eta + b_1 \cos\mu\eta),$$

$$\mu = \left(G_0 - \frac{\beta^2}{4}\right)^{1/2}, \tag{35}$$

$$\chi_2 = A a_2 \exp(\beta\eta/2) \sin m\pi\eta \cos 2k\xi, \tag{36}$$

in which a_2 is arbitrary. This means we can start with any two wave amplitudes for the wave trains of wavenumbers k and $2k$. When (35) and (36) are included in Ψ_1 in (13a) and (13a) is substituted into (22), terms of $O(A^2)$ are

collected, and then terms with factors $\sin k\xi$ and $\cos 2k\xi$ are separated, we obtain two equations:

$$L\theta_1 = a_1 g_1(\eta) + b_1 h_1(\eta) + a_2 g_2(\eta), \tag{37}$$

where L is the operator defined by (32), and

$$\left(\frac{d^2}{d\eta^2} - \beta\frac{d}{d\eta} + G_0 - 4k^2\right)\theta_2 = g_0(\eta) + a_1 a_2 g_3(\eta)$$
$$+ b_1 a_2 g_4(\eta). \tag{38}$$

By making the right-hand sides of Eqs. (37) and (38) orthogonal to $\exp(\beta\eta/2)\sin n\pi\eta$ and $\exp(\beta\eta/2)\sin m\pi\eta$, respectively, we can determine a_1 and b_1. The solution θ_2 then replaces the coefficient of $\cos 2k\xi$ in (27) and the solution $\theta_1 \sin k\xi$ is the additional part which is now necessary.

Note that to f_1, f_2, and f_3 in (28) could be added solutions of the equation

$$\left(\frac{d^2}{d\eta^2} - \beta\frac{d}{d\eta} + G_0\right)\theta_0 = 0. \tag{39}$$

This is the reason that Thorpe[6] decided that parallel flows (currents), which can be added to the flow sought by him, can be determined only if one knows how the waves have been created. Actually, there does not appear to be any hope that these currents can really be determined from the circumstances of generation of the waves. Rather, the purpose is to isolate waves of fundamental wavenumber k as much as possible, avoiding adding any terms not having this wavenumber at *all* stages of approximation unless addition of such terms is necessary as particular solutions at higher approximations than the first, or even at the first approximation, as in the case $\gamma = m\pi$ discussed in the preceding paragraph. With this decision, the parallel currents are no longer arbitrary, but uniquely determined, except in the case $\gamma = m\pi$ discussed above, where a_2 is arbitrary and hence also a_1 and b_1. That exceptional case arises because waves of wavenumbers k and $2k$ are no longer isolatable at the order $O(A)$.

One more point must be clarified before we go on to deal with terms of $O(A^2)$. If γ is not equal to $m\pi$ exactly but very near to it, the value of a in (30) can be very large, particularly if m is even. Then, Ψ_2 can be very large except for certain values of η, indeed very much larger than Ψ_1, and this seems strange and unreasonable. The apparent difficulty is removed when we remember that in the next stage of approximation large contributions are fed back in the same way to the term containing the factor $\sin k\xi$, and the amplitude will not be A but redetermined. Then, the ratio of Ψ_2 to Ψ_1 will not be so large. Difficulties of the kind discussed in this and the preceding paragraphs are typical of nonlinear problems. Their resolutions are never immediately clear and often, as in this case, require a great deal of thought. Note that if $n = 1$ (for the first mode), then nonzero value of m does not exist, and the apparent difficulties discussed in the preceding paragraphs do not exist. For $n = 1$, however, there is still the possibility that the M defined in (29), which never vanishes, may nevertheless be of $O(\beta^2)$, thus making f_2 and f_3 in (28) very large. For the convenience of later discussions, we shall only deal with those values of k^2 which satisfy

$$3\pi^2 - k^2 = O(1), \tag{40a}$$

for $n = 1$. For higher values of n, to avoid the case in which γ is equal or near $m\pi$, we shall assume that Eq. (34) is never exactly or nearly satisfied, or that, with $n = 2$ and $m = 1$ to obtain the safe bound for k^2,

$$\pi^2 - k^2 = O(1). \tag{40b}$$

If (40b) is satisfied, then M defined in (29) is not small. Hence for $n > 1$, we impose (40b) only. Since we have carried out our calculations only to $O(A^2)$ in (13a, b), our conclusions will necessarily be valid only to this order. This imposes a limit (undetermined) on the magnitude of $|A|$.

Before going on with our calculation, it is now necessary to recalculate $\rho^{-1}d\rho/d\Psi$. Using (13a) and (27), we obtain

$$\bar{\eta} = \Psi + \tfrac{1}{8}A^2 \exp(\beta\Psi)(\beta - \beta \cos 2n\pi\Psi + 2n\pi\Psi \sin 2n\pi\Psi)$$
$$+ \beta A^2[B_1 f_1(\Psi) + B_2 f_2(\Psi) + B_3 f_3(\Psi)] + O(A^4). \tag{41}$$

Substituting (41) into (22), using (13), and collecting terms of $O(A^3)$, we have

$$\left(\nabla^2 - \beta\frac{\partial}{\partial\eta} + G_0\right)\Psi_3 = T_1 + T_2 + T_3 - G_2\Psi_1, \tag{42}$$

where

$$T_1 = \beta^2\phi'[B_1 f_1' + B_2 f_2' + B_3 f_3'$$
$$+ 0.5(B_1' f_4' + B_2' f_5' + B_3 f_6')(\sin k\xi - \sin 3k\xi)]$$
$$+ k^2\beta^2\phi(B_1' f_4 + B_2' f_5 + B_3 f_6)(\sin 3k\xi - \sin k\xi),$$
$$8T_2 = (\beta\phi' - G_0\phi)[\exp(\beta\eta)(\beta - \beta \cos 2n\pi\eta$$
$$+ 2n\pi \sin 2n\pi\eta)]' \sin k\xi,$$
$$T_3 = \beta(\beta\phi' - G_0\phi)(B_1 f_1' + B_2 f_2' + B_3 f_3') \sin k\xi \tag{43}$$

with

$$\phi = \exp(\beta\eta/2) \sin n\pi\eta. \tag{44}$$

The accents in (43) indicate differentiation with respect to η, and the functions f_1 to f_6 are functions of η.

To determine G_2, we again demand that the right-hand side of (42) be orthogonal to Ψ_1, that is to say, the sum J of the coefficients of $\sin k\xi$ of the right-hand side of (42) be orthogonal to ϕ in the sense that

$$\int_0^1 \exp(-\beta\eta)J\phi\, d\eta = 0. \tag{45}$$

After we determine G_2, we can find Ψ_3 by solving (42). We shall determine G_2 to see how the amplitude A affects the wave velocity, but we shall not attempt to determine Ψ_3. That determination is straightforward, but tedious.

Note that T_1 arises from the term containing $|\nabla\Psi|^2$ in (22), T_2 and T_3 arise from the displacement of isopycnic lines as the result of Ψ_1 and Ψ_2, respectively. For all cases important in practice, β is very small; therefore, we shall consider β to be small. This will simplify the presentation of the results, although G_2 can be determined from (45) completely, with all terms included, in a straightforward

although lengthy way. For small β, we shall show that the dominant term in G_2 comes from T_2.

If (40) is satisfied for $n = 1$ and (40b) satisfied for $n > 1$, it can be shown that all the contributions to G_2 from T_1 (or rather those terms of T_1 that contain $\sin k\xi$) are $O(\beta^2)$. The same is true of the contributions from T_3. The details supporting these statements can be obtained in a straightforward manner, but are very lengthy. We shall omit their presentation to save space.

Carrying out in full the contributions of T_2, we find that

$$8\int_0^1 \exp(-\beta\eta)T_2\phi\, d\eta$$
$$= 0.5\beta^4 I(\beta, n\pi) + \beta^2(n^2\pi^2 - 0.25\beta^2)[I(\beta, 3n\pi)$$
$$- I(\beta, n\pi)] + n\pi\beta^3[R(\beta, n\pi) - R(\beta, 3n\pi)]$$
$$+ 0.5n\pi\beta\{\beta^2 I(\beta, 2n\pi) + (2n^2\pi^2 - 0.5\beta^2)I(\beta, 4n\pi)$$
$$+ 2n\pi\beta[R(\beta, 0) - R(\beta, 4n\pi)]\}$$
$$- \tfrac{1}{2}G_0\{\beta^2 R(\beta, 0) + (4n^2\pi^2 - 2\beta^2)R(\beta, 2n\pi)$$
$$+ 4n\pi\beta I(\beta, 2n\pi) - 2n\pi\beta I(\beta, 4n\pi)$$
$$+ (0.5\beta^2 - 2n^2\pi^2)[R(\beta, 0) + R(\beta, 4n\pi)]\}, \tag{46}$$

in which the functions R and I are defined by

$$R(p, q) + iI(p, q) = \int_0^1 \exp[(p + iq)\eta]\, d\eta$$
$$= \frac{1}{p^2 + q^2}[p(\exp(p)\cos q - 1) + q\exp(p)\sin q]$$
$$+ \frac{i}{p^2 + q^2}[p\exp(p)\sin q - q(\exp(p)\cos q - 1)]. \tag{47}$$

If $q = r\pi$ (r is an integer),

$$R(p, r\pi) = \frac{p}{p^2 + r^2\pi^2}[\exp(p)(-1)^r - 1],$$
$$I(p, r\pi) = \frac{r\pi}{p^2 + r^2\pi^2}[\exp(p)(-1)^r - 1].$$

Thus

$$R(\beta, 0) = 1 + 0.5\beta + O(\beta^2),$$

and, with s equal to any positive integer,

$$R(\beta, (2s-1)\pi) = O(\beta), \quad R(\beta, 2s\pi) = O(\beta^2),$$
$$I(\beta, (2s-1)\pi) = O(1), \quad I(\beta, 2s\pi) = O(\beta).$$

The right-hand side of (46) is therefore equal to

$$n^2\pi^2 G_0(1 + 0.5\beta) + O(\beta^2),$$

and, applying (45) and remembering the restrictions (40a) and (40b),

$$8G_2 = n^2\pi^2 G_0(2 + \beta) + O(\beta^2). \tag{48}$$

That G_2 is positive means that F_i^{-2} increases with A^2, according to (13b), or that c^2 *decreases* with A^2. This is a rather unexpected result, since we are so used to the increase of wave velocity with amplitude for progressive gravity waves, as for the well-known Stokesian waves. We note, however, that already for gravity waves in two superposed layers of homogeneous liquids Hunt[9] and Thorpe[6] (who made some corrections of Hunt's work) have shown that it is possible for c^2 to decrease with amplitude. (In their case it happens for long waves and small density differences.) The result (48) is remarkable in that for a continuously stratified fluid c^2 always decreases with the amplitude. Perhaps this result needs some interpretation. In this writer's opinion, it happens because a larger amplitude in a wave motion "squeezes" the isopycnic lines against the upper solid boundary near the crests, thereby increasing the vertical density gradient near the upper solid boundary and decreasing the density gradient below. Similarly, the wave motion also "squeezes" the isopycnic lines against the lower solid boundary near the troughs, increasing the density gradient there and decreasing it above. Since the increase of density gradient *near* solid boundaries are quite ineffective in increasing c^2, whereas the decrease of it in a wider region is more effective in decreasing it, c^2 decreases with the amplitude.

We have specified the stratification of ρ to be exponential by (11). However, the conclusions concerning the decrease of c^2 with A^2 for small β will remain valid for any stratification for which

$$\frac{1}{\rho}\frac{d\rho}{d\bar{\eta}} = \beta + O(\beta^2), \ \beta \ll 1. \tag{49}$$

In particular, they remain valid for the important case of a linear stratification, for which

$$\frac{d\rho}{d\bar{\eta}} = \text{const.}$$

Whether β is small or not, and for any stratification, the method of solution presented here applies to finite-amplitude waves in any stratified fluid.

Before we conclude this section, we note that the averaging process leading to (21) is valid only if there are no regions of closed streamlines. This requirement places a restriction on the admissible values of A^2. However, if A^2 is so large that regions of closed streamlines do occur, the modification required is obvious: All we have to do is to find how much fluid there is between any two streamlines (or isopycnic lines). The only thing that has to be kept in mind is that the solution must be such that when the fluid is allowed to quiet down it will have the stratification we specify for it.

IV. THE EXISTENCE OF INTERNAL SOLITARY WAVES

Solitary waves are classified as long waves, and they invariably owe their existence to the crucial requirement that the "local" wave velocity at the point of greatest vertical displacement be greater than the wave velocity of infinitesimal long waves. For a layer of homogeneous liquid, this requirement is satisfied (Ref. 10, p. 424). For two semi-infinite homogeneous liquids with an interface, Hunt[9]

has shown that this requirement is met. (See Ref. 6, p. 570.) For two homogeneous liquids of equal, finite depths bounded above and below by solid boundaries, whether this requirement is met or not depends on the relative magnitudes of the wave length and the density difference [Hunt,[9] as corrected by Thorpe,[6] p. 571, Eq. (2.1.6)]. This fact agrees with the conclusion of Long.[11]

Solitary waves in a continuously stratified fluid of finite depth, bounded above and below by horizontal boundaries have been treated elegantly by Benjamin[12] and ingeniously by Long.[10] In both papers it was *assumed*, for the existence of solitary waves, that the velocity of finite-amplitude waves increases with amplitude. See Benjamin[12] (p. 243, first paragraph) and Long[11] [Eqs. (18), (42), and (66)]. Neither author has inquired whether this assumption can be met, and their treatments based on this assumption are indeed correct. [In (4.21) of Benjamin's paper, c^2 (c is the velocity of solitary waves) is shown to be greater than c_n^2 (c_n is the velocity of corresponding long waves of infinitesimal amplitude) on the assumption that his Δ, or $\mathcal{J}$, or γ_n, is positive. All this is very consistent, but γ_n has not been independently shown to be positive.] Yet, it is difficult to escape the impression that they never doubted the truth of this assumption. The conclusion we have reached in the preceding paragraph shows that this crucial assumption is indeed not met for one continuously and weakly stratified fluid of finite depth between two solid boundaries, and strongly indicates that solitary waves, in such a fluid, as illustrated in Fig. 2 of Thorpe's paper,[6] may not exist. Note that we have expanded the eigenfunction and the eigenvalue in powers of the amplitude A, with β and k appearing in the coefficients of this expansion in a complete and indeed closed manner, so that the treatment here is somewhat more accurate and reliable than an expansion in A, β, and k concurrently, as was done by Long.[11]

All this is not to say that solitary waves do not exist if the density is discontinuous, or if, although continuous, extend to infinity. Indeed, Davis and Acrivos[8] have shown experimentally that solitary waves exist in a stratified fluid layer imbedded between two homogeneous layers of great depths (in comparison to the stratified layer), of densities ρ_1 and ρ_2, and thus vindicating their own theory as well as Benjamin's[13] for such a fluid system. Since infinite extensions are unrealistic, and the experiments of Davis and Acrivos were necessarily for finite depths, a reconciliation of this fact with the implication of the results in Sec. III is necessary. The author believes that the explanation lies in the importance of the magnitude of the wavenumber k. If the length scale is that of the stratified layer in Davis and Acrivos' experiment, waves that are long with respect to that scale may be short with respect to the *total* depth. Since in our study the wavelength is measured in terms of the total depth, our wavenumber may be very large for waves that are long with respect to the stratified layer, and therefore even for weak stratifications terms of order $O(\beta^2)$, which are neglected in reaching the conclusion that wave velocity decreases with the amplitude, may not be negligible because the coefficients are high. This seems to indicate that the existence or nonexistence of solitary waves in a continuously stratified fluid not only depends on the weakness of the stratification, but also on the distribution of stratification. If the density *gradient* is nearly uniform *throughout* in the sense of (49), solitary waves may not exist, for a calculation for any such fluid, not necessarily exponentially stratified, will lead to the same conclusion that we reached in Sec. III.

We do not, however, wish to be very dogmatic about our doubt of the nonexistence of solitary waves between fixed boundaries even for a fluid satisfying (49), for the link between progressive periodic waves and solitary waves is only the tenuous one of long wave length. This may be too tenuous a link on which to base any strong conclusions. For instance, in the calculation of $\bar{\eta}$ in terms of ψ in (21), the periodicity played an important role, and solitary waves are not periodic. What this discussion is intended to point out is that to be convincing, it is desirable, in any study of solitary waves, to show *independently* that the speed of finite-amplitude waves, especially solitary waves, is indeed greater than the velocity of waves of infinitesimal amplitude.

V. VALIDITY OF THE BOUSSINESQ APPROXIMATION

In the present context, the Boussinesq approximation amounts to ignoring the term $|\nabla\psi|^2$ and writing $\rho_0^{-1}d\rho/d\psi$ for $\rho^{-1}d\rho/d\psi$ in (1), ρ_0 being a constant, mean density. Thus, the Boussinesq approximation does not necessarily make (1) linear. If we make the Boussinesq approximation in the present problem, Ψ_1 will be modified to the extent of a term of $O(\beta)$, and Ψ_2 will be modified. The term G_2 will be modified by an amount of at most $O(\beta)$ if k satisfies (40a) or (40b). Thus, the Boussinesq approximation will not affect the value of F_i^{-2} by an appreciable amount if β is small and k is not too large.

If we merely ignore the term $|\nabla\psi|^2$ in (1) and carry out the calculations for the exponentially stratified fluid, as in Sec. III, we shall find that Ψ_0 and Ψ_1 are unaffected, Ψ_2 is zero, and (48) always holds.

VI. THE EXACTLY LINEAR CASES OF (3)

As shown by Yih,[5] the exactly linear cases of (1) can be found most easily from (3), by simply setting $d\rho/d\psi'$ and $h(\psi')$ to be linear functions of ψ'. The solutions for (3), when it is exactly linear, can then be obtained for any amplitude of the waves. The exactly linear cases all require a parallel flow of nonuniform velocity superposed on the wave motion. Granted this requirement, it is generally accepted that waves of any mode propagate with the same velocity regardless of the amplitude, in a stratified fluid permitting (3) to be exactly linear.

This, however, would be a somewhat superficial conclusion because the distribution of density in space varies with the amplitude, as we have shown, and the density stratification, if the waves are allowed to die out, would be different for different amplitudes of the waves. Hence, when we say the wave velocity is the same for any amplitude for the exactly linear cases, we are really comparing solutions not only for different wave amplitudes but for different fluids. This much neglected fact reduces the significance of the exactly linear cases.

VII. CONCLUSIONS

On the assumption that the procedure of solution used in this paper is convergent, from the foregoing analysis and discussion we conclude that

1. Finite-amplitude waves of permanent form in any stably stratified fluid between two horizontal boundaries exist, and there are infinitely many modes. (The stability of these waves is another question.)

2. The method of solution presented in this paper can be applied to find the eigenfunction and the wave velocity for internal waves of finite amplitude in any stratified fluid.

3) In exceptional cases described by equations like (34), it is necessary to start with more than one wavenumber even at the first approximation.

4. For the first mode, calculations up to the order $O(A^2)$ for the eigenfunction and for the wave velocity (contained in F_i^2) show that for an exponentially stratified fluid and for a weak stratification the square of the wave velocity always *decreases* with the square of the amplitude provided (40a) is satisfied, so that the wavelength is not too small. This conclusion is especially accurate when the amplitude is small, and holds for other weakly stratified fluids too.

5. Conclusion 4 is valid for higher modes also, provided (40b) holds. Otherwise, further approximations are necessary to insure sufficient accuracy.

6. As a consequence of conclusions 4 and 5, the existence of internal solitary waves in a weakly stratified fluid between solid boundaries, whose density satisfies (49), is somewhat in doubt.

7. For weak stratifications and if the wavelengths are not very short, the Boussinesq approximation indeed gives reliable results for the wave velocity.

8. The solutions for different amplitudes for any of the exactly linear cases of (1) or (3) really correspond not to the same fluid, but to different fluids.

ACKNOWLEDGMENTS

This work has been jointly sponsored by the Office of Naval Research and the National Science Foundation.

[1] M. L. Dubreil-Jacotin, Atti Accad. Naz. Linei Cl. Sci. Fis. Mat. Nat. Rend. 15, 814 (1932).
[2] R. R. Long, Tellus 5, 42 (1953).
[3] C.-S. Yih, in *Proceedings of the Third U. S. National Congress on Applied Mechanics* (American Society of Mechanical Engineers, New York, 1958), p. 857.
[4] R. R. Long, Q. J. R. Meteorol. Soc. 84, 159 (1958).
[5] C.-S. Yih, J. Fluid Mech. 9, 161 (1960).
[6] S. A. Thorpe, Phil. Trans. R. Soc. Lond. 263, 563 (1968).
[7] C.-S. Yih. Phys. Fluids 6, 321 (1963).
[8] R. E. Davis and A. Acrivos, J. Fluid Mech. 29, 593 (1967).
[9] J. N. Hunt, La Houille Blanche 4, 515 (1961).
[10] H. Lamb, *Hydrodynamics* (Cambridge University Press, Cambridge, 1932).
[11] R. R. Long, Tellus 17, 46 (1965).
[12] T. B. Benjamin, J. Fluid Mech. 25, 241 (1966).
[13] T. B. Benjamin, J. Fluid Mech. 29, 559 (1967).

SIAM J. APPL. MATH.
Vol. 28, No. 4, June 1975

VORTICES AND VORTEX RINGS OF STRATIFIED FLUIDS*

CHIA-SHUN YIH†

Abstract. Exact solutions for finite-amplitude motion of an inviscid, incompressible and stratified fluid corresponding to rectilinear vortices or vortex rings are found. Some of the rectilinear vortex pairs, in circular-cylindrical form, can propagate with a constant horizontal velocity in a surrounding homogeneous fluid, and some of the spherical vortex rings can be placed in a surrounding quiescent homogeneous fluid without translational propagation. Equations governing finite-amplitude two-dimensional motion and axisymmetric motion with swirl in the presence of a magnetic field are derived for a stratified conducting fluid, and the effects of a magnetic field on vortex motion are ascertained.

1. Introduction. Vortices and vortex rings in an inviscid fluid of constant density are well known. Of special interest are the propagation of a pair of counter-revolving rectilinear vortices [4, p. 221] of the same intensity in an otherwise quiescent fluid, and the spherical vortex for axisymmetric flows, discovered by Hill [3], or [4, p. 245], which can also propagate with a constant velocity and a permanent form in an otherwise quiescent fluid.

In this paper infinitely many solutions for pairs or clusters of rectilinear vortices and for vortex rings, all of a stratified fluid, will be given. The fluid is assumed inviscid and incompressible, although of variable density. These solutions are for steady and finite-amplitude motions. In the case of vortex rings, the velocity may have a swirling component. Of the infinitely many solutions for rectilinear vortices, a subset, also infinite in number, is of special interest in that each solution of the subset corresponds to a vortex pair which occupies the space of a circular cylinder and which, if placed in an inviscid fluid of constant density, will propagate horizontally with a constant velocity and with permanent form. As to the infinitely many solutions for vortex rings, there is also a subset of it, infinite in number. Each member of this subset represents a vortex ring which occupies a spherical volume and which can maintain its spherical form in a surrounding inviscid fluid of constant density at rest. Finally we shall derive the equations governing finite-amplitude two-dimensional motion and axisymmetric motion with swirl for a stratified and conducting fluid in a magnetic field, and the effects of the magnetic field on vortex motion are ascertained.

2. Two-dimensional vortices. Let x and y be Cartesian coordinates, with y measured in the direction of the vertical, and let g be the gravitational acceleration. The equation governing steady two-dimensional flows of an inviscid and incompressible fluid of variable density was given by Madame Dubreil-Jacotin [2] and independently by Long [5], with the stream function ψ as the dependent variable. This equation was simplified by Yih [10], or [11, p. 76], who made the transformation

$$(1) \qquad d\psi' = \sqrt{\rho/\rho_0}\, d\psi,$$

in which ρ is the density, ρ_0 a (constant) reference density, and ψ' is a modified

---

* Received by the editors December 3, 1973.

† Department of Applied Mechanics and Engineering Science, University of Michigan, Ann Arbor, Michigan 48104. This work was supported by the National Science Foundation and the Office of Naval Research.

900   CHIA-SHUN YIH

stream function. The equation for ψ' is [10]

$$(2) \qquad \left(\frac{\partial^2}{\partial x^2} + \frac{\partial^2}{\partial y^2}\right)\psi' + \frac{gy}{\rho_0}\frac{d\rho}{d\psi'} = h(\psi').$$

The functions ρ and h of ψ' can be determined at any section, usually far upstream, where the density and the velocity distributions are known, or are assumed to be known. In the present case we are considering the flow within a circular cylinder (or a circle in the x, y-plane), and there is not any section which can be properly considered an upstream section. Instead of determining ρ and h, we simply assume them. As usual, only when ρ and h are such that (2) is linear can we hope to obtain any exact solutions.

Suppose that the fluid fills the cylinder

$$(3) \qquad x^2 + y^2 = a^2.$$

We shall use the dimensionless variables

$$x_1 = \frac{x}{a}, \quad y_1 = \frac{y}{a}, \quad \psi'_1 = \frac{\psi'}{(ga^3)^{1/2}}, \quad \rho_1 = \frac{\rho}{\rho_0}, \quad h_1 = h\sqrt{ga}.$$

Then (2) becomes, after the subscripts are dropped,

$$(4) \qquad \left(\frac{\partial^2}{\partial x^2} + \frac{\partial^2}{\partial y^2}\right)\psi' + y\frac{d\rho}{d\psi'} = h(\psi'),$$

and (3) becomes

$$(5) \qquad x^2 + y^2 = 1.$$

The cases for which we can obtain exact solutions of (4), with $\psi' = 0$ on (5) are those for which

$$\frac{d\rho}{d\psi'} = A \quad \text{and} \quad h(\psi') = B\psi',$$

A and B being constant. We seek, then, solutions of

$$(6) \qquad \left(\frac{\partial^2}{\partial x^2} + \frac{\partial^2}{\partial y^2}\right)\psi' + Ay = B\psi',$$

with

$$(7) \qquad \psi' = 0 \quad \text{on } x^2 + y^2 = 1.$$

The following solutions are obtained.

Case 1. $B = 0$. In this case the solution satisfying (6) and (7) is

$$(8) \qquad \psi' = (A/8)y(x^2 + y^2 - 1).$$

The flow pattern is shown in Fig. 1. It is a simple matter to show that, on (5), the speed of the fluid is, with (r, θ) denoting polar coordinates ($x = r\cos\theta$, $y = r\sin\theta$),

$$(9) \qquad |\text{grad } \psi'| = (A/4)\sin\theta.$$

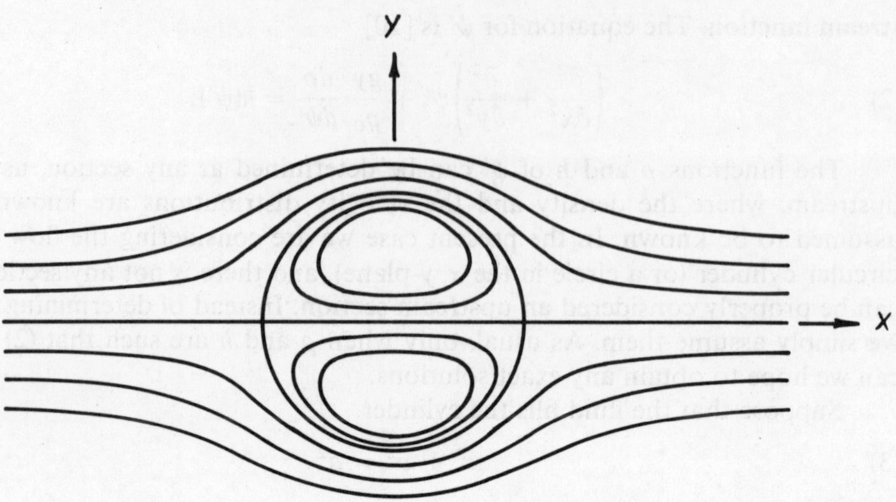

Fig. 1. *Flow pattern of a pair of vortices occupying a circular-cylindrical space and in contact with an external homogeneous fluid in two-dimensional irrotational motion. The density of the stratified fluid and that of the external fluid are equal at the surface of the cylinder. If a uniform flow with a velocity equal and opposite to that at infinity is superposed on this pattern, the pattern of flow due to a pair of vortices of a stratified fluid advancing in a homogeneous fluid at rest at infinity is obtained. ψ-value differences are 0.2 for streamlines outside the circle, and ψ'-value differences are 0.1 for streamlines inside it.*

If we recall that for steady two-dimensional irrotational flow of an inviscid fluid of uniform density ρ_0 past the circular cylinder (5), the speed on the cylinder is $2U \sin \theta$, θ being measured from a horizontal radius of (5) and U being the (horizontal) velocity at infinity, equation (9) suggests that the pair of vortices shown in Fig. 1 is dynamically possible even if it is placed in an inviscid fluid of density ρ_0, provided ρ_0 is the density of the stratified fluid on (5), and provided

$$U = A/8, \tag{10}$$

for when the tangential velocities are equal on (5), the pressures found from the Bernoulli equation for the stratified and the ambient homogeneous fluid will be equal on the interface (5).

But this can be interpreted in another way. If the ambient fluid is quiescent save for the motion of the stratified fluid, the pair of vortices of a stratified fluid occupying the space of a circular cylinder will move horizontally with speed $A/8$ in the ambient fluid. Whether it moves to the left or right depends on the sign of A. Note that since ρ/ρ_0 is a linear function of ψ', and since ψ' is an odd function of y, the averaged density of the stratified fluid is simply ρ_0, if ρ_0 is the density on $\psi' = 0$. Thus the stratified-fluid cylinder is neutrally buoyant. This makes the horizontal motion of the stratified fluid (superimposed on the internal circulation) possible. This vortex pair can be produced, approximately, by intermittent opening of a slit containing a linearly stratified fluid issuing into a homogeneous fluid with the density equal to that at the center of the slit.

Case 2. Neither A nor B vanishes. In this case let

$$\psi' = (A/B)y + F(r)\sin \theta, \qquad B = -\beta^2. \tag{11}$$

                         CHIA-SHUN YIH

Then

$$F'' + \frac{F'}{r} + \left(\beta^2 - \frac{1}{r^2}\right)F = 0,$$

the regular (at $r = 0$) solution which is

$$F = CJ_1(\beta r),$$

J_1 being the Bessel function of the first order. The constant C is determined by the condition

$$\psi' = 0 \quad \text{for } r = 1,$$

or by

(12) $$-A/\beta^2 + CJ_1(\beta) = 0.$$

The tangential velocity on $r = 1$ is

$$u_\theta = -\frac{\partial \psi'}{\partial r} = \left[\frac{A}{\beta^2} - C\beta J_1'(\beta)\right]\sin\theta,$$

in which the prime on J_1 denotes its derivatives with respect to the argument. Thus if the pair or vortices of stratified fluid is placed in an ambient inviscid fluid of constant density ρ_0, ρ_0 being the density of the stratified fluid on the surface of the cylinder (5), it will be held in place if the ambient fluid has a horizontal velocity U at infinity, provided

(13) $$2U = \frac{A}{\beta^2} - C\beta J_1'(\beta) = \frac{A}{\beta^2}\left[1 - \frac{\beta J_1'(\beta)}{J_1(\beta)}\right].$$

If the ambient fluid is quiescent at infinity, then $-U$, with U given by (13), is the (horizontal) velocity of propagation of the vortex pair, permanently in circular shape. Again, the cylinder of stratified fluid is neutrally buoyant.

If $A = 0$, we have a homogeneous fluid. Then (12) determines the infinitely many eigenvalues of β satisfying

$$J_1(\beta) = 0.$$

For these values of β, and any C,

(14) $$2U = -C\beta J_1'(\beta).$$

For the nth eigenvalue β_n, there are $n - 1$ circles with radius less than 1, on which $\psi' = 0$. The streamlines are still symmetric with respect to $y = 0$ (and to $x = 0$), and ψ' is still an odd function of y. For $\beta = \beta_1$, the flow is the two-dimensional counterpart of Hill's spherical vortex.

Case 3. $A = 0$. In this case the fluid is homogeneous. In Case 2 we have already discussed the vortex pairs of a homogeneous fluid that can propagate in a surrounding fluid (of the same density) in irrotational flow. There are other solutions which correspond to vortices contained in a circle, which do not enjoy the property of permanence when placed in a surrounding fluid. We shall now present these.

The governing equation is now

$$(15) \qquad \left(\frac{\partial^2}{\partial x^2} + \frac{\partial^2}{\partial y^2}\right)\psi' = B\psi',$$

which is (6) with $A = 0$. In polar coordinates this equation has the form

$$(16) \qquad \left(\frac{\partial^2}{\partial r^2} + \frac{1}{r}\frac{\partial}{\partial r} + \frac{1}{r^2}\frac{\partial^2}{\partial \theta^2} - B\right)\psi' = 0.$$

If we write again $-\beta^2$ for B, the solution of (16) regular at $r = 0$ is, with n an integer,

$$(17) \qquad \psi' = J_n(\beta r)(C \sin n\theta + D \cos n\theta).$$

In order to satisfy (7), we must have

$$(18) \qquad J_n(\beta) = 0,$$

which determines the infinitely many values of β for which finite cellular convection in the circle (5) is possible. Let us denote these values by β_m, with $m = 1$, 2, 3, and so on. For any m and any n, there are mn pairs of vortices or $2mn$ vortices, each of which is bounded by two concentric circular arcs and two segments of radial lines.

For any β satisfying (18), the solution (17) can be superposed on the solution (11) to obtain a solution for Case 2. The constant C is still determined by (12), but the resulting superposed flow does not enjoy permanence of form if it is placed in a surrounding homogeneous fluid.

3. Equation for steady axisymmetric swirling flows of stratified fluids. The equation governing steady axisymmetric flow of an inviscid and incompressible stratified fluid without swirl was given by Yih [9], or [11, pp. 10–11]. The equation governing steady swirling axisymmetric flows of an inviscid fluid of constant density, first given by Bragg and Hawthorne [1, (18), p. 244], is

$$(19) \qquad \left(\frac{\partial^2}{\partial r^2} - \frac{1}{r}\frac{\partial}{\partial r} + \frac{\partial^2}{\partial z^2}\right)\psi + \frac{f'(\psi)}{2} = r^2 h(\psi),$$

where r and z are two of the three cylindrical coordinates, ψ is Stokes' stream function,

$$(20) \qquad f(\psi) = (vr)^2,$$

v being the swirling velocity, and

$$(21) \qquad h(\psi) = \frac{dH}{d\psi},$$

H being the Bernoulli quantity and a function of ψ only. The functions f and h are determined by the knowledge of the velocity distribution at some section. For axisymmetric flows in a cylinder, if far upstream, the longitudinal velocity is constant and the swirling motion is that of solid-body rotation; then (19) becomes linear. This linear form in cylindrical coordinates was first used by Long [5].

However the linear form of (19) in spherical coordinates was already used by Taylor [8, (8), p. 182] much earlier.

For use in the next section, we shall now derive the equation governing steady axisymmetric swirling flows of a stratified fluid. The Euler equations are, in cylindrical coordinates and for axisymmetric flows,

$$(22) \qquad \rho(uu_r + wu_z - v^2/r) = -p_r,$$

$$(23) \qquad \rho(uv_r + wv_z + uv/r) = 0,$$

$$(24) \qquad \rho(uw_r + ww_z) = -p_z - g\rho,$$

in which subscripts indicate partial differentiation, u, v and w are components of the velocity in the directions of the cylindrical coordinates (r, θ, z), g is the gravitational acceleration, ρ the density, and p the pressure. Equation (23) can be written as

$$(25) \qquad u\frac{\partial(rv)}{\partial r} + w\frac{\partial(rv)}{\partial z} = 0,$$

which states that rv remains constant along a streamline and is thus a function of the stream function only.

Since the fluid is incompressible,

$$(26) \qquad u\rho_r + w\rho_z = 0.$$

Because of (26), the transformation [10]

$$(27) \qquad (u', v', w') = \sqrt{(\rho/\rho_0)}\,(u, v, w)$$

reduces (22) and (24) to

$$(28) \qquad \rho_0\left(u'u'_r + w'u'_z - \frac{v'^2}{r}\right) = -p_r,$$

$$(29) \qquad \rho_0(u'w'_r + w'w'_z) = -p_z - g\rho,$$

in which ρ_0 is a constant reference density. The equation of continuity can be written, again because of (26),

$$(ru')_r + (rw')_z = 0,$$

which allows the use of a stream function ψ' in terms of which

$$(30) \qquad ru' = -\psi'_z, \qquad rw' = \psi'_r.$$

The relation between ψ' and ψ is simply

$$(31) \qquad d\psi' = \sqrt{(\rho/\rho_0)}\,d\psi.$$

Since both ρ and rv are functions of ψ only, and since v is related to v' through (27) and ψ' to ψ through (31), it is evident that ρ and $(rv')^2$ are functions of ψ' only. We shall write

$$(32) \qquad (rv')^2 = f(\psi').$$

Equations (28) and (29) can be written as

$$(33) \qquad -\rho_0 w' \eta' - \frac{\rho_0 f(\psi')}{r^3} = -\frac{\partial}{\partial r}\left[p + \frac{\rho}{2}(u^2 + w^2) \right],$$

$$(34) \qquad \rho_0 u' \eta' = -\frac{\partial}{\partial z}\left[p + \frac{\rho}{2}(u^2 + w^2) \right] - g\rho,$$

in which

$$(35) \qquad \eta' = w_r' - u_z' = \frac{1}{r}\left(\psi_{rr}' - \frac{1}{r}\psi_r' + \psi_{zz}' \right),$$

$$\rho(u^2 + w^2) = \rho_0(u'^2 + w'^2).$$

Multiplying (33) by dr and (34) by dz, using (30) on the left-hand side, and adding the results, we have, after a uniform change of sign,

$$(36) \qquad \rho_0 r^{-1}\eta' \, d\psi' + \rho_0 r^{-3} f(\psi') \, dr = d[p + (\rho/2)(u^2 + w^2)] + g\rho \, dz.$$

But

$$\frac{1}{2}d(\rho_0 v'^2) = \frac{\rho_0}{2}d\left(\frac{f(\psi')}{r^2} \right) = \frac{\rho_0}{2r^2}\frac{df}{d\psi'}d\psi' - \rho_0 f(\psi')r^{-3} \, dr,$$

$$\rho \, dz = d(\rho z) - z \, d\rho.$$

Hence we can write (36) as

$$(37) \qquad \rho_0 r^{-1}\eta' \, d\psi' + \frac{\rho_0}{2r^2}\frac{df}{d\psi'}d\psi' = dH - gz \, d\rho,$$

where

$$H = p + \frac{\rho}{2}(u^2 + v^2 + w^2) + g\rho z$$

is the Bernoulli quantity. It is well known, and it can be readily shown, that for steady flows, H is a constant along a streamline. Hence H is a function of ψ' alone, and we obtain from (37) and (35)

$$(38) \qquad \left(\frac{\partial^2}{\partial r^2} - \frac{1}{r}\frac{\partial}{\partial r} + \frac{\partial^2}{\partial z^2} \right)\psi' + \frac{1}{2}\frac{df}{d\psi'} + \frac{gzr^2}{\rho_0}\frac{d\rho}{d\psi'} = r^2 h(\psi'),$$

in which

$$\rho_0 h = \frac{dH}{d\psi'}.$$

4. Vortex rings of a swirling stratified fluid. The solutions of (38) to be presented are all for the following linear form of (38):

$$(39) \qquad \left(\frac{\partial^2}{\partial r^2} - \frac{1}{r}\frac{\partial}{\partial r} + \frac{\partial^2}{\partial z^2} \right)\psi' + B\psi' + Ar^2 z = Cr^2.$$

906 CHIA-SHUN YIH

This equation results if

$$\frac{df}{d\psi'} = 2B\psi', \quad \frac{g}{\rho_0}\frac{d\rho}{d\psi'} = A, \quad h(\psi') = C.$$

If A and B are both zero, (39) is the equation that Hill [3] solved to obtain the spherical vortex. We shall consider now the case of nonzero A and B.

Let

(40) $$\psi' = (r^2/B)(C - Az) + r\chi,$$

so that

(41) $$\left(\frac{\partial^2}{\partial r^2} + \frac{1}{r}\frac{\partial}{\partial r} - \frac{1}{r^2} + \frac{\partial^2}{\partial z^2} + B\right)\chi = 0.$$

We shall first give the solution for a flow in a circular cylinder of height b and radius a, and let z be $\pm b/2$ at the ends of the cylinder. The boundary condition is that ψ' must vanish on the surface of the cylinder, and the solution is (40), with

(42) $$\chi = \frac{a}{BJ_1(\beta a)}(Az - C)J_1(\beta r) + \sum_{n=1}^{\infty}(A_n \cosh \gamma_n z + B_n \sinh \gamma_n z)J_1(\lambda_n r),$$

in which

$$\beta^2 = B, \quad J_1(\lambda_n a) = 0, \quad \gamma_n^2 = \lambda_n^2 - B,$$

$$A_n I_n \cosh \frac{\gamma_n b}{2} = \frac{C}{B}K_n, \qquad B_n I_n \sinh \frac{\gamma_n b}{2} = -\frac{Ab}{2B}K_n,$$

$$I_n = \int_0^a rJ_1^2(\lambda_n r)\,dr,$$

$$K_n = \int_0^a \left(\frac{arJ_1(\beta r)}{J_1(\beta a)} - r^2\right)J_1(\gamma_n r)\,dr,$$

provided

$$\gamma_n^2 \neq -\left(\frac{N\pi}{b}\right)^2,$$

with N equal to any integer.

This solution corresponds to a cylindrical vortex ring, which gives a qualitative picture of what happens when the stratification of the fluid is not stable and convection results—before viscosity damps out the motion or diffusivity destroys the stratification. Nevertheless the solution is not very interesting, because the vortex ring must be contained in a container and cannot be placed in a surrounding homogeneous fluid. We shall now seek solutions of spherical vortex rings which can be so placed.

In spherical coordinates (R, θ, φ), equation (41) becomes

$$(43) \qquad \frac{1}{R^2}\frac{\partial}{\partial R}\left(R^2\frac{\partial\chi}{\partial R}\right) + \frac{1}{R^2\sin\theta}\frac{\partial}{\partial\theta}\left(\sin\theta\frac{\partial\chi}{\partial\theta}\right) - \frac{\chi}{R^2\sin^2\theta} + B\chi = 0.$$

Let

$$(44) \qquad \chi = F(R)G(\theta).$$

Then F and G satisfy the equations

$$(45) \qquad F'' + \frac{2F'}{R} + BF - \frac{\lambda}{R^2}F = 0,$$

$$(46) \qquad \frac{1}{\sin\theta}(\sin\theta G')' - \frac{G}{\sin^2\theta} + \lambda G = 0,$$

where λ is a constant arising from the separation of variables. Let

$$\mu = \cos\theta.$$

Then (46) is just Legendre's differential equation:

$$(47) \qquad [(\mu^2 - 1)G']' - \lambda G + G/(1 - \mu^2) = 0,$$

in which the primes now indicate differentiation with respect to μ. It is well known that in order to have a solution of (47) regular at $\mu^2 = 1$, we must have

$$(48) \qquad \lambda = n(n + 1),$$

where n is an integer. With (48), the solution of (47) is then Legendre's associated function of the first kind, $P_n^1(\mu)$. As to (45), when λ takes on the value given by (48) we can make the substitution

$$(49) \qquad F = R^{-1/2}H,$$

and obtain

$$(50) \qquad H'' + \frac{H'}{R} + \left(B - \frac{(n - \frac{1}{2})^2}{R^2}\right)H = 0.$$

Again writing β^2 for B, the solution of (50) is

$$(51) \qquad H = J_{(n-\frac{1}{2})}(\beta R).$$

Now let us return to (40), which has the form

$$(52) \qquad \psi' = -AB^{-1}R^3\mu(1 - \mu^2) + R(1 - \mu^2)^{1/2}\chi.$$

The C in (40) has been put equal to zero for the spherical vortex, because with a nonvanishing C there is no regular solution if B is not zero. The solution of (43) satisfying the conditions

$$(53) \qquad \psi' = 0 \quad \text{at } \sin\theta = 0 \quad \text{and at } R = a \quad \text{(radius of the sphere)}$$

is

$$(54) \qquad \psi' = -AB^{-1}R^3\mu(1 - \mu^2) + KR^{1/2}(1 - \mu^2)^{1/2}J_{3/2}(\beta R)P_2^1(\mu),$$

     CHIA-SHUN YIH

in which

$$P_2^1(\mu) = 3\mu(1 - \mu^2)^{1/2}.$$

The solution (54) satisfies (53) if

$$(55) \qquad AB^{-1}a^{5/2} = 3KJ_{3/2}(\beta a),$$

which determines K. So far B (or β^2) has been arbitrary. If we impose the condition that the velocity along the surface of the sphere is zero, we have

$$0 = \frac{1}{a \sin \theta} \left. \frac{\partial \psi'}{\partial R} \right|_{R=a}$$

or

$$(56) \qquad -\frac{3a^2 A}{B} + 3K \frac{d}{dR}[R^{1/2}J_{3/2}(\beta R)]_{R=a} = 0.$$

Combining (55) with (56), we have an equation of the form

$$(57) \qquad J'_{3/2}(\beta a) = \text{const.}\, J_{3/2}(\beta a),$$

in which the prime indicates differentiation with respect to the argument of the function. Equation (57) has infinitely many roots β_n. For

$$B = \beta_n^2,$$

then, it is possible to have a spherical vortex ring (with 4 compartments of flow in any meridianal plane, because $\psi' = 0$ at the vertical axis of symmetry and at the equatorial plane $\theta = \pi/2$) capable of maintaining its spherical shape in a homogeneous fluid at rest and of the same density as the stratified fluid on the spherical surface.

5. Vortices in a stratified and conducting fluid. We shall now see whether solutions similar to those obtained so far can be obtained for a stratified and electrically conducting fluid in the presence of a magnetic field. In this section steady two-dimensional flows are considered. Cartesian coordinates (x, y, z) will be used, with y measured in the direction of the vertical. The corresponding velocity components will be denoted by u, v and w, and the corresponding components of the magnetic field will be denoted by f, g and h. All quantities are supposed to be independent of z, and w is zero since the flows considered are two-dimensional. However, h need not be assumed to be zero.

The fluid is still assumed to be incompressible, so that the equation of continuity is

$$(58) \qquad u_x + v_y = 0,$$

which allows the use of the stream function ψ, in terms of which

$$(59) \qquad u = \psi_y, \qquad v = -\psi_x.$$

The equation of continuity of the magnetic field is

$$f_x + g_y = 0,$$

which allows one to write

$$(60) \qquad f = \Lambda_y, \qquad g = -\Lambda_x,$$

in which Λ is the stream function for the magnetic field in the x, y-plane.

The equation governing the magnetic field is

$$(61) \qquad \operatorname{curl}(\mathbf{v} \times \mathbf{H}) = 0,$$

if magnetic diffusivity is assumed zero, and if $\mathbf{v}$ denotes the velocity vector and $\mathbf{H}$ the magnetic field vector. The three component equations of (61) are

$$(62) \qquad \frac{\partial}{\partial y}(ug - vf) = 0,$$

$$(63) \qquad -\frac{\partial}{\partial x}(ug - vf) = 0,$$

$$(64) \qquad -\frac{\partial}{\partial x}(uh) - \frac{\partial}{\partial y}(vh) = 0.$$

Integration of (62) and (63) gives

$$(65) \qquad ug - vf = 0,$$

the constant of integration being zero if there is a stagnation point in the flow. In view of (59), (60) and (65) we have

$$(66) \qquad \Lambda = \Lambda(\psi).$$

On account of (59), (60) and (66),

$$(67) \qquad f = \Lambda'u, \quad g = \Lambda'v, \quad \Lambda' = \frac{d\Lambda}{d\psi}.$$

In virtue of (58), (64) can be written as

$$(68) \qquad uh_x + vh_y = 0,$$

which implies

$$(69) \qquad h = h(\psi).$$

The equations of motion are, with H denoting $|\mathbf{H}|$ and μ now denoting the permeability,

$$(70) \qquad \rho(uu_x + vu_y) = -\frac{\partial}{\partial x}\left(p + \frac{\mu}{8\pi}H^2\right) + \frac{\mu}{4\pi}(ff_x + gf_y),$$

$$(71) \qquad \rho(uv_x + vv_y) = -\frac{\partial}{\partial y}\left(p + \frac{\mu}{8\pi}H^2\right) + \frac{\mu}{4\pi}(fg_x + gg_y) - g\rho,$$

$$(72) \qquad 0 = \frac{\mu}{4\pi}(fh_x + gh_y).$$

Because of (67) and (68), equation (72) is automatically satisfied. It is easy to show from (67) that

$$ff_x + gf_y = \Lambda'^2(uu_x + vu_y),$$
$$fg_x + gg_y = \Lambda'^2(uv_x + vv_y).$$

Thus (70) and (71) can be written as

$$(73) \qquad \left(\rho - \frac{\mu}{4\pi}\Lambda'^2\right)(uu_x + vu_y) = -p'_x,$$

$$(74) \qquad \left(\rho - \frac{\mu}{4\pi}\Lambda'^2\right)(uv_x + vv_y) = -p'_y - g\rho,$$

in which

$$p' = p + (\mu/8\pi)H^2.$$

Since the fluid is assumed incompressible and nondiffusive,

$$u\rho_x + v\rho_y = 0, \qquad u\mu_x + v\mu_y = 0,$$

so that, Λ' being a function of ψ, we have

$$\left(u\frac{\partial}{\partial x} + v\frac{\partial}{\partial y}\right)\left(\rho - \frac{\mu}{4\pi}\Lambda'^2\right) = 0.$$

We shall now make the transformation [12, p. 267]

$$(75) \qquad (u', v') = \left(\frac{4\pi\rho - \mu\Lambda'^2}{4\pi\rho_0}\right)^{1/2}(u, v).$$

Then (73) and (74) become

$$(76) \qquad \rho_0(u'u'_x + v'u'_y) = -p'_x,$$

$$(77) \qquad \rho_0(u'v'_x + v'v'_y) = -p'_y - g\rho,$$

which are the Euler equations for an ordinary incompressible fluid. Since

$$u'_x + v'_y = 0,$$

we have

$$u' = \psi'_y, \qquad v = -\psi'_x,$$

and from (76) and (77) we again obtain (2). Thus all the results obtained in §2 have their counterparts for a stratified conducting fluid in the presence of a magnetic field, and we need not repeat the calculations and arguments, except to state the very important fact that the Bernoulli equation for steady flow is still

$$p + (\rho/2)(u^2 + v^2) + \rho gy = \text{function of } \psi',$$

which permits the dynamical considerations at the interface of a stratified fluid and a homogeneous nonconducting fluid to remain unaffected even if the fluid is conducting and there is a magnetic field present. It has been explained [12] that if the square root factor in (75) vanishes, no real difficulty is encountered.

6. Vortex rings in a stratified and conducting fluid. For axisymmetric swirling flows of an incompressible, inviscid and conducting fluid of constant density the governing equation has been obtained by Long [6] and simplified by Yih [12]. If the fluid is stratified in addition, the governing equation can be found in the following way:

(i) Make the transformations (27) and (31).

(ii) Note that μ and ρ were assumed constant by Long [6] but are not assumed constant in this paper, and that our definition of f, g and h differ from Long's by a factor $\mu/4\pi\rho$. With this in mind, and following through Long's derivation, we obtain

$$(78) \quad \psi'_{zz} + \psi'_{rr} - \frac{1}{r}\psi'_r - \frac{\alpha\Lambda'\Lambda''}{E}[(\psi'_z)^2 + (\psi'_r)^2] + \frac{gzr^2}{\rho_0 E}\frac{d\rho}{d\psi'} + \frac{A'}{2E} + \frac{B'r^4}{2E} = \frac{Mr^2}{E},$$

in which ψ' is the same ψ' as in (38),

$$\alpha = \frac{\mu(\psi')}{4\pi\rho_0}, \qquad \Lambda(\psi') = \text{stream function for the magnetic field},$$

$$E = 1 - \alpha\Lambda'^2, \quad A = \frac{L^2}{E}, \quad B = \frac{K^2}{E},$$

$$L(\psi') = v'r - \alpha\Lambda'gr, \qquad K(\psi') = \frac{g - \Lambda'v'}{r},$$

$$\rho_0 = \text{a constant reference density}.$$

All the quantities L, K, A, B, E, M, ρ, μ and Λ are functions of ψ', and the accents on them indicate differentiation with respect to ψ'. The accents on ψ' and v' do not indicate differentiation.

(iii) Now make the transformation (essentially in [12])

$$d\Psi = E^{1/2}\, d\psi'.$$

Then (78) becomes

$$(79) \quad \Psi_{zz} + \Psi_{rr} - \frac{1}{r}\Psi_r + \frac{gzr^2}{\rho_0}\frac{d\rho}{d\Psi} + \frac{1}{2}\frac{dA}{d\Psi} + \frac{r^4}{2}\frac{dB}{d\Psi} = r^2 N(\Psi).$$

Equation (79) can be compared with (38). (Note that the f and h in (38) have nothing to do with the magnetic field, and that the A and B in (79) are not the constant A and B in (39).) If the B in (79) is constant, then (38) and (79) are identical in form, and we need not repeat the finding of the solutions. If $B \neq$ const. in (79) but is proportional to ψ, the development in § 4 can still be applied to the solution of (79) for a cylindrical container, but regular solutions for a spherical geometry[1] are not possible under the assumptions

$$\frac{1}{\Psi}\frac{dA}{d\Psi} = \text{const.}, \qquad \frac{d\rho}{d\Psi} = \text{const.}, \qquad N = \text{const.}$$

---

[1] For a spherical eddy of a viscous conducting fluid in Stokes flow, see [7].

912	CHIA-SHUN YIH

Finally we note that in case it is possible to immerse the stratified conducting fluid in a homogeneous nonconducting fluid, there is a current sheet at the interface for the two-dimensional cases but not for the axisymmetric cases, since in these latter cases the speed q and the magnitude of the magnetic field H are both zero at the interface. (The spherical vortex ring does not propagate in the homogeneous nonconducting fluid.)

REFERENCES

[1] S. L. BRAGG AND W. R. HAWTHORNE, *Some exact solutions of the flow through annular cascade actuator discs*, J. Aero. Sci., 17 (1950), pp. 243–249.

[2] M. L. DUBREIL-JACOTIN, *Complément à une note antérieure. sur les ondes de type permanent dans les liquides hétérogènes*, Atti Accad. Naz. Lincei Rend. Cl. Sci. Fis. Mat. Natur. (6), 21 (1935), pp. 344–346.

[3] M. J. M. HILL, *On a spherical vortex*, Philos. Trans. Roy. Soc. London Ser. A., 185 (1894).

[4] H. LAMB, *Hydrodynamics*, Cambridge University Press, Cambridge, 1932.

[5] R. R. LONG, *Some aspects of the flow of stratified fluids*, I: *A theoretical investigation*, Tellus, 5 (1953), pp. 42–57.

[6] ———, *Steady finite motions of a conducting liquid*, J. Fluid Mech., 7 (1960), pp. 108–114.

[7] H. K. MOFFATT, *Magnetic eddies in an incompressible viscous fluid with high electrical conductivity*, Ibid., 17 (1963), pp. 225–239.

[8] G. I. TAYLOR, *The motion of a sphere in a rotating liquid*, Proc. Roy. Soc. Ser. A, 102 (1922), pp. 180–189.

[9] C.-S. YIH, *On stratified flows in a gravitational field*, Tellus, 9 (1957), pp. 220–227.

[10] ———, *On the flow of a stratified fluid*, Proc. 3rd Nat'l. Congr. Appl. Mech., 1958, pp. 857–861.

[11] ———, *Dynamics of Nonhomogeneous Fluids*, Macmillan, New York, 1965.

[12] ———, *On large-amplitude magnetohydrodynamics*, J. Fluid Mech., 23 (1965), pp. 261–271.

INTERNAL WAVES IN PIPES
ETUDE DES ONDES INTERNES DANS LES CONDUITES

by/par

CHIA-SHUN YIH

Professor, Department of Applied Mechanics and Engineering Science,
The University of Michigan, U.S.A.

1. Summary

Internal waves of a stratified fluid in a circular or elliptic pipe are investigated. Solutions for all modes are given, and explicit results for long waves are obtained.

1. Résumé

Nous présentons une étude des ondes internes se propageant au sein d'un liquide stratifié dans une conduite de section circulaire ou elliptique, et nous proposons des solutions valables pour tous modes de mouvement ondulatoire. Enfin, nous présentons des résultats explicites que nous avons pu déterminer pour le cas des ondes longues.

2. Introduction

Results for gravity waves in channels of variable depth are extremely rare. The difficulty arises from the fact that when the depth of the fluid is not uniform the method of separation of variables cannot in general be applied. The few solutions cited in Lamb's book [1932, pp. 442–447] are for inviscid fluids with constant density in symmetric triangular channels with vertex angle equal to 90° and 120°, respectively, and for edge waves. The solution for the 120° channel is restricted to the first symmetric mode only.

It is known that Stokes' solution [1846] for edge waves is also applicable to stratified fluids [YIH 1965]. In addition, Gerstner's

2. Introduction

On ne dispose que de quelques rares résultats en ce qui concerne les ondes de gravité dans les canaux de profondeur variable. La difficulté de ce problème provient de ce que, lorsque la hauteur du liquide n'est pas uniforme, le procédé dit „de séparation des variables" devient généralement inapplicable. Les quelques solutions proposées dans l'ouvrage de LAMB (1932, pages 442–447) sont valables pour les fluides non-visqueux, de densité constante, contenus dans des canaux de section triangulaire symétrique présentant un angle au sommet égal à 90° ou 120°, et pour les ondes aux parois. La solution proposée pour le cas d'un angle au sommet

Received January 30, 1974.

Reçu le 30 janvier 1974.

solution given in LAMB [1932, p. 421] for rotational wave motion of finite amplitude, found by Madame DUBREIL-JACOTIN [1932, p. 819] to apply to incompressible fluids of any stratification, has been shown [YIH 1966], by a rotation of coordinate axes, to apply to edge waves. These are virtually all the exact solutions for gravity waves propagating in channels, with the depth varying in a horizontal direction normal to the direction of wave propagation.

In this paper we shall give the solution for all modes of internal waves in a stratified fluid filling a horizontal pipe of circular or elliptic cross section, and explicit results for long waves.

de 120° n'est valable que pour le premier mode symétrique.

On sait que la solution de STOKES (1846) concernant les ondes aux parois s'étend également au cas des fluides stratifiés (YIH, 1965). D'autre part, Madame DUBREIL-JACOTIN (1932, page 819) s'était rendue compte que la solution de GERSTNER (présentée dans l'ouvrage de LAMB en 1932 – page 421), relative au mouvement rotationnel des ondes d'amplitude finie, était valable pour les fluides incompressibles stratifiés, quel qu'en soit le schéma de stratification, et il a été démontré par YIH (1966) qu'il était possible, par rotation des axes de coordonnées, de transposer cette solution au cas des ondes aux parois.

Telles sont, en fait, pratiquement les seules solutions exactes dont nous disposons pour le problème des ondes de gravité se propageant dans des canaux dans lesquels la hauteur du liquide est variable dans une direction horizontale, et normale à celle de la propagation des ondes.

Nous présentons ici une solution pouvant s'appliquer aux ondes internes de n'importe quel mode, présentes en milieu liquide stratifié dans une conduite en charge horizontale, de section elliptique ou circulaire, ainsi que des résultats explicites pour le cas des ondes longues.

3. The differential system

The density of the incompressible stratified fluid, when it is undisturbed by wave motion, will be denoted by ϱ_0. We shall use Cartesian coordinates x, y, and z, with the direction of increasing z coinciding with the direction of the vertical. In the case of a channel, x will be measured along its axis, and y will be measured across the channel. Thus ϱ_0 is a function of z alone. The mean pressure p_0 is related to ϱ_0 by

3. Système d'équations différentielles

Soit ϱ_0 la densité d'un liquide incompressible stratifié, et non perturbé par des mouvements ondulatoires, et adoptons les coordonnées cartésiennes x, y et z (z augmentant sur la verticale). Pour un canal, nous mesurerons la grandeur x le long de l'axe, et la grandeur y suivant la largeur du canal. Ainsi, ϱ_0 ne sera fonction que de z. Dans ces conditions, la relation liant la pression moyenne p_0 à la densité ϱ_0 s'écrit:

$$\frac{\mathrm{d}p_0}{\mathrm{d}z} = -g\varrho_0 \tag{1}$$

Using u, v, and w to denote the components of the velocity in the directions of increasing x, y, and z, respectively, and p and ϱ to denote the perturbations in pressure and density, the linearized equations of motion, after Eq. (1) has been used, are

D'autre part, soient u, v et w les composantes de la vitesse en direction des valeurs croissantes de x, y et z, et affectons aux perturbations de la pression et de la densité les notations p et ϱ: compte tenu de l'équation (1), nous aboutissons aux équations linéarisées du mouvement:

$$\varrho_0 \frac{\partial}{\partial t}(u,v,w) = -\left(\frac{\partial}{\partial x}, \frac{\partial}{\partial y}, \frac{\partial}{\partial z}\right) p + (0, 0, -g\varrho) \tag{2}$$

in which t is the time and g the gravitational acceleration. The linearized equation of incompressibility is

Dans celles-ci, t représente le temps, et g l'accélération de la pesanteur. La forme linéarisée de l'équation d'incompressibilité s'écrit:

$$\frac{\partial \varrho}{\partial t} + w\varrho_0' = 0 \tag{3}$$

in which the accent denotes differentiation with respect to z. Since the fluid is incompressible, the equation of continuity is exactly

dans laquelle la grandeur „primée" désigne une dérivée par rapport à z. Etant donné l'incompressibilité du fluide, nous obtenons, pour l'équation de continuité exacte:

$$\frac{\partial u}{\partial x} + \frac{\partial v}{\partial y} + \frac{\partial w}{\partial z} = 0 \tag{4}$$

Since we are dealing with wave motion, and the equations have been linearized, we shall assume all unknown quantities to have the exponential time factor $\epsilon^{-i\sigma t}$, where σ is the circular frequency.

For convenience we shall define a quantity φ by

Puisqu'il s'agit d'un mouvement ondulatoire et les équations sont linéarisées, nous attribuons à toutes les inconnues le même facteur de temps exponentiel, $e^{-i\sigma t}$, σ étant la fréquence circulaire. Pour plus de commodité, nous définissons une grandeur φ:

$$\varphi = -\frac{i}{\sigma} p \tag{5}$$

Then the first two equations in Eqs. (2) give

Dans ces conditions, nous tirons des deux premières équations comprises dans (2) les relations:

$$\varrho_0 u = \varphi_x, \quad \varrho_0 v = \varphi_y \tag{6}$$

Eliminating ϱ between the third equation in Eqs. (2) and (3), we have

Puis, en éliminant ϱ de la troisième équation comprise dans (2) et (3):

$$w = \frac{\sigma^2 \varphi_z}{\sigma^2 \varrho_0 + g\varrho_0'} \tag{7}$$

In Eqs. (6) and (7), subscripts indicate partial differentiation. Using these equations, we obtain from Eq. (4) the following partial differential equation governing three-dimensional wave motion of a stratified incompressible fluid:

Dans les équations (6) et (7), la présence d'un indice inférieur indique une dérivée partielle. Ces équations nous permettent de tirer de l'équation (4) celle aux dérivées partielles qui définit le mouvement spatial des ondes dans un fluide incompressible stratifié:

$$\frac{\partial^2 \varphi}{\partial x^2} + \frac{\partial^2 \varphi}{\partial y^2} + \sigma^2 \varrho_0 \frac{\partial}{\partial z}\left(\frac{\varphi_z}{\sigma^2 \varrho_0 + g\varrho_0'}\right) = 0 \tag{8}$$

If the direction numbers of the normal to a stationary rigid boundary are (l, m, n) the boundary condition at that boundary is

Soient (l, m, n) les coefficients directionnels de la normale par rapport à une frontière rigide stationnaire: la condition aux limites à cette frontière est définie par la relation:

$$lu + mv + nw = 0 \tag{9}$$

In what follows we shall consider an exponentially stratified fluid but shall follow Boussinesq in neglecting the inertial effect of density variation. It should be noted that if the Boussinesq approximation is used then the differential equation for wave motion in an exponentially stratified fluid is the same as that for wave motion in a linearly stratified fluid. In practical cases the density stratification is always slight, the Boussinesq approximation valid, and the stratification is nearly linear. Hence the solutions to be presented are not without practical interest.

Nous examinerons par la suite le cas d'un fluide stratifié selon une loi exponentielle, mais comme Boussinesq, nous négligerons les forces d'inertie découlant des variations de la densité. Remarquons que, si l'on adopte la solution approchée de Boussinesq, l'équation différentielle définissant le mouvement ondulatoire dans un fluide stratifié selon une loi exponentielle est la même que celle correspondant à un fluide de stratification linéaire. Dans la réalité, la stratification de densité est toujours peu prononcée, la solution approchée de Boussinesq est valable, et la loi de stratification est quasi-linéaire. De ce fait, les solutions que nous proposons présentent un certain intérêt pratique.

4. Tree-dimensonal waves in circular or elliptic pipes

4. Ondes spatiales dans les conduites de section circulaire ou elliptique

Let the density distribution of the fluid be given by

Soit la répartition des densités du fluide telle que:

$$\varrho_0 = Ce^{-\beta z} \tag{10}$$

and consider waves in the fluid filling an elliptic pipe with cross section

et examinons le cas des ondes présentes dans une conduite de section elliptique en charge, d'équation:

$$\frac{y^2}{b^2} + \frac{z^2}{c^2} = 1 \tag{11}$$

The x-dependence of φ will be assumed to have the form

Enfin, admettons l'hypothèse selon laquelle la fonction $\varphi = f(x)$ serait de la forme:

$$f(y, z) \exp ikx$$

Then, if the Boussinesq approximation is used, Eq. (8) becomes

Dans ces conditions, et moyennant la solution approchée de Boussinesq, l'équation (8) s'écrit:

$$\lambda^2(f_{yy} - k^2 f) - f_{zz} = 0 \tag{12}$$

where   avec:

$$\lambda^2 = \frac{g\beta - \sigma^2}{\sigma^2} \tag{13}$$

The boundary condition is that the velocity component normal to the elliptic boundary (11) must vanish, or

La condition aux limites impose que la composante de la vitesse normale à la frontière elliptique s'annule, soit:

$$-\lambda^2 \frac{y f_y}{b^2} + \frac{z f_z}{c^2} = 0 \tag{14}$$

on the ellipse. Equations (12) and (14) define an eigenvalue problem, and the task is to find the eigenvalues of λ^2 (and hence of σ^2) and the corresponding eigenfunctions.

First of all let all lengths be measured in units of the reference length b, including the wave length, so that now

Les équations (12) et (14) définissent un problème relevant des valeurs propres, et il s'agit de déterminer celles de λ^2 (donc de σ^2), ainsi que les fonctions propres correspondantes.

Ramenons d'abord toutes les longueurs (longueurs d'onde comprises) à la longueur de référence b; il vient:

$$k = \frac{2\pi b}{L}$$

L = wave length in the x-direction.

Then Eq. (12) remains invariant, with x, y, z, and k all dimensionless.

Equations (11) and (14) become

L = longueur d'onde suivant x.

Dans ces conditions, l'équation (12) reste invariante, x, y, z et k étant des grandeurs réduites. Les équations (11) et (14) prennent les formes, respectivement:

$$\frac{y^2}{} + \frac{z^2}{c^2} = 1 \tag{11a}$$

$$-\lambda^2 c^2 y f_y + z f_z = 0 \tag{14a}$$

in both of which c is now measured in units of b and is dimensionless.

We now make the transformation

dans lesquelles c est une grandeur réduite, ramenée à la longueur de référence b. Nous pouvons dès lors effectuer la transformation:

$$z' = \frac{z}{c}, \quad \lambda'^2 = \lambda^2 c^2 \tag{15}$$

Then Eqs. (11a) and (14a) become, after dropping the primes,

D'où, en laissant tomber les termes „primés" des équations (11a) et (14a), nous obtenons pour celles-ci:

$$y^2 + z^2 = 1 \tag{16}$$

$$-\lambda^2 y f_y + z f_z = 0 \tag{17}$$

and Eq. (12) is invariant in form after the primes are dropped:

D'autre part, après élimination des termes „primés", l'équation (12) prend la forme invariante:

$$\lambda^2 (f_{yy} - k^2 f) - f_{zz} = 0 \tag{18}$$

in which y, z, and k are now dimensionless. Thus we can treat the case of a circular channel, and after we have obtained the solution replace z by z' and λ by λ', and use Eq. (15) to obtain the λ (and hence the σ) and the eigenfunction for the corresponding mode for the elliptic channel.

We shall, then, henceforth treat the case of the circular channel only. Transformation (15) is essentially the same as that made by HOILAND (1962) for rotating fluids in elliptic channels.

The geometry (now circular) of the problem requires a transformation of coordinates allowing a separation of variables one or other of which is constant on the circle given by Eq. (16). The required transformation is

dans laquelle y, z et k sont des grandeurs réduites. Ainsi, nous sommes en mesure d'aborder le problème d'un canal de section circulaire, et une fois déterminée, la solution correspondante, de remplacer z par z', et λ par λ', et enfin, de déterminer λ (et par conséquent σ) à partir de l'équation (15), ainsi que la fonction propre du mode correspondant pour le cas d'un canal de section elliptique.

Ceci étant, nous limiterons désormais notre examen au seul cas d'un canal de section circulaire. La transformation (15) est essentiellement de même que celle appliquée par HØILAND [1962] au cas des fluides en rotation dans les canaux de section elliptique.

Les caractéristiques géométriques (celles du cercle) intervenant dans le présent problème imposent une transformation permettant la séparation des variables, dont l'une ou l'autre reste constante sur le cercle déterminé par l'équation (16). Cette transformation est la suivante:

$$y = \frac{\cos\mu\cos\nu}{\cos\alpha}, \quad z = \frac{\sin\mu\sin\nu}{\sin\alpha} \tag{19}$$

where α is defined by

avec les définitions suivantes de l'angle:

$$\frac{\sigma}{\sqrt{g\beta}} = \cos\alpha \quad \text{or/ou} \quad \lambda = \tan\alpha \quad \text{with/avec} \quad \alpha < \frac{\pi}{2} \tag{20}$$

The transformation (19) is the same as the one employed by BARCILON [1968] to study *two-dimensional* waves in rotating fluids, although the definition of α is necessarily different.

Although Barcilon's transformation was used by him to study transverse oscillations only, it is equally useful for studying three-dimensional waves. The area inside the circle (16) is mapped many times over into rectangles in the $\mu-\nu$ plane. We shall choose the rectangle

La transformation (19) est identique à celle employée par BARCILON [1968] dans son étude des ondes planes dans les fluides en rotation, bien que l'angle α soit évidemment défini différemment.

Bien que BARCILON n'ait utilisé sa transformation que pour étudier les oscillations transversales, elle peut aussi servir utilement dans le cas des ondes spatiales. On décompose la surface du cercle défini par l'équation (16) plusieurs fois de suite en rectangles dans le plan $\mu-\nu$, dont nous choisissons celui défini par

$$-\alpha \leqq \mu \leqq \alpha, \quad \alpha \leqq \nu \leqq \pi-\alpha \tag{21}$$

as the domain for our analysis. By virtue of Eq. (20), Eq. (18) can be written as

pour notre domaine d'analyse. Compte tenu de l'équation (20), nous pouvons écrire l'équation (18) de la forme suivante:

$$f_{yy} - \cot^2\alpha\, f_{zz} - k^2 f = 0 \tag{22}$$

which, upon the use of Eq. (19), becomes

d'où, après application de l'équation (19):

$$\cos^2\alpha(f_{\mu\mu} - f_{\nu\nu}) - \frac{k^2}{2}(\cos 2\nu - \cos 2\mu)f = 0 \tag{23}$$

The circle (16) is, in the $\mu-\nu$ domain, the boundary of the rectangle (21). That is, it is transformed onto four line segments:

Le cercle défini par l'équation (16) correspond, dans le domaine $\mu-\nu$, aux limites du rectangle (21), étant transformé sur 4 segments linéaires:

$$\mu = \alpha, \quad \alpha \leqq \nu \leqq \pi-\alpha$$
$$\mu = -\alpha, \quad \alpha \leqq \nu \leqq \pi-\alpha$$
$$\nu = \alpha, \quad -\alpha \leqq \mu \leqq \alpha$$
$$\nu = \pi-\alpha, \quad -\alpha \leqq \mu \leqq \alpha$$

The boundary condition (17) is

Nous avons, pour la condition aux limités (17):

$$\frac{\partial f}{\partial \mu} = 0 \quad \text{at} \quad \mu = \pm \alpha \tag{24}$$

on the first two segments, and

pour les deux premiers segments, et:

$$\frac{\partial f}{\partial v} = 0 \quad \text{at} \quad v = \alpha \quad \text{and at} \quad v = \pi - \alpha \tag{25}$$

on the second two segments.

Substituting

pour les deux derniers segments.

Substituons dans l'équation (23):

$$f = F(\mu)G(v) \tag{26}$$

into Eq. (23) and separating variables, we have

et séparons les variables; il vient:

$$F'' + (a - 2q \cos 2\mu)F = 0 \tag{27}$$

$$G'' + (a - 2q \cos 2v)G = 0 \tag{28}$$

with

avec:

$$q = -\frac{k^2}{2\cos^2\alpha} \tag{29}$$

Equations (27) and (28) have identical forms. The quantity a is a constant arising from the separation of variables. These are in the canonical form of the Mathieu equation. We now make the important observation that y and z, as given by Eq. (19) have the period 2π in μ and v, and any solutions of Eqs. (27) and (28), to have a unique value at any point (y, z), must also have the same* period 2π in μ and v. This condition determines a as a function of q. There are infinitely many characteristic values of a for each value of q [McLachlan 1947]:

Les équations (27) et (28) sont de forme identique. La grandeur a est une constante résultant de la séparation des variables, lesquelles se présentent sous la forme canonique de l'équation de Mathieu. Ici, nous faisons une constatation importante: les grandeurs y et z définies par l'équation (19) ont une période de 2π en μ et en v, et pour que toute solution des équations (27) et (28) ait une valeur unique en tout point (y, z), il faut qu'elle présente aussi cette même période* de 2π en μ et en v. Cette condition détermine a en fonction de q. A chaque valeur de q correspond un nombre infini de valeurs caractéristique de a [McLachlan [1947]:

$$a_0 = -\tfrac{1}{2}q^2 + \tfrac{7}{128}q^4 + 0(q^6)$$

$$b_1 = 1 - q - \tfrac{1}{8}q^2 + \tfrac{1}{64}q^3 + 0(q^4), \quad a_1 = b_1(-q)$$

$$b_2 = 4 - \tfrac{1}{12}q^2 + 0(q^4), \quad a_2 = 4 - \tfrac{5}{12}q^2 + 0(q^4)$$

$$b_3 = 9 + \tfrac{1}{16}q^2 - \tfrac{1}{64}q^3 + 0(q^4), \quad a_3 = b_3(-q)$$

---

* Or the period $2\pi/N$, N being an integer.

* Ou la période $2\pi/N$, N étant un nombre entier.

and so on. It is important to note that the first term of a_n or b_n is n^2, the eigenfunction associated with a_n is denoted by ce_n, and that associated with b_n is denoted by se_n. The function $ce_{2p}(\mu, q)$ (p = integer) contains the functions $\cos 2m\mu$, m being any integer, and the functions $ce_{2p+1}(\mu, q)$ contains the functions $\cos(2m+1)\mu$. Similarly, $se_{2p}(\mu, q)$ contains $\sin 2m\mu$, se_{2p+1} contains $\sin(2m+1)\mu$. It is well known, and it can be easily demonstrated by starting with $q = 0$, that $ce_n(\mu, q)$ has $2n$ internal zeros in $(0, 2\pi)$, and $se_n(\mu, q)$ has $2n - 1$ internal zeros in $(0, 2\pi)$, but vanishes at $\mu = 0$ and $\mu = 2\pi$. What has been said of the functions of μ is of course also true for the functions of v.

The solution of Eqs. (23), (24), and (25) is of the following two classes:

et ainsi de suite. Il importe de noter que le premier terme de a_n ou b_n est n^2, que la fonction propre liée à a_n est désignée par ce_n, et que celle liée à b_n est désignée par se_n. La fonction $ce_{2p}(\mu, q)$ (p étant un nombre entier) contient les fonctions $\cos 2m\mu$ (m pouvant être n'importe quel nombre entier), et la fonction $ce_{2p+1}(\mu, q)$ contient les fonctions $\cos(2m+1)\mu$. De même, $se_{2p}(\mu, q)$ contient $\sin 2m\mu$, et se_{2p+1} contient $\sin(2m+1)\mu$. On sait, et il est facile de le démontrer en partant de $q = 0$, que $ce_n(\mu, q)$ contient $2n$ zéros internes dans $(0, 2\pi)$, et que $se_n(\mu, q)$ en contient $2n - 1$ dans $(0, 2\pi)$, mais s'annule lorsque $\mu = 0$ et $\mu = 2\pi$.

Ce qui a été dit à propos des fonctions de μ s'applique évidemment aussi à celles de v.

La solution des équations (23), (24) et (25) appartient aux deux classes suivantes:

$$f = ce_n(\mu, q)ce_n(v, q), \qquad n = 0, 1, 2, \ldots \tag{30}$$

$$f = se_n(\mu, q)se_n(v, q), \qquad n = 1, 2, 3, \ldots \tag{31}$$

The eigenvalues α are determined by Eq. (24):

Les valeurs propres de α se déterminent à partir de l'équation (24):

$$ce_n'(\mu, q) \equiv \frac{d}{d\mu} ce_n(\mu, q) = 0 \quad \text{for} \quad \mu = \pm\alpha \tag{32a}$$

or $\qquad$ soit:

$$se_n'(\mu, q) \equiv \frac{d}{d\mu} se_n(\mu, q) = 0 \quad \text{for} \quad \mu = \pm\alpha \tag{32b}$$

Because $\qquad\qquad\qquad$ En effet:

$$ce_n'(\alpha, q) = -ce_n'(-\alpha, q)$$

$$se_n'(\alpha, q) = se_n'(-\alpha, q)$$

we can impose Eq. (32a) and Eq. (32b) for $\mu = \alpha$ only. Also, in regard to v,

Les équations (32a) et (32b) ne sont valables que lorsque $\mu = \alpha$. D'autre part, en ce qui concerne v:

$$ce_n'(\alpha, q) = (-1)^{n+1} ce_n'(\pi - \alpha, q)$$

$$se_n'(\alpha, q) = (-1)^n se_n'(\pi - \alpha, q)$$

so that Eq. (25) is automatically satisfied if Eq. (24) is for $\mu = \alpha$. We must, however, obviously rule out

L'équation (25) est ainsi automatiquement satisfaite si l'équation (24) correspond à $\mu = \alpha$. Par contre, il est évident que nous ne devons par tenir compte des racines de l'équation (32a) que représentent:

$$\alpha = 0 \quad \text{and} \quad \alpha = \pi/2$$

which are roots of Eq. (32a). The actual determination of α depends on n and q, and is in general rather complicated. In the next subsection we shall determine α for long waves.

La détermination proprement dite de α dépend de n et de q; elle est, en général, assez compliquée. Nous déterminons dans le paragraphe suivant la grandeur α pour le cas des ondes longues.

5. Long waves

We shall solve the differential system consisting of Eqs. (24) to (28) by expansion in power series in k^2, since we have seen that it suffices to solve Eq. (27) together with

5. Ondes longues

Il s'agit ici de résoudre le système d'équations différentielles comprenant les équations (24) à (28), moyennant le développement d'une série de puissance en k^2; en effet nous avons vu, d'une part, qu'il suffit de résoudre les équations (27), et

$$F'(\alpha) = 0 \tag{33}$$

and that F and G are identical functions of the variables μ and v we shall assume

et d'autre part, que F et G sont des fonctions identiques des variables μ et v. Nous admettons les hypothèses suivantes:

$$F = F_0 + k^2 F_1 + k^4 F_2 + \ldots$$

$$\alpha = \alpha_0 + k^2 \alpha_1 + k^4 \alpha_2 + \ldots$$

Substituting these into Eq. (27) and collecting terms of the zeroth order in k, we have

que nous introduisons dans l'équation (27), et nous rassemblons les termes du zéro-ième ordre en k, d'où nous obtenons:

$$a = n^2 \quad (n = \text{integer/nombre entier})$$

and the solutions correspond exactly to those found by BARCILON (the only difference being in the relation of σ with α), and are of two classes:

Nos solutions correspondent exactement à celles de BARCILON (la seule différence résidant dans la relation entre σ et α); elles se regroupent dans 2 classes:

$$\text{(i)} \quad f_0 = \cos n\mu \cos nv, \quad \alpha_0 = \frac{m\pi}{n}$$

$$n = 3, 4, \ldots$$

$$m = 1, 2, \ldots, \quad N^{(1)} = \begin{cases} \dfrac{n}{2} - 1 \text{ for } n \text{ even/si } n \text{ est pair} \\[2ex] \dfrac{n-1}{2} \text{ for } n \text{ odd/si } n \text{ est impair} \end{cases}$$

(ii) $f_0 = \sin n\mu \sin n\nu, \quad \alpha_0 = \dfrac{2m+1}{2n}\pi$

$$n = 2, 3, \ldots$$

$$m = 0, 1, \ldots, \quad N^{(2)} = \begin{cases} \dfrac{n}{2} - 1 \text{ for } n \text{ even/si } n \text{ est pair} \\[2ex] \dfrac{n-1}{2} - 1 \text{ for } n \text{ odd/si } n \text{ est impair} \end{cases}$$

Collecting terms of order k^2 Eq. (27), and recalling that, for class (i), $F_0 = \cos n\mu$, we have

Rassemblons les termes d'ordre k^2 de l'équation (27): compte tenu de ce que, pour la classe (i), $F_0 = \cos n\mu$, nous pouvons écrire:

$$f_1'' + n^2 f_1 = -\frac{1}{\sigma_0^2} \cos 2\mu \cos n\mu$$

the solution of which is

dont la solution est la suivante:

$$f_1 = -\frac{1}{8\sigma_0^2}\left[\frac{\cos(n-2)\mu}{n-1} - \frac{\cos(n+2)\mu}{n+1}\right]$$

Application of Eq. (33) to the order k^2 then produces

Et il vient de l'application de l'équation (33) à l'ordre k^2:

$$\alpha_1 = -\frac{n^2-2}{2n^2(n^2-1)}\tan\alpha_0$$

A similar calculation for class (ii) gives

Un calcul semblable pour la classe (i) conduit au résultat:

$$f_1 = \frac{1}{8\sigma_0^2}\left[\frac{\sin(n+2)\mu}{n+1} - \frac{\sin(n-2)\mu}{n-1}\right]$$

$$\alpha_1 = -\frac{n^2-2}{2n^2(n^2-1)}\tan\alpha_0$$

Recall that α_0 for class (i) is different from α_0 for class (ii).

Further calculation for higher orders in k^2 can be performed without any difficulty. We

Dans ces calculs, nous devons tenir compte de la différence des termes α_0 des classes (i) et (ii).

La suite des calculs des ordres supérieurs

note that $\sigma = \cos \alpha$ increases with k, since a decreases with k.

To visualize the flow pattern, we first consider the two-dimensional flow (without x-variation) represented by (34) or (35). For this two-dimensional flow let

en k^2 ne présente aucune difficulté. Remarquons que $\sigma = \cos \alpha$ croît en fonction de k, puisque α décroît avec k.

Afin de pouvoir nous faire une image du schéma d'écoulement, nous examinons tout d'abord l'écoulement plan (sans variation de x) défini par les relations (34) ou (35). Pour cet écoulement plan, soit:

$$(v, w) = (V, W) \tag{36}$$

Then   d'où:

$$\varrho_0 V = f_y, \quad \varrho_0 W = -\frac{1}{\lambda^2} f_z \tag{37}$$

and Eq. (13), with $k = 0$, leads to

Avec $k = 0$, l'équation (13) conduit à la relation:

$$\frac{\partial(\varrho_0 V)}{\partial y} + \frac{\partial(\varrho_0 W)}{\partial z} = 0 \tag{38}$$

which is not exactly right but is consistent with the Boussinesq approximation. Then we obtain

Bien qu'elle ne soit pas tout à fait exacte, cette expression est compatible avec la relation approchée de Boussinesq. Nous obtenons ensuite:

$$\psi_z = f_y, \quad \psi_y = \lambda^{-2} f_z \tag{39}$$

which allows us to compute ψ once f is known. For instance, if $n = 2$ and $m = 0$ in Eq. (35), we have (since $f - f_0$ and $\alpha = \alpha_0$ for two-dimensional flow), from Eq. (19),

Ainsi, connaissant f, nous pouvons calculer ψ. Si, par exemple, $n = 2$ et $m = 0$ dans l'équation (35), il vient de l'équation (19) (puisque, pour l'écoulement plan, $f - f_0$ et $\alpha = \alpha_0$):

$$f = 2yz$$

From Eq. (39) it follows then

Et d'après l'équation (39):

$$\psi = y^2 + z^2 - 1 \tag{40}$$

the constant of integration -1 is to make $\psi = 0$ on the circle.

Similarly, if $n = 3$ and $m = 0$ in Eq. (35),

Avec cette constante d'intégration égale à -1, on a $\psi = 0$ sur le cercle. De même, si $n = 3$ et $m = 0$ dans l'équation (35):

$$\psi = y(y^2 + z^2 - 1) \tag{41}$$

if $n = 3$ and $m = 1$ in Eq. (34),

Si $n = 3$ et $m = 1$ dans l'équation (34):

$$\psi = z(y^2 + z^2 - 1) \qquad (42)$$

and if $n = 4$ and $m = 1$ in Eq. (34),

Enfin, si $n = 4$ et $m = 1$ dans l'équation (34):

$$\psi = yz(y^2 + z^2 - 1) \qquad (43)$$

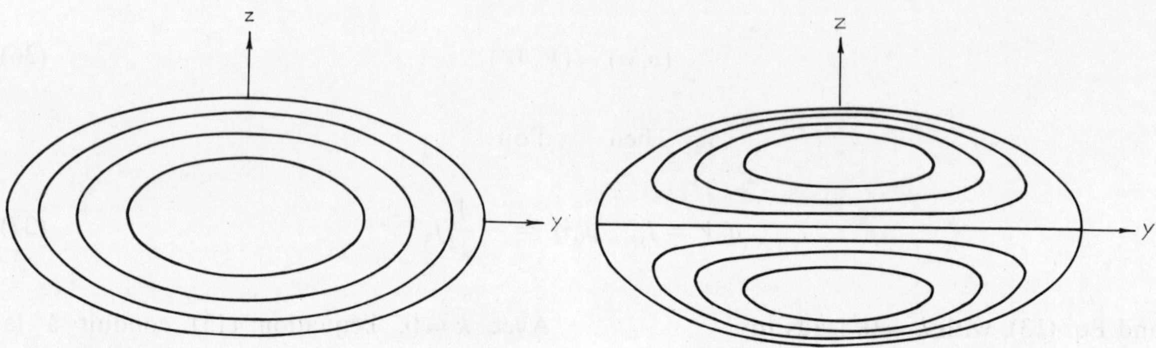

Fig. 1. Streamline pattern for two-dimensional sloshing mode of internal-wave motion in an elliptic channel, with the ratio of semi-axes equal to $\frac{1}{2}$. The stream function is given by Eq. (40a), and the interval for ψ is -0.25.

Schémas d'écoulement dans une conduite de section elliptique. Propagation d'ondes planes, en régime de clapotis sloshing mode. Rapport des demi-axes de l'ellipse: $\frac{1}{2}$. Fonction de courant selon l'équation (40a) intervalle de ψ: $-0,25$.

Fig. 3. Streamline pattern for two-dimensional sloshing mode of internal-wave motion in an elliptic channel, with the ratio of semi-axes equal to $\frac{1}{2}$. The stream function is given by Eq. (42a), and the interval for ψ is -0.1.

Schémas d'écoulement dans une conduite de section elliptique. Propagation d'ondes planes, en régime de clapotsis sloshing mode. Rapport des demi-axes de l'ellipse: $\frac{1}{2}$. Fonction de courant selon l'équation (42a) intervalle de ψ: $-0,1$.

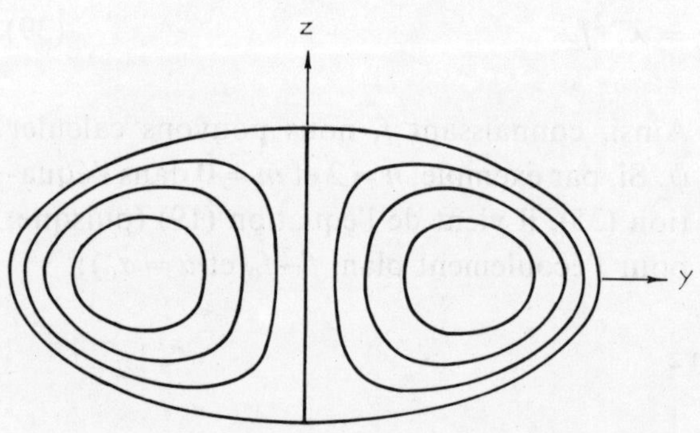

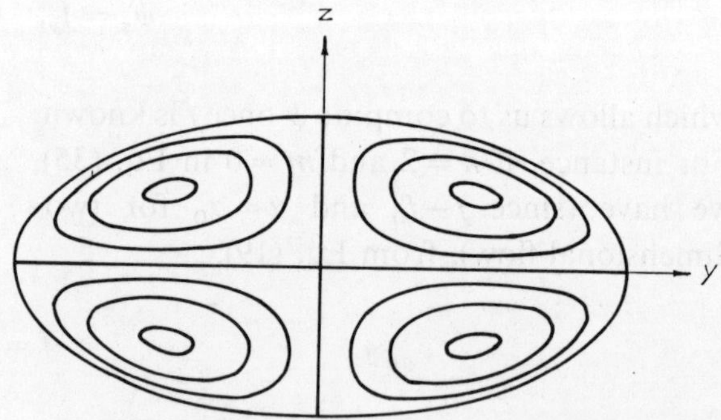

Fig. 2. Streamline pattern for two-dimensional sloshing mode of internal-wave motion in an elliptic channel, with the ratio of semi-axes equal to $\frac{1}{2}$. The stream function is given by Eq. (41a), and the interval for ψ is -0.1.

Schémas d'écoulement dans une conduite de section elliptique. Propagation d'ondes planes, en régime de clapotis sloshing mode. Rapport des demi-axes de l'ellipse: $\frac{1}{2}$. Fonction de courant selon l'équation (41a) intervalle de ψ: $-0,1$.

Fig. 4. Streamline pattern for two-dimensional sloshing mode of internal-wave motion in an elliptic channel, with the ratio of semi-axes equal to $\frac{1}{2}$. The stream function is given by Eq. (43a), and the interval for ψ is -0.04.

Schémas d'écoulement dans une conduite de section elliptique. Propagation d'ondes planes, en régime de clapotis sloshing mode. Rapport des demi-axes de l'ellipse: $\frac{1}{2}$. Fonction de courant selon l'équation (43a) intervalle de ψ: $-0,04$.

For an ellipse, we can use Eq. (15) to obtain the stream functions corresponding to Eq. (40) to (43). These are:

Pour une ellipse, l'équation (15) nous permet de déterminer la fonction de courant correspondant aux équations (40) à (43). Elles sont:

$$\psi = y^2 + \frac{z^2}{c^2} - 1 \tag{40a}$$

$$\psi = y\left(y^2 + \frac{z^2}{c^2} - 1\right) \tag{41a}$$

$$\psi = \frac{z}{c}\left(y^2 + \frac{z^2}{c^2} - 1\right) \tag{42a}$$

$$\psi = \frac{yz}{c}\left(y^2 + \frac{z^2}{c^2} - 1\right) \tag{43a}$$

in which c is the semi-axis in the z-direction divided by the semi-axis in the y-direction. The flow patterns represented by Eqs. (40a) to (43a) are shown in Figs. 1 to 4. It should be kept in mind that the motion is not steady but oscillatory. When waves propagate in the x-direction, one can visualize the motion by superposing the flow patterns in Figs. 1 to 4 on a three-dimensional flow sinusoidally varying with x.

dans lesquelles c est le quotient du demi-axe dans la direction z par celui dans la direction y. Les figures 1 à 4 présentent les schémas d'écoulement définis par les équations (40a) à (43a). Il ne faut pas oublier que le mouvement n'est pas permanent, mais oscillatoire. Lorsque les ondes se propagent dans la direction x, il est possible de se faire une image du mouvement de celles-ci en superposant les schémas d'écoulement des figures 1 à 4 sur un écoulement spatial dont les variations obéissent à une loi sinusoïdale en fonction de x.

Acknowledgments

This work has been jointly sponsored by the National Science Foundation and the Office of Naval Research.

Remerciements

La présente étude a été patronnée par la „National Science Foundation" et le „Office of Naval Research", auxquels organismes l'Auteur tient à faire part de ses plus sincères remerciements.

References **Bibliographie**

Barcilon, V. 1968, Axi-symmetric inertial oscillations of a rotating ring of fluid, Mathematika **15**, pp. 93–102.
Dubreil-Jacotin, M. L. 1932, Sur les ondes de type permanent dans les liquides hétérogènes. Atti Accad. Lincei, Rend. Cl. Sci. Fis. Mat. Nat. (6), 15, 814–819.
Hoiland, E. 1962, Geofys, Pub. **24**, p. 211.
Lamb, H. 1932, Hydrodynamics, Sixth Edition, Cambridge University Press.
McLachlan, N. W. 1947, Theory and Applications of Mathieu Functions, Oxford.
Stokes, G. G. 1846, Brit. Ass. Rep. 1846 (see Lamb 1932, p. 447).
Yih, C.-S. 1965, Dynamics of Nonhomogeneous Fluids, MacMillan, New York.
Yih, C.-S. 1966, Note on edge waves in a stratified fluid, J. Fluid Mech. 24, 765–767.

J. Fluid Mech. (1976), *vol.* 74, *part* 1, *pp.* 183–192

Internal waves in a circular channel

By W. H. YANG AND CHIA-SHUN YIH

Department of Applied Mechanics and Engineering Science,
University of Michigan, Ann Arbor

(Received 29 May 1975)

The frequencies of the first four sloshing internal wave modes in two superposed
fluid layers contained in a circular channel are calculated for two positions of
the free surface and for various ratios of the depths of the two layers. Flow patterns
are given for the first four sloshing modes for the case in which the fluids occupy
a semicircular space and the depth of the upper layer is one-quarter of the radius.

It is hoped that the results obtained will provide a guide for estimating the
frequencies of sloshing internal wave modes in long lakes.

1. Introduction

It is well known that exact solutions for water waves in channels of variable
depth are extremely few (Lamb 1932, pp. 442–450). For internal waves in superposed layers each of uniform density, no exact solutions are known if the depth
of the container is not uniform except the edge-wave solutions given by Yih
(1965, p. 57; 1966).

Internal waves occupy an important position in limnology, since lakes are
thermally stratified most of the time. Limnologists generally use a model consisting of two superposed layers, each homogeneous in itself, to approximate the
actual distribution of temperature and density. But, as stated above, nonuniformity of depth always presents difficulties surmountable only by resorting
to numerical computations.

In order to provide some guide for limnologists we have carried out calculations of the frequencies of the first four sloshing internal wave modes in two
superposed fluid layers in a circular channel (see figure 1) for different ratios of
the depths of the layers and for two positions of the free surface. Also, the flow
patterns for the first four sloshing modes are given for the case when the fluids
occupy a semicircular space and the depth of the upper layer is one-quarter of
the radius of the channel.

The frequencies for the cases of an extremely shallow upper or lower layer
have been obtained analytically by adapting the solutions of Budiansky (1960)
for a homogeneous fluid to the present case. All the other calculations are
numerical ones carried out by replacing the differential system governing internal
waves by linear algebraic equations.

W. H. Yang and C.-S. Yih

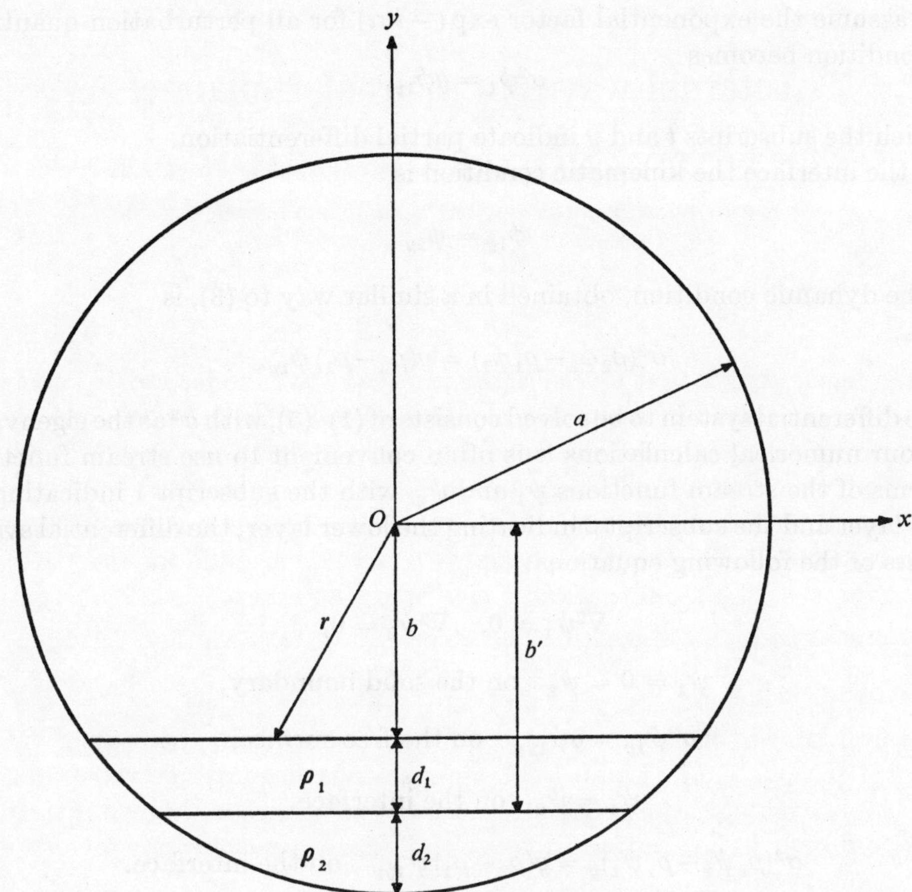

FIGURE 1. Definition sketch.

2. The differential system

We shall denote the density of the upper fluid by ρ_1 and that of the lower fluid by ρ_2. Since each layer is homogeneous, we shall assume the flow in each layer to be irrotational, and denote the velocity potential for the upper layer by ϕ_1 and that for the lower layer by ϕ_2.

Then

$$\nabla^2\phi_1 = 0, \quad \nabla^2\phi_2 = 0, \tag{1}$$

where

$$\nabla^2 = \partial^2/\partial x^2 + \partial^2/\partial y^2,$$

x and y being Cartesian co-ordinates, with y measured in the vertical direction. The condition at the solid boundary of the channel is, for either layer,

$$\partial\phi/\partial n = 0, \tag{2}$$

where n is measured in a direction normal to the boundary.

At the free surface the pressure is constant. By combining the kinematic condition with the Bernoulli equation we get the free-surface condition

$$\partial^2\phi_1/\partial t^2 + g\,\partial\phi_1/\partial y = 0.$$

If we assume the exponential factor $\exp(-i\sigma t)$ for all perturbation quantities, this condition becomes

$$\sigma^2 \phi_1 = g\phi_{1y}, \tag{3}$$

in which the subscripts t and y indicate partial differentiation.

On the interface the kinematic condition is

$$\phi_{1y} = \phi_{2y} \tag{4}$$

and the dynamic condition, obtained in a similar way to (3), is

$$\sigma^2(\rho_2\phi_2 - \rho_1\phi_1) = g(\rho_2 - \rho_1)\,\phi_{1y}. \tag{5}$$

The differential system to be solved consists of (1)–(5), with σ^2 as the eigenvalue.

In our numerical calculations it is often convenient to use stream functions. In terms of the stream functions ψ_1 and ψ_2, with the subscript 1 indicating the upper layer and the subscript 2 indicating the lower layer, the differential system consists of the following equations:

$$\nabla^2\psi_1 = 0, \quad \nabla^2\psi_2 = 0, \tag{6}$$

$$\psi_1 = 0 = \psi_2 \quad \text{on the solid boundary,} \tag{7}$$

$$\sigma^2\psi_{1y} = g\psi_{1yy} \quad \text{on the free surface,} \tag{8}$$

$$\psi_1 = \psi_2 \quad \text{on the interface,} \tag{9}$$

$$\sigma^2(\rho_2\psi_2 - \rho_1\psi_1)_y = g(\rho_2 - \rho_1)\,\psi_{1yy} \quad \text{on the interface.} \tag{10}$$

Conditions (8) and (10) are obtained by differentiating (3) and (5) with respect to x and using the Cauchy–Riemann equations, and (9) follows directly from (4) on using the Cauchy–Riemann equations.

3. Asymptotic solutions for the special cases in which one layer is extremely thin

We shall give some exact results for the extreme cases in which either the upper layer or the lower layer is exceedingly thin, which cannot be conveniently solved by numerical computation. These results will provide some check on the trend of the numerical results and some guidance as to the curves representing them. For internal waves the free surface can be considered fixed.

For the case of an extremely thin upper layer, when the maximum total depth is fixed, the result is simply that for *internal* waves

$$\sigma = 0.$$

The reasoning is briefly as follows. Compare the case with the case of internal waves in a rectangular channel with the total depth equal to the maximum total depth in the circular channel, the upper-layer depth exactly equal to that for the case under consideration and the width equal to the width of the interface.

The σ for the circular channel can be shown to be less (Yih 1975) than that for the rectangular channel, for the interfaces are of the same width, the excess area occupied by the thin upper fluid in the circular channel over that in the rect-angular channel is negligibly small, whereas the domain of the lower fluid in the rectangular channel contains that in the circular channel. For *internal* waves in the rectangular channel the upper surface can be taken as flat, and the frequency is given, after a simple calculation using (1), (2), (4) and (5), by

$$\sigma^2 = g_1' \tanh k d_1,$$

where d_1 is the depth of the upper fluid,

$$g_1' = (\Delta\rho/\rho_1)g, \quad \Delta\rho = \rho_2 - \rho_1$$

and
$$k = (2n+1)\pi/b \quad \text{or} \quad 2n\pi/b,$$

b being the width of the rectangular channel and n a positive integer. It is clear then that the σ for the rectangular channel approaches zero as d_1 approaches zero, and *a fortiori* the σ for the circular channel must approach zero. This calculation also illustrates the well-known fact that when either layer is thin we can replace g by $g\Delta\rho/(\rho$ for the thin layer), and ignore the existence of the deep layer. This fact will be recalled when we calculate σ for the case of a thin lower layer in the following paragraphs.

For the case of an extremely thin lower layer, we note first that, as has been mentioned, when the lower layer is very thin the frequency of any internal wave mode is the same as that of the corresponding free-surface wave mode for a single layer (the thin lower layer), as though the upper fluid did not exist, if g is changed to

$$g' = \frac{\rho_2 - \rho_1}{\rho_2} g. \tag{11}$$

Thus to find the σ for the case of a very thin lower layer, we need to find only the σ for free-surface waves on that layer, but with g replaced by g'.

For the first sloshing mode, we take

$$\phi_2 = \theta = -\arctan(x/y),$$

which satisfies (11) and (12). On the free surface, where $y = -b'$, we have, after some simple calculations and using (3), with ϕ_2 replacing ϕ_1,

$$\sigma^2 = g'/b',$$

if terms $O[(x/b')^3]$ are neglected. Note that x'/b is small if the lower layer is thin, or $a - b' \ll a = $ radius of circular channel. In the limit,

$$\sigma^2 = g'/a. \tag{12}$$

Solutions for higher modes can be obtained similarly. But the solutions for the modes can also all be obtained at once by adapting Budiansky's solutions for a single thin layer, by merely replacing his g by our g'. The long-wave equation used by Budiansky becomes, after replacement of ϕ_2 by ϕ and g by g',

$$\frac{\partial}{\partial x}(h_2\phi_x) + \frac{\sigma^2}{g'}\phi = 0, \tag{13}$$

where $\quad h_2 = (a^2 - x^2)^{\frac{1}{2}} - b' \doteq (a - b') - x^2/2a.$

With $\xi^2 = 2a(a-b')\,x^2$, (13) can be written as

$$\frac{\partial}{\partial \xi}[(1 - \xi^2)\,\phi_\xi] + \frac{2a\sigma^2}{g'}\phi = 0, \tag{14}$$

which is Legendre's equation. In order not to have any singularities at $\xi^2 = 1$, it is necessary that

$$2\sigma^2 a/g' = n(n+1), \tag{15}$$

n being an integer representing the mode. For $n = 1$, (15) gives (12), as expected.

4. Algebraic method for the numerical solutions

When the differential system (1)–(5) is discretized by either a finite-difference or a finite-element method, it reduces to an algebraic eigenvalue problem approximating the original equations, but not the standard algebraic eigenvalue problem

$$\mathbf{Ax} = \lambda\mathbf{x}. \tag{16}$$

It is possible to reduce the differential system only to

$$\mathbf{Ax} = \lambda\mathbf{Bx}, \tag{17}$$

where $\mathbf{A}$ and $\mathbf{B}$ are constant matrices and λ and $\mathbf{x}$ denote the eigenvalues and eigenvectors, respectively. When the variables on the free surface and interface are eliminated, the algebraic eigenvalue problem takes the form

$$\mathbf{N}(\lambda)\,\mathbf{x} = 0, \tag{18}$$

where the eigenvalue λ appears nonlinearly in the elements of the matrix $\mathbf{N}$. The dimension of $\mathbf{N}$ is smaller than that of $\mathbf{A}$. Such an eigenvalue problem has been studied recently (Kublanovskaya 1970). Efficient algorithms are just being developed for its solution.

For the algebraic formulation, subscripts are reserved for vector and matrix components. We shall denote the velocity potential in the domain D_1 of the lighter fluid by $\phi^{(1)}(x,y,t)$ and that in the domain D_2 of the heavier fluid by $\phi^{(2)}(x,y,t)$. For convenience in a parametric analysis for the various locations of the interface to be considered in this study, a regular grid with a constant mesh is most desirable. As a result, the finite-difference method with a constant mesh size H is used, with linear interpolation for the curved boundaries.

Let $\boldsymbol{\phi}_F^{(1)}$, a vector, be the projection of the potential function on the free surface in the approximating finite-dimensional space and $\boldsymbol{\phi}_1^{(1)}, \boldsymbol{\phi}_2^{(1)}, ..., \boldsymbol{\phi}_m^{(1)}$ be the vector representations of the potential function in D_1 at consecutive levels of the grid downwards from the free surface. Let $\boldsymbol{\phi}_I^{(1)}$ and $\boldsymbol{\phi}_I^{(2)}$ represent the potential

 W. H. Yang and C.-S. Yih

functions on the interface, and $\phi_1^{(2)}, \phi_2^{(2)}, \ldots, \phi_n^{(2)}$ represent the potential function in D_2 at consecutive grid levels downwards from the interface. With the condition at the container's boundary taken into consideration, the algebraic system of equations approximating (1) and (2) may be written in the matrix form

$$
\begin{bmatrix}
\mathbf{A}_F\,\mathbf{A}_{11}\,\mathbf{A}_{12} & & & & \\
& \mathbf{A}_{21}\,\mathbf{A}_{22}\,\mathbf{A}_{23} & & & \\
& \cdots\ \cdots\ \cdots & & & \\
& \mathbf{A}_{m,m-1}\,\mathbf{A}_{m,m}\,\mathbf{A}_I & & & \\
& & \mathbf{B}_I\,\mathbf{B}_{11}\,\mathbf{B}_{12} & & \\
& & \mathbf{B}_{21}\,\mathbf{B}_{22}\,\mathbf{B}_{23} & & \\
& & \cdots\ \cdots\ \cdots & & \\
& & & \mathbf{B}_{n,n-1}\,\mathbf{B}_{n,n}
\end{bmatrix}
\begin{pmatrix}
\phi_F^{(1)} \\
\phi_1^{(1)} \\
\vdots \\
\phi_m^{(1)} \\
\phi_I^{(1)} \\
\phi_I^{(2)} \\
\phi_1^{(2)} \\
\vdots \\
\phi_n^{(2)}
\end{pmatrix}
= 0, \qquad (19)
$$

where the $\mathbf{A}$'s and $\mathbf{B}$'s with different subscripts are constant matrices of dimensions compatible with that of the ϕ's, and the blanks in the global matrix denote zero entries.

The approximate algebraic form of the free-surface condition (3) is

$$
\phi_F^{(1)} = (1-\lambda)^{-1}\,\phi_1^{(1)}, \qquad (20)
$$

where

$$
\lambda = (H/g)\,\sigma^2.
$$

The interface continuity conditions (4) and (5) can be reduced to

$$
\begin{pmatrix} \phi_I^{(1)} \\ \phi_I^{(2)} \end{pmatrix} = \frac{1}{\lambda\delta(1+\gamma)-1}
\begin{bmatrix} \lambda\delta\gamma - 1 & \lambda\delta\gamma \\ \lambda\delta & \lambda\delta - 1 \end{bmatrix}
\begin{pmatrix} \phi_m^{(1)} \\ \phi_1^{(2)} \end{pmatrix}, \qquad (21)
$$

where

$$
\delta = \rho_1/(\rho_2-\rho_1), \quad \gamma = \rho_2/\rho_1.
$$

After the use of (20) and (21) the matrix equation (19) can be rearranged to give

$$
\begin{bmatrix}
\mathbf{A}_{11}' & \mathbf{A}_{12} & & & \\
& \mathbf{A}_{21}\,\mathbf{A}_{22}\,\mathbf{A}_{23} & & & \\
& \cdots\ \cdots\ \cdots & & & \\
& \mathbf{A}_{m,m-1}\,(\mathbf{A}_{m,m}+g_1\mathbf{A}_I)\,g_2\mathbf{A}_I & & \\
& g_3\mathbf{B}_I\quad(\mathbf{B}_{11}+g_4\mathbf{B}_I)\,\mathbf{B}_{12} & & \\
& \cdots\ \cdots\ \cdots & & \\
& & \mathbf{B}_{n,n-1}\,\mathbf{B}_{n,n}
\end{bmatrix}
\begin{pmatrix}
\phi_1^{(1)} \\
\vdots \\
\phi_m^{(1)} \\
\phi_1^{(2)} \\
\vdots \\
\phi_n^{(2)}
\end{pmatrix}
= 0, \qquad (22)
$$

where g_1, g_2, g_3 and g_4 are functions of λ:

$$
\left.
\begin{aligned}
& g_1(\lambda) = (\lambda\delta\gamma - 1)/g(\lambda), \quad g_2(\lambda) = \lambda\delta\gamma/g(\lambda), \\
& g_3(\lambda) = \lambda\delta/g(\lambda), \quad g_4(\lambda) = (\lambda\delta - 1)/g(\lambda), \\
& g(\lambda) = (1+\gamma)\lambda\delta - 1, \quad \mathbf{A}_{11}' = \mathbf{A}_{11} + (1+\lambda)^{-1}\mathbf{A}_F.
\end{aligned}
\right\} \qquad (23)
$$

Equation (22) has the form of the general eigenvalue problem given in (18). We shall thus write (22) in the compact notation

$$
\mathbf{N}(\lambda)\,\phi = 0. \qquad (24)
$$

This equation is solved by an iterative method (Yang 1975). For a given estimate of the eigenvalue λ, we seek an improvement $\mu = \Delta\lambda$ satisfying

$$\det\left(\mathbf{N}(\lambda+\mu)\right) = 0. \tag{25}$$

μ is obviously a function of λ. This function can be expressed as

$$\mu(\lambda) = -\left(\operatorname{tr}\left(\mathbf{L}^{-1}\mathbf{P}\mathbf{N}'\mathbf{U}^{-1}\right)\right)^{-1}, \tag{26}$$

where the matrices $\mathbf{P}$, $\mathbf{L}$ and $\mathbf{U}$ are permutation, lower-triangular and upper-triangular matrices, respectively. They are the $\mathbf{LU}$ decomposition (Forsythe & Moler 1967, p. 36) of $\mathbf{N}(\lambda)$ such that $\mathbf{N}(\lambda) = \mathbf{P}^{\mathrm{T}}\mathbf{LU}$ and

$$\mathbf{N}'(\lambda) = d\mathbf{N}(\lambda)/d\lambda.$$

$\operatorname{tr}(\ )$ denotes the trace of a matrix.

The improved estimate of the eigenvalue is given by

$$\lambda_{k+1} = \lambda_k + \mu(\lambda_k), \quad k = 0, 1, 2, \ldots. \tag{27}$$

The condition for and properties of convergence of this iteration procedure are known (Yang 1975).

We are interested in only the first (smallest) few eigenvalues. The first four eigenvalues and the associated eigenvectors were calculated and plotted in the form of contours of equal potential and the orthogonal set of streamlines. The streamlines were calculated from the Cauchy–Riemann conditions. A more accurate solution for the streamlines may be obtained from the formulation in terms of the stream function. The equi-potentials and streamlines for the first four modes are shown in figures 2(a)–(d).

It is noted that, for all four modes, the free-surface velocity is nearly horizontal. The largest amplitudes of the waves as well as the kinetic energy are concentrated about the interface. Since the amplitude of surface waves is small for low frequencies, we may approximate the free surface by a rigid surface. Such an approximation further simplifies the algebraic equation (19). Now, only the equations involving the interface contain the eigenvalue. If the stream function is used in the formulation, the differential system (6)–(10) reduces to the approximate algebraic representation

$$\begin{bmatrix} \mathbf{C}_{11} & \mathbf{C}_{12} \\ \mathbf{C}_{21} & \mathbf{C}_{22} & \mathbf{C}_{23} \\ & \cdots & \cdots & \cdots \\ & & \mathbf{C}_{m,m-1} & \mathbf{C}_{m,m} & \mathbf{C}_I \\ & & & \mathbf{D}_I & \mathbf{D}_{11} & \mathbf{D}_{12} \\ & & & & \mathbf{D}_{21} & \mathbf{D}_{22} & \mathbf{D}_{23} \\ & & & & & \cdots & \cdots & \cdots \\ & & & & & & \mathbf{D}_{n,n-1} & \mathbf{D}_{n,n} \end{bmatrix} \begin{pmatrix} \boldsymbol{\psi}_1^{(1)} \\ \vdots \\ \boldsymbol{\psi}_m^{(1)} \\ \boldsymbol{\psi}_I \\ \boldsymbol{\psi}_1^{(2)} \\ \vdots \\ \boldsymbol{\psi}_n^{(2)} \end{pmatrix} = 0, \tag{28}$$

where the $\mathbf{C}$'s and $\mathbf{D}$'s are constant matrices and $\boldsymbol{\psi}_1^{(1)}, \ldots, \boldsymbol{\psi}_m^{(1)}$ are vectors representing the stream function at different levels of the finite-difference grid in the domain D_1. $\boldsymbol{\psi}_I$ approximates the interface stream function and $\boldsymbol{\psi}_1^{(2)}, \ldots, \boldsymbol{\psi}_n^{(2)}$ represent the stream function in the domain D_2.

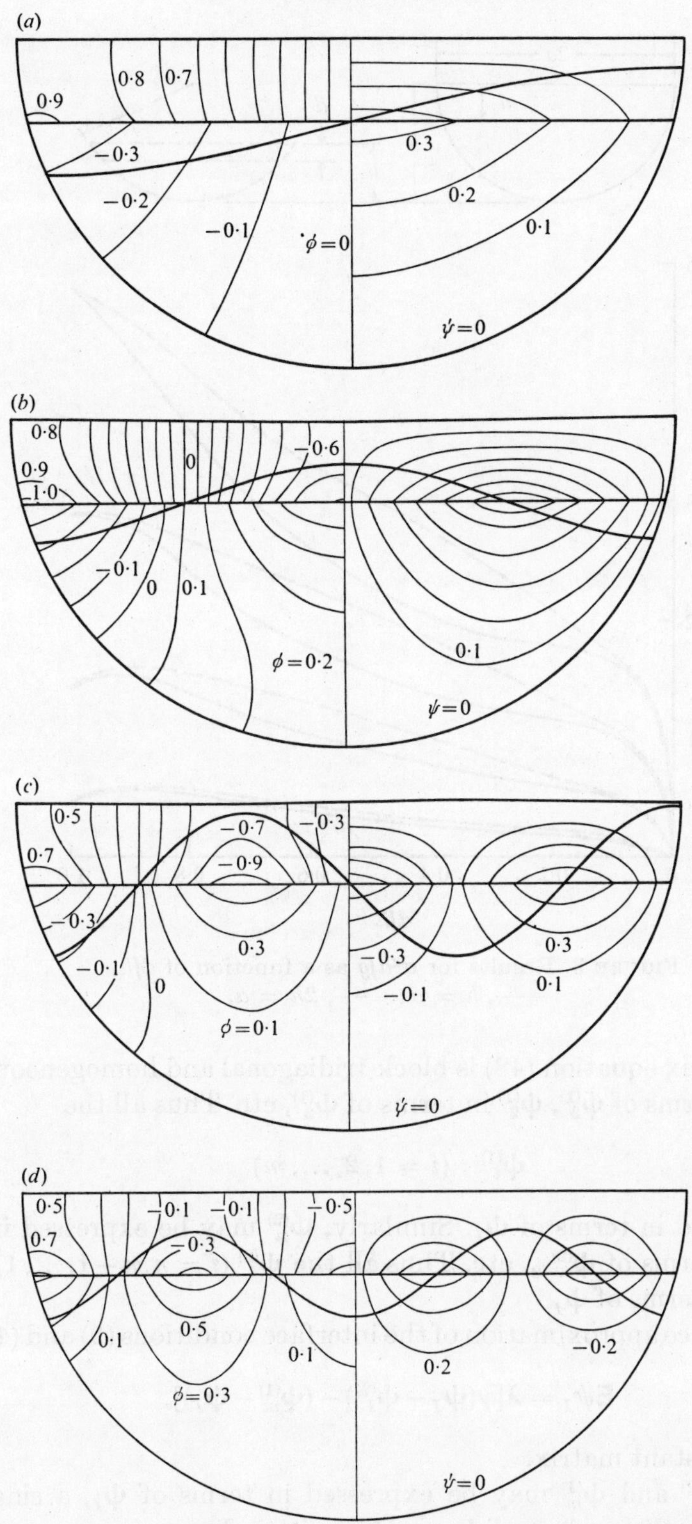

FIGURE 2. Flow patterns for the first four sloshing internal wave modes. The free surface is not assumed flat. The height of the interface is exaggerated. (a) First mode, $\sigma^2 a/g = 0.0152$; contour intervals for the stream function ψ and velocity potential ϕ 0·1 throughout. (b) Second mode, $\sigma^2 a/g = 0.0465$; contour intervals 0·1. (c) Third mode, $\sigma^2 a/g = 0.794$; contour intervals 0·2. (d) Fourth mode, $\sigma^2 a/g = 0.10843$; contour intervals 0·2.

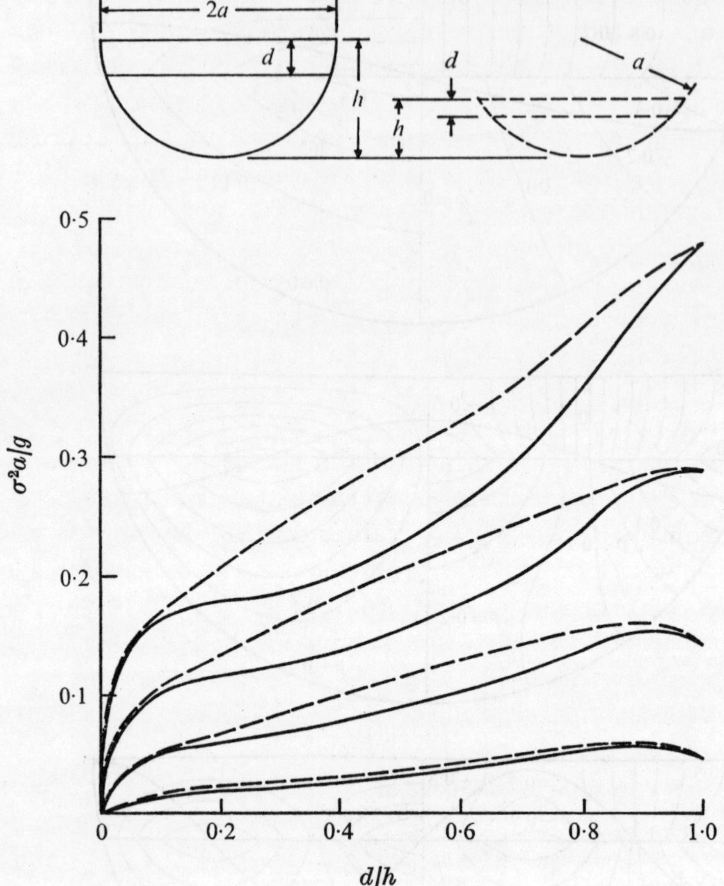

FIGURE 3. Results for $\sigma^2 a/g$ as a function of d/h.
——, $h = a$; – – –, $2h = a$.

Since the matrix equation (48) is block-tridiagonal and homogeneous, we may express $\boldsymbol{\psi}_1^{(1)}$ in terms of $\boldsymbol{\psi}_2^{(1)}$, $\boldsymbol{\psi}_2^{(1)}$ in terms of $\boldsymbol{\psi}_3^{(1)}$, etc. Thus all the

$$\boldsymbol{\psi}_i^{(1)} \quad (i = 1, 2, ..., m)$$

may be expressed in terms of $\boldsymbol{\psi}_I$. Similarly, $\boldsymbol{\psi}_n^{(2)}$ may be expressed in terms of $\boldsymbol{\psi}_{n-1}^{(2)}$, $\boldsymbol{\psi}_{n-1}^{(2)}$ in terms of $\boldsymbol{\psi}_{n-2}^{(2)}$, etc. Thus all the $\boldsymbol{\psi}_i^{(2)}$ $(i = n, n-1, ..., 1)$ may also be expressed in terms of $\boldsymbol{\psi}_I$.

Finite-difference approximation of the interface conditions (9) and (10) leads to

$$\mathbf{E}\psi_I = \lambda[\gamma(\boldsymbol{\psi}_I - \boldsymbol{\psi}_1^{(2)}) - (\boldsymbol{\psi}_m^{(1)} - \boldsymbol{\psi}_I)], \tag{29}$$

where $\mathbf{E}$ is a constant matrix.

Since both $\boldsymbol{\psi}_1^{(2)}$ and $\boldsymbol{\psi}_m^{(1)}$ may be expressed in terms of $\boldsymbol{\psi}_I$, a single matrix equation with the dimensions of $\boldsymbol{\psi}_I$ can be written down:

$$\mathbf{E}\boldsymbol{\psi}_I = \lambda\mathbf{F}\boldsymbol{\psi}_I, \tag{30}$$

where $\mathbf{F}$ is a composite matrix made up of the $\mathbf{C}$'s and $\mathbf{D}$'s.

192   *W. H. Yang and C.-S. Yih*

The advantage of this approximate formulation is obvious. It involves small dimensions and a standard form of algebraic eigenvalue problem for which efficient subroutines are readily available in every major computing centre. As expected, the solutions differ little from those of the original problem with a free surface at low frequencies. The economy provided by this approximation enabled an extended parametric analysis for various depth ratios of the two layers. The program developed here should be a very efficient tool for studying internal waves in superposed liquid layers in arbitrarily shaped containers. The frequencies of the first four modes for a circular container for various ratios of the depths of the two layers are presented in figure 3 for two positions of the free surface.

5. Results

As mentioned before, we have considered the cases $h = a$ and $h = \frac{1}{2}a$, with $\rho_2/\rho_1 = 1\cdot05$. For each case the numerical calculation was carried out for several values of d/h from $0\cdot10$ to $0\cdot90$. The values of $\sigma^2 a/g$ are shown in figure 3, in which the curves were extrapolated from zero to $0\cdot10$ and from $0\cdot90$ to $1\cdot00$.

We note that, if the Boussinesq approximation is used, approximate values of $\sigma^2 a/g$ for other density ratios can be obtained from figure 3 by multiplying the values given therein by $21(\rho_2 - \rho_1)/\rho_2$.

We note that for the first sloshing mode $\sigma^2 a/g$ varies but little with h/a.

This work has been jointly supported by the National Science Foundation and the Office of Naval Research.

REFERENCES

BUDIANSKY, B. 1960 Sloshing of liquids in circular canals and spherical tanks. *J. Aerospace Sci.* **27**, 161–173.

FORSYTHE, G. & MOLER, C. B. 1967 *Computer Solution of Linear Algebraic Systems.* Prentice-Hall.

KUBLANOVSKAYA, V. N. 1970 *SIAM J. Numer. Anal.* **7**, no. 4, 1970.

LAMB, H. 1932 *Hydrodynamics*, 6th edn. Cambridge University Press.

YANG, W. H. 1975 A method for eigenvalues of λ-matrices. *University of Michigan, AMES Rep.* no. 1702.

YIH, C.-S. 1965 *Dynamics of Nonhomogeneous Fluids.* Macmillan.

YIH, C.-S. 1966 Note on edge waves in a stratified fluid. *J. Fluid Mech.* **24**, 765–767.

YIH, C.-S. 1975 Comparison theorems for water waves in basins of variable depth. *Quart. Appl. Math.* To be published.

J. Fluid Mech. (1981), *vol.* 108, *pp.* 241–246

Similarity of steady stratified flows

By CHIA-SHUN YIH

The University of Michigan, Ann Arbor, Michigan 48109

(Received 30 April 1980)

Steady flows of an incompressible, inviscid, and non-diffusive fluid of variable density in a gravitational field are first considered. By a transformation it is shown conclusively that there are infinitely many flows with the same flow pattern, provided the density gradients of these flows at any section (e.g. far upstream) differ only by a multiplicative constant. These flows have identical local internal Froude numbers at all corresponding points of the flows and, hence, identical local Richardson numbers. They are therefore dynamically similar. Every time a solution for one stratification is obtained, one has in fact obtained the solutions for infinitely many stratifications.

The creation of vorticity in steady stratified flows is then examined, and it is shown that this creation can be divided into two parts, one part being entirely due to the inertial effect and the other originating from the gravity effect of density variation.

Finally, compressibility is considered and the results on similarity of stratified flows and on vorticity and circulation are extended to apply to steady flows of gases stratified in entropy.

---

1. Similarity of steady stratified flows of an incompressible fluid

For an incompressible and non-diffusive fluid stratified in density, the equation of incompressibility is

$$D\rho/Dt = 0, \tag{1}$$

where, since only steady flows are considered,

$$D/Dt = u_\alpha \partial/\partial x_\alpha. \tag{2}$$

In (1) and (2), ρ is the density, x_1, x_2, and x_3 are Cartesian co-ordinates, and u_1, u_2, and u_3 are the corresponding velocity components. The summation convention is used in (2). The equation of continuity is, by virtue of (1),

$$\partial u_i/\partial x_i = 0. \tag{3}$$

If the fluid is also assumed inviscid, the equations of motion are

$$\rho u_\alpha \, \partial u_i/\partial x_\alpha = -\partial p/\partial x_i - g\rho\delta_{i3} \quad (i = 1, 2, 3), \tag{4}$$

where p is the pressure, g is the gravitational acceleration acting in the direction of decreasing x_3, and δ_{i3} is the Kronecker delta.

Let the density be put in the form

$$\rho = \rho_0 + \rho_1(x_1, x_2, x_3), \tag{5}$$

242   *C.-S. Yih*

where ρ_0 is a constant, and consider another stratified fluid with the density distribution

$$\hat{\rho} = \hat{\rho}_0 + \hat{\rho}_1(\hat{x}_1, \hat{x}_2, \hat{x}_3), \tag{6}$$

where $\hat{\rho}_0$ is another constant and the circumflexes on the x's denote the co-ordinates for the flow with density $\hat{\rho}$. Since two flows can be similar only if the geometry of the boundaries are similar, we denote the length scales of the two flows by L and $\hat{L}$, and write

$$m = \hat{L}/L. \tag{7}$$

A point in the flow with length scale L is said to be corresponding to a point in the flow with length scale $\hat{L}$ if the dimensionless co-ordinates (measured in units of L or $\hat{L}$) of the two points are identical. For dynamical similarity to exist, we must have

$$\hat{\rho}_1/\rho_1 = r \tag{8}$$

at corresponding points of the two flows, r being a positive constant.

The question is then posed: Can a flow have the density distribution ρ and be similar to a given flow with the density distribution $\hat{\rho}$? We shall show that the answer is in the affirmative.

If the solution with distribution $\hat{\rho}$ has velocity components $\hat{u}_i$, we have

$$\hat{\rho}\hat{u}_\alpha\,\partial\hat{u}_i/\partial\hat{y}_\alpha = -\partial\hat{\pi}/\partial\hat{y}_i - \hat{L}g\hat{\rho}_1\delta_{i3}, \tag{9}$$

where

$$\hat{\pi} = \hat{p} + \hat{\rho}_0 gx_3, \quad \hat{y}_i = x_i/\hat{L}. \tag{10}$$

We also have

$$\hat{u}_\alpha\,\partial\hat{\rho}/\partial\hat{y}_\alpha = 0 \tag{11}$$

and

$$\partial\hat{u}_i/\partial\hat{y}_i = 0. \tag{12}$$

Now let (actually an arbitrary constant can be added to π or $\hat{\pi}$)

$$u_i = (\hat{\rho}/rm\rho)^{\frac{1}{2}}\hat{u}_i, \quad \pi = \hat{\pi}/rm, \quad y_i = x_i/L, \tag{13}$$

where π is defined by

$$\pi = p + \rho_0 gx_3. \tag{14}$$

Then, the first equation in (13), and (5), (6), and (8) guarantee that

$$u\,\partial\rho/\partial y_\alpha = 0, \tag{15}$$

provided (11) is satisfied. Furthermore, obviously

$$u_\alpha\,\partial\hat{\rho}/\partial y_\alpha = 0. \tag{16}$$

Equations (7), (8) and (13) allow us to write†

$$\rho u_\alpha\,\partial u_i/\partial y_\alpha = (\hat{\rho}/rm)\hat{u}_\alpha\,\partial\hat{u}_i/\partial\hat{y}_\alpha. \tag{17}$$

Thus (9) can be written as

$$rm\rho u_\alpha\,\partial u_i/\partial y_\alpha = -rm\,\partial\pi/\partial y_i - r\hat{L}g\rho_1\delta_{i3}, \tag{18}$$

---

† Remember that $y_i = \hat{y}_i$ at corresponding points, so that $\partial/\partial y_\alpha = \partial/\partial\hat{y}_\alpha$. This would be even clearer if we had used $\hat{x}_i = mx_i$.

which, after division by rm, is

$$\rho u_\alpha \, \partial u_i / \partial y_\alpha = - \partial \pi / \partial y_i - L g \rho_1 \delta_{i3}. \tag{19}$$

This is exactly (4) with the Cartesian co-ordinates in dimensionless form. Thus, if (9) is satisfied by $\hat{u}_i$ and $\hat{\pi}$, u_i and π given by (13) satisfy (19), or (4).

Also, because of (15) and (16), (3) is satisfied if (12) is. Hence we have proved what we set out to prove. The boundary conditions, if they are kinematical, are identical since the boundary geometries are identical, and, if they are dynamical (such as at density discontinuities), are also identical since dynamic boundary conditions are natural boundary conditions derivable from the differential equations. Hence the boundary conditions are satisfied by the flow (u_1, ρ, p) if they are satisfied by the flow $(\hat{u}_i, \hat{\rho}, \hat{p})$.

If we define the local internal Froude number F at any point of the flow by

$$F^2 = \rho u_\alpha u_\alpha / g |\nabla \rho| L^2 \tag{20}$$

(and similarly for the flow with density $\hat{\rho}$), and the local Richardson number Ri at any point of the flow by

$$Ri = g |\nabla \rho| / \rho |\nabla q|^2, \quad q^2 = u_\alpha u_\alpha, \tag{21}$$

(and similarly for the flow with density $\hat{\rho}$), then we can say that the two flows have identical local internal Froude numbers at corresponding points (i.e. for $y_i = \hat{y}_i$), and consequently the same local Richardson numbers at these points. The flow patterns are also similar, by virtue of the first equation in (13). The two flows are indeed similar geometrically, kinematically, and dynamically.

But since ρ_0 and r are arbitrary, we are not merely treating one flow similar to the flow $\hat{\rho}$; we are treating a doubly infinite family of flows, all of which are similar to the flow for $\hat{\rho}$, and hence to one another. This result is new, and I think it is very useful for laboratory simulation of natural phenomena. Note that density discontinuities are not ruled out. But, for similarity to exist between any two flows, they must occur at corresponding places, and, wherever they occur, their ratio must be the same constant (denoted by r in this paper). We note that when the density variation is small as compared with the mean density, the factor $(\hat{\rho}/\rho)^{\frac{1}{2}}$ in (13) can be replaced by $(\hat{\rho}_0/\rho_0)^{\frac{1}{2}}$ (and by 1 if water is used in the laboratory to model lakes or oceans), and the effect of density variation, important at low Froude numbers, is embodied in the factor r and is entirely associated with gravity.

In conclusion, to ensure similarity, the requirements expressed by (8) and the first equation in (13) must be satisfied at corresponding sections somewhere, say far upstream. Note that ρ does not have to be proportional to $\hat{\rho}$ at corresponding points.

2. Creation of vorticity in steady stratified flows of an incompressible fluid

Let ρ_0 now denote some constant reference density. We shall use the transformation (Yih 1958)

$$u_i' = (\rho/\rho_0)^{\frac{1}{2}} = u_i, \tag{22}$$

and study the creation of vorticity. With the vorticity vector ξ_i defined by

$$\boldsymbol{\xi} = \mathrm{curl}\, \mathbf{u}, \quad \boldsymbol{\xi} = (\xi_1, \xi_2, \xi_3), \quad \mathbf{u} = (u_1, u_2, u_3), \tag{23}$$

C.-S. Yih

we define the vorticity of the associated velocity $\mathbf{u}' \equiv (u_1', u_2', u_3')$, and

$$\boldsymbol{\xi}' = \operatorname{curl} \mathbf{u}'. \tag{24}$$

The Euler equations can be written as

$$\rho_0 u_\alpha' \, \partial u_i'/\partial x_\alpha = -\partial p/\partial x_i - \rho \, \partial \Omega/\partial x_i, \tag{25}$$

where Ω is the body-force potential, and the equation of continuity can be written as

$$\partial u_i'/\partial x_i = 0. \tag{26}$$

From (25) and (26), by cross-differentiation, we obtain

$$\rho_0 (\mathbf{u}' . \nabla) \boldsymbol{\xi}' = \rho_0 (\boldsymbol{\xi}' . \nabla) \mathbf{u}' - \nabla \rho \times \nabla \Omega. \tag{27}$$

The first term in (27) is the substantial derivative of the vorticity vector, the second term gives the effects of stretching and turning on the three components of $\boldsymbol{\xi}'$, so that the last term represents the rate of creation of the vorticity $\boldsymbol{\xi}'$ (or the components of it) as a result of density variation in the presence of a gravitational field. It is always a horizontal vector. The true vorticity is then created in the following two ways:

(i) by the inertial effect of the density variation, through the transformation (22); for instance, if gravity were absent, a steady flow originating from a large reservoir, where the velocity is zero, would have zero $\boldsymbol{\xi}'$, which means $\boldsymbol{\xi}$ would be created – by inertia alone if ρ is not uniform.

(ii) by the creation of $\boldsymbol{\xi}'$ by density variation in the presence of a gravitational field. In general (i.e. except for the unlikely case $\boldsymbol{\xi}' \neq 0$ but $\boldsymbol{\xi} = 0$) vorticity will be created. This creation is attributed to the action of gravity on a stratified fluid.

Note that although the pseudo-vorticity created is always horizontal, it does not necessarily remain so because of the turning of the pseudo-vorticity lines.

Since the pseudo-vorticity $\boldsymbol{\xi}'$ is associated with the pseudo-circulation Γ' defined by

$$\Gamma' = \oint u_i' \, dx_i, \tag{28}$$

we can profitably consider the rate of change of Γ' around a closed material circuit. Let D/Dt stand for the substantial derivative. Then, using (25) and

$$(D/Dt) \, dx_i = du_i, \tag{29}$$

we have

$$\frac{D}{Dt} \Gamma' = \oint \left\{ \left(-\frac{1}{\rho_0} \frac{\partial p}{\partial x_i} - \frac{\rho}{\rho_0} \frac{\partial \Omega}{\partial x_i} \right) dx_i + d(\tfrac{1}{2} u_\alpha u_\alpha) \right\} = \oint \frac{\Omega}{\rho_0} d\rho, \tag{30}$$

showing clearly that Γ' would be constant if gravity were not present, and that gravity can change the pseudo-circulation Γ' in a stratified fluid and through it change the true circulation Γ defined by

$$\Gamma = \oint u_i \, dx_i.$$

In the absence of gravity, Γ' would remain constant, but Γ would in general change with time – as a result of the inertial effect of density variation.

The creation of vorticity and circulation in a nonhomogeneous fluid is the subject of Bjerknes' theorems, of course. But since these theorems apply to unsteady flows as well as steady flows, their content is necessarily less far-reaching: they say that the creation of vorticity or circulation arises from a term containing the factor

$$\rho^{-2} \nabla p \times \nabla \rho,$$

but can say no more about the constitution of p. By restricting attention to steady flows, I have been able, in effect, to separate p into a dynamical part which accounts for the inertial effect of density variation, and a static part which accounts for the gravity effect of the constant part of the density. As a corollary of (30), we see that, if the material circuit is taken on a constant density surface,

$$D\Gamma'/Dt = 0 \quad \text{and} \quad D\Gamma/Dt = 0,$$

which implies that any vorticity created lies in the constant density surface (by the use of Stokes' theorem).

3. Extension to entropy stratification in gases

The results obtained above will now be extended to steady flows of compressible fluids stratified in entropy. We shall consider ideal gases and denote the ratio of the specific heat at constant pressure (c_p) to that at constant volume by the usual symbol γ, and we shall write, with the subscript c denoting some constant reference quantity,

$$\lambda = (\rho/\rho_c)/(p_c/p)^\gamma, \tag{31}$$

which is equal to a constant times $\exp(-S/c_p)$, S being the entropy. Since the flow is steady and heat conduction and viscous dissipation are neglected, the entropy does not change along a streamline, and we have

$$u_\alpha \, \partial\lambda/\partial x_\alpha = 0. \tag{32}$$

Again, we consider two λ-distributions:

$$\hat{\lambda} = \hat{\lambda}_0 + \hat{\lambda}_1, \tag{33}$$

$$\lambda = \lambda_0 + \lambda_1, \tag{34}$$

where the λ_0 and $\hat{\lambda}_0$ are assumed constant and

$$r = \hat{\lambda}_1/\lambda_1 \tag{35}$$

at corresponding points of the two flows, r being a positive constant. And, again, the question is posed: Can a flow have the entropy distribution given by λ and be similar to a given flow with the entropy distribution given by $\hat{\lambda}$? The answer is again in the affirmative but, instead of (13), the transformation demonstrating this is (with L, $\hat{L}$, y_i, y, and $\hat{y}_i$ retaining their meanings as before and with m given by (7))

$$u_i = (\hat{\lambda}/rm\lambda)^{\frac{1}{2}}\hat{u}_i, \quad \pi = \hat{\pi}/rm, \tag{36}$$

where π and $\hat{\pi}$ are defined by

$$\pi = \int dp/\rho' + \lambda_0 g x_3, \quad \hat{\pi} = \int d\hat{p}/\hat{\rho}' + \hat{\lambda}_0 g x_3, \tag{37}$$

and

$$\rho' = \rho/\lambda, \quad \hat{\rho}' = \hat{\rho}/\hat{\lambda}. \tag{38}$$

C.-S. Yih

The demonstration that the flow (u_i, π, λ) satisfies the equations of motion, the equation of continuity, and (32) is quite similar to the corresponding demonstration given above for incompressible fluids. It is sufficient to recall the results of Yih (1960 or 1980, p. 6). In particular, from (31),

$$\rho'/p^\gamma = \rho'_c/p^\gamma_c = \text{constant}, \tag{39}$$

so that the integrals in (37) exist.

Again, given geometrical similarity, dynamical similarity is assured if at some section far upstream (33), (34), and (35) hold, and the velocity distributions for the two flows are related according to the first equation in (36).

As to the creation of circulation and vorticity, we note that (Yih 1960), with

$$u'_i = \lambda^{\frac{1}{2}} u_i, \quad \rho' = \rho/\lambda, \quad p = p', \tag{40}$$

we have

$$\partial(\rho' u'_\alpha)/\partial x_\alpha = 0, \tag{41}$$

and

$$\rho' u'_\alpha \, \partial u'_i/\partial x_\alpha = -\partial p'/\partial x_i - g\rho\delta_{i,3}. \tag{42}$$

Since (39) is satisfied, by cross differentiation of (42) after division by ρ' we have

$$(\mathbf{u}'.\nabla)(\boldsymbol{\xi}'/\rho') = (\boldsymbol{\xi}'/\rho').\nabla\mathbf{u}' - \nabla\lambda \times \nabla\Omega, \tag{43}$$

where Ω is the body-force potential gx_3. Again, the last term is a horizontal vector, and represents the creation of pseudo-vorticity. The pseudo-vorticity, however, is not necessarily horizontal, because of the turning of the pseudo-vorticity lines.

If Γ' is again defined by (28), with u'_i given by (40), we have, instead of (30),

$$D\Gamma'/Dt = \oint \Omega \, d\lambda, \tag{44}$$

showing that $D\Gamma'/Dt$ is zero if gravity does not exist or if the material circuit along which Γ' is taken lies on a surface of constant entropy. Equation (44) shows the effect of the last term in (43), as (30) shows the effect of the last term in (27).

These are again two means of creation of true vorticity, as in the case of the incompressible fluid, and we shall not repeat the nearly identical statements.

This work has been supported by the Office of Naval Research.

REFERENCES

YIH, C.-S. 1958 On the flow of a stratified fluid. *Proc. 3rd U.S. Nat. Congr. Appl. Mech.*, pp. 857–861.

YIH, C.-S. 1960 A transformation for non-homentropic flows, with an application to large-amplitude motion in the atmosphere. *J. Fluid Mech.* **9**, 68–80.

YIH, C.-S. 1980 *Stratified Flows*. Academic.

QUARTERLY OF APPLIED MATHEMATICS
APRIL 1982

ON THE NONEXISTENCE OF SOLUTION OF A DIFFERENTIAL SYSTEM GOVERNING AXISYMMETRIC FLOW OF A STRATIFIED FLUID*

By CHIA-SHUN YIH (*The University of Michigan*)

The differential equation governing steady axisymmetric flow of an incompressible fluid was first derived by Yih [3]. If cylindrical coordinates (r, y, z) are used with z measured vertically upward, and if g denotes the gravitational acceleration, ρ denotes the density, and ρ_0 denotes a constant reference density, the equation is [3, 4, 5]

$$\frac{1}{r^2}\left(\frac{\partial^2}{\partial r^2} - \frac{1}{r}\frac{\partial}{\partial r} + \frac{\partial^2}{\partial z^2}\right)\psi' + \frac{g}{\rho_0}\frac{d\rho}{d\psi'}\, z = \frac{1}{\rho_0}\frac{dH}{d\psi'} = h(\psi'). \tag{1}$$

Here ψ' is a stream function related to the usual stream function ψ of Stokes by

$$\psi' = \int \left(\frac{\rho}{\rho_0}\right)^{1/2} d\psi, \tag{2}$$

and H is the Bernoulli quantity defined by

$$H = p + \frac{\rho}{2}(u^2 + w^2) + g\rho z, \tag{3}$$

p being the pressure and u and w being the velocity components in the directions of increasing r and z, respectively. From ψ' we obtain

$$u' = -\frac{1}{r}\frac{\partial \psi'}{\partial z} = \left(\frac{\rho}{\rho_0}\right)^{1/2} u, \qquad w' = \frac{1}{r}\frac{\partial \psi'}{\partial r} = \left(\frac{\rho}{\rho_0}\right)^{1/2} w. \tag{4a,b}$$

In order to solve (1), it is necessary to determine the functions $\rho(\psi')$ and $h(\psi')$, and for this determination one goes to an upstream section, where the density and velocity distributions are assumed. (Note that for steady flows ρ does not change along a streamline and hence is a function of ψ'.) Let us consider an axisymmetric flow between two horizontal planes at a distance d apart, and let the fluid flow into a point sink located on the axis of symmetry. For the problem of selective withdrawal of a stratified fluid the sink is usually assumed to be located on the upper or lower boundary.

If the flow far upstream, i.e. at large r, is assumed to be purely radial, then ψ' is a function of z only at $r = \infty$, and assuming that ρ, ψ', and $\partial\psi'/\partial z$ all exist at $r = \infty$ and are differentiable with z, we see from (1) that

$$\frac{g}{\rho_0}\frac{d\rho}{d\psi'} = h(\psi') \quad \text{at} \quad r = \infty. \tag{5}$$

The only linear case is obtained if we assume that at $r = \infty$ the density is given by

$$\rho = \rho_0 - \beta z \tag{6}$$

---

* Received January 19, 1981. This work has been sponsored by the Office of Naval Research.

and ψ' is given by

$$\psi' = U'z, \tag{7}$$

a constant having been omitted in (7) because it is of no consequence. The coefficients β and U' in (6) and (7) are constants. Then

$$d\rho/d\psi' = -\beta/U', \tag{8}$$

and

$$h(\psi') = -g\beta/\rho_0 U'^2. \tag{9}$$

Defining

$$(\xi, \zeta) = \left(\frac{r}{d}, \frac{z}{d}\right), \qquad \Psi = \frac{\psi'}{U'd}, \qquad F^2 = \frac{U'^2}{g'd}, \qquad g' = \frac{g\beta d}{\rho_0}, \tag{10}$$

we can write Eq. (1) as

$$\frac{1}{\xi^2}\left(\frac{\partial^2}{\partial\xi^2} - \frac{1}{\xi}\frac{\partial}{\partial\xi} + \frac{\partial^2}{\partial\zeta^2}\right)\Psi - F^{-2}\zeta = -F^{-2}\Psi. \tag{11}$$

The boundary conditions are

$$\Psi = 0 \quad \text{at} \quad \zeta = 0, \tag{12}$$

$$\Psi = 1 \quad \text{at} \quad \zeta = 1 \quad \text{and at} \quad \xi = 0. \tag{13}$$

The jump of the value of Ψ from 0 to 1 at the origin corresponds to the point source. The differential system consisting of (11), (12), and (13) was treated by Hino and Onishi in a series of papers starting in 1968 [1]). But, as will be seen below, their solution is fallacious**, and the differential system they treated has no solution.

To solve (11), let

$$\Psi = \eta + \phi. \tag{14}$$

Then ϕ must satisfy

$$\frac{1}{\xi^2}\left(\frac{\partial^2}{\partial\xi^2} - \frac{1}{\xi}\frac{\partial}{\partial\xi} + \frac{\partial^2}{\partial\zeta^2}\right)\phi - F^{-2}\phi = 0, \tag{15}$$

$$\phi = 0 \quad \text{at} \quad \zeta = 0, \tag{16}$$

$$\phi = 0 \quad \text{at} \quad \zeta = 1, \tag{17}$$

$$\phi = 1 - \zeta \quad \text{at} \quad \xi = 0. \tag{18}$$

Using the method of separation of variables, one obtains

$$\phi = \sum_{n=1}^{\infty} A_n f_n(\xi)\sin n\pi\zeta, \tag{19}$$

** The fallacy is akin to the assertion that $e^{-x+x} = e^{-x}(1 + x + (x^2/2) + \cdots)$ approaches zero as x approaches infinity, on the ground that each term of the expansion does so.

where f_n satisfies

$$f_n'' - \frac{1}{\xi} f_n' + (F^{-2}\xi^2 - n^2\pi^2)f_n = 0, \tag{20}$$

and

$$\sum_{n=1}^{\infty} A_n f_n(0)\sin n\pi\zeta = 1 - \zeta. \tag{21}$$

It is necessary, for (7) to hold at infinity, that

$$f_n(\infty) = 0. \tag{22}$$

We shall see that no solution of (20) can possibly satisfy (22).

Let

$$\eta = iF^{-1}\xi^2. \tag{23}$$

Then (20) becomes

$$\frac{d^2 f_n}{d\eta^2} + \left(-\frac{1}{4} + \frac{k}{\eta} \right)f_n = 0, \tag{24}$$

where

$$k = -\frac{in^2\pi^2 F}{4}. \tag{25}$$

This is a special case of the Whittaker equation [2, p. 337]

$$\frac{d^2 W}{d\eta^2} + \left(-\frac{1}{4} + \frac{k}{\eta} + \frac{1 - 4m^2}{4\eta^2} \right)W = 0, \tag{26}$$

since (25) reduces to (24) if $4m^2 = 1$. One of the solutions is [2, p. 340], apart from a constant multiplier which is inconsequential in our case,

$$W_{k,\,1/2}(\eta) = e^{-\eta/2}\eta^k \int_0^{\infty} t^{-k}\left(1 + \frac{t}{\eta} \right)^k e^{-t}\, dt. \tag{27}$$

Note that the integral is convergent for the k given by (25). The other solution is [2, p. 343] $W_{-k,\,1/2}(-\eta)$.

For large $|\eta|$,

$$W_{k,\,1/2}(\eta) = e^{-\eta/2}\eta^k[1 + O(\eta^{-1})], \tag{28}$$

$$W_{-k,\,1/2}(-\eta) = e^{\eta/2}(-\eta)^{-k}[1 + O(\eta^{-1})]. \tag{29}$$

Since both η and k are imaginary, it is evident from (28) and (29) that both are complex, oscillatory, and undamped at $\xi = \infty$. Hence neither of them, nor any linear combination thereof, vanishes at infinite ξ.

Hence (22) can never be satisfied by any solution of (20). Thus, a solution by separation of variables does not exist. Furthermore, if a solution for ϕ in (14) exists at all, at any fixed r (or ξ) it must be expressible as a Fourier series in terms of $\sin n\pi\zeta$, because the set of functions $\sin n\pi\zeta$ $(n = 1, 2, \ldots)$ is complete and because the series satisfies the boundary conditions on ϕ. The coefficients are functions of r, since the solution is a function of r. If the differential system does not allow separation of variables, we have no easy way to determine these r-dependent coefficients. But the differential system under consideration does allow separation of variables, and thereby also allows a conclusive demonstration of the asymptotic behavior of $f_n(\xi)$. This is fortunate, but in no way restricts the validity of the conclusion of nonexistence of the solution that has been reached. In other words, the expansion (19) is valid if a solution exists, whether or not the variables can be separated. That the variables can indeed be separated is the lucky circumstance that allows the conclusion of nonexistence of the solution to be reached beyond doubt.

Thus if the density distribution at $r = \infty$ is given by (6), the ψ' at infinity cannot be given by (7), and the differential equation (1) will be nonlinear. If (6) does not hold at infinity, then (1) will be nonlinear, whether or not (7) holds. In either case separation of variables is out of the question. Hence in any case a nonlinear partial differential equation has to be solved, and furthermore one can only *assume* ψ' to be some function of z at infinite r, and see whether a solution can be found.

The problem, then, is extremely difficult, and even a powerful computer is not likely to be of much help. For a computer is no more, indeed very much less, able than the human mind to decide the distribution of ψ' at infinity, and, when a solution does not exist for an assumed ψ'-distribution at infinity, is not only unable to find the solution, but also unable to see the futility of such an attempt and thus to decide to abandon the effort. I should like, by this note, to call attention to the necessity of continuing the classical discipline traditional in fluid mechanics, even if, and perhaps especially because, the computer has been so helpful to us in the solution of problems in fluid mechanics.

REFERENCES

[1] M. Hino and S. Onishi, *Analysis on stratified flow into a point sink*, Tech. Rep. No. 5, Dept. of Civil Eng., Tokyo Inst. of Tech., 1–18 (1958)

[2] E. T. Whittaker and G. N. Watson, *Modern analysis*, Macmillan Co., New York (1945)

[3] C.-S. Yih, *On stratified flows in a gravitational field*, Tellus **9**, 220–227 (1957)

[4] C.-S. Yih, *Dynamics of nonhomogeneous fluids*, Macmillan Co., New York, 1965, 120

[5] C.-S. Yih, *Stratified flows*, Academic Press, New York, 152, 1980

QUARTERLY OF APPLIED MATHEMATICS
JULY 1982

ON STEADY STRATIFIED FLOWS IN POROUS MEDIA*

By

CHIA-SHUN YIH

University of Michigan

Summary.   Steady flows of an incompressible and nondiffusive fluid stratified in viscosity and in density that take place in porous media are considered, and conditions necessary for similarity between any two such flows are given with proof. Results on the vorticity and circulation in such flows are also given.

Then the problem of axisymmetric steady flow of a stratified fluid into a point sink is solved by the use of Whittaker functions, and the solution for two-dimensional flow of a stratified and diffusive fluid into a line sink is presented. The solution of these two problems illustrate many of the general results mentioned above.

1. Introduction.   Flows of a fluid stratified in salinity (and therefore in density) in porous media bear on agriculture and domestic water supply, notably in Holland, and flows of a fluid stratified in viscosity in porous media occur in oil-recovery operations. Thus the modeling of stratified flows in porous media is of environmental, agricultural, and industrial interest. And yet the laws of modeling such flows have never been clearly stated. In this short note steady stratified flows in porous media are considered, and the conditions of similarity between two such flows stated, with a proof of the similarity (or at least the possibility of similarity) when these conditions are satisfied. Results on the vorticity and the circulation in steady stratified flows in porous media will also be given.

Then the problem of axisymmetric steady flow of a stratified fluid into a point sink is considered and solved in terms of Whittaker functions. Finally, the problem studied by List (1969), two-dimensional steady flow of a stratified diffusive fluid into a line sink, is considered, and it is found that List's solution does not satisfy the symmetry condition for the density at the plane of symmetry. An approximation to the correct solution for low Péclet numbers is presented here. The formulation and solution of the two special problems considered here illustrate many of the general results given in Secs. 2 and 3 of this paper, thus providing a sense of unity to the various subjects considered.

2. Governing equations.   With $x_i (i = 1, 2, 3)$ denoting the ith Cartesian coordinate, u_i denoting the velocity component in the direction of increasing x_i, μ denoting the viscosity, and $k, p, \rho,$ and g denoting the permeability, the pressure, the density, and the gravitational

* Received September 1, 1981. This work has been supported by the Office of Naval Research. It is presented to Ralph D. Cooper at the occasion of his retirement from government service, as a token of respect and friendship.

acceleration, respectively, the equations of motion are given by (Yih 1961)

$$\frac{\mu}{k} u_i = -\frac{\partial p}{\partial x_i} - \rho g \delta_{i3},$$

(1)

where δ_{i3} is the Kronecker delta, if we take the direction of increasing x_3 to be opposite to that of the gravitational acceleration. In this study, we assume k to be constant.

The equation of continuity is

$$\partial(\rho u_\alpha)/\partial x_\alpha = 0,$$

(2)

where the summation convention is used. We shall neglect diffusive effects, so that

$$u_\alpha \frac{\partial \mu}{\partial x_\alpha} = 0,$$

(3)

$$u_\alpha \frac{\partial \rho}{\partial x_\alpha} = 0.$$

(4)

From (2) and (4) follows

$$\partial u_\alpha/\partial x_\alpha = 0.$$

(5)

which can be used in lieu of (2).

Now let $(u_i^*, u^*, \rho^*, p^*)$ represent a solution of Eqs. (1)—(4), or Eqs. (1), (3), (4), and (5). To fix ideas, let us consider this solution to represent a flow E^* (E is the first letter of *écoulement*; we wish to avoid the letter F, which has been used for the Froude number) in nature, and let

$$\rho^* = \rho_0^* + \rho_1^*,$$

(6)

where ρ_0^* is a constant. We wish to produce a flow E in the laboratory which is similar to E^*. The first question that arises is "what constitutes similarity?" and the second question is "what must one do to achieve it?"

To answer the first question we note first of all that the boundary geometry of E must be similar to that of E^*. That is to say, the boundary shape must be the same for both flows, although the sizes do differ. Let the length scale of E^* be L^* and that of E be L, and let

$$\lambda = L^*/L,$$

(7)

$$y_i^* = x_i/L^*, \qquad y_i = x_i/L.$$

(8)

A point in E^* with (dimensionless) coordinates y_i^* and a point in E with coordinates y_i are called corresponding points if $y_i^* = y_i$. The flows E^* and E are said to be similar if at corresponding points

(a) The direction of the velocities $\mathbf{u}^*$ and $\mathbf{u}$ are the same, i.e., the flow patterns are similar, and

(b) ρ can be found from ρ^* by a linear operation, specifically

$$\rho = \rho_0 + \rho_1,$$

(9)

where ρ_0 is a constant, and

$$r = \rho_1^*/\rho_1 = (\rho^* - \rho_0^*)/\rho_1,$$

(10)

r being a constant.

We have thus defined similarity. It is an indication of the power of the transformation (Yih 1961), which is contained in the transformation to be given below, that we do not mention the μ-distribution at all in our definition of similarity, apart from the consequence of (a) and (3) that μ or μ^* is constant along a streamline in E or E^*, and the streamline patterns are similar for E and E^*. Given the upstream distribution of μ^* in E^*, any upstream distribution of μ in E will do.

The answer to the second question posed above is that, to achieve dynamical similarity, we must have, apart from the geometrical similarity stated above, the satisfaction of (9) and (10) at some upstream section, and the u_i at that section related to the u_i^* at the corresponding section in E^* in a definite way to be described below. To demonstrate this, we first write (1) in the form

$$\frac{\mu}{k} L u_i = -\frac{\partial \pi}{\partial y_i} - L\rho_1 g \delta_{i3} \tag{11}$$

where π is defined by

$$\pi = p + \rho_0 g x_3, \tag{12}$$

and ρ_0 is the constant part of ρ. Correspondingly, π^* is defined as

$$\pi^* = p^* + \rho_0^* g x_3, \tag{13}$$

and if E^* is a possible flow the equation

$$\frac{\mu^*}{k^*} L^* u_i^* = -\frac{\partial \pi^*}{\partial y_i^*} - L^* \rho_1^* g \delta_{i3} \tag{14}$$

is satisfied for $i = 1, 2, 3$.

Then we consider ρ_1 given by (10) and the u_i and π given by[1] (remember $y_i = y_i^*$ in similarity considerations)

$$u_i = \frac{\mu^*}{r\kappa\mu} u_i^*, \quad \pi = \frac{1}{r\lambda} \pi^* + \text{any constant}, \tag{15a, b}$$

with

$$\kappa = k^*/k, \tag{16}$$

and see whether (10) and (15) satisfy (11). In demonstrating this, we are of course borrowing (10), but (10) stands everywhere if it stands at some upstream section in E (and the corresponding section in E^*), which we demand, and if the velocity relationship (15a) is satisfied. Upon substitution of (10) and (15) into (14), we obtain (11) after division by λr throughout. Thus, if we choose a ρ_0 and arrange to have (10) and (15a) satisfied at some upstream section in E, the quantities (u_i, μ, ρ, p) represent a possible flow, since they satisfy the equation of motion and (3), (4), and (5) as well. That they satisfy (3) follows from (15a). For (15a) gives the flow pattern in E, and along the streamlines we simply assign to μ its upstream value, whatever it is, so that the satisfaction of (3) is trivial. Similarly, we demand the satisfaction of (4), and since at an upstream section (9) and (10) are satisfied, they are

---

satisfied at any two corresponding points downstream from that section, justifying the use of (9) and (10) to go from the satisfaction of (14) to that of (11). Thus it remains only to show that (5) is satisfied if

$$\partial u_\alpha^*/\partial x_\alpha = 0. \tag{17}$$

But from (15a) and (17), on account of (3) and (4), whose satisfaction has just been shown, and of

$$u_\alpha^* \frac{\partial \mu^*}{\partial x_\alpha} = 0 \qquad \text{and} \qquad u_\alpha^* \frac{\partial \rho^*}{\partial x_\alpha} = 0,$$

whose satisfaction has been presumed, it is an easy though far from trivial exercise to show that (5) is indeed satisfied by the u_i given by (15a).

Finally, we note that the boundaries may either be impermeable boundaries or free surfaces. The former kind needs no comment. We note here that if ρ_0 and ρ_0^* are taken to be zero, π is p and π^* is p^*. If π^* is constant on a free surface, (15b) shows that π is also constant on the corresponding surface in the laboratory flow E. Thus free surfaces are not excluded.

We note also that although we assume the macro-geometry to be similar, we do not include in this geometry the micro-geometry of the grains and interstices constituting the porous media. Indeed, we allow κ to take any value, larger or less than 1. This gives some freedom in the choice of the porous medium used in the laboratory.

3. Generation of vorticity and circulation.   Let the components of a pseudo-velocity, denoted by u_i', be defined by (Yih 1961)

$$u_i' = \frac{\mu}{\mu_0} u_i, \tag{18}$$

where μ_0 is a constant viscosity. Then, because of (3), it can be shown trivially that

$$\frac{\mu_0}{k} u_i' = -\frac{\partial p}{\partial x_i} - \rho g \delta_{i3}, \tag{19}$$

and not so trivially that, on account of (3),

$$\partial(\rho u_\alpha')/\partial x_\alpha = 0. \tag{20}$$

Eqs. (3) and (4) can be written as

$$u_\alpha' \frac{\partial \mu}{\partial x_\alpha} = 0, \tag{21}$$

$$u_\alpha' \frac{\partial \rho}{\partial x_\alpha} = 0. \tag{22}$$

On account of (22), (20) can be replaced by

$$\partial u_\alpha'/\partial x_\alpha = 0. \tag{23}$$

Thus we have reduced the flow of a fluid stratified in viscosity to that of a fluid of constant density. This is known (Yih 1961). We have reproduced this result here only because we need to use (19), and its use without a mention of the significance or rather the admissibility of the velocity field u_i' as a solution for seepage of a fluid of constant viscosity (though stratified in density) would seem incomplete.

The vorticity of the flow is defined by

$$\xi = \text{curl } \mathbf{u}, \tag{24}$$

which has the components (ξ_1, ξ_2, ξ_3). Similarly, we define a pseudo-vorticity by

$$\xi' = \text{curl } \mathbf{u}', \tag{25}$$

which has components (ξ_1', ξ_2', ξ_3').

From the first two equations in (19), i.e., for $i = 1$ and 2, we obtain

$$\xi_3' = 0 \tag{26}$$

by cross-differentiation. Thus the vertical component of the pseudo-vorticity is always zero. That, however, does not mean that ξ_3 is zero. Next, from (19) we easily obtain

$$\frac{\mu_0}{k} \xi_1' = -g \frac{\partial \rho}{\partial x_2}, \qquad \frac{\mu_0}{k} \xi_2' = g \frac{\partial \rho}{\partial x_1}, \tag{27}$$

which can be combined with (26) into the vector form

$$\frac{\mu_0}{k} \xi' = -g \text{ curl}(\rho \mathbf{k}), \tag{28}$$

where $\mathbf{k}$ is a unit vertical vector. The significance of (28) or (27) is that it is the horizontal variation of ρ that produces the pseudo-vorticity.

Thus true vorticity is produced in two ways: (1) by the viscosity variation which would produce true vorticity even in the absence of density variation (or of gravity), even though it would not produce any pseudo-vorticity, and (2) through the creation of pseudo-vorticity by the density variation in the presence of a gravitational field.

The circulation along any circuit is defined by

$$\Gamma = \oint u_i \, dx_i. \tag{29}$$

We shall define a pseudo-circulation by

$$\Gamma' = \oint u_i' \, dx_i. \tag{30}$$

From (19) we have

$$\frac{\mu_0}{k} \Gamma' = -g \oint \rho \, dx_3. \tag{31}$$

If ρ is constant, or if on the circuit it is constant, Γ' is zero. Also, of course if the circuit is horizontal Γ' is zero. This is to be expected since $\xi_3' = 0$, and an application of Stokes theorem will give a zero Γ'.

4. Steady flows into a point sink. To illustrate the general results obtained in the preceding sections, we consider axisymmetric flows of a stratified fluid confined between two horizontal boundaries into a point sink.

In cylindrical coordinates (r, ϕ, z), with z increasing vertically upward, and with the pseudo-velocity (Yih 1961) defined by

$$(u', w') = \frac{\mu}{\mu_0} (u, w),$$

(32)

the equations of motion are

$$\frac{\mu_0}{k} u' = -\frac{\partial p}{\partial r} \frac{\mu_0}{k}, \qquad w' = -\frac{\partial p}{\partial z} - g\rho.$$

(33)

Note that the r is now not the r defined in (10); we use the same symbol since there is little danger of confusion. In (32) and (33), μ_0 is a (constant) reference viscosity, u and w are the velocity components in the directions of increasing r and z, respectively, and the other symbols have the same meanings as they have in (1). As shown by Yih (1961), because μ does not change along a streamline in steady flows, u' and w' satisfy the equation of continuity and we can use a new stream function ψ' and write

$$u' = -\frac{1}{r} \frac{\partial \psi'}{\partial z}, \qquad w' = \frac{1}{r} \frac{\partial \psi'}{\partial r}.$$

(34)

The final equation governing the flow is then, upon elimination of p in (33), if the fluid is incompressible and therefore ρ is a function only of ψ' in steady flows (Yih 1961),

$$\left(\frac{\partial^2}{\partial r^2} - \frac{1}{r} \frac{\partial}{\partial r} + \frac{\partial^2}{\partial z^2} \right) \psi' = -\frac{kgr}{\mu_0} \frac{d\rho}{d\psi'} \frac{\partial \psi'}{\partial r}.$$

(35)

The horizontal boundaries are at $z = 0$ and $z = d$, and the sink is at $r = 0$, $z = d$. First, we note that the flow at infinite r must be horizontal, since there the velocity is zero and from (33) we see that the pressure is hydrostatic and the isopycnic lines horizontal. Then at infinite r the streamlines are also horizontal and ψ' must be a function only of z, and (35) shows that ψ' must be linear in z at infinite r. Hence the flow at infinity is given by

$$u' = -\frac{Q}{2\pi rd},$$

(36)

where Q is a pseudo-discharge which will be used to measure the strength of the sink. At infinite r, then,

$$\psi' = \frac{Q}{2\pi d} z.$$

(37)

We emphasize that whatever the sink distribution at the axis may be, (37) always holds. Let the density at infinite r be given by

$$\rho = \rho_0 \left(1 - \frac{\beta z}{d} \right).$$

(38)

Then

$$\frac{d\rho}{d\psi'} = -\frac{2\pi\beta\rho_0}{Q}.$$

(39)

We now use the dimensionless quantities

$$(\xi, \zeta) = \left(\frac{r}{d}, \frac{z}{d}\right), \qquad \Psi = \frac{2\pi\psi'}{Q}. \tag{40}$$

Then (35) becomes

$$\left(\frac{\partial^2}{\partial \xi^2} - \frac{1}{\xi}\frac{\partial}{\partial \xi} + \frac{\partial^2}{\partial \zeta^2}\right)\Psi = \lambda^2 \xi \frac{\partial \Psi}{\partial \xi}, \tag{41}$$

where

$$\lambda^2 = 2\pi\beta\rho_0\, kgd^2/\mu_0\, Q. \tag{42}$$

The boundary conditions are

$$\Psi = 0 \qquad \text{at} \qquad \zeta = 0, \tag{43}$$

$$\Psi = 1 \qquad \text{at} \qquad \zeta = 1, \tag{44}$$

$$\Psi = 0 \qquad \text{at} \qquad \xi = 0, \tag{45}$$

$$\Psi = \zeta \qquad \text{at} \qquad \xi = \infty. \tag{46}$$

The discontinuity of Ψ at $\xi = 0$ and $\zeta = 1$ represents the sink.

The solution by the separation of variables is of the form

$$\Psi = \zeta + \sum_{n=1}^{\infty} A_n f_n(\xi) \sin n\pi\zeta, \tag{47}$$

which satisfies (43) and (44). The coefficients A_n are determined by (45) to be

$$A_n = \frac{2(-1)^n}{n\pi f_n(0)}, \tag{48}$$

and the condition (46) is satisfied if

$$f_n(\infty) = 0. \tag{49}$$

It is evident that the solution $f_n(\xi)$ must satisfy not only (49), but also

$$f_n(0) \neq 0, \tag{50}$$

in order for A_n to be finite.

The differential equation satisfied by $f_n(\xi)$ is

$$f_n'' - \left(\lambda^2 \xi + \frac{1}{\xi}\right)f_n' - n^2\pi^2 f_n = 0. \tag{51}$$

Power-series expansion by the Frobenius method gives two independent solutions for f_n: f_{n2} which is a power series in ξ^2 starting with ξ^2, and f_{n1} which is of the form

$$f_{n1}(\xi) = 1 + a_1\xi^2 + \cdots + f_{n2}(\xi) \ln \xi. \tag{52}$$

It is evident that $f_{n2}(\xi)$ does not satisfy (50). So the solution has to be f_{n1} or a linear combination of f_{n1} and f_{n2}. The crititerion is that it has to satisfy (49). The determination of the right combination is far from trivial. We choose to give an explicit solution of (51) that satisfies both (49) and (50).

226   CHIA-SHUN YIH

Let

$$\eta = \lambda^2 \xi^2 / 2.$$

(53)

Then (51) becomes

$$\frac{d^2 f}{d\eta^2} - \frac{df}{d\eta} + \frac{k_n}{\eta} f = 0,$$

(54)

where

$$k_n = -n^2 \pi^2 / 2\lambda^2.$$

(55)

Now let

$$f = e^{\eta/2} h(\eta),$$

(56)

which transforms (54) to

$$\frac{d^2 h}{d\eta^2} + \left(-\frac{1}{4} + \frac{k_n}{\eta} \right) h = 0.$$

(57)

The Whittaker equation in its cannonical form (Whittaker and Watson 1945, p. 337), is

$$\frac{d^2 W}{d\eta^2} + \left(-\frac{1}{4} + \frac{k}{\eta} + \frac{1 - 4m^2}{4\eta^2} \right) W = 0.$$

(58)

Taking $2m = 1$, and identifying our k_n with the k in (58), we obtain

$$h = e^{-\eta/2} \eta^{k_n} \int_0^\infty t^{-k_n} \left(1 + \frac{t}{\eta} \right)^{k_n} e^{-t} \, dt,$$

(59)

which, except for a multiplicative constant which is inconsequential here, is the same as that given for $W_{k,\,0.5}(\eta)$ by Whittaker and Watson (1945, p. 340). Thus

$$f_n(\eta) = \eta^{k_n} \int_0^\infty t^{-k_n} \left(1 + \frac{t}{\eta} \right)^{k_n} e^{-t} \, dt.$$

(60)

It is a simple calculation by the use of (60) to show that

$$f_n(0) = 1.$$

(61)

Hence (48) gives

$$A_n = \frac{2}{n\pi} (-1)^n.$$

(62)

Furthermore, it is evident that (49) is satisfied. Thus (47), (60), and (62) gives the solution. We note in passing that w' on the axis of symmetry cannot be obtained by differentiation of (47) with respect to ξ term by term. This is a peculiarity arising from eigenfunction expansions, and has been noted before in similar problems (Yih, O'Dell, Debler 1962).

The flow patterns for various values of λ^2 are similar to those given for the two-dimensional case by Yih (1961). The larger λ^2 is, the more gradually the streamlines rise to the sink. We therefore refrain from presenting the flow patterns. Instead, we make the following observations on the connection of the results for this problem with the general results given in Secs. 2 and 3.

STEADY STRATIFIED FLOWS IN POROUS MEDIA 227

First we note that two flows into a point sink are similar if the λ^2 defined by (42) is the same for both flows. And for linear upstream density distributions, such as given by (38), this statement is quite equivalent to requiring the constancy of r in (10) and the requirement of (15a) far upstream.

Then we note that the left-hand side of (35), divided by $-r$, is the pseudo-vorticity, and this pseudo-vorticity is zero at infinite r, but is created by the combined action of gravity and stratification as the streamlines deviate from horizontality, in agreement with (28).

The fact that (37) holds for *any* sink distribution on the axis is of practical importance. For if one wishes to draw a lighter fluid (say oil) and does not wish to have water underlying the oil come out with the oil, one merely has to use two sinks of the appropriate strengths calculated from the depths of the oil and the water far upstream and from their viscosities. The upper sink will then draw only oil and the lower one only water. So while it is futile to try to separate oil and water by using only one sink, however small the discharge is (since (37) always holds), it is possible to separate oil from water by using two sinks of the appropriate strengths—and it does not seem very inconvenient to do so.

5. Sink flows when diffusion is taken into account.   List (1969) gave an exact solution for a two-dimensional diffusive flow of a stratified fluid into a line sink, and showed that my solution (1961) for nondiffusive flow remains intact when diffusion is considered. The simplicity of his solution has an elegance that is very appealing. However, upon closer examination one notes that the boundary condition for the temperature (or density) at the plane of symmetry has not been considered by List. The most natural form of this condition is

$$\partial\rho/\partial\xi = 0 \qquad \text{at} \qquad \xi = 0, \tag{63}$$

if we write now

$$(\xi, \eta) = \left(\frac{x}{d}, \frac{y}{d}\right). \tag{64}$$

where x is measured horizontally and y increases vertically upward, d being the spacing between two impermeable planes. The sink is situated at

$$\xi = 0, \qquad \eta = 1.$$

List's solution does not satisfy (63). Therefore his solution requires a heat-sink distribution on the plane of symmetry $\xi = 0$. Nor is the ρ given by his solution constant on $\xi = 0$. It varies linearly with η. Thus his solution is for an unrealistic temperature distribution at the plane of symmetry, where this distribution is artificially maintained. It does not solve the problem of symmetric flow into the sink from left and right. The elegance of his solution is therefore illusory, and this is most unfortunate since the solution has such appealing simplicity.

The problem admits only an approximate solution if it is to be solved properly. We shall consider the effect of temperature variation on the viscosity μ to be small, and take μ to be constant. Furthermore, we shall use ρ instead of the temperature, implicitly assuming the variation of ρ with the temperature to be linear. Then the equation of motion is (Yih 1961)

$$\mu\nabla^2\psi = gk\rho_x, \tag{65}$$

where ψ is the usual stream function and k again denotes permeability, as in Sec. 2.

The velocity given by Darcy's law at any "point" is the mean velocity over not just the pores but over a mean, sufficiently small area. We therefore do not use the porosity as List (1968, 1969) did in his diffusion equation. To be consistent we also consider the diffusivity α (thermal or saline, as the case may be) to be determined in a similar average way, and not to be the molecular diffusivity in the absence of the grain matrix. Then the diffusion equation is

$$\psi_y \rho_x - \psi_x \rho_y = \alpha \nabla^2 \rho. \tag{66}$$

We shall deal with the region $x \leq 0$ first.

To render the equations dimensionless, and to make things convenient, let

$$\frac{\psi}{Ud} = \eta + F(\xi, \eta), \tag{67}$$

$$\frac{\rho}{\rho_0} = 1 - \beta\eta + \theta(\xi, \eta), \tag{68}$$

where U is the velocity at $x = -\infty$, ρ_0 is the density at $y = 0$, and $1 - \beta\eta$ is the ρ/ρ_0 at $x = -\infty$. Then (65) becomes

$$\nabla^2 F = A\theta_\xi, \tag{69}$$

where

$$A = gk\rho_0/\mu U, \tag{70}$$

and (66) becomes

$$\nabla^2\theta - \text{Pé}(\theta_\xi + \beta F_\xi) = \text{Pé}(F_\eta \theta_\xi - F_\xi \theta_\eta), \tag{71}$$

where Pé is the Péclet number Ud/α. In (69) and (71), ∇^2 now is

$$\frac{\partial^2}{\partial\xi^2} + \frac{\partial^2}{\partial\eta^2}.$$

The boundary conditions are

$$F(\xi, 0) = 0 = F(\xi, 1), \tag{72}$$

$$F(-\infty, \eta) = 0, \tag{73}$$

$$F(0, \eta) = -\eta, \tag{74}$$

$$\theta(\xi, 0) = 0 = \theta(\xi, 1), \tag{75}$$

$$\theta(-\infty, \eta) = 0, \tag{76}$$

$$\theta_\xi(0, \eta) = 0. \tag{77}$$

The solution by Yih (1961) is for infinite Pé. Now we shall consider the case of low Pé only. For this case we can expand F and θ in powers of Pé. But this is not an efficient way of finding the solution. The most efficient way is to multiply the right-hand side of (71) by ε, solve the equations by a power expansion in ε, and then make ε equal to 1. In this way the terms containing Pé on the left-hand side of (71) appear in the first approximation already. For the first approximation, then, we have (69) and

$$\nabla^2\theta = \text{Pé}(\theta_\xi + \beta F_\xi). \tag{78}$$

Elimination of θ between (69) and (78) gives

$$\nabla^2\nabla^2 F - \text{Pé}(\nabla^2 F_\xi + A\beta F_{\xi\xi}) = 0. \tag{79}$$

Using the method of separation of variables, we have

$$F = \sum_{n=1}^{\infty} A_n F_n(\xi)\sin n\pi\eta, \tag{80}$$

$$\theta = \sum_{n=1}^{\infty} A_n \theta_n(\xi)\sin n\pi\eta, \tag{81}$$

which satisfies (72) and (75) exactly. The function F_n satisfies

$$[(D^2 - n^2\pi^2)^2 - \text{Pé}(D^2 - n^2\pi^2 + A\beta D)D]F_n = 0. \tag{82}$$

Of the four independent solutions of (82), all exponential functions, only two satisfy (73), and these are $\exp(-a_n\,\xi)$ and $\exp(-b_n\,\xi)$, where, when terms of $O(\text{Pé})$ are neglected (since the right-hand side of (71) has been dropped in this approximation),

$$a_n = n\pi(1 + Q), \tag{83}$$

$$b_n = n\pi(1 - Q), \tag{84}$$

with

$$Q = (\text{Pé}A\beta)^{1/2}. \tag{85}$$

The solution for $F_n(\xi)$ is

$$F_n(\xi) = e^{-a_n\xi} + \gamma e^{-b_n\xi}, \tag{86}$$

where γ will be determined by (77). Substituting (86) into (69) and applying (77), we find, by using (83) and (84), that $\gamma = 1$. Then integrating (78), using (86), we obtain

$$\theta_n = \frac{1}{1 - Q^2}\left(\frac{\text{Pé}\beta}{A}\right)^{1/2}(-b_n e^{-a_n\xi} + a_n e^{-b_n\xi}), \tag{87}$$

which satisfies (76) and (77).

Only (74) needs to be satisfied by determining the Fourier coefficients A_n. These are found to be

$$A_n = \frac{2}{\pi n}(-1)^n.$$

Thus

$$F = \frac{2}{\pi}\sum_{n=1}^{\infty}\frac{(-1)^n}{n}F_n(\xi)\sin n\pi\eta, \tag{88}$$

$$\theta = \frac{2}{\pi}\sum_{n=1}^{\infty}\frac{(-1)^n}{n}\theta_n(\xi)\sin n\pi\eta, \tag{89}$$

and the solution is obtained for the first approximation. Higher approximations can be found by successive substitution of the results of the previous approximation into the right-hand side of (71) and integration. But it should be remembered that the indicial equation for (82) has to be solved to higher orders in Pé, since terms of $O(\text{Pé})$ have been neglected in (83) and (84). The higher approximations present no real difficulty, and we

230   CHIA-SHUN YIH

content ourselves with the solution given by (67), (68), (88), and (89) for low Péclet numbers.

The solution for $x \geq 0$ is given by

$$\psi/Ud = -\eta - F(-\xi, \eta),$$

$$\rho/\rho_0 = 1 - \beta\eta + \theta(-\xi, \eta),$$

with F and θ given by (88) and (89). The reflection of the solution across the axis of symmetry is possible because

$$\psi = 0 \quad \text{and} \quad \left(\frac{\rho}{\rho_0}\right)_\xi = 0 \quad \text{at} \quad \xi = 0.$$

A similar solution for the axisymmetric case is possible. But to save space we shall not present it, and note here only that it involves Hankel functions that vanish at large distances from the axis of symmetry.

The solution given by (88) and (89) is in a sense already the second approximation. A truly first approximation is obtained if we drop all terms containing Pé in (71). Then we obtain

$$\theta = 0$$

exactly, and (69) shows that the flow will be irrotational. We mention this fact to show that when ρ_ξ (or ρ_x) is zero there is no vorticity, in agreement with (28) in Sec. 3, where ξ' is the true vorticity ξ in the present case of constant μ. The results in Secs. 4 and 5 illustrate the general results given in Secs. 1 and 2, thus providing a sense of unity to the various subjects treated in this paper.

REFERENCES

[1] J. List, 1968. *A two-dimensional sink in a density-stratified porous medium*, J. Fluid Mech. **33**, 529–544

[2] J. List, 1969. *An exact solution for a diffusive flow in porous medium*, J. Fluid Mech. **36**, 17–20

[3] E. T. Whittaker and G. N. Watson, 1945. *Modern analysis*, MacMillan, New York

[4] C. -S. Yih, 1961. *Flow of a non-homogeneous fluid in a porous medium*, J. Fluid Mech. **10**, 133–140.

[5] C. -S. Yih, W. O'Dell and W. R. Debler, 1962. *Prevention of stagnation zones in flows of a stratified or rotating fluid*, in *Proc. 4th U. S. Nat'l Congr. of Applied Mech.*, 1441–1453

Part B
Theory of Hydrodynamic Stability

Reprinted from
QUARTERLY OF APPLIED MATHEMATICS
Vol. XII, No. 4, January, 1955

STABILITY OF TWO-DIMENSIONAL PARALLEL FLOWS FOR THREE-DIMENSIONAL DISTURBANCES*

By CHIA-SHUN YIH (*State University of Iowa*)

The object of this note is to establish a relationship between the stability of two-dimensional parallel flows for three-dimensional disturbances and that for two-dimensional ones. The special case of confined flow of a homogeneous fluid has been considered by Squire[1]. In the present note neither is the upper surface of the fluid necessarily assumed to be fixed, nor are the gravitational force and variations in density and viscosity neglected. The variations in density and viscosity, which for two-dimensional flow can occur only in the direction normal to the plane boundary along which the fluid flows, may be continuous or discontinuous.

For the disturbance, a stream function of the type

$$\psi' = \varphi(y) \exp i(mx + nz - mct) \tag{1}$$

can be taken, in which x is measured in the direction of the primary flow, y is measured in the direction normal to the plane boundary, z is taken along an axis normal to the x, y plane, and $m, n,$ and c are constants. If a rotation about the y-axis is performed so that the x'-axis has the direction numbers $(m, 0, n)$ with respect to the original coordinate system, then

$$mx + nz = m'x' \tag{2}$$

in which $m' = (m^2 + n^2)^{1/2}$. If, furthermore, c' is defined by $m'c' = mc$, Eq. (1) can be written as

$$\psi' = \varphi(y) \exp im'(x' - c't) \tag{3}$$

which represents a two-dimensional disturbance progressing in the x'-direction with wave number m' and celerity c'. Similarly, the stream function

$$\psi'' = \varphi(y) \exp i(mx - nz - mct) = \varphi(y) \exp im'(x'' - c't) \tag{4}$$

represents the same disturbance progressing in the x''-direction with direction numbers $(m, 0, -n)$.

Now the stream function

$$\psi = \psi' + \psi'' = 2\varphi(y) \cos (nz) \exp im(x - ct) \tag{5}$$

represents a three-dimensional disturbance progressing in the x-direction with celerity c and having wave numbers m and n in the x- and z-directions, respectively. Since by symmetry ψ' and ψ'' are physically identical, it follows that the flow is stable or unstable for ψ according as it is stable or unstable for ψ', because the differential system governing stability is linear and homogeneous in the quantity representing the stream function of the disturbance, so that the rule of superposition applies.

Now if the Reynolds number, slope, and pressure gradient of the primary flow are

---

*Received February 10, 1954.

[1]H. B. Squire, *On the stability for three-dimensional disturbances of viscous fluid flow between parallel walls*, Proc. Roy. Soc. London A142, 621-628 (1933).

denoted respectively by R, s, and $\partial p/\partial x$, those for that component of the primary flow pertinent to ψ', denoted by R', s', and $\partial p'/\partial x'$, are determined by

$$m'R' = mR, \qquad m's' = ms, \qquad \frac{\partial p'}{\partial x'} \csc \beta' = \frac{\partial p}{\partial x} \csc \beta \qquad (6)$$

in which β and β' are the angles of inclination of the boundary to the horizontal in the x- and x'-directions, respectively, so that $s = \tan \beta$ and $s' = \tan \beta'$. As can be easily seen, the cross flow (in the z'-direction) for the case of ψ' makes no consequential contribution to either the equations of motion or the equation of continuity, and does not affect in any way the satisfaction of the boundary conditions. Hence, the primary flow is stable or unstable for a three-dimensional disturbance according as it is stable or unstable for a two-dimensional one at a lower Reynolds number, a milder slope, and a reduced pressure gradient: the laws of reduction for the three quantities being given by Eqs. (6).

The writer arrived at the foregoing conclusion by using Squire's approach. Whereas many details were obtained as by-products, the rather cumbersome calculations involved are unnecessary if only the principal conclusion is desired. The general approach used here was suggested by the reviewer of the original manuscript of this paper, who attributed it to Professor C. C. Lin of the Massachusetts Institute of Technology.

THERMAL INSTABILITY OF VISCOUS FLUIDS*

BY

CHIA-SHUN YIH

University of Michigan

I. Introduction

The stability of a viscous fluid in an insulated vertical tube or between insulated vertical planes when a negative temperature gradient is maintained in the upward direction depends on the magnitude of this gradient, the gravity, the geometry of the solid boundary, the properties of the fluid, and the wave length of the disturbance. The purpose of this paper is to present the relationships between these variables for neutral stability, and the results concerning the effect of rotation on stability.

The problem of stability of two superposed fluids in a cylindrical tube with surface tension at the common interface was solved by Maxwell in [1], without consideration of viscosity or wall effects. The stability of a layer of viscous fluid between two infinite horizontal planes when heated from below was investigated by Rayleigh [2], Jeffrey [3], Low [4], and Pellew and Southwell [5]. The problem under consideration resembles Maxwell's in geometry and Rayleigh-Jeffrey's in the means of producing instability as well as in the nature of the physical process through which stability is maintained under certain conditions. This problem has already been considered by Hales [11], Taylor [12], and Ostrach [13], but only incompletely. The contributions of these authors will be referred to at the appropriate places in this paper.

As will be seen, the curves for neutral stability differ from those ordinarily obtained in investigations of hydrodynamic stability in that the critical Rayleigh number occurs at zero wave number, and hence that these curves have no lower branch.

The "principle of exchange of stabilities", which is assumed in many investigations of hydrodynamic stability but proved only in one instance (Pellew and Southwell, [5]), has been shown to be valid without general rotation. With the presence of general rotation, this principle is valid under certain restrictions. The investigation of the effect of rotation lends some support to the belief that rotation has no effect on the onset of instability.

II. Stability of Fluid Between Plane Walls

1. Formulation of the problem. If a layer of heat-conducting viscous fluid between two vertical planes is heated from below, free convection will occur only if the (negative) temperature gradient in the vertical direction is sufficiently great in magnitude. The stability of such a fluid layer is discussed in this section.

Using Cartesian coordinates (x_1 , x_2 , x_3), with x_3 measured in the upward vertical direction, one can write the equations of motion as

$$\rho\left(\frac{\partial u_i}{\partial \tau} + u_i \frac{\partial u_i}{\partial x_i}\right) = (0, 0, -g)\rho - \frac{\partial p}{\partial x_i} + \nu \frac{\partial}{\partial x_i}\left(\rho \frac{\partial u_i}{\partial x_i}\right), \qquad (i = 1, 2, 3) \qquad (1)$$

in which the summation convention has been used, ρ is the density, τ is the time, g is the gravitational acceleration, p is the pressure, and ν is the kinematic viscosity, which

*Received December 13, 1957.

Reprinted from *Quart. Appl. Math.* 17 (1959) 25–42.

is assumed to be constant. The velocity component in the ith direction is denoted by u_i, and the three quantities in the parenthesis on the right-hand side of Eq. (1) are associated with indices 1, 2, and 3, respectively. The equation of continuity is

$$\frac{\partial \rho}{\partial \tau} + u_i \frac{\partial \rho}{\partial x_i} + \rho \frac{\partial u_i}{\partial x_i} = 0, \tag{2}$$

and the diffusion equation is

$$\rho \left(\frac{\partial T}{\partial \tau} + u_i \frac{\partial T}{\partial x_i} \right) = \kappa \frac{\partial}{\partial x_i} \left(\rho \frac{\partial T}{\partial x_i} \right), \tag{3}$$

in which T is the absolute temperature and κ the thermal diffusivity, assumed to be constant. For moderate temperature differences the equation of state can be approximated by

$$\rho = \rho_0 [1 - \alpha(T - T_0)], \tag{4}$$

in which T_0 and ρ_0 are the temperature and density, respectively, of the fluid at a point chosen to be the origin, and α is the thermal expansivity.

If convection is present, the temperature, pressure, and density will differ from their mean values. One can write

$$T = T_m + T',$$
$$p = p_m + p', \tag{5}$$
$$\rho = \rho_m + \rho',$$

in which the subscript m indicates primary quantities and the primes indicate the perturbation quantities. For the primary temperature distribution

$$T_m = T_0 + \beta x_3, \tag{6}$$

one has, from Eq. (4),

$$\rho_m = \rho_0 (1 - \alpha \beta x_3), \tag{7}$$

so that the hydrostatic pressure is given by

$$\frac{\partial p}{\partial x_3} = -g \rho_0 (1 - \alpha \beta x_3). \tag{8}$$

The thermal expansivity for water under normal conditions is of the order of $0.0001/°F$, that for air is of the order of $0.002/°F$. Thus if the maximum temperature difference is not excessive, the actual change in density is small. It will be assumed here once and for all that the only effect of density change is on the body force per unit volume due to gravity—the effect on the inertia or specific heat capacity being neglected. Although the change in specific weight is small because α is small, it must in no circumstances be neglected, because this change is the motivating force of any convection, and the sole cause of instability.

The requirement of small change in density imposed a limitation to the magnitude of the maximum value of βx_3 or of x_3. If later one does not hesitate to speak of "zero wave number," which corresponds to infinite wave length in the x_3-direction, it will be with the understanding that that term is only a convenient expression for "long wave lengths." As will be seen, the rate of change of the Rayleigh number with wave number at neutral stability is small when the latter is small, so that the result for "zero wave number" applies rather accurately for long wave lengths.

Under the assumptions made on the effects of the density change, neglecting quadratic terms of the perturbation quantities, and remembering that the undisturbed state is one of dynamic and thermal equilibrium, one can write Eqs. (1) to (3) as

$$\frac{\partial u_i}{\partial \tau} = (0,\, 0,\, g\alpha T') - \frac{1}{\rho_0}\frac{\partial p}{\partial x_i} + \nu \Delta u_i\,, \tag{9}$$

$$\frac{\partial \rho'}{\partial \tau} - \alpha\beta\rho_0 u_3 + \rho_0 \frac{\partial u_i}{\partial x_i} = 0, \tag{10}$$

$$\left(\frac{\partial}{\partial \tau} - \kappa\Delta\right)T' = -\beta u_3\,, \tag{11}$$

in which Δ is the Laplacian operator in Cartesian coordinates. By virtue of Eq. (4), Eq. (10) can be written as

$$-\alpha\left(\frac{\partial T'}{\partial \tau} + \beta u_3\right) + \frac{\partial u_i}{\partial x_i} = 0,$$

which, because of the smallness of the thermal expansivity, becomes

$$\frac{\partial u_i}{\partial x_i} = 0. \tag{12}$$

In other words, the effect of change of density on continuity can be neglected. Eliminating p' from the first and third equations contained in Eq. (9), one has,

$$\frac{\partial}{\partial \tau}\left(\frac{\partial u_1}{\partial x_3} - \frac{\partial u_3}{\partial x_1}\right) = -g\alpha\frac{\partial T'}{\partial x_1} + \nu\Delta\left(\frac{\partial u_1}{\partial x_3} - \frac{\partial u_3}{\partial x_1}\right). \tag{13}$$

For further discussion u_2 will be assumed to be zero. This does not mean that the motion under consideration is necessarily two dimensional in the usual sense of the word, for u_1 and u_3 may still depend on x_2. If u_2 is zero, however, the equation of continuity permits the use of Lagrange's stream function:

$$u_1 = -\frac{\partial \psi}{\partial x_3}\,, \qquad u_3 = \frac{\partial \psi}{\partial x_1}. \tag{14}$$

Thus Eqs. (11) and (13) can be written as

$$\left(\frac{\partial}{\partial \tau} - \kappa\Delta\right)T' = -\beta\frac{\partial \psi}{\partial x_1}\,, \tag{15}$$

$$\left(\frac{\partial}{\partial \tau} - \nu\Delta\right)\Delta\psi = g\alpha\frac{\partial T'}{\partial x_1}. \tag{16}$$

If the origin of the coordinates is taken midway between the plates and the half spacing is denoted by d, the boundary conditions are

$$\psi = 0, \qquad \frac{\partial \psi}{\partial x_1} = 0, \quad \text{and} \quad \frac{\partial T'}{\partial x_1} = 0 \quad \text{at} \quad x_1 = \pm d. \tag{17}$$

For convective motion independent of the coordinate x_2 and periodic in the x_3-direction, one tries solutions of the form

$$\psi = \kappa f(x) \cos az\, e^{\sigma t}, \tag{18}$$

$$T' = \beta\, d\theta(x) \cos az\, e^{\sigma t}, \tag{19}$$

in which

$$(x, y, z) = \left(\frac{x_1}{d}, \frac{x_2}{d}, \frac{x_3}{d}\right), \qquad t = \frac{\kappa\tau}{d^2},$$

a is the dimensionless wave number, and σ (equal to $\sigma_r + i\sigma_i$) is the complex amplification factor. Equations (15) and (16) now become

$$[\sigma - (D^2 - a^2)]\theta = -Df, \tag{20}$$

$$[\sigma - Pr(D^2 - a^2)](D^2 - a^2)f = -R\, Pr\, D\theta, \tag{21}$$

in which D denotes differentiation with respect to x, Pr is the Prandtl number ν/κ, and

$$R = -\frac{g\alpha\beta\, d^4}{\kappa\nu} \tag{22}$$

is the Rayleigh number. The boundary conditions are

$$f = 0, \qquad Df = 0, \quad \text{and} \quad D\theta = 0 \quad \text{at} \quad x = \pm 1. \tag{23}$$

If u_2 is zero but the motion is assumed to be periodic both in x_2 and x_3 , one tries solutions of the type

$$\psi = \kappa f(x) \cos\ by\ \cos az\, e^{\sigma t}, \tag{24}$$

$$T' = \beta\, d\theta(x) \cos\ by\ \cos az\, e^{\sigma t}. \tag{25}$$

Equations (15) and (16) now have the form

$$[\sigma - (D^2 - b^2 - a^2)]\theta = -Df, \tag{26}$$

$$[\sigma - Pr(D^2 - b^2 - a^2)](D^2 - b^2 - a^2)f = -R\, Pr\, D\theta. \tag{27}$$

The boundary conditions are the same as those for the strictly two-dimensional case, but the differential equations now correspond to truly cellular convection of a viscous fluid. Since Eqs. (26) and (27) would be identical to Eqs. (20) and (21) if $a^2 + b^2$ were replaced by a^2, the stability or instability against cellular convection can be predicted from that against the formulation of vortex tubes. This result is similar to that of Squire [6].

2. **Principle of exchange of stabilities.** In investigations of hydrodynamic stability other than that of the Tollmien-Schlichting type, it has often been assumed that the imaginary part of the factor σ is equal to zero as well as the real part at neutral stability. This is the so-called principle of exchange of stabilities. Only in the case of thermal instability of a viscous fluid between horizontal plates has it been rigorously proved (Pellew and Southwell, [5]). This principle will now be proved for the problem formulated in the last section, but without any assumption concerning boundary geometry.

If the velocity and the pressure are assumed to be periodic vertically, and if

$$u_i = U_i e^{\sigma\tau}, \qquad p' = P e^{\sigma\tau}, \qquad T' = \theta e^{\sigma\tau}, \tag{28}$$

the proof can be achieved by the use of Green's theorems:

$$\iint m_i F_i \, dS = \iiint_V \frac{\partial F_i}{\partial x_i} \, dV, \tag{29}$$

$$\iint_S F \frac{\partial G}{\partial n} \, dS = \iiint_V (\text{grad } F)\cdot(\text{grad } G) \, dV + \iiint_V F \Delta G \, dV, \tag{30}$$

in which m_i are the direction cosines of the outwardly drawn normal to the surface S enclosing a cellular space, and n is the distance along this normal. Multiplying Eq. (9) by u_i^*, summing over i, and utilizing Eq. (12), one has

$$\sigma J_0 = g\alpha H - \frac{1}{\rho_0} \iiint_V \frac{\partial (PU_i^*)}{\partial x_i} \, dV + \nu \iiint_V U_i^* \Delta U_i \, dV, \tag{31}$$

in which

$$J_0 = \iiint_V U_i U_i^* \, dV, \qquad H = \iiint_V \theta U_3^* \, dV.$$

The second integral on the right-hand side of Eq. (31) is, by Green's first theorem, equal to

$$\iint_S m_i P U_i^* \, dS,$$

which is zero because on the solid boundary U_i^* is zero and the quantity PU_i^* is periodic in x_3, the volume V being a cellular space of the convection. The third integral on the right-hand side is, for the same reasons and by virtue of Green's second theorem,

$$-\iiint (\text{grad } U_i)(\text{grad } U_i^*) \, dV = -J_1 \quad (\text{say}).$$

Thus Eq. (31) can be written as

$$\sigma J_0 + \nu J_1 = g\alpha H. \tag{32}$$

If now Eq. (11) is multiplied by T'^* and integrated, one has, by Green's second theorem and because of periodicity and the insulation of the wall,

$$\sigma I_0 + \kappa I_1 = -\beta H^* \tag{33}$$

in which

$$I_0 = \iiint_V \theta \theta^* \, dV, \qquad I_1 = \iiint_V |\text{grad } \theta|^2 \, dV.$$

From Eqs. (32) and (33) it follows that

$$-\beta(\sigma^* J_0 + \nu J_1) = g\alpha(\sigma I_0 + \kappa I_1),$$

or

$$\sigma_r(g\alpha I_0 + \beta J_0) + g\alpha\kappa I_1 + \beta\nu J_1 = 0. \tag{34}$$

$$\sigma_i(g\alpha I_0 - \beta J_0) = 0. \tag{35}$$

From Eq. (35) one concludes that if σ_i is not zero β must be positive. If so, from Eq. (34) σ_r must be negative and the fluid stable—as is also to be expected from the physical point of view. Thus, under the restrictions of periodicity in the vertical direction and of infinitesimal disturbances, the principle of exchange of stabilities is valid for a viscous fluid contained in an insulated tube and heated from below.

If there are two horizontal planes intersecting the tube just considered, which are kept at constant temperatures to create a temperature gradient β, periodicity in the x_3-direction is no longer necessary for the proof, because the integral involving the pressure in Eq. (31) now vanishes on account of the vanishing of the velocity components on a solid boundary. Since the temperature fluctuations on the horizontal plates are zero, the proof presented in the last paragraph remains valid.

3. Solution of the differential system governing stability. The differential system consisting of Eqs. (20), (21), and (23) will now be solved. Since the principle of exchange of stabilities is valid, for neutral stability one needs only to consider the system (with $h = R\theta$).

$$(D^2 - a^2)h = R\,Df, \tag{36}$$

$$(D^2 - a^2)^2 f = Dh, \tag{37}$$

$$f = 0 \quad \text{and} \quad Df = 0 \quad \text{at} \quad x = \pm 1, \tag{38}$$

$$Dh = 0 \quad \text{at} \quad x = \pm 1. \tag{39}$$

Differentiating Eq. (36) and substituting Eq. (37) into the result, one has

$$(D^2 - a^2)^3 f = R\,D^2 f, \tag{40}$$

with the boundary conditions

$$f = 0, \qquad Df = 0, \qquad (D^2 - a^2)^2 f = 0 \quad \text{at} \quad x = \pm 1. \tag{41}$$

Equations (40) can be written in the form

$$(L^3 - RL - Ra^2)f = 0, \qquad (L \equiv D^2 - a^2). \tag{42}$$

The solution of the indicial equation

$$m^3 - Rm - Ra^2 = 0$$

is

$$m = \left(n + \frac{1}{n}\right)\left(\frac{R}{3}\right)^{1/2}, \tag{43}$$

in which

$$n^3 = \frac{3a^2(3/R)^{1/2} \pm (27R^{-1}a^4 - 4)^{1/2}}{2}. \tag{44}$$

Only one of the two signs need be taken, and either one can be taken. If the three roots of m are denoted by

$$m_i = \omega_i^2 - a^2, \qquad (i = 1, 2, 3) \tag{45}$$

which may be complex, the solutions of Eq. (42) are exponential functions with exponents $\pm\omega_i x$. The form of Eq. (40) permits one to resolve the problem into two parts—in the one f is even, and in the other f is odd. The solutions for even f are $\cosh \omega_i x$ and those for odd f are $\sinh \omega_i x$. The secular equation obtained from the boundary conditions and determining the relationship between a and R is, if f is even,

$$\begin{vmatrix} \cosh \omega_1 & \cosh \omega_2 & \cosh \omega_3 \\ \omega_1 \sinh \omega_1 & \omega_2 \sinh \omega_2 & \omega_3 \sinh \omega_3 \\ m_1^2 \cosh \omega_1 & m_2^2 \cosh \omega_2 & m_3^2 \cosh \omega_3 \end{vmatrix} = 0 \tag{46}$$

which, though complex as it stands, is only one real equation, on account of either the conjugacy of the two complex roots of m, or the fact that the three roots are all not complex. The secular equation for odd f is similar to Eq. (46), the only difference being that the symbols cosh and sinh are exchanged.

It can be readily shown that

$$\frac{\partial \omega_i}{\partial a} \quad \text{and} \quad \frac{\partial m_i}{\partial a} \qquad (i = 1, 2, 3)$$

contain the factor a, hence vanish as a vanishes. To find the minimum Rayleigh number, one differentiates Eq. (46) or the corresponding equation for odd f with respect to a and sets the derivative dR/da to zero. Thus, for the critical condition and as far as the first derivative, R can be considered as a constant and all differentiations with respect to a can be considered as ordinary differentiations. After differentiating Eq. (46) or the corresponding equation for odd f, one obtains three determinants having one row with its three members containing the factors

$$\frac{\partial \omega_1}{\partial a}, \frac{\partial \omega_2}{\partial a}, \frac{\partial \omega_3}{\partial a} \quad \text{or} \quad \frac{\partial m_1}{\partial a}, \frac{\partial m_2}{\partial a}, \frac{\partial m_3}{\partial a},$$

respectively. Since these vanish for a equal to zero, the minimum Rayleigh number corresponds to zero wave number in the direction of gravitation—the possibility of a maximum being ruled out by physical considerations.

The task of finding the minimum Rayleigh number is now very much lightened. One may set a equal to zero forthwith and solve the differential system directly. The equation to be solved is now

$$(D^6 - R\,D^2)f = 0, \tag{47}$$

with boundary conditions

$$f = 0, \qquad Df = 0, \qquad D^4 f = 0 \quad \text{at} \quad x = \pm 1. \tag{48}$$

For antisymmetric motion (even f), the solution can be shown by a direct calculation to be

$$-\tan R^{1/4} = \tanh R^{1/4},$$

with

$$\frac{\pi}{2} < R^{1/4} < \pi.$$

Thus

$$R_{cr}^{1/4} = 2.365, \qquad R_{cr} = 31.29 \tag{49}$$

for even f. After the writer found this number, he was informed by Dr. G. K. Batchelor that Sir Geoffrey Taylor already possessed it in 1953, though he never published it. The equation leading to this number was also found by Ostrach for different boundary conditions.

For symmetric motion (odd f), the solution is

$$\tan R^{1/4} = \tanh R^{1/4}$$

with

$$\pi < R^{1/4} < 3\pi/2.$$

Thus, approximately,

$$R_{cr}^{1/4} = \frac{5\pi}{4} = 3.927, \qquad R_{cr} = 237.6 \tag{50}$$

which, it must be remembered, is based on half of the spacing of the plates. This Rayleigh number was given specifically as the critical one for the stated problem by Ostrach

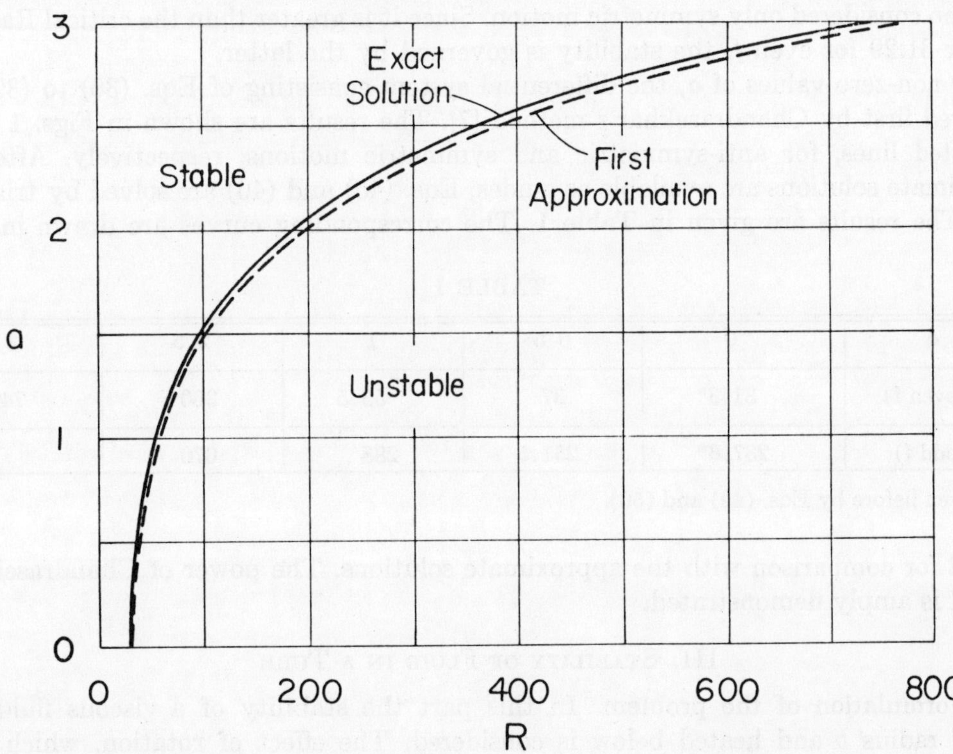

FIG. 1. Approximate and exact neutral-stability curves for antisymmetric convection between plane boundaries.

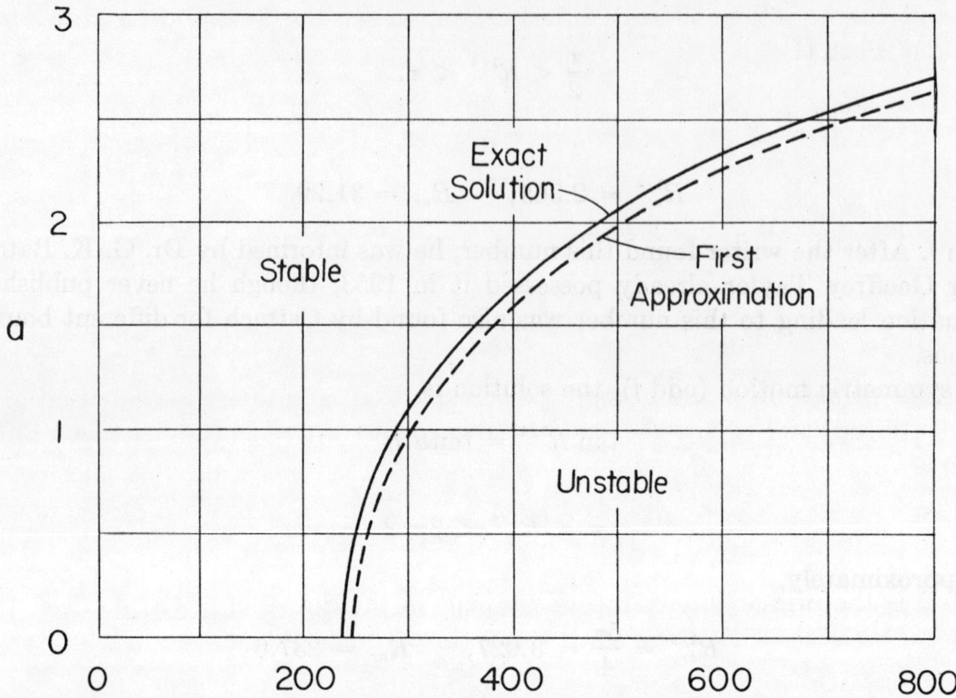

FIG. 2. Approximate and exact neutral-stability curves for symmetric convection between plane boundaries.

[13], who considered only symmetric motion. Since it is greater than the critical Rayleigh number 31.29 for even f, the stability is governed by the latter.

For non-zero values of a, the differential system consisting of Eqs. (36) to (39) will be solved first by Chandrasekhar's method [7]. The results are shown in Figs. 1 and 2 by dotted lines, for anti-symmetric and symmetric motions, respectively. After the approximate solutions are available as guides, Eqs. (45) and (46) are solved by trial and error. The results are given in Table 1. The corresponding curves are drawn in Figs.

TABLE 1

d	0	0.5	1	2.5	3
R (even f)	31.3*	37	53.5	360	742
R (odd f)	237.6*	251.5	288	670	

*Given before by Eqs. (49) and (50).

1 and 2 for comparison with the approximate solutions. The power of Chandrasekhar's method is amply demonstrated.

III. STABILITY OF FLUID IN A TUBE

1. **Formulation of the problem.** In this part the stability of a viscous fluid in a tube of radius b and heated below is considered. The effect of rotation, which for a horizontal layer of fluid has been discussed by Chandrasekhar [10], will be investigated.

If (x_1 , x_2 , x_3) are cylindrical coordinates, the linearized forms of the equations of motion and the equation of heat diffusion are, under the assumptions stated at the beginning of Part II

$$\rho_0\left(\frac{\partial u_1}{\partial \tau} + \Omega\,\frac{\partial u_1}{\partial x_2} - 2\Omega u_2\right) = -\frac{\partial p'}{\partial x_1} + \rho_0\nu\left(\Delta u_1 - \frac{u_1}{x_1^2} - \frac{2}{x_1^2}\frac{\partial u_2}{\partial x_2}\right), \tag{51}$$

$$\rho_0\left(\frac{\partial u_2}{\partial \tau} + \Omega\,\frac{\partial u_2}{\partial x_2} + 2\Omega u_1\right) = -\frac{1}{x_1}\frac{\partial p'}{\partial x_2} + \rho_0\nu\left(\Delta u_2 - \frac{u_2}{x_1^2} + \frac{2}{x_1^2}\frac{\partial u_1}{\partial x_2}\right), \tag{52}$$

$$\rho_0\left(\frac{\partial u_3}{\partial \tau} + \Omega\,\frac{\partial u_3}{\partial x_2}\right) = -\frac{\partial p'}{\partial x_3} + \rho_0\nu\Delta u_3 + \rho_0 g\alpha T', \tag{53}$$

in which the primes on p and T indicate perturbation quantities, the equation of state has been utilized, and ρ_0 has the same meaning as in Eq. (4). The linearized diffusion equation is

$$\frac{\partial T'}{\partial \tau} + \Omega\,\frac{\partial T'}{\partial x_2} + \beta u_3 = \kappa\Delta T' \tag{54}$$

in which β is the primary temperature gradient in the direction of the vertical. If now one sets

$$\left(\frac{x_1}{b},\, x_2,\, \frac{x_3}{b}\right) = (r, \varphi, z)$$

$$\left(\frac{bu_1}{\kappa},\, \frac{bu_2}{\kappa},\, \frac{bu_3}{\kappa}\right) = (u, v, w)$$

$$T' = \beta b\Theta, \qquad \tau = \frac{b^2 t}{\kappa}, \qquad q = \frac{b^2 p'}{\rho_0 \kappa^2}$$

the linearized equations become, with B for $\Omega b^2/\kappa$

$$\frac{\partial u}{\partial t} + B\left(\frac{\partial u}{\partial \varphi} - 2v\right) = -\frac{\partial q}{\partial r} + Pr\left(\Delta u - \frac{u}{r^2} - \frac{2}{r^2}\frac{\partial v}{\partial \varphi}\right), \tag{55}$$

$$\frac{\partial v}{\partial t} + B\left(\frac{\partial v}{\partial \varphi} + 2u\right) = -\frac{1}{r}\frac{\partial q}{\partial \varphi} + Pr\left(\Delta v - \frac{v}{r^2} + \frac{2}{r^2}\frac{\partial u}{\partial \varphi}\right), \tag{56}$$

$$\frac{\partial w}{\partial t} + B\,\frac{\partial w}{\partial \varphi} = -\frac{\partial q}{\partial z} + Pr\,\Delta w - Pr\,R\Theta, \tag{57}$$

$$\frac{\partial \Theta}{\partial t} + B\,\frac{\partial \Theta}{\partial \varphi} + w = \Delta\Theta, \tag{58}$$

in which Δ is now dimensionless and R is the Rayleigh number based on b. The equation of continuity is

$$\frac{\partial(ru)}{\partial r} + \frac{\partial v}{\partial \varphi} + \frac{\partial(rw)}{\partial z} = 0. \tag{59}$$

After the case of no rotation has been discussed the effect of rotation will then be investigated only for the rotationally symmetric case. If (as it turns out to be the case) rotation has no effect on the stability of the most unstable mode, the most important aspect of the problem is solved. For axisymmetric convection, Eqs. (55) to (59) become

$$\frac{\partial u}{\partial t} - 2Bv = -\frac{\partial q}{\partial r} + Pr\left(\Delta u - \frac{u}{r^2}\right), \tag{60}$$

$$\frac{\partial v}{\partial t} + 2Bu = Pr\left(\Delta v - \frac{v}{r^2}\right), \tag{61}$$

$$\frac{\partial w}{\partial t} = -\frac{\partial q}{\partial z} + Pr\,\Delta w - Pr\,R\Theta, \tag{62}$$

$$\frac{\partial \Theta}{\partial t} + w = \Delta\Theta, \tag{63}$$

$$\frac{\partial(ru)}{\partial} + \frac{\partial(rw)}{\partial z} = 0, \tag{64}$$

in which

$$\Delta = D^2 + \frac{1}{r}D + \frac{\partial^2}{\partial z^2}, \qquad D = \frac{\partial}{\partial r}, \qquad R = -\frac{g\alpha\beta b^4}{\nu\kappa}.$$

Equation (64) permits the use of Stokes' stream function ψ in terms of which the velocity components are

$$u = \frac{1}{r}\frac{\partial\psi}{\partial z}, \qquad w = -\frac{1}{r}D\psi. \tag{65}$$

Eliminating q between Eqs. (60) and (62), one has

$$\left[\frac{\partial}{\partial t} - Pr\left(\Delta - \frac{1}{r^2}\right)\right]\left(\frac{\partial u}{\partial z} - \frac{\partial w}{\partial r}\right) = 2B\frac{\partial v}{\partial z} + Pr\,R\,D\Theta$$

which, by virtue of Eqs. (65), can be written as

$$\left[\frac{\partial}{\partial t} - Pr\left(\Delta - \frac{1}{r^2}\right)\right]\left(\Delta - \frac{1}{r^2}\right)\frac{\psi}{r} = 2B\frac{\partial v}{\partial z} + Pr\,R\,D\Theta \tag{66}$$

since

$$\frac{\partial u}{\partial z} - \frac{\partial w}{\partial r} = \left(D\frac{1}{r}D + \frac{1}{r}\frac{\partial^2}{\partial z^2}\right)\psi = \left(\Delta - \frac{1}{r^2}\right)\frac{\psi}{r}.$$

Equations (61) and (63) can be written as

$$\left[\frac{\partial}{\partial t} - Pr\left(\Delta - \frac{1}{r^2}\right)\right]v = -2B\frac{\partial}{\partial z}\frac{\psi}{r}, \tag{67}$$

$$\left(\frac{\partial}{\partial t} - \Delta\right)\Theta = \frac{1}{r}D\psi. \tag{68}$$

If one tries a solution of the type

$$\frac{\psi}{r} = \Psi(r)\,\cos az\,e^{\sigma t},$$

$$v = V(r)\,\sin az\,e^{\sigma t},$$

$$\Theta = \theta(r)\,\cos az\,e^{\sigma t},$$

Eqs. (66) to (68) become

$$(\sigma - Pr\,L)L\Psi = 2aBV + Pr\,R\,D\theta, \qquad (69)$$

$$(\sigma - Pr\,L)V = 2aB\Psi, \qquad (70)$$

$$(\sigma - L')\theta = \frac{1}{r}\,Dr\Psi, \qquad (71)$$

in which

$$L = D^2 + \frac{1}{r}D - \frac{1}{r^2} - a^2 = D\frac{1}{r}Dr - a^2,$$
$$\qquad (72)$$
$$L' = D^2 + \frac{1}{r}D - a^2 = \frac{1}{r}Dr\,D - a^2.$$

The boundary conditions are

$$\Psi = 0, \qquad D\Psi = \text{finite}, \qquad V = 0, \qquad D\theta = 0 \quad \text{at} \quad r = 0, \qquad (73)$$

$$\Psi = 0, \qquad D\Psi = 0, \qquad V = 0, \qquad D\theta = 0 \quad \text{at} \quad r = 1. \qquad (74)$$

The differential system consisting of Eqs. (69) to (74) governs the stability against axisymmetric convection of the fluid column under rotation and heated from below. If there is no rotation, B can simply be set equal to zero.

2. **The principle of exchange of stabilities.** By a procedure similar to that used in Part II, it can be demonstrated that for axisymmetric motion a time-independent solution exists if

$$\frac{Pr^2a^8}{B^2R} \geq 4, \quad \text{or if} \quad \frac{Pr^3a^8}{B^2R} \geq 4$$

which means that for any given wave number a time-independent solution exists for sufficiently small Rayleigh number and sufficiently weak rotation. Furthermore it has been demonstrated* that, for zero wave number and undamped motion,

$$\sigma_i = -nB = -\frac{nb^2\Omega}{\kappa}, \qquad (75)$$

in which $2\pi/n$ is the period of motion in the direction of φ. Equation (75) states that the convection pattern progresses with angular speed Ω. For axisymmetric motion, $n = 0$, and $\sigma_i = 0$ if the disturbances are undamped. Thus for neutral stability axisymmetric motion is time-independent for zero wave number.

3. **Solution for the case of no rotation.** Since for the case of no rotation a time-independent solution corresponding to neutral stability exists, the differential systems to be solved are (with $h = -R\theta$)

$$L^2\Psi = Dh, \qquad (76)$$

$$L'h = \frac{R}{r}\,Dr\Psi, \qquad (77)$$

---

*The demonstration is omitted to save space.

and

$$\Psi = 0, \quad D\Psi = 0, \quad Dh = 0 \quad \text{at} \quad r = 0, 1. \tag{78}$$

The differential equation and boundary conditions for V can be simply satisfied by taking V to be zero. Differentiating Eq. (77), one has

$$LDh = R(L + a^2)\Psi.$$

Thus Eq. (76) can be written as

$$L^3\Psi = R(L + a^2)\Psi, \tag{79}$$

with boundary conditions

$$\Psi = 0, \quad D\Psi = 0, \quad L^2\Psi = 0 \quad \text{at} \quad r = 0, 1.$$

Since the indicial equation is exactly the same as that preceding Eq. (43), the fundamental solutions of Eq. (79) are the Bessel functions

$$J_1(i\omega_1 r), \qquad J_1(i\omega_2 r), \qquad J_1(i\omega_3 r),$$

in which the ω's have the same values as in Part II (with the Rayleigh number based on b, of course). The secular equation obtained from the boundary conditions is

$$\begin{vmatrix} J_1(i\omega_1) & J_1(i\omega_2) & J_1(i\omega_3) \\ \omega_1 J_0(i\omega_1) & \omega_2 J_0(i\omega_2) & \omega_3 J_0(i\omega_3) \\ m_1^2 J_1(i\omega_1) & m_2^2 J_1(i\omega_2) & m_3^2 J_1(i\omega_3) \end{vmatrix} = 0, \tag{80}$$

since

$$\frac{dJ_1(i\omega r)}{dr} = i\omega J_0(i\omega r) - \frac{1}{r} J_1(i\omega r).$$

The determinant equation in which the ω's contain R and a, is a single equation though in the form given it is complex, and is the solution of the problem. With precisely the same arguments as in Part II, one concludes that the critical Rayleigh number occurs at zero wave number.

For zero wave number a, the secular equation can be shown by a direct calculation to be

$$J_1(R^{1/4})J_0(R^{1/4}i) + iJ_0(R^{1/4})J_1(R^{1/4}i) = 0,$$

the first root of which is

$$R^{1/4} = 4.611, \quad \text{or} \quad R = 452.1. \tag{81}$$

This number was first given by Hales [11], who considered only the axisymmetric case which, as will be seen, does not correspond to the true critical Rayleigh number.

Although only for the axisymmetric case has it been proved that the most unstable condition is associated with a wave number of zero, this situation can be expected to hold even for the other modes of motion. If one investigates the stability at zero wave number for the other modes (not axisymmetric), the conclusion reached in Sec. 2 of Part II enables one to write Eqs. (62) and (63) as

$$L_n W = R\theta, \tag{82}$$

$$L_n \theta = W, \tag{83}$$

in which

$$w = W(r) \cos n\varphi, \qquad \Theta = \theta(r) \cos n\varphi, \qquad L_n \equiv D^2 + \frac{1}{r} D - \frac{n^2}{r^2}$$

since one may assume the z-gradient of q (the perturbation pressure term) to be zero. This assumption can be justified physically from the symmetry of the flow, which is upward as well as downward and is motivated as much by the buoyancy of the hotter fluid as by the negative buoyancy of the colder fluid. The boundary conditions are

$$W = 0, \qquad D\theta = 0 \quad \text{at} \quad r = 1.$$

$$W \quad \text{and} \quad \theta \quad \text{non-singular at} \quad r = 0.$$

From Eqs. (82) and (83) it follows that

$$L_n^2 W = RW,$$

the adequate solutions of which are

$$J_n(R^{1/4}r) \quad \text{and} \quad i^n J_n(iR^{1/4}r),$$

a combination of which is to satisfy the boundary conditions

$$W = 0, \qquad DL_n W = 0 \quad \text{at} \quad r = 1.$$

The secular equation is

$$J_n(iR^{1/4})J_n'(R^{1/4}) + iJ_n'(iR^{1/4})J_n(R^{1/4}) = 0, \qquad (84)$$

in which

$$J_n'(x) = -\frac{n}{x} J_n(x) + J_{n-1}(x),$$

the primes denoting differentiation with respect to the entire argument. The equation preceeding Eq. (81) can be obtained from Eq. (84) by taking n to be zero. The first roots of Eq. (84) for integral values of n are given in Table 2. Higher roots for each n

TABLE 2

n	0	1	2
$R^{1/4}$	4.611	2.871	4.259
R	452.1	67.9	329.1

can be found, which undoubtedly correspond to neutral stability. In this case, as in the case of plane boundaries, what happens as these higher roots are crossed has not yet been rigorously investigated mathematically or understood physically. As far as the first roots go, the second mode ($n = 1$) is the most unstable, and axisymmetric disturbances are more stable not only than those of the second mode but also than those of the third mode ($n = 2$). The second mode is antisymmetric, and compared with the antisymmetric motion for the case of plane boundaries is more stable. This is not surprising, because the hydraulic radius for the latter case is, for $b = d$, exactly twice the hydraulic radius for the circular tube. The number 67.9 was first given by Taylor [12] without proof.

For non-zero wave numbers, the method of Chandrasekhar has been employed to solve the system consisting of Eqs. (76) to (78). The results are shown in Fig. 3 by the

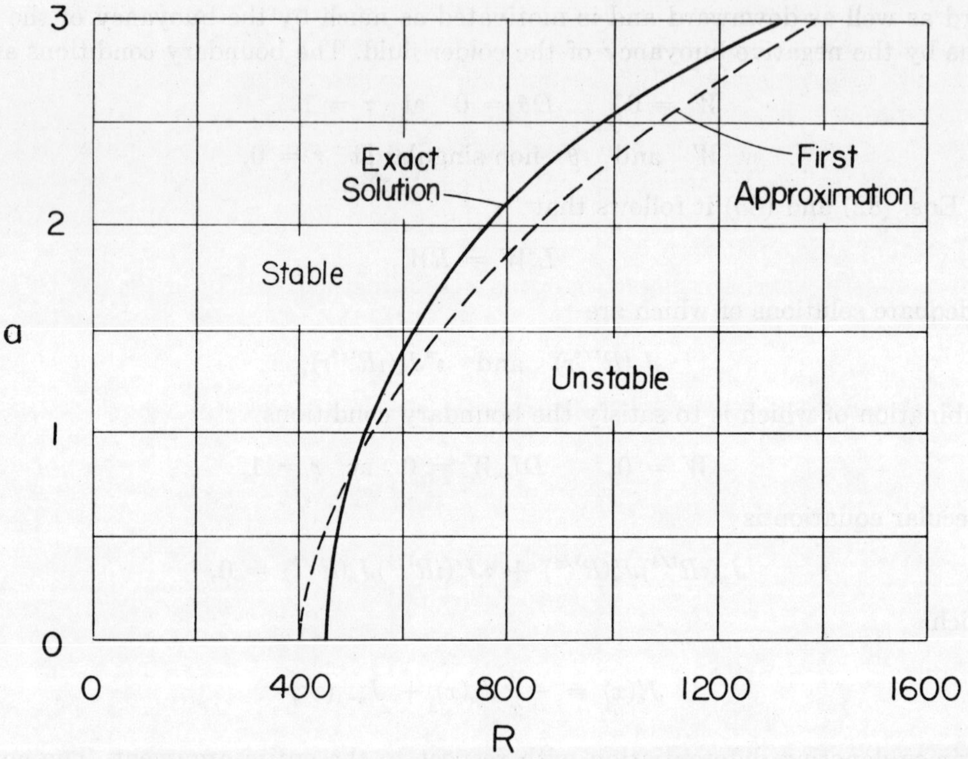

Fig. 3. Approximate and exact neutral-stability curves for axisymmetric convection in a circular tube.

dotted line. With the assistance of these results Eq. (80) is solved numerically. The results are given in Table 3 and are represented by a curve in Fig. 3. These values are in good agreement with those given by Hales [11] for a smaller range. Hales observed from his numerical data for the symmetric case but without analytic proof that the most unsteady mode corresponds to zero wave number.

TABLE 3

a	0	1	2	3
R	452.1	528	759	1322

4. **Axisymmetric motion with imposed rotation.** Although the time-independence at neutral stability has been demonstrated only under certain restrictions when a general rotation is present, indications for it are so strong that it can be assumed. Putting σ

equal to zero and eliminating V and θ among Eqs. (69) to (71), one has, for axisymmetric motion,

$$\left[L^3 + R(L + a^2) + \left(\frac{2aB}{Pr}\right)^2 \right]\Psi = 0.$$

By a process entirely the same as that used in Part II, one can show that for any definite value of B/Pr the critical Rayleigh number occurs at zero wave number. Since the effect of rotation is manifested in the number $(aB/Pr)^2$ which contains a^2, for zero wave number the general rotation has no influence whatever on the stability. The critical Rayleigh number is therefore still given by Eq. (81). Physically, this is understandable because at zero wave number there is no radial motion, which alone is inhibited by rotation. In fact, by similar reasoning one may conjecture that a vertical magnetic field has no influence whatever on the value of the critical Rayleigh number, since no magnetic lines are crossed at zero wave number.

For non-zero wave numbers Chandrasekhar's method will be extended to be used for three equations instead of two. If $V' = (2aB/Pr)V$, $\theta' = R\theta$, the equations to be solved are

$$L^2\Psi = -V' - D\theta' \tag{85}$$

$$LV' = -\left(\frac{2aB}{Pr}\right)^2 \Psi, \tag{86}$$

$$L'\theta = -R\left(\frac{1}{r}\, Dr\Psi\right), \tag{87}$$

with boundary conditions

$$V' = 0 \quad \text{at} \quad r = 0, 1; \tag{88}$$

$$\Psi = 0, \qquad D\Psi = 0 \quad \text{at} \quad r = 0, 1; \tag{89}$$

$$D\theta' = 0 \quad \text{at} \quad r = 0, 1. \tag{90}$$

If the λ's are the zeros of the Bessel function $J_1(\lambda)$, the forms

$$\theta' = \sum_{m=1}^{\infty} A_m J_0(\lambda_m r), \tag{91}$$

$$V' = \sum_{m=1}^{\infty} A'_m J_1(\lambda_m r), \tag{92}$$

are appropriate from the standpoint of the boundary conditions on V' and θ'. If these expressions are substituted in Eq. (85) and the result is solved exactly together with the boundary conditions, one obtains,

$$\Psi = \sum_{m=1}^{\infty} A_m \left[B_m i J_1(iar) + C_m r J_0(iar) + \frac{\lambda_m}{M^2} J_1(\lambda_m r) \right]$$

$$+ \sum_{m=1}^{\infty} A'_m \left[B'_m i J_1(iar) + C'_m r J_0(iar) - \frac{1}{M^2} J_1(\lambda_m r) \right] \tag{93}$$

in which

$$(B_m, B_m') = (C_m, C_m') \frac{iJ_0(ia)}{J_1(ia)}, \qquad (C_m, C_m') = (\lambda_m, -1) \frac{J_0(\lambda_m)G}{M^2},$$

$$M^2 = \lambda_m^2 + a^2, \qquad G^{-1} = \frac{ia^2 J_0^2(ia)}{J_1(ia)} - 2J_0(ia) + iaJ_1(ia).$$

Substituting Eq. (93) in (87) and expanding in a series of $J_0(\lambda_m r)$, one has

$$-\frac{M}{R} A_n = \sum_{n=1}^{\infty} \left\{ A_m \left[\frac{-a^2 B_m P_m}{N_{0m}} + \frac{C_m Q_m}{N_{0m}} - \frac{\lambda_m^2}{M^2} \right] + A_m' \left[\frac{-a^2 B_m' P_m + C_m' Q_m}{N_{0m}} + \frac{\lambda_m}{M} \right] \right\}, \quad (94)$$

with

$$P_m = \frac{iJ_0(\lambda_m)J_1(ia)}{M},$$

$$Q_m = -2aP_m + a \int_0^1 ir^2 J_1(iar) J_0(\lambda_m r) \, dr.$$

Substituting Eq. (93) in (86) and expanding in a series of $J_1(\lambda_m r)$, one obtains

$$M\left(\frac{Pr}{2aB}\right)^2 A_n' = \sum_{m=1}^{\infty} A_m \left[\frac{-\lambda_m B_m P_m}{N_{1m}} + \frac{C_m S_m}{N_{1m}} + \frac{\lambda_m^2}{M^2} \right]$$

$$+ \sum_{m=1}^{\infty} A_m' \left[\frac{-\lambda_m B_m' P_m + C_m' S_m}{N_{1m}} - \frac{1}{M^2} \right] \quad (95)$$

in which

$$S_m = \int_0^1 r^2 J_0(iar) J_1(\lambda_m r) \, dr,$$

$$N_{1m} = -\tfrac{1}{2} J_0(\lambda_m) J_2(\lambda_m).$$

Taking m and n to be 1 in Eqs. (94) and (95) and demanding that A_1 and A_1' not be both zero, one arrives at the condition

$$\chi_1 \Phi_2 = \chi_2 \Phi_1 \quad (96)$$

in which

$$\chi_1 = \frac{M_1}{R} + \frac{C_1 Q_1 - a^2 B_1 P_1}{N_{01}} - \frac{\lambda_1^2}{M_1^2},$$

$$\chi_2 = \frac{C_1' Q_1 - B_1' P_1}{N_{01}} + \frac{\lambda_1}{M_1^2},$$

$$\Phi_1 = \frac{C_1 S_1 - \lambda_1 B_1 P_1}{N_{11}} + \frac{\lambda_1^2}{M_1^2},$$

$$\Phi_2 = -M_1\left(\frac{Pr}{2aB}\right)^2 + \frac{C_1' S_1 - \lambda_1 B_1' P_1}{N_{11}} - \frac{1}{M_1^2}.$$

Equation (96) represents the first approximation to the relationship between a, R, and $(B/Pr)^2$ for neutral stability. Its graph for any fixed value of B/Pr intersects the neutral curve for no rotation at the R-axis, and can be expected to lie to the right of the latter curve for non-zero values of a.

42   CHIA-SHUN YIH   [Vol. XVII, No. 1

IV. Conclusions

From the foregoing it can be concluded that

(1) With no rotation, convection at neutral stability is time-independent. With rotation the time-independence of axisymmetric motion for neutral stability can be proved only under certain conditions, but is valid if the wave number is zero. For other modes of motion in a rotating circular tube the undamped motion is time-independent relative to a frame of reference rotating with the tube, provided the wave number is zero.

(2) With no rotation the critical Rayleigh numbers occur at zero wave number for plane boundaries and for axisymmetric motion, and can be expected to occur at zero wave number for other modes of motion in a circular tube. Antisymmetric modes are more unstable. For such modes the critical Rayleigh number is 31.3 for plane boundaries, and 67.9 for a circular boundary. (The priority of these numbers belongs to Taylor.)

(3) Detailed relationships between the Rayleigh number and the wave number at neutral stability are given by Eq. (46), one similar to it, and Eq. (80), and by the graphs and tables. An approximate relationship connecting the Rayleigh number, rotation parameter, and wave number is given by Eq. (96) for neutral stability in the presence of rotation. Since the effect of rotation on the mean orientation of the fluid has been neglected in this paper, the results concerning the effects of rotation are only approximate. The results for zero rotation are rigorous.

V. Acknowledgment

This work is sponsored by the Office of Ordnance Research, U. S. Army. The assistance rendered by Mr. Walter R. Debler in numerical computation, checking, and drafting is greatly appreciated. The writer wishes to thank Dr. G. K. Batchelor for pointing out the previous work of Hales, Taylor, and Ostrach, to which references have already been made in this paper.

References

1. J. C. Maxwell, *Scientific papers*, Dover, 1890, p. 587
2. Lord Rayleigh, *On convection currents in a horizontal layer of fluid when the higher temperature is on the under side*, Scientific Papers **6**, Cambridge University Press, 1916, pp. 432-446
3. H. Jeffrey, *The stability of a layer of fluid heated below*, Phil. Mag. (7) **2**, 833-844 (1926)
4. A. R. Low, *On the criterion for stability for a layer of viscous fluid heated from below*, Proc. Roy. Soc. **A125**, 180-195 (1929)
5. A. Pellew and R. V. Southwell, *On maintained convective motion in a fluid heated from below*, Proc. Roy. Soc. **A176**, 312-343 (1940)
6. H. B. Squire, *On the stability for three-dimensional disturbances of viscous fluid flow between parallel walls*, Proc. Roy. Soc. **A142**, 621-628 (1933)
7. S. Chandrasekhar, *The stability of viscous flow between rotating cylinders*, Mathematika **1**, 5-13 (1954)
8. Sir Geoffrey Taylor, *Stability of viscous fluids contained between two rotating cylinders*, Phil. Trans. **A223**, 289-343 (1923)
9. S. Chandrasekhar, *On characteristic value problems in high order differential equations which arise in studies on hydrodynamic and hydromagnetic stability*, Am. Math. Monthly **61** (7), 32-45 (1954)
10. S. Chandrasekhar, *The instability of a layer of fluid heated below and subject to Coriolis forces*, Proc. Roy. Soc. **A217**, 306-327 (1953)
11. A. L. Hales, *Convection currents in geysers*, Monthly Notices Royal Astronom. Soc., Geophys. Suppl. **4**, 122 (1937)
12. Sir Geoffrey Taylor, *Diffusion and mass transport in tubes*, Proc. Phys. Soc. **B67**, 868 (1954)
13. S. Ostrach, *On the flow, heat transfer, and stability of viscous fluids subject to body forces and heated from below in vertical channels*, 50 Jahre Grenzschichtforschung, Verlag Friedr. Vieweg und Sohn, Braunschweig, Germany, 1955

Reprinted without change of pagination from the
Journal of Fluid Mechanics, *volume* 5, *part* 3, *pp*. 436–444, 1959

Ring vortices generated electromagnetically

By CHIA-SHUN YIH

Department of Engineering Mechanics, University of Michigan

(Received 9 September 1958)

If an electric current of uniform density j_0 is passed axially through a stationary fluid between concentric cylinders of radii r_1 and r_2 ($> r_1$), the fluid is stable to axisymmetric disturbances only if the damping provided by viscosity and electrical resistivity is sufficiently large. It is shown herein that the fluid may also be stabilized by passing a line current J along the axis, sufficient conditions for stability being

$$J \leqslant - \pi j_0(r_2^2 - r_1^2), \quad \text{or} \quad J \geqslant \pi j_0 r_1^2.$$

The values of J needed to stabilize the fluid when the fluid has non-zero viscosity and finite conductivity are calculated for the case $r_2 - r_1 \ll r_1$. In this latter case, the ring vortices which exist under conditions of neutral stability are exactly the same as those for flow between rotating cylinders if J and j_0 have the same sign, and if J is not very small compared with $\pi j_0 r^2$.

1. Introduction

In a remarkable paper (Taylor 1923), Taylor presented the results of his analytical and experimental investigation of the stability of a viscous fluid between two rotating cylinders. The vortices which he found in the fluid for unstable conditions have since been found to be present in many fluid flows with curved streamlines. The cause of these vortices is here dynamical in nature, i.e. it is due to the centripetal acceleration of the fluid which is tantamount to a centrifugal force. Can similar ring vortices be created in a quiescent fluid? The answer is in the affirmative if electromagnetic forces are allowed. In the following sections, it will be shown that Taylor vortices can occur in a fluid between concentric cylinders if a longitudinal electric current passes along the axis of the cylinders and another passes through the fluid. Specific results are given for small differences in radii. The cause of instability is the *centripetal* electromagnetic body force acting on the fluid in the undisturbed state.

2. The undisturbed state

The relationship between magnetic field strength **H** and current density **j** is

$$\text{curl}\,\mathbf{H} = 4\pi\mathbf{j}. \tag{1}$$

In cylindrical co-ordinates (r, θ, z), a current J along the centre line (z-axis) of the cylinders will give rise to a circular magnetic field equal to $2J/r$, current being counted as positive if it is in the positive z-direction. The circular magnetic field due to a current of density j_0 passing between the cylinders in the axial direction is $2\pi j_0(r^2 - r_1^2)/r$, if the radii of the cylinders are denoted by r_1 and $r_2\,(\, > r_1)$. Thus the undisturbed state is characterized by

$$\bar{H}_r = \bar{H}_z = 0, \quad \bar{H}_\theta = 2\pi\left(\frac{J'}{\pi r} + j_0 r\right), \quad J' = J - \pi j_0 r_1^2. \tag{2}$$

It can be shown that a quiescent state of the fluid is consistent with the magnetic field given by equations (2), and that the only effect the field has is to change the (hydrostatic) pressure by an amount consistent with the equation of equilibrium.

The electromagnetic body force per unit volume of the fluid is $-\mu j_0 H_\theta$ acting in the (outward) radial direction. Since this body force is similar to the pseudo-body-force (so-called centrifugal force) in the case of a fluid under rotation, instability of the fluid can be expected to occur under suitable conditions.

3. Formulation of the problem

With (u, v, w) and (H_r, H_θ, H_z) denoting the components of the velocity and of the magnetic field strength in the directions of the (r, θ, z)-co-ordinate lines, the equations of motion for an incompressible fluid are

$$\rho\left(\frac{Du}{D\tau} - \frac{v^2}{r}\right) = -\frac{\partial\chi}{\partial r} + \rho\nu\left(\nabla^2 u - \frac{u}{r^2} - \frac{2}{r^2}\frac{\partial v}{\partial\theta}\right) + \frac{\mu}{4\pi}\left(\frac{\mathscr{D}H_r}{\mathscr{D}\tau} - \frac{H_\theta^2}{r}\right),$$

$$\rho\left(\frac{Dv}{D\tau} + \frac{uv}{r}\right) = -\frac{1}{r}\frac{\partial\chi}{\partial\theta} + \rho\nu\left(\nabla^2 v - \frac{v}{r^2} + \frac{2}{r^2}\frac{\partial u}{\partial\theta}\right) + \frac{\mu}{4\pi}\left(\frac{\mathscr{D}H_\theta}{\mathscr{D}\tau} + \frac{H_r H_\theta}{r}\right),$$

$$\rho\frac{Dw}{D\tau} = -\frac{\partial\chi}{\partial z} + \rho\nu\nabla^2 w + \frac{\mu}{4\pi}\frac{\mathscr{D}H_z}{\mathscr{D}\tau},$$

in which
$$\chi = p + \frac{\mu|\mathbf{H}|^2}{8\pi} + \rho\Omega,$$

$$\frac{\mathscr{D}}{\mathscr{D}\tau} \equiv H_r\frac{\partial}{\partial r} + \frac{H_\theta}{r}\frac{\partial}{\partial\theta} + H_z\frac{\partial}{\partial z},$$

$$\frac{D}{D\tau} \equiv \frac{\partial}{\partial\tau} + u\frac{\partial}{\partial x} + \frac{v}{r}\frac{\partial}{\partial\theta} + w\frac{\partial}{\partial z},$$

$$\nabla^2 \equiv \frac{\partial^2}{\partial r^2} + \frac{1}{r}\frac{\partial}{\partial r} + \frac{1}{r^2}\frac{\partial^2}{\partial\theta^2} + \frac{\partial^2}{\partial z^2},$$

and ρ is the density, τ the time, ν the kinematic viscosity, μ the magnetic permeability, and Ω the gravitational potential per unit mass. The equations for the magnetic field are

$$\frac{DH_r}{D\tau} = \frac{\mathscr{D}u}{\mathscr{D}\tau} + \eta\left(\nabla^2 H_r - \frac{H_r}{r^2} - \frac{2}{r^2}\frac{\partial H_\theta}{\partial\theta}\right),$$

$$\frac{DH_\theta}{D\tau} + \frac{vH_r}{r} = \frac{\mathscr{D}v}{\mathscr{D}\tau} + \frac{H_\theta u}{r} + \eta\left(\nabla^2 H_\theta - \frac{H_\theta}{r^2} + \frac{2}{r^2}\frac{\partial H_r}{\partial\theta}\right),$$

$$\frac{DH_z}{D\tau} = \frac{\mathscr{D}w}{\mathscr{D}\tau} + \eta\nabla^2 H_z,$$

in which η is the magnetic diffusivity.

A disturbance of the stationary fluid will give rise to small velocity components (u, v, w), and a deviation from the equilibrium magnetic field denoted by (h_r, h_θ, h_z). The total magnetic field is then given by

$$h_r, \quad 2\pi\left(\frac{J'}{\pi r} + j_0 r\right) + h_\theta, \quad h_z.$$

If these are substituted in the equations of motion and the equations of magnetic diffusion and all quadratic terms in u, v, w, and the h's are neglected, and if axisymmetry is assumed, the following linearized equations are obtained:

$$\rho\frac{\partial u}{\partial \tau} = -\frac{\partial \chi'}{\partial r} + \rho\nu\left(\nabla^2 u - \frac{u}{r^2}\right) - \mu\left(\frac{J'}{\pi r^2} + j_0\right)h_\theta, \tag{3}$$

$$\rho\frac{\partial v}{\partial \tau} = \rho\nu\left(\nabla^2 v - \frac{v}{r^2}\right) + \mu j_0 h_r, \tag{4}$$

$$\rho\frac{\partial w}{\partial \tau} = -\frac{\partial \chi'}{\partial z} + \rho\nu\nabla^2 w, \tag{5}$$

$$\frac{\partial h_r}{\partial \tau} = \eta\left(\nabla^2 h_r - \frac{h_r}{r^2}\right), \tag{6}$$

$$\frac{\partial h_\theta}{\partial \tau} = \frac{4J'}{r^2}u + \eta\left(\nabla^2 h_\theta - \frac{h_\theta}{r^2}\right), \tag{7}$$

$$\frac{\partial h_z}{\partial \tau} = \eta\nabla^2 h_z. \tag{8}$$

in which
$$\nabla^2 \equiv \frac{\partial^2}{\partial r^2} + \frac{1}{r}\frac{\partial}{\partial r} + \frac{\partial^2}{\partial z^2}, \quad \chi' = p' + \frac{\mu}{4\pi}\bar{H}_\theta h_\theta,$$

with p' denoting the pressure perturbation. The equation of continuity is

$$\frac{\partial(ru)}{\partial r} + \frac{\partial(rw)}{\partial z} = 0, \tag{9}$$

since compressibility can be neglected.

From the form of equations (6) and (8) we can conclude that h_r and h_z will be damped out if they are not initially everywhere zero (see Yih 1959). Then from equation (4) we conclude further that v will also be damped out. The differential equations to be dealt with are then equations (3), (5) and (7). Eliminating χ' from equations (3) and (5), we have

$$\rho\frac{\partial}{\partial \tau}\left(\frac{\partial w}{\partial r} - \frac{\partial u}{\partial z}\right) = \rho\nu\left(\nabla^2 - \frac{1}{r^2}\right)\left(\frac{\partial w}{\partial r} - \frac{\partial u}{\partial z}\right) + \mu\left(\frac{J'}{\pi r^2} + j_0\right)\frac{\partial h_\theta}{\partial z}. \tag{10}$$

We define dimensionless variables

$$(r', z') = \left(\frac{r}{r_1}, \frac{z}{r_1}\right), \quad t = \frac{\tau\nu}{r_1^2},$$

$$(u_1, w_1) = \left(\frac{ur_1}{\nu}, \frac{wr_1}{\nu}\right), \quad h_1 = \frac{h_\theta}{j_0 r_1},$$

where r_1 and r_2 are the radii of the inner and outer cylinders. Then, on dropping the primes on r and z, we can write equations (10) and (7) as

$$\frac{\partial}{\partial t}\left(\frac{\partial w_1}{\partial r}-\frac{\partial u_1}{\partial z}\right)=\left(\nabla^2-\frac{1}{r^2}\right)\left(\frac{\partial w_1}{\partial r}-\frac{\partial u_1}{\partial z}\right)+A\left(\frac{B}{r^2}+1\right)\frac{\partial h_1}{\partial z},\tag{11}$$

$$\frac{\partial h_1}{\partial t}=\frac{\eta}{\nu}\left(\nabla^2-\frac{1}{r^2}\right)h_1+\frac{4\pi B}{r^2}u_1,\tag{12}$$

in which
$$A=\frac{\mu j_0^2 r_1^4}{\rho\nu^2},\quad B=\frac{J'}{\pi j_0 r_1^2}.\tag{13}$$

Following Taylor, we can make the following substitutions:

$$(u_1,w_1,h_1)=[U(r)\cos mz,\quad W(r)\sin mz,\quad h(r)\cos mz]\,e^{\sigma t},$$

in which m is the wave number for the z-direction. The equation of continuity then becomes
$$rU'+U+mrW=0,\tag{14}$$

and equations (11) and (12) become

$$(L-m^2-\sigma)(L-m^2)U=-m^2A\left(\frac{B}{r^2}+1\right)h,\tag{15}$$

$$\left(L-m^2-\frac{\sigma\nu}{\eta}\right)h=-\frac{4\pi B\nu}{\eta r^2}U,\tag{16}$$

in which
$$L=D\left\{\frac{1}{r}D(r\ )\right\},\quad D=\frac{d}{dr}.$$

With
$$U=-m^2Af\quad\text{and}\quad N=\frac{4\pi AB\nu}{\eta},$$
equations (15) and (16) can be written as

$$(L-m^2-\sigma)(L-m^2)f=\left(\frac{B}{r^2}+1\right)h,\tag{17}$$

$$\left(L-m^2-\frac{\sigma\nu}{\eta}\right)h=m^2N\frac{f}{r^2}.\tag{18}$$

The boundary conditions corresponding to

$$U=W=0\quad\text{at}\quad r=1\quad\text{and}\quad r=\frac{r_2}{r_1}=\alpha$$

are
$$f=Df=0\quad\text{at}\quad r=1\text{ and }r=\alpha.\tag{19}$$

The simplest realistic boundary condition for h is that which corresponds to zero electrical conductivity of the walls, that is, to $j_r=0$. But

$$j_r=\frac{1}{r}\frac{\partial h_3}{\partial\theta}-\frac{\partial h_\theta}{\partial z}=-\frac{\partial h_\theta}{\partial z}\quad\text{(for axisymmetry)},$$

and so the boundary condition for h is

$$h=0\quad\text{at}\quad r=1\text{ and }r=\alpha\tag{20}$$

for non-conducting walls. The task is to find the relationship between N and m for a given value of B, from the differential system consisting of equations (17) and (20).

Chia-Shun Yih

440

4. Sufficient condition for stability

A sufficient condition for stability can be given on physical grounds, in the manner of Rayleigh (1916), or on mathematical grounds, in the manner of Synge (1938). The physical proof relies upon the fact that for a magnetically non-diffusive fluid ($\eta = 0$) the lines of force move with the fluid. The proof for this well-known fact is identical with the proof for vorticity lines in an inviscid fluid (Lamb 1945, p. 204), and is available elsewhere. In §3 of this paper it has been shown that H_r and H_z (or h_r and h_z) will be damped out. In a discussion of the sufficient condition for stability it can thus be assumed that only H_θ is different from zero. Since the total magnetic flux round a thin material ring of fluid is constant, and since by continuity the volume of this ring must be constant, so that its cross-section varies inversely as its radius r', H_θ must be equal to kr' (r' dimensional), with k as the constant (for the ring as it moves) of proportionality. The body force per unit volume in the r-direction, which is in general (Yih 1959)

$$\frac{\mu}{4\pi}\left(-\frac{\frac{1}{2}(\partial|\mathbf{H}|^2)}{\partial r} + H_r\frac{\partial H_r}{\partial r} + \frac{H_\theta}{r}\frac{\partial H_r}{\partial \theta} + H_z\frac{\partial H_r}{\partial z} - \frac{H_\theta^2}{r}\right),$$

can in the present discussion be written as

$$-\frac{\mu}{4\pi}H_\theta\left(\frac{\partial H_\theta}{\partial r} + \frac{H_\theta}{r}\right).$$

Now imagine the thin material ring with a magnetic flux in the θ-direction to be instantaneously situated at the position indicated by r'. The sole effect of the term

$$-\frac{\mu}{4\pi}H_\theta\frac{\partial H_\theta}{\partial r}$$

is to reduce the pressure throughout the ring by an amount $\mu H_\theta^2/8\pi$, and therefore has no effect on the work done by the ring against pressure applied externally on the surface of the ring. Consequently, the only force acting on the ring which can be properly counted as a body force is

$$-\frac{\mu}{4\pi}\frac{H_\theta^2}{r}.$$

Since the instantaneous value for r is r' for the thin ring, and since $H_\theta = kr'$, this force can be written as

$$-\frac{\mu}{4\pi}k^2 r'.$$

The potential energy due to this centripetal force is then $\mu k^2 r'^2/8\pi$, which increases with r' for any particular value of k.

Returning to the distribution of the mean field $\bar{H}_\theta$ specified earlier in this paper, we can imagine the fluid in its mean configuration to be composed of thin shells, each with a different value for k given by

$$k = \frac{\bar{H}_\theta}{r} = 2\pi\left(\frac{J'}{\pi r^2} + j_0\right).$$

441 *Ring vortices generated electromagnetically*

Since a higher value of k^2 corresponds to a 'heavier' fluid, and since stability will ensue if a 'heavier' fluid shell occupies a position of lower potential energy (hence smaller r), one concludes that a sufficient condition for stability is that the quantity

$$\left(\frac{J'}{\pi r^2}+j_0\right)^2$$

does not increase outwards—a situation which is possible only if

$$J \leqslant -\pi j_0(r_2^2-r_1^2) \quad \text{or} \quad J \geqslant j_0 r_1^2.$$

In this physical proof magnetic diffusivity has been neglected. It is tacitly assumed that, if a fluid with no magnetic diffusivity is stable, one with magnetic diffusivity will be so *a fortiori*. For the type of instability under discussion, this is a valid assumption, as will be demonstrated by a mathematical proof (of the sufficient conditions just reached), in which the effects of viscosity and magnetic diffusivity are not neglected. Whether magnetic diffusivity can have a de-stabilizing effect on certain flows, in the manner that viscosity can sometimes be destabilizing, is not known. An investigation of this possibility would be highly interesting.

For a mathematical proof of the same result one turns to the dimensionless equations (17) to (20). Multiplying equation (17) by $r\bar{f}$ ($\bar{f}$ being the complex conjugate of f) and integrating (by parts if necessary) with respect to r between 1 and α, we have, upon utilization of the boundary conditions on f,

$$I_2 + (2m^2+\sigma)\,I_1 + m^2(m^2+\sigma)\,I_0 = \int_1^\alpha \left(\frac{B}{r^2}+1\right)rh\bar{f}\,dr, \tag{21}$$

in which

$$I_0 = \int_1^\alpha r\,|f|^2\,dr, \quad I_1 = \int_1^\alpha \frac{1}{r}\,|Drf|^2\,dr, \quad I_2 = \int_1^\alpha r\,|Lf|^2\,dr.$$

Similarly, by multiplying equation (18) by $r\bar{h}$ and $r^3\bar{h}$ and integrating, one obtains, respectively,

$$H_1 + \left(m^2+\frac{\nu\sigma}{\eta}\right)H_0 = -m^2 N \int_1^\alpha \frac{f\bar{h}}{r}\,dr, \tag{22}$$

$$H_3 + \left(m^2+\frac{\nu\sigma}{\eta}\right)H_2 + 2\int_1^\alpha r\bar{h}D(rh)\,dr = -m^2 N \int_1^\alpha rf\bar{h}\,dr, \tag{23}$$

in which

$$H_0 = \int_1^\alpha r\,|h|^2\,dr, \quad H_1 = \int_1^\alpha \frac{1}{r}\,|Drh|^2\,dr, \quad H_2 = \int_1^\alpha r^3\,|h|^2\,dr, \quad H_3 = \int_1^\alpha r\,|Drh|^2\,dr.$$

Equations (21) to (23) can be suitably combined to eliminate the integrals on the right-hand sides. The result is

$$m^2N(I_2 + 2m^2 I_1 + m^4 I_0) + B(H_1 + m^2 H_0) + (H_3 + m^2 H_2)$$

$$-2\int_1^\alpha r\bar{h}D(rh)\,dr + \sigma\left(m^2 N I_1 + m^4 N I_0 + \frac{B\nu}{\eta}H_0 + \frac{\nu}{\eta}H_2\right) = 0. \tag{24}$$

But since
$$\int_1^\alpha r\bar{h}D(rh)\,dr + \int_1^\alpha rh D(r\bar{h})\,dr = r^2 h\bar{h}\,|_1^\alpha = 0,$$

the real part of the integral in equation (24) is zero. Taking the real part of (24), we have

$$m^2 N (I_2 + 2m^2 I_1 + m^4 I_0) + B(H_1 + m^2 H_0) + (H_3 + m^2 H_2)$$

$$+ \sigma_r \left(m^2 N I_1 + m^4 N I_0 + \frac{B\nu}{\eta} H_0 + \frac{\nu}{\eta} H_2 \right) = 0. \qquad (25)$$

Now from the definitions of the integrals denoted by H, it is evident that

$$\alpha^2 H_0 > H_2, \quad \text{and} \quad \alpha^2 H_1 > H_3.$$

Thus, since N and B are of the same sign, if

$$-B \geqslant \alpha^2, \quad \text{or} \quad B > 0, \qquad (26)$$

it follows from equation (25) that σ_r is negative, and the fluid is stable. With the definition of B given by (13), the sufficient condition of stability is therefore again found to be

$$J \leqslant -\pi j_0 (r_2^2 - r_1^2) \quad \text{or} \quad J \geqslant \pi j_0 r_1^2. \qquad (27)$$

5. Solution for small spacings

For small spacings of the cylinders, the operator L in (17) and (18) can be replaced by D^2. If the dimensionless parameters are now re-defined as

$$t = \frac{\tau \nu}{d^2}, \quad \xi = \frac{r - r_1}{d} \ (r \text{ dimensional}), \quad m = \frac{2\pi d}{\lambda},$$

in which d is $r_2 - r_1$, and λ is the wavelength in the z-direction, equations (17) and (18) can be replaced by

$$(D^2 - m^2 - \sigma)(D^2 - m^2) f = \left(\frac{d}{r_1}\right)^4 \left[(B+1) - \frac{2Bd}{r_1} \xi \right] h, \qquad (28)$$

$$\left(D^2 - m^2 - \frac{\nu \sigma}{\eta} \right) h = m^2 N \left(1 - \frac{2d}{r_1} \xi \right) j, \qquad (29)$$

where D stands now for $d/d\xi$. The boundary conditions are

$$f = Df = 0 \quad \text{at} \quad \xi = 0 \text{ and } 1, \qquad (30)$$

$$h = 0 \quad \text{at} \quad \xi = 0 \text{ and } 1. \qquad (31)$$

We shall investigate the stability for the cases in which the two currents are in the same direction $(-B < 1)$, so that the electromagnetic body force on the undisturbed state is contripetal. If B is not nearly equal to -1, equations (28) and (29) become (since d/r_1 is assumed to be very small)

$$(D^2 - m^2 - \sigma)(D^2 - m^2) f = (B+1) \left(\frac{d}{r_1}\right)^4 h, \qquad (32)$$

$$\left(D^2 - m^2 - \frac{\nu \sigma}{\eta} \right) h = m^2 N f. \qquad (33)$$

Effectively the same equations with the same boundary conditions as for the problem at hand have been solved exactly by Pellew & Southwell (1940), who also proved that for neutral stability σ is zero and not purely imaginary. Comparing equations (32) and (33) with Pellew & Southwell's equations (see Lin 1955, p. 108), we find that the parameter corresponding to Pellew & Southwell's R (Rayleigh number) is

$$T \equiv -(1+B)\,N\left(\frac{d}{r_1}\right)^4 = \frac{\mu J(\pi j_0 r_1^2 - J)}{\pi \rho \nu \eta}\left(\frac{d}{r_1}\right)^4.$$

According to Pellew & Southwell's solution, then,

$$T = 1707 \cdot 8. \tag{34}$$

If $1+B$ is positive but of the same magnitude as d/r_1, and if the principle of exchange of stabilities is assumed, equations (28) and (29) become

$$(D^2 - m^2)^2 f = (1+B)\left(\frac{d}{r_1}\right)^4 (1+\beta\xi)\,h, \tag{35}$$

$$(D^2 - m^2)\,h = m^2 N f. \tag{36}$$

where

$$\beta = -\frac{2dB}{r_1(1+B)}. \tag{37}$$

The boundary conditions are still specified by (30) and (31). Solution of the differential system for three values of β by the method of Chandrasekhar (1954) yields the corresponding critical values of T as given in table 1.

β ...	0·25		0·5		1·0	
m ...	3·12	3·13	3·12	3·13	3·12	3·13
T (1st approx.)	1524·5	1524·6	1372·1	1372·1	1143·4	1143·4
T (2nd approx.)	1524·4	1524·4	1371·6	1371·7	1142·4	1142·4
T (3rd approx.)	1518·0	1518·0	1365·9	1366·0	1137·7	1137·7

TABLE 1

Computation for the case of negative $J(1+B<0)$ has not been performed. However, from the definition of N it can be seen that N is negative for negative J, and from the forms of (35) and (36) it can be seen that the fluid is probably stable for negative J unless $|1+B|$ is very small and β large. For very small $|1+B|$, the modified parameter

$$T' = \beta T$$

can be advantageously used instead of T. A table for T' can be easily constructed from table 1. The value of T' for negative J of small magnitude or for small $|1+B|$ is not much different from that for small positive J, so that a rough measure of it can be obtained by extrapolation from the table for T'. This measure can be improved by extending the range of β in Table 1, and hence in the T'-table derived therefrom.

6. Feasibility of experiment

For an experiment the most favourable value of B for the occurrence of ring vortices is of course $-1/2$. If d/r_1 is $0\cdot1$, for the critical case

$$\frac{\mu}{4}\frac{\pi j_0^2 r_1^4}{\rho \nu \eta} = 1707 \cdot 8 \times 10^4.$$

For mercury, we have, in e.m.u.,

$$\eta = \frac{1}{4\pi\mu\sigma} = 8000 \, \text{cm}^2/\text{sec}, \quad \mu = 1 \, \text{e.m.u.},$$

$$\nu = 1{\cdot}12 \times 10^{-3} \, \text{cm}^2/\text{sec}, \quad \rho = 13{\cdot}6 \, g/\text{c.c.}$$

For r_1 equal to 10 cm and d equal to 1 cm,

$$j_0 = 257 \, \text{e.m.u.} = 2570 \, \text{amp/cm}^2.$$

The total current through the annular space is then

$$20\pi j_0 = 1{\cdot}62 \times 10^5 \, \text{amp},$$

which is obviously a tremendous current. However, this current is the same (for the same d/r_1) regardless of the size of the apparatus, and the total power per metre (which is roughly 4160 kW for $r = 10$ cm) decreases in inverse proportion to the square of the lateral dimension of the apparatus. Furthermore, the heat capacity of mercury per metre of length increases in direct proportion to the square of the lateral dimension. Thus the danger of boiling decreases rapidly as the lateral size increases. For highly ionized gases with a density much smaller than that of mercury and with very high conductivity, the necessary current for ring vortices to occur will be very much reduced. Unfortunately a simple experiment with a small apparatus does not appear feasible.

This work was jointly sponsored by the University of Michigan and the Office of Ordnance Research of the U.S. Army. The computational service of Mr Wei Lai was supplied through a faculty research fund by the Rackham Graduate School of the University of Michigan.

REFERENCES

CHANDRASEKHAR, S. 1954 The stability of viscous flow between rotating cylinders. *Mathematika*, **1**, 5–13.

LAMB, H. 1945 *Hydrodynamics*. New York: Dover.

LIN, C. C. 1955 *The Theory of Hydrodynamic Stability*. Cambridge University Press.

PELLEW, A. & SOUTHWELL, R. V. 1940 On maintained convective motion in a fluid heated from below. *Proc. Roy. Soc.* A, **176**, 312–343.

RAYLEIGH, LORD 1916 On the dynamics of revolving fluids. *Scientific Papers*, **6**, 447–453. Cambridge University Press.

SYNGE, J. L. 1938 On the stability of a viscous liquid between two rotating coaxial cylinders. *Proc. Roy. Soc.* A, **167**, 250–256.

TAYLOR, G. I. 1923 Stability of a viscous liquid contained between two rotating cylinders. *Phil. Trans.* A, **223**, 289–343.

YIH, C.-S. 1959 Inhibition of hydrodynamic instability by an electric current. (To be published.)

Reprinted from

THE PHYSICS OF FLUIDS　　VOLUME 2, NUMBER 2　　MARCH-APRIL, 1959

Inhibition of Hydrodynamic Instability by an Electric Current

CHIA-SHUN YIH
University of Michigan, Ann Arbor, Michigan
(Received October 24, 1958)

The inhibition of instability of a viscous fluid contained in a circular cylinder and heated from below by an electric current is investigated. Previous results indicate that, for a thermally nonconducting wall, the critical Rayleigh number is 452.1 for symmetric convection, and 67.9 for the first (and critical) mode of unsymmetric convection. It has been found in this investigation that unsymmetric convections can be delayed or completely inhibited by an electric current, whereas symmetric convection is not at all affected. This indicates a very interesting physical situation at Rayleigh number 452.1, for an electric current just strong enough to inhibit unsymmetric convection. If the current is slightly increased, only symmetric motion will occur. If it is slightly decreased, unsymmetric convection, being more unstable, will prevail. Thus the physically significant solution of a differential system may have a sudden change of behavior at certain critical values of its parameters.

I. INTRODUCTION

ALTHOUGH it is well known that the presence of a magnetic field often inhibits the onset of hydrodynamic instability, the great variation of the effectiveness of the inhibition with the mode of instability has not been widely recognized. The purpose of this paper is to present a striking example showing the great difference in the effectiveness of a circular magnetic field in inhibiting different modes of instability of a viscous fluid heated from below. The fluid is contained in a circular cylinder, and in its quiescent state has an adverse linear temperature gradient. At sufficiently large Rayleigh numbers, convection will occur, with the incipient Rayleigh number varying widely for different modes of convection.[1] If an electric current is allowed to pass longitudinally through the fluid, a circular magnetic field is created, and it can be expected that this field will inhibit or delay any hydrodynamic instability that would otherwise occur. It turns out that, although it does inhibit or delay all unsymmetric modes of convection with different degrees of effectiveness, it does not affect axisymmetric convection at all. Since the fluid is most unstable for the first unsymmetric mode, the interesting situation arises that, for the Rayleigh number 452.1 (critical for axisymmetric convection), at a certain critical value of this current axisymmetric convection and the first mode of unsymmetric convection can start simultaneously, and that for a current stronger than the critical one only axisymmetric convection can occur, whereas for a current weaker than the critical one the first mode of unsymmetric convection will prevail. Thus, this paper presents an example of

how the behavior of the physically significant solution of a differential system can change *abruptly* at certain critical values of the parameters of the system.

II. GOVERNING EQUATIONS

Specifically, one considers a viscous fluid contained in a cylinder of radius b and with a mean temperature decreasing linearly with the vertical distance. If cylindrical coordinates (r, θ, z) are used, and if z is used to denote the vertical distance along the axis of the cylinder, the mean-temperature distribution considered is

$$T_m = T_0 + \beta z, \tag{1}$$

in which T_0 is the temperature at the level from which z is measured, and β is the temperature gradient, assumed to be negative. The mean density is then

$$\rho_m = \rho_0(1 - \alpha\beta z), \tag{2}$$

in which ρ_0 is the density at $z = 0$, and α is the coefficient of volume expansion. The hydrostatic pressure distribution is given by

$$\partial p_m/\partial z = -g\rho_0(1 - \alpha\beta z), \tag{3}$$

with g denoting the gravitational acceleration. As shown by Hales,[2] Taylor,[3] and Yih,[1] for a given fluid and a given geometry the fluid configuration is unstable for a sufficiently large adverse temperature gradient. It is the express purpose of this paper to show the manner in which a longitudinal electric current through the fluid inhibits or delays the

---

[1] C.-S. Yih, "Thermal instability of viscous fluids," Quart. Appl. Math. (to be published).

[2] A. L. Hales, Monthly Notices Roy. Astron. Soc., Geophys. Suppl. 4, 122 (1937).
[3] Sir Geoffrey Taylor, Proc. Phys. Soc. (London) **B67**, 857 (1954).

thermal instability that would otherwise occur.

If the density of the electric current is denoted by j_0, the strength of the circular magnetic field is given in cylindrical coordinates by

$$H_\theta = 2\pi j_0 r, \tag{4}$$

since the curl of the magnetic field is equal to 4π times the current density. In order to proceed with the analysis, it is necessary to present the equations of motion and the equations of magnetic diffusion in cylindrical coordinates. Although these equations are known, it seems that they have never been systematically derived before. In the following paragraph, the well-known vector forms of these equations in Cartesian coordinates will be given first, which will then be written in general coordinates in a tensorially correct form. The desired equations in cylindrical coordinates then follow in a straightforward manner.

The vector equation of motion is, in Cartesian coordinates,

$$\rho \frac{D\mathbf{v}}{D\tau} = -\mathrm{grad}\left(p^{-\lambda\theta'} + \frac{\mu}{8\pi}|\mathbf{H}|^2\right)$$
$$+ \rho\mathbf{g} + \rho\nu\nabla^2\mathbf{v} + \mathrm{div}\,\frac{\mu\mathbf{H}\mathbf{H}}{4\pi}, \tag{5}$$

in which $\mathbf{v}$ is the velocity vector, τ is the time, $\mathbf{g}$ is the gravitational acceleration, μ is the magnetic permeability, $\mathbf{H}$ is the (solenoidal) magnetic field strength, $D/D\tau$ signifies substantial derivative, and the other symbols have their usual meanings. The "diffusion equation" for the vector $\mathbf{H}$ is

$$\frac{\partial\mathbf{H}}{\partial\tau} = \mathrm{curl}\,(\mathbf{v}\times\mathbf{H}) + \eta\nabla^2\mathbf{H}, \tag{6}$$

in which η is the magnetic diffusivity. In general coordinates x^i, with u^i and u_i denoting the contravariant and the covariant velocity vector, and H^i and H_i the contravariant and the covariant magnetic field vector, Eqs. (5) and (6) assume the forms

$$\rho\left(\frac{\partial u^i}{\partial\tau} + u^\alpha\frac{Du^i}{Dx^\alpha}\right) = \rho g^i$$
$$- g^{i\alpha}\frac{D}{Dx^\alpha}\left(p - \lambda\theta' + \frac{\mu|\mathbf{H}|^2}{8\pi}\right)$$
$$+ g^{\beta\alpha}\frac{D}{Dx^\beta}\left[\rho\nu g^{\gamma i}\left(\frac{Du_\alpha}{Dx^\gamma} + \frac{Du_\gamma}{Dx^\alpha}\right)\right]$$
$$+ \frac{\mu}{4\pi}H^\alpha\frac{DH^i}{Dx^\alpha}, \tag{7}$$

$$\frac{\partial H^i}{\partial\tau} = H^\alpha\frac{Du^i}{Dx^\alpha} - u^\alpha\frac{DH^i}{Dx^\alpha}$$
$$+ g^{\beta\alpha}\frac{D}{Dx^\beta}\left[\eta g^{\gamma i}\left(\frac{DH_\alpha}{Dx^\gamma} + \frac{DH_\gamma}{Dx^\alpha}\right)\right]. \tag{8}$$

In these equations g^i is the contravariant vector for the gravitational acceleration, θ' is the velocity dilatation, λ has the usual meaning, g^{ii} is the contravariant fundamental tensor (or metric) for the coordinates, D/Dx^i signifies covariant differentiation, and the summation convention has been used. The last term in Eq. (7) corresponds to that in (5) because the divergence of the magnetic field is zero.

In cylindrical coordinates (r, θ, z),

$$g_{11} = g^{11} = g_{33} = g^{33} = 1, \qquad g_{22} = r^2,$$
$$g^{22} = r^{-2}, \qquad g_{ii} = 0 \quad \text{for} \quad i \neq j.$$

With (u, v, w) and (H_r, H_θ, H_z) denoting the physical components of the velocity and the magnetic field strength, the equations of motion are, with $\mathbf{g}$ acting in the direction opposite to that of z,

$$\rho\left(\frac{Du}{D\tau} - \frac{v^2}{r}\right) = -\frac{\partial\chi}{\partial r}$$
$$+ \rho\nu\left(\nabla^2 u - \frac{u}{r^2} - \frac{2}{r^2}\frac{\partial v}{\partial\theta}\right)$$
$$+ \frac{\mu}{4\pi}\left(\frac{\mathfrak{D}H_r}{\mathfrak{D}\tau} - \frac{H_\theta^2}{r}\right), \tag{9}$$

$$\rho\left(\frac{Dv}{D\tau} + \frac{uv}{r}\right) = -\frac{1}{r}\frac{\partial\chi}{\partial\theta}$$
$$+ \rho\nu\left(\nabla^2 v - \frac{v}{r^2} + \frac{2}{r^2}\frac{\partial u}{\partial\theta}\right)$$
$$+ \frac{\mu}{4\pi}\left(\frac{\mathfrak{D}H_\theta}{\mathfrak{D}\tau} + \frac{H_r H_\theta}{r}\right), \tag{10}$$

$$\rho\frac{Dw}{D\tau} = -\frac{\partial\chi}{\partial z} + \rho\nu\nabla^2 w + \frac{\mu}{4\pi}\frac{\mathfrak{D}H_z}{\mathfrak{D}\tau}, \tag{11}$$

in which (with $D/D\tau$ redefined)

$$\chi = p - \lambda\theta' + \frac{\mu|\mathbf{H}|^2}{8\pi}, \tag{12}$$

$$\frac{D}{D\tau} \equiv \frac{\partial}{\partial\tau} + u\frac{\partial}{\partial r} + \frac{v}{r}\frac{\partial}{\partial\theta} + w\frac{\partial}{\partial z},$$

$$\nabla^2 \equiv \frac{\partial^2}{\partial r^2} + \frac{1}{r}\frac{\partial}{\partial r} + \frac{1}{r^2}\frac{\partial^2}{\partial\theta^2} + \frac{\partial^2}{\partial z^2}, \tag{13}$$

$$\frac{\mathfrak{D}}{\mathfrak{D}\tau} \equiv H_r\frac{\partial}{\partial r} + \frac{H_\theta}{r}\frac{\partial}{\partial\theta} + H_z\frac{\partial}{\partial z}. \tag{14}$$

The equations of magnetic diffusion are

$$\frac{DH_r}{D\tau} = \frac{\mathfrak{D}u}{\mathfrak{D}\tau} + \eta\left(\nabla^2 H_r - \frac{H_r}{r^2} - \frac{2}{r^2}\frac{\partial H_\theta}{\partial\theta}\right), \tag{15}$$

$$\frac{DH_\theta}{D\tau} + \frac{vH_r}{r} = \frac{\mathfrak{D}v}{\mathfrak{D}\tau} + \frac{H_\theta u}{r}$$
$$+ \eta\left(\nabla^2 H_\theta - \frac{H_\theta}{r^2} + \frac{2}{r^2}\frac{\partial H_r}{\partial\theta}\right), \tag{16}$$

$$\frac{DH_z}{D\tau} = \frac{\mathfrak{D}w}{\mathfrak{D}\tau} + \eta\nabla^2 H_z. \tag{17}$$

The equation for thermal diffusion is

$$\frac{DT}{D\tau} = \kappa\nabla^2 T, \tag{18}$$

with ∇^2 given by (13) for cylindrical coordinates and κ denoting thermal diffusivity. The equations of continuity are

$$\frac{\partial(ru)}{\partial r} + \frac{\partial v}{\partial\theta} + \frac{\partial(rw)}{\partial z} = 0, \tag{19}$$

$$\frac{\partial(rH_r)}{\partial r} + \frac{\partial H_\theta}{\partial\theta} + \frac{\partial(rH_z)}{\partial z} = 0. \tag{20}$$

With the disturbances in temperature, pressure, and density denoted, respectively, by T', p', and ρ', and the disturbance in the magnetic field denoted by (h_r, h_θ, h_z), one has

$$T = T_m + T', \quad p = p_m + p', \quad \rho = \rho_m + \rho', \tag{21}$$

$$\mathbf{H} = (h_r, 2\pi j_0 r + h_\theta, h_z). \tag{22}$$

If Eqs. (2), (21), and (22) are substituted into (9) to (20), and if all quadratic and higher order terms involving α (assumed small) and all disturbance quantities are dropped, then since the mean quantities satisfy the equations separately, the equations to the first order are

$$\frac{\partial u}{\partial t} = -\frac{\partial q}{\partial r} + \mathrm{Pr}\left(\nabla^2 u - \frac{u}{r^2} - \frac{2}{r^2}\frac{\partial v}{\partial\theta}\right)$$
$$+ Q\left(\frac{\partial h_r}{\partial\theta} - 2h_\theta\right), \tag{23}$$

$$\frac{\partial v}{\partial t} = -\frac{1}{r}\frac{\partial q}{\partial\theta} + \mathrm{Pr}\left(\nabla^2 v - \frac{v}{r^2} + \frac{2}{r^2}\frac{\partial u}{\partial\theta}\right)$$
$$+ Q\left(\frac{\partial h_\theta}{\partial\theta} + 2h_r\right), \tag{24}$$

$$\frac{\partial w}{\partial t} = -\frac{\partial q}{\partial z} + \mathrm{Pr}\,\nabla^2 w - \mathrm{Pr}\,R\Theta + Q\frac{\partial h_z}{\partial\theta}, \tag{25}$$

$$\frac{\partial h_r}{\partial t} = 2\pi\frac{\partial u}{\partial\theta} + \frac{\eta}{\kappa}\left(\nabla^2 h_r - \frac{h_r}{r^2} - \frac{2}{r^2}\frac{\partial h_\theta}{\partial\theta}\right), \tag{26}$$

$$\frac{\partial h_\theta}{\partial t} = 2\pi\frac{\partial v}{\partial\theta} + \frac{\eta}{\kappa}\left(\nabla^2 h_\theta - \frac{h_\theta}{r^2} + \frac{2}{r^2}\frac{\partial h_r}{\partial\theta}\right), \tag{27}$$

$$\frac{\partial h_z}{\partial t} = 2\pi\frac{\partial w}{\partial\theta} + \frac{\eta}{\kappa}\nabla^2 h_z, \tag{28}$$

$$\frac{\partial\Theta}{\partial\tau} + w = \nabla^2\Theta \tag{29}$$

$$\frac{\partial(ru)}{\partial r} + \frac{\partial v}{\partial\theta} + \frac{\partial(rw)}{\partial z} = 0, \tag{30}$$

$$\frac{\partial(rh_r)}{\partial r} + \frac{\partial h_\theta}{\partial\theta} + \frac{\partial(rh_z)}{\partial z} = 0, \tag{31}$$

in which all distances (r and z) are now measured in terms of b, all velocities in terms of κ/b, all h's in terms of $j_0 b$, ∇^2 is now dimensionless, and

$$t = \tau\kappa/b^2, \quad q = \frac{2b^2(p' - \lambda\theta') + \mu j_0 r h_0}{2\rho_0\kappa^2}$$

(r and h_θ dimensional),

$$\mathrm{Pr}\text{ (Prandtl number)} = \nu/\kappa, \quad Q = \frac{\mu b^4 j_0^2}{2\rho_0\kappa^2},$$

$$\mathrm{R}\text{ (Rayleigh number)} = -\frac{g\alpha\beta b^4}{\nu\kappa}, \quad \theta = \frac{T'}{\beta b}.$$

III. AXISYMMETRIC CONVECTION

For axisymmetric convection all physical quantities are independent of θ, and from the forms of Eqs. (24) and (26) to (28) the quantities v and the h's will eventually be damped out. The equation governing the diffusion of h_z is, for axisymmetry, identical with that for heat conduction in solids. Now if h_z is zero at infinity or if it is zero at large radial distances but is periodic longitudinally, conduction through several media (the fluid in the cylinder, the wall, the fluid or air outside of the cylinder) must reduce it to zero everywhere because there are no internal sources, as indicated by Eq. (28) for axisymmetry. As for h_r and h_θ, the equations governing their diffusion are the same as that for the swirling velocity of a viscous fluid moving axisymmetrically. True, there are three media, and the value of η/κ varies from medium to medium, but if h_r and h_θ are zero at infinity or if they vanish at large r but are periodic in z, the eventual vanishing of h_r and h_θ is evident from the physical point of view. If h_r is zero, then for axisymmetry equation (24) is the equation for axisymmetric swirling motion of a viscous fluid in the absence of a magnetic field, with the boundary condition that v is zero at $r = 1$. If v is zero at large absolute values of z or if it is periodic in z, again it must vanish everywhere eventually.

The mathematical substantiation of the foregoing physical arguments is simple. Since the case of h_θ is similar to that of h_r, the case of h_z is simpler than that of h_r, and the vanishing of v follows from that of h_r for axisymmetry, a mathematical proof of the vanishing of h_r only will suffice. If the outer radius of the cylinder in terms of the inner radius b is c (so that the wall thickness is $bc - b$), the quantity η/κ for $1 < r \leq c$ will be denoted by $(\eta/\kappa)_w$, and that for $c < r$ will be denoted by $(\eta/\kappa)_0$. For periodicity in z, the region to be considered is, with l as the dimensionless period in the z direction,

$$0 \leq r, \qquad 0 \leq z \leq l.$$

For h_r vanishing at all points at infinity, the entire space is the region under consideration. Since the demonstration is quite the same, only the periodic case will be presented. For axisymmetry, Eq. (26) is, with $a = 2\pi/l$ as the wave number and D for $\partial/\partial r$,

$$\frac{\partial h_r}{\partial t} = \frac{\eta}{\kappa}\left(\nabla^2 h_r - \frac{h_r}{r^2}\right) = \frac{\eta}{\kappa}\left(D\frac{1}{r}Dr - a^2\right)h_r. \quad (32)$$

Multiplying Eq. (32) by $\kappa r h_r/\eta$ and integrating for the fluid in the cylinder, one has

$$\frac{\partial}{\partial t} I_0 = \int_0^l \left(h_r \frac{1}{r} Dr h_r\right)_0^1 dz \\ - \int_0^l \int_0^1 \left[\frac{1}{r}(Dr h_r)^2 + a^2 h_r{}^2\right] dr\, dz, \quad (33)$$

in which

$$I_0 = \frac{\kappa}{\eta} \int_0^l \int_0^1 r h_r{}^2\, dr\, dz.$$

Similarly,

$$\frac{\partial}{\partial t} I_1 = \int_0^l \left(h_r \frac{1}{r} Dr h_r\right)_1^c dz \\ - \int_0^l \int_1^c \left[\frac{1}{r}(Dr h_r)^2 + a^2 h_r{}^2\right] dr\, dz, \quad (34)$$

$$\frac{\partial}{\partial t} I_2 = \int_0^l \left(h_r \frac{1}{r} Dr h_r\right)_c^\infty dz \\ - \int_0^l \int_c^\infty \left[\frac{1}{r}(Dr h_r)^2 + a^2 h_r{}^2\right] dr\, dz, \quad (35)$$

in which

$$I_1 = \left(\frac{\kappa}{\eta}\right)_w \int_0^l \int_1^c r h_r{}^2\, dr\, dz,$$

$$I_2 = \left(\frac{\kappa}{\eta}\right)_0 \int_0^l \int_c^\infty r h_r{}^2\, dr\, dz.$$

Since h_r is zero at $r = 0$ and at $r = \infty$, addition of Eqs. (33) to (35) yields, if $h_r \neq 0$,

$$\frac{\partial}{\partial t}(I_0 + I_1 + I_2) = \text{negative definite.}$$

Since the I's are positive definite for $h_r \neq 0$, this equation means that h_r must eventually vanish. Similarly, v, h_θ, and h_z must eventually vanish. From Eqs. (23) to (31) it can then be concluded that a longitudinal electric current does not affect at all the stability of a fluid heated from below with respect to axisymmetric convection. This is perhaps not surprising, because, loosely speaking, the magnetic lines are not "cut"—only enveloped—by the motion of the fluid.

The Rayleigh number R for axisymmetric convection in the absence of a magnetic field was first found by Hales[2] to be 452.1. Hales' numerical results indicate that this critical Rayleigh number corresponds to zero wave number of the disturbance—a fact later analytically proved by Yih.[1]

IV. CONVECTION WITH ZERO WAVE NUMBER

Although only for axisymmetric convection has it been proved that the most unstable disturbance is that with zero wave number, the same situation can be assumed to prevail in other modes of convection. In fact, Taylor[3] has tacitly assumed this situation to be true for the first mode of unsymmetric convection, and has found what is truly the critical Rayleigh number—67.9. The critical Rayleigh number for the second mode of unsymmetric convection, assumed to correspond to zero wave number, was found by Yih[1] to be 329.1. It seems reasonable to assume that the critical Rayleigh numbers for the various modes will still correspond to zero wave number even in the presence of a circular magnetic field created by the electric current, and to investigate the stability of the fluid in this field for zero wave number.

For zero wave number all physical quantities are independent of z. Furthermore, u and v can be assumed to be zero. Since Eq. (31) becomes

$$\partial h_\theta/\partial\theta = -\partial(r h_r)/\partial r,$$

Eq. (26) can be written in terms of h_r alone, and by the method of Sec. II it can be shown mathematically that h_r must eventually vanish. Then Eq. (27) becomes the same as that for axisymmetric convection and the result of Sec. III shows that h_θ must also vanish. However, h_z will not vanish because w now depends on θ. The governing equations are then Eqs. (25), (28), and (29), with $\partial q/\partial z$ equal to zero in (25).

The boundary condition for the flow is that

$$w = 0 \quad \text{at} \quad r = 1. \tag{36}$$

The thermal boundary condition is, if the wall is a poor* heat conductor,

$$\partial\Theta/\partial r = 0 \quad \text{at} \quad r = 1. \tag{37}$$

If the boundary is a much better conductor of electricity than the fluid, then the θ component of electric field strength along the wall must be zero, so that in the fluid

$$j_\theta = 0,$$

or, since

$$j_\theta = \frac{\partial h_r}{\partial z} - \frac{\partial h_z}{\partial r} = -\frac{\partial h_z}{\partial r},$$
$$\partial h_z/\partial r = 0 \quad \text{at} \quad r = 1. \tag{38}$$

The case of a thermally insulated wall which is a good conductor (circumferentially) of electricity may seem to be artificial. But it can be realized by a thin shell of copper in the inside of a glass tube, for instance. The wall will be insulated (thermally or electrically) radially but not circumferentially. If the boundary is a poor conductor of electricity as well as of heat, then at the wall

$$j_r = \frac{1}{r}\frac{\partial h_z}{\partial \theta} - \frac{\partial h_\theta}{\partial z} = 0,$$

or, since $\partial h_\theta/\partial z$ is zero for zero wave number and unsymmetric convection is expressly under consideration,

$$h_z = 0 \quad \text{at} \quad r = 1. \tag{39}$$

With the substitutions ($n = $ integer)

$$(w, \Theta, h_z) = [W(r)\cos n\theta, f(r)\cos n\theta, h(r)\sin n\theta], \tag{40}$$

Eqs. (25), (28), and (29) become (with $D = d/dr$), under the assumption of the so-called marginal stability,

$$\left(\frac{1}{r} Dr\, D - \frac{n^2}{r^2}\right)W = \mathrm{R}f - \frac{nQ}{\mathrm{Pr}}h, \tag{41}$$

$$\frac{\eta}{\kappa}\left(\frac{1}{r} Dr\, D - \frac{n^2}{r^2}\right)h = 2\pi n W, \tag{42}$$

$$\left(\frac{1}{r} Dr\, D - \frac{n^2}{r^2}\right)f = W. \tag{43}$$

---

* The linear temperature gradient may be maintained by a wall which is an excellent heat conductor with an imposed linear temperature distribution, but this is a rather artificial case. We do not wish to discuss this case though it can be treated readily enough.

The boundary conditions are either

$$W = 0, \qquad Df = 0, \qquad Dh = 0 \tag{44}$$
(wall perfect electricity conductor) at $r = 1$,

or

$$W = 0, \qquad Df = 0, \qquad h = 0 \tag{45}$$
(wall poor conductor) at $r = 1$.

It is understood that at $r = 0$, W, f, and h must not be singular.

For the first set of boundary conditions, one can simply take

$$h = \frac{2\pi\eta\kappa f}{\eta}, \tag{46}$$

and the differential system then becomes

$$\left(\frac{1}{r} Dr\, D - \frac{n^2}{r^2}\right)W = (\mathrm{R} - n^2Q')f, \tag{47}$$

$$\left(\frac{1}{r} Dr\, D - \frac{n^2}{r^2}\right)f = W, \tag{48}$$

with boundary conditions

$$W = Df = 0 \quad \text{at} \quad r = 1 \tag{49}$$

and

$$Q' = \frac{\pi\mu b^4 j_0{}^2}{\rho_0\nu\eta}. \tag{50}$$

Now the system consisting of Eqs. (47)–(49) has been solved for $n = 0$ by Hales,[2] for $n = 1$ by Taylor,[3] and for $n = 0$, 1, and 2 by Yih.[1] The results are, *mutatis mutandis*,

$$\mathrm{R} \qquad\quad = 452.1 \quad \text{for} \quad n = 0,$$
$$\mathrm{R} - Q' = 67.9 \quad \text{for} \quad n = 1,$$
$$\mathrm{R} - 4Q' = 329.1 \quad \text{for} \quad n = 2.$$

From these results it can be seen that $n = 2$ cannot be a critical case. Whether $n = 0$ or $n = 1$ is the critical case now depends on Q'. If Q' is larger than 384.2, any instability that occurs must necessarily be axisymmetric. If Q' is less than 384.2, unsymmetric convection ($n = 1$) will set in first, before any axisymmetric convection is possible. There is thus a sudden change of fluid behavior at $\mathrm{R} = 452.1$ and Q' equal to 384.2, at which the two modes of convection ($n = 0$ or 1) can set in simultaneously— a most interesting situation. A plot of the critical Rayleigh number against Q' is shown in Fig. 1.

The most realistic case is the one in which the wall of the cylinder is insulated both thermally and electrically, so that the boundary conditions are

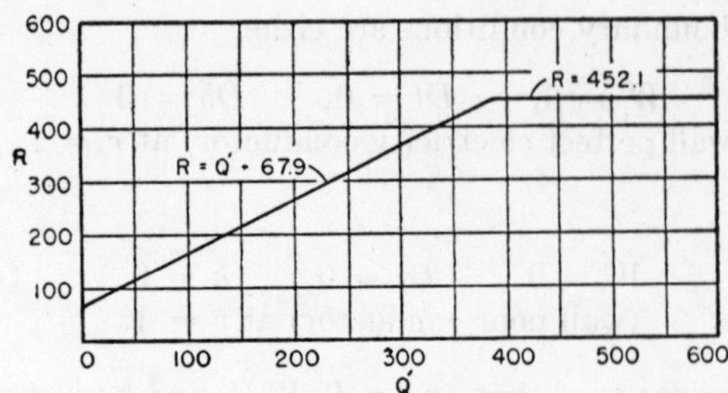

FIG. 1. Variation of critical Rayleigh number with Q', the wall being a perfect conductor of electricity.

given by Eqs. (45). Substituting Eqs. (42) and (43) in (41), we have

$$L_n^2 W - SW = 0 \qquad (51)$$

with

$$S = R - n^2 Q', \qquad L_n = \frac{1}{r} Dr\, D - (n^2/r^2).$$

The solution of (51) that satisfies the condition $W = 0$ *at* $r = 1$ and is nonsingular at $r = 0$ is

$$W = Ai^n[J_n(iS^{\frac14})J_n(S^{\frac14}r) - J_n(S^{\frac14})J_n(iS^{\frac14}r)]. \qquad (52)$$

This expression for W can be substituted in Eq. (42), which can then be solved for h. The solution satisfying the condition $h = 0$ at $r = 1$ is

$$h = -\frac{4\pi n\kappa}{\eta} S^{-\frac14} Ai^n[J_n(iS^{\frac14})J_n(S^{\frac14}r)$$
$$+ J_n(S^{\frac14})J_n(iS^{\frac14}r) - 2J_n(S^{\frac14})J_n(iS^{\frac14}r^n]. \qquad (53)$$

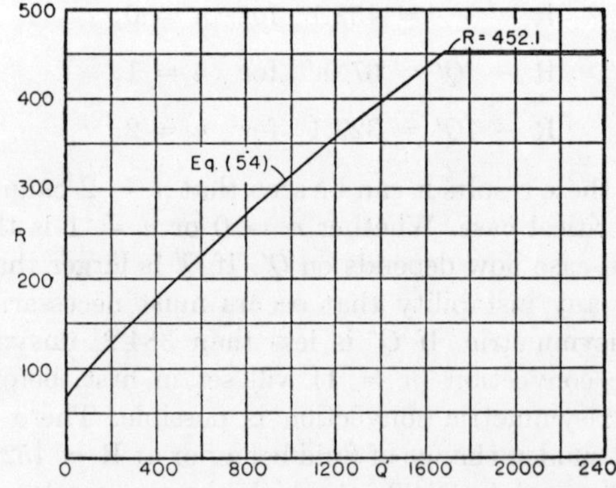

FIG. 2 Variation of critical Rayleigh number with Q', the wall being a poor conductor.

Equations (52) and (53) can then be substituted in (41) to find f. If one now demands that the resulting expression for f satisfy $Df = 0$ at $r = 1$, and that the solution be not identically zero, one arrives at the secular equation (after utilizing some known relationships of the Bessel functions and their derivatives),

$$2n(S - 2R)J_n(S^{\frac14})J_n(iS^{\frac14})$$
$$+ S^{\frac14}R[J_{n-1}(S^{\frac14})J_n(iS^{\frac14}) \qquad (54)$$
$$+ iJ_{n-1}(iS^{\frac14})J_n(S^{\frac14})] = 0.$$

This equation is solved numerically for the most important case of $n = 1$. The procedure is as follows. Assuming S, one can solve (54) for R straightforwardly, and then compute Q' from S and R. The resulting Q' is plotted against R and the relationship between Q' and R for zero wave number is given approximately in Table I. At R equal to

TABLE I. Relationship between Q' and R for zero wave number.

Q'	0	104	208	303	412	480	558	749	1132	1290	1465	1762
R	67.9	99	127	153	181	197	217	261	343	375	410	466

452.1, Q' is equal to 1682. This is the transition (or critical) value for Q' at which axisymmetric and unsymmetric ($n = 1$) convections can set in simultaneously, and above which only axisymmetric convection is physically possible. A plot of the critical Rayleigh number against Q' for an electrically and thermally insulated boundary is shown in Fig. 2.

V. CONCLUSION

The foregoing investigation shows clearly that a longitudinal electric current favors axisymmetric convection, with clear-cut laws of favoritism, and that the physically significant solution of a differential system may change its behavior abruptly at certain critical values of its parameters.

ACKNOWLEDGMENTS

This work is sponsored by the Office of Ordnance Research, U. S. Army. The computational assistance rendered by Mr. William Graebel is much appreciated.

Reprinted without change of pagination from the
Proceedings of the Royal Society, A, *volume* 258, pp. 63–86, 1960

Instability of a rotating liquid film with a free surface*

By Chia-Shun Yih

Department of Engineering Mechanics, University of Michigan

With an appendix by J. F. C. Kingman

(Communicated by Sir Geoffrey Taylor, F.R.S.— Received 23 *December* 1959)

[Plate 7]

The centripetal acceleration of a rotating liquid film is tantamount to a centrifugal force, which tends to cause the liquid film to form rings around the circular cylinder to which it is attached. The stabilizing factors are surface tension and, presumably, viscosity. But it is shown in this paper that instability occurs even for large values of the surface-tension parameter and at small Reynolds numbers. The critical wave number is shown to depend predominantly on the surface tension. Its dependence on the Reynolds number, R, is slight if R is small, and nil if R is large. The effect of viscosity is therefore essentially to slow down the rate of amplification of the unstable disturbances.

The analysis is carried out for both large and small Reynolds numbers, for various ratios of film thickness to cylinder radius, and for various surface tension parameters. (The calculation for intermediate Reynolds numbers turns out to be unnecessary for the purpose of comparison with the experiments obtained. Enough information is provided by the calculations performed for practical applications.) Numerical results are given. Comparison of results obtained from 65 experiments with pure glycerine, water + glycerine mixture, and water with the analytical results shows satisfactory agreement.

1. Introduction

The phenomenon of instability of a rotating liquid film with a free surface is of importance to the paper industry because it occurs on the table rolls underneath the wire screen carrying the pulp in a Fourdrinier machine, and because, in the process of coating, rotating cylinders are often used to carry the coating material in the form of liquid films. This phenomenon can be described briefly as follows: when a cylinder carrying a thin film of fluid on its outside surface rotates with sufficient speed, fluid rings will be developed and will in general grow in height and subsequently disintegrate (see figure 17, plate 7). The cause of instability is essentially centripetal acceleration of the liquid film in the presence of a free surface, although Coriolis acceleration does play a role in this phenomenon. Instability phenomena similar to the one under consideration have been considered by Sir Geoffrey Taylor. In a well-known paper (Taylor 1923) he considered the instability of a fluid between concentric rotating cylinders. However, the absence of a free surface in his problem makes it quite different from the one under study. In a later paper (1950), Taylor considered the instability of the free surface of a liquid accelerated downward, but neglected the effects of viscosity or Coriolis acceleration (which does not exist in his problem). The phenomenon under investigation here is thus in a sense a combination of the phenomena considered by Taylor, to whose

* This work has been sponsored by the Fluid Mechanics Section of the Technical Association of Pulp and Paper Industries.

64   Chia-Shun Yih

wide scientific inspiration the present work bears testimony. The effects of viscosity, surface tension, and Coriolis acceleration will be taken into consideration, and the effect of gravity will be accounted for in the interpretation of the experimental results.

The stability analysis is based on the assumption of axisymmetry of the disturbances. Although the experiments performed did indicate the predominance of axisymmetry, at least at low Reynolds numbers, it is in fact not known whether this predominance is inherent, or merely due to the particular experimental arrangement used. The stability of two-dimensional disturbances (independent of distance in the axial direction) is now being analyzed. The result will be presented elsewhere.

2. Formulation of the problem

The radius of the cylinder (see figure 17, plate 7) will be denoted by a, and its angular speed of rotation by ω. If the cylindrical co-ordinates r and z are measured in terms of a, all velocities in terms of ωa, the pressure in terms of $\rho \omega^2 a^2$ (with ρ denoting the density of the liquid), the mean velocity is described simply by

$$\overline{V} = r, \tag{1}$$

and the mean pressure gradient is simply

$$\mathrm{d}\overline{p}/\mathrm{d}r = r. \tag{2}$$

If, furthermore, the time t is measured in terms of $1/\omega$, the linearized equations of motion for the perturbation velocity (u, v, w) and the perturbation pressure p are, for axisymmetry,

$$\frac{\partial u}{\partial t} - 2v = -\frac{\partial p}{\partial r} + \frac{1}{R_a}\left(\nabla^2 u - \frac{u}{r^2}\right), \tag{3}$$

$$\frac{\partial v}{\partial t} + 2u = \frac{1}{R_a}\left(\nabla^2 v - \frac{v}{r^2}\right), \tag{4}$$

$$\frac{\partial w}{\partial t} = -\frac{\partial p}{\partial z} + \frac{1}{R_a}\nabla^2 w, \tag{5}$$

in which

$$\nabla^2 \equiv \frac{\partial^2}{\partial r^2} + \frac{1}{r}\frac{\partial}{\partial r} + \frac{\partial^2}{\partial z^2}, \tag{6}$$

and

$$R_a = \frac{\rho \omega a^2}{\mu} = \frac{\omega a^2}{\nu} \tag{7}$$

is the Reynolds number based on a, with μ and ν denoting the dynamic and kinematic viscosity, respectively.

The equations of motion are to be solved simultaneously with the equation of continuity

$$\frac{\partial u}{\partial r} + \frac{u}{r} + \frac{\partial w}{\partial z} = 0, \tag{8}$$

with the appropriate boundary conditions. The boundary conditions at the surface of the cylinders are

$$u = v = w = 0 \quad \text{at} \quad r = 1. \tag{9}$$

With η denoting the (dimensionless) deviation of the free surface from its mean position, the kinematic condition at the free surface is, for axisymmetry,

$$\partial \eta / \partial t = u. \tag{10}$$

Instability of a rotating liquid film with a free surface   65

The dynamic conditions at the free surface are (with r, θ and z as the cylindrical co-ordinates):

$$\text{shear stresses} \quad \tau_{r\theta} = \tau_{rz} = 0 \quad \text{at} \quad r = 1 + d/a, \tag{11}$$

and

$$\text{normal stress} \quad \tau_{rr} = 0 \quad \text{at the free surface.} \tag{12}$$

The symbol d in conditions (11) denotes the mean thickness of the liquid film.

In terms of velocity components, conditions (11) become

$$r\frac{\partial}{\partial r}\left(\frac{v}{r}\right) = 0 \quad \text{and} \quad \frac{\partial u}{\partial z} + \frac{\partial w}{\partial r} = 0,$$

which can be imposed at $r = 1 + d/a$ because there are no shear stresses $\tau_{r\theta}$ and τ_{rz} for the *mean* flow. The condition (12), translated in terms of velocity components, is more complicated, because there is a gradient for the mean pressure $\overline{p}$ at the free surface. With axisymmetric rings spaced in the z-direction, condition (12) can be written in the form (see note added in proof on p. 86)

$$-p - \frac{d\overline{p}}{dr}\eta - \frac{T}{\rho\omega^2 a^3}\frac{\partial^2\eta}{\partial z^2} + \frac{2}{R_a}\frac{\partial u}{\partial r} = 0,$$

with all quantities evaluated at $r = 1 + d/a$, η being calculated from equation (10).

Equations (2) to (12a) constitute the differential system to be solved. Since the system is homogeneous and linear, it is obvious that all unknowns admit of the trivial solution zero. For a non-trivial solution a relation between the pertinent parameters of the system must be satisfied. Thus the problem has the structure of an eigenvalue problem, like all problems of hydrodynamic instability formulated according to a linear theory. Without further simplifications, however, the problem is still not very tractable. Following Taylor, we shall assume that

$$(u, v, p, \eta) = (U, V, P, H)\,e^{\sigma t}\cos nz. \tag{13}$$

$$w = W\,e^{\sigma t}\sin nz, \tag{14}$$

in which σ is the exponential growth factor, and n is the wave number in the z-direction defined by

$$n = 2\pi a/\lambda, \tag{15}$$

λ being the wavelength in the z-direction. With

$$L \equiv D^2 + \frac{1}{r}D - \frac{1}{r^2}, \quad L' \equiv D^2 + \frac{1}{r}D, \quad D \equiv \frac{d}{dr},$$

the equations of motion are

$$\sigma U - 2V = -\frac{\partial P}{\partial r} + R_a^{-1}(L - n^2)\,U, \tag{16}$$

$$\sigma V + 2U = R_a^{-1}(L - n^2)\,V, \tag{17}$$

$$\sigma W = nP + R_a^{-1}(L' - n^2)\,W, \tag{18}$$

and the equation of continuity is

$$DU + U/r + nW = 0. \tag{19}$$

Chia-Shun Yih

After P has been eliminated, equations (16) to (18) become

$$(L-n^2-\sigma R_a)(L-n^2)U = 2n^2 R_a V, \tag{20}$$

$$(L-n^2-\sigma R_a)V = 2R_a U. \tag{21}$$

The boundary conditions at $r = 1$ are now

$$U = DU = V = 0, \tag{22}$$

since the vanishing of W can be replaced by that of DU, in virtue of equation (20). The kinematic condition (10) and the boundary conditions (11a) become

$$\sigma H = U, \quad DV - V/r = 0, \quad (L+n^2)U = 0 \quad \text{at} \quad r = 1+d/a, \quad (23a,b,c)$$

the last of which has been obtained through the use of equation (20). In virtue of equations (20) and (23a) the boundary condition (12a) becomes

$$\sigma(L'-n^2-\sigma R_a)\frac{1}{r}D(rU) - 2\sigma n^2 DU + \left(r - \frac{T}{\rho\omega^2 a^3}n^2\right)n^2 R_a U = 0, \tag{24}$$

to be imposed at $r = 1+d/a$.

For small values of d/a, the differential system consisting of equations (21) to (24) can be considerably simplified. With

$$R = \frac{\omega d^2}{\nu}, \quad m = \frac{nd}{a}, \quad D = \frac{d}{d\xi}, \quad \xi = \frac{a(r-1)}{d}, \tag{25}$$

and with D^2 replacing L (because $|DU| \gg |U|/r$, etc.), the equations of motion become

$$(D^2-m^2-\sigma R)(D^2-m^2)U = 2m^2 RV, \tag{26}$$

$$(D^2-m^2-\sigma R)V = 2RU, \tag{27}$$

and the boundary conditions become

$$U = DU = V = 0 \quad \text{at} \quad \xi = 0, \tag{28}$$

$$(D^2+m^2)U = 0, \quad DV = 0 \quad \text{at} \quad \xi = 1, \tag{29}$$

$$\sigma(D^2-3m^2-\sigma R)DU + \left(b - \frac{Tm^2}{\rho\omega^2 d^3}\right)m^2 RU = 0 \quad \text{at} \quad \xi = 1. \tag{30}$$

in which $b = 1+a/d$. In terms of U alone, the equations constituting the differential system to be solved are, finally

$$(D^2-m^2-\sigma R)^2(D^2-m^2)U = 4m^2 R^2 U, \tag{31}$$

$$U = 0, \quad DU = 0, \quad (D^2-m^2-\sigma R)(D^2-m^2)U = 0 \quad \text{at} \quad \xi = 0, \quad (32a,b,c)$$

$$(D^2+m^2)U = 0, \quad D(D^2-m^2-\sigma R)(D^2-m^2)U = 0 \quad \text{at} \quad \xi = 1, \quad (33a,b)$$

$$\sigma(D^2-3m^2-\sigma R)DU + (b-Sm^2)m^2 RU = 0 \quad \text{at} \quad \xi = 1, \tag{34}$$

with

$$S = T/\rho\omega^2 d^3. \tag{35}$$

The purpose of the subsequent calculation is to find the relation between m, R, S, b and σ which will allow a non-trivial solution of the differential system just obtained.

3. Principle of exchange of stabilities

Since the growth rate σ is in general complex, it is very desirable to show that when its imaginary part σ_i is not zero, its real part σ_r is always negative, i.e. the flow is always stable. The proof is rigorous, and does not involve a detailed solution of the differential system governing the phenomenon. For the sake of completeness, equations (20) to (24) will be used instead of the simplified equations.

Multiplying equations (20) by $r\overline{U}$ ($\overline{U}$ being the conjugate of U) and integrating (by parts if necessary), we have, with c denoting $1+d/a$,

$$I_2 + (2n^2 + \sigma R_a)I_1 + n^2(n^2 + \sigma R_a)I_0$$
$$+ [\overline{U}\mathrm{D}(rLU) - (\mathrm{D}(rU))LU - (2n^2 + \sigma R_a)\overline{U}\mathrm{D}(rU)]_{r=c}$$
$$= 2n^2 R_a \int_1^c rV\overline{U}\,\mathrm{d}r, \qquad (36)$$

in which
$$I_0 = \int_1^c rU\overline{U}\,\mathrm{d}r, \quad I_1 = \int_1^c \frac{1}{r}|\mathrm{D}(rU)|^2\,\mathrm{d}r, \quad I_2 = \int_1^c r|LU|^2\,\mathrm{d}r.$$

Similarly, multiplication of equation (21) by $r\overline{V}$ and integration yields

$$(\overline{V}\mathrm{D}(rV))_{r=c} - J_1 - (n^2 + \sigma R_a)J_0 = 2R_a \int_1^c r\overline{V}U\,\mathrm{d}r, \qquad (37)$$

in which
$$J_0 = \int_1^c r|V|^2\,\mathrm{d}r, \quad J_1 = \int_1^c \frac{1}{r}|\mathrm{D}(rV)|^2\,\mathrm{d}r.$$

From equation (23b)
$$(\overline{V}\mathrm{D}(rV))_c = 2(V\overline{V})_c. \qquad (38)$$

Furthermore, from the definition of L',

$$rL'\left(\frac{1}{r}\mathrm{D}(rU)\right) = \mathrm{D}(rLU), \qquad (39)$$

so that equation (24) can be written as

$$\mathrm{D}(rLU) - (n^2 + \sigma R)\,\mathrm{D}(rU) - 2n^2 rDU + \frac{1}{\sigma}\left(c - \frac{T}{\rho\omega^2 a^3}n^2\right)n^2 R_a U = 0. \qquad (40)$$

If equations (36) and (37) are combined, and equations (23c) and (38) are used

$$\{\overline{U}[\mathrm{D}(rLU) - (n^2 + \sigma R_a)\,\mathrm{D}(rU) - 2n^2 rDU] + n^2[\overline{U}\mathrm{D}(rU) + U\mathrm{D}(r\overline{U})] - 2n^2 U\overline{U}\}_c$$
$$+ I_2 + 2n^2 I_1 + n^4 I_0 + \sigma R_a(I_1 + n^2 I_0) = n^2[(2V\overline{V})_c - J_1 - n^2 J_0 - \overline{\sigma}RJ_0].$$

In virtue of equations (23a) and (40), this becomes

$$\overline{\sigma}\left(c - \frac{T}{\rho\omega^2 a^3}n^2\right)n^2 R_a H\overline{H} + \{n^2[\overline{U}\mathrm{D}(rU) + U\mathrm{D}(r\overline{U})] - 2n^2 U\overline{U}\}_c$$
$$+ I_2 + 2n^2 I_1 + n^4 I_0 + \sigma R_a(I_1 + n^2 I_0) = n^2[(2V\overline{V})_c - J_1 - n^2 J_0 - \overline{\sigma}R_a J_0]. \qquad (41)$$

But

$$[\overline{U}\mathrm{D}(rU) + U\mathrm{D}(r\overline{U}) - 2U\overline{U}]_c = \int_1^c r(\overline{U}LU + UL\overline{U})\,\mathrm{d}r + 2\int_1^c \frac{1}{r}|\mathrm{D}(rU)|^2\,\mathrm{d}r$$

$$-2\int_1^c \mathrm{D}(U\overline{U})\,\mathrm{d}r = \int_1^c r(\overline{U}LU + UL\overline{U})\,\mathrm{d}r + 2\int_1^c \left(r|DU|^2 + \frac{1}{r}|U|^2\right)\mathrm{d}r,$$

and
$$I_2 + n^4 I_0 + n^2 \int_1^c r(\overline{U}LU + UL\overline{U})\,\mathrm{d}r = \int_1^c r|LU + n^2 U|^2\,\mathrm{d}r \geqslant 0,$$

so that
$$I_3 = n^2\{[\overline{U}\mathrm{D}(rU) + U\mathrm{D}(r\overline{U})] - 2U\overline{U}\}_c + I_2 + n^4 I_0 \tag{42}$$

is positive definite. Similarly,

$$J_2 = J_1 - 2(V\overline{V})_c = \int_1^c \frac{1}{r}\,|\mathrm{D}(rV)|^2\,\mathrm{d}r - 2\int_1^c (V\mathrm{D}\overline{V} + \overline{V}\mathrm{D}V)\,\mathrm{d}r$$

$$= \int_1^c \left(r|\mathrm{D}V|^2 + \frac{1}{r}V\overline{V}\right)\mathrm{d}r - \int_1^c (V\mathrm{D}\overline{V} + \overline{V}\,\mathrm{D}V)\,\mathrm{d}r$$

$$= \int_1^c \frac{1}{r}\,|r\,\mathrm{D}V - V|^2\,\mathrm{d}r \tag{43}$$

is positive definite. Thus equation (41) can be written

$$I_3 + 2n^2 I_1 + n^2 J_2 + n^2 J_0 = -\sigma R_a(I_1 + n^2 I_0) - \overline{\sigma}n^2 R_a\left[J_0 + \left(c - \frac{T}{\rho\omega^2 a^3}n^2\right)H\overline{H}\right],$$

or, with real and imaginary parts separated,

$$I_3 + 2n^2 I_1 + n^2 J_2 + n^2 J_0 = -\sigma_r R_a\left[I_1 + n^2 I_0 + n^2 J_0 + \left(c - \frac{T}{\rho\omega^2 a^3}n^2\right)n^2 H\overline{H}\right] \tag{44}$$

and
$$0 = -\sigma_i R_a\left[I_1 + n^2 I_0 - n^2 J_0 - \left(c - \frac{T}{\rho\omega^2 a^3}n^2\right)n^2 H\overline{H}\right]. \tag{45}$$

If σ_i is not equal to zero, then the bracket in equation (45) is zero. Hence the bracket in equation (44) is positive, and σ_r is negative. Thus all waves travelling along the length of the cylinder are necessarily stable, and for unstable or neutrally stable disturbances σ_i must be equal to zero. Since we are chiefly concerned with unstable (or neutrally stable) modes, σ_i will henceforth be taken to be zero.

4. Neutral stability

Before the details of the solution are presented, it is very instructive to investigate the case of neutral stability. It will be shown in this section that the condition for neutral stability is *independent* of the Reynolds number, and that for neutral stability there is no *perturbation motion* whatsoever, though there is a corrugation of the free surface. Lack of recognition of this situation has led to confusion and controversy in the past, in connexion with the problem of stability of a liquid film flowing under the action of gravity.

The original differential system consisting of equations (3) to (10), (11a) and (12a) is satisfied by
$$u = v = w = p = 0$$

provided η does not depend on time (neutral stability) and
$$\left(1 + \frac{d}{a}\right)\eta + \frac{T}{\rho\omega^2 a^3}\frac{\mathrm{d}^2\eta}{\mathrm{d}z^2} = 0$$

(See note added in proof on p. 86).

Instability of a rotating liquid film with a free surface   69

If η depends on z as specified in (13), this condition becomes

$$\left(1+\frac{d}{a}\right)-\frac{T}{\rho\omega^2 a^3}n^2 = 0. \tag{46}$$

On physical grounds we can conclude then that the flow is stable, neutrally stable, or unstable according as

$$\left(1+\frac{d}{a}\right)-\frac{T}{\rho\omega^2 a^3}n^2$$

is negative, zero, or positive. It is peculiar to problems of free-surface instability that the state of neutral stability may (as it does in this case) correspond to a state of *perturbed configuration but no perturbation motion*. It is also very interesting that the condition for neutral stability is entirely independent of the Reynolds number. This is perhaps not surprising, since for the state of neutral stability there is no perturbation motion and hence no Coriolis acceleration. The centripetal acceleration corresponds then to a centrifugal gravitational field for a static fluid, and viscosity certainly should not affect the *neutral* stability of what is essentially a *static* configuration.

For any Reynolds number and any surface tension T, there is always a range of the wave number n for which the flow is unstable. To find the critical wave number for which the instability is greatest, equation (46) is no longer sufficient, and a detailed calculation for the degree of instability is necessary. In the next two sections the calculation for large and small Reynolds numbers, respectively, will be presented.

When ω is zero, there is no mean motion, so long as gravity is neglected, as in the present analysis. In the absence of gravity and a virtual gravitational field created by rotation, there is no energy supply, and any *motion*, infinitesimal or finite, of whatever combination of modes, will definitely be damped out. However, static corrugations can remain if surface tension is zero. If surface tension is not zero, only surface deviations of infinite wavelength will not be damped out. If ω is not zero, then however small it may be and whatever the surface tension is, the flow is unstable for disturbances of sufficiently large wavelengths.

5. Solution for large Reynolds numbers

For problems of importance in engineering that involve the instability phenomenon under investigation the Reynolds number R may vary over a considerable range. Although the method of attack presented herein is entirely general if equation (47) is solved exactly, the numerical results presented in this section are for Reynolds numbers which are not too small, say not less than 100. Actually, the formulae presented can be used for computation at Reynolds numbers less than 100, but if only the first term involving R is taken in the formula, its application is limited to R's larger than 100, with increasing accuracy for increasing R.

With L^* denoting $D^2 - m^2$, equation (31) becomes

$$(L^{*3} - 2\sigma R L^{*2} + \sigma^2 R^2 L^* - 4m^2 R^2)\,U = 0,$$

the indicial equation of which is

$$x^3 - 2\sigma R x^2 + \sigma^2 R^2 x - 4m^2 R^2 = 0. \tag{47}$$

If the solutions of the indicial equation are denoted by x_1, x_2 and x_3, and

$$a_i^2 = m^2 + x_i \quad (i = 1, 2, 3), \tag{48}$$

the general solution of equation (31) is

$$U = \sum_{i=0}^{2} (A_{1+2i} \cosh a_{1+i}\xi + A_{2i} \sinh a_{1+i}\xi). \tag{49}$$

The six boundary conditions are

$$A_1 + A_3 + A_5 = 0,$$

$$a_1 A_2 + a_2 A_4 + a_3 A_6 = 0,$$

$$E_1 A_1 + E_2 A_3 + E_3 A_5 = 0,$$

$$a_1'^2(A_1 \cosh a_1 + A_2 \sinh a_1) + a_2'^2(A_3 \cosh a_2 + A_4 \sinh a_2)$$
$$+ a_3'^2(A_5 \cosh a_3 + A_6 \sinh a_3) = 0,$$

$$a_1 E_1(A_1 \sinh a_1 + A_2 \cosh a_1) + a_2 E_2(A_3 \sinh a_2 + A_4 \cosh a_2)$$
$$+ a_3 E_3(A_5 \sinh a_3 + A_6 \cosh a_3) = 0,$$

$$A_1(F_1 \sinh a_1 + S'm^2 R \cosh a_1) + A_2(F_1 \cosh a_1 + S'm^2 R \sinh a_1)$$
$$+ A_3(F_2 \sinh a_2 + S'm^2 R \cosh a_2) + A_4(F_2 \cosh a_2 + S'm^2 R \sinh a_2)$$
$$+ A_5(F_3 \sinh a_3 + S'm^2 R \cosh a_3) + A_6(F_3 \cosh a_3 + S'm^2 R \sinh a_3) = 0,$$

in which
$$a_i'^2 = a_i^2 + m^2 = 2m^2 + x_i, \quad E_i = x_i(x_i - \sigma R),$$

$$F_i = \sigma a_i(x_i - 2m^2 - \sigma R), \quad S' = b - Sm^2.$$

For a non-trivial solution, the A's must not all vanish. The condition for the non-vanishing of the A's is

$$\begin{vmatrix} 1 & 0 & 1 & 0 & 1 & 0 \\ 0 & a_1 & 0 & a_2 & 0 & a_3 \\ E_1 & 0 & E_2 & 0 & E_3 & 0 \\ b_1 & c_1 & b_2 & c_2 & b_3 & c_3 \\ d_1 & e_1 & d_2 & e_2 & d_3 & e_3 \\ f_1 & g_1 & f_2 & g_2 & f_3 & g_3 \end{vmatrix} = 0, \tag{50}$$

in which

$$b_i = a_i'^2 \cosh a_i, \qquad\qquad c_i = a_i'^2 \sinh a_i,$$

$$d_i = a_i E_i \sinh a_i, \qquad\qquad e_i = a_i E_i \cosh a_i,$$

$$f_i = F_i \sinh a_i + S'm^2 R \cosh a_i, \quad g_i = F_i \cosh a_i + S'm^2 R \sinh a_i.$$

For large R, two of the roots of (47), say x_1 and x_2, are large and nearly equal, as will be seen. Consequently, terms involving e^{-a_1} or e^{-a_2} as a factor can be neglected, but in all other respects the calculation needs very careful handling. If the second column of the determinant is subtracted from the first and the fourth from the third, and the new first column subtracted from the second and the new third column from the

Instability of a rotating liquid film with a free surface **71**

fourth, and the resulting second and fourth columns are divided respectively by e^{a_1} and e^{a_2} the resulting determinant is, after elements involving e^{-a_1} and e^{-a_2} are neglected,

$$\begin{vmatrix} 1 & 0 & 1 & 0 & 1 & 0 \\ -a_1 & 0 & -a_2 & 0 & 0 & a_3 \\ E_1 & 0 & E_2 & 0 & E_3 & 0 \\ 0 & a_1'^2 & 0 & a_2'^2 & b_3 & c_3 \\ 0 & a_1 E_1 & 0 & a_2 E_2 & d_3 & e_3 \\ 0 & F_1 + S'm^2R & 0 & F_2 + S'm^2R & f_3 & g_3 \end{vmatrix} = 0.$$

Now the first column is subtracted from the third and the fifth, and then the third row is multiplied by $(a_1 - a_2)/(E_2 - E_1)$ and subtracted from the second row. Finally, the second column is multiplied by 1, $\cosh a_3$, $\sinh a_3$ and subtracted respectively from the fourth, fifth, and sixth columns. The resulting determinant is

$$\begin{vmatrix} 0 & 0 & a_1 - \dfrac{E_3 - E_1}{E_2 - E_1}(a_1 - a_2) & a_3 \\ a_1'^2 & x_2 - x_1 & (x_3 - x_1)\cosh a_3 & (x_3 - x_1)\sinh a_3 \\ a_1 E_1 & a_2 E_2 - a_1 E_1 & a_3 E_3 \sinh a_3 - a_1 E_1 \cosh a_3 & a_3 E_3 \cosh a_3 - a_1 E_1 \sinh a_3 \\ F_1 + S'm^2R & F_2 - F_1 & F_3 \sinh a_3 - F_1 \cosh a_3 & F_3 \cosh a_3 - F_1 \sinh a_3 \end{vmatrix} = 0.$$

The determinant equation can finally be written in the following form

$$S'm^2R = \frac{a_1'^2 F_2 - a_2'^2 F_1}{F_2 - F_1}\frac{D_1}{D_2}, \tag{51}$$

in which

$$D_1 = \begin{vmatrix} 0 & B & C \\ \dfrac{x_2 - x_1}{r^*} - (a_2 E_2 - a_1 E_1) & a_3 E_3 & \dfrac{x_3 - x_1}{r^*} + a_1 E_1 \\ F_2 - F_1 & -F_3 & -F_1 \end{vmatrix},$$

$$D_2 = \begin{vmatrix} 0 & B & C \\ x_2 - x_1 & 0 & x_3 - x_1 \\ a_2 E_2 - a_1 E_1 & -a_3 E_3 & -a_1 E_1 \end{vmatrix},$$

with

$$B = a_1 - \frac{E_3 - E_1}{E_2 - E_1}(a_1 - a_2) - a_3 \coth a_3,$$

$$C = \left[a_1 - \frac{E_3 - E_1}{E_2 - E_1}(a_1 - a_2) \right]\coth a_3 - a_3,$$

$$r^* = \frac{a_1'^2 F_2 - a_2'^2 F_1}{a_1 E_1 F_2 - a_2 E_2 F_1}.$$

The detailed calculation, though straightforward, is very lengthy and laborious. For the record, and in order to show the degree of accuracy achieved, only the expressions for the basic quantities needed for the calculation will be registered here. The roots of equation (47) for large R are

$$\begin{pmatrix} x_2 \\ x_1 \end{pmatrix} = \sigma R \left(1 \pm \frac{1}{\beta} - \frac{1}{2\beta^2} \pm \frac{5}{8\beta^3} - \frac{1}{\beta^4} + O(\beta^{-5}) \right),$$

$$x_3 = \sigma \alpha^2 \left(1 + \frac{2}{\beta^2} + \frac{7}{\beta^4} \right),$$

in which $\qquad \beta = \dfrac{R^{\frac{1}{2}}}{\alpha} \quad$ and $\quad \alpha = \dfrac{2m}{\sigma^{\frac{3}{2}}}.$

Furthermore, with c *henceforth* denoting $\frac{1}{4}\sigma^2$,

$$\begin{pmatrix} a_2 \\ a_1 \end{pmatrix} = (\sigma R)^{\frac{1}{2}} \left[1 \pm \frac{1}{2\beta} + \left(\frac{c}{2} - \frac{3}{8} \right) \frac{1}{\beta^2} \pm \left(\frac{1}{2} - \frac{c}{4} \right) \frac{1}{\beta^3} - \left(\frac{105}{128} - \frac{5c}{16} + \frac{c^2}{8} \right) \frac{1}{\beta^4} \right],$$

$$a_3 = \alpha \sqrt{\{\alpha(1+c)\}} \left[1 + \frac{1}{(1+c)\beta^2} + \frac{6+7c}{2(1+c)^2 \beta^4} \right];$$

$$\begin{pmatrix} E_2 \\ E_1 \end{pmatrix} = (\sigma R)^2 \left(\pm \frac{1}{\beta} + \frac{1}{2\beta^2} \mp \frac{3}{8\beta^3} + \frac{1}{2\beta^4} \right),$$

$$E_3 = -(\sigma \alpha)^2 R \left(1 + \frac{1}{\beta^2} + \frac{3}{\beta^4} \right);$$

$$\begin{pmatrix} F_2 \\ F_1 \end{pmatrix} = \sigma^2 R (\sigma R)^{\frac{1}{2}} \left[\pm \frac{1}{\beta} - \frac{2c}{\beta^2} \mp \frac{c}{2\beta^3} + \left(\frac{c}{4} - c^2 \right) \frac{1}{\beta^4} \right],$$

$$F_3 = -\alpha \sigma^2 R \sqrt{\{\sigma(1+c)\}} \left(1 + \frac{2c^2 + c}{1+c} \frac{1}{\beta^2} + \frac{c}{2(1+c)^2} \frac{1}{\beta^4} \right);$$

$$B = (\sigma R)^{\frac{1}{2}} \left[1 - \frac{\sqrt{(1+c)} \coth P}{\beta} + \left(\frac{c}{2} - \frac{5}{8} \right) \frac{1}{\beta^2} - \frac{\sqrt{(1+c)} L_1}{\beta^3} - \left(\frac{181}{128} - \frac{7c}{16} + \frac{c^2}{8} - \frac{\sinh P}{\sigma^2 \alpha^4} \right) \frac{1}{\beta^4} \right],$$

$$C = (\sigma R)^{\frac{1}{2}} \left[\coth P - \frac{\sqrt{(1+c)}}{\beta} + \frac{(4c-5) \coth P + 8M}{8\beta^2} - \frac{1}{\sqrt{(1+c)} \beta^3} \right],$$

and $\qquad r^* = \dfrac{1}{\alpha \sigma (1+2c) \sqrt{(\sigma R)}} \left(1 + \dfrac{96c^2 + 54c - 13}{16(1+2c)} \dfrac{1}{\beta^2} \right),$

in which

$$P = \alpha \sqrt{\{\sigma(1+c)\}}, \quad M = -\frac{m}{\sqrt{(c+c^2)}} \operatorname{cosech}^2 P, \quad L_1 = \frac{\coth P}{1+c} + M.$$

The determinant equation has the final form

$$(b - Sm^2)\, m = 2\sigma \sqrt{(1+c)} \left[\coth P + \frac{G}{\beta} + \frac{\{K + \frac{1}{2}(7c-1)\} \coth P + Q}{\beta^2} \right.$$

$$\left. + \frac{X(K-1) + Y + G\{\frac{1}{2}(7c-1)\} + Z + \sqrt{(1+c)} \coth^2 P}{\beta^3} \right], \quad (52)$$

in which

$$X = \sqrt{(1+c)(1+\coth^2 P)}, \quad G = X - \frac{2c+1}{\sqrt{(1+c)}}\left(1-\frac{1}{\alpha}\right),$$

$$K = \frac{5c^2+2c-1}{2(c+1)} - \frac{1+2c}{\alpha}, \quad Q = M + (1+c)\coth P \operatorname{cosech}^2 P$$

$$Y = \frac{1}{\sqrt{(1+c)}}\left\{-1+(1+c)\left[-\left(\frac{c}{2}-\frac{5}{8}\right)\operatorname{cosech}^2 P + (M+L_1)\coth P\right]\right.$$

$$\left. + (1+c)^2 \coth^2 P \operatorname{cosech}^2 P\right\},$$

$$Z = \frac{32\alpha c^2 - 28\alpha c + 10\alpha + 16c^2 + 62c + 11}{16\alpha\sqrt{(1+c)}}.$$

If, for large R, only the first two terms in the bracket of the right-hand side of equation (52) are used, we have

$$m(b-Sm^2) = 2\sigma\sqrt{(1+c)}\left(\coth P + \frac{\alpha G}{R^{\frac{1}{2}}}\right). \tag{53}$$

To find the critical wave number $m_{\mathrm{cr.}}$ corresponding to maximum σ, we differentiate equation (53) with respect to m, and set $d\sigma/dm$ to zero. The result is

$$b - 3Sm^2 = 2\sigma(1+c)\left\{-\frac{2}{\sigma}\operatorname{cosech}^2 P + \frac{2}{\sigma}(\sigma R)^{-\frac{1}{2}}\right.$$

$$\left. \times \left[\coth^2 P - \frac{c}{c+1} - 2\sqrt{\{\sigma(1+c)\}}\,\alpha \coth P \operatorname{cosech}^2 P\right]\right\}. \tag{54}$$

Elimination of S between equations (53) and (54) gives (with $m = m_{\mathrm{cr.}}$)

$$2mb - 2\sigma\sqrt{(1+c)}\,(3\coth P + \operatorname{cosech}^2 P)$$

$$= \frac{2\sigma(1+c)}{\sqrt{R}}\left\{3\alpha(\coth^2 P + 1) - \frac{6c+3}{c+1}(\alpha-1) + 2\alpha P \coth P \operatorname{cosech}^2 P\right.$$

$$\left. - \left(\coth^2 P - \frac{c}{c+1}\right)\alpha\right\}. \tag{55}$$

Equations (54) and (55) jointly give the critical wave number $m_{\mathrm{cr.}}$ and the corresponding σ for any assigned values of b, S, and R. The results (for large R) are plotted in figures 1 to 6. It appears that the curves $\sigma = $ constant in the $m_{\mathrm{cr.}} - S$ plane coincide where they overlap, giving a single curve to determine $m_{\mathrm{cr.}}$ once S is given, provided R is large. This fact indicates that viscosity, so long as it is small, has no effect on the critical wave number. As shown in figures 2, 4, and 6, its principal role is to determine σ, after $m_{\mathrm{cr.}}$ is determined from S.

For infinite Reynolds number, equation (52) reduces to

$$(b-Sm^2)m = 2\sigma\sqrt{(1+c)}\coth P, \tag{56}$$

which is what one would get if viscosity were neglected from the very beginning. The fact that R has little effect on the (single) $m_{\mathrm{cr.}}$–S curve for each b indicates that the $m_{\mathrm{cr.}}$–S curves obtained directly from equation (56) would be nearly identical with the ones obtained. If $m_{\mathrm{cr.}}$ is above 3 (an assumption which can be verified *a posteriori*), from figures 2, 4 and 6 it can be seen that σ is large for the range of b

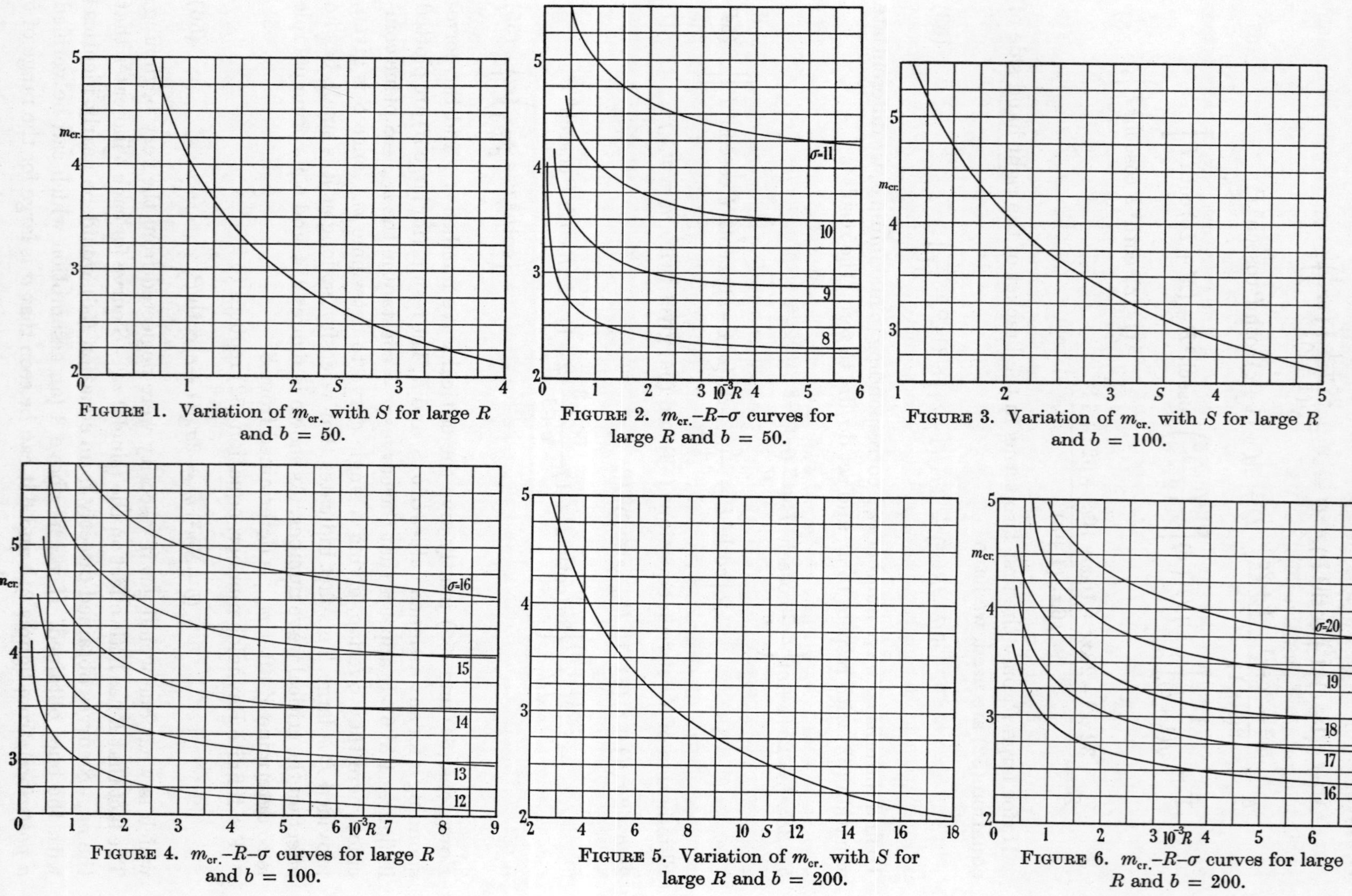

FIGURE 1. Variation of $m_{cr.}$ with S for large R and $b = 50$.
FIGURE 2. $m_{cr.}$–R–σ curves for large R and $b = 50$.
FIGURE 3. Variation of $m_{cr.}$ with S for large R and $b = 100$.
FIGURE 4. $m_{cr.}$–R–σ curves for large R and $b = 100$.
FIGURE 5. Variation of $m_{cr.}$ with S for large R and $b = 200$.
FIGURE 6. $m_{cr.}$–R–σ curves for large R and $b = 200$.

Instability of a rotating liquid film with a free surface **75**

covered and for greater b, and hence $P = m$ approximately and $\coth P$ is equal to 1 and varies slowly with m. Thus a good estimate of $m_{\mathrm{cr.}}$ is provided by the following simplified form of equation (54):

$$b - 3Sm_{\mathrm{cr.}}^2 = 0, \quad \text{or} \quad m_{\mathrm{cr.}} = \sqrt{(b/3S)}, \tag{57}$$

provided of course that the resulting $m_{\mathrm{cr.}}$ is above 3. The corresponding σ calculated from equations (56) and (57) is (since b is large) approximately

$$\sigma_{\mathrm{max.}} = \sqrt{\left(\frac{2bm_{\mathrm{cr.}}}{3}\right)} = \left(\frac{4b^3}{27S}\right)^{\frac{1}{4}}. \tag{58}$$

Comparison of equation (57) with figures 1, 3 and 5 shows excellent agreement, as it should, since these figures are constructed for large Reynolds numbers. Comparison of equation (58) with figures 2, 4 and 6 shows that equation (58) invariably overestimates $\sigma_{\mathrm{max.}}$, as indeed is to be expected.

In any special application, equation (57) can be used if $m_{\mathrm{cr.}}$ is above 3. Otherwise extrapolation of the graphs in figures 1, 3 and 5 may be necessary. If so, extrapolation can most conveniently be done on logarithmic paper, owing to the asymptotically hyperbolic character of the graphs.

6. SOLUTION FOR SMALL REYNOLDS NUMBERS

For small Reynolds numbers the general method can still be used, but the method of solution actually used is radically different and much more convenient. The method adopted is that initiated in a previous paper (Yih 1954) to apply to the problem of hydrodynamic stability of a flowing liquid film. The unknown quantity U in equation (31) is expanded in an ascending power series in R, and the said equation is solved by equating the coefficient of each power of R on the left-hand side to that on the right. Thus

$$U = U_0 + RU_1 + R^2U_2 + \dots, \tag{59}$$

in which the coefficients (functions of ξ) of the series satisfy

$$(\mathrm{D}^2 - m^2)^3 U_0 = 0, \tag{60}$$

$$(\mathrm{D}^2 - m^2)^3 U_1 = 2\sigma(\mathrm{D}^2 - m^2)^2 U_0, \tag{61}$$

$$(\mathrm{D}^2 - m^2)^3 U_2 = 2\sigma(\mathrm{D}^2 - m^2)^2 U_1 - \sigma^2(\mathrm{D}^2 - m^2) U_0 + 4m^2 U_0, \text{ etc.} \tag{62}$$

The solution of equation (60) is

$$U_0 = A \cosh m\xi + B \sinh m\xi + C\xi \cosh m\xi + D\xi \sinh m\xi + E\xi^2 \cosh m\xi$$
$$+ F\xi^2 \sinh m\xi. \tag{63}$$

This solution is very favourable for finding the particular solution of U in equation (61), because the function on which operation by the simple operator $(\mathrm{D}^2 - m^2)^3$ will produce any of the terms on the right-hand side of equation (63) can be found in a straightforward manner. The situation would be less favourable if the terms in equation (63) were not of either of the types

$$\xi^n \begin{Bmatrix} \cosh m\xi \\ \sinh m\xi \end{Bmatrix} \quad \text{and} \quad \xi^n \begin{Bmatrix} \cos m\xi \\ \sin m\xi \end{Bmatrix},$$

76   Chia-Shun Yih

or if the operator were more complicated. Similarly, equation (62) and the subsequent equations can be readily solved. It should be noticed here that only particular solutions of equations (61), (62), etc., are needed, because using the complementary solution of equation (61) for U in equation (62) obviously amounts to starting the whole procedure all over again, beginning with U_1 this time instead of U_0. The effect, if *all* the infinite number of functions U_n were found, would only amount to changing $A, B, ..., F$ in equation (63), which are arbitrary anyway. If the operation is truncated (as it will be), then of course there will be a difference between the results obtained by including or excluding the complementary solutions. However, in that case it is obvious that inclusion of the complementary solutions *reduces* the accuracy because it reduces the degree of approximation by starting the original process over again, without having the chance to go as far as the original process. The results are, up to U_2,

$$U_1 = E\left(\frac{\xi^3 \sinh m\xi}{3m} - \frac{\xi^2 \cosh m\xi}{2m^2} + \frac{\xi \sinh m\xi}{2m^3}\right) + F\left(\frac{\xi^3 \cosh m\xi}{3m} - \frac{\xi^2 \sinh m\xi}{2m^2} + \frac{\xi \cosh m\xi}{2m^3}\right),$$

$$(64)$$

$$U_2 = \frac{A\xi^3 \sinh m\xi}{12m} + \frac{B\xi^3 \cosh m\xi}{12m} + C\left(\frac{\xi^4 \sinh m\xi}{48m} - \frac{(36\sigma^2 - 1)\,\xi^3 \cosh m\xi}{288m^2}\right)$$

$$+ D\left(\frac{\xi^4 \cosh m\xi}{48m} - \frac{(36\sigma^2 - 1)\,\xi^3 \sinh m\xi}{288m^2}\right)$$

$$+ E\left(\frac{\xi^5 \sinh m\xi}{120} + \frac{\sigma^2 - m}{16m^2}\,\xi^4 \cosh m\xi + \frac{(\sigma^2 - m)\,(12m - 1)}{96m^3}\,\xi^3 \sinh m\xi\right)$$

$$+ F\left(\frac{\xi^5 \cosh m\xi}{120} + \frac{\sigma^2 - m}{16m^2}\,\xi^4 \sinh m\xi + \frac{(\sigma^2 - m)\,(12m - 1)}{96m^3}\,\xi^3 \cosh m\xi\right). \quad (65)$$

The subsequent U_n $(n \geqslant 3)$ can be found if needed, and the boundary conditions can be applied to obtain the secular equation wanted.

Before proceeding further with the presentation of the calculation, a remark may be made on the desirability of a slightly different approach for the solution of equation (31). Since this paper will have demonstrated analytically and experimentally that the instability under investigation occurs even at very low Reynolds numbers, and since stability calculations at low Reynolds numbers, though tedious, are straightforward, it might appear profitable to some to write equation (31) in a slightly different way (by arranging the terms in descending orders of D^2, for instance) and solve it by a power series in ξ. It is therefore appropriate to discuss the merit of the approach adopted in this paper relative to the approach by use of a power series in ξ.

The method of solution by power series (in ξ) is an old and a well-known one, attributed by most mathematicians to Frobenius. If the differential equation is such that particular solutions for U_n $(n \geqslant 1)$ are difficult or impossible to obtain, there is definitely a merit in using a power series in ξ. This is not the case for most problems of hydrodynamic stability at low Reynolds numbers, for the operator applied to U_n is either $(D^2 - m^2)^2$, as in film stability, or $(D^2 - m^2)^3$, as in this case. However, in general U_n becomes very involved as n is increased, so that if it is

Instability of a rotating liquid film with a free surface **77**

necessary to carry the calculation to the order R^{12} say, the ξ-power-series method may be more advantageous. If, on the other hand, comparison is made of the relative accuracy of the solutions by the two approaches, both carried to the *same* power of R, the solution by the method adopted here is undoubtedly the more accurate, since for all powers in R up to the highest one, the solution is *complete* in ξ. It is, of course, not fair to compare a ξ-power solution, carried to ξ^{16} and R^{12}, say, with an R-power solution carried to the first power in R. Patience is a virtue that seldom goes unrewarded. In this paper, calculations will be carried only to the first power in R. This is not only because experimental results indicate the solution to be sufficiently accurate, but also because calculation for large R and small R alike have shown that stability is predominantly controlled by surface tension, viscosity only playing a secondary role—even at low Reynolds numbers if S is not small. A ξ-power solution would in this case be inadequate if carried only to the first power in R, and wasteful if carried to a high power in R. (Furthermore, with six boundary conditions, carrying the ξ-power series to ξ^{16}, say, would tax the patience of even the most purposeful.)

With
$$U = U_0 + RU_1,$$

and U_0 and U_1 given by equations (63) and (64), application of the boundary conditions—equations (32)—at the cylinder surface yields

$$A = 0, \quad c = -\frac{\sigma RF}{2m^3} - mB, \quad E = \frac{m\sigma R}{4m^2 + \sigma R}D = \frac{\sigma R}{4m}D.$$

Application of the boundary conditions (33) and (34) yields the secular equation

$$R[(b - Sm^2)\, 2m \cosh m\, (\sinh m \cosh m - m)$$
$$+ \sigma^2(-7\cosh^3 m - 4m \sinh m\, \cosh^2 m - 7m^2 \cosh m - 2m^3 \sinh m)]$$
$$- 4\sigma m^2 \cosh m(\cosh^2 m + m^2) = 0. \tag{66}$$

For maximum σ at fixed b, S and R, $\mathrm{d}\sigma/\mathrm{d}m = 0$. Thus to obtain the critical wave number $m_{\mathrm{cr.}}$ (which corresponds to $\sigma_{\mathrm{max.}}$), one needs only to differentiate (66) with respect to m, treating σ as a constant. The result is (in which m is $m_{\mathrm{cr.}}$)

$$R\{2(b - Sm^2)\,(2m\cosh m \sinh^2 m + m\cosh^3 m + \cosh^2 m \sinh m - m^2 \sinh m$$
$$- 2m \cosh m) + 4Sm^2 \cosh m(m - \cosh m \sinh m)$$
$$+ \sigma^2[-\sinh m \cosh m(25\cosh m + 8m\sinh m) - 4m\cosh^3 m - 13m^2 \sinh m$$
$$- (14 + 2m^2)\, m \cosh m]\}$$
$$- 4m\sigma(3m\cosh^2 m \sinh m + 2\cosh^3 m + m^3 \sinh m + 4m^2 \cosh m) = 0. \tag{67}$$

If R is eliminated between equations (66) and (67), the variation of $m_{\mathrm{cr.}}$ (which for simplicity is written m in the equation) with S for various values of σ is given by

$$\sigma^2[\cosh^5 m(14\cosh m + 4m\sinh m) + m^2 \cosh^3 m(24\cosh m + 10m\sinh m)$$
$$+ 4m^4 \cosh^2 m(3 - \cosh^2 m) + 2m^5(\sinh m\, \cosh m - m)]$$
$$+ 4Sm^3 \cosh^2 m(\cosh^2 m + m^2)\,(m - \cosh m \sinh m)$$
$$+ (b - Sm^2)\, 2m \cosh m[-\cosh^4 m \sinh m + m\cosh^3 m - m^2 \cosh^2 m \sinh m$$
$$+ m^3 \cosh m(2\cosh^2 m + 1)] = 0. \tag{68}$$

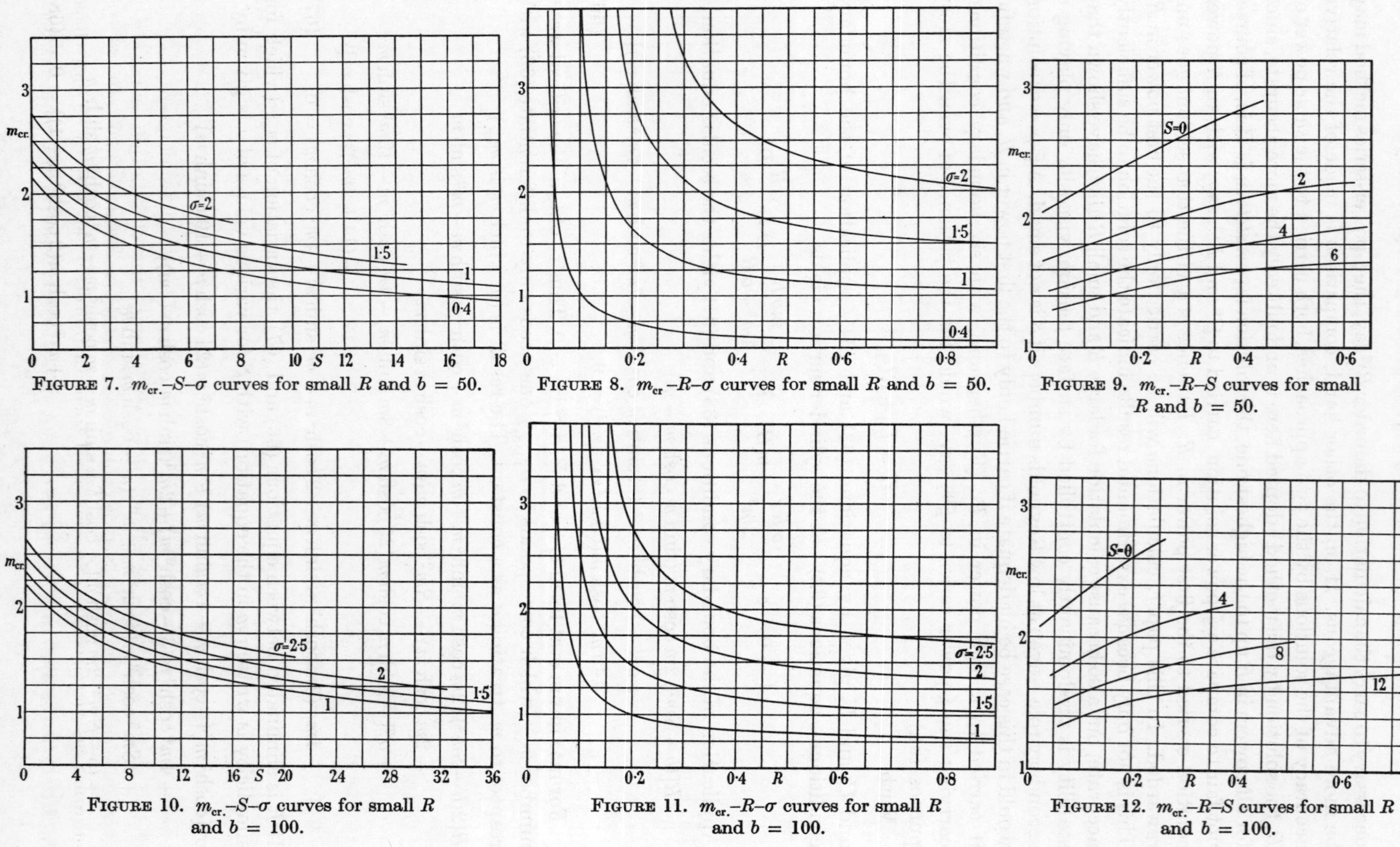

FIGURE 7. $m_{cr.}$–S–σ curves for small R and $b = 50$.

FIGURE 8. $m_{cr.}$–R–σ curves for small R and $b = 50$.

FIGURE 9. $m_{cr.}$–R–S curves for small R and $b = 50$.

FIGURE 10. $m_{cr.}$–S–σ curves for small R and $b = 100$.

FIGURE 11. $m_{cr.}$–R–σ curves for small R and $b = 100$.

FIGURE 12. $m_{cr.}$–R–S curves for small R and $b = 100$.

Instability of a rotating liquid film with a free surface 79

On the other hand, elimination of S between equations (66) and (67) yields

$$-4R\beta m \cosh^2 m(\sinh m \cosh m - m)^2 + 4\sigma m^2 \cosh m[\cosh^4 m \sinh m$$

$$- m \cosh^3 m + m^2 \cosh^2 m \sinh m + m^3 \cosh m(2 \cosh^2 m - 1)]$$

$$+ R\sigma^2[21 \cosh^5 m \sinh m + m \cosh^4 m(-29 + 8 \cosh^2 m) + 9m^2 \cosh^3 m \sinh m$$

$$+ m^3 \cosh^2 m(22 \cosh^2 m - 25) + 2m^4 \cosh m \sinh m(2 \sinh^2 m - 1) + 2m^5] = 0, \quad (69)$$

in which, again, m is written for $m_{\mathrm{cr.}}$. Equation (68) is represented graphically in figures 7, 10 and 13, and equation (69) in figures 8, 11 and 14, for three values of b.

FIGURE 13. $m_{\mathrm{cr.}}$–S–σ curves for small R and $b = 200$.

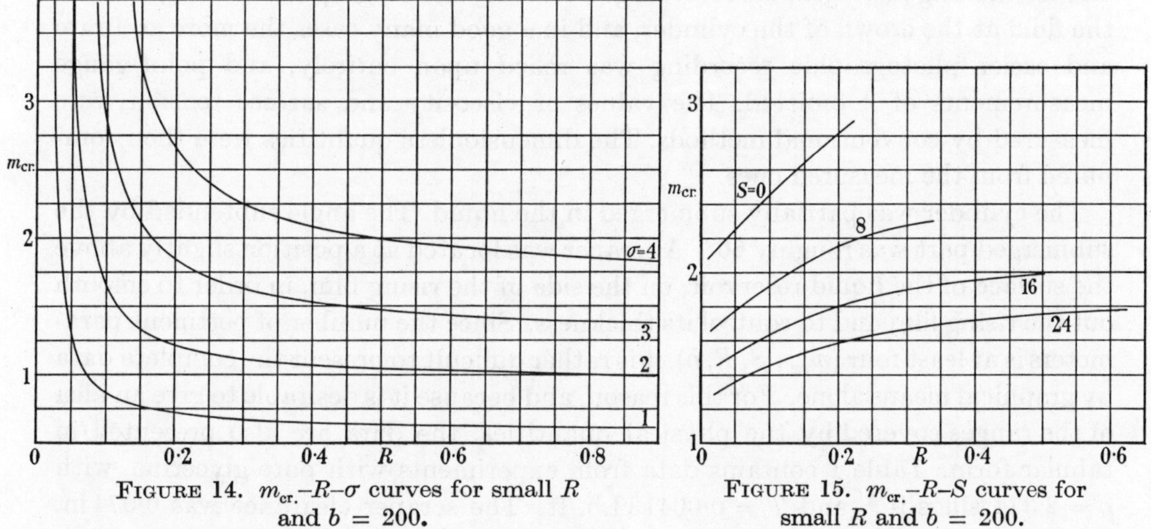

FIGURE 14. $m_{\mathrm{cr.}}$–R–σ curves for small R and $b = 200$.

FIGURE 15. $m_{\mathrm{cr.}}$–R–S curves for small R and $b = 200$.

From these figures it can be seen that at small Reynolds numbers the relation between $m_{\mathrm{cr.}}$ and S is no longer represented by a single curve for each b, as a result of the slight dispersive effect of viscosity. However, the dispersion of the $m_{\mathrm{cr.}}$–S curves is much smaller than that of the $m_{\mathrm{cr.}}$–R curves, and the critical wave number is still predominantly determined by S. To see the $m_{\mathrm{cr.}}$–S–R relation more clearly, σ is eliminated from equations (66) and (67). But since σ occurs in them quadratically, the resulting expression is rather involved (though the elimination is perfectly straightforward, involving *no* solution of a quadratic equation). The results of the elimination are presented in graphical form in figures 9, 12 and 15. From these figures it can be seen that so long as S is not small, the variation of $m_{\mathrm{cr.}}$ with R is very

80   Chia-Shun Yih

gradual, and is practically nil for R greater than 0·6. As will be seen, nearly all the experimental results obtained except those for pure glycerine are in the range $148 \geqslant R > 0.6$. For pure glycerine, many of the data are for R between 0·1 and 0·6. However, for all these data and for the five data for water + glycerine mixture with R less than 0·6, S varies from 74 to 4868, and hence is very high. Thus for the range covered by experiments $m_{\text{cr.}}$ is predominantly determined by S. Detailed comparison of theoretical and experimental results will be presented in the next section.

7. Experimental results

The experimental apparatus is shown in figure 17, plate 7. A lucite horizontal cylinder of radius (a) 0·365 ft. was driven by a motor with variable speed, the value of which was set by a dial. The depth of the liquid film was measured by a point gauge directly above the crown of the cylinder, brought to zero (before the cylinder rotates) when the point just touches the surface of the cylinder. The film depth was then measured at crests and troughs (and other stations) by the point gauge, which could be moved in the axial direction. The mean depth d could then be computed. The point gauge could also measure the wave length λ. The measurements of λ were checked photographically. When the flow was very unstable, the rings broke down stream, making photographic recording rather easy. Photographs were also taken of the fluid at the crown of the cylinder, and in a good many cases the more accurate and easier photographic recording was relied upon entirely, and point-gauge measurements of λ omitted. The values of viscosity and surface tension were measured by conventional methods. The dimensionless quantities were then computed from the measured ones.

The cylinder was partially submerged in the liquid. The angle subtended by the submerged part was roughly 60°. A scraper was located at a position slightly above the surface of the liquid reservoir, on the side of the rising film, in order to smooth out the rising film and to control its thickness. Since the number of pertinent parameters is at least four ($m_{\text{cr.}}$, S, R, b), it is rather difficult to present the complete data by graphical means alone. For this reason, and because it is desirable to give an idea of the ranges covered by the physical quantities, the data are also presented in tabular form. Table 1 contains data from experiments with pure glycerine, with $\rho = 2.374$ slugs/ft.^{3}, and $T = 0.00413$ Lb./ft. The scraper clearance was 0·074 in. Table 2 contains data from experiments with a water + glycerine mixture, nearly but not exactly 50–50 by volume, with $\rho = 2.231$ slugs/ft.^{3} and $T = 0.00407$ Lb./ft. The scraper clearance was 0·074 in. for the first 17 experiments and 0·050 in. for the rest. Table 3 contains data for water, with $\rho = 1.935$ slugs/ft.^{3}, and $T = 0.00496$ Lb./ft. The scraper clearance was 0·050 in. throughout. The viscosity ν is recorded in the tables.

As the liquid film re-entered the reservoir, some air was entrained into the latter. Some of the air bubbles present in the reservoir were carried along with the rising liquid film, and no doubt some additional air was entrained as the film left the reservoir. The air bubbles present in the film were not visible to the unaided eye, but could be made visible by a blinking light. The amount by volume was not large,

FIGURE 17

TABLE 1

glycerine: $\rho = 2{\cdot}374$ slugs/ft.^{3}, $T = 0{\cdot}00413$ Lb./ft., scraper clearance $= 0{\cdot}074$ in., $a = 0{\cdot}365$ ft.

ω (rad/s)	$10^3 d$ (ft.)	$10^3 \lambda$ (ft.)	$10^4 \nu$ (ft.^{2}/s)	$m = 2\pi d/\lambda$	$b = (a+d)/d$	$R = d^2\omega/\nu$	$S = T/\rho\omega^2 d^3$	$\Pi = g/\omega^2 dm^2$	$Se = S+\Pi$
16·01	3·54	52·6	12·15	0·42	104	0·17	153	198	351
17·08	3·66	47·6	9·89	0·48	101	0·23	121	129	250
13·10	3·61	66·7	9·62	0·34	102	0·18	215	445	660
10·48	3·61	76·9	9·62	0·30	102	0·14	337	925	1262
9·43	3·51	71·4	9·62	0·31	105	0·12	452	1070	1522
11·51	3·67	71·4	9·62	0·32	100	0·16	266	632	898
14·44	3·37	66·7	10·74	0·32	109	0·15	218	450	668
13·11	3·44	62·5	10·00	0·35	107	0·16	249	452	701
10·37	3·53	71·4	10·00	0·31	104	0·13	368	870	1238
15·80	4·54	55·5	9·62	0·51	81	0·34	74	107	181
19·16	6·57	55·5	9·45	0·75	57	0·88	17	24	41
17·38	5·55	55·5	9·25	0·63	67	0·58	34	49	83

TABLE 2

glycerine + water mixtue: $\rho = 2 \cdot 231$ slugs/ft.^{3}, $T = 0 \cdot 00407$ Lb./ft., $a = 0 \cdot 365$ ft.

ω (rad/s)	$10^3 d$ (ft.)	$10^3 \lambda$ (ft.)	$10^4 \nu$ (ft.^{2}/s)	$m = 2\pi d/\lambda$	$b = (a+d)/d$	$R = d^2\omega/\nu$	$S = T/\rho\omega^2 d^3$	$\Pi = g/\omega^2 dm^2$	$Se = S + \Pi$
				scraper clearance $= 0 \cdot 074$ in.					
12·88	2·01	71·5	0·686	0·18	183	0·76	1354	3100	4454
13·60	2·04	55·5	0·694	0·23	180	0·82	1162	1590	2752
10·45	2·02	100·0	0·720	0·13	182	0·59	2027	8280	10307
11·50	1·90	83·4	0·709	0·14	193	0·59	2011	6220	8231
12·54	1·92	71·5	0·709	0·17	191	0·65	1639	3730	5369
13·50	2·03	55·5	0·709	0·23	181	0·79	1197	1635	2832
14·00	2·07	66·6	0·709	0·20	177	0·85	1051	2070	3121
15·70	2·29	62·5	0·699	0·23	160	1·18	617	1075	1692
16·74	2·33	50·0	0·694	0·29	158	1·31	515	571	1086
17·80	2·48	62·5	0·686	0·25	148	1·60	378	660	1038
18·83	2·44	66·6	0·686	0·23	151	1·63	354	698	1052
19·90	2·93	62·5	0·678	0·30	126	2·52	183	317	500
20·90	3·21	50·0	0·678	0·40	115	3·18	126	141	267
22·00	4·29	55·5	0·678	0·49	86	5·95	48	65	113
23·00	3·90	66·7	0·666	0·37	95	5·25	58	116	174
24·20	5·40	62·5	0·666	0·54	69	10·6	20	34	54
25·30	8·17	50·0	0·666	1·03	46	25·3	5	6	11
				scraper clearance $= 0 \cdot 050$ in.					
9·74	1·58	125·0	0·753	0·08	232	0·32	4868	34300	39168
11·20	1·75	100·0	0·747	0·11	210	0·46	2713	12200	14913
12·25	1·75	83·5	0·736	0·13	210	0·51	2268	7150	9418
13·30	2·00	83·5	0·736	0·15	184	0·72	1289	4050	5339
14·23	2·00	71·5	0·736	0·18	184	0·77	1126	2560	3686
15·40	2·16	62·5	0·736	0·22	170	0·98	762	1330	2092
16·42	2·58	55·5	0·736	0·29	142	1·49	394	542	936
17·80	2·92	55·5	0·736	0·33	126	2·06	231	319	550
18·21	2·92	71·5	0·764	0·26	126	2·04	221	494	715
19·6	3·08	66·7	0·736	0·29	120	2·52	162	324	486
20·9	3·08	55·5	0·736	0·35	120	2·69	143	198	341
21·9	2·92	50·0	0·731	0·37	126	2·55	153	171	324
22·9	3·91	50·0	0·720	0·49	94	4·86	58	64	123
24·0	4·91	43·5	0·715	0·71	75	8·10	27	23	50
25·5	5·91	35·7	0·710	1·04	63	12·6	14	8	22

TABLE 3

water: $\rho = 1{\cdot}935$ slugs/ft.^{3}, $T = 0{\cdot}00496$ Lb./ft. scraper clearance $= 0{\cdot}050$ in., $a = 0{\cdot}365$ ft.

ω (rad/s)	10^3d (ft.)	$10^3\lambda$ (ft.)	$10^4\nu$ (ft.^{2}/s)	$m = 2\pi d/\lambda$	$b = (a+d)/d$	$R = d^2\omega/\nu$	$S = T/\rho\omega^2 d^3$	$\Pi = g/\omega^2 m^2$	$Se = S+\Pi$
9·85	1·17	83·3	0·093	0·09	314	1·44	16625	36900	53525
11·2	1·08	83·3	0·093	0·08	338	1·41	16126	35800	51926
9·01	1·08	125·0	0·095	0·05	338	1·11	24918	123000	147918
9·85	1·08	100·0	0·095	0·07	338	1·21	20850	66000	86850
10·9	1·08	83·3	0·095	0·08	338	1·35	17026	37400	54426
11·6	1·17	83·3	0·094	0·09	314	1·68	11987	26600	38587
12·6	1·08	77·0	0·094	0·09	338	1·57	12741	24000	36741
13·6	1·17	83·3	0·094	0·09	314	1·97	8721	19350	28071
14·7	1·25	77·0		0·10	293	2·47	6071	11450	17521
15·7	1·67	71·5		0·15	220	4·66	2241	3690	5931
16·6	1·75	71·5		0·15	210	5·46	1735	2810	4545
17·7	2·17	71·5		0·19	169	8·93	801	1310	2111
18·7	2·33	55·5		0·26	158	10·9	579	567	1146
19·8	2·92	55·5		0·33	126	18·2	262	257	519
21·0	4·25	55·5		0·48	87	41·0	76	75	151
22·0	4·75	52·6	0·093	0·57	78	53·7	49	44	93
22·8	4·66	45·4		0·65	79	53·6	49	32	81
24·3	5·34	62·5		0·54	69	74·7	29	35	64
25·2	5·42	55·5		0·61	68	80·0	25	25	50
26·2	5·58	47·5		0·74	66	88·1	21	16	37
27·2	6·42	47·5		0·85	58	121	13	9	22
28·3	6·75	45·4		0·94	55	139	10	7	17
29·4	6·84	43·5		0·99	54	148	9	6	15

Remark: Π is accurate to 3 significant figures only. Hence S_e as computed is also only accurate to 3 significant figures.

84   Chia-Shun Yih

and it was not thought worth while to go into the rather considerable trouble of eliminating them completely. Nevertheless, they constitute a source of error that must be recorded here.

Before the experimental results are graphically compared with the theoretical ones, it must be remembered that gravity has been entirely neglected in the analysis. This neglect was necessary because the effect of gravity is different at different parts of the cylinder, and for the sake of neatness it was judged better to consider the effect of gravity separately. Since the measurements were taken at the crown of the cylinder, where gravity and surface tension conspire to stabilize the flow, the effective S must be increased. A review of equation $(12a)$ shows that the only term that need be added is through the term $-\eta\, d\bar{p}/dr$, which now also contains the term $\rho g \eta$. The final effect is to change S to

$$S_e = S + g/\omega^2 \mathrm{d}m^2. \tag{70}$$

The term $g/\omega^2 \mathrm{d}m^2$ was computed and included in the tables, and the S_e obtained is the effective S used for comparing the experimental results with the curves obtained from analysis. Of course, the question may be raised as to the adequacy of taking account of gravity effects entirely locally, without regard for the flow before the crown is reached, where the effect of gravity is less. The most important defence of the procedure is that since the growth is exponential, the most *recent* growth is the most effective and important. Therefore gravity effect can be accounted for locally without serious error. Another point is that for a relatively large distance near the crown the slope is nearly horizontal, therefore the additiveness of the effects of surface tension and gravity is valid over a relatively long distance immediately before and after the crown is reached.

Now the graphical comparison will be made. The range of S (or rather S_e) realized in the experiments is so extensive that extrapolation of the theoretical curves is necessary. (Since the $m_{\mathrm{cr.}}$–S curves are more and more hyperbolic as S is increased, extrapolation is best done on logarithmic paper, on which the curves become straight lines for large S.) For the case of pure glycerine, the first nine experiments are for values of b very nearly equal to 100, and for Reynolds numbers between 0·1 and 0·2. The critical wave numbers are in the range between 0·3 and 0·5. From figure 11 it can be seen that the mean σ is 0·35. The curve $\sigma = 0·35$ is then obtained by extrapolation (in values of σ) on figure 10, put on figure 16 in logarithmic scale, and extended beyond $S = 36$. The experimental points are plotted on the same figure, with S_e for S, as explained, to account for the effect of gravity. Of the remaining data, only ten experiments have b-values much above 200, which is the highest b-value for which computation has been made. Close examination of the data reveals that $m_{\mathrm{cr.}}$ varies from 0·11 to 0·23 approximately, for b nearly equal 200. The Reynolds number varies from 0·46 to 5·46. For this range the variation with R is very small, as can be seen from figure 14. Extrapolation of the curves to $m_{\mathrm{cr.}} = 0·25$ shows that $\sigma = 0·05$ approximately. This curve is plotted in figure 16 to provide an upper limit for all experimental points with b near 200 or below 200. For data with b near 50, a sharp lower limit should be provided by a line for $b = 50^*$ and $\sigma = 0·6$, as drawn in figure 16.

* From figure 8, since for b near 50 the lowest m_c is 0·75, corresponding to $b = 57$ for glycerine.

To show how slightly the curve shifts for a different σ and to provide a better lower limit, the curve for $b = 50$ and $\sigma = 0\cdot1$ is also drawn in the figure. It can be seen from the figure that the agreement between theoretical and experimental results is indeed rather satisfactory, although those points for b greater than 300 seem to be lower than they should be.

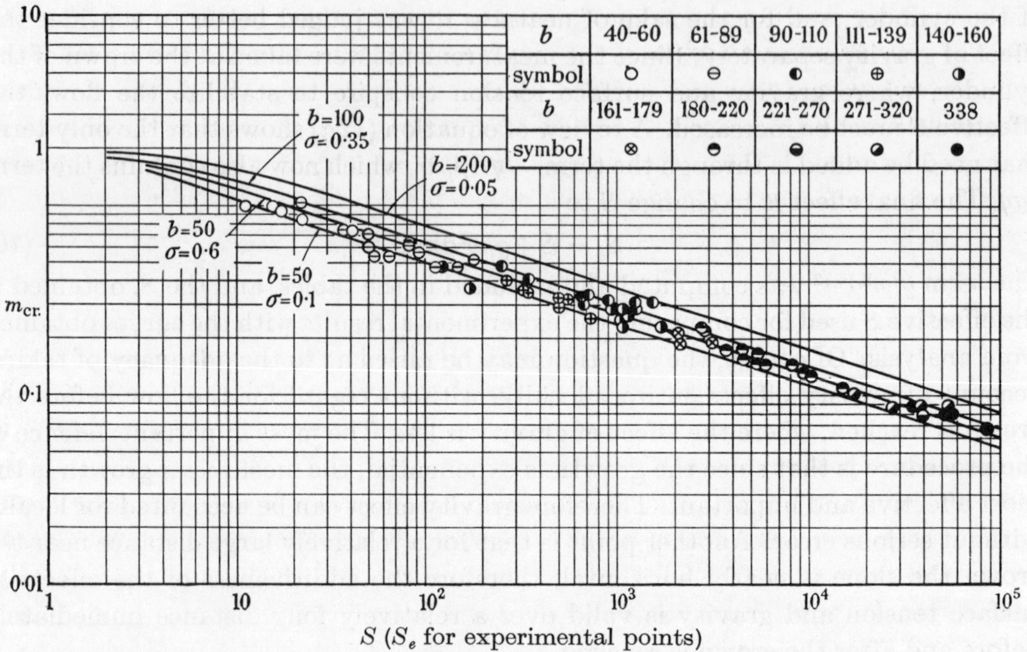

b	40-60	61-89	90-110	111-139	140-160
symbol	○	⊖	◑	⊕	◐
b	161-179	180-220	221-270	271-320	338
symbol	⊗	⊜	⊝	◓	●

S (S_e for experimental points)

FIGURE 16. Comparison of analytical and experimental results.

Since the value of σ selected for plotting depends on the range of $m_{\rm cr.}$ obtained experimentally, the meaning of the comparison can be questioned. The most important thing to remember is that the variation of $m_{\rm cr.}$ with σ is very slight (see the two curves for $b = 50$ in figure 16), so that, for any b, any choice of σ will result in a curve near the curve plotted for the σ-value that has actually been selected. This relieves the comparison from undue reliance on experimental results. Furthermore, even after a particular σ is chosen, there is no *a priori* reason why there should be good agreement in the $m_{\rm cr.}$–S plane, if the analysis is not good.

Since the calculations leading to the analytical curves used for comparison were performed for small Reynolds numbers only, the use of the curves for comparison with data obtained at moderate values of the Reynolds number may also be subject to question. The justification for using the analytical results at moderate R lies in the theoretically demonstrated fact that above $R = 0\cdot6$ or so the variation of $m_{\rm cr.}$ with R is very small, so that the calculation, performed originally for small R only, turns out to be useful for greater R as well—a very welcome situation indeed.

Since the time for the liquid film to travel from the reservoir to the crown was rather short (about $\frac{1}{3}$ s or less), the point may be raised that the fluid did not have time to be in purely rotational motion, as assumed in the analysis. (In fact, gravity may also change the mean velocity distribution somewhat.) This is certainly the

Chia-Shun Yih

most important objection. It is indeed quite possible that herein lies the explanation why the experimental points lie lower than they should, because an incompletely developed velocity profile implies an incompletely realized destabilizing factor, and therefore a smaller critical wave number. (Remember surface tension, which is stabilizing, tends to reduce $m_{\mathrm{cr.}}$.)

In conclusion, one may state that for any given situation (with S_e replacing S) $m_{\mathrm{cr.}}$ can either be obtained from figure 16, with the best fitting curve ($b = 50$, $\sigma = 0.6$) considered as an experimental curve,* or from figures 1, 3 and 5 for large R and from figures 7 to 15 for small R, if b is near 50, 100, or 200 (otherwise interpolation will be necessary). For large R the corresponding σ is found from figures 2, 4 and 6. For small R the values of $m_{\mathrm{cr.}}$ and σ are found simultaneously from the $m_{\mathrm{cr.}}$–S and $m_{\mathrm{cr.}}$–R curves.† In general, $m_{\mathrm{cr.}}$ depends much more on S than on R. The effect of viscosity is chiefly to reduce the rate of amplification; its effect on $m_{\mathrm{cr.}}$ is overshadowed by that of surface tension, particularly when the Reynolds number is large.

Note added in proof, 31 May 1960

Strictly speaking, the term $\partial^2\eta/\partial z^2$ in the equations immediately preceding (13) and (46) should be replaced by $\eta + \partial^2\eta/\partial z^2$. However, since in these equations z is measured in terms of a, and the wave number based on a is large for the fairly thin (compared with a) films herein considered, the term $\partial^2\eta/\partial z^2$ is very large compared with η, which can therefore be neglected. If the term η is to be included in the equation preceding (46), the conclusions reached in §4 can be made exactly valid simply by replacing n^2 in the right-hand side of (46) by $n^2 - 1$.

This work has been carried out at the University of Michigan and is the outcome of an industrial-research project sponsored by the Technical Association of Pulp and Paper Industries, to which the author wishes to express his appreciation for the support received. The assistance rendered by Mr Chintu Lai in numerical computation, by Mr A. Engerer in collecting the experimental data, and by Dr W. P. Graebel in calculation for the case of small Reynolds numbers is gratefully acknowledged. The author also wishes to express his appreciation to members of the Fluid-Mechanics Committee of T.A.P.P.I. for the stimulation which has led to the undertaking of this investigation, and to the T.A.P.P.I. magazine for permission to use figures 1 to 6 contained in a preliminary report by the author.

REFERENCES

Taylor, G. I. 1923 *Phil. Trans.* A, **223**, 289–343.
Taylor, G. I. 1950 *Proc. Roy. Soc.* A, **201**, 192–4.
Yih, C.-S. 1954 *Proc. 2nd U.S. Nat. Congr. Appl. Mech.*, pp. 623–28.

* Certainly for the ranges of b, R, and S realized experimentally in the present work.

† Alternatively, $m_{\mathrm{cr.}}$ is found for given b, R and S from figures 9, 12 and 15 if b is 50, 100, or 200 (otherwise interpolation or extrapolation is necessary). The value of σ can then be found from the $m_{\mathrm{cr.}}$–σ–R curves.

Reprinted from

THE PHYSICS OF FLUIDS   VOLUME 4, NUMBER 7   JULY, 1961

Dual Role of Viscosity in the Instability of Revolving Fluids of Variable Density

CHIA-SHUN YIH

The University of Michigan, Ann Arbor, Michigan
(Received February 24, 1961, revised version received April 6, 1961)

The stability of a viscous fluid between rotating cylinders and with a radial temperature gradient against the formation of axisymmetric disturbances (Taylor vortices) is considered, and it has been found that viscosity has a dual role. If the circulation increases radially outward (so that the flow would be stable in the absence of density variation) but the density decreases with the radial distance, the situation can arise that viscosity actually has a destabilizing effect. In the opposite circumstance, thermal diffusivity is always destabilizing. Detailed results for small spacing of the cylinders and sufficient conditions for stability of a revolving fluid of variable density or entropy also are given.

I. INTRODUCTION

$\mathbf{F}$OR a homogeneous fluid flowing between rotating concentric cylinders, Synge[1] has shown that if the circulation increases with radial distance the flow is always stable. If the density of the fluid also has a radial variation, the arguments of von Kármán, as presented in the book by Lin,[2] can be used to show that, in the *absence* of viscosity, the flow in the case of a liquid is always stable if $\rho \Gamma^2$ increases with the radial distance, with ρ denoting the density and Γ the circulation of the fluid in its undisturbed state. In this paper the stability of a liquid between coaxial rotating cylinders and with a radial density gradient is considered. The disturbances are assumed to be axisymmetric, not two dimensional, as assumed by Chandrasekhar.[3] The chief points to be made are that, even if $\rho \Gamma^2$ increases with the radial distance, the flow can actually become less stable or even unstable (1) for increasing kinematic viscosity if Γ increases but ρ decreases outward, and (2) for increasing thermal diffusivity if Γ decreases but ρ increases outward, and that the flow is stable if both ρ (of a liquid) and Γ increase with radial distance.

The destabilizing effect of thermal diffusivity in case (2) is almost exactly the same as in the very interesting case of gravitational instability discovered by Stommel *et al.*[4] In their case a fluid (water) has a temperature increasing and a salinity increasing with height in such a way that their combined effect is to make the density decrease with height, and, *superficially*, to make the fluid

stable. However, since the thermal diffusivity of water is much greater than its salinity diffusivity, a displaced particle will harmonize with its new surroundings more readily in temperature than in salinity. Consequently, the original cause for stability can be diminished to such a degree that instability due to adverse salinity gradient actually occurs. In the present case (2) thermal diffusivity plays exactly the same role, although the cause of instability is not gravity but centripetal acceleration.

The destabilizing effect in case (1) lies in the fact that as a material ring is displaced, its density may harmonize with that in the ring's new surroundings less readily than the circulation along it, because of the diffusive effect of viscosity, and consequently the product $\rho \Gamma^2$ of the ring may exceed that in its new surroundings, causing the ring to move further.

Inasmuch as viscosity is a momentum diffusivity, its destabilizing effect in case (1) is similar to that of thermal diffusivity in case (2) or in the case considered by Stommel *et al.*, but not entirely. Aside from being an agent for momentum diffusion, viscosity is always a dissipative agent responsible for the eventual conversion of kinetic energy into heat. Thus, except in the case of Tollmien-Schlichting waves for which viscosity also plays a dual role, the effect of viscosity has always been to stabilize a flow. Certainly in the case of flow of a homogeneous fluid between rotating cylinders, Sir Geoffrey Taylor[5] showed, among other specific results, that viscosity is stabilizing. Therefore, if viscosity is found to be destabilizing in the case of a nonhomogeneous fluid, it must have a dual role which thermal diffusivity cannot have. In the case of Bernard cells, thermal diffusivity is entirely stabilizing. In the case of

[1] J. L. Synge, Proc. Roy. Soc. (London) **A167**, 250–256 (1938).
[2] C. C. Lin, *The Theory of Hydrodynamic Stability* (Cambridge University Press, New York, 1955), pp. 49–50.
[3] S. Chandrasekhar, J. Ratl. Mech. Analysis **3**, 181–207 (1954).
[4] H. Stommel, A. B. Arons, and D. Blanchard, Deep-Sea Research **3**, 152–153 (1956).
[5] G. I. Taylor, Phil. Trans. Roy. Soc. London **A223**, 289–343 (1923).

Stommel's "salt fountain" or in the present case (2), thermal diffusivity is entirely destabilizing. It cannot play *at once* the dual role which viscosity *simultaneously* plays. Since the destabilizing effect of viscosity is so rare that it is now exclusively associated with Tollmien-Schlichting waves, it seems worthwhile to present an essentially distinct instance of the same effect.

The second part of this paper is a discussion of the effect of compressibility on the stability of a revolving gas. A new criterion for stability is derived by neglecting the effects of viscosity and diffusivity. But since either viscosity or diffusivity can be destabilizing, as will be shown, even this criterion is not very useful and must be replaced by a more stringent one in the form of two conditions to be *simultaneously* satisfied.

II. FORMULATION OF THE PROBLEM

The radii of the cylinders will be denoted by r_1 and r_2 (with $r_2 > r_1$). The angular velocities of the cylinders will be denoted by Ω_1 and Ω_2. Thus the velocity of mean flow is, in cylindrical coordinates (r, θ, z),

$$V = A_* r + (B_*/r), \tag{1}$$

in which

$$A_* = \frac{\Omega_2 r_2^2 - \Omega_1 r_1^2}{r_2^2 - r_1^2}, \quad B_* = -\frac{(\Omega_2 - \Omega_1) r_1^2 r_2^2}{r_2^2 - r_1^2}. \tag{2}$$

If the temperatures at the walls are T_1 and T_2, the temperature distribution in the primary flow is given by

$$T = T_1 + (T_2 - T_1) \frac{\ln r - \ln r_1}{\ln r_2 - \ln r_1}, \tag{3}$$

The density distribution is then given by

$$\rho = \rho_1 [1 - \alpha(T - T_1)], \tag{4}$$

in which α is the coefficient of volume expansion.

If axisymmetry of the disturbance is assumed, the linearized equations of motion are, with θ as the temperature perturbation,

$$\rho_1 \left[\frac{\partial u}{\partial t} - \frac{2Vv}{r} + \alpha\theta \frac{V^2}{r} \right]$$
$$= -\frac{\partial p}{\partial r} + \mu\left(\nabla^2 u - \frac{u}{r^2}\right), \tag{5}$$

$$\rho_1 \left(\frac{\partial v}{\partial t} + 2A_* u\right) = \mu\left(\nabla^2 v - \frac{v}{r^2}\right), \tag{6}$$

$$\rho_1 \frac{\partial w}{\partial t} = -\frac{\partial p}{\partial z} + \mu \nabla^2 w, \tag{7}$$

in which u, v, and w are the components of the velocity of the disturbance, p the perturbation pressure, t the time, μ the viscosity, which is assumed constant, and

$$\nabla^2 = \frac{\partial^2}{\partial r^2} + \frac{1}{r}\frac{\partial}{\partial r} + \frac{\partial^2}{\partial z^2}. \tag{8}$$

The equation of continuity is

$$[\partial(ru)/\partial r] + [\partial(rw)/\partial z] = 0. \tag{9}$$

The diffusion equation is

$$\partial\theta/\partial t + u(dT/dr) = \kappa\nabla^2\theta, \tag{10}$$

in which, as stated before, θ is the temperature perturbation (not the second coordinate which is not needed because of axisymmetry), and κ is the thermal diffusivity.

Assuming, after Taylor,

$$(u, v, \theta) = [u_1(r), v_1(r), \theta_1(r)] \cos \lambda z \, e^{\sigma t},$$

$$w = w_1(r) \sin \lambda z \, e^{\sigma t},$$

and utilizing the equation of continuity, we can write the equations of motion and of diffusion as

$$\nu L\left(L - \lambda^2 - \frac{\sigma}{\nu}\right) u_1 = 2\lambda^2 \frac{V}{r} v_1 - \alpha\lambda^2 \frac{V^2}{r} \theta_1, \tag{11}$$

$$\nu[L - \lambda^2 - (\sigma/\nu)]v_1 = 2A_* u_1, \tag{12}$$

$$\kappa[L' - \lambda^2 - (\sigma/\kappa)]\theta_1 = (dT/dr)u_1, \tag{13}$$

in which

$$L' = \frac{d^2}{dr^2} + \frac{1}{r}\frac{d}{dr}, \quad L = L' - \frac{1}{r^2}.$$

The conditions that the velocity components vanish at the boundaries can be written, by virtue of (9), in the following form:

$$u_1 = 0, \quad du_1/dr = 0, \quad v_1 = 0$$
$$\text{at} \quad r = r_1 \text{ and } r_2. \tag{14a}$$

The boundary conditions for θ_1 are, if the walls are assumed much more conductive than the fluid,

$$\theta_1 = 0 \quad \text{at} \quad r = r_1 \text{ and } r_2. \tag{14b}$$

The differential system consisting of (11)–(13) and the boundary conditions define an eigenvalue problem.

III. CASE OF SMALL SPACING

Since the purpose of this paper is to investigate the roles of ν and κ, we shall, for simplicity, assume

$r_2 - r_1 \ll r_1$. In this case it is appropriate to use the dimensionless quantities

$$\xi = (r - r_1)/(r_2 - r_1), \qquad k = \lambda(r_2 - r_1),$$

$$R' = \Omega_1(r_2 - r_1)^2/\nu, \qquad (15)$$

in which ξ varies from zero to 1, k is the dimensionless wave number, and R' a Reynolds number. If, furthermore, the substitutions

$$(u_2, v') = (\Omega_1 r_1)^{-1}(u_1, v_1) \quad \text{and} \quad \theta' = \alpha\theta_1 \qquad (16)$$

are made, Eqs. (11) to (13) become, if higher powers of $(r_2 - r_1)/r_1$ are neglected in the differential operators on the left-hand sides,

$$(D^2 - k^2)\left(D^2 - k^2 - \frac{\sigma R'}{\Omega_1}\right)u_2$$

$$= 2k^2\omega R'v' - k^2\omega^2 R'\left(1 + \frac{r_2 - r_1}{r_1}\xi\right)\theta', \qquad (17)$$

$$[D^2 - k^2 - (\sigma R'/\Omega_1)]v' = 2AR'u_2, \qquad (18)$$

$$\left(D^2 - k^2 - \frac{\sigma R'}{\Omega_1}\Pr\right)\theta' = \text{Pé}\left(\alpha r_1 \frac{dT}{dr}\right)u_2. \qquad (19)$$

In these equations, Pr is the Prandtl number ν/κ, $D = d/d\xi$,

$$\text{Pé} = \Omega_1(r_2 - r_1)^2/\kappa \qquad (20)$$

is the Péclet number, and

$$\omega = V/r\Omega_1 = A + B[1 + (r_2 - r_1)\xi/r_1]^{-2}, \qquad (21)$$

with

$$A = \frac{\Omega_2 r_2^2 - \Omega_1 r_1^2}{(r_2^2 - r_1^2)\Omega_1}, \qquad B = \frac{(\Omega_1 - \Omega_2)r_2^2}{(r_2^2 - r_1^2)\Omega_1}. \qquad (22)$$

Thus

$$A + B = 1,$$

and

$$\omega = 1 + \alpha'\xi, \qquad \alpha' = (\Omega_2/\Omega_1) - 1, \qquad (23)$$

with higher powers in $(r_2 - r_1)/r_1$ neglected. Now, from (3) it follows that

$$\frac{dT}{dr} = \frac{T_2 - T_1}{r_2 - r_1}\left(1 - \frac{r_2 - r_1}{r_1}\xi\right)$$

$$= \beta\left(1 - \frac{r_2 - r_1}{r_1}\xi\right), \qquad (24)$$

so that for $r_2 - r_1 \ll r_1$,

$$dT/dr = \beta = (T_2 - T_1)/(r_2 - r_1). \qquad (25)$$

It will now be assumed that for neutral stability σ is zero, and not merely equal to a purely imaginary

number. Furthermore, the following calculation is based on the assumption that α' is moderately small, so that $\alpha'^2 \ll 1$. Under these assumptions, (17), (18), and (19) become, after the term $\xi(r_2 - r_1)/r_1$ is neglected in (17),

$$(D^2 - k^2)^2 u_2 = 4AR'^2 k^2(1 + \alpha'\xi)v_2$$

$$- \text{Pé}\, R'\alpha\beta r_1 k^2(1 + 2\alpha'\xi)\theta_2, \qquad (26)$$

$$(D^2 - k^2)v_2 = u_2, \qquad (27)$$

$$(D^2 - k^2)\theta_2 = u_2, \qquad (28)$$

with

$$v_2 = v'/2AR' \quad \text{and} \quad \theta_2 = \theta'/\text{Pé}\,(\alpha\beta r_1). \qquad (29)$$

The boundary conditions are

$$u_2 = 0, \qquad Du_2 = 0 \quad \text{at} \quad \xi = 0 \text{ and } 1, \qquad (30)$$

$$v_2 = 0, \qquad \theta_2 = 0 \quad \text{at} \quad \xi = 0 \text{ and } 1. \qquad (31)$$

Since the differential equations and the boundary conditions are identical for v_2 and θ_2, and the left-hand sides of (27) and (28) are not zero, we conclude that

$$\theta_2 = v_2, \qquad (32)$$

and can write (26) and (27) as

$$(D^2 - k^2)^2 u_2 = k^2[(C - D) + \alpha'(C - 2D)\xi]v_2, \qquad (33)$$

$$(D^2 - k^2)v_2 = u_2. \qquad (34)$$

with

$$C = 4AR'^2, \qquad D = \text{Pé}\,R'\alpha\beta r_1. \qquad (35)$$

Comparing this pair of equations with that treated by Chandrasekhar,[6] we see that

$$D - C = T, \qquad (36)$$

$$\alpha'(C - 2D)/(C - D) = \alpha_0, \qquad (37)$$

in which T is the Taylor number $-4AR'^2$ obtained by Chandrasekhar in the case of no density gradient, and α_0 (denoted by α in his paper) is the value of $(\Omega_2 - \Omega_1)/\Omega_1$ for that case. Chandrasekhar found the critical value (T_c) of T for a variety of values of α_0, all corresponding to Ω_2/Ω_1 less than 1. Later, in considering a case of hydromagnetic instability, Yih[7] encountered a similar differential system and found the relationship between T_c and α_0 (denoted by β in Yih's paper) for three values of α_0 which are positive.[8]

[6] S. Chandrasekhar, Mathematika **1**, 5–13 (1954).

[7] C. -S. Yih, J. Fluid Mech. **5**, 436–44 (1959).

[8] These positive values of α_0 correspond to stability (for whatever T) in the problem studied by Taylor and Chandrasekhar, but not in the problem studied by Yih.

TABLE I. Critical Taylor numbers for various values of Ω_2/Ω_1.

Ω_2/Ω_1	2	1.5	1.25	1	0.50	0.25	
α_0	1	0.5	0.25	0	−0.50	−0.75	
k	3.12[a]	3.12[a]	3.12[a]	3.12	3.12	3.12	
T_c	1138[a]	1366[a]	1518[a]	1708	2275	2725	
Ω_2/Ω_1	0	−0.25	−0.50	−0.60	−0.70	−0.80	−0.90
α_0	−1	−1.25	−1.50	−1.60	−1.70	−1.80	−1.90
k	3.12	3.13	3.20	3.24	3.34	3.49	3.70
T_c	3390	4462	6417	7688	9433	11820	14940
Ω_2/Ω_1	−0.95	−1.00	−1.25	−1.50	−1.75	−2.00	
α_0	−1.95	−2.00	−2.25	−2.50	−2.75	−3.00	
k	3.86	4.00	4.61	5.06	5.60	6.05	
T_c	16760	18680	30460	46190	67590	95630	

[a] Values given by Yih.[7] The rest of the values were given by Chandrasekhar.[6]

The values of T_c against α_0 are given in Table I, with the corresponding wave numbers. The first three lines are reproduced from Yih and the rest from Chandrasekhar.[6] With T_c substituted for T in (36), solution of (36) and (37) yields the parametric relationship between C and D:

$$C = [(\alpha_0/\alpha') - 2]T_c, \tag{38}$$

$$D = [(\alpha_0/\alpha') - 1]T_c. \tag{39}$$

For a given α', values of α_0 are assumed, and the corresponding values of T_c read off from Table I, and C and D are then computed. Since both C and D contain R', in order to separate the effects of viscosity and diffusivity, the value of $D/|C|^{\frac{1}{2}}$ is plotted against C. The curves for various values of α' are given in Fig. 1. For each value of α' (corresponding to a positive value of Ω_2/Ω_1) there is a curve consisting of one or two branches, above which the flow is unstable and below which the flow is stable. The ordinate of the curves is

$$D/|C|^{\frac{1}{2}} \quad \text{or} \quad \text{Pé } \alpha\beta r_1/2\,|A|^{\frac{1}{2}}, \tag{40}$$

which is independent of the viscosity. The graphs show that for a given value of this parameter, there is a region in which the flow is destabilized as the viscosity is increased, i.e., the region to the right of the point of relative minimum of the ordinate of the curve for the particular value of α' considered. Outside of this region viscosity is always stabilizing. Furthermore, for negative values of C the curves eventually dip below the horizontal axis. For each such curve the region below the horizontal axis is a

region in which thermal diffusivity has a destabilizing effect. Outside of this region thermal diffusivity is always stabilizing.

A. Special Case of Nearly Rigid Rotation

For the special case $\Omega_2 \simeq \Omega_1$, $\alpha' \simeq 0$, and by virtue of (37) α_0 also vanishes approximately. This makes $T_c = 1708$. With

$$S = -4AR'^2 + \text{Pé } R'\alpha\beta r_1, \tag{41}$$

the dual roles of viscosity and diffusivity can be brought forth very clearly by means of graphs. There are six cases, which are given in Table II. The first four cases are realistic because α' is only nearly, not exactly, zero. The cases in which $\beta = 0$ will not be discussed here, because they have been discussed thoroughly in the existing literature. It may be mentioned here that for α' equal to zero the method of Pellew and Southwell[9] can be used

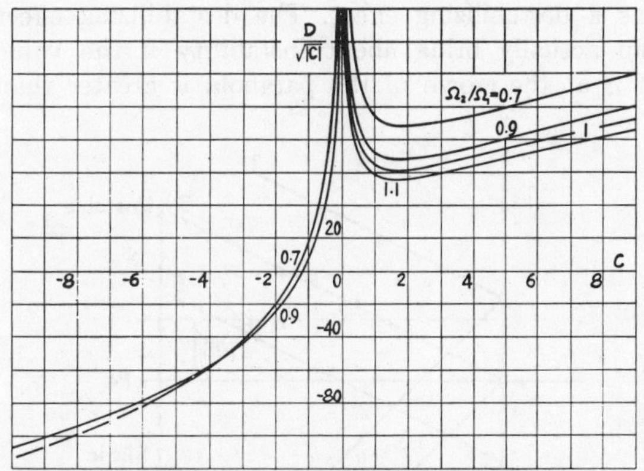

FIG. 1. Stability chart for the case of small spacing. $C = 4AR'^2$, $D = \text{Pé } R'\alpha\beta r_1$, so that $D/|C|^{\frac{1}{2}} = (1/|4A|^{\frac{1}{2}})\text{ Pé } \alpha\beta r_1$. For each value of Ω_2/Ω_1, the region above the curve or curves corresponds to instability, and the region below corresponds to stability.

TABLE II. Classification of cases.

Case 1	$A < 0,$	$\beta > 0,$
Case 2	$A < 0,$	$\beta < 0,$
Case 3	$A = 0,$	$\beta > 0,$
Case 4	$A = 0,$	$\beta < 0,$
Case 5	$A > 0,$	$\beta > 0,$
Case 6	$A > 0,$	$\beta < 0.$

[9] A. Pellew and R. V. Southwell, Proc. Roy. Soc. (London) **A176**, 312–343 (1940).

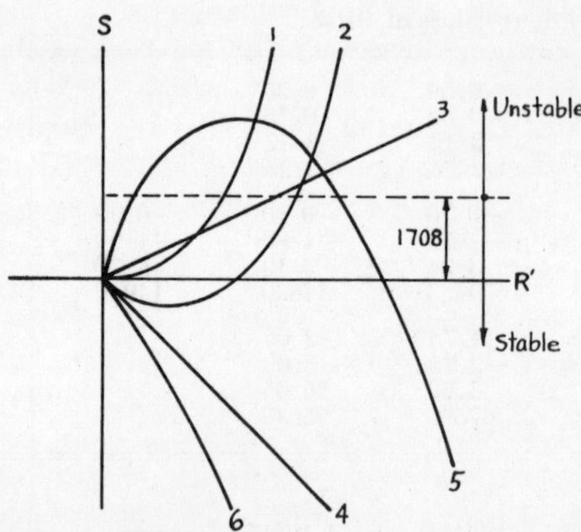

FIG. 2. A schematic drawing showing the stabilizing or destabilizing effect of viscosity for the special case $\Omega_2 \simeq \Omega_1$. Here $S = -4AR'^2 + \text{P\'e } R'\alpha\beta r_1$, and the numbering of the curves corresponds to the six cases (or subcases) considered.

to show that for neutral stability $\sigma = 0$ exactly.

If S is plotted against R' (Fig. 2), the curves are parabolas (concave upward) in cases 1 and 2, straight lines in cases 3 and 4, and parabolas (concave downward) in cases 5 and 6. In cases 1 and 3 the effect of viscosity is stabilizing. The reverse is true in cases 4 and 6, although the destabilizing effect is never great enough to make the flow actually unstable. In case 2 the effect of viscosity is mainly to stabilize, although there is a region in which viscosity can render the flow less stable. This destabilizing effect is again never great enough to make the flow actually unstable. Case 5 is the most interesting. To the left of the crown of the parabola, viscosity has a stabilizing effect. To the right, it has a destabilizing effect. The destabilizing effect can actually bring about instability if the value of S at the crown of the parabola is greater than

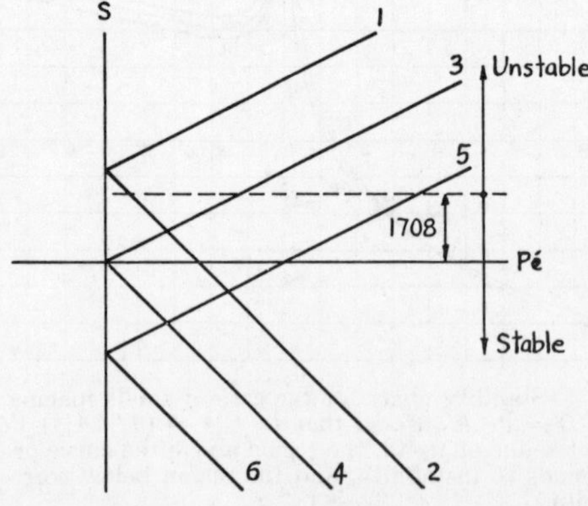

FIG. 3. A schematic drawing showing the stabilizing or destabilizing effect of thermal diffusivity. The symbol S and the numbering of the curves have the same meanings as in Fig. 2.

1708 (as shown in Fig. 2). In general, the effect of viscosity is to stabilize if $dS/dR' > 0$, and to destabilize if $dS/dR' < 0$.

S can also be plotted against Pé (Fig. 3). The effect of diffusivity is clear-cut. In cases 1, 3, and 5, diffusivity has a stabilizing effect. In cases 2, 4, and 6, the opposite is true. Except in case 2, the destabilizing effect is never great enough to make the flow actually unstable.

From Figs. 2 and 3 it can be seen that in cases 4 and 6, i.e., when neither the circulation nor the density decreases outward, the flow is stable. This is not limited either to the case of small spacing or to the special case of $\Omega_2 \simeq \Omega_1$, so long as Ω_2/Ω_1 is positive. Indeed, there are only two causes for instability: outwardly decreasing circulation and outwardly decreasing density. When both causes are present, viscosity and thermal diffusivity can only be stabilizing. When only the first cause is present, thermal diffusivity has the effect of removing the stabilizing effect of the positive radial density gradient and of bringing out the destabilizing effect of circulation variation, possibly to such an extent for actual instability to occur. When only the second cause is present, viscosity has a dual role, as mentioned before. On the one hand it is, as usual, a dissipative agent. On the other, it tends to equalize the circulation of a displaced fluid ring with that of its new surrounding, and thus to remove the stabilizing effect of the outward increase of circulation and to bring the destabilizing effect of negative density gradient in the radial direction into prominence. When neither cause is present, the flow is definitely stable. Consequently, the criterion that the flow is stable

$$d(\rho V^2 r^2)/dr \geq 0,$$

derived by Rayleigh and von Kármán (see Lin[2]) from different viewpoints is not only not necessary, but also not sufficient for stability, if diffusive effects are taken into account. The criterion is much more stringent when ρ also varies, and now reads that the flow is stable if

$$d\rho/dr \geq 0 \quad \text{and} \quad d(Vr)^2/dr \geq 0, \qquad (42)$$

or, in the case under consideration, if

$$\beta \leq 0 \quad \text{and} \quad A \geq 0. \qquad (43)$$

IV. EFFECT OF COMPRESSIBILITY

Since the stability of the flow of a gas between rotating cylinders kept at different temperatures bears upon that of the flow of a gas around a convex

INSTABILITY OF REVOLVING FLUIDS   811

surface, which has been discussed by several authors, it is appropriate to discuss here very briefly the effect of compressibility.

With V denoting the velocity parallel to a solid surface and r the normal distance measured from the center of curvature, the criterion that for

$$d(\rho V^2 r^2)/dr \geq 0 \qquad (44)$$

the flow of a fluid along a convex surface must be stable is correct only if the fluid is a liquid and if the effects of viscosity and diffusivity are neglected. For a gas, a material ring displaced from $r = r_1$ to $r = r_2$ will not maintain its density, and it is not true that the strongest destabilizing effect is obtained if we take $\tilde{\rho}_1 = \rho_1$, in which $\tilde{\rho}_1$ is the density of the fluid ring when it has reached its new position $r = r_2$. In fact, the radial pressure gradient is $\rho V^2/r$, so that the pressure increases outward, and the fluid in a material ring will be compressed as it moves out, and have a density $\tilde{\rho}_1$ greater than its original density ρ_1. Thus, assuming isentropic process, we obtain

$$\tilde{\rho}_1 = \rho_1 (p_2/p_1)^{1/\gamma}, \qquad (45)$$

and (44) should be replaced by

$$d(\rho V^2 r^2/p^{1/\gamma})/dr \geq 0, \qquad (46)$$

or

$$d[V^2 r^2 \exp(-S/c_p)]/dr \geq 0, \qquad (47)$$

in which S is now the entropy and c_p the specific heat of the gas at constant pressure. The criterion (44) obtained by Lees[10] and Lessen[11] is therefore approximately correct if the change of pressure is small. The pressure gradient, being equal to $\rho V^2/r$, is usually not large enough to cause any significant pressure variation with r, provided the pressure at $r = r_1$ is not exceedingly low. If only the stability of the boundary layer (which is usually very thin)

is considered, the approximate criterion used by these authors is practically identical with (46), and, within the implied limitations, usually quite accurate. However, if $\rho V^2 r^2$ does not change with r, the destabilizing effect of pressure variation is quite critical, and, but for mitigating circumstances brought about by diffusive and dissipative agents, would actually cause instability. This is true both in gas flow between cylinders and in gas flows around a convex surface.

Actually, the density $\tilde{\rho}_1$ defined by (45) is a potential density (at a reference pressure p_2, say), the concept of which is very familiar to meteorologists. Thus if we identify the ρ in (44) as the potential density, (44) and (46) become identical.

Neglecting pressure variation with r, Lees[10] has reached the conclusion that cooling at a convex surface can never cause instability. This is again usually true, provided the effects of diffusivities can be neglected. But even under this provision it may not be true when pressure variation plays an important role, such as when the pressure at the surface is low (so that pressure variation contributes heavily to density variation), or when there exists a region where $d(Vr)/dr$ is nearly zero (presumably outside of the boundary layer).

As has been demonstrated for the case of incompressible fluids, the effects of viscosity and thermal diffusivity can be destabilizing, so that even (47) is insufficient for the stability of real fluids. The sufficient conditions for stability of real fluids are more stringent, and are

$$dS/dr \leq 0 \quad and \quad d(Vr)^2/dr \geq 0.$$

ACKNOWLEDGMENTS

It is a pleasure to express my appreciation to my colleague, Professor A. M. Kuethe, for kindly calling my attention to the papers by Lees and Lessen.

This work has been done for a research project sponsored by the Army Research Office (Durham).

[10] L. Lees, J. Aeronaut. Sci. **25**, 407–8 (1958).
[11] M. Lessen, "Hydrodynamic stability of curved laminar compressible flows," IAS Preprint No. 812 (cited by Lees) (1958).

Formation of Rings in a Liquid Film Attached to the Inside of a Rotating Cylinder

Walter R. Debler and Chia-Shun Yih*
University of Michigan, Ann Arbor, Mich.
September 19, 1961

IN AN EXPERIMENTAL INVESTIGATION sponsored by the Technical Association of Pulp and Paper Industries we found that rings formed in a liquid film attached to the inside of a rotating cylinder, as the cylinder was suddenly stopped or slowed down. In the former case the rings (Fig. 1) lasted a few seconds before gravity pulled the liquid down to the lower part of the drum. (The axis of the drum was horizontal.) In the latter case the rings appeared for a shorter length of time but disappeared again, leaving a smooth film rotating at a smaller speed, so long as the final speed was great enough to withstand the pull of gravity.

All this is really to be expected, since it is well-known that a revolving fluid is, generally speaking, unstable if the circulation decreases monotonically radially outward, as it indeed did in the present case. The investigation was carried out because the instability of the free surface of the film is very pertinent to the phenomenon of spouting of stock in the paper-making process. We wish to call attention to the ring formation here for a different reason. Professor S. F. Shen of Cornell University recently informed the second author that experiments by Donald Coles at the California Institute of Technology showed that Tollmien-Schlichting instability occurred in a fluid between rotating cylinders as the outer cylinder was stopped. We do not know the details of Coles' experiments, but understand that his inner cylinder was stationary, so that a large portion of the fluid was stable against Taylor instability (for revolving fluids). Only in a thin layer attached to the outer cylinder was Taylor instability possible, and there it was evidently dominated by Tollmien-Schlichting instability, so that only longitudinal ridges formed. In our case the free surface (or the inner boundary) rotated before the cylinder was stopped, and continued to do so at about the same speed shortly after it was stopped. Thus the bulk of the liquid was in our case unstable with regard to ring formation. The two cases are different, and apparently there must be intermediate cases in which Taylor instability and Tollmien-Schlichting instability are equally significant.

FIG. 1.

---

* Professor of Engineering Mechanics.

Reprinted from *J. Aerospace Sci.* 29 (1962) 364.

Reprinted from TAPPI, Vol. 45, No. 4, April 1962
Copyright, 1962, by Technical Association of the Pulp and Paper Industry, and reprinted by permission of the copyright owner

On the Instability of Stock on a Fourdrinier Wire*

WALTER R. DEBLER AND CHIA-SHUN YIH

A case of free-surface instability closely related to the phenomenon of spouting on a fourdrinier wire is investigated. As a rotating cylinder with a liquid film attached to its inner surface is slowed down or stopped instantaneously, the liquid will be retarded near the surface of the cylinder while farther away the speed remains high. This is an unstable situation, and is similar to the situation prevailing at a stock-carrying fourdrinier wire as it leaves a table roll. In the latter case the fluid is slowed down at the near-stagnation region on the wire as it leaves the table roll, while the free-surface velocity remains high. Experimental data obtained indicate that the critical wavenumber (2π times the film thickness divided by the critical wavelength) of the most unstable mode is 2.7, approximately.

1. INTRODUCTION

THE VERY pronounced instability of stock on a fourdrinier wire as it leaves the table rolls has been one of the major problems encountered by the pulp and paper industry. Although much effort has been expended to ascertain the degree and characteristics of this instability, the cause of it has not been clarified up to now. One possible cause of the post-roll instability of stock on a fourdrinier wire is the slowing down of fluid near the wire in the near-stagnation region. If so, the cause of instability is exactly the same as that of the flow studied by Sir Geoffrey Taylor (1923), although the presence of the free surface (which does not exist in his well-known investigation) does make the instability phenomenon even more pronounced and easily visible.

For those readers who may not be familiar with the spouting phenomenon, it will be described briefly here.

As a wire mesh, called the fourdrinier wire, carries the stock over a series of table rolls, it winds around the top portions of these rolls, and separates from them afterwards (Fig. 1). Near the points of separation† the stock is slowed down, while the speed of the stock at the free surface remains essentially unchanged. Since the faster fluid is nearer the center of curvature of the wire than the slower fluid (the curvature of the wire is opposite to that of the table rolls after separation of the wire from these rolls), the fluid is unstable. The cause of instability is the same as for a fluid between two rotating cylinders, the instability of which was investigated by Sir Geoffrey Taylor in 1923.

To clarify a possible cause of the spouting phenomenon, and to provide a sound basis for guiding the control of spouting, the instability of a liquid film attached to the inner surface of a rotating cylinder is considered. The cylinder, rotating at a constant speed, is slowed down, and as the mean velocity profile changes with time, instability will occur. The rate of amplification of the ring-shaped disturbances is not

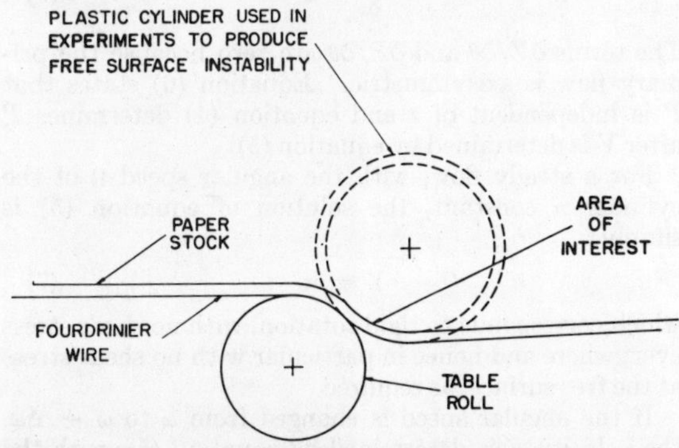

Fig. 1. Region of fourdrinier machine examined by the instability analysis and the experimental study.

WALTER R. DEBLER and CHIA-SHUN YIH, Department of Engineering Mechanics, The University of Michigan, Ann Arbor, Mich.
* This investigation has been sponsored by the Technical Association of Pulp and Paper Industry through its Fluid Mechanics Committee.
† It is in the neighborhood of these points that water is removed by the suction built up between the (separating) wire and the rollers. But this paper is not concerned with water removal.

constant, but can be computed for each instant. Thus the growth of the disturbances can be calculated by integration. The effects of Coriolis acceleration and surface tension will be taken into account, but the effect of viscosity will be considered only insofar as viscosity affects the velocity of the primary flow, which is unsteady.

2. THE PRIMARY FLOW

Cylindrical coordinates r, θ, and z will be used, with the Z-axis coinciding with the axis of the cylinder, and r measured radially from that axis. The coordinate θ is measured from a radial line and in a plane perpendicular to the axis of the cylinder. The velocity components in the directions of increasing r, θ, and z will be denoted by u, $V + v$, and w, in which V is the velocity of the primary flow and u, v, and w are the components of the velocity due to the disturbance. The pressure will be denoted by $P + p$, in which P is for the primary flow and p for the disturbance. The equations of motion are

$$\frac{\partial u}{\partial t} + u\frac{\partial u}{\partial r} + \frac{V + v}{r}\frac{\partial u}{\partial \theta} + w\frac{\partial u}{\partial z} - \frac{(V + v)^2}{r} =$$
$$-\frac{1}{\rho}\frac{\partial (P + p)}{\partial r} + \nu\left(\nabla^2 u - \frac{u}{r^2} - \frac{2}{r^2}\frac{\partial v}{\partial \theta}\right) \quad (1)$$

$$\frac{\partial (V + v)}{\partial t} + u\frac{\partial (V + v)}{\partial r} + \frac{V + v}{r}\frac{\partial (V + v)}{\partial \theta} +$$
$$w\frac{\partial (V + v)}{\partial z} + \frac{u(V + v)}{r} = -\frac{1}{\rho r}\frac{\partial (P + p)}{\partial \theta} +$$
$$\nu\left[\nabla^2(V + v) - \frac{V + v}{r^2} + \frac{2}{r^2}\frac{\partial u}{\partial \theta}\right] \quad (2)$$

$$\frac{\partial w}{\partial t} + u\frac{\partial w}{\partial r} + \frac{V + v}{r}\frac{\partial w}{\partial \theta} + w\frac{\partial w}{\partial z} =$$
$$-\frac{1}{\rho}\frac{\partial (P + p)}{\partial z} + \nu\nabla^2 w \quad (3)$$

in which t is time, ν is the kinematic viscosity of the fluid, and

$$\nabla^2 = \frac{\partial^2}{\partial r^2} + \frac{1}{r}\frac{\partial}{\partial r} + \frac{\partial^2}{\partial z^2}$$

is the Laplacian operator.

To determine the primary flow, one simply lets u, v, w, and p vanish. The resulting equations are:

$$\frac{\partial P}{\partial r} = \frac{\rho V^2}{r} \quad (4)$$

$$\frac{\partial V}{\partial t} = \nu\left(\nabla^2 V - \frac{V}{r^2}\right) \quad (5)$$

$$\frac{\partial P}{\partial z} = 0 \quad (6)$$

The terms $\partial V/\partial \theta$ and $\partial P/\partial \theta$ are zero because the primary flow is axisymmetric. Equation (6) states that P is independent of z and equation (4) determines P after V is determined by equation (5).

For a steady flow, with the angular speed Ω of the cylinder a constant, the solution of equation (5) is simply:

$$V = \omega r \quad (7)$$

which corresponds to rigid rotation, with no shear stress everywhere and hence in particular with no shear stress at the free surface, as required.

If the angular speed is changed from ω to $\omega - \Delta\omega$, the velocity V is determined by equation (5), with the boundary conditions that

the shear deformation rate $\mu e_{r\theta} = r\frac{\partial}{\partial r}\left(\frac{V}{r}\right) = 0$ at $r = a$,

$$\quad (8)$$

and

$$V = (\omega - \Delta\omega)\, r \text{ at } r = b \text{ and } t > 0 \quad (9)$$

in which a is the r for the free surface, and b the radius for the surface of the cylinder. The initial condition is equation (7), at $t = 0$. The final condition is

$$V = (\omega - \Delta\omega)r \text{ at } t = \infty \quad (10)$$

The solution can be obtained by the method of separation of variables, and is

$$V = (\omega - \Delta\omega)r + \Delta\omega\sum_{n=1}^{\infty} A_n Z_1(\lambda_n r)e^{-\lambda^2_n \nu t} \quad (11)$$

in which

$$Z_1(\lambda_n r) = J_1(\lambda_n r) + C_n N_1(\lambda_n r) \quad (12)$$

with J_1 denoting the Bessel function and N_1 the Neumann function, all of the first order. The eigenvalues λ_n are determined by equations (8) and (9), which demand that

$$\lambda_n r_1 Z'_1(\lambda_n a) - Z_1(\lambda_n a) = 0 \quad (13)$$
$$Z_1(\lambda_n b) = 0 \quad (14)$$

Equations (12), (13), and (14) yield the secular equation

$$\frac{\lambda_n a J'_1(\lambda_n a) - J_1(\lambda_n a)}{\lambda_n a N'_1(\lambda_n a) - N_1(\lambda_n a)} = \frac{J_1(\lambda_n b)}{N_1(\lambda_n b)} \quad (15)$$

from which the roots λ_n can be calculated. In equations (13) and (15), the primes indicate differentiation with respect to the argument in the parenthesis. The constant C_n in equation (12) is

$$C_n = -\frac{J_1(\lambda_n b)}{N_1(\lambda_n b)} \quad (16)$$

and the coefficients A_n in equation (11) are determined by the condition (corresponding to the initial condition)

$$\sum_{n=1}^{\infty} A_n Z_1(\lambda_n r) = r \quad (17)$$

by utilizing the well-known orthogonality properties of the eigenfunctions $Z_1(\lambda_n r)$.

For a very thin film, the calculation can be considerably simplified. In this case the curvature effects can be neglected, and the variable

$$\xi = r - a$$

can be used advantageously instead of r. The solution must satisfy the equation

$$\frac{\partial V}{\partial t} = \nu\frac{\partial^2 V}{\partial \xi^2}$$

the boundary conditions

$$\frac{\partial V}{\partial \xi} = 0 \text{ at } \xi = 0$$

and

$$V = b(\omega - \Delta\omega) \text{ at } \xi = b - a \text{ for all } t > 0$$

the initial condition

$$V = \omega(a + \xi) \text{ at } t = 0$$

and the final condition

$$V = (\omega - \Delta\omega)(a + \xi) \text{ at } t = \infty$$

The solution can be found by the method of separation of variables to be

$$V = (\omega - \Delta\omega)(a + \xi) + \sum_{n=1}^{\infty} A_n e^{-\lambda^2_n \nu t} \cos \lambda_n \xi \quad (18)$$

in which

$$\lambda_n = \frac{\pi(2n - 1)}{2(b - a)}$$

and A_n is determined from

$$\sum_{n=1}^{\infty} A_n \cos \lambda_n \xi = \Delta\omega(a + \xi)$$

to be

$$A_n = \frac{2\Delta\omega}{b - a} \int_0^{b-a} (a + \xi) \cos \lambda_n \xi \, d\xi =$$
$$\frac{4\Delta\omega}{\pi(2n - 1)} \left[b(-1)^{n-1} - \frac{1}{\lambda_n} \right] \quad (19)$$

Duhamel's principle can be applied to equation (18) if the speed variations is time-dependent, as it is indeed here. The result is

$$V = \omega(a + \xi) - \int_0^t \left[(a + \xi) + \sum A'_n e^{-\lambda^2_n \nu(t-\tau)} \cos \lambda_n \xi \right]$$
$$\frac{d[\Delta\omega(\tau)] \, d\tau}{d\tau} - \Delta\omega(0) \left[(a + \xi) + \sum A'_n e^{-\lambda^2_n \nu t} \cos \lambda_n \xi \right]$$
$$(19A)$$

in which $\Delta\omega(0)$ is the change of speed at $t = 0$, and

$$A'_n = \frac{4}{\pi(2n - 1)} \left[b(-1)^n - \frac{1}{\lambda_n} \right]$$

3. STABILITY OF THE PRIMARY FLOW

If the effect of viscosity on the disturbance is neglected, and if the disturbance is assumed to be axisymmetric, the first-order terms in u, v, w, and p in equations (1), (2), and (3) satisfy the equations

$$\frac{\partial u}{\partial t} - \frac{2Vv}{r} = -\frac{1}{\rho} \frac{\partial p}{\partial r} \quad (20)$$

$$\frac{\partial v}{\partial t} + u \frac{\partial V}{\partial r} + \frac{Vu}{r} = 0 \quad (21)$$

$$\frac{\partial w}{\partial t} = -\frac{1}{\rho} \frac{\partial p}{\partial z} \quad (22)$$

The equation of continuity is

$$\frac{\partial(ru)}{\partial r} + \frac{\partial(rw)}{\partial z} = 0 \quad (23)$$

Assuming

$$(u, v, p) = e^{\sigma t} [u(r), v(r), p(r)] \cos \lambda z, \; w = e^{\sigma t} w(r) \sin \lambda z, \quad (24)$$

and using henceforth u, v, w, and p to denote $u(r)$, $v(r)$, etc., one has, with primes indicating differentiation with respect to r,

$$\sigma u - \frac{2V}{r} v = -\frac{1}{\rho} p' \quad (25)$$

$$\sigma v = -\left(\frac{V}{r} + V' \right) u \quad (26)$$

$$\sigma w = \frac{\lambda}{\rho} p \quad (27)$$

The equation of continuity becomes

$$w = -\frac{1}{\lambda} \left(u' + \frac{u}{r} \right) \quad (28)$$

Elimination of p from equations (25) and (27) produces

$$\sigma(-\lambda u - w') + \frac{2V}{r} \lambda v = 0 \quad (29)$$

Finally, combination of equations (26), (28), and (29) yields

$$u'' + \frac{u'}{r} - \frac{u}{r^2} - \frac{\lambda^2}{\sigma^2} [K(r) + \sigma^2]u = 0 \quad (30)$$

in which

$$K(r) = \frac{2V}{r} \left(\frac{V}{r} + V' \right) \quad (31)$$

The boundary condition at the surface of the cylinder is simply

$$u(b) = 0 \quad (32)$$

With $(e^{\sigma t} \cos \lambda z)\eta(r)$ denoting the deviation of the free surface from its mean position (Fig. 1), the boundary condition at the free surface is

$$\frac{dP}{dr} \eta + p - \frac{T}{a^2} \left(\eta + a^2 \frac{\partial^2 \eta}{\partial z^2} \right) = 0 \quad (33)$$

in which T is the surface tension. Now the kinematic condition at the free surface is

$$u = \sigma\eta \quad (34)$$

This, together with equations (4), (27), and (28), enables one to write equation (33) as

$$u' + \frac{u}{a} - \frac{\lambda^2}{\sigma^2} \left[\frac{V^2}{a} - \frac{T}{a^2\rho} (1 - a^2\lambda^2) \right] u = 0 \text{ at } r = a \quad (35)$$

The next task is to determine σ for given V, T, and λ, from equations (30), (31), (32), and (35). V will be evaluated at various values of t, and will then for those instants be considered as functions of r only. The Ritz method will be used to solve the eigenvalue problem. First the functions

$$\phi_m (r) = \sin \left(\beta_m \frac{b - r}{b - a} \right) \quad (36)$$

will be chosen, with β_m determined from the equation

$$\beta_m = -Q \tan \beta_m \quad (37)$$

in which

$$Q = \frac{\lambda^2(b - a)}{\sigma^2} \left[\frac{V^2}{a} - \frac{T}{a^2\rho} (1 - a^2\lambda^2) \right] - \frac{b - a}{a} \quad (38)$$

with V evaluated at $r = a$. The functions ϕ_m satisfy the boundary conditions (32) and (35). Now u can be expressed as a linear combination of ϕ_m:

$$u = \sum_{m=1}^{N} c_m \phi_m(r) \quad (39)$$

Equation (30) will be rewritten in the form

$$L(u) - \lambda^2 \left[\frac{K(r)}{\sigma^2} + 1 \right] u = 0 \quad (40)$$

in which the operator L is defined by

$$L = \frac{d^2}{dr^2} + \frac{1}{r} \frac{d}{dr} - \frac{1}{r^2} \quad (41)$$

It is more desirable to deal with dimensionless members only. If r is measured in terms of a and all velocities in terms of ωa, equations (39), (40), (41) and (31) can retain their forms, with all quantities understood to be dimensionless, and with the new λ equal to a times the old λ, and the new σ equal to the old σ divided by ω. Thus

$$Q = \left\{\frac{\lambda^2}{\sigma^2}\left[V^2 - S(1 - \lambda^2)\right] - 1\right\}\frac{b - a}{a} \quad (42)$$

in which

$$S = \frac{T'}{\rho\omega^2 a^3} \quad (43)$$

The objective is to obtain the relationship between λ, σ, and S, given a, b, and V.

The procedure is as follows. The quantities σ and Q are first assumed. Then the β's are found from equation (37), and the functions ϕ_m thus determined. Now, with μ denoting the approximate value (or values) of λ^2, which is to be obtained by the use of equation (39), equation (40) can be multiplied by u as expressed in equation (39) to yield

$$\int_1^\alpha uL(u)dr - \mu \int_1^\alpha \left(\frac{K(r)}{\sigma^2} + 1\right)u^2 dr =$$
$$\sum_{m,n=1}^N (A_{mn} - \mu B_{mn})C_m C_n \quad (44)$$

If the condition is imposed that the right-hand side of this equation be stationary for variations of the C's, the N equations

$$\sum_{m=1}^N (A_{mn} - \mu B_{mn})C_m = 0, \ (n = 1, 2, \ldots, N) \quad (45)$$

are obtained. Since the C's must not all vanish, the values of μ must satisfy the secular equation

$$\begin{vmatrix} A_{11} - \mu B_{11} & A_{12} - \mu B_{12} \ldots A_{1N} - \mu B_{1N} \\ A_{21} - \mu B_{21} & A_{22} - \mu B_{22} \ldots A_{2N} - \mu B_{2N} \\ \cdots\cdots\cdots\cdots\cdots\cdots\cdots\cdots\cdots\cdots \\ A_{N1} - \mu B_{N1} & A_{N2} - \mu B_{N2} \ldots A_{NN} - \mu B_{NN} \end{vmatrix} = 0 \quad (46)$$

With μ or (the approximate) λ^2 found, the value of S is calculated from the assumed value of Q. Since there are N values of λ^2, there will be N corresponding values of S for the same σ. Thus the curves $\sigma = $ constant can possibly be traced out with *one* assumption of Q. However, it is laborious to solve equation (46) if N is too large. We shall be contented with $N = 1$, which usually gives very good approximations, and endeavor to trace out the curves $\sigma = $ constant by assuming various values of Q.

For small spacings equation (30) can be replaced by

$$\frac{d^2u}{d\eta^2} - \frac{\lambda'^2}{\sigma^2}\left[G(\eta) + \sigma^2\right]u = 0 \quad (47)$$

in which

$$\eta = \frac{r - a}{b - a}, \ \lambda' = \frac{b - a}{a}\lambda, \ \text{and} \ G(\eta) = K(r)$$

Equation (36) can be written

$$\phi_m(\eta) = \sin \beta_m(1 - \eta) \quad (48)$$

The procedure is quite unchanged. The result is a relationship between σ, λ', and S.

The σ's so found are for an instant t. Therefore σ is really a function of t. A disturbance will grow in accordance with the time factor

$$A(t) = \exp \int_0^t \omega\sigma(\tau)\,d\tau \quad (49)$$

in which $\sigma(\tau)$ is the dimensionless σ for a given S and λ or λ', after the σ-S-λ ie σ-S-λ' chart is available. The

most unstable mode for any S corresponds to the largest value of equation (49), and a particular λ or λ', which is magnified the fastest. Of course of value of $A(t)$ depends on t. We can define the most unstable mode to be the one corresponding to the maximum value of

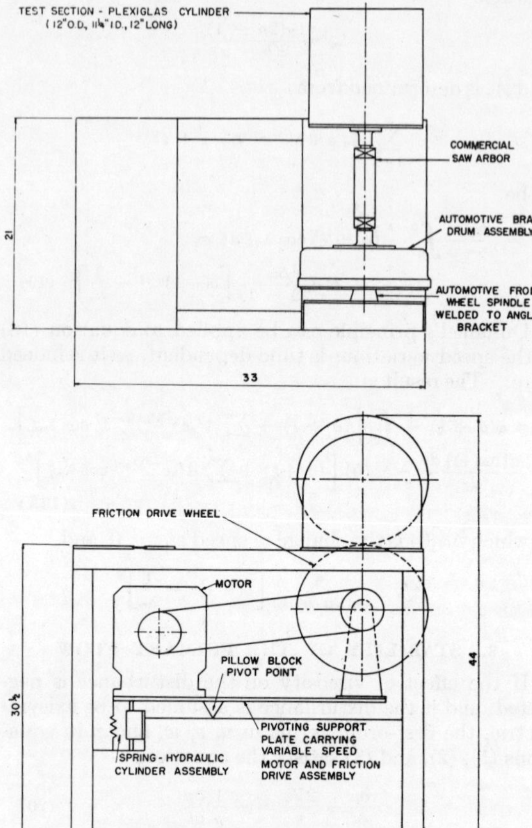

Fig. 2. Diagram of experimental apparatus.

$A(\infty)$, for a given S. The integral $A(t)$ is convergent if the final state given by equation (10) is stable under the action of surface tension.

4. EXPERIMENTAL INVESTIGATION

An experimental program was initiated to produce, with a laboratory apparatus, a free-surface instability which would be similar to the post-roll spouting encountered on the fourdrinier machine. In addition it was intended to make quantitative measurements.

Accordingly, the apparatus shown in Figs. 2 and 3 was designed and built. The test section consists of a plastic drum with a horizontal axis. Water (or any other suitable fluid) is added to the drum in a predetermined amount so that, when the drum is rotated at high speed, the fluid is forced out against the inside surface of the plastic cylinder, forming a fluid cylinder of the desired thickness. The plastic drum (or test section) is connected to an automotive brake drum by a steel shaft running in ball bearings. This brake drum was dynamically balanced, and the rim machined to obtain a surface concentric with the assembly's centerline to reduce vibration. The plastic drum was supported at its end by ball bearing supports which kept it concentric with the drive shaft and eliminated the cantilever loads and deflections. One could not sense any vibration in the test apparatus if he were to touch it. A complete brake shoe assembly was mounted within the drum and to a modified, automotive wheel spindle. The spindle was welded to an angle plate which in turn was bolted to the test stand.

A rubber wheel, driven with a V-belt by a variable speed motor, was in contact with the brake drum. The friction wheel with its associated bearings and supports, along with the motor, were mounted on a pivoting platform that was located below the brake drum. A tension spring attached to one end of the platform causes it to rotate about its pivot and to swing into contact with the rim of the brake drum. Thus the brake drum served not only to stop the test cylinder once it was in motion, but also to transmit the motion during a portion of the operating schedule. A hydraulic cylinder was placed in parallel with the spring so that, upon its activation, the cylinder's piston would pivot the platform and the friction wheel away from the brake rim. This latter action separated the rotating test section from the power source and thereby served as the clutch. Upon disengagement of the friction wheel from the brake rim, fluid was admitted to the hydraulic cylinder in the brake assembly, applying pressure to the brake shoes and thereby stopping the rotating test section. The stopping of the test section was usually abrupt; however, as will be mentioned

Fig. 4. *End view of test section showing surface waves generated in water with a depth of 0.295 in.*

tioned later, one could also manually operate the clutch and have gradual stopping.

Prior to applying the brakes, the water in the plastic cylinder would be in solid-body rotation and completely transparent. Subsequent to stopping, the fluid away from the solid boundary would continue to rotate and a series of longitudinally spaced and essentially axisymmetric waves were generated on the free surface. These waves persisted (for a sudden halting of the test section) until the entire fluid mass had decelerated to such a degree that gravity effects caused the fluid to leave the uppermost portions of the cylinder and fall to the bottom. The waves were made visible by suitable lighting of the test section, which yielded highlights and shadows from the wave crests and troughs. After completion of one test run the friction drive wheel could be engaged again by releasing the pressure in the hydraulic brake unit. The spring would pull the friction wheel into contact with the brake drum rim and it, along with the connected test section, would commence rotating.

During the course of an individual test run, photographs were taken of the waves which formed within the test section. The apparatus was instrumented so that the speed of the drum before braking could be read by means of a photoelectric cell that was connected to an electric counter. This equipment could not be used during the period immediately after the application of the brakes because of its disadvantageous response-time characteristics. To overcome this, a microswitch was attached to the rotating test section and the output of this fed to a two-channel recorder. One channel was used to measure speed, while the other channel recorded a signal that was emitted each time a photograph was taken. In this way, it was

Fig. 3. *Experimental apparatus and recording equipment.*

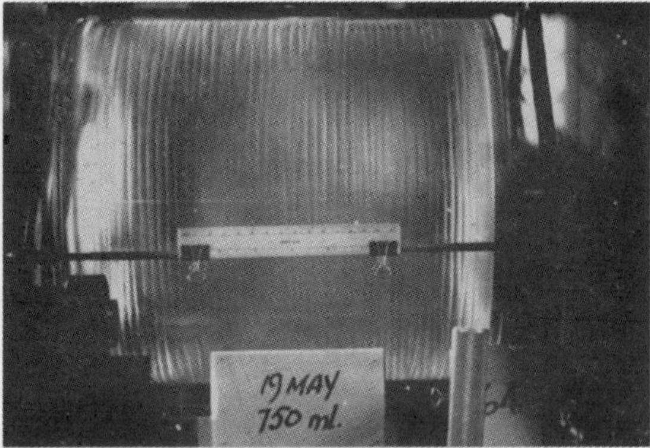

Fig. 5. *Axial view of test section showing waves in 0.105 in. of water after an abrupt stop from 600 r.p.m.; wavelength = 0.236 in.*

possible to determine accurately not only the drum speed when the photographs were taken but also the time interval between successive photographs. Examples of the results of these tests are shown in Figs. 4, 5, 6, 7, and 8.

The apparatus was originally designed with the intent that the halting of the test cylinder would be abrupt. However, tests were also conducted for which the brake was applied gradually and the stopping process occurred over an extended period of time. The photographs obtained from these tests showed less contrast than those taken after a sudden stop, because the waves appear immediately after the first application of the brake and subsequently disappear. This phenomenon is easily explained because the redistribution of momentum by the secondary flow removes the mechanism for the occurrence and growth of the waves.

5. EXPERIMENTAL RESULTS

The physical parameters associated with this problem are (see Fig. 9):

λ_{cr} = critical wavelength
b = the inside radius of the cylinder
a = the inside radius of the fluid film
$b - a$ = the fluid depth
ω = the angular speed of the cylinder prior to an abrupt stop
ρ = fluid density
μ = fluid viscosity
T = surface tension

Fig. 6. *Axial view of test section showing waves in 0.295 in. of water after an abrupt stop from 500 r.p.m.; wavelength = 0.576 in.*

Fig. 7. *Axial view of test section showing waves in 0.175 in. of kerosene after an abrupt stop from 600 r.p.m.; wavelength = 0.464 in.*

The above variables may be combined into dimensionless parameters by the well-known methods of dimensional analysis. The result is:

$$\frac{\lambda_{cr}}{b - a} = F_1\left(\frac{b}{b - a}, \frac{T}{\rho\omega^2(b - a)^3}, \frac{b^2\omega}{\nu}\right)$$

Viscosity will of course modify the mean velocity as soon as the motion of the cylinder is stopped. If the effects of viscosity on the disturbance are neglected, for the time being, the result can be reduced to:

$$\frac{\lambda_{cr}}{b - a} = F_2\left(\frac{b}{b - a}, S\right)$$

in which

$$S = \frac{\sigma T}{\rho\omega^2(b - a)^3}$$

The functions F_1 and F_2 are to be determined.

The experimental results, taken over a broad range of free-surface curvature parameter (i.e., $b/(b - a)$) are shown in Fig. 10. These data show that the ratio of (critical) wavelength to fluid thickness is between 2.0 and 3.0 and, while the ratio is nearly independent of the free-surface curvature, it tends to increase slightly as $b/(b - a)$ is increased. The results show some spread with regard to the surface-tension parameter. This spread is most pronounced at both the high and low

Fig. 8. *Axial view of test section showing waves in 0.295 in. of a 5% mixture of water and Long-Lac pulp after an abrupt stop from 400 r.p.m.; wavelength = 0.709 in.*

curvatures and results from the increased difficulty in interpreting the photographs taken under those conditions. At the low values of $b/(b-a)$, the fluid thickness is high and the waves are extremely unstable in form. As a result, they are accompanied by addi-

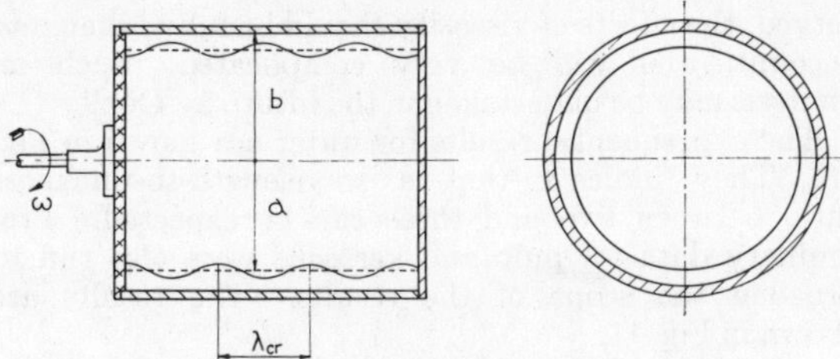

Fig. 9. Definition drawing

tional surface discontinuities which must be sorted out by the person reading the photograph. One can note in Fig. 7 the presence of other surface undulations. Nevertheless, the primary wave pattern is clearly evident. For large values of $b/(b-a)$ the waves appear to be very stable; but the wave amplitude is small and they tend to give a very poor image. Both of these difficulties were examined and a great many photographs were taken so that reliable data could be obtained.

Each data point shown in Fig. 10 results from averaging the results from five to fifteen photographs. On each photograph from five to ten waves, depending upon the wavelength, were used to obtain the value of the wavelength. For most tests (each for a constant S and $b/(b-a)$) the wavelength obtained from different photographs was quite consistent, although one of the 21 tests conducted showed a 3 to 1 variation between the shortest and longest wavelength obtained. Thus, it is believed that the data, although somewhat scattered, are representative of the phenomena which were under study.

The pattern of the points associated with a particular value of the surface tension parameter is not consistent. It is regretted that with the data at hand

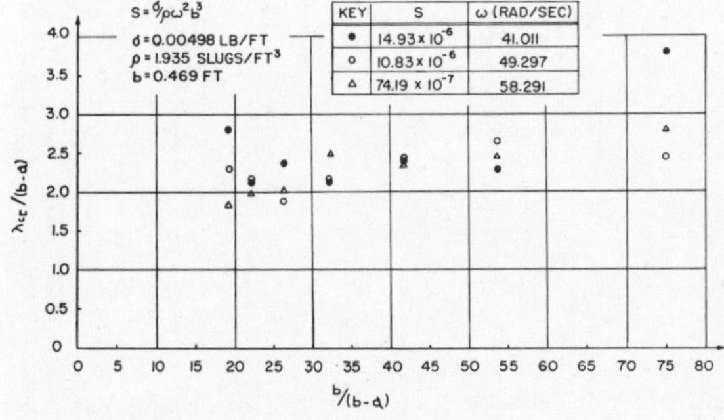

Fig. 10. Experimentally determined critical wavelengths for water

it was not possible to isolate to a greater degree the role of the surface tension parameter on the wavelength. Nevertheless, it is indicated from the present results that the role is a minor one. This is possibly because the faster motion of the free surface stiffens and stabilizes it against wave formation, and any waves

which do occur are primarily due to the unstable momentum distribution in the liquid film. The instability is therefore more like that studied by Sir Geoffrey Taylor (1923) than that studied by Yih (1960). Indeed, since 3.13 is approximately the critical wave number obtained by Taylor, and the value 2.3 for $\lambda_{cr}/(b-a)$ corresponds to the value 2.7 for the critical wavenumber $2\pi(b-a)\lambda_{cr}$, the agreement is really rather remarkable. The weak dependence of the critical wave number on S does not mean, of course, that S does not affect the rate of growth, for the latter must depend very much on S. It merely says that whatever the value of S, $\lambda_{cr}/(b-a)$ is nearly 2.3.

After the experimental evidence indicated how very closely the instability considered resembles the instability investigated by Sir Geoffrey Taylor, it was realized that any analysis in which the effects of viscosity are not fully taken into account will not adequately predict the critical wavenumber, since in Taylor's analysis the effects of viscosity are (and must

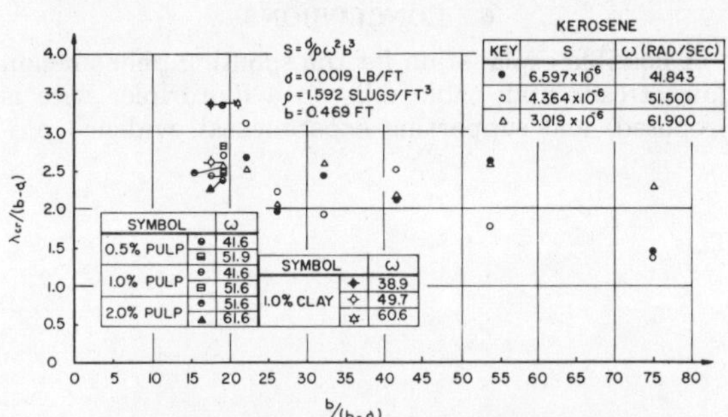

Fig. 11. Experimentally determined critical wavelengths for paper pulp and clay solutions and kerosene

be) fully taken into account. Numerical calculation according to the analysis presented in Section 3 of this paper was then abandoned.

It is believed that additional tests could be conducted using the present techniques and procedures. A consequence of this might be more consistent average values with a greater expectancy of occurrence. The use of high-speed motion picture equipment could be valuable in studying the growth of the waves. Both of these courses of action would not materially increase the understanding of the spouting phenomenon. The high-speed motion pictures would help, however, to determine the variation of the wavelength before the stabilizing effect of gravity destroys the wave pattern. Some variation in the results from individual photographs could be ascribed to the fact that they were taken "early" or "late" in wave formation process. Most of the pictures were taken about one-half second after the test section was abruptly stopped.

On Fig. 11 some data points for pulp‡ are shown. These test points are from a brief test program with pulp and were done only to verify the existence of the wave formation phenomena with a nonhomogeneous and non-Newtonian fluid. It is believed that the wave formation in a pulp solution, shown less clearly in Fig. 7 than in actuality, indicates that the analysis given in this paper and the associated test program

‡ KC Long Lac 17; kraft (softwood); 65% spruce, 35% jack pine; 25–35 micron fiber diameter; 2.5–3.5 mm. fiber length.

are applicable to the operation of the fourdrinier machine.

Some data were also taken with kerosene, which has a surface tension about one-half that of water. (This was done to significantly increase the parameter S without raising ω beyond the limit set by structural stability considerations.) These data (Fig. 11) are not as complete as the water data and are considered preliminary. Additional work is concurrently going on so as to give a better picture of the surface tension parameter.

The pulp data mentioned before were plotted using the surface tension of pure water. It is recognized that this may not be correct. However, no other figure seemed more appropriate or readily obtainable. The pulp data, while restricted in number of runs, were also limited to solutions of less than 3% concentration. Above 3% it was found that the mixture was extremely "thick" and there was also a marked tendency for the water and pulp to separate in the centrifugal field.

6. CONCLUSIONS

A possible explanation for the spouting phenomenon downstream from table rolls on a fourdrinier wire is proposed, and supporting experimental evidence presented. Whether the proposed mechanism adequately explains the spouting phenomenon on a fourdrinier wire depends on whether the actual velocity distribution in the stock in the post-roll region is favorable for the proposed mechanism to be effective in producing instability. In an analysis of the phenomenon observed, the effects of viscosity should be fully taken into account, and will be very complicated. Such an analysis may be undertaken in the future by Debler.

The experimental results for water are shown in Fig. 10. They indicate that a wavelength-to-thickness ratio between two and three can be expected. Preliminary data for pulp and kerosene were also run to broaden the scope of the results. The results are shown in Fig. 11.

LITERATURE CITED

1. Taylor, Sir Geoffrey, *Phil. Trans.* A, 223, 289–343 (1923).
2. Yih, C.-S., *Proc. Roy. Soc.* Series A, 258, 63–86 (1960).

RECEIVED Aug. 23, 1961. Presented at the 16th Engineering Conference of the Technical Association of the Pulp and Paper Industry, held in Washington, D. C., Oct. 15–19, 1961.

The success of the experimental work is due in large measure to R. Montgomery, a graduate student in the Department of Engineering Mechanics, The University of Michigan. Without his help in the design of the equipment and his subsequent test work with the apparatus, the experimental work would not have progressed as easily as it did. This work has been sponsored by the Fluid-Mechanics Committee of the *Tappi* through a contract with The University of Michigan.

THE PHYSICS OF FLUIDS   VOLUME 6, NUMBER 3   MARCH 1963

Stability of Liquid Flow down an Inclined Plane

CHIA-SHUN YIH

Department of Engineering Mechanics, The University of Michigan, Ann Arbor, Michigan
(Received 11 October 1962)

The stability of a liquid layer flowing down an inclined plane is investigated. A new perturbation method is used to furnish information regarding stability of surface waves for three cases: the case of small wavenumbers, of small Reynolds numbers, and of large wavenumbers. The results for small wavenumbers agree with Benjamin's result obtained by the use of power series expansion, and the results for the two other cases are new. The results for large wavenumbers, zero surface tension, and vertical plate contradict the tentative assertion of Benjamin. The three cases are then re-examined for shear-wave stability, and the results compared with those for confined plane Poiseuille flow. The comparison serves to indicate the vestiges of shear waves in the free-surface flow, and to give a sense of unity in the understanding of the stability of both flows. The case of large wavenumbers also serves as a new example of the dual role of viscosity in stability phenomena.

The topological features of the c_i curves for four cases (surface tension = 0 or $\neq$ 0 and angle of plate inclination = or $< \frac{1}{2}\pi$) are depicted. The effect of variability of surface tension is briefly assessed.

I. INTRODUCTION

THE stability of the laminar flow of a liquid layer, analyzed inexactly by Kapitza,[1] was first rigorously formulated by Yih[2] (henceforth referred to as I), who solved the Orr–Sommerfeld equation by an expansion in powers of αR. The resulting secular equation was solved by numerical computation, involving the solution of simultaneous nonlinear algebraic equations. Whereas the numerical computation produced the result that

the flow down a vertical plane is unstable for Reynolds numbers larger than 1.5, thus establishing the instability of the flow at low Reynolds numbers, it was not accurate enough, and both the shape of the neutral stability curve and the values of the wave speed given in I are incorrect. In a paper based on Yih's formulation and on a variation of his method, Benjamin[3] performed a new calculation, with the important difference that his neutral-stability curves were obtained analytically, instead of numerically. His calculation established the result that free-surface flow down a vertical plane is unstable for all finite Reynolds numbers, and

---

[1] P. L. Kapitza, Zh. Eksperim. i Teor. Fiz. **18**, 3 (1948); **18**, 20 (1948); **19**, 105 (1949).

[2] C.-S. Yih, "Stability of Parallel Laminar Flow with a Free Surface," *Proceedings of the Second U. S. National Congress of Applied Mechanics* (American Society of Mechanical Engineers, New York, 1955), pp. 623–628.

[3] T. B. Benjamin, J. Fluid Mech. **2**, 554 (1957).

gave values for the wave speed which are more in accord with experiments.[4] The present paper, on the same subject, has been written for the following reasons.

Yih's numerical computation and Benjamin's power expansion are both very laborious. It is desirable to have a simple method for the solution of problems of the same kind. A perturbation procedure based on Yih's expansion (I) provides just such a method. The agreement of the results obtained by this new method with Benjamin's should dispel the feeling in the minds of some of the people working on free-surface instability that there is a fundamental difference between Yih's expansion and Benjamin's. But quite apart from this, the perturbation procedure provides a powerful method for solving stability problems involving free surfaces or interfaces, and is itself worth presenting. It is presented in this paper.

The nature of the axis $\alpha = 0$ (α is the wavenumber) and the topology of the curves for constant c_i in the α–R plane ($\alpha c_i \sim$ rate of amplification or damping, R is the Reynolds number) have not been clarified. It is hoped that this paper will provide such a clarification.

The plane Poiseuille flow is known to be unstable only at rather high Reynolds numbers. Since free-surface flow is one-half the plane Poiseuille flow, it is rather surprising that the free surface should make it unstable at very much lower Reynolds numbers. Should not there remain some features of the stability of the free-surface flow which are similar to those of the plane Poiseuille flow? Why should the features of the stability of the plane Poiseuille flow disappear so completely when a free surface is present? Clarification of this point leads not only to the understanding of the correct choice of mathematical approximations to be made in dealing with problems of free-surface instability, but also to a better understanding of the physics of the phenomenon. This paper contains such a clarification.

Benjamin's calculation is based on the assumption that α is small. For this reason Benjamin did not consider his calculation applicable to values of α which are not small. For the case of vertical flow with zero surface tension, he gave the dashed line $\alpha = 0.43$ (approximately) as the estimated neutral-stability curve. This is incorrect, and has misled some people to obtain such a neutral-stability curve with a high-speed computer. Here Yih's method,[2]

coupled with the new perturbation procedure, provides results at low Reynolds numbers for any value of α, however large. These results, which cannot be obtained by Benjamin's power series expansion, are presented in this paper. They show that the entire axis $R = 0$ is part of a neutral-stability curve for vertical film flows if surface tension is zero, and that there is no bifurcation point enabling the curve to branch out. The greater versatility of the expansion in powers of αR is thus demonstrated.

The question at large values of the wavenumber α has so far not been touched. It will be discussed in this paper. The pertinent result furnishes a new example of the dual role of viscosity, i.e., a new example of the destabilizing effect of viscosity.

The free-surface boundary condition involving shear will be formulated with variable surface tension taken into account, and the effect of this variability is briefly assessed in this paper.

II. FORMULATION OF THE PROBLEM

For the sake of completeness, the formulation of the problem is presented. With reference to Fig. 1, the primary flow, assumed steady, is parallel to the X axis, with the velocity $\bar{u}$ varying only with Y. Since the pressure gradient in the X direction and the velocity component parallel to Y are zero, the Navier–Stokes equations are simply

$$\rho g \sin \beta + \mu \, d^2 \bar{u}/dY^2 = 0, \qquad (1)$$

$$d\bar{p}/dY = \rho g \cos \beta, \qquad (2)$$

in which ρ is the (constant) density, g the gravitational acceleration, μ the viscosity, and $\bar{p}$ is the pressure of the primary flow. The coordinates X and Y and the angle of inclination β of the plane boundary are all defined in Fig. 1.

Equation (1) can be integrated with the boundary conditions $\bar{u} = 0$ at $Y = d$, and $du/dY = 0$ at $Y = 0$, since d is the depth of the primary flow and the mean free surface is at $Y = 0$, where the shear stress must vanish. The result is

$$\bar{u} = (g \sin \beta/2\nu)(d^2 - Y^2),$$

or

$$U(y) = \tfrac{3}{2}(1 - y^2), \qquad (3)$$

in which

$$U = \bar{u}/\bar{u}_a, \ \bar{u}_a = \text{average velocity of the}$$

$$\text{primary flow} = g \, d^2 \sin \beta/3\nu, \ y = Y/d. \qquad (4)$$

---

[4] A. M. Binnie, J. Fluid Mech. **2**, 551 (1957).

The Reynolds number and Froude number will be defined to be

$$R = \bar{u}_a d/\nu, \qquad F = \bar{u}_a/(gd)^{\frac{1}{2}}. \tag{5}$$

The second equation in (4) can be written as

$$3F^2 = R \sin \beta. \tag{6}$$

Squire's result[5] for the stability of three-dimensional disturbances in unidirectional flows between rigid boundaries has been extended to flows with free surfaces, interfaces, or density stratification.[6] For these flows, the primary flow is stable or unstable for a three-dimensional disturbance according as it is stable or unstable for a two-dimensional disturbance at a lower Reynolds number, a milder slope, and a reduced pressure gradient in the direction of flow. (For the flow under study, the pressure gradient in the X direction is zero. Hence no reduction is necessary.) Consequently, it is sufficient to consider two-dimensional disturbances only.

With the origin of the Cartesian coordinates (shown in Fig. 1) at the free surface, and with u

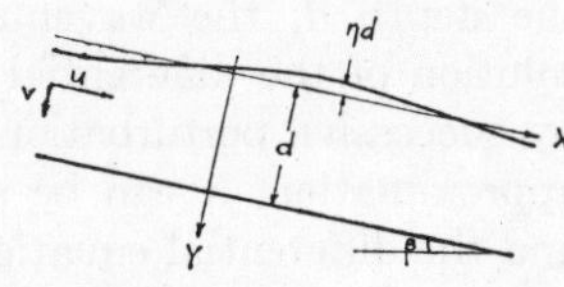

Fig. 1. Definition sketch.

and v denoting the velocity components in the directions of X and Y, respectively, the Navier–Stokes equations are

$$\frac{\partial u}{\partial t} + u \frac{\partial u}{\partial X} + v \frac{\partial u}{\partial Y} = -\frac{1}{\rho} \frac{\partial p}{\partial X} + g \sin \beta + \nu \Delta u,$$

$$\frac{\partial v}{\partial t} + u \frac{\partial v}{\partial X} + v \frac{\partial v}{\partial Y} = -\frac{1}{\rho} \frac{\partial p}{\partial Y} + g \cos \beta + \nu \Delta v,$$

in which t is the time, p the pressure, and Δ the Laplacian operator. The equation of continuity is

$$\partial u/\partial X + \partial v/\partial Y = 0.$$

By the substitutions

$$(u_1, v_1) = (u, v)/\bar{u}_a, \qquad (x, y) = (X, Y)/d,$$

$$p_1 = p/\rho \bar{u}_a^2, \qquad \tau = t\bar{u}_a/d,$$

the equations of motion and of continuity can be written in the following dimensionless forms:

$$\frac{\partial u_1}{\partial \tau} + u_1 \frac{\partial u_1}{\partial x} + v_1 \frac{\partial u_1}{\partial y} = \frac{\partial p_1}{\partial x} + \frac{\sin \beta}{F^2} + \frac{1}{R} \Delta u_1, \tag{7}$$

[5] H. B. Squire, Proc. Roy. Soc. (London) **A142**, 621 (1933).
[6] C.-S. Yih, Quart. Appl. Math. **12**, 434 (1955).

$$\frac{\partial v_1}{\partial \tau} + u_1 \frac{\partial v_1}{\partial x} + v_1 \frac{\partial v_1}{\partial y} = -\frac{\partial p_1}{\partial y} + \frac{\cos \beta}{F^2} + \frac{1}{R} \Delta v_1, \tag{8}$$

$$\frac{\partial u_1}{\partial x} + \frac{\partial v_1}{\partial y} = 0. \tag{9}$$

Let

$$u_1 = U + u', \qquad v = v', \qquad p = P + p', \tag{10}$$

in which U and P are the (dimensionless) velocity and pressure of the primary flow, and the accented quantities are the velocity and the pressure perturbations. Substitution of (10) into (5), (6), and (7) yields

$$u'_\tau + U u'_x + U_y v' = -p'_x + (1/R)\Delta u', \tag{11}$$

$$v'_\tau + U v'_x = -p'_y + (1/R)\Delta v', \tag{12}$$

$$u'_x + v'_y = 0, \tag{13}$$

if terms quadratic in the perturbation quantities are neglected. In obtaining (11) and (12), the fact that U and P satisfy (5) and (6) has been utilized. The subscripts in (11), (12), and (13) denote partial differentiation.

Equation (13) allows the use of a (dimensionless) stream function ψ, in terms of which u' and v' can be expressed as follows:

$$u' = \psi_y, \qquad v' = -\psi_x.$$

Equations (11) and (12) can then be written as

$$\psi_{y\tau} + U\psi_{xy} - U_y\psi_x = -p'_x + (1/R)\Delta\psi_y, \tag{14}$$

$$\psi_{x\tau} + U\psi_{xx} = -p'_y + (1/R)\Delta\psi_x. \tag{15}$$

The boundary conditions at the bottom ($y = 1$) are

(i) $u' = \psi_y = 0,$ (ii) $v' = -\psi_x = 0.$

At the free surface the shear stress must vanish and the normal stress must just balance the normal stress induced by surface tension. Hence the boundary conditions at the free surface are

(iii) $\dfrac{\partial v_1}{\partial x} + \dfrac{\partial u_1}{\partial y} = 0,$

(iv) $\left(-p_1 + \dfrac{2}{R} \dfrac{\partial v_1}{\partial y}\right)\rho \bar{u}_a^2 + T \dfrac{\partial^2(\eta d)}{\partial X^2} = 0,$

or

$$-p_1 + \frac{2}{R} \frac{\partial v_1}{\partial y} + S \frac{\partial^2 \eta}{\partial x^2} = 0, \qquad S = \frac{T}{\rho d \bar{u}_a^2},$$

in which ηd is the displacement of the free surface from its mean position. The free-surface conditions must be applied at $y = \eta$, not at $y = 0$, because the gradients of the shear stress and of the pressure of the primary flow at $y = 0$ are not zero. Hence (iii) and (iv) can be rewritten in the forms

(iii) $(d^2U/dy^2)\eta + \psi_{yy} - \psi_{xx} = 0,$

(iv) $-P - P_y\eta - p' - (2/R)\psi_{xy} + S\eta_{xx} = 0,$

which, apart from the terms containing η, are now to be applied at $y = 0$. Since $P(0) = 0$, and $P_y(0) = \cos\beta/F^2$, (iv) can be written further as

(iv) $(\cos\beta/F^2)\eta + p' + (2/R)\psi_{xy} - S\eta_{xx} = 0.$

The (dimensionless) displacement η is related to ψ by the kinematic condition at the free surface

$$-\psi_x = \eta_\tau + U\eta_x. \qquad (16)$$

As usual, a sinusoidal disturbance is assumed. If the disturbance is in the form of a "cloud" vanishing at $x = \pm\infty$, it can be expressed in terms of the elemental sinusoidal disturbances by means of a Fourier integral. Assume

$$\psi = \phi(y)\exp[i\alpha(x - c\tau)], \quad p' = f(y)\exp[i\alpha(x - c\tau)],$$

$$(17)$$

in which α is the wavenumber defined by $2\pi d/\lambda$, λ being the wavelength, and $c = c_r + ic_i$, c_r being the wave velocity and αc_i being the rate of amplification or damping. The kinematic condition at the free surface becomes

$$\eta = [\phi(0)/c']\exp[i\alpha(x - c\tau)], \quad c' = c - \tfrac{3}{2}, \qquad (18)$$

and the equations of motion become

$$-i\alpha c\phi' + i\alpha U\phi' - i\alpha U'\phi$$
$$= -i\alpha f + (1/R)(\phi''' - \alpha^2\phi'), \qquad (19)$$

$$\alpha^2 c\phi - \alpha^2 U\phi = f' + (1/R)(i\alpha\phi'' - i\alpha^3\phi), \qquad (20)$$

in which the primes now denote differentiation with respect to y. If f is eliminated from (19) and (20) by cross differentiation, the well-known Orr–Sommerfeld equation results:

$$\phi'''' - 2\alpha^2\phi'' + \alpha^4\phi$$
$$= i\alpha R[(U - c)(\phi'' - \alpha^2\phi) - U''\phi]. \qquad (21)$$

The boundary conditions (i), (ii), and (iii) now assume the forms

(i) $\phi'(1) = 0,$ $\qquad\qquad\qquad\qquad (22)$

(ii) $\phi(1) = 0,$ $\qquad\qquad\qquad\qquad (23)$

(iii) $\chi(0) \equiv \phi''(0) + (\alpha^2 - 3/c')\phi(0) = 0. \qquad (24)$

The p' in boundary condition (iv) can be evaluated from the second equation in (17), with f given by

(19). The final form of the boundary condition (iv) is

(iv) $\theta(0) \equiv [\alpha(3\cot\beta + \alpha^2 SR)/c']\phi(0)$
$$+ \alpha(Rc' + 3\alpha i)\phi'(0) - i\phi'''(0) = 0. \qquad (25)$$

Equation (21) and the boundary conditions constitute an eigenvalue problem. For a nontrivial solution, a relationship

$$c = c(R, F, \alpha)$$

must exist between R, F, α, and c. This relationship is complex, and can be resolved into the relationships

$$c_r = c_r(R, F, \alpha), \qquad c_i = c_i(R, F, \alpha).$$

Since R, F, and the angle β are related by (6), on putting $c_i = 0$ the equation

$$c_i(R, F, \alpha) = 0 \qquad (26)$$

defines a relationship between R and α for a given value of β, and the graph depicting this relationship is the neutral-stability curve.

III. SOLUTION FOR LONG WAVES

For wavelengths that are long compared with the depth d, the wavenumber α is small, and a solution of the differential system defining stability by successive perturbation is possible. For the first approximation, α can be simply set equal to zero, and the differential equation becomes

$$\phi'''' = 0, \qquad (27)$$

with the boundary conditions

(i) $\qquad\qquad \phi(1) = 0,$ $\qquad$ (ii) $\quad \phi'(1) = 0,$

(iii) $\phi''(0) - (3/c')\phi(0) = 0,$ $\qquad$ (iv) $\phi'''(0) = 0.$

The differential system is indeed an extremely simple one. Integration of (27) produces

$$\phi = A + By + Cy^2 + Dy^3, \qquad (28)$$

and (iv) demands $D = 0$. Boundary conditions (i) and (ii) then give

$$A + B + C = 0, \quad\text{and}\quad B + 2C = 0,$$

or

$$C = A, \quad\text{and}\quad B = -2A.$$

Then (iii) demands

$$2C - (3/c')A = 0.$$

Hence

$$c' = \tfrac{3}{2}, \quad\text{or}\quad c = 3. \qquad (29)$$

Since the differential system is linear and homogeneous, the eigenfunction is determined only up to a multiplicative constant. We shall take $A = 1$. The eigenfunction is then simply

$$\phi(y) = 1 - 2y + y^2 = (1 - y)^2. \qquad (30)$$

For the sake of clarity, this expression will be denoted by $\phi_0(y)$ in subsequent approximations.

Equation (29) gives a value of c which is $\frac{3}{2}$ times that of Benjamin. This is because the reference velocity is taken to be the average velocity of the primary flow in this paper (and in I), whereas Benjamin uses the surface velocity of the primary flow as the reference velocity. The present result is therefore in agreement with Benjamin's.

The opinion exists that there is a difference in the results obtained, on the one hand, by putting α or R equal to zero in the differential system and, on the other, by allowing α and R to vanish in the expression for c laboriously obtained from the original, unsimplified differential system. Now the differential equation retains its order when either α or R vanishes. The eigenfunction is an entire function of α and R, as can be seen by solving (21) by a power series and considering its convergence for finite α and R, and as the boundary conditions are not singular in α or R if they are finite. Hence the aforementioned opinion has no foundation whatever. The case of infinite Reynolds number, which has occupied the attention of researchers for almost exactly three-quarters of a century, is quite another matter, for if R is set equal to infinity to start with, the order of the Orr–Sommerfeld equation is reduced by two. Hence the stability or instability of flows at large Reynolds numbers cannot be settled by considering an inviscid fluid. The opinion mentioned above results perhaps from a lack of understanding of the difference between the classical case of large Ryenolds numbers and the case under study in this paper.

Equation (28) shows that the axis $\alpha = 0$ is a part of the neutral-stability curve, whatever the angle β, the surface tension, and, indeed, the Reynolds number. It is a valid approximation for small values of α so long as αR is small, even though R may be large. The next step is to see how the eigenvalue c will be modified as α departs from zero. We note that terms of first power in α are associated with R, and that if ϕ in

$$i\alpha R[(U - c)(\phi'' - \alpha^2 \phi) - U''\phi]$$

contained the first power in α that expression would contain second powers in α. Since our first approximation for ϕ is entirely independent of α,

the above expression will not contain the second power in α if we use in it the first approximation for ϕ we have just obtained, as we shall. Hence it is inconsistent to include the term $-2\alpha^2\phi''$, let alone the term $\alpha^4\phi$, in the second approximation. Terms containing α^2 are also to be neglected in the boundary conditions (24) and (25). However, the term with the factor $\alpha^3 SR$ in (25) need not be neglected, because S appears here and nowhere else, and the inclusion of it will not lead to an error in the term containing S. With these considerations in mind, and with ϕ given by (30) denoted by ϕ_0, the differential equation for the second approximation is

$$\phi'''' = i\alpha R[(U - c_0)\phi_0'' - U''\phi_0], \qquad (31)$$

and the boundary conditions are

$$\text{(i)} \quad \phi(1) = 0, \qquad \text{(ii)} \quad \phi'(1) = 0,$$

$$\text{(iii)} \quad \phi''(0) - (3/c')\phi(0) = 0,$$

and

$$\text{(iv)} \quad [\alpha(3 \cot \beta + \alpha^2 SR)/c_0']\phi_0(0)$$
$$+ \alpha R c_0' \phi_0'(0) - i\phi'''(0) = 0.$$

Note that in (31) and in (iv) above, $c_0'(= \frac{3}{2}$, given by the first approximation) and ϕ_0 are used for c and ϕ, because the use of c and ϕ would only introduce terms of a higher order in α.

Now

$$(U - c_0)\phi_0'' - U''\phi_0$$
$$= -3(y^2 + 1) + 3(1 - y)^2 = -6y.$$

Hence the solution of (31) is

$$\phi = \phi_0 + \phi_1,$$
$$\phi_1 = -(i\alpha R y^5/20)$$
$$+ \Delta A + \Delta B y + \Delta C y^2 + \Delta D y^3. \qquad (32)$$

In the second of Eqs. (32), the term involving α is the particular solution, and the rest constitutes the complementary solution, necessitated by the inclusion of the first-power terms in α in the differential system.

In view of the fact that

$$\phi_0''(0) - (3/c_0')\phi_0(0) = 0,$$

the boundary condition (iii) can be written as

$$\phi_1''(0) - (3/c_0')\phi_1(0) + [3\Delta c'/(c_0')^2]\phi_0(0) = 0,$$

or

$$\phi_1''(0) - 2\phi_1(0) + \tfrac{4}{3}\Delta c' = 0.$$

Substitution of (32) into the boundary conditions yield, after rearrangement and some simple divisions,

$$\Delta A + \Delta B + \Delta C + \Delta D = i\alpha R/20, \qquad (33)$$

$$\Delta B + 2\Delta C + 3\Delta D = \tfrac{1}{4}i\alpha R, \qquad (34)$$

$$\Delta C - \Delta A = -\tfrac{2}{3}\Delta c', \qquad (35)$$

$$\Delta D = -\tfrac{1}{9}i\alpha(3\cot\beta + \alpha^2 SR) + \tfrac{1}{2}i\alpha R. \qquad (36)$$

If (33), (35), and twice of (36) are added together, and (34) is subtracted from the result, all the Δ quantities disappear, and we have, after simplification,

$$\Delta c' = ic_i, \quad c_i = \frac{6\alpha R}{5} - \frac{\alpha(3\cot\beta + \alpha^2 SR)}{3}. \qquad (37)$$

Comparison of this result with Benjamin's[3] Eq. (5.3) shows that the difference is only in a factor $\tfrac{3}{2}$, arising from the different choices of the reference velocity. In other words, using a power expansion in α, which is analogous in approach to the power expansion in αR used in I, results identical to Benjamin's are obtained by taking only two terms (ϕ_0 and ϕ_1) in the expansion. Higher approximations can be carried out if desired. The two approximations cannot, and did not, take more than two hours to accomplish at the most. The method is really very simple and useful.

The eigenfunction for the second approximation will now be discussed. The left-hand sides of (33), (34), (35), and (36) are not linearly independent. In fact, with c_i given by (37), these equations are not linearly independent. We can, then, assign any value to ΔA and calculate ΔB and ΔC, with ΔD given by (36), whatever the value of ΔA. The results are

$$\Delta C = -\frac{i2c_i}{3} + \Delta A,$$

$$\Delta B = \frac{i\alpha R}{20} - \Delta D + \frac{i2c_i}{3} - 2\Delta A.$$

Thus the terms in ϕ_1 involving ΔA are

$$\Delta A(1 - y)^2,$$

which is proportional to ϕ_0. We shall therefore take ΔA to be zero, for otherwise we should be starting another first approximation at the stage of the second approximation. Whereas this would not affect the c_i obtained, it is quite unnecessary. Another point of view is as follows. An eigenfunction is determined up to a constant multiplier. This multiplier was chosen once and for all when we chose A to be unity. In fact, the successive approximations, with $\Delta A = 0$, furnish more and more accurate eigenfunctions and eigenvalues which satisfy the differential system more and more closely, and that is all that is desired. In the following section dealing with small Reynolds numbers (but any wavenumber, large or small), the same approach will be used. We shall simply take ΔA to be zero without further explanation.

Equation (37) shows that, while c_i is zero at $\alpha = 0$, c_i will increase or decrease when α increases from zero, according as

$$R > \tfrac{5}{6}\cot\beta \quad \text{or} \quad R < \tfrac{5}{6}\cot\beta.$$

In other words, the neutral-stability curve has a bifurcation point at

$$\alpha = 0, \qquad R = \tfrac{5}{6}\cot\beta, \qquad (38)$$

at which a branch goes off from the axis $\alpha = 0$, which is itself a branch of the neutral-stability curve. This consideration contributes to the qualitative description of the c_i curves given in Fig. 2.

The value $R = \tfrac{5}{6}\cot\beta$ was given by Benjamin as the critical Reynolds number. This is, however, the Reynolds number above which some disturbances will be amplified. It is not the Reynolds number below which all disturbances will be damped. As has been seen, for $\alpha = 0$ neutral disturbances exist right up to $R = 0$, even if β is less than $\tfrac{1}{2}\pi$ (so that the plate is not vertical).

IV. SOLUTION FOR SMALL REYNOLDS NUMBERS

For the case of small Reynolds numbers and any α, the first approximation will be carried out by taking R to be zero to begin with. The justification of this procedure is similar to that given for the case of small α, and need not be repeated here.

To avoid confusion in regard to the term containing SR in the boundary condition (iv), we note that

$$SR = T/\mu\bar{u}_a,$$

which will be denoted by S', to avoid the impression that it must be zero when R is zero. Since $\bar{u}_a$ will, for any given μ, approach zero as R approach zero, this term may seem troublesome. From the second of (4) it can be seen that for given values of g, d, β, and ρ, $\mu\bar{u}_a$ is finite. If μ is very large, $\bar{u}_a$ will be very small, and the Reynolds number very small. In the limit it can be zero. Hence it is not meaningless to consider the case of small Reynolds numbers and zero Reynolds numbers, even if the surface tension T is not zero. Actually $\mu\bar{u}_a$ may be very small. So long as it is not zero, which it is not unless $d = 0$, it causes no trouble. If T is assumed to be zero, the term containing SR in (iv) will of course drop out.

Setting R equal to zero in the differential system, we have

$$\phi'''' - 2\alpha^2 \phi'' + \alpha^4 \phi = 0, \qquad (39)$$

with the boundary conditions (22), (23), (24), and

$$\text{(iv)} \quad -[i\alpha(3 \cot \beta + \alpha^2 S')/c']\phi(0)$$
$$+ 3\alpha^2 \phi'(0) - \phi'''(0) = 0. \qquad (40)$$

The solution of (39) is

$$\phi = e^{\alpha y} + Be^{-\alpha y} + Cye^{\alpha y} + Dye^{-\alpha y}, \qquad (41)$$

in which the coefficient of the term $e^{\alpha y}$ has been taken to be unity, because the eigenfunction can be multiplied by any constant. Equation (24) demands

$$(2\alpha^2 - 3/c')(1 + B) + 2\alpha(C - D) = 0. \qquad (42)$$

Equation (40) yields

$$-i(3 \cot \beta + \alpha^2 S')(1 + B) + 2\alpha^2 c'(1 - B) = 0,$$

or

$$B = \frac{-i(3 \cot \beta + \alpha^2 S') + 2\alpha^2 c'}{i(3 \cot \beta + \alpha^2 S') + 2\alpha^2 c'}. \qquad (43)$$

Equations (22) and (23) have the forms

$$e^\alpha + Be^{-\alpha} + Ce^\alpha + De^{-\alpha} = 0, \qquad (44)$$

and

$$\alpha e^\alpha - B\alpha e^{-\alpha} + C(1 + \alpha)e^\alpha + D(1 - \alpha)e^{-\alpha} = 0. \quad (45)$$

Since B is known, (44) and (45) can be solved for C and D. The results are

$$D = -(1/2\alpha)[e^{2\alpha} + B(1 + 2\alpha)], \qquad (46)$$

with B given by (43), and

$$C = -1 - e^{-2\alpha}(B + D), \qquad (47)$$

with B and D given by (43) and (46). On the other hand, C is given by (42) to be

$$C = D - (1/2\alpha)(2\alpha^2 - 3/c')(1 + B).$$

Equating the two expressions given for C, we can solve for c', since B and D are known. The result is, after some intermediate calculation which is entirely straightforward,

$$c' = \frac{1}{1 + \cosh 2\alpha + 2\alpha^2}$$
$$\cdot \left[3 + \frac{i(2\alpha - \sinh 2\alpha)}{2\alpha^2}(3 \cot \beta + \alpha^2 S') \right], \qquad (48)$$

Now, for small α,

$$(2\alpha - \sinh 2\alpha)/2\alpha^2 = O(\alpha).$$

Hence at $\alpha = 0$ we have again $c' = \frac{3}{2}$, in agreement with (29). Since $\sinh 2\alpha > 2\alpha$ for all $\alpha > 0$, the flow is always stable at $R = 0$ for all nonzero wavenumbers if $\cot \beta$ is positive (i.e., if $\beta < \frac{1}{2}\pi$), as can be seen from (48). As α increases the stabilizing effect of the slope becomes less and less important as compared with the surface-tension effect, as is to be expected. When $\alpha \to \infty$,

$$c' \to -\tfrac{1}{2}iS', \quad \text{or} \quad c \to \tfrac{3}{2} - \tfrac{1}{2}iS', \qquad (49)$$

Thus, for $S' = 0$, $c = \frac{3}{2}$ at $\alpha = \infty$. This fact and Eq. (70), to be presented, contradict Benjamin's (estimated) neutral-stability curve for $S' = 0$ (corresponding to his $\zeta = 0$), drawn at $\alpha = 0.43$ approximately. Benjamin stated that the region lying above that curve represents stability. Benjamin's dashed line, meant to be a rough estimate only, was unfortunately taken seriously by some researchers, who have produced a neutral-stability curve of similar trend with a high-speed computer.

The neutral stability at $R = 0$ for zero surface tension T is of course a puzzling situation. Benjamin has carefully avoided the discussion of this limiting case, and restricted his discussion to values of R other than zero. In a note appended to his paper, the present author has sought to explain this puzzling situation. A fuller explanation will be given here. Since c is expressed in terms of a reference velocity (in the present paper and in I, in terms of $\bar{u}_a$), and this velocity is zero if d/ν is not zero and if R vanishes. Hence if c is equal to a finite number the real rate of damping, $-\alpha c_i \bar{u}_a/d$, is zero, and the disturbance will not be damped out. But now if d/ν is finite, $\bar{u}_a$ can be zero only if $g \sin \beta$ is zero, in which case gravity is not a source of energy. There is no pressure gradient in the X direction, and since T is zero the surface tension does not enter into the question. (Since the mean surface is flat, any corrugation would mean an *expenditure* of surface energy, even if S' is not zero.) How could a *disturbance motion* be maintained? The answer is that, for $T = 0$ and any α, in the limiting case of $R = 0$ there is no disturbance motion, but merely a surface corrugation, which has no reason to be damped. Benjamin's contribution is that in the neighborhood of this case of static corrugation there are unstable waves.

In the second approximation we shall concentrate on the case $\beta = \frac{1}{2}\pi$ and $S' = 0$, because if these conditions do not exist (47) already tells us that the flow will be stable for all nonzero values of α at $R = 0$. The first approximation indicates that the axis $R = 0$ is a part of the neutral stability curve if $\cot \beta$ and S' are all zero. It is important to see whether the flow will be stabilized or destabilized as R is increased slightly.

The development in I is exactly what is needed for the second approximation. Denoting by ϕ_0 the ϕ given by the first approximation, i.e., by (41), (43), (46), and (47), the ϕ for the second approximation must satisfy

$$\phi'''' - 2\alpha^2\phi'' + \alpha^4\phi$$
$$= i\alpha R[-(\tfrac{3}{2}y^2 + c_0')(\phi_0'' - \alpha^2\phi_0) + 3\phi_0]. \quad (50)$$

Now, with $\cos \beta$ and S' both zero,

$$\phi_0 = e^{\alpha y} + e^{-\alpha y} - (1/2\alpha)(2\alpha - 1 - e^{-2\alpha})ye^{\alpha y}$$
$$+ (1/2\alpha)(-2\alpha - 1 - e^{2\alpha})ye^{-\alpha y}, \quad (51)$$

as can be seen from (41), (43), (46), and (47). We shall call the particular solutions of (50) $\alpha R(\phi_{11}, \phi_{12}, \phi_{13}, \phi_{14})$ when $e^{\alpha y}$, $e^{-\alpha y}$, $ye^{\alpha y}$, and $ye^{-\alpha y}$ are substituted for ϕ_0 in (50). Then the solution of (50) is

$$\phi = \phi_0 + i\alpha R\phi_1 + \Delta Be^{\alpha y} + \Delta Cye^{\alpha y} + \Delta Dye^{-\alpha y}, \quad (52)$$

with

$$\phi_1(y) = \phi_{11} + \phi_{12} - (1/2\alpha)(2\alpha - 1 - e^{-2\alpha})\phi_{13}$$
$$- (1/2\alpha)(2\alpha + 1 + e^{2\alpha})\phi_{14}. \quad (53)$$

In (52) ΔA has been taken to be zero, for reasons given in Sec. III. The functions ϕ_{11}, ϕ_{12}, ϕ_{13}, and ϕ_{14} were given in I, in which it is also stated that these can be expressed in terms of exponential functions. [The expression for ϕ_{11} contains a misprint of a sign. The parenthesis $(3 - 2\alpha y)$ should read $(3 + 2\alpha y)$. The expression given for $\phi_{11}(\phi_1^{(1)}$ in I) later in I is in agreement with the correct sign.] These are

$$\phi_{11}(\alpha, y) = (3/16\alpha^4)[(3 - 4\alpha y + 2\alpha^2 y^2)e^{\alpha y}$$
$$- (3 + 2\alpha y)e^{-\alpha y}], \quad (54)$$

$$\phi_{12}(\alpha, y) = \phi_{11}(-\alpha, y), \quad (55)$$

$$\phi_{13}(\alpha, y) = -(3c_0'/8\alpha^3)[(3 - 4\alpha y + 2\alpha^2 y^2)e^{\alpha y}$$
$$- (3 + 2\alpha y)e^{-\alpha y}]$$
$$- (1/32\alpha^5)[(2\alpha^4 y^4 - 12\alpha^3 y^3 + 30\alpha^2 y^2$$
$$- 42\alpha y + 27)e^{\alpha y} - (12\alpha y + 27)e^{-\alpha y}], \quad (56)$$

$$\phi_{14}(\alpha, y) = \phi_{13}(-\alpha, y). \quad (57)$$

Since the derivatives of these functions are also needed, they will also be given. These are

$$\phi_{11}'(\alpha, y) = (3/16\alpha^3)[(-1 + 2\alpha^2 y^2)e^{\alpha y}$$
$$+ (1 + 2\alpha y)e^{-\alpha y}], \quad (58)$$

$$\phi_{12}'(\alpha, y) = \phi_{11}'(-\alpha, y), \quad (59)$$

$$\phi_{13}'(\alpha, y) = -(c_0'/8\alpha^2)[(-1 + 2\alpha^2 y^2)e^{\alpha y}$$
$$+ (1 + 2\alpha y)e^{-\alpha y}]$$
$$- (1/32\alpha^4)[(2\alpha^4 y^4 - 4\alpha^3 y^3 - 6\alpha^2 y^2$$
$$+ 18\alpha y - 15)e^{\alpha y} + (15 + 12\alpha y)e^{-\alpha y}], \quad (60)$$

$$\phi_{14}'(\alpha, y) = \phi_{13}'(-\alpha, y). \quad (61)$$

Although the second and third derivatives of ϕ occur in the boundary conditions (iii) and (iv), we need not give them for the functions given by (54), (55), (56), and (57). This is because these functions have been so arranged (by adding linear combinations of the complementary solutions) as to contain no power of y less than the fourth. Hence these functions and their derivatives up to the third ones all vanish at $y = 0$, where (iii) and (iv) are to be applied.

With ϕ given by (52), the boundary condition (iii) given by (24) assumes the form

$$(2\alpha^2 - 3/c_0')\Delta B + 2\alpha\Delta C - 2\alpha\Delta D + 6\Delta c/c_0'^2 = 0, \quad (62)$$

if terms quadratic in R and the Δ quantities are neglected. In (62) the last term comes from the variation of c'. In obtaining it the facts that $\phi_0(0) = 2$ and that $\Delta c' = \Delta c$ have been used. Also, $\phi_1(0) = 0$, as explained before, so that ϕ_1 does not appear in (62) at all. The c_0' in (62) is the c' given in the first approximation, by (48), with $\cot \beta$ and S' equal to zero. Hence

$$c_0' = \frac{3}{1 + \cosh 2\alpha + 2\alpha^2},$$

and

$$2\alpha^2 - \frac{3}{c_0'} = -(1 + \cosh 2\alpha). \quad (63)$$

The boundary condition (iv) has the form (since $\beta = \tfrac{1}{2}\pi$ and $S' = 0$)

$$\alpha(Rc' + 3\alpha i)\phi'(0) - i\phi'''(0) = 0.$$

Substitution of (52) into it yields, in the same way,

$$\Delta B = (iRc_0'/2\alpha^3)(2\alpha + \sinh 2\alpha). \quad (64)$$

The boundary conditions (i) and (ii), given by (22) and (23), have the forms

$$e^{-\alpha}\Delta B + e^{\alpha}\Delta C + e^{-\alpha}\Delta D = -iR\alpha\phi_1(1), \quad (65)$$

$$-\alpha e^{-\alpha}\Delta B + (1 + \alpha)e^{\alpha}\Delta C + (1 - \alpha)e^{-\alpha}\Delta D$$
$$= -iR\alpha\phi_1'(1), \qquad (66)$$

from which

$$2\alpha\Delta D = iR\alpha e^{\alpha}[\phi_1'(1) - (1 + \alpha)\phi_1(1)]$$
$$- (1 + 2\alpha)\Delta B, \qquad (67)$$

and

$$-2\alpha\Delta C = iR\alpha e^{-\alpha}[\phi_1'(1) - (1 - \alpha)\phi_1(1)] - e^{-2\alpha}\Delta B. \qquad (68)$$

Substituting (63), (64), (67), and (68) into (62), we have, after some simplifications,

$$\Delta c = \tfrac{1}{6}iRc_0'^2\{(c_0'/2\alpha^3)(2\alpha + \sinh 2\alpha)$$
$$\cdot (\cosh 2\alpha - 2\alpha - e^{-2\alpha})$$
$$+ 2\alpha[\cosh \alpha \, \phi_1'(1) - (\cosh \alpha + \alpha \sinh \alpha)\phi_1(1)]\}, \qquad (69)$$

with ϕ_1 and ϕ_1' given by Eqs. (53) through (61). For very large α, a brief calculation shows that

$$\Delta c \sim \frac{iRc_0'^2}{6}\left(\frac{3e^{3\alpha}}{16\alpha^4}\right) \sim \frac{i9Re^{-\alpha}}{8\alpha^4} \qquad (70)$$

and

$$c_i \to 0 \quad \text{as} \quad \alpha \to \infty$$

in the neighborhood of $R = 0$. (Indeed R must be so small that αR is kept small as α increases.) Equation (70) means that if α is very large, c_i is very small. For intermediate values of α it is well nigh impossible to determine the sign of the bracket in (69) algebraically. A numerical computation[7] has not turned up any negative or zero value for c_i for α from 0.2 to 4.0. The fact that dc/dR is nowhere zero for finite values of α indicates that a bifurcation point, such as the intersection of the dashed line and the axis $R = 0$ in Benjamin's Fig. 2, of the neutral-stability curve cannot exist on $R = 0$. This seems to rule out the possibility that the dashed line of Benjamin's Fig. 2 divides two regions of instability, and merely marks a valley of least c_i, which happens to be zero.

The second approximation carried out here shows that the expansion in I is useful and capable of producing definite results when only two terms in the expansion are used. Actually, Benjamin's expansion in power series of y and the expansion used in I and the present paper are identical and will produce the same results *provided* a very great number of terms are used in both expansions. If only a limited number of terms are taken, then the method presented here is more flexible and

---

[7] The author is indebted to Philip Davis for the assistance rendered in this computation.

versatile. It produces identical results as Benjamin's for small α, and for small R (but any α) it produces results hitherto unavailable.

V. STABILITY OF VERY SHORT WAVES

If α is very large, then for *any finite* R, the Orr-Sommerfeld equation can be approximated by (39), provided c is small compared with α. This provision, of course, can only be verified *a posteriori*. Since the boundary conditions will then be exactly those used in the first approximation carried out in Sec. IV, i.e., (22), (23), (24), and (40), the result is known and exactly given by (48), which shows that $c' \to -\tfrac{1}{2}iS'$ as $\alpha \to \infty$. Since $S' = T/\mu\bar{u}_a$, very short waves are damped by surface tension T, and can only be neutral if T is zero, or if $\mu\bar{u}_a$ is infinite. For any given T the dimensionless rate of damping is decreased if $\mu\bar{u}_a$ is increased. Since the complex wave velocity c has been expressed in terms of $\bar{u}_a$, so that $\alpha c_i\bar{u}_a/d$ is the actual rate of growth (and if negative, of damping), the result $c_i = -\tfrac{1}{2}S'$ shows that the actual rate of damping of very short waves is reduced in magnitude if μ is increased, for any T. This result is entirely unexpected, and is a new example of the dual role of viscosity. Of course, increasing μ can never bring about instability. But it does reduce the degree of stability at large wavenumbers.

VI. TOPOLOGICAL FEATURES OF THE c_i CURVES

From the foregoing discussions the following facts have been established:

(1) The axis $\alpha = 0$ is always a part of the neutral-stability curve.

(2) There is a bifurcation point on $\alpha = 0$ for the neutral-stability curve, at $R = \tfrac{5}{6} \cot \beta$. This point is at the origin if $\beta = \tfrac{1}{2}\pi$.

(3) The axis $R = 0$ is part of the neutral-stability curve if $T = 0$ and $\beta = \tfrac{1}{2}\pi$.

(4) If $T = 0$ but $\beta \neq \tfrac{1}{2}\pi$, c_i varies on $R = 0$, from zero at $\alpha = 0$ through a minimum to zero again at $\alpha = \infty$.

(5) If $T \neq 0$ but $\beta = \tfrac{1}{2}\pi$, c_i varies on $R = 0$ from zero at $\alpha = 0$ monotonically to $-\tfrac{1}{2}S'$ at $\alpha = \infty$. The monotonicity can be established readily by differentiating c_i given by (48) with respect to α. The result is (for $R = 0$)

$$\frac{dc_i}{d\alpha} = -\frac{1}{2\alpha^4(1 + \cosh 2\alpha + 2\alpha^2)^2}$$
$$\cdot [4\alpha^4(\cosh 2\alpha + 1)(3 \cot \beta + \alpha^2 S')$$
$$+ 6\alpha(2\alpha - \sinh 2\alpha)(1 + \cosh 2\alpha + 2\alpha^2) \cot \beta],$$

which is evidently negative if $\beta = \tfrac{1}{2}\pi$.

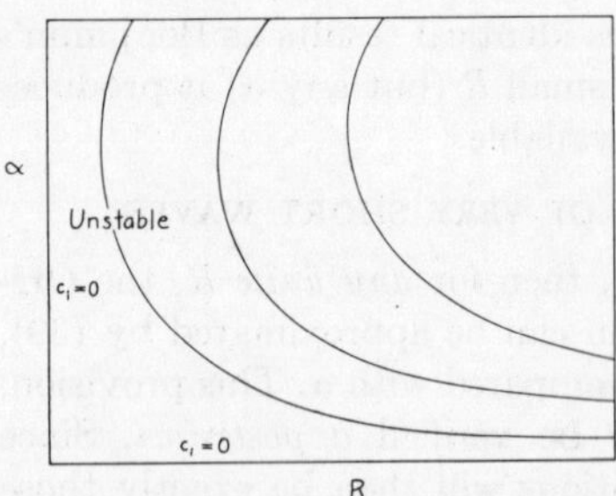

FIG. 2. Topological features of the c_i curves for the case $S' = 0$ and $\beta = \frac{1}{2}\pi$. The axes constitute the neutral-stability curve.

(6) If $T \neq 0$ and $\beta \neq \frac{1}{2}\pi$, the expression for $dc_i/d\alpha$ at $R = 0$ shows that $dc_i/d\alpha = -\cot\beta$ at $\alpha = 0$, so that, with $\beta < \frac{1}{2}\pi$, c_i will initially decrease on $R = 0$. But it is evident that as α increases (on $R = 0$) $dc_i/d\alpha$ will eventually be positive. Hence c_i will have at least one minimum on $R = 0$. (More than one minimum is very unlikely, although a conclusive algebraic proof that only one minimum exists is not obvious.) We shall assume that only one minimum exists.

(7) At large α, for any given β and R, $c_i = -\frac{1}{2}S'$.

From these facts we conclude that the topological features of the c_i curves are given in Figs. 2–5 for the four cases described in the figure captions. It can be seen that the neutral-stability curve given in I for the case $S' = 0$ and $\beta = \frac{1}{2}\pi$ is more a curve of constant nonzero c_i. The numerical calculation in I was, however, too inaccurate, and produced erroneous values for c_r, which did not seem to affect the conclusion that instability could happen at low Reynolds numbers.

Figures 2–5 are the simplest configurations that can be constructed with the information available. If new information should turn out to show that these figures are incomplete and oversimplified, the information upon which these figures have been drawn, wherever definite, should not be subjected to doubt.

VII. EFFECTS OF VARIABLE SURFACE TENSION

In case there is a thin film of contamination at the free surface, the surface tension may vary from place to place, giving rise to a variable shear stress just below the film. If the surface tension at the free surface when the film is unstretched is T_0, and the variation from this is proportional to the amount of stretching per unit length in the direction of stretching, then

$$T = T_0 + T_1 \, \partial\xi/\partial X,$$

in which ξ is the distance in the direction of stretching (assumed to be the X direction) covered by a

certain particle, and T_1 is a second constant specifying the variability of surface tension. This variability has no effect on the boundary condition (iv), but does have an effect on the boundary condition (iii). Since

$$D\xi/Dt = \bar{u} + \bar{u}_a u',$$

we have, on the free surface,

$$\xi = \bar{u}(0)t + \xi_1,$$

where

$$\frac{D\xi}{Dt} = \frac{\bar{u}_a}{d}\frac{D\xi}{D\tau} = \bar{u} + \bar{u}_a u' = \bar{u} + \bar{u}_a \phi'(0)e^{i\alpha(x-c\tau)} .$$

Thus

$$\xi_1 = (id/\alpha c')\phi'(0)e^{i\alpha(x-c\tau)}, \quad c' = c - U(0) = c - \tfrac{3}{2}.$$

Now the variation in τ_{xy} on the free surface is

$$-\frac{\partial T}{\partial X} = -\frac{iT_1}{\alpha d}\frac{\partial^2}{\partial x^2}\frac{\phi'(0)}{c'}e^{i\alpha(x-c\tau)}$$

$$= \frac{i\alpha T_1}{d}\frac{\phi'(0)}{c'}e^{i\alpha(x-c\tau)}.$$

Hence (iii) has the form

$$\text{(iii)} \quad \phi''(0) + (\alpha^2 - 3/c')\phi(0) + i\alpha S_1\,\phi'(0)/c' = 0,$$

in which

$$S_1 = T_1/\mu\bar{u}_a.$$

Since the additional term involving S_1 is associated with α, it has no effect on the first approximation for $\alpha = 0$. It does have an effect on the next approximation for c_i, which determines the stability condition, and also on the first approximation for $R = 0$. It is calculable by the method given in Sec. III. The author is indebted to Dr. T. B. Benjamin for pointing out the factor i/α in ξ_1, which was missing in the first draft.

VIII. VESTIGES OF SHEAR WAVES

The waves discussed so far in this paper are surface waves. Since they can occur at small Reynolds numbers and are only moderately damped

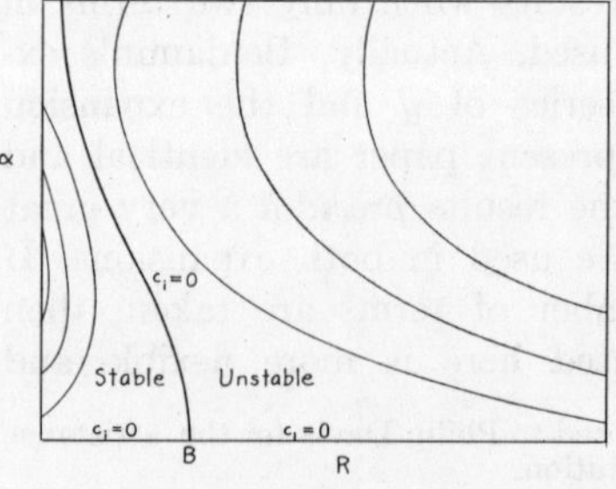

FIG. 3. Topological features of the c_i curves for the case $S' = 0$ and $\beta < \frac{1}{2}\pi$. $R = 5/6 \cot\beta$ at the bifurcation point B. $c_i = 0$ on $\alpha = 0$.

or amplified at small values of $R\alpha$, they may be called soft waves. These are distinct from the shear waves, or hard waves, in plane Poiseuille flow and other confined flows, which are highly damped at small values of $R\alpha$. But it does seem strange that the existence of a free surface should remove the possibility of shear waves altogether, particularly if the surface tension is large, so that the free surface is rather stiff against corrugation. Where are the vestiges of shear waves? In providing the answer that they are there, we shall also illustrate how to make the correct approximation to the mathematical system to be solved, gain a deeper insight into the fine structure of an arbitrary disturbance possessing different components (each represented by an eigenfunction of the differential system governing stability), and demonstrate that the differential system has infinitely many eigenvalues for c for given values of R and α.

We deal with shear waves of plane Poiseuille flows for three cases:

(1) Small Reynolds number for any α,
(2) Small wavenumber for any finite R,
(3) Large wavenumbers.

In each case it is shown that the waves are strongly damped. We then take up the shear waves in the film flow under study in this paper, deal with the same three cases, and show that the waves are again strongly damped, thus demonstrating the vestiges of shear waves in film flow. After all, the film flow is one-half of a plane Poiseuille flow, and if these vestiges could not be found it would be very strange indeed.

For plane Poiseuille flow, the differential equation is still given by (21), with U given by (3), except that U is now defined in $-1 \leq y \leq 1$. The boundary conditions are

$$\phi(\pm 1) = 0, \qquad \phi'(\pm 1) = 0.$$

It is well known that if the differential system

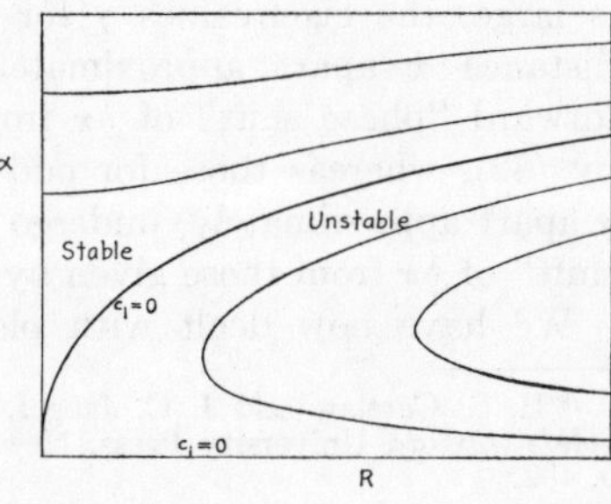

FIG. 4. Topological features of the c_i curves for the case $S' \neq 0$ and $\beta = \frac{1}{2}\pi$. $c_i = 0$ on $\alpha = 0$. c_i curves flatten and c_i approaches $-\frac{1}{2}S'$ as α increases indefinitely.

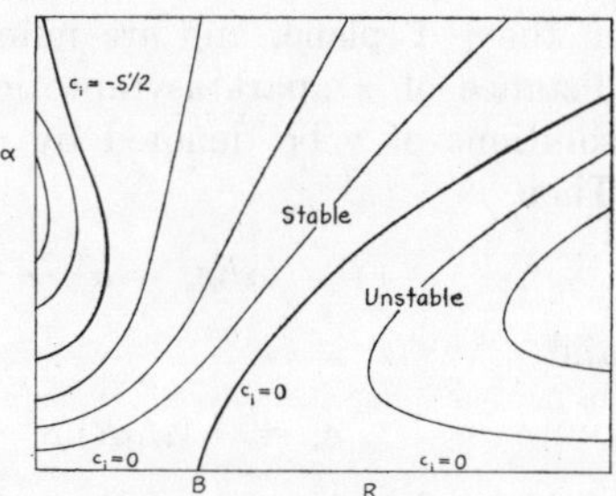

FIG. 5. Topological features of the c_i curves for the case $S' \neq 0$ and $\beta < \frac{1}{2}\pi$. $c_i = 0$ on $\alpha = 0$. $c_i \rightarrow -\frac{1}{2}S'$ as $\alpha \rightarrow \infty$. $R = 5/6$ cot β at the bifurcation point B.

governing stability is entirely symmetric, so that it admits of an odd function of y or an even function of y as a solution, the secular equation for any solution, which is neither even or odd, is factorizable into two factors, one of which is for the odd part of the solution and the other the even part. Hence even and odd solutions can be treated separately. In general, they have different eigenvalues.

Case 1. For small R, assume that Rc is not small. This is important, for otherwise c would drop out of the differential system altogether in the limiting case of $R = 0$, and the differential system could not have any nontrivial solution. For any α, the differential equation can then be written as

$$(D^2 - \beta^2)(D^2 - \alpha^2)\phi = 0, \tag{71}$$

in which $D = d/dy$, and

$$\beta^2 = \alpha^2 - i\alpha Rc. \tag{72}$$

The even solution is

$$\phi = A \cosh \alpha y + B \cosh \beta y. \tag{73}$$

The satisfaction of the boundary conditions demands

$$A \cosh \alpha + B \cosh \beta = 0,$$

$$A\alpha \sinh \alpha + B\beta \sinh \beta = 0,$$

so that the secular equation is

$$\beta \tanh \beta = \alpha \tanh \alpha. \tag{74}$$

The solution $\beta = \alpha$ is to be excluded, because in the first place it violates the assumption $Rc \neq 0$, and in the second place the solution (73) would be invalid if $\beta = \alpha$. But there are infinitely many solutions of (74). Let $\beta = \gamma i$. Then (74) becomes

$$\gamma \tan \gamma = -\alpha \tanh \alpha, \tag{75}$$

the solutions of which are the abscissas of the intersections of the curves

$$\Gamma = \tan \gamma \quad \text{and} \quad \Gamma = -\alpha \tanh \alpha/\gamma$$

in the γ–Γ plane, and are infinite in number, at a distance of π apart asymptotically. Let these real solutions of γ be denoted by γ_n ($n = 1, 2, \cdots$). Then

$$i\alpha R c_n = \alpha^2 + \gamma_n^2,$$

and

$$c_n = -(i/\alpha R)(\alpha^2 + \gamma_n^2), \tag{76}$$

giving infinitely many eigenvalues of c, all corresponding to high rate of damping since R is small. The rate increases in magnitude as n increases. Note that as n increases γ_n also does, so that $\cosh \beta_n y$ ($= \cos \gamma_n y$), hence ϕ, is more and more oscillatory. That a more and more oscillatory disturbance will be damped faster and faster is quite to be expected.

The odd solution is

$$\phi = A \sinh \alpha y + B \sinh \beta y,$$

with the secular equation

$$\beta \coth \beta = \alpha \coth \alpha.$$

Again the solution $\beta = \alpha$ is to be excluded. The other solutions are found again by putting β equal to γi and solving

$$\gamma \cot \gamma = \alpha \coth \alpha \tag{77}$$

for γ. The solutions can be obtained by finding the intersections of

$$\Gamma = \cot \gamma \quad \text{and} \quad \Gamma = \alpha \coth \alpha / \gamma.$$

Then again c_n is given by (76). The γ's are infinite in number, asymptotically at distance π apart, and asympotically at the distance $\frac{1}{2}\pi$ from the roots of (72). The γ_1 for even ϕ is smaller than γ_1 for odd ϕ if α is large (by a little less than $\frac{1}{2}\pi$ in fact), but the reverse is true if α is small. The infinity of the number of eigenvalues has now been amply demonstrated. Note that the assumption that Rc is not small has been justified *a posteriori*.

Case 2. If α is small, we shall assume that αc is not small. The differential equation can then be written as

$$\phi'''' + i\alpha R c \phi'' = 0. \tag{78}$$

The even solution is

$$\phi = A + B \cosh \beta y,$$

with β now given by

$$\beta^2 = -i\alpha R c. \tag{79}$$

The boundary conditions $\phi'(\pm 1) = 0$ give, with-

out the conjunction of the other two boundary conditions,

$$\sinh \beta = 0, \quad \text{or} \quad \beta = n\pi i.$$

This gives

$$c = -(i/\alpha R)(n\pi)^2. \tag{80}$$

The odd solution is

$$\phi = Ay + B \sinh \beta y.$$

The boundary conditions demand

$$A + B \sinh \beta = 0,$$

$$A + B\beta \cosh \beta = 0,$$

so that

$$\beta \coth \beta = 1.$$

There are no real solutions of this equation except $\beta = 1$, which is to be excluded. But, with $\beta = i\gamma$,

$$\gamma \cot \gamma = 1, \tag{81}$$

the solutions of which are[8]

$$\gamma_1 = 4.4934, \quad \gamma_2 = 7.7253, \quad \gamma_3 = 10.9041,$$

$$\gamma_4 = 14.0662, \quad \gamma_5 = 17.2208.$$

Further roots are at distance π apart, approximately. In this case it is evident that antisymmetric disturbances (even ϕ) are less stable than symmetric ones (odd ϕ).

Case 3. If α is large, we assume c is at least of the order of α. The governing equation is again (71), and the eigenvalues are given by (76), with γ_n given by (75) for antisymmetric disturbances and by (77) for symmetric disturbances. Since α is large, the γ_n for antisymmetric disturbances (even ϕ) is approximately

$$\gamma_n = \tfrac{1}{2}(2n + 1)\pi, \tag{82}$$

and the γ_n for symmetric disturbances (odd ϕ) is

$$\gamma_n = n\pi, \tag{83}$$

so long as n is not too large for either case. When n is large, the eigenvalues γ for even ϕ are still at distance π apart approximately, but there is a forward "phase shift" of $\frac{1}{2}\pi$ from the values given by (82), whereas those for odd ϕ, also at distance π apart approximately, undergo a backward "phase shift" of $\frac{1}{2}\pi$ from those given by (83).

We have now dealt with plane Poiseuille flow,

---

[8] H. S. Carslaw and J. C. Jaeger, *Conduction of Heat in Solids* (Oxford University Press, New York, 1959), 2nd ed., p. 492.

STABILITY OF LIQUID FLOW DOWN AN INCLINED PLANE   333

and shall turn our attention to the free-surface flow under study.

Cases 1 and 3. Due to the complexity of the free-surface boundary conditions, a simple, explicit solution for the eigenvalues is not possible for these two cases, although the solution of the differential equation is itself simple and explicit. For small R or large α, we shall use the method of Synge.[9] It turns out that a single demonstration is sufficient for these two cases.

Again, if R is small, we assume Rc is not small, and if α is large, we assume c is at least of the order of α. These assumptions can be verified *a posteriori*. In either case the governing differential equation is (71), or

$$(D^2 - \alpha^2)^2\phi = -i\alpha Rc(D^2 - \alpha^2)\phi. \qquad (84)$$

The boundary conditions are (22), (23),

$$\text{(iii)} \quad \phi''(0) + \alpha^2\phi(0) = 0, \qquad (85)$$

and (25). In (25) the first term can be neglected. If R is small and Rc not small, c and hence c' must be large in magnitude, hence the first term can be neglected. (Otherwise the term SR is not necessarily negligible, even if R is small; see Sec. IV for explanation.) If α is large and if c (hence c') is at least of the order of α, $|\phi'|$ is at least of the order $\alpha|\phi|$ and $|\phi'''|$ at least of the order $\alpha^3|\phi|$. Hence again the first term in (25) can be neglected. However, since it causes no trouble to keep it, we shall do so, and verify the negligibility of the term after the final result has been obtained. Since in both Case 1 and Case 3 c is very large, c' in (25) will be replaced by c.

Multiplying (84) by ϕ^*, the complex conjugate of ϕ, and integrating the result (by parts if necessary), we have, with the aid of the boundary conditions (22) and (23),

$$-\phi^*(0)\phi'''(0) + \phi'^*(0)\phi''(0) + I_2$$
$$+ 2\alpha^2\phi^*(0)\phi'(0) + 2\alpha^2 I_1 + \alpha^4 I_0$$
$$= -i\alpha Rc[-\phi^*(0)\phi'(0) - I_1 - \alpha^2 I_0], \qquad (86)$$

in which

$$I_0 = \int_0^1 |\phi|^2\, dy, \quad I_1 = \int_0^1 |\phi'|^2\, dy, \quad I_2 = \int_0^1 |\phi''|^2\, dy.$$

By the use of (85), (86) becomes

[9] C. C. Lin, *The Theory of Hydrodynamic Stability* (Cambridge University Press, New York, 1955).

$$i\alpha Rc(I_1 + \alpha^2 I_0) = I_2 + 2\alpha^2 I_1 + \alpha^4 I_0$$
$$- i\phi^*(0)\{\alpha Rc\phi'(0) - i\phi'''(0)$$
$$+ i3\alpha^2\phi'(0) + [\alpha(3\cot\beta + \alpha^2 SR)/c]\phi(0)\}$$
$$- \alpha^2[\phi'^*(0)\phi(0) + \phi'(0)\phi^*(0)]$$
$$+ [i\alpha(3\cot\beta + \alpha^2 SR)/c]\,|\phi(0)|^2. \qquad (87)$$

Since c' may be replaced by c (because both are large, so that the difference $\frac{3}{2}$ is unimportant), the first curly bracket in (87) is the left-hand side of (25), and is zero. Hence

$$i\alpha Rc(I_1 + \alpha^2 I_0) - [i\alpha(3\cot\beta + \alpha^2 SR)/c]\,|\phi(0)|^2$$
$$= I_2 + 2\alpha^2 I_1 + \alpha^4 I_0 - \alpha^2[\phi'^*(0)\phi(0) + \phi'(0)\phi^*(0)].$$

But

$$\phi'^*(0)\phi(0) + \phi'(0)\phi^*(0)$$
$$= 2\int_0^1 |\phi'|^2\, dy + \int_0^1 (\phi''^*\phi + \phi''\phi^*)\, dy$$
$$= 2I_1 + \int_0^1 (\phi''^*\phi + \phi''\phi^*)\, dy.$$

Hence

$$i\alpha Rc(I_1 + \alpha^2 I_0) - [\alpha(3\cot\beta + \alpha^2 SR)/c]\,|\phi(0)|^2$$
$$= I_2 - \alpha^2\int_0^1 (\phi''^*\phi + \phi''\phi^*)\, dy + \alpha^4 I_0$$
$$= \int_0^1 |\phi'' - \alpha^2\phi|^2\, dy. \qquad (88)$$

The right-hand side of (88) cannot be equal to zero, for otherwise

$$\phi'' - \alpha^2\phi = 0,$$

and

$$\phi = A\cosh\alpha y + B\sinh\alpha y,$$

which cannot nontrivially satisfy $\phi(1) = \phi'(1) = 0$. Hence the last integral of (88) is positive definite. Taking the real part of (88), we have

$$-\alpha Rc_i\left[I_1 + \alpha^2 I_0 + \frac{(3\cot\beta + \alpha^2 SR)}{|c|^2 R}\,|\phi(0)|^2\right]$$
$$= \int_0^1 |\phi'' - \alpha^2\phi|^2\, dy > 0,$$

which proves that

(1) c_i is negative;

(2) if R is small, the term containing $|\phi(0)|^2$ is negligible, as expected, if Rc is assumed not small;

(3) if that term is neglected then Rc is not small,

334　　　　　　　　　　　　　　　CHIA-SHUN YIH

as was assumed, hence, there is at least consistency in the assumption;

(4) if α is large, the right-hand side is of the order $\alpha^4 \, |\phi|^2$, the left-hand side of the order $Rc_i\alpha^3 \, |\phi|^2$, hence $c_i = O(\alpha)$, as assumed, and the term containing $|\phi(0)|^2$ is negligible, as expected.

The development shows rather convincingly that for small R and large α, there are highly damped modes. These modes are the vestiges of shear waves. They may be overshadowed by surface waves, but they are there.

Case 2. For small α we can obtain sharper results. Under the assumption that αc is not small, the differential equation can be written as

$$\phi'''' + i\alpha Rc\phi'' = 0,$$

the solution of which is

$$\phi = A + By + Ce^{\beta y} + De^{-\beta y},$$

with

$$\beta^2 = -i\alpha Rc.$$

The boundary conditions (iii) and (iv) are

$$\phi''(0) = 0, \qquad \beta^2\phi'(0) - \phi'''(0) = 0,$$

from which

$$C = -D, \qquad B = -4\beta D.$$

The boundary condition $\phi'(1) = 0$ gives

$$B = 2\beta \cosh \beta D.$$

Since β has been assumed to be different from zero, the two evaluations of B give

$$\cosh \beta = -2.$$

The boundary condition $\phi(1) = 0$ can be used to evaluate A in terms of D (say), and is not needed to arrive at the secular equation. Thus

$$\beta = \cosh^{-1} 2 + (2n + 1)\pi i$$

and

$$-i\alpha Rc = (\cosh^{-1} 2)^2 - (2n + 1)^2\pi^2$$
$$+ i2(2n + 1)\pi \cosh^{-1} 2,$$

with n any integer, positive or negative. Breaking this into its real and imaginary parts, we have

$$\alpha Rc_i = (\cosh^{-1} 2)^2 - (2n + 1)^2\pi^2,$$
$$\alpha Rc_r = -2(2n + 1)\pi \cosh^{-1} 2.$$

Since $\cosh^{-1} 2 = 1.32$ approximately, c_i is always negative, and very large in magnitude when α is small. Since α is always assumed positive (because the results are unchanged if α is negative) and n may be positive or negative, the waves can propagate both upstream and downstream, and if they propagate with the same speed they are damped equally fast. Note again that as $|2n + 1|$ increases the eigenfunction has more and more oscillations in $0 \leq y \leq 1$. It is therefore not surprising that the pertinent waves are damped faster and faster. We have now shown that the shear waves are indeed there, though it is the surface waves that govern stability.

We conclude with the warning that although surface waves have been shown to govern stability at small Reynolds numbers, it has not been conclusively shown that for very small β (so that $\frac{5}{6} \cot \beta$ is large) shear waves do not, after all, govern the stability of the flow.

ACKNOWLEDGMENTS

This work has been supported jointly by the National Science Foundation and the Army Research Office (Durham).

Reprinted from **TAPPI,** Vol. 47, No. 2, February 1964
Copyright, 1964, by Technical Association of the Pulp and Paper Industry, and reprinted by permission of the copyright owner

CHIA-SHUN YIH
and S. P. LIN

Effect of Variation of Acceleration on Free-Surface Instability

THE instability of stock on a fourdrinier wire occurs as it issues from the slice, as it passes over the table rolls, and especially immediately after it leaves the table rolls. There are many causes for the instability. On top of the table rolls the cause of instability is the centripetal and downward acceleration of the fluid, which can be many times as great as the gravitational acceleration. A paper dealing with this was published in the *Proceedings of the Royal Society* by Yih (*1*) with supporting experimental data. At the places where the streamlines are curved and the fluid is slowed down away from the center of the curvature, instability may take the form of the formation of Taylor-Görtler vortices. A paper dealing with this possibility was published by Yih and Debler in 1961 (*3*).

Measurements of the growth of disturbances after the table roll were made by Spengos (*4*), and by Debler (*6*). Spengos also obtained some preliminary measurements on the rate of growth of the disturbances over the table roll. But the rather violent instability of the stock after the table rolls has so far not been satisfactorily explained. This paper provides a theory, with some supporting experimental data, which explains the main cause of instability after the table rolls, and constitutes a final report to the

CHIA-SHUN YIH and S. P. LIN, Department of Engineering Mechanics, The University of Michigan, Ann Arbor, Mich.

One of the causes of stock instability on a fourdrinier wire after the table rolls—perhaps the most important—is the change of acceleration from downward to upward and back to downward as the stock goes over the table rolls. This cause is analyzed by considering a layer of fluid being subject to (1) a sudden change of acceleration and (2) a gradual change of acceleration. In both cases growth of surface waves is found when the conditions are right, and these conditions are always realized on a fourdrinier wire. To verify the theory, an apparatus was constructed to observe the effect of variable acceleration. A rectangular box containing a layer of water was allowed to fall freely to a foam-rubber pad. As soon as it hit the pad, the acceleration quickly became positive and then decreased to a negative value. Waves originally observed in the water were seen to grow, in some cases so violently that they spilled out of the container. The experiments verify the main conclusions of the theory at least qualitatively, and it is now felt that variable acceleration is indeed a very important factor in stock instability.

Technical Association of Pulp and Paper Industry which has generously sponsored the study of free-surface instability at the University of Michigan during the years 1957–59 and 1960–62.

1. A DESCRIPTIVE EXPLANATION OF THE CAUSE OF POSTROLL INSTABILITY

Consider a layer of liquid in a container and in wave motion, as shown in Fig. 1. Suppose that at time $t = 0$ the wave attains a maximum height, when the acceleration of the container is a_1, directed upward. This acceleration is maintained until the free surface is flat, at which time all the energy of the wave motion is in the form of kinetic energy. If at this time the acceleration is suddenly changed to a_2, which is less than a_1, then as the next

maximum wave height is attained it would have to be greater than the previous maximum, because the potential energy relative to the container will remain the same, whereas the *effective* gravitational acceleration has been decreased from $g + a_1$ to $g + a_2$. The reverse is true if a_2 is greater than a_1, as shown in Fig. 2. It is also evident that the phase of the waves is important at the moment of change of the acceleration, whether it is decreased or increased. Since the waves on the stock as it moves past the table rolls are in all possible phases, a change of acceleration will make certain components of the waves unstable. The change of acceleration is experienced by the stock as the wire carrying it leaves the table rolls, above which it has undergone a downward acceleration, and goes through regions of upward and then

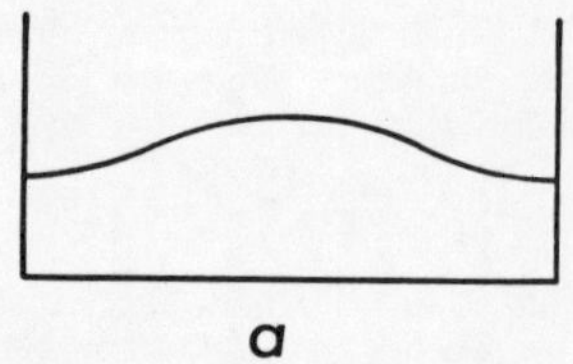

Acceleration = a_1. Wave attains max. height

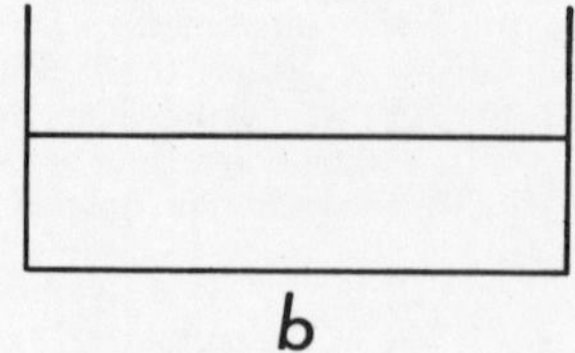

Acceleration changes to a_2, which is less than a_1. Surface is flat

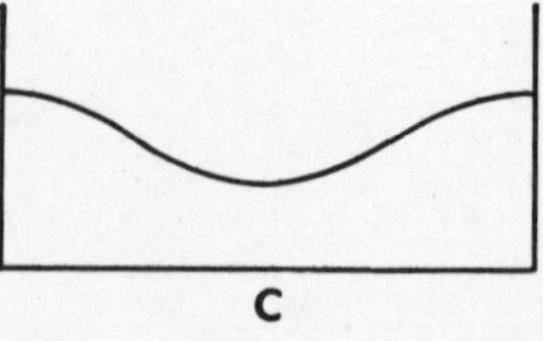

Acceleration = a_2. Wave attains next max. height

Fig. 1.

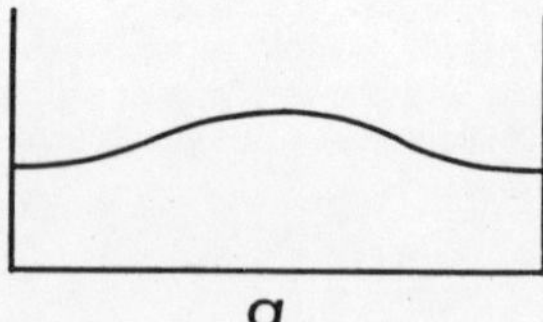

Acceleration = a_1. Wave attains max. height

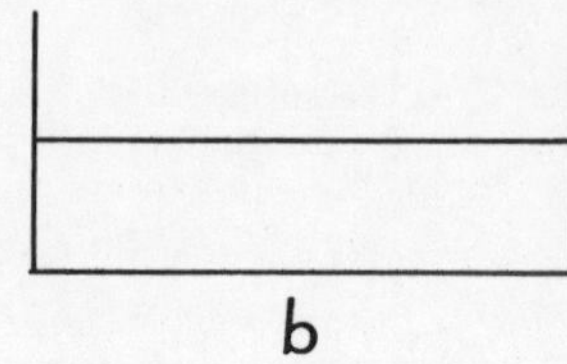

Acceleration changes to a_2, which is greater than a_1. Surface is flat

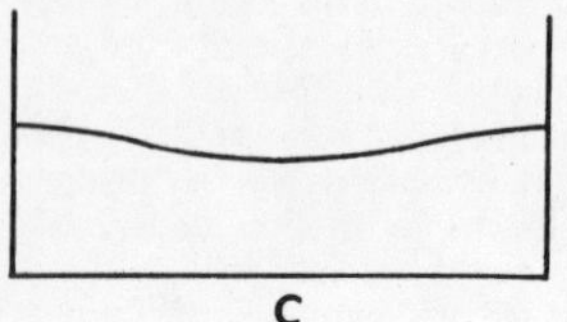

Acceleration = a_2. Wave attains next max. height

Fig. 2

again downward acceleration. The first author owes this idea to a stimulating discussion with E. J. Justus, who explained the instability in terms of pressure at the bottom of the container. A more precise explanation will be given by a mathematical analysis, which will be presented in the following two sections.

The foregoing consideration of the instability phenomenon, for the first time, also explains in *physical* terms the observation of Faraday, in 1831 (*Phil. Trans.*, p. 319), that the frequency of liquid oscillations was only half that of an oscillating vessel containing the liquid, since, as the liquid accomplishes half an oscillation (Fig. 1), the vessel has already accomplished one oscillation, ready to start the next cycle by changing a_2 to a_1 again. (The change in acceleration occurs both at extreme wave heights and at zero wave heights.)

2. FORMULATION OF THE DIFFERENTIAL EQUATION GOVERNING FREE-SURFACE INSTABILITY

Wave motion in a layer of liquid of uniform depth will be considered. The formulation of the problem is identical to that of Benjamin and Ursell (5) for instability due to periodic acceleration. In fact, the qualitative explanation given in the previous section makes it possible to understand in physical terms the mathematical results obtained by Benjamin and Ursell.

The hydrodynamic equations of motion *with reference to the container* are,

with viscous effects neglected,

$$\frac{D}{Dt}(u,v,w) =$$
$$\frac{1}{\rho}\left(\frac{\partial}{\partial x}, \frac{\partial}{\partial y}, \frac{\partial}{\partial z}\right) p + (0,0, -g-a) \quad (1)$$

in which a is the acceleration, ρ is the density, p is the pressure, g is the gravitational acceleration, and u, v, and w are the velocity components in the directions of increasing x, y, and z, respectively. The coordinates x, y, and z are Cartesian coordinates, and the symbol D/Dt stands for

$$\frac{\partial}{\partial t} + u\frac{\partial}{\partial x} + v\frac{\partial}{\partial y} + w\frac{\partial}{\partial z}$$

and is the operator for substantial differentiation. From equation (1), it can already be seen that when the frame of reference is taken to be the container, the body force g per unit mass in the negative z-direction is replaced by $g + a$, so that the potential energy with respect to the container is based on $g + a$ instead of g. Although the concept of potential energy is meaningful only if a is constant, the explanation based on constant a given in the last section is qualitatively applicable to the case of variable acceleration. The origin is taken at the bottom of the container, and the undisturbed depth of the water in it is h.

The unknowns in (1) are u, v, w, and p. Since there are only three equations in (1), a fourth one is needed. This is the equation of continuity

$$\frac{\partial u}{\partial x} + \frac{\partial v}{\partial y} + \frac{\partial w}{\partial z} = 0 \quad (2)$$

Now equations (1) are nonlinear, and are very difficult to solve although the number of equations is now sufficient with the addition of (2). Fortunately, the theorem of Helmholtz and Kelvin on the persistence of irrotationality is valid here because the acceleration a of the container can only be time-dependent, so that the effective body force with components $(0, 0, -g-a)$ is conservative, i.e., its curl is zero. This can be demonstrated quite simply. With the vorticity components denoted by

$$\xi = \frac{\partial w}{\partial y} - \frac{\partial v}{\partial z}, \eta =$$
$$\frac{\partial u}{\partial z} - \frac{\partial w}{\partial x}, \zeta = \frac{\partial v}{\partial x} - \frac{\partial u}{\partial y}, \quad (3)$$

equations governing the vorticity of the fluid can be obtained from (1) by cross-differentiation. For instance, with the second and third equation in (1) written as

$$\frac{\partial v}{\partial t} + u\zeta - w\xi =$$
$$- \frac{\partial}{\partial y}\left(\frac{p}{\rho} + \frac{u^2 + v^2 + w^2}{2}\right) \quad (4)$$

$$\frac{\partial w}{\partial t} - u\eta + v\xi =$$
$$- \frac{\partial}{\partial z}\left(\frac{p}{\rho} + \frac{u^2 + v^2 + w^2}{2}\right) - (g + a) \quad (5)$$

(5) can be differentiated with respect to y and (4) differentiated with respect to z. Utilizing (2) and the identity

$$\frac{\partial \xi}{\partial x} + \frac{\partial \eta}{\partial y} + \frac{\partial \zeta}{\partial z} = 0$$

the result can be reduced to the form

$$\frac{D\xi}{Dt} = \xi \frac{\partial u}{\partial x} + \eta \frac{\partial u}{\partial y} + \zeta \frac{\partial u}{\partial z} \quad (6)$$

Similarly,

$$\frac{D\eta}{Dt} = \xi \frac{\partial v}{\partial x} + \eta \frac{\partial v}{\partial y} + \zeta \frac{\partial v}{\partial z} \quad (7)$$

$$\frac{D\zeta}{Dt} = \xi \frac{\partial w}{\partial x} + \eta \frac{\partial w}{\partial y} + \zeta \frac{\partial w}{\partial z} \quad (8)$$

Now if the flow starts from an irrotational state, $\xi = \eta = \zeta = 0$ everywhere at $t = 0$, and (6), (7), and (8) state that the substantial derivatives of ξ, η, and ζ are zero, or that the true derivatives of ξ, η, and ζ of each particle as we follow its motion are zero. This being true of every particle originating from an irrotational state, the vorticity of every particle will remain zero, and the persistence of irrotationality is demonstrated. Since the motion under consideration can be considered to have started from rest, which is an irrotational state, the subsequent motion is irrotational.

For irrotational motion, equation (3) states that the *curl* of the velocity is zero. This implies that the velocity can be expressed as the gradient of a potential ϕ:

$$(u,v,w) = -\left(\frac{\partial}{\partial x}, \frac{\partial}{\partial y}, \frac{\partial}{\partial z}\right)\phi \quad (9)$$

Combining (2) and (9), we have

$$\left(\frac{\partial^2}{\partial x^2} + \frac{\partial^2}{\partial y^2} + \frac{\partial^2}{\partial z^2}\right)\phi = 0 \quad (10)$$

which is linear. The problem is then to solve (10) with the appropriate boundary conditions. But one of the boundary conditions, the one at the free surface, involves the pressure. It is therefore necessary to obtain an expression for p in terms of ϕ. This is supplied by the Bernoulli equation for irrotational unsteady flows:

$$-\frac{\partial \phi}{\partial t} + \frac{p}{\rho} + \frac{u^2 + v^2 + w^2}{2} + (g + a)z = F(t) \quad (11)$$

The derivation of (11) is quite simple. With the vorticity components in (4) and (5) equal to zero, and with v and w on the left-hand sides given by (9), the equations (4) and (5) can be written as

$$\frac{\partial \chi}{\partial y} = 0, \frac{\partial \chi}{\partial z} = 0$$

in which

$$\chi = -\frac{\partial \phi}{\partial t} + \frac{p}{\rho} + \frac{u^2 + v^2 + w^2}{2} + (g + a)z$$

Similarly the first equation in (1) gives

$$\frac{d\chi}{dx} = 0$$

Hence, by integration, (11) is obtained. The function $F(t)$ is independent of x, y, and z, and can be absorbed in ϕ by

adding to ϕ the function $-\int F(t)dt$, without affecting either the velocity components or p. Hence, for convenience $F(t)$ will be taken to be zero.

The conditions at the rigid boundaries are

$$\frac{\partial \phi}{\partial z} = 0 \text{ at the bottom} \quad (12)$$

and

$$\frac{\partial \phi}{\partial n} = 0 \text{ at the walls} \quad (13)$$

At the free surface,

$$p = -T\left(\frac{1}{R_1} + \frac{1}{R_2}\right) \quad (14)$$

in which T is the surface tension and R_1 and R_2 are the principal radii of the surface

$$z = \zeta(x,y,t) + h \quad (15)$$

with ζ now and henceforth denoting the surface displacement rather than the third vorticity component. Since (15) is valid for all values of time t,

$$\frac{D}{Dt}[z - \zeta(x,y,t)] = 0$$

or

$$w = \frac{\partial \zeta}{\partial t} + u\frac{\partial \zeta}{\partial x} + v\frac{\partial \zeta}{\partial y} \quad (16)$$

This is the kinematic condition at the free surface, relating w to ζ. The dynamic boundary condition is obtained from (11) and (14), and is

$$-\frac{T}{\rho}\left(\frac{1}{R_1} + \frac{1}{R_2}\right) - \frac{\partial \phi}{\partial t} +$$
$$\frac{1}{2}(u^2 + v^2 + w^2) + (g + a)\zeta = 0 \quad (17)$$

If ζ and its derivatives with respect the x and y are everywhere small, u, v, and w will be everywhere small, and squares and products in u, v, w, and ζ can be neglected. Equations (16) and (17) can then be written as

$$w = \frac{\partial \zeta}{\partial t} = -\frac{\partial \phi}{\partial z} \text{ at } z = h \quad (18)$$

$$-\frac{T}{\rho}\left(\frac{\partial^2 \zeta}{\partial x^2} + \frac{\partial^2 \zeta}{\partial y^2}\right) - \frac{\partial \phi}{\partial t}\Big|_{z=h} + (g + a)\zeta = 0 \quad (19)$$

Following Benjamin and Ursell (5) we shall take

$$\zeta(x,y,t) = \sum_0^\infty a_m(t)S_m(x,y) \quad (20)$$

and

$$\phi(x,y,z,t) = -\sum_1^\infty \frac{da_m(t)}{dt}\frac{\cosh k_m z}{k_m \sinh k_m h} \times$$
$$S_m(x,y) + G(t) \quad (21)$$

in which $S_m(x,y)$ satisfies

$$\left(\frac{\partial^2}{\partial x^2} + \frac{\partial^2}{\partial y^2} + k_m^2\right)S_m(x,y) = 0 \quad (22)$$

in which the k's are the eigenvalues that make $[\partial S_m(x,y)]/\partial n$ equal to zero, and

of course depend only on the shape of the container. Note that (13) and (18) imply that

$$\frac{\partial \zeta}{\partial n} = 0 \text{ at the walls}$$

and that equation (20) satisfies this condition. Also, ϕ given in (21) satisfies (12) and (13), as well as (18).

The eigenvalue $k_0 = 0$ corresponds to $S_0(x,y) = 0$. As explained by Benjamin and Ursell, $a_0(t)$ is constant, since the total volume of the liquid is constant. If the origin of ζ is taken from the mean free surface, $a_0(t) = 0$. Hence, it follows from (19) that $G(t)$ can only be a constant, which can be taken to be zero without affecting anything. With (20) and (21) substituted into (19), the result is

$$\sum_1^\infty \frac{S_m(x,y)}{k_m \tanh k_m h}\left[\frac{d^2 a_m}{dt^2} + k_m \tanh k_m h\left(\frac{k_m^2 T}{\rho} + g + a\right)\right] = 0 \quad (23)$$

Since the functions $S_m(x,y)$ are linearly independent,

$$\frac{d^2 a_m}{dt^2} + (p_m + q_m)a_m = 0 \quad (24)$$

in which

$$p_m = k_m \tanh k_m h\left(\frac{T}{\rho}k_m^2 + g\right), q_m = a(t)k_m \tanh k_m h \quad (25)$$

Equation (24) is the basis for the analyses in the subsequent sections.

3. FREE-SURFACE INSTABILITY DUE TO A SUDDEN CHANGE OF ACCELERATION

To bring out the effect of variable acceleration on the amplitude of waves, consider the simplest case in which the acceleration is zero at first, then assumes a constant finite value a, and finally becomes zero again, as shown in Fig. 3.

For simplicity the quantity a_m, which is a time-dependent amplitude in the sense that it is proportional to the maximum surface height (with respect to x and y) at time t for the mth mode, will be denoted by A. If attention is focused on the mth mode, (24) reads

$$\frac{d^2 A}{dt^2} + (p_m + q_m)A = 0 \quad (26)$$

Suppose that the acceleration $a(t)$ is changed from zero to the constant a at time $t = 0$. Then for $t < 0$

$$A = B_1 \cos(s_1 t + \theta_1), B_1 > 0 \quad (27)$$

in which $s_1^2 = p_m$, and θ_1 is the angle specifying the phase of A at $t = 0$. For $t > 0$ the acceleration is a, so that the solution of (26) is

$$A = B_2 \cos(s_2 t + \theta_2) \quad (28)$$

in which

$$s_2^2 = p_m + q_m, \text{ with } a(t) = a \text{ in } q_m$$

Now at $t = 0$ both A and dA/dt must be continuous. Hence

$$B_1 \cos\theta_1 = B_2 \cos\theta_2 \qquad (29)$$

$$s_1 B_1 \sin\theta_1 = s_2 B_2 \sin\theta_2 \qquad (30)$$

If (29) is squared and (30) is divided by s_2 and squared, and the results are added, the following equation is obtained.

$$B_2{}^2 = B_1{}^2 \left[\cos^2\theta_1 + \left(\frac{s_1}{s_2} \sin\theta_1 \right)^2 \right] = B_1{}^2[1 - (1 - r^2)\sin^2\theta_1] \qquad (31)$$

in which

$$r = \frac{s_1}{s_2}$$

Thus, whatever the value of r, $|B_2| = |B_1|$ if $\theta_1 = 0$. That is to say, the amplitude is unchanged if the change of acceleration from zero to a occurs at the time of maximum A. This is understandable, because at that moment the kinetic energy is zero, and a sudden change in acceleration only brings about a sudden change in potential energy in the proportion $(g + a)/g$. If the acceleration is maintained constant $(= a)$, the subsequent maximum A will remain unchanged.

If, on the other hand, $\theta_1 = \pi/2$, then

$$|B_2| = r\,|B_1| \qquad (32)$$

and the amplitude is reduced by the ratio r. We can, indeed, compute the maximum and minimum of $(B_2/B_1)^2$ from (31). Thus

$$\frac{d}{d\theta_1}\left(\frac{B_2}{B_1} \right)^2 = -2(1 - r^2)\sin\theta_1 \cos\theta_1 = -(1 - r^2)\sin 2\theta_1$$

which is zero for $\theta_1 = 0$, $\pm\pi/2$, $\pm\pi$, $\pm 3\pi/2$, etc. Since $r < 1$, it is easy to see that the values 0 and $\pm n\pi$ ($n =$ integer) correspond to the maximum values of $|B_2/B_1|$, and the values $\pm(2n + 1)\pi/2$ correspond to the minimum values. In other words, the most severe amplitude-reduction ratio is simply s_1/s_2.

When the acceleration suddenly drops from a to zero, the analysis is similar, but physically the situation is quite different. Since we are going to consider all possible phase angles, we can again take, without loss of generality, the moment of acceleration change to be the origin of time. For $t < 0$, we have

$$A = B_2 \cos(s_2 t + \theta_2{}') \qquad (33)$$

in which s_2 is as defined before, $|B_2|$ maintains the same magnitude, but $\theta_2{}'$ is no longer θ_2, because we have changed the origin of time for convenience. For $t > 0$

$$A = B_3 \cos(s_1 t + \theta_3) \qquad (34)$$

in which $s_1 = \sqrt{p_m}$ as before. Continuity in A and dA/dt at $t = 0$ demands that

$$B_2 \cos\theta_2{}' = B_3 \cos\theta_3$$

$$s_2 B_2 \sin\theta_2{}' = s_1 B_3 \sin\theta_3$$

which produce

$$B_3{}^2 = B_2{}^2[1 + (r^{-2} - 1)\sin^2\theta_2{}'] \qquad (35)$$

in which r has the same meaning as before. A similar calculation gives the maximum value of $|B_3/B_2|$ to be r^{-1}, and the minimum value to be 1. The minimum value, corresponding to no change of amplitude, is again understandable. Since it corresponds to $\theta_2{}' = 0$ or $n\pi$, it corresponds to the state of maximum potential energy and no kinetic energy. The maximum value of $|B_3/B_2|$ corresponds to $\theta_2{}' = \pi/2$ or $\pm(2n + 1)\pi/2$. For $0 < \theta_2{}' < \pi/2$, the value of $|B_3/B_2|$ is between 1 and $1/r$. This brings out the importance of the phase angle $\theta_2{}'$. (The same is true of θ_1.) Since waves with all phases are assumed to exist, the maximum ratio of amplitude increase is s_2/s_1.

Consider now the acceleration graph given in Fig. 3. If $t_0 = 0$ and $\theta_1 = 0$, the amplitude suffers no change on passing through t_0. At $t = t_1$ the value of $\theta_2{}'$ is really $s_2(t_1 - t_0) + \theta_2 = s_2 t_1 + \theta_2$. Depending on s_1, s_2, and t_1 (or $t_1 - t_0$), it may or may not be one of the values $\pm(2n + 1)\pi/2$. But as t_1 is varied, it can be one of these values. Thus the absolute maximum for $|B_3/B_1|$, or the greatest ratio of amplitude increase, is

s_2/s_1. If the value a is very large, say $48g$, this ratio is exactly 7 if surface-tension effect is neglected, because $(a + g)/g = 7^2$. It is significant that it is the region of acceleration decrease that causes the increase in amplitude. At the postroll region on a fourdrinier wire, the velocity changes from a downward one along the roll to a slightly upward one along the wire a short distance after a reverse curvature (concave upward), then becomes horizontal again. There is a region where the acceleration changes from a large positive value (upward acceleration) to zero. This is the narrow region of dramatic increase in the amplitudes of the disturbances.

Figure 7 shows the three regions of vertical acceleration of the stock as it is carried by a fourdrinier wire over a table roll. Where the wire wraps around the roll (*Region I*), the acceleration is centripetal and downward. As the wire leaves the roll, there is a region of positive curvature (concave upward), where the acceleration is upward. This is *Region II*. After *Region II* there follows necessarily a region of negative curvature (*Region III*), before the wire can become level again.

The acceleration schedule described by Fig. 4 is more realistic. The downward acceleration a_1 corresponds to *Region I*. The upward acceleration, a, corresponds to *Region II*. *Region II* in Fig. 7 corresponds to downward acceleration a_2. At $t = t_0$ the greatest ratio is 1, whatever the values of a_1 and a. At $t = t_1$ the maximum possible amplitude ratio is $[(g + a)/(g - a_2)]^{1/2}$, which is also the maximum ratio of the amplitude after t_1 to the amplitude before t_1. Since a_2 may be quite near to g, this ratio can be very large. This explains the rather dramatic amplification of disturbances in the postroll region.

4. FREE-SURFACE INSTABILITY DUE TO A GRADUAL CHANGE OF ACCELERATION

An acceleration schedule representing the actual situation on a fourdrinier wire is given in Fig. 5. The region $t < t_0$ represents the region of downward

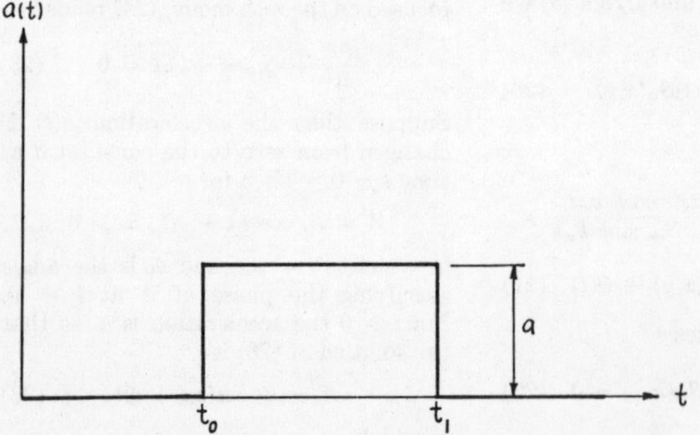

Fig. 3. An idealized acceleration schedule

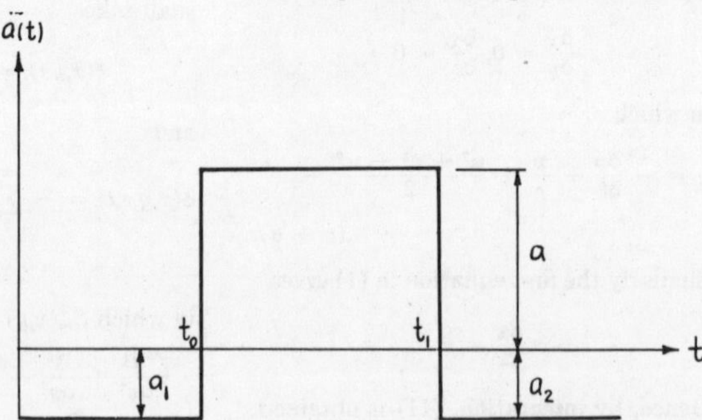

Fig. 4. A more realistic acceleration schedule

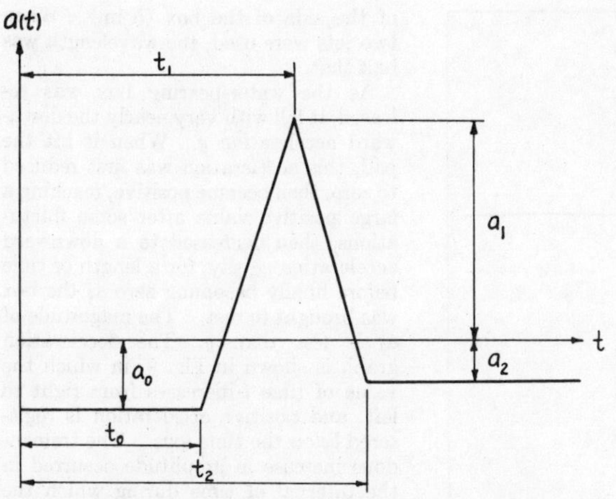

Fig. 5. An acceleration schedule representing the actual situation on a fourdrinier wire

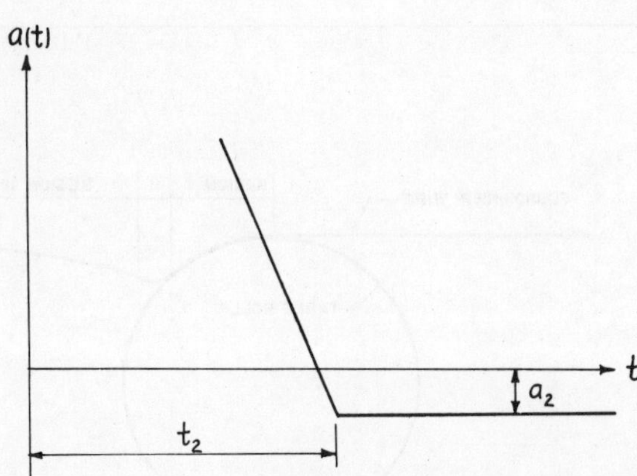

Fig. 6. That portion of Fig. 5 used for experimental verification of the theory

acceleration over the table rolls. The region $t_0 \leq t \leq t_1$ represents the region of increasing upward acceleration. The region $t_1 \leq t \leq t_2$ represents the region of decreasing acceleration. For $t > t_2$, a region of negative (downward) acceleration exists, which corresponds to a region of upward-convexity of the fourdrinier wire, following the region of reverse curvature (concave upward) where the acceleration is positive.

The governing equation is still (26), in which p_m and q_m retain their forms in (25), so that

$$\frac{q_m}{k_m \tanh k_m h} = a(t) =$$

$$\begin{cases} -a_0 \text{ for } t \leq t_0 \\ a_0 + \dfrac{a_1 + a_0}{t_1 - t_0}(t - t_0) \text{ for } t_0 \leq t \leq t_1 \\ a_1 - \dfrac{a_1 + a_2}{t_2 - t_1}(t - t_1) \text{ for } t_1 \leq t \leq t_2 \\ -a_2 \text{ for } t \geq t_2 \end{cases}$$

Thus it is easy to see that (26) has in all four regions the general form

$$\frac{d^2 A}{dt^2} + (\alpha + \beta t)A = 0 \qquad (36)$$

If β is zero, as for $t \leq t_0$ or $t \geq t_2$, then the solution is of the form

$$A = B \cos(\sqrt{\alpha}\, t + \theta) \qquad (37)$$

If β is not zero, as in the region of increasing or decreasing acceleration, the solution of (36) is

$$A = (\alpha + \beta t)^{1/2} \left[B J_{1/3} \left(\frac{2}{3} \sqrt{\beta} \left(t + \frac{\alpha}{\beta} \right)^{3/2} \right) + N_{1/3} \left(\frac{2}{3} \sqrt{\beta} \left(t + \frac{\alpha}{\beta} \right)^{3/2} \right) \right] \qquad (38)$$

Matching of the solutions of type (37) and (38) at $t = t_0$ and $t = t_2$, and of two solutions of the type (38) at $t = t_1$, can be made on the demand that A and dA/dt be continuous at the moments t_0, t_1, and t_2. Since the possibility of tremendous increase in amplitude has already been demonstrated in the last

Table I

Max. acceleration = 10.7g h = 0.25 in.	λ = 3.6 in. Max. (2A) = 3.19 in.		t_2 = 16 millisec. $\sqrt{\dfrac{t_2}{\alpha}}$ = 3.06 rad/sec.
t, millisec.	5	20	25	35
2A Calculated, in.	0.0015	0.04	0.09	0.19
2A Measured, in.	0.0010	0.04	0.10	0.22

Table II

Max. acceleration = 10.7g h = 0.25 in.	λ = 3.4 in. Max. (2A) = 3.48 in.	t_2 = 16 millisec. $\sqrt{\dfrac{t_2}{\alpha}}$ = 3.49 rad/sec.
t, millisec.	5	25	35
2A Calculated, in.	0.0057	0.12	0.24
2A Measured, in.	0.0010	0.15	0.25

Table III

Max. acceleration = 12.81g h = 0.25 in.	λ = 3.6 in. Max. (2A) = 3.09 in.	t_2 = 14 millisec. $\sqrt{\dfrac{t_2}{\alpha}}$ = 3.24 rad/sec.
t, millisec.	5	25	35
2A Calculated, in.	0.0015	0.12	0.22
2A Measured, in.	0.0010	0.10	0.20

Table IV

Max. acceleration = 12.8g h = 0.25 in.	λ = 3.4 in. Max. (2A) = 3.27 in.		t_2 = 14 millisec. $\sqrt{\dfrac{t_2}{\alpha}}$ = 3.68 rad/sec.
t, millisec.	5	25	30	35
2A Calculated, in.	0.006	0.14	0.20	0.26
2A Measured, in.	0.001	0.12	0.16	0.22

Table V

Max. acceleration = 18.65g h = 0.25 in.	λ = 3.6 in. Max. (2A) = 3.16 in.	t_2 = 11 millisec. $\sqrt{\dfrac{t_2}{\alpha}}$ = 3.16 rad/sec.
t, millisec.	5	25	40
2A Calculated, in.	0.012	0.19	0.34
2A Measured, in.	0.010	0.19	0.30

Table VI

Max. acceleration = 18.65g h = 0.25 in.	λ = 3.3 in. Max. (2A) = 2.72 in.	t_2 = 11 millisec. $\sqrt{\dfrac{t_2}{\alpha}}$ = 3.68 rad/sec.
t, millisec.	5	25	40
2A Calculated, in.	0.004	0.20	0.45
2A Measured, in.	0.010	0.18	0.35

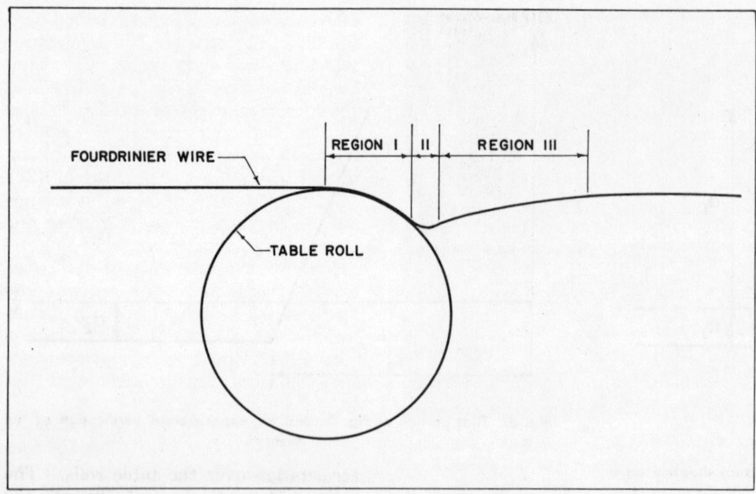

Fig. 7. Schematic drawing for regions of acceleration on a fourdrinier wire as it passes over a table roll. *Region I*: downward aceleration. *Region II*: strong upward acceleration. *Region III*: downward acceleration

section for acceleration schedules described by Figs. 3 and 4, and the demonstration for the present case would differ only in some detail, it will not be given here. Instead, (37) and (38) will be used to correlate the experimental data, because the actual acceleration schedule in the experiments is not far from that given in Fig. 5.

5. EXPERIMENTAL VERIFICATION

The theory has been advanced that variable acceleration in a direction normal to the free surface can bring about a tremendous increase in amplitude of surface disturbances. To test the validity of this theory, an apparatus was constructed (Fig. 8) which allowed a plastic 5-in.-sq box containing a layer of water to fall about 2 to 3 in. onto a pad of foam-rubber layers. Surface disturbances were made by either one line-jet of air blowing at the middle of the water surface or two such jets parallel to two sides of the box and blowing at two symmetric quarter positions (hence not at the center line). Thus the wavelengths were controlled. When only one jet was used, the wavelength λ is equal to the inner measure

Fig. 8. Apparatus

of the side of the box (5 in.). When two jets were used, the wavelength was half that.

As the water-bearing box was released, it fell with very nearly the downward acceleration g. When it hit the pad, this acceleration was first reduced to zero, then became positive, reaching a large positive value after some fluctuations, then decreased to a downward acceleration a_2, say, for a length of time before finally becoming zero as the box was brought to rest. The magnitude of a_2 is less than g. The acceleration graph is shown in Fig. 9, in which the value of time t increases from right to left, and positive acceleration is registered *below* the time axis. The tremendous increase in amplitude occurred in the interval of time during which the acceleration decreased to a_2 and was maintained at a_2, as described schematically in Fig. 6. Attention will be focused on this period. The magnitude of a_2 is near g. Hence, a_2 is assumed to be $-g$ in the calculations.

Table VII

Max. acceleration = 11.65g h = 0.5 in.		λ = 3.4 in. Max. (2A) = 1.12 in.		t_2 = 14 millisec. $\sqrt{\alpha}$ = 4.52 rad/sec.	
t, millisec.	5		40		50
2A Calculated, in.	0.003		0.14		0.18
2A Measured, in.	0.001		0.12		0.20

Table VIII

Max. acceleration = 11.65g h = 0.5 in.		λ = 3.5 in. Max. (2A) = 1.41 in.		t_2 = 14 millisec. $\sqrt{\alpha}$ = 4.27 rad/sec.	
t, millisec.	5	25		35	45
2A Calculated, in.	0.006	0.10		0.18	0.22
2A Measured, in.	0.008	0.10		0.15	0.20

Table IX

Max. acceleration = 13.42g h = 0.5 in.		λ = 3.2 in. Max. (2A) = 0.61 in.		t_2 = 12 millisec. $\sqrt{\alpha}$ = 5.0 rad/sec.	
t, millisec.	5		40		70
2A Calculated, in.	0.004		0.09		0.18
2A Measured, in.	0.001		0.10		0.18

Table X

Max. acceleration = 13.42g h = 0.5 in.		λ = 3.4 in. Max. (2A) = 1.11 in.		t_2 = 12 millisec. $\sqrt{\alpha}$ = 4.51 rad/sec.	
t, millisec.	5	20		30	40
2A Calculated, in.	0.0014	0.05		0.10	0.15
2A Measured, in.	0.0020	0.04		0.09	0.15

Table XI

Max. acceleration = 19.2g h = 0.5 in.		λ = 3.1 in. Max. (2A) = 0.57 in.		t_2 = 12 millisec. $\sqrt{\alpha}$ = 5.3 rad/sec.	
t, millisec.	5		30		40
2A Calculated, in.	0.0017		0.06		0.09
2A Measured, in.	0.0020		0.08		0.12

Table XII

Max. acceleration = 19.2g h = 0.5 in.		λ = 3.3 in. Max. (2A) = 2.34 in.		t_2 = 12 millisec. $\sqrt{\alpha}$ = 3.43 rad/sec.	
t, millisec.	5	15		25	35
2A Calculated, in.	0.012	0.05		0.13	0.21
2A Measured, in.	0.010	0.05		0.11	0.18

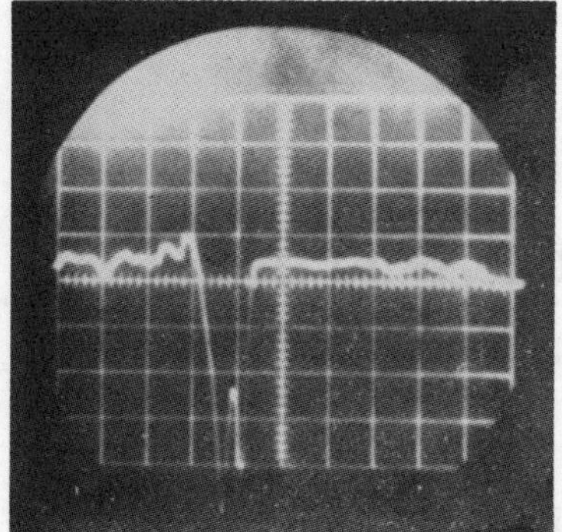

Fig. 9. Acceleration graph

Fig. 10. Wave form soon after a_2 (nearly equal to $-g$) is reached by a, after decreasing from a large positive value

A movie camera took the motion pictures at 250 frames per second. The surface waves had the form and magnitude shown in Fig. 10 when the acceleration was a_2, very shortly after $t = t_2$. The surface form a few milliseconds after a_2 was reached is shown in Fig. 11, from which the tremendous increase in amplitude is very evident indeed.

A more detailed check of the theory was provided by the following procedure. Two values of A were taken from the motion pictures for two values of t very near t_2 but less than t_2. Then from the solution (38), in which, as in (36), α and β can be calculated from the experimental data, B and C are determined. Then the value of A calculated for a value of t less than t_2 is compared with the experimental value. Similarly, with A and dA/dt known at $t = t_2$ (the latter from two values of A at two instants near $t = t_2$), A for $t > t_2$ can be calculated. The values so calculated can be compared with the measured ones. The comparison is shown in Tables I to XII. Due to the

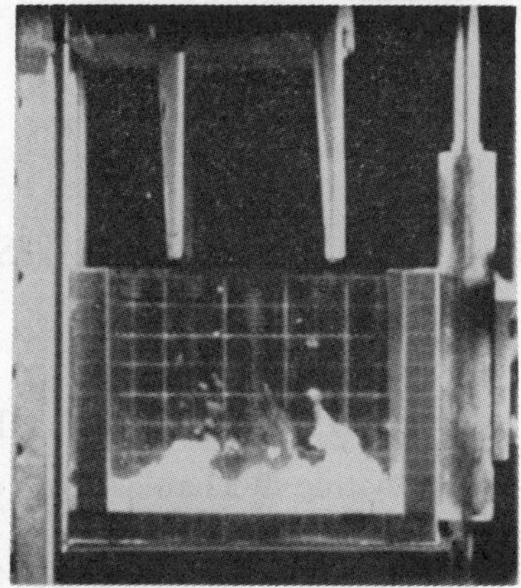

Fig. 11. A few milliseconds after the condition in Fig. 10 was reached (but this picture is not in the same sequence as that in Fig. 10)

smallness of A for $t < t_2$, and the consequent difficulty of measurement, the calculated and experimental values of A for $t < t_2$ agreed only in order of magnitude. The agreement between the calculated and experimental values is much better for $t > t_2$. The values of $\sqrt{\alpha}$ given in Tables I through XII are those calculated from (37) for $t > t_2$.

Both the pictorial description provided by Figs. 9 and 10 and the more detailed record provided by Tables I and XII demonstrate very vividly the striking effect of acceleration variation on amplitude increase. The comparison of calculated and experimental values given in these tables also indicates the general validity of the theory given in Sections 2 and 3.

6. APPLICATION TO POSTROLL INSTABILITY OF STOCK ON FOURDRINIER WIRES

The striking effect of acceleration variation on the amplitude of surface disturbances has been demonstrated both theoretically and experimentally. The pertinence of this effect on postroll instability of stock on a fourdrinier wire can be seen from the acceleration schedule of the stock as it passes over the table rolls. On top of a table roll the acceleration is downward. Then it increases to a large positive value at a region of reverse curvature which must exist as the wire leaves the roll. As the wire has to become horizontal eventually, the reverse curvature will have to pass over to a region of concave-downward curvature again. This is a region of downward acceleration. Thus the acceleration schedule is much like that given in Fig. 5. The latter part of the schedule (Fig. 6) is chiefly responsible for the amplitude increase.

One point of great interest is the phase shift of the surface disturbances as they leave the table rolls. A quali-

tative explanation can be supplied here. For simplicity consider the acceleration schedule described in Fig. 3. (The same general conclusion can be reached by considering more complicated and realistic acceleration schedules.) In the region of upward acceleration the solution is given by (28) instead of (27). In (28) s_2 can be very large if a is large, and a large s_2 means a greater frequency and a shorter period of time required for a phase shift of $180°$, i.e., for the ridges to become troughs and vice versa. This is true for a disturbance of any wavelength in any direction whatsoever, and in particular true for the disturbance already prominent over the table roll.

The growth of surface instability as the stock passes over the table rolls has been adequately explained in ref. (1). The cause of instability is the downward acceleration which can be considerably greater than g. In ref. (3) the velocity distribution in the postroll region was considered a possible cause of an instability of the Taylor-Görtler type, with the presence of growing longitudinal vortex tubes. For correlation with experimental data, the analysis given in ref. (3) would have to be modified to include the velocity distribution in the stock in *Region II* and the effect of viscosity. Although instability of the Taylor-Görtler type remains a possibility, the violence of amplitude growth in the postroll region seems to favor the variability of acceleration as the main cause of instability, particularly since this explanation is entirely independent of the velocity distribution in the postroll region. For this reason further pursuit of the Taylor-Görtler instability was abandoned. The authors believe that the variability of acceleration is indeed the main cause not only of postroll instability, but also of the instability of the free surface as the stock leaves the slice.

LITERATURE CITED

1. Yih, C.-S., *Proc. Roy. Soc.* **A258:** 63–86, 1960.
2. Yih, C.-S., *Tappi* **45** (6): 524–527 (1962).
3. Debler, W. R. and Yih, C.-S., *Tappi* **45** (4): 272–279 (1962).
4. Yih, C.-S. and Spengos, A. C., *Tappi* **42** (5): 398–403 (1959).
5. Benjamin, T. B. and Ursell, F., *Proc. Roy. Soc.* **A225:** 505–515 (1954).
6. Debler, W. R., *Tappi* **44** (8): 589–592 (1961).

RECEIVED July 16, 1963. Presented at the 18th Engineering Conference of the Technical Association of the Pulp and Paper Industry, held in New Orleans, La., Oct. 28–31, 1963.

This paper serves as a final report on the research sponsored by TAPPI on free-surface instability for the past several years. The writer of this paper (C.-S. Yih), who has served as supervisor of this research, wishes to express his sincere thanks to TAPPI for this sponsorship, and to the members of the several fluid-mechanics committees of TAPPI, for their interest and many stimulating discussions. The authors also wish to thank Dr. W. R. Debler and Messrs. Milo Kaufman and A. Engerer for assistance in the experimental program.

J. Fluid Mech. (1965), *vol.* 22, *part* 3, *pp.* 579–586

Gravitational instability of a viscous fluid in a magnetic field

By CHIA-SHUN YIH

Department of Engineering Mechanics, University of Michigan

(Received 16 November 1964)

The instability of a viscous fluid between two infinite vertical plates and heated from below in the presence of a magnetic field perpendicular to the plates is investigated, and the most critical stability boundary in the space of the Rayleigh number R, Hartmann number M, and the horizontal wave number a is determined. It is found that the most unstable mode is a symmetric mode with zero wave-number, and that for any M the fluid is unstable for any non-zero R, however small.

1. Introduction

The problem studied concerns the stability of a viscous fluid contained between two vertical infinite plates and heated from below in the presence of a uniform magnetic field perpendicular to the plates. The mean temperature field is given by

$$\overline{T} = T_0 + \beta z, \tag{1}$$

with z measured vertically upward, and β indicating the (negative) vertical gradient of the temperature. The mean density is then

$$\overline{\rho} = \rho_0(1 - \alpha\beta z), \tag{2}$$

in which α is the thermal expansivity. The gradient of the hydrostatic pressure $\overline{p}$ is then

$$d\overline{p}/dz = -g\rho_0(1 - \alpha\beta z), \tag{3}$$

in which g is the gravitational acceleration. The quantities T_0 and ρ_0 are the values of $\overline{T}$ and $\overline{\rho}$ at $z = 0$. The only component of the magnetic field when the fluid is undisturbed is $\overline{H}_x$, which is in the direction normal to the plates. Its magnitude is denoted by H_0. The direction of y is therefore horizontal and parallel to the plates.

The problem with zero magnetic field has been considered by Ostrach (1955), Yih (1959), and Wooding (1960). Ostrach considered purely vertical motion. Yih considered the stability of disturbances with wavelengths in the z-direction, proved the validity of the principle of exchange of stabilities, and showed that the most unstable mode is the one with infinite wavelength, or zero wave-number in the direction of the vertical. The results of Ostrach and Yih, for both symmetric and antisymmetric convection, are actually in agreement, although Yih did not realize that the number 31·29 for antisymmetric convection had already been given in Ostrach's paper. However, Wooding (1960) showed that both Ostrach

 Chia-Shun Yih

and Yih had missed the most unstable mode. By considering motion in the y-direction he showed that, for motion symmetric with respect to x, the critical Rayleigh number (to be defined later in this paper) is indeed zero, corresponding to zero wave-number in the y-direction. Zero indeed is a root of the secular equation obtained by Ostrach and Yih for symmetric convection. But its significance escaped them both!

Wooding gave, for the case of zero magnetic field, an expansion of the Rayleigh number in powers of the wave-number in the y-direction, here indicated by a to distinguish it from the customary symbol α for the thermal expansivity,

$$R = 3a^2\{1 + \tfrac{8}{21}a^2 + O(a^4)\}. \tag{4}$$

Wooding's demonstration that the fluid is unstable for all Rayleigh numbers is beyond doubt, so long as the plates are infinite in the y-direction.

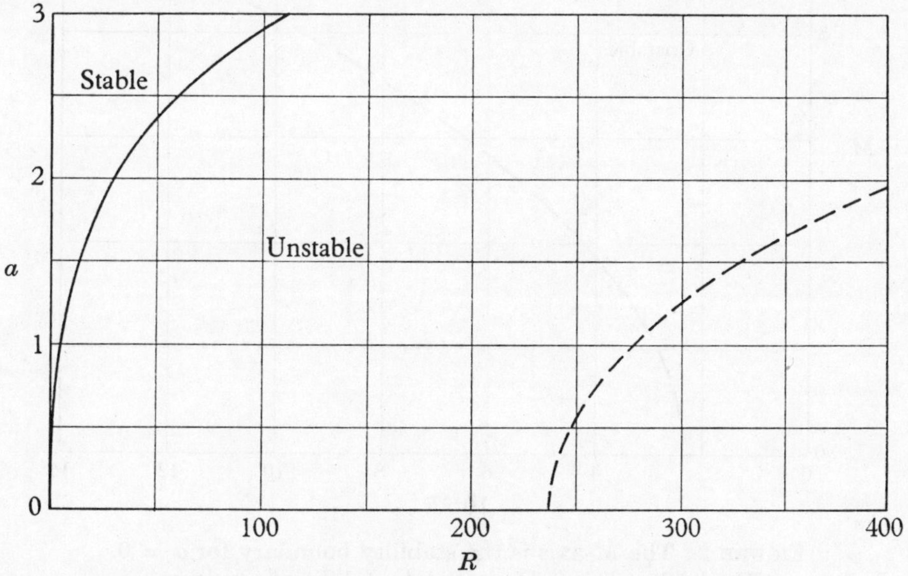

FIGURE 1. The solid line is the true stability boundary for $M = 0$. The broken line is Dunwoody's stability boundary.

The problem stated in this section has been studied by Dunwoody (1964). His results for symmetric convection are given in broken lines in figure 1 for the case of zero magnetic field and in figure 2 for the case of a non-zero magnetic field (with M indicating the Hartmann number and $a = 0$ in this case). It is clear that Dunwoody's curves do not pass through the origin and that his results are at variance with Wooding's finding. Dunwoody regards Wooding's result for $a = 0$ and $H_0 = 0$ (or $M = 0$) as correct. But he seems to consider that result to be an isolated incident, and has ignored the expansion (4) entirely. The 'stable' regions in his figures 2 and 4 are not stable regions if Wooding's results are correct. If, as Dunwoody agrees, the fluid is incipiently unstable at $R = 0$ and $M = 0$, how can it be stable for $M = 0$ and $0 < R < 237{\cdot}6$, as indicated by his figures 2 and 4? To put it another way, how can R jump from zero (given in Dunwoody's

Gravitational instability of a viscous fluid in a magnetic field   581

table 1) to $237 \cdot 6 + O(\epsilon^2)$ as a changes from zero to ϵ? Or from zero (given in Dunwoody's table 2) to $237 \cdot 6 + O(\epsilon^2)$ as M changes from zero to ϵ? These jumps are indicated in his figures 2 and 4, and implied in his tables 1 and 2.

These puzzling points led the writer to investigate the present problem anew. It will be shown that Dunwoody missed the most unstable mode of symmetric convection, that the results for that mode are consistent with Wooding's finding for $M = 0$, and that, contrary to Dunwood's conclusion, the most critical symmetric mode is more unstable than the most critical antisymmetric mode.

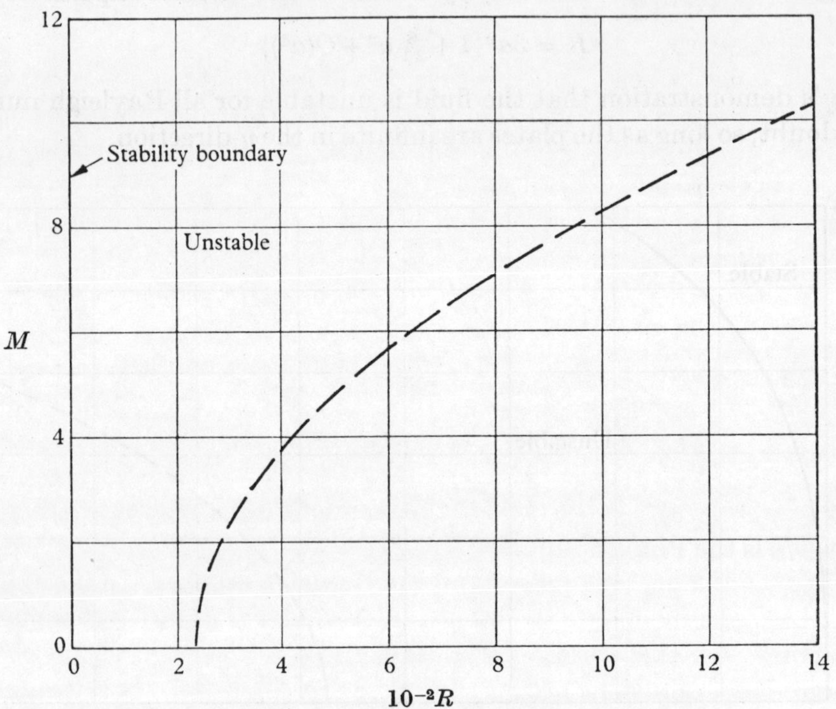

FIGURE 2. The M-axis is the stability boundary for $a = 0$.
The broken line is Dunwoody's stability boundary.

2. The governing differential system

Since some of the equations in Dunwoody's formulation of the mathematical problem will be referred to in this discussion, the key equations in his paper will be reproduced here. There will be a slight change in notation. The wave-number will be denoted by a instead of α, the thermal expansivity by α instead of ϕ, and the bars over a symbol denote mean quantities here rather than dimensionless variables. In the following, $2d$ denotes the spacing of the plates, ν the kinematic viscosity, κ the thermal diffusivity, t the time, T' the temperature perturbation, w the vertical velocity, p' the pressure perturbation, and H_z the vertical component of the magnetic field. Dunwoody assumes that the velocity components u and v in the directions of x and y are zero, that the only component of the induced magnetic field is H_z, so that

$$H_x = H_0, \quad H_y = 0. \tag{5}$$

 Chia-Shun Yih

Furthermore, the perturbation quantities w, T', and H_z are supposed independent of z, and the co-ordinates

$$x' = \frac{x}{d}, \quad y' = \frac{y}{d}, \quad t' = \frac{\nu t}{d^2},$$

will be used *without* the accents. The exponential time factor will be assumed for the perturbation quantities, so that

$$\frac{wd}{\kappa} = W(x,y)\,e^{\lambda t}, \quad \frac{T'}{\beta d} = \theta(x,y)\,e^{\lambda t}, \quad \frac{H_z}{H_0} = H(x,y)\,e^{\lambda t}, \quad \frac{\partial p'}{\partial z} = \Pi\,e^{\lambda t}. \tag{6}$$

However, Π must be zero, for otherwise p' will be infinite at $z = \pm\infty$, violating the basis of the linear theory. (This rules out the Hartmann flow, which would otherwise be a perfectly acceptable solution of (7), (8), and (9) below, for $\lambda = 0$ and $R = 0$, as a possible neutral mode.)

The linearized equations of motion in the z-direction, of thermal diffusion, and, for the magnetic field are then

$$\lambda W = -R\theta + \nabla^2 W + \eta M^2 \frac{\partial H}{\partial x}, \tag{7}$$

$$P\lambda\theta = \nabla^2\theta - W, \tag{8}$$

$$P\lambda H = \eta\nabla^2 H + \partial W/\partial x, \tag{9}$$

in which $\eta = (4\pi\mu\sigma\kappa)^{-1}$ is the ratio of the magnetic diffusivity to thermal diffusivity, $P = \nu/\kappa$ is the Prandtl number, and $M^2 = \sigma u^2 H_0^2 d^2/\rho_0\nu$ and $R = -\alpha\beta g d^4/\nu\kappa$, are the Hartmann number squared and the Rayleigh number. In the expressions for η and M, μ is the magnetic permeability, and σ the electrical conductivity. The symbol ∇^2 denotes the Laplacian in x and y.

The boundary conditions are: (a) the non-slip condition, (b) the condition of insulation at the wall, and (c) the continuity of H_z at the wall, in which it is assumed to be zero. Thus they are

$$W = 0, \quad \partial\theta/\partial x = 0, \quad \text{and} \quad H = 0 \quad \text{at} \quad x = \pm 1, \tag{10}$$

if the origin of the co-ordinates is located midway between the plates.

The quantity λ is in general complex. Since the principle of exchange of stabilities has been shown to be valid by Dunwoody, for neutral stability it can be taken to be zero. If, further,

$$W(x,y) = f(x)\cos ay, \tag{11}$$

the equations (7), (8) and (9) can be reduced to the single equation in $f(x)$, which is

$$\{(D^2 - a^2)^2 - M^2 D^2\}f = Rf, \tag{12}$$

with D denoting d/dx. The boundary conditions can be reduced to

$$f = 0 \quad \text{and} \quad (D^2 - a^2 - M^2)Df = 0 \quad \text{at} \quad x = \pm 1. \tag{13}$$

3. Solution for symmetric convection

The system consisting of (12) and (13) admits even and odd solutions separately. There is no error of omission in Dunwoody's work for odd f, corresponding to antisymmetric convection. We shall concentrate on even f on symmetric convection. The secular equation for that has been correctly obtained by Dunwoody, and is

$$(\epsilon_1^2 - a^2 - M^2)\,\epsilon_1 \tanh \epsilon_1 = (\epsilon_2^2 - a^2 - M^2)\,\epsilon_2 \tanh \epsilon_2, \tag{14}$$

in which

$$2\epsilon_1^2 = 2a^2 + M^2 + B, \quad 2\epsilon_2^2 = 2a^2 + M^2 - B, \quad B = (M^4 + 4M^2 a^2 + 4R)^{\frac{1}{2}}. \tag{15}$$

The solutions of (14) for $M = 0$ or for $a = 0$ obtained by Dunwoody are indicated in figures 1 and 2 by broken lines. They are without errors in so far as they satisfy (14). But the most unstable mode has escaped notice, and, as mentioned in the introduction, many puzzling points raised by these broken lines demand explanation. Inspection of (15) shows that $B = 0$ satisfies (14). But this will not do, because the indicial equation of (12) then has a double root, and (14) must be modified because of the solutions in the form of x times a hyperbolic sine. When the modification is made, it is found that $B = 0$ does not satisfy the secular equation.

But, for any M whatever, the equations

$$a = 0 \quad \text{and} \quad R = 0 \tag{16}$$

do satisfy (14). This indicates that R is small if a is non-zero but small. In fact, as will be verified *a posteriori*, $R = O(a^2)$ for small a. Considering small a and *any* M small enough for a four-term expansion of $\tanh \epsilon_1$ or of $\tanh \epsilon_2$ to be sufficiently accurate, we can calculate R from (14). We do not make any stronger assumption concerning M. It may be greater or smaller than a, and M^4 may be greater than R. It turns out that we never have to expand the radical equal to B in (15), because only B^2 or its powers are involved after the factor B has been cancelled. The result in fact is

$$-30a^2 + 10a^4 - 4a^6 + \tfrac{34}{21}a^8 + (M^4 - B^2)\left[-\tfrac{5}{2} + 3a^2 - \tfrac{17}{7}a^4 + M^2 - \tfrac{34}{21}M^2 a^2 \right.$$
$$\left. - \tfrac{17}{168}(3M^4 + B^2)\right] = 0,$$

which involve R and R^2, but no radicals. The final evaluation of R gives

$$R = Aa^2 + Ba^4 + O(a^6), \tag{17}$$

in which $\qquad A = 315(105 - 42M^2 + 17M^4)^{-1} - M^2,$

$$B = (10 - 4M^2 + \tfrac{34}{21}M^4)^{-1}\{-10 + 12M^2 - \tfrac{170}{21}M^4 + A(12 - \tfrac{68}{7}M^2 - \tfrac{34}{21}A)\}.$$

For $M = 0$, (17) reduces to (4). For small M, both A and B increases with M. Although (17) has been obtained by taking only four terms in $\tanh \epsilon_1$ and $\tanh \epsilon_2$, and is therefore valid only for small values of M and a, the increase of A and B with M can be expected to hold for any M, however large, on physical grounds. Thus the intersection of the stability boundary with the plane $M = \text{constant } C$

 Chia-Shun Yih

is a curve embracing the R-axis, and doing so more and more closely as C increases.

We have not evaluated R for very large values of M because there has been no need to do so. For large M series expansions of $\tanh \epsilon_1$ and $\tanh \epsilon_2$ are of course impractical. A referee of this paper has shown by assuming $M^4 \gg R$ that $R = Ma^2$ for large M. This does not contradict what has been obtained and said above in the least. In fact it confirms the statement that the stability boundary intersects the plane $M = C$ in a curve that embraces the R-axis more and more closely as C increases.

For $M = 0$, (14) reduces to (3.14) in Dunwoody (1964), or

$$\xi \tanh \xi = \zeta \tan \zeta, \tag{18}$$

with
$$\xi = (R^{\frac{1}{2}} + a^2)^{\frac{1}{2}}, \quad \zeta = (R^{\frac{1}{2}} - a^2)^{\frac{1}{2}}.$$

The (R, a) curve for $M = 0$ is given in figure 1 in solid line. This has been obtained directly from (18) by numerical calculation, by insisting on $\zeta < \frac{1}{2}\pi$. It is evident that it is not only generally more 'critical' than the broken line, but gives a critical Rayleigh number far less than 237·6. For $a = 0$, the neutral-stability curve is simply $R = 0$, or the M-axis, as shown in figure 2. It is again evident that the broken line lies entirely within the unstable region.

The solid line in figure 1 is based on figures kindly provided by Mr S. P. Lin and given in the following table:

a	0·5	1	2	3
R	0·82	4·1	29·5	113·6

To visualize the true stability boundary in the (R, a, M)-space, one may consider it as an infinite sail. The M-axis is the mast and the R-axis the centre-line of the sail boat or the projection of the keel on the deck. The solid line in figure 1 is a curved boom. The positive direction of the R-axis points toward the stern. The broken line in figure 1 is a second curved boom attached to a curved secondary mast indicated by the broken line in figure 2. The 'stern jib' that extends from the second boom to the secondary mast is the stability boundary for one of the infinitely many higher and more stable modes.

Before concluding, it is desirable to clarify the rather puzzling situation that the fluid can be unstable at zero Rayleigh number, even in the presence of a magnetic field. Inspection of (7)–(10), with $\lambda = 0$, reveals that for $a = 0$ the solution is

$$W = 0, \quad H = 0, \quad \theta = \text{const.} \tag{19}$$

provided $R = 0$. For this mode there is no motion and no induced magnetic field, and the definition of θ in (6) shows that T' is equal to a constant (since $\lambda = 0$) times βd. Now for a given fluid R can be zero if β or d is zero. In either case T' is zero. Hence the case of neutral stability corresponding to $a = 0$ and $R = 0$ is characterized by the absence of motion, of induced magnetic field, and of induced temperature. This removes the apparent difficulty of accepting *neutral* stability at zero Rayleigh number, but also raises the question of whether a formal solution characterized by no perturbation of physical quantities at all is qualified to represent a situation of neutral stability. But then we have just shown that in the neighbourhood of such a seemingly insignificant solution are solutions indicating instability at any non-zero Rayleigh number, however small.

We shall make the result $R \to 0$ as $a \to 0$ more palatable by showing that λ is proportional to R. This is done in the following way. As has been said in the last paragraph, for $a = 0$ equations (19) hold. Let the constant for θ be θ_0. As R is increased slightly, Π still must be zero for the reason stated before. But W and H will be different from zero, and θ will be equal to $\theta_0 + \theta_1$. Equations (7)–(9) become

$$\lambda W = -R\theta_0 + W'' + \eta M^2 H',$$
$$P\lambda\theta_0 = \theta_1'' - W,$$
$$P\lambda H = \eta H'' + W'.$$

Now since $\lambda = 0$ at $R = 0$, we expect λ to be small compared with 1 for small R. Thus these equations can be further simplified to

$$0 = -R\theta_0 + W'' + \eta M^2 H', \tag{20}$$
$$P\lambda\theta_0 = \theta_1'' - W, \tag{21}$$
$$0 = \eta H'' + W'. \tag{22}$$

From these it is immediately clear that W and H are proportional to R. In fact, on setting

$$W = RW_1 \quad \text{and} \quad H = RH_1, \tag{23}$$

we can write (20) and (22) as

$$0 = -\theta_0 + W_1'' + \eta M^2 H_1', \tag{24}$$
$$0 = \eta H_1'' + W_1', \tag{25}$$

combination of which yields

$$\theta_0 = \eta H_1''' + \eta M^2 H_1'. \tag{26}$$

Odd as it may appear at first sight, this can be solved with (25) to satisfy the four boundary conditions on W and H in (10). The solution is simply†

$$\left. \begin{array}{l} H_1 = Ax + B\sin Mx, \\ W_1 = -\eta H_1' + D, \end{array} \right\} \tag{27}$$

in which

$$A = \theta_0(\eta M^2)^{-1}, \quad B = -A(\sin M)^{-1} \quad \text{and} \quad D = \eta A(1 - M\cot M).$$

This in fact confirms the adequacy of (23). Now multiplication of (21) by θ_0 and integration between $x = -1$ and $x = 1$ yield

$$2P\lambda\theta_0^2 = -\theta_0\!\int W\,dx = -R\!\int \theta_0 W_1\,dx, \tag{28}$$

since θ_1' vanishes at both limits. Multiplication of (24) by W_1 and integration between the same limits yield

$$\int\theta_0 W_1\,dx = \int W_1'' W_1\,dx + \eta M^2\!\int H_1' W_1\,dx,$$

or, upon integration by parts and utilization of (10) and (25),

$$\int\theta_0 W_1\,dx = -\int W_1'^2\,dx - \eta M^2\!\int H_1 W_1'\,dx$$
$$= -\int W_1'^2\,dx - \eta^2 M^2\!\int H_1'^2\,dx. \tag{29}$$

† This demonstration is based on $M \neq 0$. That for $M = 0$ is similar.

586   *Chia-Shun Yih*

Substitution of (29) in (28) produces, finally,

$$2P\lambda\theta_0^2 = R \int [(W_1')^2 + (\eta M H_1')^2]\, dx. \tag{30}$$

Hence λ is proportional to R and is positive for any positive R, however small.

4. Conclusions

We are then in a position to conclude that, whether a magnetic field H_x is present or not:

1. Symmetric convection is more unstable than antisymmetric convection;
2. The fluid is unstable for any non-zero Rayleigh number, however small;
3. For any Hartmann number M, the most unstable mode corresponds to $a = 0$;
4. The (R, a) curve for neutral stability in a plane with constant M embraces the R-axis more and more closely as the value of M increases, giving a smaller and smaller region of instability but keeping zero as the critical Rayleigh number.

Conclusion 3 is in agreement with Dunwoody's conclusion. The other conclusions are new, and are at variance with the results of Dunwoody. All the conclusions are consistent with the results of Wooding (1960) for $M = 0$.

This work is among the many researches sponsored jointly by the National Science Foundation and the Army Research Office (Durham).

REFERENCES

DUNWOODY, N. T. 1964 *J. Fluid Mech.* **20**, 103.

OSTRACH, S. 1955 50 *Jahre Grenzschichtforschung.* Brunswick: Verlag Friedr. Vieweg und Sohn.

WOODING, R. A. 1960 *J. Fluid Mech.* **7**, 501.

YIH, C.-S. 1959 *Quart. Appl. Math.* **17**, 25.

Reprinted from

THE PHYSICS OF FLUIDS   VOLUME 8, NUMBER 7   JULY 1965

Stability of a Non-Newtonian Liquid Film Flowing Down an Inclined Plane

Chia-Shun Yih

The University of Michigan, Ann Arbor, Michigan
(Received 5 October 1964; final manuscript received 15 March 1965)

A layer of a non-Newtonian liquid, of which the constitutive equation is triply nonlinear, flows down an inclined plane under the action of gravity. The stability of the flow against wave formation is investigated. With M denoting a parameter involving the first and the second viscosities, the critical Reynolds number is given as a function of M and the slope of the plane, for small values of M. The theory presented here shows how free-surface instability of non-Newtonian fluids can be attacked, and provides a basis for stability experiments with non-Newtonian fluids.

1. INTRODUCTION

THE problem of the stability of a Newtonian liquid film flowing down an inclined plane was formulated by Yih[1] and solved by Benjamin.[2] Further features of the phenomenon were discussed by Yih,[3] who also gave a simple method for dealing with stability problems involving a free surface or an interface. Since free-surface instability of non-Newtonian fluids is of much practical interest, and at present no analysis of it is available, it seems desirable to provide an analysis which illustrates how problems involving such an instability can be at-

tacked, and provides a basis for experiments on the stability of non-Newtonian fluids. The method of analysis is the same as that used in Yih.[3]

The specific problem considered is the stability of a layer of a triply nonlinear isotropic liquid flowing down an inclined plane, with the angle of inclination denoted by β, as shown in Fig. 1. The direction of the gravitational acceleration is vertical.

2. EQUATIONS OF MOTION

The velocity components in the directions of the increasing Cartesian coordinate $x_i (i = 1, 2, \text{ and } 3)$ will be denoted by u_i, with i ranging from 1 to 3. With ρ, t, and X_i denoting the density, the time, and the body-force components, respectively, and with τ_{ij} denoting the components of the stress tensor,

[1] C.-S. Yih, in *Proceedings of the Second U. S. National Congress of Applied Mechanics* (American Society of Mechanical Engineers, New York, 1955), pp. 623–628.
[2] T. B. Benjamin, J. Fluid Mech. **2**, 554 (1957).
[3] C.-S. Yih, Phys. Fluids **6**, pp. 321–334 (1963).

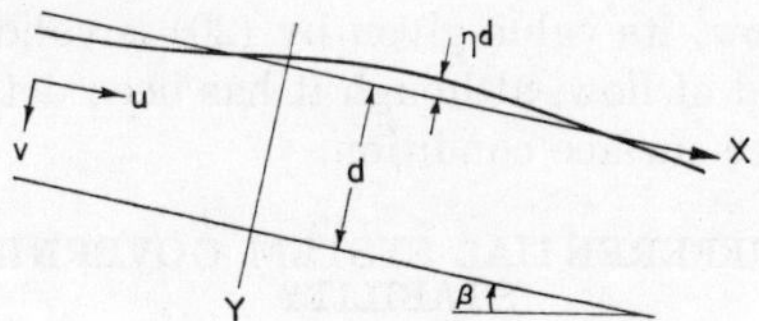

FIG. 1. Definition sketch.

the equations of motion are still

$$\rho\left(\frac{\partial u_i}{\partial t} + u_\alpha \frac{\partial u_i}{\partial x_\alpha}\right) = \frac{\partial \tau_{\alpha i}}{\partial x_\alpha} + \rho X_i, \tag{1}$$

in which repeated indices in the same term indicate summation. As usual, the second index in τ_{ij} indicates the direction of the corresponding force component, and the first index indicates the axis perpendicular to the plane in which it acts.

Since the liquid is isotropic, the relationship between the stress components and the rates of deformation e_{ij} is, in the most general form,

$$\tau_{ij} = f_0(I)\delta_{ij} + f_1(I)e_{ij} + f_2(I)e_{i\alpha}e_{\alpha j}, \tag{2}$$

in which

$$e_{ij} = \partial u_j/\partial x_i + \partial u_i/\partial x_j, \tag{3}$$

and I is a collective symbol indicating the three invariants of the tensor e_{ij}, i.e.,

$$I_1 = \partial u_\alpha/\partial x_\alpha, \tag{4}$$

$$I_2 = \begin{vmatrix} e_{11} & e_{12} \\ e_{21} & e_{22} \end{vmatrix} + \begin{vmatrix} e_{22} & e_{23} \\ e_{32} & e_{33} \end{vmatrix} + \begin{vmatrix} e_{11} & e_{13} \\ e_{31} & e_{33} \end{vmatrix}, \tag{5}$$

$$I_3 = \begin{vmatrix} e_{11} & e_{12} & e_{13} \\ e_{21} & e_{22} & e_{23} \\ e_{31} & e_{32} & e_{33} \end{vmatrix}. \tag{6}$$

The three functions f_0, f_1, and f_3 are functions of I_1, I_2, and I_3. Equation (2) is called the constitutive equation. In the present case, the liquid can be considered incompressible, so that

$$I_1 = 0, \tag{7}$$

which is the equation of continuity of an incompressible fluid. Of course f_0, f_1, and f_2 can be very complicated functions[4] of I_2 and I_3. For the triply non-linear fluid under consideration,

$$f_0(I) = -p + \lambda_2 I_2 + \lambda_3 I_3,$$
$$f_1(I) = \mu - \mu_2 I_2, \qquad f_2(I) = \mu_3, \tag{8}$$

---

[4] Non-Newtonian fluids for which the shear stress varies as a power of the shearing rate of deformation are known to exist. For such fluids $f_1(I) = \mu_2 I_2^n$. The method given in this paper applies to such fluids and to a fluid with any constitutive equation.

in which p is a function of space (but is no longer the mean pressure, as it would be for a Newtonian fluid), μ is the ordinary viscosity, and μ_2 and μ_3 can be called the second and third viscosities. All the coefficients μ, μ_2, μ_3, λ_2, and λ_3 are assumed to be constant. The coefficients λ_2 and μ_3 have the same dimension M/L, λ_3 and μ_2 have the same dimension MT/L, and μ has the dimension M/TL, with M, L, and T denoting the dimensions of mass, length, and time, respectively.

The equations of motion in terms of velocity components only are obtained by substituting (8) in (2) and then (2) in (1), and are

$$\rho\left(\frac{\partial u_i}{\partial t} + u_\alpha \frac{\partial u_i}{\partial x_\alpha}\right) = -\frac{\partial}{\partial x_i}(p - \lambda_2 I_2 - \lambda_3 I_3) + \rho X_i$$
$$+ \frac{\partial}{\partial x_\alpha}\left[\mu\left(\frac{\partial u_i}{\partial x_\alpha} + \frac{\partial u_\alpha}{\partial x_i}\right) - \mu_2 I_2\left(\frac{\partial u_i}{\partial x_\alpha} + \frac{\partial u_\alpha}{\partial x_i}\right)\right]$$
$$+ \frac{\partial}{\partial x_\alpha}\left[\mu_3\left(\frac{\partial u_k}{\partial x_\alpha} + \frac{\partial u_\alpha}{\partial x_k}\right)\left(\frac{\partial u_k}{\partial x_i} + \frac{\partial u_i}{\partial x_k}\right)\right]. \tag{9}$$

3. THE PRIMARY FLOW

The primary flow is unidirectional, with the only nonzero velocity component $\bar{u}_1$ in the direction of x_1, or X as shown in Fig. 1. Further, $\bar{u}_1$ depends only on x_2 or Y, so that I_3 is zero. If the body force is assumed to be conservative,

$$X_i = -\partial\Omega/\partial x_i,$$

in which Ω is the body-force potential. The second and third equations in (9) state, since $\bar{u}_2 = 0 = \bar{u}_3$, that

$$\frac{\partial}{\partial x_1}(p + \rho\Omega - \lambda_2 I_2 - \lambda_3 I_3)$$

cannot be a function of x_2 and x_3. The first equation in (8) then states that

$$\frac{\partial}{\partial x_1}(p + \rho\Omega - \lambda_2 I_2 - \lambda_3 I_3) = -K \text{ (a constant)}, \tag{10}$$

because $\bar{u}_1$ is not a function of x_1. Since

$$I_2 = -(d\bar{u}_1/dY)^2, \quad \text{and} \quad I_3 = 0,$$

the first equation in (9) is

$$0 = K + \frac{d}{dY}\left(\mu \frac{d\bar{u}_1}{dY}\right) + \frac{d}{dY}\left[\mu_2\left(\frac{d\bar{u}_1}{dY}\right)^3\right], \tag{11}$$

integration of which yields

$$\mu \frac{d\bar{u}_1}{dY} + \mu_2\left(\frac{d\bar{u}_1}{dY}\right)^3 = -KY, \tag{12}$$

the constant of integration being zero because the shear stress (τ_{21}) is zero at $Y = 0$. Let

$$U = \mu \bar{u}_1/Kd^2, \qquad x = X/d, \qquad y = Y/d, \qquad (13)$$

in which d is the depth of the liquid. Equation (12) then assumes the form

$$U' + M(U')^3 = -y, \qquad (14)$$

in which the accent indicates differentiation with respect to y, and

$$M = \mu_2(Kd)^2/\mu^3. \qquad (15)$$

The parameter M is a measure of the importance of the first relative to the second viscosity. If M is large, the second viscosity predominates, and the fluid is predominantly non-Newtonian. If M is small, the first viscosity predominates, and the fluid is only slightly non-Newtonian. In this paper M is supposed to be small, say less than 0.2. The sign of M may be positive or negative.

Equation (14) can be solved exactly for U', and the result, after expansion in power series of M, can be integrated to obtain U. Alternatively, we can use

$$U' = -y \qquad (16)$$

as the first approximation, substitute (16) in the cubic term of (14) and integrate to get a second approximation, and repeat the iteration process as many times as we wish. The result can be integrated to obtain U. In either way we obtain, to the second power in M,

$$U' = -y + My^3 - 3M^2y^5 \qquad (17)$$

and

$$U = \tfrac{1}{2}(1 - y^2) - \tfrac{1}{4}M(1 - y^4) + \tfrac{1}{2}M^2(1 - y^6), \qquad (18)$$

in which the constant of integration has been determined by the nonslip condition

$$U = 0 \quad \text{at} \quad y = 1. \qquad (19)$$

It can be shown that the root for U', of which the one given by (17) is the approximation, is the only real root of (14).

The value of K in (10) is determined from the fact that $\tau_{22} = 0$ along the free surface, so that

$$p - \lambda_2 I_2 - \lambda_3 I_3$$

is independent of x on the free surface. Thus

$$K = -\frac{\partial}{\partial x_1}\,\rho\Omega = \rho g \sin\beta, \qquad (20)$$

in which g is the gravitational acceleration. Since K has been shown to be a constant for the entire

field of flow, its value given by (20) is valid for the entire field of flow, although it has been determined from a free-surface condition.

4. DIFFERENTIAL SYSTEM GOVERNING STABILITY

Only two-dimensional flows are considered in this paper. For two-dimensional flows, the general equations of motion given by (9) can be considerably simplified. Utilizing the equation of continuity

$$\partial u_1/\partial X + \partial u_2/\partial Y = 0, \qquad (21)$$

and using Δ to denote the Laplacian

$$\partial^2/\partial X^2 + \partial^2/\partial Y^2,$$

we can reduce (9) to the form

$$\rho\left(\frac{\partial u_1}{\partial t} + u_1\frac{\partial u_1}{\partial X} + u_2\frac{\partial u_1}{\partial Y}\right)$$
$$= -\frac{\partial}{\partial X}\,(p - \lambda_2 I_2 + \mu_3 I_2) + \rho g \sin\beta + \mu\Delta u_1$$
$$- 2\mu_2\frac{\partial}{\partial X}\left(I_2\frac{\partial u_1}{\partial X}\right) - \mu_2\frac{\partial}{\partial Y}\left[I_2\left(\frac{\partial u_1}{\partial Y} + \frac{\partial u_2}{\partial X}\right)\right],$$

$$\rho\left(\frac{\partial u_2}{\partial t} + u_1\frac{\partial u_2}{\partial X} + u_2\frac{\partial u_2}{\partial Y}\right) \qquad (22)$$
$$= -\frac{\partial}{\partial Y}\,(p - \lambda_2 I_2 + \mu_3 I_2) + \rho g \cos\beta + \mu\Delta u_2$$
$$- \mu_2\frac{\partial}{\partial X}\left[I_2\left(\frac{\partial u_2}{\partial X} + \frac{\partial u_1}{\partial Y}\right)\right] - 2\mu_2\frac{\partial}{\partial Y}\left(I_2\frac{\partial u_2}{\partial Y}\right).$$

In addition to those introduced in (13), the following dimensionless variables will be used:

$$(u, v) = (u_1, u_2)\,\frac{\mu}{Kd^2}, \qquad \tau = \frac{tKd}{\mu},$$

$$P = \frac{1}{\rho}\left(\frac{\mu}{Kd^2}\right)^2(p - \lambda_2 I_2 + \mu_3 I_2).$$

The equations of motion (22) can then be written as

$$\frac{\partial u}{\partial \tau} + u\frac{\partial u}{\partial x} + v\frac{\partial u}{\partial y} = -\frac{\partial P}{\partial x} + \frac{\sin\beta}{F^2} + \frac{1}{R}\,\Delta u$$
$$- \frac{M}{R}\left\{\frac{\partial}{\partial x}\left(2J_2\frac{\partial u}{\partial x}\right) + \frac{\partial}{\partial y}\left[J_2\left(\frac{\partial u}{\partial y} + \frac{\partial v}{\partial x}\right)\right]\right\},$$
$$\frac{\partial v}{\partial \tau} + u\frac{\partial v}{\partial x} + v\frac{\partial v}{\partial y} = -\frac{\partial P}{\partial y} + \frac{\cos\beta}{F^2} + \frac{1}{R}\,\Delta v \qquad (23)$$
$$- \frac{M}{R}\left\{\frac{\partial}{\partial x}\left[J_2\left(\frac{\partial u}{\partial y} + \frac{\partial v}{\partial x}\right)\right] + \frac{\partial}{\partial y}\left(2J_2\frac{\partial v}{\partial y}\right)\right\},$$

in which Δ now stands for the Laplacian in terms of x and y, and J_2 is the dimensionless form of I_2. The symbols R and F represent the Reynolds number and the Froude number based on the reference velocity

$$V = \frac{Kd^2}{\mu} = \frac{gd^2 \sin \beta}{\nu}, \qquad (24)$$

ν being the kinematic viscosity μ/ρ. Thus

$$R = \frac{Vd}{\nu} = \frac{gd^3 \sin \beta}{\nu^2} \qquad F^2 = \frac{V^2}{gd} = \frac{gd^3 \sin^2 \beta}{\nu^2}, \qquad (25)$$

so that

$$F^2 = R \sin \beta.$$

As usual, the variables u, v, and P will each be resolved into a part representing the primary flow and a part representing the perturbation, or

$$u = U + u', v = v', P = \Pi + p', \qquad (26)$$

in which U and Π are for the primary flow, and the accented quantities are perturbation quantities. Substituting (26) into (23), cancelling out the terms corresponding entirely to the primary flow, and neglecting quadratic terms in the perturbation quantities, we obtain

$$u'_\tau + Uu'_x + U_y v' = -p'_x + \frac{1}{R}\Delta u' - \frac{M}{R}$$
$$\cdot [U_y^2 u'_{xx} - 3U_y^2 u'_{yy} - 6U_y U_{yy}(v'_x + u'_y)], \qquad (27)$$

$$v'_\tau + Uv'_x = -p'_y + \frac{1}{R}\Delta v' - \frac{M}{R}$$
$$\cdot (-U_y^2 u'_{yx} - 3U_y^2 v'_{xx} - 4U_y U_{yy}v'_y), \qquad (28)$$

in which the subscripts indicate partial differentiation.

The equation of continuity now takes the form

$$\partial u'/\partial x + \partial v'/\partial y = 0,$$

which permits the use of the stream function ψ, in terms of which

$$u' = \psi_y, \qquad v' = -\psi_x. \qquad (29)$$

Assuming

$$\psi = \phi(y) \exp i\alpha(x - c\tau), \qquad (30)$$

substituting (30) into (29) and the result into (27) and (28), and eliminating p' in (27) and (28) by cross differentiation, we obtain finally

$$\phi'''' - 2\alpha^2 \phi'' + \alpha^4 \phi + 3M(U'^2 \phi'')''$$
$$+ 2M\alpha^2(U'^2\phi'' + 2U'U''\phi' + 3U''^2\phi + 3U'U'''\phi)$$
$$+ 3M\alpha^4 U'^2 \phi = i\alpha R[(U - c)(\phi'' - \alpha^2\phi) - U''\phi],$$
$$(31)$$

in which the primes now indicate differentiation with respect to y. In (30) and (31), α is the wavenumber $2\pi d/\lambda$, λ being the wavelength, and

$$c = c_r + ic_i,$$

c_r being the wave velocity and αc_i the rate of amplification. If c_i is positive, the waves grow exponentially. If it is negative, they are damped out exponentially. The chief concern of this paper is to determine the sign of c_i for various values of R, M, and β, and for small values of α.

Equation (31) is the differential equation governing the perturbation motion. The boundary conditions at the bottom of the layer are

$$u' = 0 = v' \quad \text{at} \quad y = 1,$$

or

$$\phi'(1) = 0 \quad \text{and} \quad \phi(1) = 0. \qquad (32)$$

The surface conditions are more complicated, since they must be applied on the free surface and not merely at $y = 0$. Let ηd be the (dimensional) deviation of the free surface from its mean position, so that

$$\eta_\tau + U(0)\eta_x = v' = -i\alpha\phi(0) \exp i\alpha(x - c\tau),$$

or

$$\eta = [\phi(0)/c'] [\exp i\alpha(x - c\tau)], c' = c - U(0). \qquad (33)$$

The mean shear $\bar{\tau}_{21}$ in the primary flow is given by the equation of equilibrium (since there is no acceleration for that flow):

$$(d/dy)\bar{\tau}'_{21} = -\rho gd \sin \beta,$$

in which the sign is negative because of the convention that the direction of the shear force on a surface with its *outward* normal in the *positive* y direction determines its sign. The shear at the free surface due to the perturbation motion is

$$\tau'_{21} = \frac{\mu V}{d}\left(\frac{\partial u'}{\partial y} + \frac{\partial v'}{\partial x}\right) + \frac{3\mu_2 V^3}{d^3} U'^2\left(\frac{\partial u'}{\partial y} + \frac{\partial v'}{\partial x}\right)$$
$$- (\rho gd \sin \beta)\eta, \qquad (34)$$

the last term in which gives the effect of variation in mean shear as the free surface deviates from its mean position. The first two terms on the right-hand side of (34) are evaluated at $y = 0$. Since $U(0) = 0$, (34) can be simplified. With η given by (33), V by (24), and u' and v' by (29) and (30), the condition $\tau'_{21} = 0$ on the free surface becomes, finally,

$$\phi''(0) + (\alpha^2 - 1/c')\phi(0) = 0, \qquad (35)$$

which is the same as that for a Newtonian fluid.

[See Yih[3], Eq. (24), in which the factor 3 arose from a different choice of the reference velocity.]

To evaluate the normal stress on the free surface, we need p' at $y = 0$, which can be obtained from (27), and the variation of the normal stress in the primary flow with y, which is given by

$$(d/dy)\bar{\tau}_{22} = -\rho g \cos \beta. \tag{36}$$

A development similar to that leading to (35) then gives the fourth boundary condition

$$\frac{\alpha(\cot \beta + \alpha^2 SR)\phi(0)}{c'}$$
$$+ \alpha(Rc' + 3\alpha i)\phi'(0) - i\phi'''(0) = 0, \tag{37}$$

in which

$$S = T/\rho V^2 d, \tag{38}$$

T being the surface tension, and V being given by (24). Condition (37) is the same as for a Newtonian fluid, because $U'(0) = 0$. [See Yih,[3] Eq. (25), in which the factor 3 before $\cot \beta$ arose from a different choice of the reference velocity.]

Equations (31), (32), (35), and (37) define an eigenvalue problem. Given β, α, S, R, and M, there is a value of c. We shall adopt the approach in Yih,[3] and first consider very long waves ($\alpha = 0$). With the eigenvalue c so obtained, we can then proceed to find the change in c as α is increased. It will be seen that c is real for $\alpha = 0$, and as α is increased the change in c is purely imaginary, giving a c_i positive or negative according as the R is greater or less than a critical value.

5. FIRST APPROXIMATION

For the first approximation, all terms containing α in (31) and the boundary conditions are dropped. The differential equation to be solved is then

$$\phi_0'''' + 3M(U'^2\phi_0'')'' = 0. \tag{39}$$

The boundary conditions (32) stand unmodified. But (35) and (37) are replaced by

$$\phi_0''(0) - (1/c_0')\phi_0(0) = 0 \tag{40}$$

and

$$\phi_0'''(0) = 0, \tag{41}$$

in which, as subsequently, the subscript zero is used to indicate the first approximation.

The solution of (39) is accomplished by four quadratures, the first two of which give

$$\phi_0'' = (Ay + B)/(1 + 3MU'^2). \tag{42}$$

After (42) has been expanded in a power series in M, two more quadratures produce, to the order of M^2,

$$\phi_0 = A\phi_{01} + B\phi_{02} + Cy + D, \tag{43}$$

in which

$$\phi_{01} = \frac{1}{6} y^3 - \frac{3M}{20} y^5 + \frac{5M^2}{14} y^7,$$

$$\phi_{02} = \frac{1}{2} y^2 - \frac{M}{4} y^4 + \frac{M^2}{2} y^6. \tag{44}$$

Equation (41) demands that $A = 0$, and we can take $B = 1$ once and for all. Equations (32), now for ϕ_0, determine C and D to be

$$C = -\phi_{02}'(1) \quad \text{and} \quad D = \phi_{02}'(1) - \phi_{02}(1).$$

Equation (40) then gives

$$c_0' = \tfrac{1}{2} - \tfrac{3}{4}M + \tfrac{5}{2}M^2, \tag{45}$$

so that

$$c_0 = c_0' + U(0) = 1 - M + 3M^2. \tag{46}$$

Incidentally, $c_0' = \phi_0(0) = D$. The eigenfunction ϕ_0 is

$$\phi_0 = \tfrac{1}{2}y^2 - y + \tfrac{1}{2} + M(-\tfrac{1}{4}y^4 + y - \tfrac{3}{4})$$
$$+ M^2(\tfrac{1}{2}y^6 - 3y + \tfrac{5}{2}). \tag{47}$$

For the second approximation, the equation to be solved is

$$\phi_1'''' + 3M(U'^2\phi_1'')'' = i\alpha R[(U - c_0)\phi_0'' - U''\phi_0]. \tag{48}$$

The boundary conditions for ϕ_1 at $y = 1$ are

$$\phi_1(1) = 0, \qquad \phi_1'(1) = 0. \tag{32a}$$

Since only terms of first order in α are retained in the differential system, (37) becomes

$$(\alpha \cot \beta/c_0')\phi_0(0) + \alpha Rc_0'\phi_0'(0) - i\phi_1'''(0) = 0. \tag{49}$$

As to (35), care must be taken that c' suffers a change in the second approximation, so that the proper form of (35) is now

$$\phi_1''(0) - \frac{1}{c_0'} \phi_1(0) + \frac{\Delta c}{c_0'^2} \phi_0(0) = 0, \tag{50}$$

since

$$\frac{d}{dc'}\left(\frac{1}{c'}\right) = -\frac{1}{(c')^2}, \quad \text{and} \quad \Delta c' = \Delta c.$$

The quantity Δc in (49) denotes the change in c.

1262   CHIA-SHUN YIH

Substitution of (47) in (48) and solving for ϕ_1, we have

$$\phi_1(y) = \Delta A\phi_{01} + \Delta Cy + \Delta D + i\alpha Rf(y), \qquad (51)$$

with

$$f(y) = -\frac{1}{120} y^5 + M\left(\frac{13}{840} y^7 + \frac{1}{120} y^5\right)$$
$$- M^2\left(\frac{463}{10080} y^9 + \frac{13}{840} y^7 + \frac{1}{40} y^5\right). \qquad (52)$$

In (51), the first three terms can be considered either as the complementary solution of (48), or as the correction of ϕ_0 necessitated by $i\alpha Rf(y)$. The term $\Delta B\phi_{02}$ has been suppressed because we have taken B to be unity once and for all. The result is not at all affected by this suppression. For detailed arguments, see Yih.[3]

Since $\phi_0(0) = c_0'$, (49) becomes

$$\Delta A = -i[\alpha \cot \beta + \alpha Rc_0'\phi_0'(0)].$$

Since, furthermore, $\phi_1(0) = 0$, (50) reduces to

$$\Delta c = \Delta D.$$

From the boundary conditions (32a) we can compute ΔD and obtain Δc. The result is

$$\Delta c = i\alpha R[f'(1) - f(1)]$$
$$- i[\phi_{01}'(1) - \phi_{01}(1)][\alpha \cot \beta + \alpha Rc_0'\phi_0'(0)]. \qquad (53)$$

After (52), (44), and (47) have been substituted in (53) and only terms up to M^2 are included, it becomes

$$\Delta c = i\alpha\left[R\left(\frac{2}{15} - \frac{62M}{105} + \frac{128M^2}{45}\right)\right.$$
$$\left. + \left(-\frac{1}{3} + \frac{3M}{5} - \frac{15M^2}{7}\right) \cot \beta\right]. \qquad (54)$$

The critical Reynolds number is

$$R_{cr} = \left(\frac{1}{3} - \frac{3M}{5} + \frac{15M^2}{7}\right)$$
$$\cdot \left(\frac{2}{15} - \frac{62M}{105} + \frac{128M^2}{45}\right)^{-1} \cot \beta, \qquad (55a)$$

which can be simplified to

$$R_{cr} = \left(\frac{5}{2} + \frac{46}{7} M - \frac{2399}{294} M^2\right) \cot \beta. \qquad (55b)$$

If $R > R_{cr}$, c_i is positive, and the flow is unstable. If $R < R_{cr}$, c_i is negative, and the flow is stable. For $M = 0$,

$$R_{cr} = \tfrac{5}{2} \cot \beta,$$

which can be compared to Benjamin's (1957)

$$R_{cr} = \tfrac{5}{4} \cot \beta.$$

and Yih's (1963)

$$R_{cr} = \tfrac{5}{6} \cot \beta.$$

The differences have arisen from the choice of the reference velocity. Benjamin chose it to be the surface velocity, Yih[3] chose it to be the average velocity, and in the present paper it has been chosen, for simplicity, to be Kd^2/μ, which for $M = 0$ is exactly twice the surface velocity or three times the average velocity of the primary flow. There is therefore agreement for the case $M = 0$ with existing results.

From (2), (5), (8), and (15) it can be seen that if M (or μ_2) is positive the second viscosity μ_2 stiffens the fluid, and that if M is negative the second viscosity reduces the shear stress and "softens" the fluid. It is therefore reasonable that for small M the critical Reynolds number is increased if M is positive and reduced if M is negative. Thus the second viscosity stabilizes or destabilizes according as it is positive or negative.

ACKNOWLEDGMENTS

The initial stages of this work were jointly sponsored by the National Science Foundation and the Army Research Office (Durham). The final stage was completed in Geneva, Switzerland, during the tenure of a Guggenheim Fellowship. To all three sponsoring organizations the writer wishes to express his appreciation.

J. Fluid Mech. (1967), *vol.* 27, *part* 2, *pp.* 337–352

Instability due to viscosity stratification

By CHIA-SHUN YIH

Department of Engineering Mechanics, University of Michigan, Ann Arbor

(Received 14 December 1965 and in revised form 20 April 1966)

The principal aim of this paper is to show that the variation of viscosity in a fluid can cause instability. Plane Couette–Poiseuille flow of two superposed layers of fluids of different viscosities between two horizontal plates is considered, and it is found that both plane Poiseuille flow and plane Couette flow can be unstable, however small the Reynolds number is. The unstable modes are in the neighbourhood of a hidden neutral mode for the case of a single fluid, which is entirely ignored in the usual theory of hydrodynamic stability, and are brought out by the viscosity stratification.

1. Introduction

In this paper the stability of two superposed fluids of different viscosities in plane Couette and Poiseuille flow is considered. General formulas for calculating the eigenvalues of the complex wave velocity and thus for determining the stability or instability are given. Numerical calculations based on these formulas for plane Couette flow and plane Poiseuille flow for equal densities of the fluids have brought out the rather surprising result that the flow can be unstable at any Reynolds number, however small. Since for a single fluid plane Couette flow is known to be stable for all Reynolds numbers, however large, and plane Poiseuille flow is stable except at large Reynolds numbers, the instability mentioned above can only arise from the viscosity difference. The instability is even more striking if we consider first the plane Couette flow of a single fluid, which is stable. Upon *increasing* the viscosity of a layer of this flow, it becomes unstable.

The instability mentioned can already be inferred from the thesis of Sangster (1964). But his work was limited to an almost vertical flow. Therefore the instability he found is still mainly due to the longitudinal component of gravity. Only the increase of the degree of instability by viscosity variation found by him is pertinent to the present work, in which the body force has no longitudinal component.

2. The primary flow

Since it has been shown by Squire (1933) for channel flow of a uniform fluid between rigid boundaries, and later by Yih (1955) for stratified fluids, that it is sufficient to consider two-dimensional disturbances, we need only to write down the equations governing two-dimensional motion of viscous fluids. From these

22

338   *Chia-Shun Yih*

the primary flow can be readily determined. These equations are the Navier–Stokes equations

$$\frac{Du}{Dt} = -\frac{1}{\rho}\frac{\partial p}{\partial X} + \nu\Delta u, \tag{1}$$

$$\frac{Dv}{Dt} = -\frac{1}{\rho}\frac{\partial p}{\partial Y} - g + \nu\Delta v, \tag{2}$$

in which u and v are the velocity components in the directions of increasing X and Y, as shown in figure 1, t is the time, ρ the density, p the pressure, ν the kinematic viscosity (μ/ρ), Δ the Laplacian in X and Y, and

$$\frac{D}{Dt} = \frac{\partial}{\partial t} + u\frac{\partial}{\partial X} + v\frac{\partial}{\partial Y}.$$

The direction of increasing Y is the direction of the vertical, so that the X-direction is horizontal. This is to avoid having a longitudinal component of gravity, which has been known to be destabilizing (Benjamin 1957; Yih 1954, 1963; Kao 1965), and thus to focus the cause of any instability to be found on the viscosity variation.

The primary flow (figure 1) has only one velocity component $\overline{u}$, which is independent of t and X. (2) states that $\overline{p}+\rho g Y$ is independent of Y, and (1) states that $d\overline{p}/dX$ is independent of X. Hence

$$K = -d\overline{p}/dX, \tag{3}$$

in which K is a constant. (1) then can be written as

$$d^2\overline{u}/dY^2 = -K/\mu, \tag{4}$$

in which μ takes the value μ_1 for the upper fluid and μ_2 for the lower fluid. (4) is to be solved for each fluid, with the boundary conditions that $\overline{u}$ is equal to a specified U_0 on the upper boundary and zero on the lower boundary, and that $\overline{u}$ and the shear stress $\mu\, d\overline{u}/dY$ must be continuous at the interface.

If U_0 is not zero, the dimensionless mean velocities in the two layers are defined to be

$$U_1 = \overline{u}_1/U_0, \quad U_2 = \overline{u}_2/U_0. \tag{5}$$

In terms of the dimensionless co-ordinates

$$x = X/d_1, \quad y = Y/d_1, \tag{6}$$

the mean-velocity distributions are

$$U_1 = A_1 y^2 + a_1 y + b, \tag{7}$$

$$U_2 = A_2 y^2 + a_2 y + b, \tag{8}$$

in which

$$\left.\begin{aligned}
&A_2 = -(\tfrac{1}{2}K/\mu_2 U_0)\,d_1^2, \quad A_1 = mA_2, \\
&a_2 = \{1 + A_2(n^2 - m)\}/(m+n), \quad a_1 = ma_2, \\
&b = \{1 - A_1(1+n)\}\,n/(m+n),
\end{aligned}\right\} \tag{9}$$

with

$$m = \mu_2/\mu_1, \quad n = d_2/d_1. \tag{10}$$

If $\overline{u}(d_1) = 0$, it is convenient to define

$$U_1 = \overline{u}_1/\overline{u}(0), \quad U_2 = \overline{u}_2/\overline{u}(0). \tag{11}$$

The general expressions for U_1 and U_2 can be easily written. Since for $U_0 = 0$ we shall treat only the special case in which $\rho_1 = \rho_2$ and $d_1 = d_2$, these expressions will be given only for the case $n = 1$ and $r = \rho_2/\rho_1 = 1$:

$$U_1 = 1 + a_1 y + b_1 y^2, \tag{12}$$

$$U_2 = 1 + a_2 y + b_2 y^2, \tag{13}$$

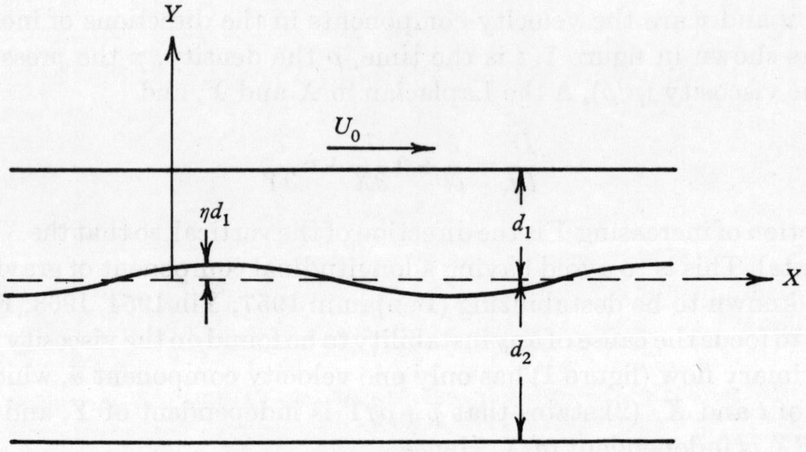

FIGURE 1. Definition sketch.

in which the subscripts 1 and 2 refer to the upper and lower fluids, respectively,

$$\left. \begin{array}{ll} a_1 = \tfrac{1}{2}(m-1), & b_1 = -\tfrac{1}{2}(m+1), \\ a_2 = \tfrac{1}{2}(1-1/m), & b_2 = -\tfrac{1}{2}(1+1/m). \end{array} \right\} \tag{14}$$

The reference velocity is the interfacial velocity, or $\bar{u}$ at $y = 0$. For the case $U_0 = 0$, $n = 1$ and $r = 1$, it is quite immaterial whether m is greater or less than 1. For definiteness we shall assume $m > 1$ in that case.

The velocity gradients at the interface are different for the two fluids if $m \neq 1$. This is what makes the instability considered here possible.

3. The differential system governing stability

It is well known that the differential equation governing stability is the Orr–Sommerfeld equation. In order to derive the normal-stress condition at the interface, one equation occurring in the derivations of the Orr–Sommerfeld equation is needed. For this reason, and for the sake of clarity and completeness, a brief derivation of that equation is included.

Apart from the equations of motion, the equation of continuity

$$\frac{\partial u}{\partial X} + \frac{\partial v}{\partial Y} = 0 \tag{15}$$

must be satisfied. We shall consider the upper layer first. With V denoting U_0 or $\bar{u}(0)$, as the case may be, the substitutions

$$\left. \begin{array}{l} (\hat{u}, \hat{v}) = (u, v)/V, \quad (x, y) = (X, Y)/d_1, \\ \hat{p} = p/\rho_1 V^2 \quad \text{and} \quad \tau = tV/d_1 \end{array} \right\}$$

340   *Chia-Shun Yik*

can be used to put (1), (2) and (15) in the dimensionless forms:

$$\frac{D\hat{u}}{D\tau} = -\frac{\partial \hat{p}}{\partial x} + \frac{1}{R}\Delta\hat{u}, \tag{1a}$$

$$\frac{D\hat{v}}{D\tau} = -\frac{\partial \hat{p}}{\partial y} + \frac{1}{R}\Delta\hat{v}, \tag{2a}$$

and

$$\frac{\partial \hat{u}}{\partial x} + \frac{\partial \hat{v}}{\partial y} = 0, \tag{15a}$$

in which R is the Reynolds number $\rho_1 V d_1/\mu_1$, Δ now stands for the Laplacian

$$\frac{\partial^2}{\partial x^2} + \frac{\partial^2}{\partial y^2},$$

and

$$\frac{D}{D\tau} = \frac{\partial}{\partial \tau} + \hat{u}\frac{\partial}{\partial x} + \hat{v}\frac{\partial}{\partial y}.$$

As usual, the motion is resolved into the primary motion and the perturbation motion. Thus

$$\hat{u} = U_1 + u', \quad \hat{v} = v', \quad \hat{p} = P + p', \tag{16}$$

in which P is the dimensionless pressure for the primary flow. The equation of continuity is now in the form

$$\frac{\partial u'}{\partial x} + \frac{\partial v'}{\partial y} = 0,$$

which permits the use of the stream function ψ, in terms of which

$$u' = \psi_y, \quad v' = -\psi_x, \tag{17}$$

with the subscripts indicating partial differentiation. We shall now assume an exponential time factor for all perturbation quantities, and write

$$(\psi, p') = \{\phi(y), f(y)\}\exp i\alpha(x - c\tau), \tag{18}$$

in which $c = c_r + ic_i$. The stability or instability is then decided by the sign of c_i. If (16), (17), and (18) are substituted into (1a) and (2a), terms pertaining only to the primary flow are cancelled out, and quadratic terms in perturbation quantities are neglected, we have

$$i\alpha\{(U_1 - c)\phi' - U_1'\phi\} = -i\alpha f + R^{-1}(\phi''' - \alpha^2\phi'), \tag{19}$$

$$\alpha^2(c - U_1)\phi = f' + (i\alpha/R)(\phi'' - \alpha^2\phi), \tag{20}$$

in which primes on ϕ and U indicate differentiation with respect to y. Elimination of f from (19) and (20) produces the well-known Orr–Sommerfeld equation

$$\phi^{iv} - 2\alpha^2\phi'' + \alpha^4\phi = i\alpha R\{(U_1 - c)(\phi'' - \alpha^2\phi) - U_1''\phi\}, \tag{21}$$

which, together with the boundary conditions, governs the stability problem.

Equations (19), (20) and (21) are for the upper fluid. For the lower fluid, we choose to retain the substitutions (15) and the meanings of R and f, and to write χ for ϕ. (19) and (20) then become

$$i\alpha r\{(U_2 - c)\chi' - U_2'\chi\} = -i\alpha f + (m/R)(\chi''' - \alpha^2\chi'), \tag{19a}$$

$$\alpha^2 r(c - U_2)\chi = f' + (i\alpha m/R)(\chi'' - \alpha^2\chi), \tag{20a}$$

Instability due to viscosity stratification **341**

and (21) becomes

$$\chi^{\mathrm{iv}} - 2\alpha^2\chi'' + \alpha^4\chi = i\alpha Rm^{-1}r\{(U_2 - c)(\chi'' - \alpha^2\chi) - U_2''\chi\}. \tag{21a}$$

The boundary conditions are

$$\phi(1) = 0, \quad \phi'(1) = 0, \tag{22}$$

$$\chi(-n) = 0, \quad \chi'(-n) = 0 \tag{23}$$

(expressing the condition of no slip at the rigid boundaries) and the interfacial conditions. The latter group consists of the conditions of continuity of velocity and of stresses. The continuity of v' (on which the accent does not indicate differentiation) demands

$$\phi(0) = \chi(0). \tag{24}$$

The continuity of u' must be formulated with more care, because the quantity U' is not continuous across the interface, and because the condition is to be imposed at $y = \eta$ (deviation of interface from its mean position) rather than at $y = 0$. Since

$$\left(\frac{\partial}{\partial\tau} + U\frac{\partial}{\partial x}\right)\eta = v' = -i\alpha\phi(0)\exp i\alpha(x - c\tau),$$

we have

$$\eta = \frac{\phi(0)}{c'}\exp i\alpha(x - c\tau), \quad c' = c - U(0). \tag{25}$$

The continuity in u' then demands

$$\phi'(0) + \frac{\phi(0)}{c'}U_1'(0) = \chi'(0) + \frac{\chi(0)}{c'}U_2'(0),$$

or

$$\phi'(0) - \chi'(0) = \frac{\phi(0)}{c'}(a_2 - a_1). \tag{26}$$

The continuity of shear stress is expressed by

$$\phi''(0) + \alpha^2\phi(0) = m\{\chi''(0) + \alpha^2\chi(0)\}. \tag{27}$$

Note that this boundary condition can be applied right at $y = 0$, for the gradient of shear stress is the same for both layers, so that the displacement of the surface can be ignored as far as the shear-stress condition at the interface is concerned.

The normal-stress condition at the interface is more complicated. The difference of the quantity

$$\rho g d_1 \eta - p'\rho_1 V^2 + \frac{2\mu V}{d_1}\frac{\partial v'}{\partial y} \tag{28}$$

evaluated for the upper fluid and that for the lower fluid must be

$$-\frac{T}{d_1}\frac{\partial^2\eta}{\partial x^2}. \tag{29}$$

In (28), the first term gives the negative of the hydrostatic pressure increment as y varies from zero to η, and the other terms are evaluated at $y = 0$, for either fluid. In (29) T denotes the surface tension. Expressed in dimensionless terms, the normal-stress condition is, upon utilization of (19) to evaluate f and hence p' for either fluid and of (25) to evaluate η,

$$-i\alpha R(c'\phi' + a_1\phi) - (\phi''' - \alpha^2\phi') + 2\alpha^2\phi' + ir\alpha R(c'\chi' + a_2\chi)$$
$$+ m(\chi''' - \alpha^2\chi') - 2\alpha^2 m\chi' = i\alpha R(F^{-2} + \alpha^2 S)\phi/c', \tag{30}$$

342   *Chia-Shun Yih*

in which all variables are evaluated at $y = 0$, and

$$F^2 = \frac{\rho_2 - \rho_1}{\rho_1}\frac{gd_1}{V^2}, \quad S = \frac{T}{\rho_1 d_1 V^2}, \quad c' = c - U(0). \tag{31}$$

(In any comparison of (30) with equation (25) in Yih (1963), the reader has to keep in mind the change of direction of the Y-axis.)

In the special case $\rho_1 = \rho_2$, or $r = 1$, (30) assumes the simpler form

$$m(\chi''' - 3\alpha^2\chi') - (\phi''' - 3\alpha^2\phi') = i\alpha^3 RS\phi/c' \quad \text{at} \quad y = 0. \tag{30a}$$

The differential system governing the stability problem consists of (21), (21a), (22), (23), (24), (26), (27) and (30). It defines an eigenvalue problem in the sense that given m, n, r, F, R and S, c has to take on certain values for the solution not to be identically zero. The flow is unstable, neutrally stable, or stable according as c_i is positive, zero, or negative.

4. Solution for the case of moving upper boundary

In this case $\bar{u} \neq 0$ at $Y = d_1$, and V is U_0. We shall adopt the method used by Yih (1963), which is essentially a method of non-singular perturbation around the case of $\alpha = 0$, which corresponds to very long waves. The quantity αR is assumed to be small compared with 1. Thus, however large R is, there is a small enough range of α for which the perturbation procedure is valid.

In the first approximation, all terms containing α in the differential system are ignored. In the second approximation, all terms containing α^2 and higher orders of α are ignored. Thus for the first approximation (21) and (21a) become

$$\phi_0^{\mathrm{iv}} = 0 \quad \text{and} \quad \chi_0^{\mathrm{iv}} = 0, \tag{32}$$

in which the subscripts zero indicate the first approximation. The boundary conditions (22), (23), (24), and (26) remain as they stand except that the variables all have subscripts zero, whereas (27) and (30) become

$$\phi_0''(0) - m\chi_0''(0) = 0, \tag{27a}$$

and

$$\phi_0'''(0) - m\chi_0'''(0) = 0. \tag{30b}$$

Solution of the differential system just formulated for $\alpha = 0$ gives

$$\left.\begin{aligned}
\phi_0 &= 1 + B_1 y + C_1 y^2 + D_1 y^3, \\
\chi_0 &= 1 + B_2 y + C_2 y^2 + D_2 y^3,
\end{aligned}\right\} \tag{33}$$

in which

$$B_1 = -\frac{m + 3n^2 + 4n^3}{2n^2(1+n)},$$

$$B_2 = \frac{2(m+n^3)}{mn} + \frac{n^2}{m}B_1,$$

$$C_1 = mC_2, \quad C_2 = \frac{m+n^3}{mn^2(1+n)},$$

$$D_1 = mD_2, \quad D_2 = \frac{n^2 - m}{2mn^2(1+n)}.$$

The eigenvalue c_0' is $c_0 - b$, and is determined by (26), which gives

$$c_0' = \frac{a_2 - a_1}{B_1 - B_2} = \frac{2mn^2(1+n)(a_1 - a_2)}{m^2 + 2mn(2 + 3n + 2n^2) + n^4}. \tag{34}$$

When $m = 1$, a_1 is equal to a_2, and $c_0' = 0$. If $\phi_0(0)$ is not zero, the vanishing of c_0' would seem to make η infinite and present a difficulty. Actually if the magnitude of η is taken to be the standard, this situation merely means that when $c_0' = 0$ the velocity perturbations represented by $\phi(y)$ and $\phi'(y)$ are all zero, and only a corrugation remains. This point is intimately related to the difference in character of the unstable modes to be presented in this paper and the unstable modes treated in the usual theory of hydrodynamic stability.

The equations to be solved in the second approximation are

$$\phi_1^{\mathrm{iv}} = i\alpha R\{(U_1 - c_0)\phi_0'' - 2A_1\phi_0\}, \tag{35}$$

and

$$\chi_1^{\mathrm{iv}} = i\alpha R m^{-1} r\{(U_2 - c_0)\chi_0'' - 2A_2\chi_0\}, \tag{36}$$

in which $2A_1$ has been written for U_1'' and $2A_2$ for U_2'', according to (7) and (8). The solution for (35) is

$$\phi_1 = \Delta B_1 y + \Delta C_1 y^2 + \Delta D_1 y^3 + i\alpha R h_1(y), \tag{37}$$

in which

$$h_1(y) = \frac{A_1 D_1}{210} y^7 + \frac{a_1 D_1}{60} y^6 + \frac{a_1 C_1 - 3c_0' D_1 - A_1 B_1}{60} y^5 - \frac{c_0' C_1 + A_1}{12} y^4. \tag{38}$$

The solution of (36) is

$$\chi_1 = \Delta B_2 y + \Delta C_2 y^2 + \Delta D_2 y^3 + i\alpha R m^{-1} r h_2(y), \tag{39}$$

in which

$$h_2(y) = \frac{A_2 D_2}{210} y^7 + \frac{a_2 D_2}{60} y^6 + \frac{a_2 C_2 - 3c_0' D_2 - A_2 B_2}{60} y^5 - \frac{c_0' C_2 + A_2}{12} y^4. \tag{40}$$

In (37), the first three terms constitute the complementary solution necessitated by the last term, which is the particular solution. The term of zero degree in y is taken to be zero in (37). The argument is that the solution of the eigenvalue problem is determined only up to an arbitrary constant factor. We have taken the constant term of ϕ in (33) to be 1. We can and shall keep it at that value once and for all. That this will not deprive us of the possibility of satisfying the boundary conditions will presently be seen. For more detailed arguments, see Yih (1963, p. 326). Then the term of zero degree in y must also be zero in (39), as demanded by (24). The boundary conditions (22), (23), and (27) assume the forms

$$\Delta B_1 + \Delta C_1 + \Delta D_1 + i\alpha R h_1(1) = 0, \tag{22a}$$

$$\Delta B_1 + 2\Delta C_1 + 3\Delta D_1 + i\alpha R h_1'(1) = 0, \tag{22b}$$

$$-\Delta B_2 n + \Delta C_2 n^2 - \Delta D_2 n^3 + i\alpha R m^{-1} r h_2(-n) = 0, \tag{23a}$$

$$\Delta B_2 - 2\Delta C_2 n + 3\Delta D_2 n^2 + i\alpha R m^{-1} r h_2'(-n) = 0, \tag{23b}$$

$$m\Delta C_2 = \Delta C_1. \tag{27b}$$

344   *Chia-Shun Yih*

We are then left with (26) and (30) to contend with. To the present order of approximation, (30) assumes the form

$$m\chi_1''' - \phi_1''' = i\alpha R\{(\phi_0/c_0' F^2) - r(c_0'\chi_0' + a_2\chi_0) + (c_0'\phi_0' + a_1\phi_0)\}, \qquad (30c)$$

to be applied at $y = 0$. But (24) and (26), when applied to the first approximation, were

$$\phi_0'(0) - \chi_0'(0) = \{\phi_0(0)/c_0'\}(a_2 - a_1) \quad \text{and} \quad \phi_0(0) = \chi_0(0).$$

Hence $(30c)$ can be written further as

$$m\chi_1''' - \phi_1''' = i\alpha R\{(\phi_0/c_0' F^2) - (r-1)(c_0'\phi_0' + a_1\phi_0)\}, \qquad (30d)$$

to be applied at $y = 0$. Thus

$$6m\Delta D_2 - 6\Delta D_1 = i\alpha R\{(1/c_0' F^2) - (r-1)(c_0' B_1 + a_1)\}. \qquad (30e)$$

As to (26), its form for the second approximation takes some care, because c' also suffers a perturbation. With this in mind, and remembering that both $\phi_1(0)$ and $\chi_1(0)$ are zero, (26) becomes

$$\phi_1'(0) - \chi_1'(0) = -\{\Delta c\phi_0(0)/c_0'^2\}(a_2 - a_1),$$

in which Δc is the change in c and is of course identical with $\Delta c'$, since $U(0)$ does not change. Hence

$$(\Delta B_1 - \Delta B_2)c_0'^2 = -\Delta c(a_2 - a_1). \qquad (26a)$$

The six Δ-coefficients can be found by solving $(22a,b)$, $(23a,b)$, $(27b)$, and $(30e)$. Then Δc can be found from $(26a)$. The result is

$$\Delta c = ic_i, \quad c_i = \alpha R J(m, n, r, A_1), \qquad (41)$$

in which

$$J = \frac{m^{-1}c_0'^2}{a_1 - a_2}\left\{m(h_1' - 2h_1) - J_2 - \frac{2}{n}H_2 + \frac{m - n^2}{2(1+n)}\left(h_1 - h_1' - \frac{J_2}{n} - \frac{H_2}{n^2}\right)\right\}, \qquad (42)$$

with
$$h_1' = h_1'(1), \quad h_1 = h_1(1)$$

$$H_2 = rh_2(-n) - \tfrac{1}{6}n^3\{(1/c_0' F^2) - (r-1)(c_0' B_1 + a_1)\},$$

$$J_2 = rh_2'(-n) + \tfrac{1}{2}n^2\{(1/c_0' F^2) - (r-1)(c_0' B_1 + a_1)\}.$$

The method of regular perturbation adopted here has greatly reduced the algebraic work which otherwise would be necessary. But it is still desirable to provide an independent check of the correctness of (34), and the final results (41) and (42). For (34), the check is provided by the requirement that $c_0' = c_0 - b$ (b = mean velocity at the interface) must be equal in magnitude and opposite in sign if $r = 1$ and the depths and the viscosities of the layers are interchanged— or if m is replaced by m^{-1} and n by n^{-1}. Equation (34) withstands this test. For (41), the test is that the same interchanges should leave c_i (though not J) unchanged. (41) and (42) withstand this test. The author has checked these equations several times, and Mr Chin-Hsiu Li has checked them independently. They are free from errors. The numerical results obtained by the use of a computer also withstand the tests, indicating that the numerical results are also free from errors.

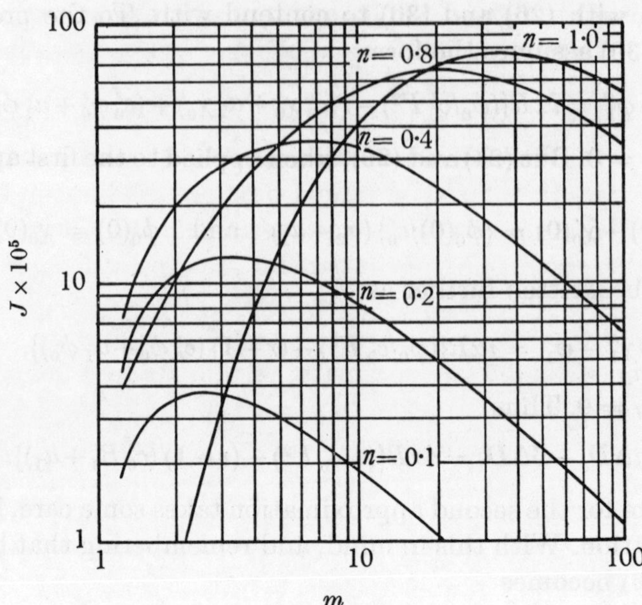

FIGURE 2(a). Variation of J with the viscosity ratio m for various values of the depth ratio $n \leqslant 1$ for plane Couette flow with uniform density, showing instability.

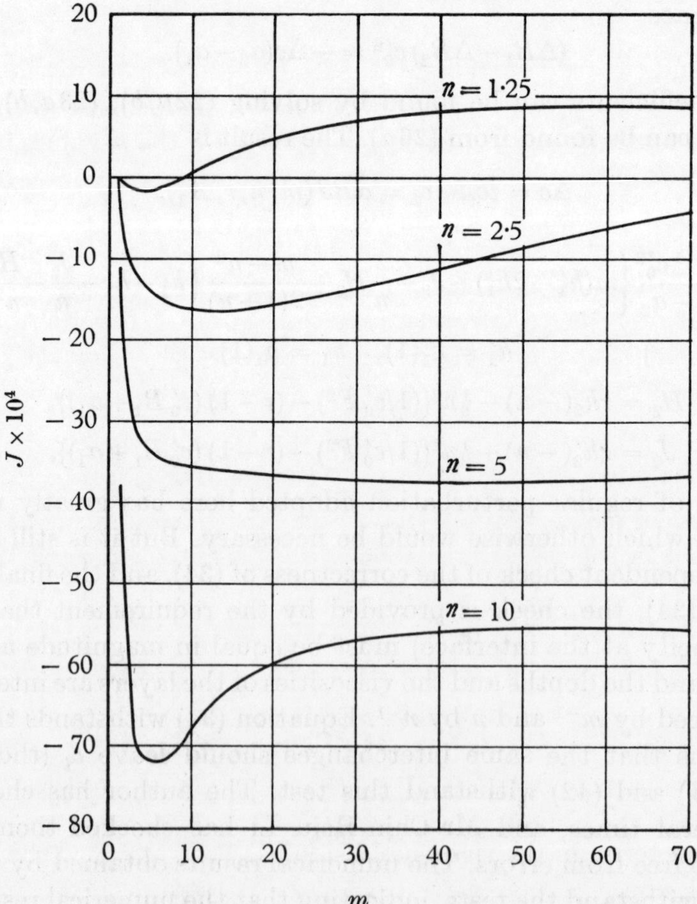

FIGURE 2(b). Variation of J with the viscosity ratio m for various values of the depth ratio $n > 1$ for plane Couette flow with uniform density, showing extensive regions of instability.

From the definition of J given by (42) and for $r = 1$, the writer has verified that J vanishes as $(m-1)^2$ for $n = 1$ and as $m - 1$ for $n \neq 1$, as m approaches 1. This point will be discussed further later.

To see whether the c_i calculated from (41) can be positive, numerical calculations have been carried out for the special case $A_1 = 0$ and $r = 1$. This is plane Couette flow, since there is no longitudinal pressure gradient in the mean flow. Since $r = 1$, there is no density difference, so that gravity has no effect on the phenomenon whatsoever, aside from imparting a hydrostatic part to the pressure. Keeping (41) in mind, one concludes from figure 2(a) that for $n \leqslant 1$ the flow is unstable for all m greater than 1, with the instability greatest, for fixed αR, at some value of m between 2·5 (approximate) for $n = 0·1$ and 35 for $n = 1$.

For $n > 1$ and $m > 1$ the variation of J with m and n is given in figure 2(b). The value of J for $m = 1$ and different values of n is zero although the scale of figure 2(b) does not allow two of the curves to be continued conveniently further to the left. Keeping this in mind, one can see from figure 2(b) that for $n = 1·25$ a region of stability exists between $m = 1$ and $m = 9$ approximately, and that for $n = 2·5$, 5 and 10 the flow is stable up to $m = 70$ at least.

It can be directly verified from (42) that

$$\frac{m}{n^2} J(m, n) = J\left(\frac{1}{m}, \frac{1}{n}\right),$$

which corresponds to the statement that c_i is unchanged if the depths and viscosities of the layers are interchanged. This formula has been verified numerically. With this formula, the values of J for $m < 1$ for the n-values in figure 2(b) can be obtained from the values of J given by the lower four curves in figure 2(a) for $m > 1$, and vice versa.

Whenever the flow is unstable, the instability occurs at all Reynolds numbers, however small, although c_i does approach zero as R approaches zero. The instability is entirely due to viscosity variation. If $r > 1$, the gravity term in H_2 and J_2 will be stabilizing, and the destablizing effect of viscosity variation may be overshadowed.

5. Solution for the case of stationary boundaries

This is the case of plane Poiseuille flow. Since the general formulation has been amply illustrated in the preceding section, we shall further restrict ourselves to the case $r = 1$ and $n = 1$. Thus the two layers are of equal depth and have the same density. The mean velocity in the layers are given by (12) and (13). As mentioned in §2, m can be assumed greater than 1 in the special case considered here.

Following the same approach as in §4, we have

$$\phi_0 = 1 + B_1 y + C_1 y^2 + D_1 y^3, \tag{43}$$

of which the first term on the right-hand side has been assigned the value unity once and for all, and

$$\chi_0 = 1 + B_2 y + C_2 y^2 + D_2 y^3. \tag{44}$$

The first term in (44) has been determined by (24). The other boundary conditions determine the other coefficients to be

$$B_1 = -\tfrac{1}{4}(7+m), \quad B_2 = \tfrac{1}{4}(1+7m)/m, \quad C_1 = \tfrac{1}{2}(1+m),$$
$$C_1 = mC_2, \quad D_1 = \tfrac{1}{4}(1-m), \quad D_1 = mD_2, \tag{45}$$

and the eigenvalue to be

$$c_0 = 1 + 2(m-1)^2/(m^2+14m+1). \tag{46}$$

Before going to the second approximation, we shall pause to consider (46) and see whether the velocity of the primary flow is equal to c_0 at some point in the flow. Such a point has been called the critical point in the literature. It needs special attention if the viscous terms in the Orr–Sommerfeld equation are neglected at large Reynolds numbers to provide two (out of a total of four) asymptotic solutions, or if the diffusive terms in the linearized diffusion equation (if diffusion is part of the problem) are neglected. In the present problem we are not using any asymptotic solutions of the sort that require special treatment of the critical point. Hence the point at which $U = c$ is really not critical except perhaps at $y = 0$, where one boundary condition, (26), involves $c - U(0)$ or $c - 1$. But since n is not equal to 1, (46) shows that c_0 is never equal to 1.

We now proceed to the second approximation, and to solve the equations

$$\phi_1^{iv} = i\alpha R\{(U_1 - c_0)\,\phi_0'' - U_1''\phi_0\},$$

and
$$\chi_1^{iv} = i\alpha Rm^{-1}\{(U_2 - c_0)\,\chi_0'' - U_2''\chi_0\}.$$

The solutions are

$$\phi_1 = \Delta B_1 y + \Delta C_1 y^2 + \Delta D_1 y^3 + i\alpha R h_1(y), \tag{47}$$
$$\chi_1 = \Delta B_2 y + \Delta C_2 y^2 + \Delta D_2 y^3 + i\alpha Rm^{-1}h_2(y), \tag{48}$$

in which the variation of the first term in (44) is zero because of (24), and

$$h_1(y) = \frac{m^2-1}{1680}\,y^7 - \frac{(m-1)^2}{480}\,y^6 + \frac{m^4+18m^3-156m^2-98m-21}{480(m^2+14m+1)}\,y^5$$
$$- \frac{m^3-17m^2-17m+1}{24(m^2+14m+1)}\,y^4, \tag{49}$$

$$h_2(y) = \frac{m^2-1}{1680m^2}\,y^7 - \frac{(m-1)^2}{480m^2}\,y^6 + \frac{21m^4+98m^3+156m^2-18m-1}{480m^2(m^2+14m+1)}\,y^5$$
$$- \frac{m^3-17m^2-17m+1}{24m(m^2+14m+1)}\,y^4. \tag{50}$$

The boundary conditions lead, in a manner similar to that explained in §4, to

$$\Delta c = ic_i, \quad c_i = 8\alpha R H_3, \tag{51}$$

in which

$$H_3 = \left(\frac{1-m}{m^2+14m+1}\right)^2 \left[-\tfrac{1}{2}(m+1)\{h_1(1)+h_2(-1)+h_2'(-1)-h_1'(1)\}\right.$$
$$\left.-\tfrac{1}{4}(m-1)\{h_1(1)-h_1'(1)-h_2(-1)-h_2'(-1)\} - mh_1(1)-h_2(-1)\right]. \tag{52}$$

Equations (46) and (51) must pass the test that if the viscosities are interchanged, that is, if m is replaced by $1/m$, both c_0' ($=c_0-1$) and c_i must remain unchanged. They do pass the test.

 Chia-Shun Yih

The function H_3 is plotted against m in figure 3, in which it can be seen that, for the case of equal depths and equal densities at least, plane Poiseuille flow is always unstable at any Reynolds number, however small. Note that since (52) indicates that H_3 vanishes as $(m-1)^2$ as m approaches zero, the curve in figure 3 dips asymptotically near the axis $m = 1$ as m approaches 1.

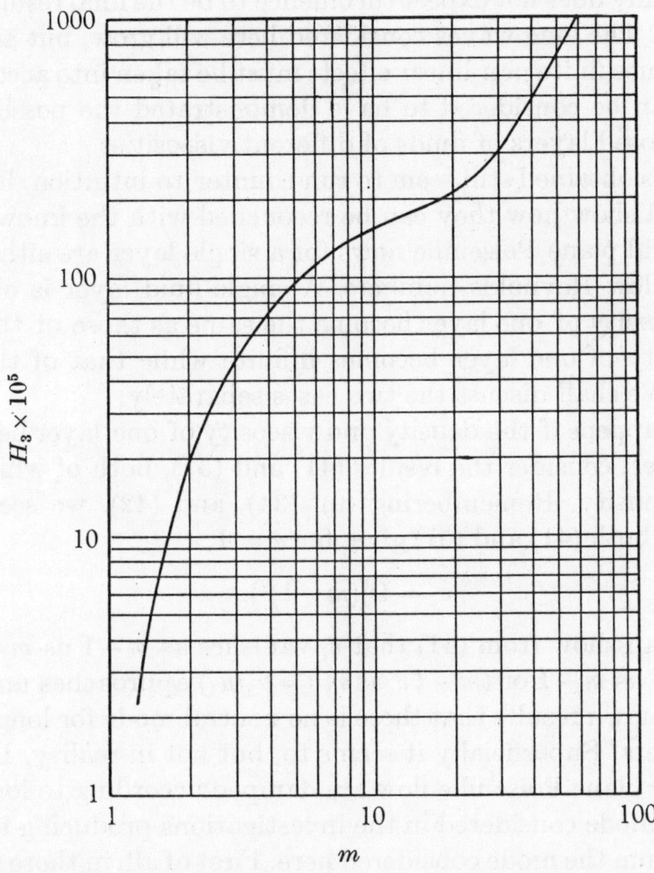

FIGURE 3. Curve showing instability of plane Poiseuille flow, $n = 1 = r$.

6. Discussion

The instability found in this paper can be regarded in two ways. In the first, the fluid is considered to be viscous to start with, and flows which are known to be stable for all Reynolds numbers or unstable only at high Reynolds numbers have been found to be unstable for any Reynolds number whatsoever if the viscosity varies from layer to layer and the depth ratio and the viscosity ratio are within certain ranges. In the second, the fluid can be regarded as inviscid and the velocity profile is assumed to have a discontinuity in slope. The stability of such flows have been studied by Rayleigh (1894, pp. 382–98) who found that the flows are stable when the slope of the velocity profile varies monotonically and unstable otherwise. The analogue of this conclusion when the velocity profile is continuous is well known. In the present work flows (such as plane Couette flow with a broken-line velocity profile) which are stable when the fluid is considered inviscid have been shown to be unstable when the viscosity is considered. From this point of view, the instability found here is due to the existence of viscosity. Of course, to obtain the velocity profiles treated in this work, the viscosity must vary from layer to layer.

What does finally become of the flow when it is unstable and disturbed slightly? Since the instability, when it exists, exists for any Reynolds number however small, one certainly does not expect turbulence to be the final result of instability when R is small. The long waves considered here will grow, but as soon as their amplitude becomes finite non-linear effects must be taken into account. Thus the present work can be considered to have demonstrated the possibility of finite waves in superposed layers of fluids of different viscosities.

But the results obtained still seem to run counter to intuition. To make them credible we shall show how they can be reconciled with the known results that plane Couette and plane Poiseuille flows for a single layer are either stable or at least stable for low Reynolds numbers. A single-fluid layer is obtained if the viscosity and density of one layer become the same as those of the other layer, or if the viscosity of one layer becomes infinite while that of the other layer remains finite. We shall discuss the two cases separately.

To see what happens if the density and viscosity of one layer become equal to those of the other, consider the results (41) and (51), both of which are for the case of equal density. Remembering (9), (34), and (42), we see after a brief calculation that both (41) and (51) give, for $n = 1$,

$$c_i = O\{(m-1)^2\}. \tag{53}$$

For $n \neq 1$ one can show from (41) that c_i vanishes as $m - 1$ as m approaches 1. Thus c_i vanishes as $m - 1$ or $(m-1)^2$ as m $(= \mu_2/\mu_1)$ approaches unity. Does this contradict the known results that there is no neutral mode for long waves at low Reynolds numbers? Superficially it seems to, but not in reality. Long waves in plane Couette or plane Poiseuille flow are damped according to long established results. But the mode considered in the investigations producing those results is quite different from the mode considered here. First of all, in those investigations αc is supposed finite. This already rules out finite c for the very long waves (vanishing α) considered here. For a detailed discussion, see Yih (1963, pp. 330–4). The mode considered in this paper reduces to a neutral mode for long waves as m approaches 1, but it is quite a different mode. Not only is c finite, but $U - c$ is zero at the imaginary interface—imaginary when m actually becomes unity. Since ϕ is not zero at $y = 0$ according to (33) and (43) for any m different from 1, and therefore is not zero in the limiting case of $m = 1$, and since we can take the magnitude of η as the standard magnitude of the perturbation, when $U - c$ vanishes at $y = 0$ in the limiting case of $m = 1$ the only conclusion to be drawn is that when m is equal or nearly equal to unity ϕ is generally an order of magnitude smaller than η, so that the mode is characterized by zero† perturbation in velocity and the existence of only a corrugation of the interface, in the limiting case, or by very small velocity perturbation compared with η, in case m is nearly equal to unity. The mode being discussed here for the limiting case of $m = 1$ is so drastically different from the damped long-wave modes in the usual theory, that

† After demanding that η be finite.

it may serve to dramatize the difference by calling it the 'soft' mode and the corresponding waves 'soft' waves as opposed to the Tollmien–Schlichting waves which may be considered 'hard'. In the neighbourhood of the 'soft' mode for $m = 1$, wherever the imaginary interface is, we have shown that there are unstable modes when m is different from 1. In other words the unstable modes discussed in this paper are not 'near' the damped modes considered in the usual theory, but near the soft modes ignored by it, and are brought out when there is a discontinuity in viscosity.

The arguments advanced here are quite similar to those I gave in an appendix to Benjamin's (1957) paper and again in my own (1963) paper to explain the instability of a liquid layer flowing down a vertical plane at very low Reynolds numbers, which at first also seemed unbelievable. Now it is generally accepted and it is understood that its cause is the longitudinal component of gravity, which supplies the power to the unstable disturbance. What supplies the power to the unstable disturbances treated in this paper is either the moving plate or the pressure gradient. Whether the disturbance can derive power from the mean flow sustained by these sources through the non-linear terms in the Navier–Stokes equations of motion can only be determined from a detailed study of the Orr–Sommerfeld equation and the boundary conditions. And such a study is precisely what has been done here. One can in fact obtain an integral formula from the Orr–Sommerfeld equation and the boundary conditions and interpret the formula from the point of view of energy. When the eigenfunction ϕ found in the solution is substituted in the integrals of that formula, c_i will be what we have given. That means unstable disturbances can be sustained by the available sources of power.

The limiting case of infinite viscosity in either layer will now be discussed. In that case only one layer is flowing, and the flow becomes an ordinary plane Couette–Poiseuille flow. The two special flows treated in numerical detail in this paper then become either an ordinary plane Couette flow (§ 4) or an ordinary plane Poiseuille flow. The former is known to be stable for all Reynolds numbers. The latter, as shown by Heisenberg (1924) and Lin (1945), is certainly stable at low Reynolds numbers. Do the results of these limiting cases contradict the present results? This is a question that is certain to occur in the minds of workers in hydrodynamic stability.

The answer is in the negative. The most important thing to recognize is that a rigid plane boundary is not a proper limit of the interface as μ_1 or μ_2 approaches infinity. If μ_1 (or μ_2) is large, the rate of deformation is very small in the very viscous layer. But given enough time the interface will deform and become wavy. Thus, however large μ_1 or μ_2 is, the interface should not be considered a rigid plane boundary. Thus the apparent contradiction does not really exist.

But it would be reassuring to see what happens to the analysis as μ_1 or μ_2 approaches infinity. It is sufficient to consider the case treated in § 4 ($U_0 \neq 0$) as μ_1 approaches infinity, or as $m \to 0$, because the other limiting cases behave similarly. In this case (9) shows that A_2, a_2, and b are all of order 1 as far as μ_1 or m is concerned. A_1 and a_1 are of the order of m. So is c_0', from (34). From the equations preceding (34) it is evident that B_1, C_1, and D_1 are all of order 1, whereas B_2, C_2, and D_2 are of order m^{-1}. This makes h_2, h_2' of order $1/m$, and hence J of order 1. Hence from (41) c_i is of the order of R, which is of the order of m (or μ_1^{-1}). Thus in the limit not only c_0' but also $\Delta c' = ic_i$ are both zero. Thus even to the second approximation c' is zero. From (25) it can be seen that η is of the order m^{-1} and therefore greater than $\phi(0)$ or v' by an order of magnitude. If the magnitude of η is taken to be the standard, then $\phi(0)$ or $\chi(0)$ should be zero. Why are they not zero in (33)? Remembering that the eigenfunctions of the differential system are determined only up to a multiplicative constant, we see that multiplication of (33) by m would make ϕ_0 equal to zero in the limit and, what is more revealing, would in the limit remove only the constant term from χ_0, since B_2, C_2, and D_2 are of order m^{-1}. This shows that $\chi_0(0)$ is indeed zero in the limit. Higher-order approximations do not change the fact that $\chi(0)$ is zero. Thus the apparent difficulty encountered in (25), (26), and (30) as $c' \to 0$ is resolved for the case $\mu_1 \to \infty$, and similarly for the case $\mu_2 \to 0$. The limiting flow corresponds in fact to the flow with a wavy interface, on which the velocity perturbations u' and v' are exactly zero. It is a case of neutral stability because it is simply the flow in a channel with a wavy wall. And we have demonstrated that in the neighbourhood of this seemingly insignificant case of neutral stability are innumerable cases of instability due to viscosity variation.

Finally, two points will be emphasized. First, the analysis presented here is fully applicable to two fluids of different densities as well as viscosities. Examples have been given for two fluids of equal density and different viscosities only to dramatize the fact that the instability is due to viscosity variation alone, and cannot be attributed to anything else. Secondly, since the fluids have been considered to be non-diffusive in viscosity as well as in density, the criticism might be raised that the instability discovered might be a result of neglecting to treat properly the so-called critical layer when the diffusion equation

$$D\mu/Dt = \kappa\,\Delta\mu$$

is truncated to

$$D\mu/Dt = 0$$

upon the neglect of diffusivity. There is no basis for this criticism. For in the results given here c is never equal to U at the interface, implying that, had the viscosity variation been continuous, the place where c is equal to U_1 or U_2 for the *corresponding* mode would fall outside of the range of viscosity variation. The question of the critical layer therefore does not arise. Note that the question concerning the ordinary critical layer also does not arise since Rayleigh's equation is never used instead of the Orr–Sommerfeld equation. The instability found here simply is unaffected by the non-consideration of the function of the critical layer in the analogous case of continuous viscosity variation. From the physical point of view non-diffusity is not unrealistic since there are many oils which do not mix at all with water, for instance.

This work was started in Geneva, Switzerland, early in 1964, during the tenure of a Guggenheim Fellowship. Subsequently it is jointly sponsored by the National Science Foundation and the Army Research Office (Durham). The author is grateful to Mr Chin-Hsiu Li for computational and drafting assistance.

352   *Chia-Shun Yih*

REFERENCES

BENJAMIN, T. B. 1957 Wave formation in laminar flow down an inclined plane. *J. Fluid Mech.* **2**, 554.

HEISENBERG, W. 1924 Über stabilität und Turbulenz von Flüssigkeiteströmen. *Ann. Phys. Lpz.* (4), **74**, 577–627

KAO, T. W. 1965 Stability of two-layer viscous stratified flow down an inclined plane. *Phys. Fluids* **8**, 812.

LIN, C. C. 1945 On the stability of two-dimensional parallel flows. Parts I, II, III. *Quart. Appl. Math.* **3**, 117–142, 218–234, 277–301.

LORD RAYLEIGH 1894 *Theory of Sound*, 2nd ed. London: MacMillan.

SANGSTER, W. M. 1964 The stability of stratified flows on nearly vertical slopes. Dissertation, State University of Iowa.

SQUIRE, H. B. 1933 On the stability for three-dimensional disturbances of viscous fluid flow between parallel walls. *Proc. Roy. Soc.* A **142**, 621.

YIH, C.-S. 1954 Stability of parallel laminar flow with a free surface. *Proc. 2nd U.S. Congr. of Appl. Mech.*, p. 623.

YIH, C.-S. 1955 Stability of two-dimensional parallel flows for three-dimensional disturbances. *Quart. Appl. Math.* **12**, 434.

YIH, C.-S. 1963 Stability of liquid flow down an inclined plane. *Phys. Fluids*, **6**, 321.

J. Fluid Mech. (1967), *vol.* 28, *part* 3, *pp.* 493–500

Instability of laminar flows due to a film of adsorption

By CHIA-SHUN YIH

Department of Engineering Mechanics,
The University of Michigan, Ann Arbor, Michigan

(Received 20 May 1966 and in revised form 1 September 1966)

When a horizontal layer of viscous liquid with an adsorption film of varying concentration as its upper boundary is set in motion by a steady translation of its lower boundary, plane Couette flow with zero surface velocity is possible. In this paper the stability of this flow is considered, and it is found that the liquid layer can be unstable for long waves. The instability found for this flow, however, exists also for other laminar flows with an adsorbed film, and plane Couette flow has been chosen only as a simple means of demonstration.

1. Introduction

When surface-active material is present in an adsorbed film at the surface of a liquid, the surface tension of the liquid may change from place to place, giving rise to non-zero shear stresses at the surface. If the surface concentration of the adsorbed material is denoted by γ, the surface diffusivity by D, and the time by t, the equation of continuity for the adsorbed material is (Levich 1962, p. 393)

$$\partial\gamma/\partial t + \mathbf{div}\,(\gamma\mathbf{v} - D\,\mathbf{grad}\,\gamma) + j_n = 0, \tag{1}$$

in which $\mathbf{v}$ is the velocity of the fluid at the surface, j_n is the flux of the material from the surface to the interior of the liquid, per unit time and per unit area, and the divergence applies to the surface only. The normal flux j_n is usually assumed negligible compared with the other terms. We shall make the same assumption here and shall furthermore assume D to be constant. Thus the preceding equation will be written as

$$\partial\gamma/\partial t + \mathbf{div}\,(\gamma\mathbf{v}) = D\Delta\gamma, \tag{2}$$

Δ being the Laplacian operator.

Landau & Lifshitz (1959, pp. 242-3) presented a solution for a flow in a deep channel joining two reservoirs and driven by surface shear arising from the non-homogeneity of γ on the surface. Instead of (2) they presented its non-diffusive form

$$\partial\gamma/\partial t + \mathbf{div}\,(\gamma\mathbf{v}) = 0; \tag{2a}$$

but the solution given does not satisfy $(2a)$ or (2) and is therefore not valid. Landau & Lifshitz attributed the solution to Levich, and gave reference to the Moscow edition (1952) of the latter's book *Physicochemical Hydrodynamics*. The only edition of that book at the present writer's disposal is the second edition in its English version (Levich 1962). When the writer searched the second edition he could not find the solution Landau & Lifshitz referred to. It is not clear whether

494   *Chia-Shun Yih*

Levich realized his solution was wrong and therefore withdrew it in the second edition of his book, or he merely suppressed it for other reasons. At any rate any interested reader can demonstrate to his own satisfaction that the solution quoted by Landau & Lifshitz is incorrect. It turns out that if one insists on giving a valid solution of Levich's original problem one must take into consideration the longitudinal variation of velocity and the surface height. If one still wants to have a simple and truly one-dimensional solution, one must consider a different problem, in which the free surface must be stationary, in order that (2) can be satisfied. Since in a one-dimensional flow the surface must be flat, and since on that flat surface the pressure must be constant, the flow can either be a horizontal plane Couette flow with the lower boundary moving, or a plane Poiseuille-Couette flow, with the lower boundary inclined to the horizontal but not necessarily moving.

For simplicity we consider the former flow in this paper, and investigate its stability. It will be seen that this flow can be unstable for long waves. The motion of the lower boundary does make the flow rather special, and this speciality is of course not attractive. But the instability to be demonstrated no doubt exists also for more natural free-surface flows with an adsorbed film, such as (*a*) flow of a liquid layer down an inclined plane, or (*b*) the nearly parallel flow of a liquid layer on a horizontal bottom, with a nearly parabolic velocity distribution in each section due to a longitudinal pressure gradient which is in turn due to the slope of the free surface induced by the motion of the surface film. We wish to demonstrate the kind of instability which can occur for flows with an adsorbed film, and have chosen plane Couette flow merely as a simple vehicle for demonstration.

2. Primary flow

Consider a unidirectional steady flow in the X-direction of a layer of viscous liquid of depth d. The velocity, denoted by $\bar{u}$, is a function of Y only. The lower boundary moves with a constant speed V (see figure 1). We shall consider only the case $\bar{u}(0) = 0$. Since the flow is unsteady, the solution of (2) is, with $\bar{\gamma}$ denoting the γ for the primary flow,

$$\bar{\gamma} = \gamma_0 + \gamma_1 X, \tag{3}$$

in which γ_0 is the value of $\bar{\gamma}$ at the origin, and

$$\gamma_1 = [\bar{\gamma}(L) - \bar{\gamma}(-L)]/2L. \tag{4}$$

The length of the channel is $2L$ and supposed to be very large compared with d. The reservoir with greater concentration of the adsorbed material is situated at $X = L$, and the other reservoir at $x = -L$. Note that, if $\bar{u}(0)$ is not zero, (3) is not a solution of (2). This is the reason for demanding zero velocity at the surface.

If the surface tension is denoted by T, the shear stress on the surface, where $Y = 0$, is, for the co-ordinates chosen in agreement with an earlier work (Yih 1963),

$$\tau_{21} = -\partial T/\partial X = \delta\,\partial\bar{\gamma}/\partial X = \delta\gamma_1, \tag{5}$$

in which $-\delta = \partial T/\partial \gamma \tag{6}$

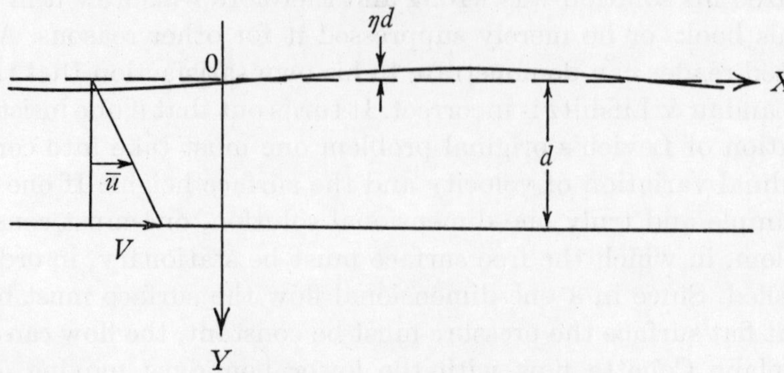

FIGURE 1. Definition sketch.

is supposed to be constant. It is obvious that the flow due to a moving lower boundary in the presence of a stationary upper surface at constant pressure must be a plane Couette flow described by

$$U = y, \tag{7}$$

in which

$$U = \bar{u}/V, \quad y = Y/d. \tag{8}$$

However (5) must be satisfied. Hence, with μ denoting the viscosity,

$$\mu \, d\bar{u}/d\gamma = \gamma_1 \delta. \tag{9}$$

This implies

$$\delta \gamma_1 d/\mu V = 1. \tag{10}$$

Equations (3) and (7), with the restriction (10), describe the plane Couette flow under consideration. The pressure gradient is of course zero, so that, if $\bar{p}$ denotes the pressure of the primary flow,

$$\partial \bar{p}/\partial X = 0. \tag{11}$$

3. General formulation of the stability problem

We consider, as usual, only two-dimensional disturbances. With u and v denoting the velocity components in the directions of increasing X and Y, respectively, and with p indicating the pressure, the Navier–Stokes equations are

$$\frac{\partial u}{\partial t} + u \frac{\partial u}{\partial X} + v \frac{\partial u}{\partial Y} = -\frac{1}{\rho} \frac{\partial p}{\partial X} + \nu \Delta u, \tag{12}$$

$$\frac{\partial v}{\partial t} + u \frac{\partial v}{\partial X} + v \frac{\partial v}{\partial Y} = -\frac{1}{\rho} \frac{\partial p}{\partial Y} + g + \nu \Delta v, \tag{13}$$

in which ν is the kinematic viscosity. The co-ordinates X and Y are defined in figure 1. The equation of continuity is

$$\partial u/\partial X + \partial v/\partial Y = 0. \tag{14}$$

The substitutions

$$(u_1, v_1) = (u, v)/V, \quad (x, y) = (X, Y)/d,$$
$$p_1 = p/\rho V^2 \quad \text{and} \quad \tau = tV/d, \tag{15}$$

Chia-Shun Yih

can be used to reduce (12), (13) and (14) to their dimensionless forms:

$$\frac{\partial u_1}{\partial \tau} + u_1 \frac{\partial u_1}{\partial x} + v_1 \frac{\partial u_1}{\partial y} = -\frac{\partial p_1}{\partial x} + \frac{1}{R}\Delta u_1, \tag{16}$$

$$\frac{\partial v_1}{\partial \tau} + u_1 \frac{\partial v_1}{\partial x} + v_1 \frac{\partial v_1}{\partial y} = -\frac{\partial p_1}{\partial y} + F^{-2} + \frac{1}{R}\Delta v_1, \tag{17}$$

$$\frac{\partial u_1}{\partial x} + \frac{\partial v_1}{\partial y} = 0, \tag{18}$$

in which Δ is now in terms of x and y, and

$$R = Vd/\nu \quad \text{and} \quad F = V(gd)^{-\frac{1}{2}} \tag{19}$$

are the Reynolds number and Froude number, respectively.

Let
$$u_1 = U + u', \quad v_1 = v', \quad \text{and} \quad p = P + p', \tag{20}$$

in which U is the dimensionless velocity of the primary flow given by (7), P is the dimensionless pressure of the primary flow, and the accented quantities are perturbation quantities of magnitude very much smaller than unity. Substituting (20) into (16), (17) and (18), subtracting out the terms representing the primary flow only and neglecting quadratic terms in the perturbation quantities, we have

$$u'_\tau + Uu'_x + U_y v' = -p'_x + R^{-1}\Delta u', \tag{21}$$

$$v'_\tau + Uv'_x = -p_y + R^{-1}\Delta v', \tag{22}$$

$$u'_x + v'_y = 0, \tag{23}$$

with subscripts denoting partial differentiation. Equation (23) permits the use of a stream function ψ, in terms of which

$$u' = \psi_y, \quad v' = -\psi_x. \tag{24}$$

Equations (21) and (22) can be written as

$$\psi_{y\tau} + U\psi_{xy} - U_y\psi_x = -p'_x + R^{-1}\Delta\psi_y, \tag{25}$$

$$\psi_{x\tau} + U\psi_{xx} = p'_y + R^{-1}\Delta\psi_x. \tag{26}$$

The boundary conditions at the bottom are

$$\text{(i)} \quad u' = \psi_y = 0 \quad \text{and} \quad \text{(ii)} \quad v' = -\psi_x = 0.$$

Before we can formulate the boundary conditions at the free surface an equation governing the perturbation in γ is needed. With

$$\gamma = \overline{\gamma} + \gamma_0 \gamma', \tag{27}$$

in which γ' is the dimensionless perturbation quantity in γ, the linearized and dimensionless form of (1) is

$$\frac{\partial \gamma'}{\partial \tau} + \frac{u'\gamma_1 d}{\gamma_0} + \frac{\overline{\gamma}}{\gamma_0}\frac{\partial u'}{\partial x} = \frac{1}{P\acute{e}}\Delta\gamma', \tag{28}$$

in which $$P\acute{e} = Vd/D, \qquad (29)$$

and Δ is in terms of x and y. In obtaining (28), it is understood that the curvilinear distance along the free surface can be identified with x, since the amplitude of the waves under consideration is supposed small. Equation (28) can be written as

$$\gamma'_\tau + \frac{\gamma_1 d}{\gamma_0}\,\psi_y + \frac{\bar{\gamma}}{\gamma_0}\,\psi_{xy} = \frac{1}{P\acute{e}}\Delta\gamma'. \qquad (28a)$$

The boundary condition *at the free surface* regarding the shear stress is then

$$\mu\left(\frac{\partial u}{\partial Y} + \frac{\partial v}{\partial X}\right) = \delta\gamma_1 + \delta\gamma_0\frac{\partial\gamma'}{\partial X},$$

or, in dimensionless terms,

$$\frac{\partial u_1}{\partial y} + \frac{\partial v_1}{\partial x} = \frac{d\delta\gamma_1}{\mu V} + \frac{\delta\gamma_0}{\mu V}\gamma'_x. \qquad (30)$$

Since (30) is, *a priori*, to be applied at the free surface rather than at $y = 0$, its final form is, after (20), (5), (10) and (24) have been utilized,

$$\text{(iii)} \qquad \frac{d^2U}{dy^2}\,\eta + \psi_{yy} - \psi_{xx} = \frac{\gamma_0}{\gamma_1 d}\gamma'_x,$$

in which η is the dimensionless displacement of the free surface, as shown in figure 1. Equation (30) can now be applied at $y = 0$. Of course, for plane Couette flow, the first term is zero, and it would not have made any difference if (30) had been applied at $y = 0$ to start with.

The normal-stress condition at the free surface is

$$\left(-p_1 + \frac{2}{R}\frac{\partial v_1}{\partial y}\right)\rho V^2 + T\frac{\partial^2(\eta d)}{\partial X^2} = 0,$$

or $$-p_1 + \frac{2}{R}\frac{\partial v_1}{\partial y} + S\frac{\partial^2\eta}{\partial x^2} = 0, \qquad S = \frac{T}{\rho d V^2}.$$

Since this has to be applied at the free surface, and not merely at $y = 0$, it can be written further in the form

$$-P - P_y\eta - p' - 2R^{-1}\psi_{xy} + S\eta_{xx} = 0.$$

Now $P(0) = 0$ and $P_y(0) = F^{-2}$, so that the normal-stress condition can be written as

$$\text{(iv)} \qquad F^{-2}\eta + p' + 2R^{-1}\psi_{xy} - S\eta_{xx} = 0.$$

The conditions (iii) and (iv) all involve η. To determine η in terms of ψ, we use the kinematic condition

$$-\psi_x = v' = \eta_\tau. \qquad (31)$$

We now consider a spatially growing or damping disturbance of (dimensionless) angular frequency ω, and assume

$$(\psi, p', \gamma') = [\phi(y), f(y), \chi(y)]\exp i\left[\int\alpha\,dx - \omega\tau\right], \qquad (32)$$

in which α is a function of x. The reason for not assuming α to be independent of x is that the surface tension is not constant, and therefore the diffusion equation of the surface material and one free-surface boundary condition have x-dependent coefficients. We shall retain the x-dependence of these coefficients, and shall consider the instability of the disturbance when α and ω are both small. Since

$$\alpha = \alpha_r + i\alpha_i,$$

the flow is unstable or stable according as α_i is positive or negative, provided the waves propagate upstream† (toward decreasing values of x). Equation (31) then assumes the form

$$\eta = \frac{\alpha\phi(0)}{\omega}\exp i\left[\int \alpha\,dx - \omega\tau\right]. \tag{33}$$

The equations of motion become

$$i(\alpha U - \omega)\phi' - i\alpha U'\phi = -i\alpha f + R^{-1}(\phi''' - \alpha^2\phi'), \tag{34}$$

$$\alpha(\omega - \alpha U)\phi = f' + i\alpha R^{-1}(\phi'' - \alpha^2\phi), \tag{35}$$

and $(28a)$ becomes

$$-i\omega\chi + \frac{\gamma_1 d}{\gamma_0}\phi' + \frac{i\alpha\overline{\gamma}}{\gamma_0}\phi' = -\frac{\alpha^2}{P\acute{e}}\chi, \tag{36}$$

in which $\overline{\gamma}$ is not constant but a linear function of x. In (34), (35) and (36), the primes denote differentiation with respect to y. Elimination of f between (34) and (35) produces the Orr–Sommerfeld equation

$$\phi^{\mathrm{iv}} - 2\alpha^2\phi'' + \alpha^4\phi = iR[(\alpha U - \omega)(\phi'' - \alpha^2\phi) - \alpha U''\phi]. \tag{37}$$

We shall now write the boundary conditions in terms of ϕ and χ. These are

(i) $\phi'(1) = 0,$

(ii) $\phi(1) = 0,$

(iii) $\phi''(0) + \alpha^2\phi(0) = (i\alpha\gamma_0/\gamma_1 d)\chi(0),$

(iv) $[\alpha^2(RF^{-2} + \alpha^2 SR)/\omega]\phi(0) + \alpha RU'(0)\phi(0) + (R\omega + 3\alpha^2 i)\phi'(0) - i\phi'''(0) = 0.$

In obtaining the final form of (iv), p' has been evaluated from (32), with f given by (34), and with $U(0) = 0$.

The formulation is now complete. We should note that, since T is not constant for all x, nor is S. Since S is associated with α^3 in (iv), we can, to the stage of approximation achieved in this paper, ignore it, and write the last boundary condition as

(iv) $R[\alpha/F^2\omega + U'(0)]\phi(0) + (R\omega + 3a^2 i)\phi'(0) - i\phi'''(0) = 0.$

The x-dependence of S, however, should be retained in higher-order approximations.

† As will be shown, the waves treated in this paper propagate upstream. In case the waves propagate downstream, the flow is unstable if α_i is negative, and stable if α_i is positive.

4. Solution of the stability problem for plane Couette flow

In solving the differential system governing stability formulated in the last section, we shall adopt the procedure in Yih (1963). Since $U'' = 0$ in the present case, the first approximation is governed by the equations

$$\phi_0^{\mathrm{iv}} = 0, \tag{37a}$$

$$-i\omega\chi_0 + (\gamma_1 d/\gamma_0)\,\phi_0' = 0, \tag{36a}$$

and the boundary conditions

(i) $\phi_0'(1) = 0$, (ii) $\phi_0(1) = 0$,

(iii) $\phi_0''(0) = (i\alpha_0\gamma_0/\gamma_1 d)\,\chi_0(0)$, (iv) $\phi_0'''(0) = 0$.

Note that $\alpha\chi$ or $\omega\chi$ is of the same order as ϕ and its derivatives, and hence must be kept in (36 a) and (iii). Combining these two equations, we have

$$\phi_0''(0) = \omega^{-1}\alpha_0\,\phi_0'(0). \tag{38}$$

The solution of (37 a), with conditions (i), (ii), (iv) and (38), is straightforward and is

$$\phi_0 = (1-y)^2, \quad \alpha_0 = -\omega. \tag{39}$$

Thus the waves propagate in the negative x-direction with dimensionless speed 1, or dimensional speed V.

The next approximation involves the equation

$$\phi_1^{\mathrm{iv}} = -i2\omega R(1+y), \tag{40}$$

whose solution is†

$$\phi_1 = -i2\omega R(\tfrac{1}{24}y^4 + \tfrac{1}{120}y^5) + \Delta By + \Delta Cy^2 + \Delta Dy^3.$$

Two of the boundary conditions for ϕ_1 are

(i) $\phi_1'(1) = 0$, (ii) $\phi_1(1) = 0$.

Condition (iv) now has the form

(iv) $-\omega R(3 - F^{-2}) - i\phi_1'''(0) = 0$.

As to the equation corresponding to (38), (36) and the original form of (iii) at this stage give it the form

$$\phi_1'' + \phi_1' = 2\left(\frac{\Delta\alpha}{\alpha_0} - \frac{i\omega}{P\acute{e}} - \frac{i\omega\overline{\gamma}}{\gamma_1 d}\right). \tag{41}$$

Thus

$$\Delta B + \Delta C + \Delta D = \tfrac{1}{10}i\omega R, \quad \Delta B + 2\Delta C + 3\Delta D = \tfrac{1}{12}i5\omega R, \quad 6\Delta D = i\omega R(3 - F^{-2}),$$

$$\Delta B + 2\Delta C = 2\left(\frac{\Delta\alpha}{\alpha_0} - \frac{i\omega}{P\acute{e}} - \frac{i\omega\overline{\gamma}}{\gamma_1 d}\right),$$

from which (since $\alpha_0 = -\omega$)

$$\Delta\alpha = i\omega^2 R\left(\frac{13}{24} - \frac{1}{RP\acute{e}} - \frac{1}{4F^2} - \frac{\overline{\gamma}}{\gamma_1 dR}\right). \tag{42}$$

† See Yih (1963) for the reason for not providing a term ΔA.

500 *Chia-Shun Yih*

By utilizing (10) one can interpret (42) in the following dimensional terms: if

$$\frac{gd}{4}+\frac{D\nu}{d^2}+\frac{\delta\overline{\gamma}}{\rho d} < \frac{13}{24}\left(\frac{\delta\gamma_1 d}{\mu}\right)^2,\tag{43}$$

the flow is unstable. This criterion is x-dependent. The surface-active agent is placed at $x = L$, and therefore $\overline{\gamma}$ increases with x. Thus, if the flow is neutral for one value of x, it is unstable for all algebraically smaller values of x, and the degree of instability increases as x decreases.

For higher approximations ΔB, ΔC, and ΔD must be evaluated. These are functions of x.

In (43), the first term represents the stabilizing effect of gravity, and the second the stabilizing effect of the diffusivity of the material and of viscosity. The third, having its origin in the third term in (36) and eventually in the third term in (28a), represents the stabilizing effect of the *stretching* of the film. The right-hand side of (43) represents the destabilizing effect of the gradient of surface tension. It is equal to $13V^2/24$, in which V is the necessary bottom velocity to make the surface velocity of the primary flow equal to zero, and thus to make truly parallel flow possible. We may also consider it to represent the destabilizing effect of inertia, since it has its origin in the inertial terms on the right-hand side of (40). But these inertial terms in turn owe their origin to the primary flow, which is intimately related to the surface-tension gradient.

Finally, we may wonder whether the inequality (43) for instability is ever satisfied in a realistic situation. It is not unrealistic to consider a layer of water of depth 0.02 ft. flowing from one reservoir to another 1 ft. away, where the surface contamination reduces the surface tension to one half of its value without such contamination. The surface tension of water at 70 °F is 0.005 lb./ft. Thus $\delta\overline{\gamma}$ (δ assumed constant) has one half of that value at the surface of the contaminated reservoir. The quantity $\delta\gamma_1 \times 1$ ft. also has the value 0.0025 lb./ft. Since $\rho = 1.94$ slug/ft.^{3}, $g = 32.2$ ft./sec^2, $\nu = 1.05 \times 10^{-5}$ ft.^{2}/sec, $\mu = 2.04 \times 10^{-5}$ lb.-sec/ft.^{2}, and D can be assumed to be of the same order as ν and will be assumed equal to 10ν on the safe side, we have, in units of ft.^{2}/sec^2,

$$\tfrac{1}{4}gd = 0.160, \quad D\nu/d^2 = 2.75 \times 10^{-6},$$
$$\delta\overline{\gamma}/\rho d = 0.013, \quad \tfrac{13}{24}(\delta\gamma_1 d/\mu)^2 = \tfrac{13}{4}.$$

Thus (43) is definitely satisfied. It is also evident that, of the three stabilizing effects, that due to gravity is the most important.

This work has been jointly supported by the Army Research Office (Durham) and the National Science Foundation. The writer wishes to thank the referees for their criticisms of the first version of this paper, which have led to its improvement.

REFERENCES

LANDAU, L. D. & LIFSHITZ, E. M. 1959 *Fluid Mechanics*. Oxford: Pergamon Press.

LEVICH, V. G. 1962 *Physicochemical Hydrodynamics*. New York: Prentice-Hall.

YIH, C.-S. 1963 Stability of liquid flow down an inclined plane. *Physics of Fluids* 6, 321–34.

Reprinted from

THE PHYSICS OF FLUIDS VOLUME 11, NUMBER 7 JULY 1968

Stability of a Horizontal Fluid Interface in a Periodic Vertical Electric Field

CHIA-SHUN YIH

Department of Engineering Mechanics, The University of Michigan, Ann Arbor, Michigan
(Received 4 January 1968)

The stability of the interface in the presence of a periodic electric field is considered. It is shown that the stability is governed by a Mathieu equation, that the interface can be unstable even if the electric field is at all times weaker than that needed for instability in the case of a steady field, and that, when instability occurs, the waves may either be synchronous with the electric field, or have twice its frequency.

I. INTRODUCTION

The stability of a horizontal fluid interface between a conducting and a nonconducting fluid in a steady vertical electric field was treated by Taylor and McEwan.[1] In their paper the forces arising from the electric field, from gravity, and from surface tension are balanced at the interface, and a stability criterion is found from this balance. Although the hydrodynamics of the conducting fluid was not considered in the paper by Taylor and McEwan, identical results are obtained if it is taken into consideration.

In this paper the instability of the interface in a vertical electric field varying periodically with time is considered. Because of the time dependence of the electric field, the simple equation of force balance can no longer be utilized to obtain the stability criterion, and the hydrodynamics of the fluid or fluids must be taken into account. When this is done, and the viscous effects are negligible, the stability of the interface can be shown to be governed by a Mathieu equation whose coefficients depends on the gravitational acceleration, the surface tension, the magnitude and frequency of the periodic electric field, the depth (or depths), and the geometry of the container.

II. THE EQUILIBRIUM STATE

Suppose that the upper fluid which can be a gas or a liquid, is nonconductive and the lower fluid, which is invariably a liquid, is conductive of electricity. The depth of the upper fluid is denoted by h_1 and that of the lower fluid by h_2. (See Fig. 1) The upper fluid, which is bounded above by an electrode with potential V_1 and below by the interface, has depth h_1, and the lower fluid, bounded below by an electrode with potential

$$V_2 = V_0 \cos \omega t, \tag{1}$$

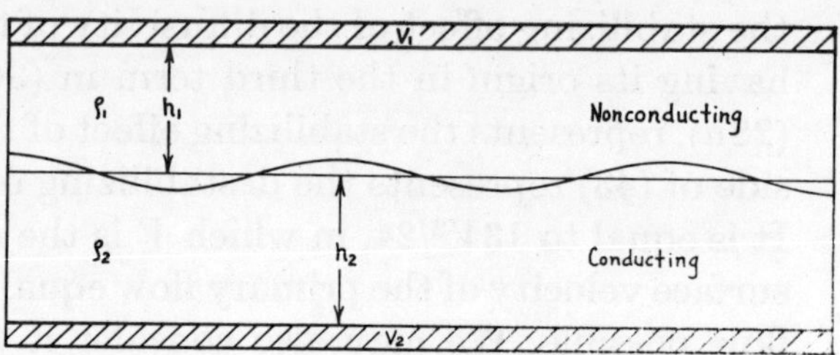

FIG. 1. Definition sketch.

has depth h_2. In Eq. (1) t is the time and ω the circular frequency of V_2. (Note that the usage of V_0 in this paper is different from that in the paper by Taylor and McEwan.) We will assume that the Reynolds number based on either the depth or the wavelength of the disturbance to be large for either fluid, so that viscous effects are negligible.

If the densities of the upper and lower fluids are denoted by ρ_1 and ρ_2, respectively, and the gravitational acceleration by g, the hydrostatic pressure distributions in the two fluids are given by

$$p_1 = p_0 - g\rho_1 z,$$
$$p_2 = p_0 - \frac{K}{8\pi}\left(\frac{V_1 - V_2}{h_1}\right)^2 - g\rho_2 z, \tag{2}$$

if z is measured vertically from the interface, and K is the dielectric constant of the nonconducting fluid. The pressure in the upper fluid at the interface is denoted by p_0. It can be assigned any arbitrary value without affecting anything, since both fluids can be considered incompressible. Note that the pressure p_2 at the interface (or just below it) is not p_0 but p_0 reduced by the electric part of the Maxwell stress normal to the interface.

The electric potential V is simply V_2 in the conducting fluid, so that the electric field in that fluid is zero. In the nonconducting fluid

$$V = V_2 + \frac{V_1 - V_2}{h_1} z, \tag{3}$$

[1] G. I. Taylor and A. D. McEwan, J. Fluid Mech. 22, 1 (1965).

so that the field in that fluid is

$$E_1 = \frac{V_1 - V_2}{h_1}.\qquad (4)$$

We assume that the horizontal dimensions of the container are much larger than $h_1 + h_2$, so that surface tension effects are negligible over the main part of the interface.

III. FORMULATION OF THE STABILITY PROBLEM

Suppose that the interface of the two fluids is slightly displaced, so that at any time it is described by the equation

$$z = \zeta = a(t)f(x, y),\qquad (5)$$

in which f satisfies the equation

$$\left(\frac{\partial^2}{\partial x^2} + \frac{\partial^2}{\partial y^2} + k^2\right)f = 0,$$

k^2 being an eigenvalue which makes $\partial f/\partial n = 0$ (n is the normal distance) at the wall of the cylindrical container and is thus dependent on geometry alone. The electric field and potential in the lower fluid are still given by

$$E_2 = 0 \quad \text{and} \quad V_2 = V_0 \cos \omega t.\qquad (6)$$

But the electric potential of the upper fluid, which must satisfy the Laplace equation and the boundary conditions (if we now specify $V_1 = -V_2$)

$$V = V_1 = -V_2 \quad \text{at} \quad z = h_1$$

and

$$V = V_2 \quad \text{at} \quad z = \zeta,\qquad (7)$$

is given by

$$V = V_2\left[1 - \frac{2z}{h_1} - \frac{2 \sinh k(z - h_1)}{h_1 \sinh kh_1} a(t)f(x, y)\right].\qquad (8)$$

The normal component of the electric stress (tensile) at the interface is, with K indicating the dielectric constant,

$$\frac{K}{8\pi}\left\{\left(\frac{\partial V}{\partial x}\right)^2 + \left(\frac{\partial V}{\partial y}\right)^2 + \left(\frac{\partial V}{\partial z}\right)^2\right\},\qquad (9)$$

since $z = f$ is a surface of constant potential V_2 (although it varies with time). This stress component is

$$\sigma_{en} = \frac{K}{2\pi}\frac{V_2^2}{h_1^2}[1 + 2k \coth (kh_1)a(t)f],\qquad (10)$$

if terms quadratic in $a(t)$ are neglected. The subscript e indicates that σ_e is an electric stress, and the subscript n indicates the normal component.

Now turning to the hydrodynamics of the fluids, we note that since the lower fluid has no electric

field or magnetic field, its motion is governed by the ordinary hydrodynamic equations. If we assume that the Reynolds number (based on any representative length) is large, the fluid may be treated as inviscid, and if the motion is assumed to have begun from rest it is irrotational. Hence the potential ϕ_2 for the motion of the lower fluid is

$$\phi_2 = A_2(t) \cosh k(z + h_2)f(x, y) + G_2(t),\qquad (11)$$

which satisfies the boundary conditions

$$\frac{\partial \phi_2}{\partial n} = 0 \quad \text{at the wall}, \qquad \frac{\partial \phi_2}{\partial z} = 0 \quad \text{at} \quad z = -h_2.$$

Similarly, the upper fluid, which is free of electric charges, has a constant K, and therefore possesses a velocity potential

$$\phi_1 = A_1(t) \cosh k(z - h_1)f(x, y) + G_1(t),\qquad (12)$$

which satisfied

$$\frac{\partial \phi_1}{\partial n} = 0 \quad \text{at the wall and} \quad \frac{\partial \phi_1}{\partial z} = 0 \quad \text{at} \quad z = h_1.$$

We are left to deal with the interfacial conditions. There are two such conditions, one kinematic, and the other dynamic. The kinematic condition is

$$\frac{\partial \phi_1}{\partial z} = \frac{\partial \phi_2}{\partial z} = \frac{da(t)}{dt} f(x, y) \quad \text{at} \quad z = 0,\qquad (13)$$

and the dynamic condition is

$$p_2 - p_1 + \frac{K}{8\pi}|E|^2$$
$$= -Ta(t)\left(\frac{\partial^2}{\partial x^2} + \frac{\partial^2}{\partial y^2}\right)f = k^2 Ta(t)f,\qquad (14)$$

T being the surface tension and p the pressure. Equations (13) give

$$-A_1(t)k \sinh kh_1 = \frac{da(t)}{dt} = A_2(t)k \sinh kh_2.\qquad (15)$$

In order to utilize (14), it is necessary to use the Bernoulli equations

$$\rho_1\left(\frac{\partial \phi_1}{\partial t} + \tfrac{1}{2}q_1^2\right) + p_1 - \rho_1 gz = F_1(t),\qquad (16)$$

$$\rho_2\left(\frac{\partial \phi_2}{\partial t} + \tfrac{1}{2}q_2^2\right) + p_2 - \rho_2 gz = F_2(t),\qquad (17)$$

in which q is the speed. Since an arbitrary function of time has been added to ϕ_1 and to ϕ_2, we can take $F_1(t)$ and $F_2(t)$ to be zero. Neglecting q^2, we have

$$p_2 - p_1 = gz(\rho_2 - \rho_1) + \rho_1 \frac{\partial \phi_1}{\partial t} - \rho_2 \frac{\partial \phi_2}{\partial t}.\qquad (18)$$

Putting Eqs. (18), (11), and (12) into Eq. (14), and

setting z equal to ζ in (18) and evaluating ϕ_1 and ϕ_2 in Eq. (18) by Eqs. (11) and (12), putting the result into Eq. (14), and using the σ_{en} in (10) for the electric term in (14), we have, besides

$$\frac{K}{2\pi}\frac{V_2^2}{h_1^2} = \rho_2 G_2'(t) - \rho_1 G_1'(t), \qquad (19)$$

$$\left[\frac{K}{\pi}\frac{V_2^2}{h_1^2}k\coth kh_1 - k^2 T - g(\rho_2 - \rho_1)\right]a(t) - k^{-1}$$

$$\cdot(\rho_2 \coth kh_2 + \rho_1 \coth kh_1)\frac{d^2 a(t)}{dt^2} = 0, \qquad (20)$$

or

$$\frac{d^2 a}{dt^2} + (\omega_0^2 - \beta - \beta \cos 2\omega t)a = 0, \qquad (21)$$

in which

$$\omega_0^2 = \frac{k^3 T - gk(\rho_2 - \rho_1)}{\rho_2 \coth kh_2 + \rho_1 \coth kh_1}, \qquad (22)$$

$$\beta = \frac{KV_0^2 k^2 \coth kh_1}{2\pi h_1^2(\rho_2 \coth kh_2 + \rho_1 \coth kh_1)}. \qquad (23)$$

Equation (21) can be put in the canonical form of the Mathieu equation

$$\frac{d^2 a}{d\tau^2} + (p - 2q \cos 2\tau)a = 0, \qquad (24)$$

in which p and q are not the pressure and the speed, if we put

$$\tau = \omega t, \qquad p = \frac{\omega_0^2 - \beta}{\omega^2}, \qquad q = \frac{\beta}{2\omega^2}.$$

The stability diagram for (24) is standard, and for completeness is shown in Fig. 2. It is seen that even if β is very small there may be regions of instability. Since V_2^2 has a basic frequency of 2ω, not ω, the various regions correspond to double frequency and synchronism of the hydrodynamic oscillations in relation to V_2, instead of synchronism and half-

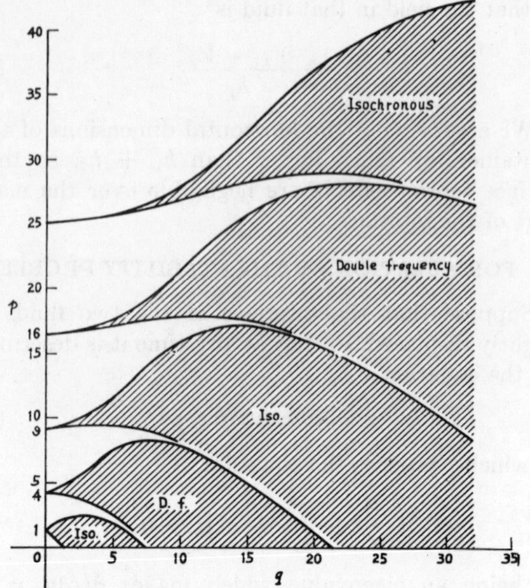

FIG. 2. The stability diagram for Mathieu's equation.

frequency, respectively. In conclusion we note that if V_1 is zero instead of $-V_2$, the V_0 in (23) should be replaced by $V_0/2$. The instability found here is akin to the one found by Benjamin and Ursell[2] for the free surface of a liquid in vertical periodic motion.

ACKNOWLEDGMENTS

This paper is a direct result of the stimulation of a public lecture given by Sir Geoffrey Taylor on October 4, 1967, which was an event in the Sesquicentennial Celebrations of The University of Michigan.

The work has been jointly sponsored by the National Science Foundation and the Army Research Office (Durham).

[2] T. B. Benjamin and F. Ursell, Proc. Roy. Soc. (London) A225, 505 (1954).

J. Fluid Mech. (1968), *vol.* 31, *part* 4, *pp.* 737–751

Instability of unsteady flows or configurations
Part 1. Instability of a horizontal liquid layer on an oscillating plane

By CHIA-SHUN YIH

Department of Engineering Mechanics, The University of Michigan

(Received 2 October 1967)

A layer of viscous liquid with a free surface is set in motion by the lower boundary moving simple-harmonically in its own plane. The stability of this motion is investigated. Since the primary flow is time-dependent, the time variable cannot be separated from at least one space variable, and a new approach must be used to investigate the problem. In this paper the stability of long waves is studied by a perturbation method which has not been applied before to problems of stability of unsteady flows, and it is found that the flow under consideration can be unstable for long waves.

1. Introduction

It is well known that problems of stability of unsteady flows are troublesome because their time-dependence precludes the use of the exponential time-factor for the perturbation quantities. Criteria for stability in integral form are not difficult to obtain. But these criteria are not very helpful because they involve the unknown eigenfunctions. One can of course follow the method of Orr (1907), obtain a formula expressing the Reynolds number R as the ratio involving integrals containing eigenfunctions as integrands, and determine a lower bound for the critical Reynolds number by minimizing R, allowing all disturbances for the integrands, whether dynamically possible or not, provided only that they satisfy the equation of continuity and the boundary conditions. The non-linearity of the equations of motion is allowed to stand. How far these lower bounds fall short of the mark can be judged by what Orr (1907) obtained for plane Couette flow and plane Poiseuille flow, for both of which he obtained 89. This has also been obtained by Conrad & Criminale (1965), who gave 88·88 for the former and 88·91 for the latter flow. Recently Joseph (1966) showed that Orr's lower bound is wrong for plane Couette flow at least, and gave the even lower number 41·3 as the new reliable lower bound. But it is known that plane Couette flow is stable for all Reynolds numbers and plane Poiseuille flow is stable if an identically defined Reynolds number is below 5250. However, the lower bounds are good for finite disturbances, and even for infinitesimal disturbances such estimates are often useful at least in a transient period, before more significant information is obtained.

                          Chia-Shun Yih

Conrad & Criminale (1965) also attempted to generalize Squire's (1933) result for three-dimensional disturbances to apply to unsteady flows. But, as they themselves indicated, the time transformation does not allow the generalization to be a useful one. In fact the stability or instability of a three-dimensional disturbance in a given unsteady two-dimensional flow can be determined by the stability or instability of a two-dimensional disturbance in *another* unsteady two-dimensional flow, which differs from the original one not merely in the Reynolds number, as in the case of steady primary flows, but also in the distribution of the velocity of the primary flow, and which will be different for a different three-dimensional disturbance.

Conrad & Criminale (1965) also attempted to obtain a Rayleigh theorem for time-dependent flows. They assumed the eigenfunction v to have the form

$$v(y, \tau) = \sum_{n=1}^{N} \theta_n(\tau)\, \phi_n(y),$$

in which τ is a time and y a spatial co-ordinate, obtained a second-order differential equation for each of ϕ_n, and from it obtained the desired theorem. The conclusion, however, cannot be reached from the equation for *each* ϕ_n, and must be arrived at by considering the *sum* they assumed. Hence the theorem has not been proved for unsteady flows.

Much of existing work on the stability of unsteady flows is based on the assumption of quasi-steadiness, that is, on the assumption that the stability of an unsteady flow is determined by whether or not it is stable for all the (varying) velocity distributions if each of these distributions is assumed to persist. The most recent study of hydrodynamic stability based on the assumption of quasi-steadiness is that of Currie (1967), in whose paper many other references can be found. It is concerned with the onset of Bénard cells when the primary temperature distribution is time-dependent. If the frequency ω_* of the primary flow (or temperature) is much less than a reference velocity V divided by a reference length d, it can be shown that the approach of quasi-steadiness can predict stability or instability over time intervals small compared with the period $T = 2\pi/\omega_*$. If it predicts instability, the slow variation of the primary flow with time may not materially affect the conclusion. But many flows predicted to be stable by the approach of quasi-steadiness may well turn out to be unstable in the long run. We know at least one instance illustrating the erroneousness of the ordinary approach of quasi-steadiness. Benjamin & Ursell (1954) showed that when a cylinder containing inviscid liquid with a free surface is shaken up and down with a simple-harmonic acceleration of amplitude a_0, the fluid can be unstable even if a_0 is very much less than the gravitational acceleration g, whereas an analysis based on quasi-steadiness predicts stability in that case. This paper presents another illustration, which is believed to be the first one for the instability of a viscous fluid. The method used can be applied to many other problems concerning hydrodynamic stability of time-dependent flows or configurations.

We consider here the stability of a primary flow which is completely unsteady, in the sense that it contains no steady part whatsoever. The approach of quasi-

Instability of unsteady flows. Part 1   739

steadiness is discarded, and we seek to investigate the instability of the flow in the long run. The particular flow under investigation is described in the next section.

2. Primary flow

A horizontal layer of liquid of depth d, viscosity μ, and density ρ is set in motion by the lower boundary moving in the X-direction (figure 1) with velocity

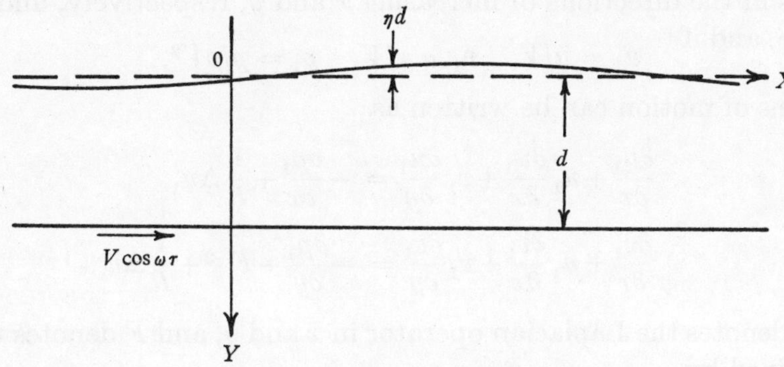

FIGURE 1. Definition sketch

$V \cos \omega_* t$, ω_* being the frequency, t the time, and V the amplitude of the forcing motion. We shall introduce the dimensionless independent variables

$$\tau = Vt/d, \quad x = X/d, \quad y = Y/d. \tag{1}$$

In terms of these, the equation governing the primary flow is

$$\frac{\partial U}{\partial \tau} = \frac{1}{R}\frac{\partial^2 U}{\partial y^2}, \tag{2}$$

in which $\quad U = \bar{u}(y,\tau)/V, \quad R = Vd/\nu = \text{the Reynolds number}, \tag{3}$

$\bar{u}$ being the velocity of the primary flow and ν the kinematic viscosity. The boundary conditions for U are

$$\partial U/\partial y = 0 \quad \text{at} \quad y = 0, \tag{4}$$

and $\quad U = \cos\omega_* t = \cos\omega\tau \quad \text{at} \quad y = 1, \quad \text{with} \quad \omega = \omega_* d/V. \tag{5}$

The solution of (2), (4) and (5) is

$$U = A[W + W^* - i\tanh\beta\tan\beta(W - W^*)], \tag{6}$$

with the asterisk as a superscript indicating complex conjugate, and

$$W = \cosh[\beta(1+i)y]e^{i\omega\tau}, \quad A = \frac{\cos\beta\cosh\beta}{2(\cos^2\beta + \sinh^2\beta)}, \quad \beta = \left(\frac{\omega R}{2}\right)^{\frac{1}{2}}.$$

The U given by (6) is real, as is obvious by inspection. It is written in that form in order to facilitate the integration to be performed later.

The pressure $\bar{p}$ for the primary flow is hydrostatic, and is zero at $y = 0$. Hence

$$\bar{p} = g\rho Y = g\rho dy. \tag{7}$$

740   *Chia-Shun Yih*

3. Formulation of the stability problem

Although Squire's theorem cannot be generalized in a useful way to justify the consideration of two-dimensional disturbances only, it is still true that the stability of a three-dimensional disturbance can be determined from that of a two-dimensional one for a different flow. Hence the method of solution for two-dimensional disturbances will apply to three-dimensional ones. We shall consider only two-dimensional disturbances in this paper. If u and v denote the velocity components in the directions of increasing x and y, respectively, and p denotes the pressure, and if

$$u_1 = u/V, \quad v_1 = v/V, \quad p_1 = p/\rho V^2,$$

the equations of motion can be written as

$$\frac{\partial u_1}{\partial \tau} + u_1 \frac{\partial u_1}{\partial x} + v_1 \frac{\partial u_1}{\partial y} = -\frac{\partial p_1}{\partial x} + \frac{1}{R}\Delta u_1, \tag{8}$$

$$\frac{\partial v_1}{\partial \tau} + u_1 \frac{\partial v_1}{\partial x} + v_1 \frac{\partial v_1}{\partial y} = -\frac{\partial p_1}{\partial y} + F^{-2} + \frac{1}{R}\Delta v_1, \tag{9}$$

in which Δ denotes the Laplacian operator in x and y, and F denotes the Froude number defined by

$$F = V(gd)^{-\frac{1}{2}}. \tag{10}$$

The equation of continuity is

$$\frac{\partial u_1}{\partial x} + \frac{\partial v_1}{\partial y} = 0. \tag{11}$$

Resolving each of the dependent variables into a primary part and a perturbation part, we have

$$u_1 = U + u', \quad v_1 = v', \quad p_1 = P + p', \tag{12}$$

in which P is $\bar{p}/\rho V^2$, and the accented quantities are the perturbation quantities. If (12) is substituted into (8) and (9), the terms pertaining to the primary flow only, being in balance, are subtracted out, and quadratic terms in the perturbation quantities are neglected, the resulting equations are

$$u'_\tau + U u'_x + U_y v' = -p'_x + \frac{1}{R}\Delta u', \tag{13}$$

$$v'_\tau + U v'_x = -p_y + \frac{1}{R}\Delta v', \tag{14}$$

with the subscripts indicating partial differentiation. Equation (11) can be replaced by

$$\frac{\partial u'}{\partial x} + \frac{\partial v'}{\partial y} = 0,$$

which permits us to use a streamfunction ψ and to write

$$u' = \psi_y, \quad v' = -\psi_x. \tag{15}$$

With (15), the equations of motion can be written as

$$\psi_{y\tau} + U \psi_{xy} - U_y \psi_x = -p'_x + \frac{1}{R}\Delta \psi_y, \tag{16}$$

$$\psi_{x\tau} + U \psi_{xx} = p'_y + \frac{1}{R}\Delta \psi_x. \tag{17}$$

Since U depends on τ as well as y, (16) and (17) do not permit the use of the exponential time-factor. However, as far as x is concerned, we can still consider any disturbance to be a Fourier integral of disturbances simply periodic in x, and (16) and (17) allow us to write

$$\psi = \phi(y,\tau)\,e^{i\alpha x}, \quad p' = f(y,\tau)\,e^{i\alpha x}, \tag{18}$$

and (16) and (17) as

$$\phi_{y\tau} + i\alpha U\phi_y - i\alpha U_y\phi = -i\alpha f + \frac{1}{R}\,(\phi_{yyy} - \alpha^2\phi_y), \tag{19}$$

$$i\alpha\phi_\tau - \alpha^2 U\phi = f_y + \frac{i\alpha}{R}\,(\phi_{yy} - \alpha^2\phi). \tag{20}$$

Elimination of f from (19) and (20) produces

$$R\left[\left(\frac{\partial}{\partial\tau} + i\alpha U\right)\phi'' - \alpha^2\phi) - i\alpha U_{yy}\phi\right] = \phi'''' - 2\alpha^2\phi'' + \alpha^4\phi, \tag{21}$$

in which the primes on ϕ indicate differentiations with respect to y.

The boundary conditions at the bottom are the non-slip conditions

$$\text{(i)} \quad \phi(1,\tau) = 0, \quad \text{(ii)} \quad \phi'(1,\tau) = 0. \tag{22}$$

The boundary conditions at the free surface are that both the shear stress and the normal stress there must be zero. Since the shear stress of the primary flow and $\bar{p}$ both vary with y, and the free surface will not be flat, the free-surface boundary conditions must include contributions from the primary flow as a result of the vertical displacement of the free surface. If this displacement is denoted by ηd, the relationship between η and ψ is provided by the kinematic condition

$$\left[\frac{\partial}{\partial\tau} + U(0,\tau)\frac{\partial}{\partial x}\right]\eta = v' = -\psi_x. \tag{23}$$

With
$$\eta = h(\tau)\,e^{i\alpha x},$$

(23) becomes
$$\left[\frac{d}{d\tau} + i\alpha U(0,\tau)\right]h = -i\alpha\phi(0,\tau). \tag{24}$$

The condition of zero shear at the free surface is
$$U_{yy}(0,\tau)\eta + \psi_{yy} - \psi_{xx} = 0,$$

or (iii)
$$U_{yy}(0,\tau)h + \phi''(0,\tau) + \alpha^2\phi(0,\tau) = 0. \tag{25}$$

The condition that the normal stress vanish at the free surface is, in its primitive form,

$$\left(-p_1 + \frac{2}{R}\frac{\partial v_1}{\partial y}\right)\rho V^2 + T\frac{\partial^2(\eta d)}{\partial X^2} = 0, \tag{26}$$

in which T is the surface tension. Since, by (7),

$$P = \frac{gd}{V^2}\,y = F^{-2}y,$$

(26) can be written as

$$-F^{-2}\eta - p' - \frac{2}{R}\psi_{xy} + S\eta_{xx} = 0, \tag{27}$$

in which
$$S = T/\rho d V^2.$$

                                   Chia-Shun Yih

Using (19) to evaluate f and then (18) to evaluate p', and substituting the result into (27), we have (remembering $U_y = 0$ at $y = 0$)

$$i\alpha(F^{-2} + S\alpha^2)\eta + \frac{1}{R}(\psi_{yyy} - 3\alpha^2\psi_y) - \psi_{y\tau} - i\alpha U\psi_y = 0,$$

or (iv) $$i\alpha(F^{-2} + S\alpha^2)h + \frac{1}{R}(\phi''' - 3\alpha^2\phi') - \phi'_\tau - i\alpha U\phi' = 0, \tag{28}$$

to be applied at $y = 0$.

The differential system governing stability consists of (21), (22), (24), (25) and (28).

4. A discussion of the approach of quasi-steadiness

Since the approach of quasi-steadiness is so often used, a discussion of its usefulness and its limitations is desirable. Consider the Orr–Sommerfeld equation (21), to be solved with linear homogeneous boundary conditions. The U in (21) is assumed to be a function of y with at least some of its coefficients containing $\cos \omega\tau$ or $\sin \omega\tau$. For clarity we shall denote $\omega\tau$ by τ'. The following expansion is assumed for ϕ:

$$\phi = e^{\sigma\tau}\{\phi_0(y, \tau') + \omega\phi_1(y, \tau') + \omega^2\phi_2(y, \tau') + \ldots\}, \tag{29}$$

with $$\sigma = \sigma_0 + \omega\sigma_1 + \omega^2\sigma_2 + \ldots. \tag{30}$$

Expansions (29) and (30) are then substituted into (21) and the boundary conditions, and terms of equal power in ω are sorted out. The first two equations so obtained are

$$L\phi_0 \equiv \phi_0'''' - 2\alpha^2\phi_0'' + \alpha^4\phi_0 = R[(\sigma_0 + i\alpha U)(\phi_0'' - \alpha^2\phi_0) - i\alpha U''\phi_0] = 0, \tag{31}$$

$$L\phi_1 = R\sigma_1(\phi_0'' - \alpha^2\phi_0) + R\frac{\partial}{\partial\tau'}(\phi_0'' - \alpha^2\phi_0), \tag{32}$$

and the other equations are similar in form. In the same way the boundary conditions can be expressed in terms of ϕ_0, ϕ_1, etc. In (31) and (32) all accents mean differentiation with respect to y. It is immediately evident that the differential system (though we have not written out the boundary conditions explicitly) governing ϕ_0 is just that used if the approach of quasi-steadiness is used. Note that σ_0 and ϕ_0 are determined with the τ' in U and U'' serving only as a parameter. Hence σ_0 is a function of τ' and ϕ_0 contains τ'. After σ_0 and ϕ_0 are determined, (32) and the pertinent boundary conditions will determine σ_1 and ϕ_1. It is very important in this connexion to observe that: (*a*) the *homogeneous parts* of the differential equations (31), (32), etc., are identical in form; (*b*) the homogeneous parts of the boundary conditions in successive stages of determination are also identical in form; (*c*) and therefore σ_0 can be considered once for all the eigenvalue pertaining to the operator L and the linear operators in the homogeneous parts of the boundary conditions. It is the item (*c*) that allows us to determine σ_1, σ_2, etc. Otherwise since (32) and the boundary conditions for ϕ_1 are non-homogeneous any σ_1 would do.

Presumably the expansions (29) and (30) are convergent for any finite ω. If ω is very small, the quasi-steadiness approach gives good results. For an ω not very small, more terms in (31) and (32) may have to be taken. Obviously if

ω is very much greater than 1 the quasi-steadiness approach cannot be relied upon to give good results.

In any practical application of the approach just outlined, the success would depend on the ease with which the particular solution of (32) for ϕ_2 is obtained. We see at once that, U being dependent on y, the task of solving for (31) is already in general rather difficult, let alone the task of finding particular solutions for (32) and the subsequent equations. However, for long waves (31) and (32) can be solved by a power expansion in α, and, provided the boundary conditions allow a determination of σ_0 which does not correspond to rapidly damped disturbances, solutions indicating long-term instability are quite readily obtainable. In fact, if a free surface or an interface exists, the boundary conditions are such that such solutions are indeed obtainable. This paper illustrates in detail how the stability of an unsteady flow with a free surface can be studied by an expansion in α. It turns out that the expansion in ω is then unnecessary.

5. Extension of the Floquet theorem

Before we present the solution to the problem formulated in §3, we shall present an extension of the famous Floquet theorem to the realm of partial differential equations. Since this extension must have wide applications to mathematical physics, we shall consider a more general equation than the Orr–Sommerfeld equation, and general linear boundary conditions. What we seek to establish is the

Theorem. Given the differential equation

$$\frac{\partial}{\partial \tau} \sum_{i=0}^{m-1} f_i(y)\, D^i\phi = D^m\phi + \sum_{i=0}^{m-1} g_i(y,\tau)\, D^i\phi \tag{33}$$

in the domain $\qquad\qquad 0 \leqslant y \leqslant 1, \quad 0 \leqslant t < \infty,$

in which $f_i(y)$ and $g_i(y,\tau)$ can be expanded into a power series in y in the domain, $g_i(y,\tau)$ is periodic in τ with period T, and $D^i\phi$ is the i-th derivative of ϕ with respect to y, and given the boundary conditions

$$\frac{\partial}{\partial \tau} \sum_{i=0}^{m-1} h_{ji} D^i\phi + \sum_{i=0}^{m-1} k_{ji} D^i\phi = 0 \quad \text{at} \quad y = 0, \tag{34}$$

$$\frac{\partial}{\partial \tau} \sum_{i=0}^{m-1} p_{ji} D^i\phi + \sum_{i=0}^{m-1} q_{ji} D^i\phi = 0 \quad \text{at} \quad y = 1, \tag{35}$$

the independent solutions can be written in the form

$$e^{\mu_1 \tau}\chi(y,\tau), \tag{36}$$

in which $\chi(y,\tau)$ is either a periodic function of τ with period T or can involve polynomials in τ as well as periodic functions in τ with period T. The h and p in (34) and (35) are constants, the k and q can be periodic functions of τ with period T.

The demonstration will be sketched out briefly here. The function ϕ can be expanded in the form

$$\phi = \phi_0(\tau) + \phi_1(\tau)y + \phi_2(\tau)y^2 + \dots + \phi_{n-1}(\tau)y^{n-1} + \dots. \tag{37}$$

If (37) is substituted into (33), (34) and (35), and equal powers in y are collected

744   *Chia-Shun Yih*

in the case of (33), and if we stop at the term $\phi_{n-1}(\tau)\,y^{n-1}$, we have a total of n first-order ordinary differential equations in τ, involving n unknowns

$$\phi_i \quad (i = 0, \ldots, n-1).$$

These can be reduced to one n-th order differential equation with the single unknown ϕ_k, say. Then Floquet's theorem (Ince 1944, p. 381; or Coddington & Levinson 1955, pp. 78–81) states that ϕ_k is of the form

$$e^{\mu_1\tau}P(\tau), \tag{38}$$

in which $P(\tau)$ is periodic with period T, if the characteristic root μ_1 is simple, or of the form
$$e^{\mu_1\tau}P(\tau) \times \text{a polynomial in } \tau, \tag{39}$$

if μ_1 is a multiple root of a secular equation. Now all the other ϕ_i $(i \neq k)$ can be expressed as a linear form of $D^i\phi_k\,(i = 0, \ldots, n-2)$, by an elimination procedure applied to the n first-order equations. Hence the factor $e^{\mu_1\tau}$ is in all the ϕ_i. If μ_1 is simple, $\phi_0, \phi_1, \ldots,$ and ϕ_{n-1} are all of the form (38). Otherwise they are of the form (39), with the same μ_1. Thus the theorem is true up to n-terms. As the number of terms taken in (37) is increased, more and more characteristic roots appear, corresponding to more and more modes. Presumably the series (37) will converge to the solution wanted, and there will be a discretely infinite number of modes. Aside from the question of convergence, which the author must leave to more capable minds, the theorem is established.

The theorem can also be established in the original manner of Floquet, if we assume that there exist a complete set of discretely infinite number of solutions

$$\phi_1(y, \tau), \quad \phi_2(y, r), \ldots.$$

Since $\phi_i(y, \tau+T)$ is obviously also a solution, we have

$$\phi_i(y, \tau+T) = \sum_{j=1}^{\infty} a_{ij}\phi_j(y, \tau). \tag{40}$$

We seek a solution $w_i(y, \tau)$ such that

$$w_i(y, \tau+T) = sw_i(y, \tau). \tag{41}$$

Now since the set $\phi_i(y, \tau)$ is complete,

$$w_i(y, \tau) = \sum_{j=1}^{\infty} b_{ij}\phi_j(y, \tau). \tag{42}$$

Substituting (40) and (42) into (41), and demanding that not all the b's be zero, we have

$$\begin{vmatrix} a_{11}-s & a_{12} & a_{13} & \cdots \\ a_{21} & a_{22}-s & a_{23} & \cdots \\ a_{31} & a_{32} & a_{33}-s & \cdots \\ \cdots & \cdots & \cdots & \cdots \\ \cdots & \cdots & \cdots & \cdots \end{vmatrix} = 0. \tag{43}$$

If μ_1 is a simple root of (43), then writing

$$s = e^{\mu_1 T},$$

(41) can be written as $\qquad \dfrac{w_1(y, \tau+T)}{e^{\mu_1(\tau+T)}} = \dfrac{w_1(y, \tau)}{e^{\mu_1\tau}},$

Instability of unsteady flows. Part 1 **745**

which is to say that
$$w_1(y,\tau)\,e^{-\mu_1\tau}$$
is periodic. Hence the form (36) follows. The case of multiple roots has been discussed in the preceding paragraph, and we shall not dwell upon the subject any longer, except to say that the convergence of any particular root of (43) to a definite value as the the number of rows (and columns) is increased has been left unproven. The arguments advanced in this section would be complete if the convergence of (37) had been established. But in their present form they are so highly plausible that we need have no doubt of the truth of the theorem.

6. Solution of the problem

We shall now apply the results of §5 to the solution of the problem. Assuming μ_1 to be a simple root of (43), we shall write
$$\phi(\tau,y) = e^{\mu_1\tau}\chi(\tau,y),$$
$$h(\tau) = e^{\mu_1\tau}H(\tau),$$
in which $\chi(\tau,y)$ and $H(\tau,y)$ are periodic in τ.

Since we expect to find instability for long waves, or small wave numbers, we shall follow the approach used in Yih (1963) and write
$$\left.\begin{aligned}
\chi(\tau,y) &= \phi_0(y,\tau)+\alpha\phi_1(y,\tau)+\alpha^2\phi_2(y,\tau)+\dots,\\
H(\tau) &= h_0(\tau)+\alpha h_1(\tau)+\alpha^2 h_2(\tau)+\dots,\\
\mu_1 &= \theta_0+\alpha\theta_1+\alpha^2\theta_2+\dots,
\end{aligned}\right\} \tag{44}$$
in which the ϕ's and h's are all periodic in τ, and the θ's are *real* constants. Collecting terms of equal powers in α in equations (21) and (24), we obtain a series of equations in y and τ. The first of the series constituting (24) is
$$\frac{\partial h_0}{\partial\tau}+\theta_0 h_0 = 0.$$
Since h_0 must be periodic in τ, it follows immediately that†
$$\theta_0 = 0,$$
and without loss of generality
$$h_0 = 1. \tag{45}$$
Then for the first approximation the differential system is
$$R\frac{\partial}{\partial\tau}\phi_0'' = \phi_0''', \tag{21a}$$

$$(ia)\quad \phi_0(1,\tau)=0, \qquad\qquad (iia)\quad \phi_0'(1,\tau)=0,$$
$$(iiia)\quad U''(0,\tau)+\phi_0''(0,\tau)=0, \qquad (iva)\quad \phi_0'''-R(\phi_0')_\tau = 0 \quad\text{at}\quad y=0.$$
The solution of the system is simply
$$\phi_0 = -U(y,\tau)+B_0(\tau)+D(V_0+V_0^*)+iE(V_0-V_0^*), \tag{46}$$
in which
$$V_0 = \sinh[\beta(1+i)y]\,e^{i\omega\tau}, \qquad B_0 = b_0 e^{i\omega\tau}+b_0 e^{-i\omega\tau},$$
$$b_0 = \frac{A(1-i\gamma)}{\cosh\beta(1+i)}, \qquad \gamma = \tanh\beta\tan\beta,$$
$$D+iE = A(1-i\gamma)\tanh\beta(1+i),$$
D and E being real numbers. Note that the τ-dependence of ϕ_0 is dictated by (iiia).

---

† The other possibility is $h_0 = 0$, $\theta_0 \neq 0$. But it can and will be shown that this leads to a damped mode as far as long waves are concerned. Imaginary values for θ_0, with $h_0 \pm 0$, lead to nothing new.

For the next approximation, (24) gives

$$\frac{dh_1}{d\tau} + \theta_1 = -iB_0(\tau).$$

Since B_0 contains only $\sin \omega\tau$ and $\cos \omega\tau$, and h_1 is purely periodic,

$$\theta_1 = 0$$

and

$$h_1 = -i\int B_0(\tau)\,d\tau = -\frac{1}{\omega}(b_0\,e^{i\omega\tau} - b_0^*\,e^{-i\omega\tau}),\tag{47}$$

the constant of integration being chosen to be zero so that the term independent of τ in h is $h_0(=1)$ once and for all. This practice will not affect the criterion of stability in the least, and will be followed in calculating h_2. Equation (32) shows that even at the second approximation no instability is manifested.

For ϕ_1, the governing system is, since $\theta_1 = 0$,

$$iR(U\phi_0'' - U''\phi_0) = \phi_1''' - R\frac{\partial}{\partial\tau}\phi_1'',\tag{21b}$$

$$(i\,b)\quad \phi_1(1,\tau) = 0, \qquad (ii\,b)\quad \phi_1'(1,\tau) = 0,$$

$$(iii\,b)\quad U''(0,\tau)h_1 + \phi_1''(0,\tau) = 0,$$

$$(iv\,b)\quad iF^{-2} + \frac{1}{R}\phi_1''' - \frac{\partial}{\partial\tau}\phi_1' - iU\phi_0' = 0 \text{ at } y=0.$$

The τ-dependence of ϕ_1 is dictated by this system. Instead of terms containing $e^{i\omega\tau}$ and $e^{-i\omega\tau}$, those containing $e^{\pm i2\omega\tau}$ or no τ at all must be used. The particular solution of $(21b)$ is

$$\phi_{1p} = iR\left\{\frac{1}{2}\iint\left[\left(\phi_0'\int U\right) - U'\int(\phi_0 - B_0)\right] - J\right\},\tag{48}$$

in which J satisfies the equation

$$J'''' - R\frac{\partial}{\partial\tau}J'' = B_0 U'',\tag{49}$$

and the integrations are with respect to y, with dy omitted in each integration. After some straightforward integrations, we obtain

$$\phi_{1p} = iR(I_0 + I_1 + I_2 + I_0^* + I_1^* + I_2^*),\tag{50}$$

in which

$$I_0 = \frac{iA^2(1+\gamma^2)}{4\omega R}\tanh\beta(1+i)(\sinh 2\beta y + i\sin 2\beta y),\tag{51}$$

$$I_1 = \frac{iA^2(1+\gamma^2)}{\omega R\cosh\beta(1-i)}\cosh[\beta(1+i)\,y],\tag{52}$$

$$I_2 = -\frac{iA^2(1-i\gamma)^2}{\omega R\cosh\beta(1+i)}\cosh[\beta(1+i)\,y]\,e^{i2\omega\tau}.\tag{53}$$

The complementary solution is of the form

$$\phi_{1c} = A_1 + B_1 y + C_1 y^2 + D_1 y^3 + E_1 V_1 + F_1 W_1 + E_1^* V_1^* + F_1^* W_1^* + G(\tau) + K(\tau)y,\tag{54}$$

in which the eight coefficients are constants, and

$$V_1 = \sinh[\beta(1+i)\,y]\,e^{i2\omega\tau}, \qquad W_1 = \cosh[\beta(1+i)\,y]\,e^{i2\omega\tau},$$

$$G(\tau) = g_1\,e^{i2\omega\tau} + g_1^*\,e^{-i2\omega\tau}, \qquad K(\tau) = k_1\,e^{i2\omega\tau} + k_1^*\,e^{-i2\omega\tau}.$$

Now a look at (24) reveals that, for prediction of stability for long waves, none but the time-independent terms in

$$\phi_1 = \phi_{1p} + \phi_{1c} \tag{55}$$

and in $U(0,\tau)\,h_1$ need be calculated. For higher approximations at larger α we need to include the terms containing I_2, E_1, F_1, $G(\tau)$ and $K(\tau)$, but not at this stage. Considering then the terms independent of τ, we have, in the place of ϕ_1, the function

$$\Phi(y) = iR(I_0 + I_0^* + I_1 + I_1^*) + A_1 + B_1 y + C_1 y^2 + D_1 y^3, \tag{56}$$

satisfying the conditions

(ic) $\Phi(1) = 0,$ (ii$c$) $\Phi'(1) = 0,$

(iii$c$) $\Phi''(0) + iA^2(1+\gamma^2)\,R[\operatorname{sech}\beta(1+i) + \operatorname{sech}\beta(1-i)] = 0,$

(iv$c$) $iF^{-2} + (1/R)\Phi''' - iA^2\beta(1+\gamma^2)[(1+i)\tanh\beta(1+i)$

$$+ (1-i)\tanh\beta(1-i)] = 0.$$

The solution is given by the equations

$$\left.\begin{aligned}
C_1 &= 0, \quad D_1 = -\frac{i}{6}RF^{-2}, \\[2mm]
A_1 &= 2D_1 - \frac{i2A^2(1+\gamma^2)}{\omega}(R_1 - R_2), \\[2mm]
B_1 &= -3D_1 - \frac{iRA^2(1+\gamma^2)}{\beta}R_2,
\end{aligned}\right\} \tag{57}$$

in which R_1 and R_2 are respectively the real part of

$$\frac{i}{4}\tanh\beta(1+i)(\sinh 2\beta + i\sin 2\beta) + \frac{i}{\cosh\beta(1-i)}\cosh\beta(1+i),$$

$$\frac{i\beta}{2}\tanh\beta(1+i)(\cosh 2\beta + i\cos 2\beta) - \frac{2\beta}{(1+i)\cosh\beta(1-i)}\sinh\beta(1+i).$$

Now, according to (24),

$$\frac{dh_2}{d\tau} = -\theta_2 - i[U(0,\tau)\,h_1 + \phi_1(0,\tau)]. \tag{58}$$

The term in $U(0,\tau)\,h_1$ which is independent of τ is

$$-\frac{i2A^2(1+\gamma^2)}{\omega}I_3, \tag{59}$$

in which I_3 is the coefficient of the imaginary part of $\operatorname{sech}\beta(1+i)$. The part of $\phi_1(0,\tau)$ which is independent of τ is

$$\Phi(0) = A_1 + \frac{i2A^2(1+\gamma^2)}{\omega}I_3. \tag{60}$$

Thus the part on the right-hand side of (58) which is independent of time is simply $-\theta_2 - iA_1$, and this must be zero since h_2 is periodic in τ. Hence

$$\theta_2 = -iA_1,$$

and the criterion sought is that the flow is unstable or stable according as $-iA_1$

 Chia-Shun Yih

is positive or negative, or according as

$$\frac{6A^2(1+\gamma^2)}{\omega R}(R_2 - R_1) > \text{ or } < F^{-2}.$$

(61)

β	$L \times 10^n$	n	β	$L \times 10^n$	n
0·10	8·0042	5	3·20	$-2\cdot4914$	3
0·20	1·2772	3	3·40	$-1\cdot7888$	3
0·30	6·4093	3	3·60	$-1\cdot1007$	3
0·40	1·9785	2	3·80	$-5\cdot7129$	4
0·50	4·6005	2	4·00	$-2\cdot2517$	4
0·60	8·7539	2	4·20	$-3\cdot1780$	5
0·80	1·9975	1	4·40	5·5388	5
1·00	2·7859	1	4·60	7·9145	5
1·20	2·7075	1	4·80	7·1305	5
1·40	2·0792	1	5·00	5·2075	5
1·60	1·3790	1	5·20	3·2385	5
1·80	8·2447	2	5·40	1·6890	5
2·00	4·4619	2	5·60	6·6071	6
2·20	2·1067	2	5·80	8·0065	7
2·40	7·5952	3	6·00	$-1\cdot8288$	6
2·60	7·1058	4	7·00	$-5\cdot2612$	7
2·80	$-2\cdot1722$	3	8·00	$-7\cdot6320$	8
3·00	$-2\cdot8502$	3	9·00	6·8866	10
			10·00	$-1\cdot6199$	9

TABLE 1

Table 1 shows the variation of the left-hand side (L) of (61) with β. The maximum value of L is 0·279. When F^{-2} is greater than this value, there is stability. Table 1 is shown graphically in figure 2. If L is positive, there can be instability even for small Reynolds numbers provided ω_* and F are sufficiently large. It is interesting to see that for certain ranges of β the value of L is negative, so that in those ranges the motion actually stabilizes the free surface against the formation of long waves. For very small frequencies such that $\omega R = 2\beta^2 \ll 1$, the criterion derived from (61) is that the flow is unstable or stable according as

$$\tfrac{4}{5}A^2\omega^2 R^2 > \text{ or } < F^{-2},$$

(61a)

or, since $A = \tfrac{1}{2}$ for small β, according as

$$\frac{\omega_*^2 d^4}{5\nu^2} > \text{ or } < F^{-2},$$

(61b)

in which $\omega_* d^2/\nu$ is the Reynolds number based on ω_*.

The result obtained is that

$$\mu_1 = -i\alpha^2 A_1 + O(\alpha^3).$$

For long waves, $\alpha \ll 1$, and the criterion (61) is valid. As α increases toward the order of 1, more terms are needed. But as long as $\alpha \ll 1$, the stability or instability found is for any period of time, however long. We were concerned with the secular instability of the flow, and we have solved the problem explicitly for long waves.

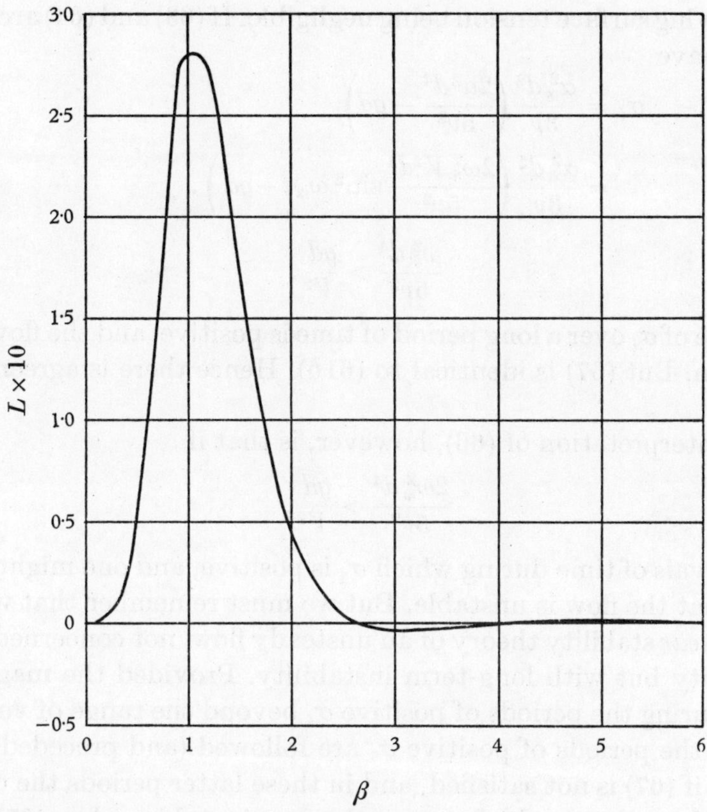

FIGURE 2. The variation of the left-hand side (L) of (61) with β. If $L > F^{-2}$, there is instability.

7. Discussion

For
$$\omega = \omega_* d/V \ll 1 \quad \text{and} \quad \beta^2 \ll 1,$$

the results obtained by the use of the approach of quasi-steadiness should be in agreement with the present results. But the former can be obtained from the results of Benjamin (1957) for the stability of the flow of a liquid layer down an inclined plane with angle of inclination θ, provided we make the correspondences

$$g' = (g^2 + a^2)^{\frac{1}{2}}, \quad \theta = \arctan(a/g), \tag{62}$$

in which a is the (dimensional) acceleration of the plane

$$a(t) = -\omega_* V \sin \omega_* t, \tag{63}$$

and g' is the g in the Benjamin–Yih problem. The average velocity (dimensional) of the flow in that problem is

$$\bar{u}_a = \tfrac{1}{3}(g' \sin \theta)\, d^2/\nu = a d^2/3\nu. \tag{64}$$

Then the σ_i in the exponential factor

$$e^{\sigma_i t} = e^{\alpha_* c_i t}$$

($\alpha_* = 2\pi/\lambda$, $\lambda =$ wavelength) is, according to the results of Benjamin,

$$\sigma_i = \frac{\alpha_*^2 \bar{u}_a^2 d^2}{\nu}\left(\frac{6}{5} - \frac{g' d \cos\theta}{3\bar{u}_a^2}\right), \tag{65}$$

                    Chia-Shun Yih

the term involving surface tension being negligible. If (63) and (64) are substituted into (65), we have

$$\sigma_i = \frac{\alpha_*^2 d^2}{3\nu} \left(\frac{2a^2 d^4}{5\nu^2} - gd \right)$$

$$= \frac{\alpha_*^2 d^2}{3\nu} \left(\frac{2\omega_*^2 V^2 d^4}{5\nu^2} \sin^2 \omega_* t - gd \right). \tag{66}$$

If

$$\frac{\omega_*^2 d^4}{5\nu^2} > \frac{gd}{V^2}, \tag{67}$$

the mean value of σ_i over a long period of time is positive, and the flow is unstable in the long run. But (67) is identical to (61b). Hence there is agreement, as one would expect.

One other interpretation of (66), however, is that if

$$\frac{2\omega_*^2 d^4}{5\nu^2} > \frac{gd}{V^2}, \tag{68}$$

there are intervals of time during which σ_1 is positive, and one might be tempted to conclude that the flow is unstable. But we must remember that we are, when considering *linear* stability theory of an unsteady flow, not concerned with short-range instability but with long-term instability. Provided the magnitude does not increase during the periods of positive σ_i beyond the range of validity of the linear theory, the periods of positive σ_i are followed (and preceded) by periods of negative σ_i if (67) is not satisfied, and in these latter periods the disturbances will be damped, so that in the long run the flow is stable unless (67) is satisfied.

Finally we shall show that the possibility of $h_0 = 0$ and $\theta_0 \neq 0$ does lead to damped modes only. In this case it is more convenient to treat (21), (22), (25) and (28) directly. If we write

$$\phi = \Phi_0 + \alpha \Phi_1 + \alpha^2 \Phi_2 + \ldots, \tag{69}$$

and further assume

$$\Phi_0 = e^{\theta_0 \tau} q(y), \tag{70}$$

then $q(y)$ satisfies

$$R\theta_0 q'' = q'''', \tag{71}$$

$$q(1) = 0, \quad q'(1) = 0, \tag{72}$$

$$q''(0) = 0, \quad q'''(0) - R\theta_0 q'(0) = 0. \tag{73}$$

Multiplying (71) by q, integrating between zero and 1 (by parts if necessary), and utilizing the boundary conditions (72) and (73), we find that

$$R\theta_0 \int_0^1 (q')^2 dy = - \int_0^1 (q'')^2 dy,$$

so that θ_0 is negative. In fact, θ_0 can be found explicitly. For the solution is

$$q = A' + B' y + C' e^{\beta' y} + D' e^{-\beta' y} \quad \text{with} \quad \beta' = (R\theta_0)^{\frac{1}{2}}.$$

The boundary conditions (73) demand†

$$C' = -D', \quad B' = 0.$$

† See Yih (1963, p. 334) for a similar discussion. One evaluation for B there was wrong, but the conclusions were correct.

The boundary conditions (72) then give

$$A' + B' + 2C' \sinh\beta' = 0, \quad B' + 2C'\beta' \cosh\beta' = 0,$$

the second of which gives $\qquad \beta' \cosh\beta' = 0.$

The solution $\beta' = 0$ must be discarded, for it leads to $q = 0$. The allowable solutions for β' are given by

$$\beta' = \frac{2n+1}{2}\pi i,$$

or

$$R\theta_0 = -\frac{2n+1^2}{2}\pi^2,$$

n being integers. Hence all modes are damped.

This work has been jointly sponsored by the Army Research Office (Durham) and the National Science Foundation. The author is grateful to Mr C. H. Li for the computation that leads to table 1 and Dr David Herbert for checking (61b).

REFERENCES

BENJAMIN, T. B. 1957 Wave formation in laminar flow down an inclined plane. *J. Fluid Mech.* **2**, 554–75.

BENJAMIN, T. B. & URSELL, F. 1954 The stability of the plane free surface of a liquid in vertical periodic motion. *Proc. Roy. Soc. Lond.* A **225**, 505–15.

CODDINGTON, E. A. & LEVINSON, N. 1955 *Theory of Ordinary Differential Equations.* New York: McGraw-Hill.

CONRAD, P. W. & CRIMINALE, W. O. 1965 The stability of time-dependent laminar flow: parallel flows. *ZAMP* **16**, 233.

CURRIE, I.G. 1967 The effect of heating rate on stability of stationary fluids. *J. Fluid. Mech.* **29**, 337–48.

INCE, E. L. 1944 *Ordinary Differential Equations.* New York: Dover.

JOSEPH, D. D. 1966 Nonlinear stability of the Boussinesq equations. *J. Rat. Mech. Analy.* **22**, 163–84.

ORR, W. McF. 1907 The stability or instability of the steady motions of a perfect liquid and of a viscous liquid. Part II: a viscous liquid. *Proc. Roy. Irish Acad.* **27**, 69–138.

SQUIRE, H. B. 1933 On the stability for three-dimensional disturbances of viscous fluid flow between parallel walls. *Proc. Roy. Soc. Lond.* A **142**, 621–8.

YIH, C.–S. 1963 Stability of liquid flow down an inclined plane. *Phys. Fluids*, **6**, 321–34.

YIH, C.–S. 1966 Instability due to viscosity stratification. *J. Fluid Mech.* **27**, 337–352.

J. Fluid Mech. (1969), *vol.* 38, *part* 2, *pp.* 273–278

Note on eigenvalue bounds for the Orr–Sommerfeld equation

By CHIA-SHUN YIH

Department of Engineering Mechanics, University of Michigan

(Received 8 November 1968 and in revised form 27 March 1969)

Bounds for the complex wave velocity c, determined by the Orr–Sommerfeld equation and the boundary conditions for channel flow, have been given by Joseph (1968 a, b). In these notes it is shown how two of Joseph's theorems can be uniformly improved.

1. Preliminary

The differential system considered consists of the Orr–Sommerfeld equation

$$i\alpha R[(U - c)(\phi'' - \alpha^2\phi) - U''\phi] = \phi^{\mathrm{iv}} - 2\alpha^2\phi'' + \alpha^4\phi \tag{1}$$

and the boundary conditions

$$\phi(\pm \tfrac{1}{2}) = 0 = \phi'(\pm \tfrac{1}{2}), \tag{2}$$

for flow between parallel plates. In (1) α is the wave-number, U the dimensionless velocity of the primary flow, R the Reynolds number based on the spacing d of the plates, $c = c_r + ic_i$ is the complex wave velocity, and accents indicate differentiation with respect to the dimensionless ordinate y measured in the direction normal to the plates. For convenience, the space occupied by the fluid is specified by the interval

$$-\tfrac{1}{2} \leqslant y \leqslant \tfrac{1}{2}, \tag{3}$$

instead of $0 \leqslant y \leqslant 1$, as in the paper of Joseph (1968). The length scale remains the same. The parameters R and α are non-negative.

By multiplying (1) by ϕ^*, the complex conjugate of ϕ, and integrating throughout the interval specified by (3), using (2) whenever necessary, Synge (1938) obtained

$$c_i = \{Q - Q^* - (\alpha R)^{-1}(I_2^2 + 2\alpha^2 I_1^2 + \alpha^4 I_0^2)\}/(I_1^2 + \alpha^2 I_0^2), \tag{4}$$

and

$$c_r = \{\textstyle\int[U|\phi'|^2 + (\alpha^2 U + \tfrac{1}{2}U'')|\phi|^2]\,dy\}/(I_1^2 + \alpha^2 I_0^2), \tag{5}$$

in which

$$I_2^2 = \textstyle\int|\phi''|^2\,dy, \quad I_1^2 = \textstyle\int|\phi'|^2\,dy,$$

$$I_0^2 = \textstyle\int|\phi|^2\,dy, \quad Q = \tfrac{1}{2}i\textstyle\int U'\phi\phi'^*\,dy.$$

The upper limit in all the integrals is $\tfrac{1}{2}$ and the lower limit $-\tfrac{1}{2}$.

Using (4) and Schwarz's inequality, Synge (1938) obtained the estimate

$$c_i \leqslant \frac{qI_0 I_1 - (\alpha R)^{-1}(I_2^2 + 2\alpha^2 I_1^2 + \alpha^4 I_0^2)}{I_1^2 + \alpha^2 I_0^2}, \tag{6}$$

where

$$q = \max|U'(y)|$$

in the interval (3).

274   *C.-S. Yih*

2. An upper bound for c_i

Using (6), Joseph (1969) concluded that

$$c_i \leqslant \frac{q}{2\alpha} - \left\{ \frac{\pi^2(4\pi^2 + \alpha^2)}{\pi^2 + \alpha^2} + \alpha^2 \right\} \Big/ \alpha R, \tag{7}$$

and that, if

$$\alpha R q < f(\alpha) \equiv \max\,[M_1, M_2], \tag{8}$$

$$\left. \begin{aligned} M_1 &= (4{\cdot}73)^2\, 2\pi + 2^{\frac{3}{2}}\alpha^3, \\ M_2 &= (4{\cdot}73)^2\, 2\pi + 2\alpha^2\pi, \end{aligned} \right\} \tag{9}$$

then c_i cannot be positive. Result (8) greatly improves the result of Synge (1938).

We shall show that (7) to (9) can be uniformly sharpened. Starting from (6), we immediately obtain

THEOREM 1.
$$c_i \leqslant \frac{q}{2\alpha} - \frac{\lambda^2}{\alpha R}, \tag{10}$$

in which
$$\lambda^2 = \min \frac{I_2^2 + 2\alpha^2 I_1^2 + \alpha^4 I_0^2}{I_1^2 + \alpha^2 I_0^2}. \tag{11}$$

Of course λ^2 must be given explicitly in terms of α. To evaluate λ^2, we shall use the variational method. That is, we shall give ϕ a variation $\delta\phi$ satisfying

$$\delta\phi(\pm\tfrac{1}{2}) = \delta\phi'(\pm\tfrac{1}{2}) = 0, \tag{12}$$

and require the ratio in (11) to be a minimum, thereby finding a differential equation to be satisfied by ϕ and containing λ^2 as a parameter. This equation is no longer (1). It, with (2), will determine λ^2. Since the ϕ in (1) is four-times differentiable, we shall assume $\delta\phi$ to be four times differentiable also. Remembering the definitions of I_0, I_1 and I_2, allowing ϕ to have the variation $\delta\phi$ satisfying (12) and four times differentiable but otherwise arbitrary, and requiring the ratio in (11) to be an extremum, we obtain, upon neglect of quadratic terms in $\delta\phi$ and its derivatives and after integrations by parts whenever necessary,

$$\frac{2}{I_1^2 + \alpha^2 I_0^2} \int (D^2 - \alpha^2 + \lambda^2)\,(D^2 - \alpha^2)\,\phi\,\delta\phi\,dy = 0,$$

the limits of integration being understood, and D denoting d/dy. Since $\delta\phi$ is arbitrary, ϕ must satisfy

$$(D^2 - \alpha^2 + \lambda^2)\,(D^2 - \alpha^2)\,\phi = 0. \tag{13}$$

This and (2) constitute a differential system which defines an eigenvalue problem, with λ^2 as the eigenvalue for any given α^2. The differential system admits even or odd solutions for ϕ. For even ϕ, it gives the secular equation

$$\sqrt{(\lambda^2 - \alpha^2)}\,\tan\tfrac{1}{2}\sqrt{(\lambda^2 - \alpha^2)} = -\alpha\tanh\tfrac{1}{2}\alpha. \tag{14}$$

The solution of (14) will be denoted by λ_e, the subscript meaning 'even'. The lowest λ_e^2 is plotted in figure 1 for comparison with the corresponding values

$$\pi^2 + \alpha^2 \quad \text{and} \quad \pi^2(4\pi^2 + \alpha^2)/(\pi^2 + \alpha^2) + \alpha^2,$$

given by Joseph in (1968) and in equation (7), respectively. That λ_e^2 is uniformly an improvement of (7) is evident.

For odd ϕ the secular equation is

$$\sqrt{(\lambda^2 - \alpha^2)}\tanh\tfrac{1}{2}\alpha = \alpha\tan\tfrac{1}{2}\sqrt{(\lambda^2 - \alpha^2)}. \tag{15}$$

The solution of this equation will be denoted by λ_o^2, the subscript meaning 'odd'. The values of the lowest λ_o^2 for various values of α^2 are also plotted in figure 1. It can be seen from figure 1 that the lowest λ_o^2 is greater than the lowest λ_e^2 for all values of α^2. It is also clear that the λ^2 in (13) is an extremum only if ϕ is even

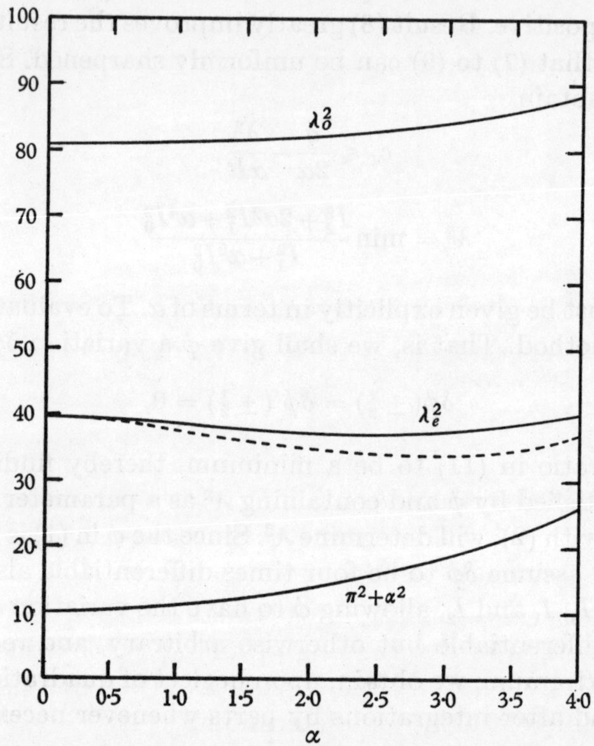

FIGURE 1. The values of Joseph's bound $\alpha^2 + \pi^2(4\pi^2 + \alpha^2)/(\pi^2 + \alpha^2)$: ----. Joseph previously gave the less sharp bound $\pi^2 + \alpha^2$. The improved bound is λ_e^2.

or odd, since, as can be shown, the general secular equation in the form of a four-by-four determinant can be factorized into two equations which are precisely (14) and (15). Near any solution of (14) λ^2 cannot be an extremum unless ϕ is even, and near any solution of (15) λ^2 cannot be an extremum unless ϕ is odd. In fact, the spectrum of λ_e^2 and the spectrum of λ_o^2 separate each other. Hence the lowest λ_e^2 is the value we want.

Note that from (13) and its boundary conditions we can easily obtain (with limits and dy omitted)

$$\int |D^2\phi|^2 + (2\alpha^2 - \lambda^2)\int |D\phi|^2 + \alpha^2(\alpha^2 - \lambda^2)\int |\phi|^2 = 0,$$

from which it is obvious that λ^2 is real. Thus it is quite unnecessary to consider complex forms of the function ϕ, for its real and imaginary parts would separately

          C.-S. Yih

satisfy (13) and its boundary conditions, and the function that gives the lowest λ^2 is proportional to the real eigenfunction ϕ corresponding to the lowest eigenvalue λ_e^2. The constant of proportionality may be complex, but the lowest λ^2 is just the λ_e^2 we have obtained.

3. A sufficient condition for stability

We shall now give the improvement of (8) and (9). From (6), we see that c_i cannot be positive if

$$\alpha Rq \leqslant \frac{I_2^2 + 2\alpha^2 I_1^2 + \alpha^4 I_0^2}{I_0 I_1}. \tag{16}$$

We shall try to minimize the right-hand side of (16), the minimum value of which will be denoted by κ^2. If

$$\kappa_1^2 = \min \frac{I_2^2 + 2\alpha^2 I_1^2 + \alpha^4 I_0^2}{I_0^2} \tag{17}$$

and

$$\kappa_2^2 = \min \frac{I_2^2 + 2\alpha^2 I_1^2 + \alpha^4 I_0^2}{I_1^2}, \tag{18}$$

then obviously

$$\kappa_1 \kappa_2 \leqslant \kappa^2. \tag{19}$$

The obviously correct statement, that c_i cannot be positive if

$$\alpha Rq \leqslant \kappa^2, \tag{20}$$

can be replaced by the less sharp

THEOREM 2*a*. c_1 *cannot be positive if*

$$\alpha Rq \leqslant \kappa_1 \kappa_2 \tag{21}$$

(less sharp, because of (19)).

The estimate (21), however, has the advantage that κ_1 and κ_2 can be simply evaluated. The method of determining κ_1^2 and κ_2^2 is the same as that used to determine λ^2 in the preceding section. Again only even functions ϕ need be considered. The differential system determining κ_1^2 is

$$(D^2 - \alpha^2)^2 \phi - \kappa_1^2 \phi = 0, \tag{22}$$

in conjunction with (2), and the differential system determining κ_2 is

$$(D^2 - \alpha^2)^2 \phi + \kappa_2^2 D^2 \phi = 0, \tag{23}$$

in conjunction with (2). The product $\kappa_1 \kappa_2$ is plotted against α in figure 2, which also shows M_1 and M_2 given by (9). That the present estimate is an improvement over Joseph's (1969) is evident for $\alpha \leqslant 2\cdot4$; but for $\alpha > 2\cdot4$ Joseph's M_1 is a better bound. We shall now proceed to find a bound for αRq for stability which is uniformly better than Joseph's.

Since for any real b

$$I_0 I_1 \leqslant \frac{1}{2b} (I_1^2 + b^2 I_0^2),$$

if we define $K(\alpha, b)$ by

$$K(\alpha, b) = \min \frac{2b(I_2^2 + 2\alpha^2 I_1^2 + \alpha^4 I_0^2)}{I_1^2 + b^2 I_0^2},$$

for any real α and b, it is evident that $\kappa^2 \geqslant K(\alpha, b)$ for *all* values of b. Hence

$$\kappa^2 \geqslant K_{\max},$$

where $K_{\max}$ is the maximum of K with respect to b, for any α^2, and we can use $K_{\max}$ as a safe and at the same time good substitute for κ^2. Using the variational method, we obtain, for the determination of $K(\alpha, b)$, the differential system

$$\phi^{\mathrm{iv}} - 2\alpha^2\phi'' + \alpha^4\phi + \frac{K}{2b}(\phi'' - b^2\phi) = 0,$$

$$\phi(\pm\tfrac{1}{2}) = 0 = \phi'(\pm\tfrac{1}{2}).$$

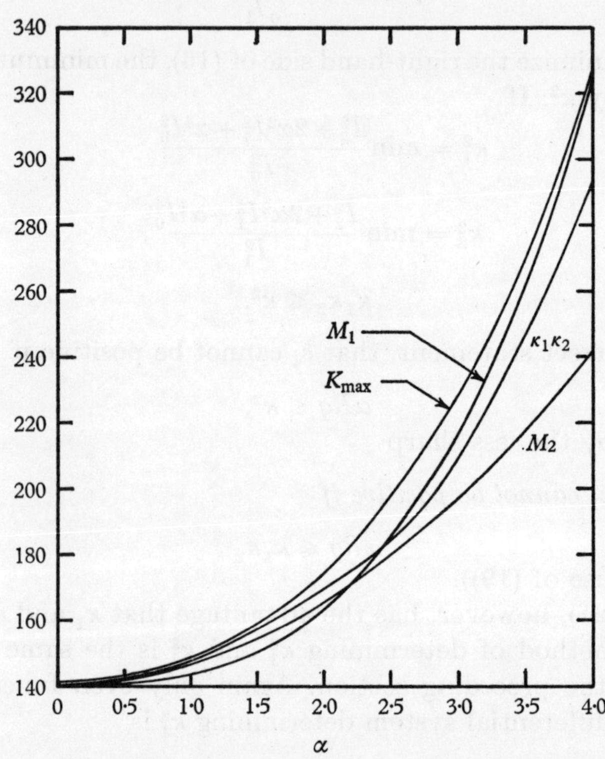

FIGURE 2. The greater of M_1 and M_2 is Joseph's bound.
The improved bound is $K_{\max}$.

We shall again consider ϕ to be even, for an odd ϕ will give higher eigenvalues for K. In this way we can find $K(\alpha, b)$ for given α and various values of b. Thus $K_{\max}$ is obtained, which is a function of α only. Its values are plotted in figure 2. All of these values correspond to the value of 3·55 for b, which does not seem to vary with α in the range of calculation. It is evident that $K_{\max}$ improves Joseph's estimate (9) uniformly. We have now the sharper

THEOREM 2. c_i *cannot be positive if*

$$\alpha Rq \leqslant K_{\max}. \tag{24}$$

This work has been jointly sponsored by the National Science Foundation and the Army Research Office (Durham). The author is indebted to Mr C. H. Li for computational assistance. To avoid duplicating the graphs, the numerical values of λ_e^2, λ_o^2, κ_1, κ_2, $\kappa_1\kappa_2$ and K_{max} have not been reproduced here in tabular form. Readers interested in these values are invited to write to the author.

REFERENCES

JOSEPH, D. D. 1968 Eigenvalue bounds for the Orr–Sommerfeld equation. *J. Fluid Mech.* **33**, 617–621.

JOSEPH, D. D. 1969 Eigenvalue bounds for the Orr–Sommerfeld equation, Part 2. *J. Fluid Mech.* **36**, 721–734.

SYNGE, J. L. 1938 Hydrodynamic stability. *Semicentenn. Publ. Am. Math. Soc.* **2**, 227–69.

J. Fluid Mech. (1972), *vol.* 54, *part* 1, *pp.* 143–152

Instability of unsteady flows or configurations.
Part 2. Convective instability

By CHIA-SHUN YIH

Department of Engineering Mechanics, The University of Michigan

AND CHIN-HSIU LI

Division of Fluid, Thermal and Aerospace Sciences,
Case Western Reserve University, Cleveland

(Received 2 September 1971 and in revised form 8 February 1972)

The formation of convective cells in a fluid between two horizontal rigid boundaries with time-periodic temperature distribution is studied by the use of the Floquet theory. Numerical results for the critical Rayleigh number are given for a Prandtl number of 0·73 (air) and for various values of the frequency and magnitude of the primary temperature oscillation. Some numerical results for a Prandtl number of 7·0 (water) are also given. The most striking feature of the results is that the disturbances (or convection cells) oscillate either synchronously or with half frequency.

1. Introduction

In numerous stability problems in mechanics, oscillation of the basic state has been found sometimes to have a stabilizing and sometimes a destabilizing effect, the latter often being associated with the reduction of the problem to Mathieu's equation. Some pertinent references in the field of fluid mechanics are Benjamin & Ursell (1954), Rosenblat (1968), Yih (1968), and the experimental work of Donnelly (1964).

The present work concerns Bénard convection with a time-dependent basic state. Three recent papers on that subject are those by Gresho & Sani (1970), who studied the effect of time-variable gravity on thermal convection, and Venezian (1969), on convection in an unsteady temperature field when the amplitude of the unsteady part is assumed small, and that of Rosenblat & Herbert (1970) on the same problem at low modulation frequency, but with the modulation amplitude not small. In this paper we study the marginal stability of a fluid layer with a symmetric temperature gradient which contains an unsteady part. Neither the amplitude nor the frequency of this unsteady part is assumed small. Solutions are obtained by a method of expansion in orthogonal functions akin to that of Chandrasekhar (1954). A similar investigation has been very recently reported by Rosenblat & Tanaka (1971); they use a slightly different basic temperature field, and Galerkin's method. The most striking feature of our results is that the disturbances, at neutral stability at least (and

                    C.-S. Yih and C.-H. Li

probably at instability), are either synchronous with the primary temperature field or have half its frequency. A similar but less extensive result was obtained by Gresho & Sani.

2. Primary temperature distribution

Consider a layer of fluid between two fixed plates, one at $x_3 = +\tfrac{1}{2}d$ and the other at $x_3 = -\tfrac{1}{2}d$, x_1, x_2 and x_3 being Cartesian co-ordinates with x_3 measured in the direction of the vertical from the plane mid-way between the plates. The temperature of the upper plate is kept at $T_1 + T_2 \cos \omega_* t$, and that at the lower plate is maintained at $T_0 - T_2 \cos \omega_* t$, t being the time and ω_* being equal to 2π times the frequency of the periodic temperature fluctuation at the lower plate.

Define the following dimensionless variables:

$$\tau = t\kappa/d^2, \quad (x, y, z) = (1/d)\,(x_1, x_2, x_3), \\ \omega = \omega_* d^2/\kappa, \quad \theta = (\overline{T} - T_1)/(T_0 - T_1), \tag{1}$$

where κ is the thermal diffusivity. Then the dimensionless equation governing the distribution of the primary (or mean) temperature T is

$$\partial\theta/\partial\tau = \partial^2\theta/\partial z^2 \tag{2}$$

and the boundary conditions are

$$\theta = 1 - b \cos \omega\tau \quad \text{at} \quad z = -\tfrac{1}{2}, \tag{3}$$

$$\theta = b \cos \omega\tau \quad \text{at} \quad z = \tfrac{1}{2}, \tag{4}$$

with
$$b = T_2/(T_0 - T_1). \tag{5}$$

The solution of (2) with the boundary conditions (3) and (4) is

$$\theta = -\tfrac{1}{2} - z + bF(z, \tau), \tag{6}$$

where
$$F(z, \tau) = (B \cos \omega\tau - C \sin \omega\tau) \sinh \beta z \cos \beta z$$
$$- (C \cos \omega\tau + B \sin \omega\tau) \cosh \beta z \sin \beta z, \tag{7}$$

with
$$B = -\sinh \beta' \cos \beta'/(\sinh^2 \beta' + \sin^2 \beta'), \quad C = -B \tan \beta' \coth \beta', \tag{8}$$

and
$$\beta = (\tfrac{1}{2}\omega)^{\frac{1}{2}}, \quad \beta' = \tfrac{1}{2}\beta. \tag{9}$$

If ρ_0 is the density at temperature T_0 and the prevailing pressure, the density ρ at any temperature not too different from T_0 is

$$\rho = \rho_0[1 - \alpha(T - T_0)], \tag{10}$$

where α is the thermal expansion coefficient of the fluid, which is assumed incompressible. The Boussinesq approximation will be made.

3. Differential system governing stability

We shall now disturb the fluid and see whether the disturbance will grow. The temperature disturbance will be denoted by T' and the velocity by (u_1, u_2, u_3). Then (see, for instance, Pellew & Southwell 1940), with the substitutions

$$u_3 = (\kappa/d)f(x, y)\, w(z, \tau), \tag{11}$$

$$T' = (T_0 - T_1)f(x, y)\, \theta(z, \tau), \tag{12}$$

where
$$f_{xx} + f_{yy} + a^2 f = 0, \tag{13}$$

a being the wavenumber of the Bénard cells, the linearized Boussinesq equations reduce to

$$\left[\frac{1}{\sigma}\frac{\partial}{\partial\tau} - (D^2 - a^2)\right](D^2 - a^2)w = -Ra^2\theta, \tag{14}$$

$$\left[\frac{\partial}{\partial\tau} - (D^2 - a^2)\right]\theta = -[-1 + bF'(z-\tau)]w, \tag{15}$$

in which $R = g\alpha(T_0 - T_1)d^3/\kappa\nu$ = Rayleigh number, $\sigma = \nu/\kappa$ = Prandtl number, $D = \partial/\partial z$ and $F'(z,\tau) = DF(z,\tau)$. The boundary conditions are

$$w = 0 = Dw \quad \text{at} \quad z = \pm\tfrac{1}{2}, \tag{16}$$

$$\theta = 0 \quad \text{at} \quad z = \pm\tfrac{1}{2}. \tag{17}$$

4. Method of approach

We note, first of all, that $F(z,\tau)$ is an odd function of z and hence $F'(z,\tau)$ is an even function of z. Inspection of (14)–(17) reveals that the eigenfunctions can be divided into two categories: those which are even functions of z and those which are odd functions of z. All previous investigations of convection cells have shown that disturbances corresponding to even eigenfunctions and hence having an *odd* number of cells in the z direction are more unstable than those corresponding to odd functions. Of these the single-celled disturbance is the most unstable. We therefore investigate only the stability of disturbances with even eigenfunctions.

Keeping in mind the boundary conditions on θ and w, we can expand θ in a series in $\cos(2n+1)\pi z$ and w in a series in $\phi_n(z)$, which is defined by the system

$$\left.\begin{array}{c}(D^2 - a^2)^2\phi_n = \cos(2n+1)\pi z, \\[6pt] \phi_n(-\tfrac{1}{2}) = 0 = D\phi_n(-\tfrac{1}{2}), \quad \phi_n(\tfrac{1}{2}) = 0 = D\phi_n(\tfrac{1}{2}).\end{array}\right\} \tag{18}$$

The solution of (18) is

$$\phi_n = P_n\cosh az + Q_n z\sinh az + c_n^2\cos[(2n+1)\pi z], \tag{19}$$

where
$$\left.\begin{array}{l}P_n = -(-1)^n(2n+1)\pi c_n^2\sinh(\tfrac{1}{2}a)/(a + \sinh a), \\[6pt] Q_n = (-1)^n 2(2n+1)\pi c_n^2\cosh(\tfrac{1}{2}a)/(a + \sinh a), \\[6pt] c_n = 1/[(2n+1)^2\pi^2 + a^2].\end{array}\right\} \tag{20}$$

We now expand θ and w as follows:

$$\theta = \sum_{n=0}^{\infty} B_n(\tau)\cos[(2n+1)\pi z], \tag{21}$$

$$w = \sum_{n=0}^{\infty} A_n(\tau)\phi_n(z). \tag{22}$$

Substituting (21) and (22) into (14) and (15), multiplying the resulting equations by $\cos[(2n+1)\pi z]$ and integrating between $z = \pm\tfrac{1}{2}$ gives

$$\frac{2}{\sigma}\sum_{n=0}^{\infty}\zeta_{mn}A_n'(\tau) - A_m(\tau) = -Ra^2 B_m(\tau) \quad (m = 0, 1, 2, \ldots), \tag{23}$$

$$B_m'(\tau) + \frac{1}{c_m}B_m(\tau)$$
$$= -2\sum_{n=0}^{\infty}(c_m\zeta_{mn} + b\lambda_{mn}\cos\omega\tau + b\xi_{mn}\sin\omega\tau)A_n(\tau) \quad (m = 0, 1, 2, \ldots), \tag{24}$$

146   *C.-S. Yih and C.-H. Li*

where

$$\zeta_{mn} = (-1)^{m+n}\, 8a(2n+1)\,(2m+1)\,\pi^2 c_n^2\, c_m \cosh^2\left(\tfrac{1}{2}a\right)/(a+\sinh a) - \tfrac{1}{2}c_n \delta_{mn}, \quad (25)$$

δ_{mn} being the Kronecker delta, and λ_{mn} and ξ_{mn} are defined by

$$\lambda_{mn}\cos\omega\tau + \xi_{mn}\sin\omega\tau = \int_{-\frac{1}{2}}^{\frac{1}{2}} F'(z,\tau)\cos\left[(2m+1)\pi z\right]\phi_n(z)\,dz. \quad (26)$$

When expanded, (26) gives

$$\lambda_{mn} = \beta \int_{-\frac{1}{2}}^{\frac{1}{2}} \left[(B-C)\cosh\beta z\cos\beta z - (B+C)\sinh\beta z\sin\beta z\right]$$
$$\times \cos\left[(2m+1)\pi z\right]\phi_n(z)\,dz, \quad (26a)$$

$$\xi_{mn} = -\beta \int_{-\frac{1}{2}}^{\frac{1}{2}} \left[(B+C)\cosh\beta z\cos\beta z + (B-C)\sinh\beta z\sin\beta z\right]$$
$$\times \cos\left[(2m+1)\pi z\right]\phi_n(z)\,dz. \quad (26b)$$

We shall now study truncated versions of the infinite set of equations (23) and (24) determining $A_n(\tau)$ and $B_n(\tau)$. If A_n and B_n remain small for all times the fluid is stable; if they grow with time in the long run (that is, cycle after cycle of period $2\pi/\omega_*$), the fluid is unstable. We shall attempt only to determine the Rayleigh number R for neutral stability.

5. Analysis

Since the coefficients in (23) and (24) are either constant or periodic functions of τ with (dimensionless) period $\tau_0 = 2\pi/\omega$, the Floquet theory applies. (See Ince 1944, pp. 381–382; Coddington & Levinson 1955, pp. 78–81.) The outstanding result of the Floquet theory is that the solution must have the form $e^{\mu_1 \tau}\,P(\tau)$, where $P(\tau)$ is either a periodic function of τ with period τ_0 or a sum of terms each of which is the product of a polynomial in τ (in particular a constant) and such a periodic function. In all cases the vanishing of the real part μ_{1r} of μ_1 evidently marks the stability boundary. Our aim is to determine the conditions under which $\mu_{1r} = 0$.

If μ_{1i}, the imaginary part of μ_1, is zero, then the disturbance is synchronous with the unsteady part of the mean temperature field. If $\mu_{1i}\tau_0$ is equal to π or $-\pi$, then the disturbance has frequency half that of the unsteady mean temperature field. Numerical calculation will show that the most unstable disturbance either is synchronous or has half the frequency of the mean temperature. Values of $\mu_{1i}\tau_0$ other than zero and $\pm\pi$ were searched for, though not exhaustively, but none were found.

We now consider the $2M$ equations obtained by putting $m = 0, 1, ..., M-1$ in (23) and (24). For convenience of exposition, let us denote $2M$ by N. In principle the N equations with N unknowns can be combined into one differential equation of order N, with N independent solutions, which we shall denote by $G_n(\tau)$ $(n = 1, 2, ..., N)$. Let us give $G_n(\tau)$ the property

$$G_n^{(k-1)}(0) = \delta_{nk}, \quad (27)$$

where
$$G_n^{(k)}(\tau) = d^k G_n(\tau)/d\tau^k. \quad (28)$$

Then, since the coefficients of the Nth-order differential equation have period τ_0,

$$G_n(\tau+\tau_0) = \sum_{m=1}^{N} a_{nm} G_m(\tau),\tag{29}$$

and we have

$$a_{nm} = G_n^{(m-1)}(\tau_0).\tag{30}$$

If we seek a solution $U(\tau)$ with the property

$$U(\tau+\tau_0) = sU(\tau),\tag{31}$$

we can write

$$U(\tau) = \sum_{m=1}^{N} b_m G_m(\tau).\tag{32}$$

Substituting (29) and (32) into (31), we have the secular equation

$$\det\{G_n^{(k-1)}(\tau_0) - s\delta_{nk}\} = 0,\tag{33}$$

which determines s. It is evident that

$$s = e^{\mu_1 \tau_0}.\tag{34}$$

We thus have a means of determining μ_1.

For the first approximation we retain only the first term in expansions (21) and (22); equations (23) and (24) then contain only A_0 and B_0. By eliminating B_0 between them, we obtain

$$A_0''(\tau) - \left(\frac{\sigma}{2\zeta_{00}} - \frac{1}{c_0}\right) A_0'(\tau) - \frac{\sigma}{\zeta_{00}}\left[\frac{1}{2c_0} + Ra^2(c_0\zeta_{00} + b\lambda_{00}\cos\omega\tau + b\xi_{00}\sin\omega\tau)\right] A_0(\tau) = 0.\tag{35}$$

For the second approximation we have four simultaneous first-order equations or two second-order simultaneous equations, which we shall not present, because they are rather lengthy.

If desired, higher order approximations can be carried out in much the same way. Numerical computations have been carried out for a Prandtl number† $\sigma = 0.73$ (air) but to the second approximation only. We are also in possession of asymptotic solutions of (35) and of the two second-order equations in the second approximations for large values (> 100) of the Prandtl number σ. However, for these high values the mean temperature varies a good deal with the co-ordinate z and the validity of a mere second approximation becomes questionable. For this reason we do not present these solutions.

6. The case $T_1 = T_0$

Before we present the results of numerical calculation we wish to discuss the case $T_1 = T_0$, which has also been investigated. The primary temperature distribution is still governed by (2), except that T_2 is now used as the temperature scale instead of $T_0 - T_1$, so that

$$\theta = (T - T_0)/T_2.\tag{36}$$

With the boundary temperatures maintained as before (see the beginning of §2),

$$\theta = \pm\cos\omega\tau \quad\text{at}\quad z = \pm\tfrac{1}{2}.\tag{37}$$

† We also have some results for $\sigma = 7.0$ (water). See table 2.

                    C.-S. Yih and C.-H. Li

The solution of (2) with (37) is

$$\theta = F(z, \tau), \tag{38}$$

with $F(z, \tau)$ given by (7).

The differential equations governing stability are still (14) and (15), except that the right-hand side of (15) is to be replaced by $-F'(z, \tau)\,w$, and the Rayleigh number R is now defined by

$$R = g\alpha T_2 d^3/\kappa\nu. \tag{39}$$

We again use the expansions (21) and (22), and once more obtain (23). Equation (24) is now replaced by

$$B'_m(\tau) + \frac{1}{c_m} B_m(\tau) = -2 \sum_{n=0}^{\infty} (\lambda_{mn} \cos \omega\tau + \xi_{mn} \sin \omega\tau) A_n(\tau) \quad (m = 0, 1, 2, \ldots), \tag{40}$$

where ζ_{mn}, c_m, λ_{mn} and ξ_{mn} are again as given in §4.

The equations for the various stages of approximation are very similar to those for the case $T_0 \neq T_1$, and the rest of the analysis is identical to that given in §5 for the case $T_0 \neq T_1$.

7. Discussion of results

The numerical computation was done by the Runge–Kutta method using 'double precision', with a UNIVAC 1108 computer. The step size h chosen was small enough for μ_1 in (34) to be accurate to the third significant digit at least.

Since for the case $T_0 = T_1$ there is one less parameter to consider, i.e. the parameter b does not appear, it is possible to obtain a relationship between the critical Rayleigh number R_c (note that R is based on T_2, not $2T_2$) and the corresponding critical wavenumber a_c in terms of functions of the dimensionless frequency ω of the oscillating primary temperature field. The critical Rayleigh number is the minimum value of R as a function of the wavenumber a for a fixed value of ω. Figure 1 shows R_c and a_c as functions of ω. In this figure the symbol S signifies 'synchronous' and the symbol H 'half-frequency'. On and above an S curve the disturbances are synchronous, and on and above an H curve the disturbances have the frequency $\frac{1}{2}\omega$. We have found that each of the cusps in the R_c–ω curve is really the intersection of an H curve with an S curve, both of which can be continued beyond the intersection. Thus in the area above an H curve there are also synchronous disturbances, but disturbances with half-frequency can be expected to be more unstable. Similarly, above an S curve there are disturbances with half-frequency, but synchronous disturbances are more unstable. The critical wavenumber appears to be discontinuous from the a_c–ω curve only because we do not continue the S curves and the H curves beyond their intersections. The a_c–ω curves are also composed of S curves and H curves.

Below $\omega = 6$ the arcs corresponding to the S curves and H curves, as indicated by the computed points, seem to have rather low amplitudes. That is to say, they do not sag much below the curve passing through their mean positions. For this reason we use a broken line to indicate the mean position of computed points only. The exact form of the R_c–ω curve must be very near this broken line.

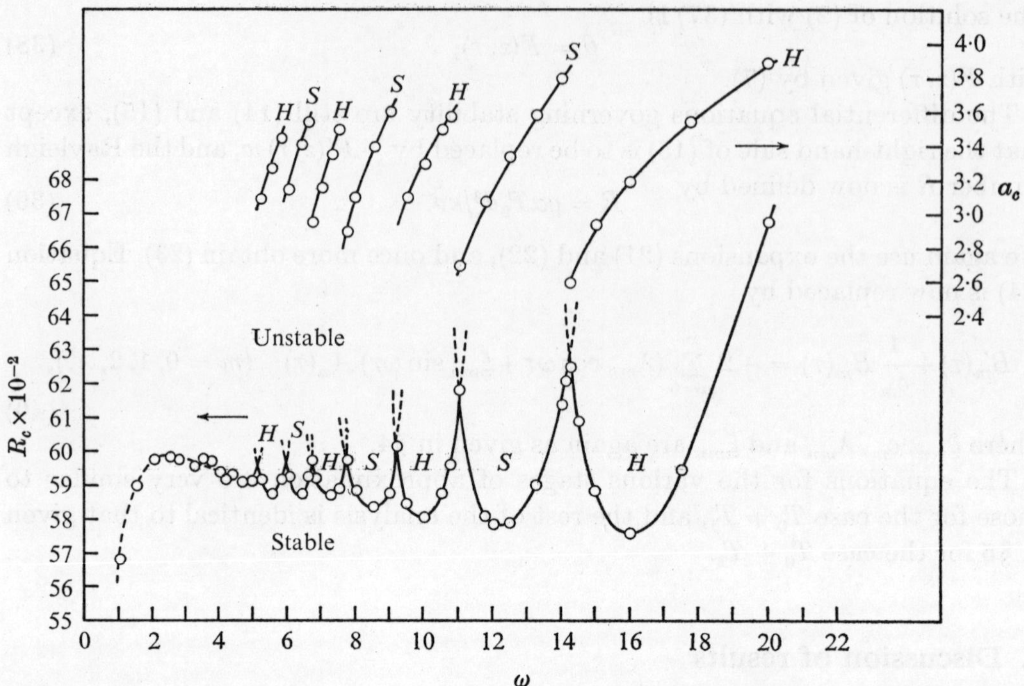

FIGURE 1. Variation of R_c and a_c with ω for $\sigma = 0.73$ (air) and $T_0 = T_1$. S signifies 'synchronous' and H signifies 'half-frequency', for the curve below.

We note that the existence of synchronous and half-frequency disturbances was already indicated in figure 4 of the paper of Gresho & Sani (1970), in which, incidentally, the vertical co-ordinate should be $R_c \times 10^{-3}$ instead of $R_c \times 10^{-5}$ (which is merely a misprint).

At high values of ω, the primary temperature field has at any instant many 'waves' in the z direction, and the validity of an approximation taking into account only A_0, A_1, B_0 and B_1 becomes questionable. However, up to $\omega = 20$ (see figure 1) examination of the expression for $F(z, \tau)$ shows that the primary temperature has about *one* wave in the direction of z, since

$$\beta/\pi = (\omega/2\pi^2)^{\frac{1}{2}} = 1 \quad \text{for} \quad \omega = 20.$$

Thus $\phi_1(z)$ and $\phi_2(z)$ are quite sufficient to give a good approximation to the eigenfunction.

We now turn to the case $T_0 \neq T_1$. Figure 2 shows the variation of the critical Rayleigh number R_c with b for $\sigma = 0.73$ (air) and $\omega = 5$. We use a dashed line to show the results of the first approximation and a solid line to show the results of the second approximation. We have marked with S (synchronous) and H (half-frequency) the first two arcs only, to avoid confusion, since the positions of the S curves and H curves shift from the first to the second approximation. For each approximation the S curves alternate with the H curves.

We note that in the mean the results of the first and second approximations do not differ very much, although the shift of the cusps is very evident. It is interesting that, as b increases from zero, at first (for small b) the unsteady part

150   *C.-S. Yih and C.-H. Li*

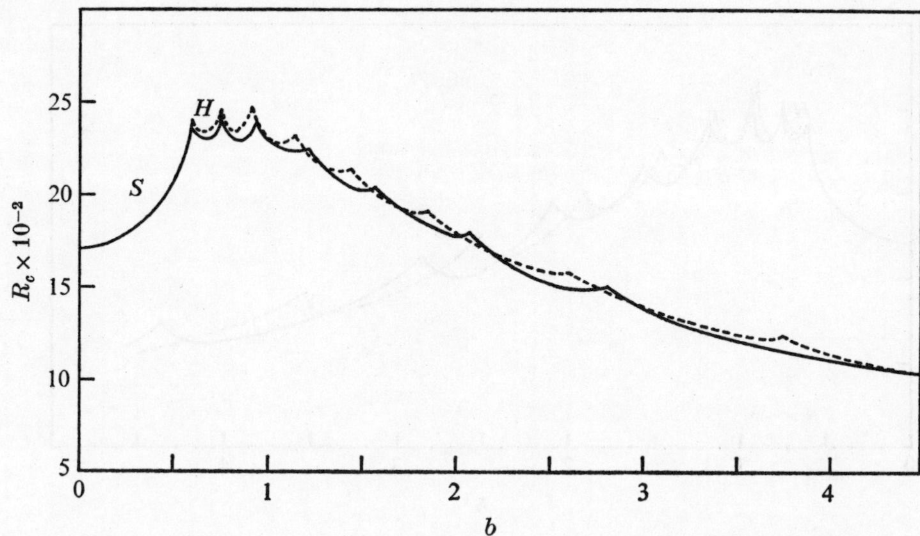

FIGURE 2. Variation of R_c with b at $\sigma = 0.73$ and $\omega = 5$. – – –, first approximation; ———, second approximation. S signifies 'synchronous' and H signifies 'half-frequency', for the curve below. S and H alternate for the curves to the right.

of the primary temperature field is stabilizing. This agrees largely with the findings of Venezian (1969), who found a (very weak) destabilizing effect of the unsteady part of the primary temperature only in one special case of σ, and treated both boundaries as 'free'. It also agrees with Donnelly's (1964) findings for the related problem of Taylor vortices that oscillation of one cylinder can only stabilize the Couette flow. Beyond $b = 1$, however, the effect of this part is generally destabilizing.

Figure 3 is similar in every respect to figure 2, with the only difference that the R is for neutral stability at $a = 3.117$ instead of $a = a_c$. Hence the R is a little more than the R_c in figure 2. The fact that they do not differ by very much shows that a_c is never very different from 3.

For both figures 2 and 3, the value of R_c or R at $b = 0$ is 1715·08 for the first approximation and 1707·94 for the second, both of which correspond to $a = 3.117$. These figures agree, as they should, with Chandrasekhar's (1961) values. With this in mind it is interesting to mention that Gresho & Sani (1970) used Galerkin's method and obtained (for their problem and for $\omega = 0$, which corresponds to the Bénard problem and to $b = 0$ in our study) for R_c the value 1825 at $a = 3.117$ with one trial function, and the value 1710·1 at $a = 3.117$ with five trial functions. The 'exact' value is 1707·8.

In view of the fact that the R_c–b or R–b curves in figures 2 and 3 are smooth for $b < 0.6$, we have computed the R_c values for various values of $b \leqslant 4.5$, for values of ω other than 5, and for $\sigma = 0.73$ (air). The results are given in table 1. For $\sigma = 7$ (water) table 2 gives R_c and a_c for $\omega = 10$ and various values of b. Both tables show that in the range of b indicated the unstable part of the primary temperature field is stabilizing.

It remains to compare our results with those of Rosenblat & Tanaka (1971). If one compares their figures 3 and 4 with our figures 2 and 3, it appears that

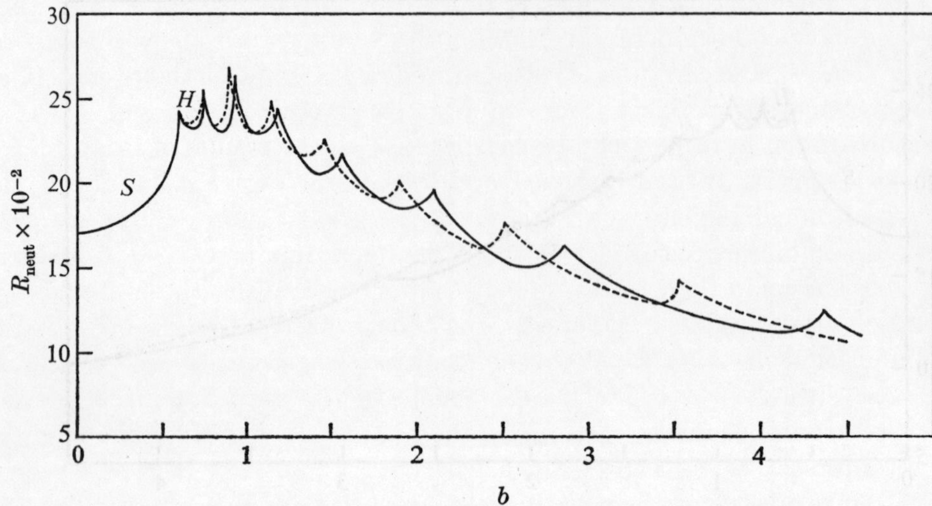

FIGURE 3. Variation of R at neutral stability with b at $\sigma = 0.73$, $\omega = 5$ and $a = 3.117$. – – –, first approximation; ——, second approximation. S signifies 'synchronous' and H signifies 'half-frequency', for the curve below. S and H alternate for the curves to the right.

b/ω	1·0	2·5	5·0	10·0
0	1715·08	1715·08	1715·08	1715·08
0·5	2040	2037	2020	1976
0·75	2450	2403	2450	2354
1·0	2382	2352	2308	2411
1·25	2253	2227	2190	2130
1·5	2113	2098	2068	2005
2·5	1592	1600	1584	1526
4·5	1034	1059	1043	1021

TABLE 1. Variation of the critical Rayleigh number R_c with the fluctuation amplitude b and frequency ω for $\sigma = 0.73$ (air); first approximation.

b	R_c	a_c
0	1715·08	3·117
0·5	1764	3·1
1·0	1951	3·0
2·5	4048	4·0
5·0	2650	3·8

TABLE 2. Variations of the critical Rayleigh number R_c and the critical wavenumber a_c with b at $\sigma = 7.0$ (water) and $\omega = 10$; first approximation.

their R_c increases monotonically with ϵ (our b), whereas for $b > 0.6$ our results show loops of alternating H curves and S curves. Possibly, for their temperature profile, R_c is monotonic with ϵ for $\epsilon < 1$. It is also possible that their calculation followed the initial S curve even after its intersection with an H curve. Up to $b = 0.6$, our R_c increases with b (as does theirs with ϵ), and is of the same order of magnitude as their R_c. In comparing our R_c with theirs, it must be kept in

152   *C.-S. Yih and C.-H. Li*

mind that our temperature profile is different from theirs (since only their bottom boundary condition involves oscillating temperature, the top temperature being steady), and that our R_c should not be the same as theirs even if all the other parameters (ω, b, etc.) were equal in the two cases.

Our results given in table 1 can be compared with the results of Rosenblat & Tanaka (1971) given in their figures 1 and 2. Although for $b = 0.5$ our R_c decreases monotonically with ω, in agreement with their figure 1 (for $\epsilon = 0.4$), for $b = 1$ (corresponding to their $\epsilon = 1$) our R_c has a minimum near $\omega = 5$, whereas the R_c values shown in their figure 2 decrease monotonically with the frequency. Taking a look at our figures 2 and 3, we think the qualitative disagreement comes from the fact that at $b = 1$ we already encounter the second H curve, whereas in their case either $\epsilon = 1$ is still in the region of the first S curve (for their temperature profile) or in the calculation they have followed their first S curve beyond an intersection with an H curve.

In brief, our results do not necessarily contradict those of Rosenblat & Tanaka.

The work of C.-S. Yih has been jointly supported by the National Science Foundation and Office of Naval Research. The work of C.-H. Li was supported by the A.F.O.S.R. through Grant AFOSR-68-1485 to the Case Western Reserve University administered by Dr S. Ostrach.

REFERENCES

BENJAMIN, T. B. & URSELL, F. 1954 The stability of the plane free surface of a liquid in vertical periodic motion. *Proc. Roy. Soc.* A **225**, 505–515.

CHANDRASEKHAR, S. 1954 The stability of viscous flow between rotating cylinders. *Mathematika,* **1**, 5–13.

CHANDRASEKHAR, S. 1961 *Hydrodynamic and Hydromagnetic Stability.* Oxford University Press.

CODDINGTON, E. A. & LEVINSON, N. 1955 *Theory of Ordinary Differential Equations,* pp. 78–81. McGraw-Hill.

DONNELLY, R. J. 1964 Experiments on the stability of viscous flow between rotating cylinders. III. Enhancement of stability by modulation. *Proc. Roy. Soc.* A **281**, 130–139.

GRESHO, P. M. & SANI, R. L. 1970 The effects of gravity modulation on the stability of a heated layer. *J. Fluid Mech.* **40**, 783–806.

INCE, E. L. 1944 *Ordinary Differential Equations.* Dover.

PELLEW, A. & SOUTHWELL, R. V. 1940 On maintained convective motion in a fluid heated from below. *Proc. Roy. Soc.* A **176**, 312–343.

ROSENBLAT, S. 1968 Centrifugal instability of time-dependent flows. Part 1. Inviscid periodic flows. *J. Fluid Mech.* **33**, 321–336.

ROSENBLAT, S. & HERBERT, D. M. 1970 Low-frequency modulation of thermal instability. *J. Fluid Mech.* **43**, 385–398.

ROSENBLAT, S. & TANAKA, G. A. 1971 Modulation of thermal convection instability. *Phys. Fluids,* **14**, 1319–1322.

VENEZIAN, G. 1969 Effect of modulation on the onset of thermal convection. *J. Fluid Mech.* **35**, 243–254.

YIH, C.-S. 1968 Instability of unsteady flows or configurations, Part 1. Instability of a horizontal liquid layer on an oscillating plane. *J. Fluid Mech.* **31**, 737–752.

J. Fluid Mech. (1973), *vol.* 58, *part* 4, *pp.* 703–708

Wave velocity in parallel flows of a viscous fluid

By CHIA-SHUN YIH

Department of Engineering Mechanics, The University of Michigan

(Received 8 December 1972)

It is shown in this note that the velocity of unstable or neutral waves in plane Poiseuille flow or plane Couette–Poiseuille flow, or of axisymmetric waves in Poiseuille flow, stable or unstable, must lie within the range of the velocity of the flow.

1. Introduction

Bounds for the real part of the complex wave velocity c appearing in the Orr–Sommerfeld equation have been given by Synge (1938) for plane Couette and Poiseuille flows. Synge's results were extended by Pai (1954) to apply to more general flows, and Pai's results were sharpened by Joseph (1968). For the plane Couette flow it is already evident from Synge's results that the real part of $c = c_r + ic_i$ must be within the range of the velocity U of the flow, whatever its imaginary part may be. For other flows the bounds of c_r given by all three authors mark an interval greater than the range of U; but their results are for all possible values of c_i, hence for all kinds of waves – amplified, neutral or damped.

In this note we shall derive some results from which we deduce immediately that the velocity c_r of unstable and neutral waves (in fact, even some damped ones) in plane Poiseuille and plane Couette–Poiseuille flows (combinations of a plane Couette flow with a plane Poiseuille flow) must be within the range of the velocity of the flow. Furthermore, we shall show that axisymmetric disturbances in Poiseuille flow (in circular pipes) always propagate with a velocity which is within the range of the velocity of the flow, whether the disturbances are stable, neutral or unstable.

2. Recapitulation of some known results for plane flows

The Orr–Sommerfeld equation is

$$(D^2 - \alpha^2)^2 \phi = i\alpha R[(U - c)(D^2 - \alpha^2)\phi - U''\phi], \tag{1}$$

in which the unknown ϕ is the (complex) amplitude of the stream function, α is the wavenumber, R the Reynolds number, U the dimensionless velocity (in the x direction), c the complex wave velocity $c_r + ic_i$ and

$$D = d/dy, \quad U'' = D^2 U,$$

y being the dimensionless Cartesian co-ordinate normal to the direction of flow, on which alone U depends. Since the stream function is

$$\psi = \phi(y) \exp\{i\alpha(x - ct)\},$$

 C.-S. Yih

the rate of growth of the waves is αc_i, and the waves are stable, neutral or unstable according as c_i is negative, zero or positive. The parameters α and R are by definition positive. With ϕ' denoting $D\phi$, the boundary conditions are

$$\phi(0) = \phi'(0) = 0 = \phi(1) = \phi'(1). \tag{2}$$

By multiplying (1) by ϕ^*, the complex conjugate of ϕ, and integrating, using (2) whenever necessary, Synge (1938) obtained

$$\int |(D^2 - \alpha^2)\phi|^2 + \alpha R c_i \int P = i\alpha R\big[-\int (U-c)P + \int U'\phi\phi'^*\big], \tag{3}$$

in which
$$P = |\phi'|^2 + \alpha^2|\phi|^2,$$

the limits of integration are understood to be zero and one, and the differential dy is omitted for all integrals, for convenience. Since

$$\mathrm{Re} \int U'\phi\phi'^* = -\tfrac{1}{2}\int U''|\phi|^2,$$

we conclude from (3), upon taking its imaginary part, that

$$\int (U-c_r)P + \tfrac{1}{2}\int U''|\phi|^2 = 0. \tag{4}$$

From (4) we obtain the following known results which were already evident from the results of Synge [see equation (3) of Joseph (1968), which is Synge's result]:

$$c_r > U_{\min} \quad \text{if} \quad U'' \geqslant 0 \text{ throughout,} \tag{5}$$

$$c_r < U_{\max} \quad \text{if} \quad U'' \leqslant 0 \text{ throughout,} \tag{6}$$

$$U_{\min} < c_r < U_{\max} \quad \text{if} \quad U'' = 0 \text{ throughout.} \tag{7}$$

These results of Synge are for any waves (or disturbances), amplified, neutral or damped.

3. New results for unstable and neutral waves in plane flows

Let $F(y)$ be defined by
$$(U-c)F = \phi. \tag{8}$$

Note that F is never infinite if $c_i \neq 0$, or if c_r is *outside* the range of U. The Orr–Sommerfeld equation then becomes

$$(D^2 - \alpha^2)^2[(U-c)F] = i\alpha R\{[(U-c)^2 F']' - \alpha^2(U-c)^2 F\}, \tag{9}$$

in which the prime indicates differentiation with respect to y. The boundary conditions on F are, so long as $U-c$ does not vanish on the boundary (we shall return to this point later),

$$F(0) = F'(0) = 0 = F(1) = F'(1). \tag{10}$$

Multiplying (9) by F^*, the complex conjugate of F, and integrating between zero and one, using (10) whenever necessary, we obtain

$$\int (U-c_r)|(D^2-\alpha^2)F|^2 - 2\int U''|F'|^2 + \tfrac{1}{2}\int U^{\mathrm{iv}}|F|^2 - ic_i\int|(D^2-\alpha^2)F|^2 - \alpha^2\int U''|F|^2$$
$$+ \int U'(F'F^{*\prime\prime} - F^{*\prime}F'') - \tfrac{1}{2}\int U'''(FF^{*\prime} - F'F^*) + \alpha^2\int U'(FF^{*\prime} - F^*F')$$
$$= i\alpha R\{-\int[(U-c_r)^2 - c_i^2]Q + i2c_i\int(U-c_r)Q\}, \tag{11}$$

in which
$$Q = |F'|^2 + \alpha^2 |F|^2. \tag{11a}$$

The last four terms on the left-hand side of (11) are imaginary. Taking the real part of (11), we obtain

$$\int (U - c_r)\left[|(D^2 - \alpha^2)F|^2 + 2\alpha R c_i Q\right] - 2\int U''|F'|^2 + \tfrac{1}{2}\int U^{iv}|F|^2 - \alpha^2\int U''|F|^2 = 0. \tag{12}$$

From this equation we conclude that

$$U_{\max} > c_r \quad \text{if} \quad c_i > 0, \quad \text{and} \quad U'' \geqslant 0, \quad U^{iv} \leqslant 0 \text{ throughout}, \tag{13}$$

$$U_{\min} < c_r \quad \text{if} \quad c_i > 0, \quad \text{and} \quad U'' \leqslant 0, \quad U^{iv} \geqslant 0 \text{ throughout}. \tag{14}$$

If $c_i = 0$, the function F is well defined if $c_r > U_{\max}$ or $c_r < U_{\min}$, and (12) states that, for neutral waves,

$$c_r > U_{\max} \text{ is impossible, or } U_{\max} \geqslant c_r, \text{ if } U'' \geqslant 0, \ U^{iv} \leqslant 0 \text{ throughout}, \tag{15}$$

$$c_r < U_{\min} \text{ is impossible, or } U_{\min} \leqslant c_r, \text{ if } U'' \leqslant 0, \ U^{iv} \geqslant 0 \text{ throughout}. \tag{16}$$

For plane Poiseuille flow or plane Couette–Poiseuille flows, U'' is either positive throughout or negative throughout, and U^{iv} is zero. Hence for such flows (5), (6), (13) and (14) give

$$U_{\min} < c_r < U_{\max} \quad \text{for} \quad c_i > 0, \tag{17}$$

and (5), (6), (15) and (16) give

$$U_{\min} < c_r \leqslant U_{\max} \quad \text{if} \quad U'' > 0, \quad c_i = 0, \tag{18}$$

$$U_{\min} \leqslant c_r < U_{\max} \quad \text{if} \quad U'' < 0, \quad c_i = 0. \tag{19}$$

In the next section we shall show that for neutral waves in plane Poiseuille or plane Couette–Poiseuille flows c_r cannot attain $U_{\max}$ or $U_{\min}$. This point is important whenever one attempts to calculate the neutral-stability curves by asymptotic methods, for if $c_r = U_{\max}$ or $c_r = U_{\min}$ the critical layer would always include the boundary, however large the Reynolds number, and the existing calculations would break down.

4. Neutral and some damped modes in plane flows

We now concentrate on plane Poiseuille and plane Couette–Poiseuille flows. Thus
$$U'' = \text{constant}, \quad U^{iv} = 0.$$

We shall define a new F by

$$(U - c_1)F = \phi, \tag{20}$$

where
$$c_1 = c_r + ic_{1i} = c_r + i[c_i + 4\pi^2(\alpha R)^{-1}]. \tag{21}$$

Note that F is never infinite if

$$c_i > -4\pi^2(\alpha R)^{-1}.$$

The Orr–Sommerfeld equation can then be written as

$$(D^2 - \alpha^2)^2 \phi + 4\pi^2(\phi'' - \alpha^2\phi) = i\alpha R[(U - c_1)(\phi'' - \alpha^2\phi) - U''\phi],$$

or

$$(D^2 - \alpha^2)\left[(D^2 - \alpha^2) + 4\pi^2\right]\left[(U - c_1)F\right] = i\alpha R\{[(U - c_1)^2 F']' - \alpha^2(U - c_1)^2 F\}, \tag{22}$$

706   *C.-S. Yih*

with the boundary conditions

$$F(0) = F'(0) = 0 = F(1) = F'(1). \tag{23}$$

By multiplying (22) by F^* and integrating between zero and 1, using (23) whenever necessary, we obtain

$$T - i4\pi^2(\alpha R)^{-1} \int |(D^2 - \alpha^2) F|^2 - 4\pi^2 \int (U - c_1) Q - 4\pi^2 \int U' F F'^*$$
$$= -i\alpha R \int (U - c_1)^2 Q = -i\alpha R \left\{ \int [(U - c_r)^2 - c_{1i}^2] Q - 2ic_{1i} \int (U - c_r) Q \right\}, \tag{24}$$

in which Q is defined by (11a), with the F therein defined by (20), and T stands for terms on the left-hand side of (11), with the F now defined by (20). Noting that

$$\mathrm{Re} \int U' F F'^* = -\tfrac{1}{2} \int U'' |F|^2,$$

and taking the real part of (24), we have (now that U'' is constant and $U^{\mathrm{iv}} = 0$)

$$\int (U - c_r) \left[|(D^2 - \alpha^2) F|^2 + 2(\alpha R c_i + 2\pi^2) Q \right] = 2U'' I + \alpha^2 \int U'' |F|^2, \tag{25}$$

in which

$$I = \int (|F'|^2 - \pi^2 |F|^2) \geqslant 0, \tag{26}$$

as is well known. Thus (25) gives

$$c_r < U_{\max} \quad \text{if} \quad U'' > 0, \quad c_i \geqslant -2\pi^2(\alpha R)^{-1}, \tag{27}$$

$$U_{\min} < c_r \quad \text{if} \quad U'' < 0, \quad c_i \geqslant -2\pi^2(\alpha R)^{-1}. \tag{28}$$

Note that for

$$c_i \geqslant -2\pi^2(\alpha R)^{-1} \tag{29}$$

F is certainly well defined (i.e. it never becomes infinite) by (20), for any values of c_r. On combining (27) and (28) with (5) and (6), we conclude that when (29) is satisfied

$$U_{\min} < c_r < U_{\max}$$

for plane Poiseuille and plane Couette–Poiseuille flows; or, ignoring the damped modes, we may state the results in the following theorem

THEOREM 1. *The velocity* (c_r) *of neutral or unstable shear waves in plane Poiseuille flow or in plane Couette–Poiseuille flows must be within the range of the velocity of the flow, and the maximum or minimum of the flow velocity is never attained by* c_r.

Recalling also that c_i is bounded (Yih 1969) above by

$$h = \frac{q}{2\alpha} - \frac{\lambda^2}{\alpha R} \tag{30}$$

with

$$\lambda^2 = \min \frac{I_2 + 2\alpha^2 I_1 + \alpha^4 I_0}{I_1 + \alpha^2 I_0},$$

$$I_2 = \int |\phi''|^2, \quad I_1 = \int |\phi'|^2, \quad I_0 = \int |\phi|^2,$$

$$q = \max |U'(y)|,$$

we can state the following theorem.

THEOREM 2. *For plane Poiseuille or plane Couette–Poiseuille flows, the eigenvalues* c *for neutral and unstable waves lie inside or on the horizontal boundaries*

Wave velocity in parallel viscous flows

of a rectangle in the complex-c plane which has the range of the flow velocity as its base and h defined by (30) as its height, provided h is positive.†

This theorem (a rectangle theorem) corresponds to Howard's semicircle theorem for the Rayleigh equation or the differential equation for flows of an inviscid stratified fluid (Howard 1961), and I present it to Professor Howard in return for the delight that his semicircle theorem has given me.

5. Results for Poiseuille flow

For Poiseuille flow the mean velocity is given by

$$W(r) = W_0(1 - r^2),$$

in which r is the radial distance from the centre-line of the circular pipe, measured in units of the pipe radius r_0. For axisymmetric disturbances the Stokes stream function ψ can be used, and the perturbation part of it, denoted by ψ', has the form

$$\psi' = \phi(r) \exp\{i\alpha(z - ct)\},$$

in which z is measured along the centre-line in units of r_0, α is the dimensionless wavenumber, c is the complex wave velocity $(c_r + ic_i)$ measured in units of W_0, and t is the time, measured in units of r_0/W_0. Then the equation governing stability is‡

$$(L - \alpha^2)^2 \phi = i\alpha R(1 - r^2 - c)(L - \alpha^2)\phi, \tag{31}$$

in which $R = W_0 r_0/\nu$ is the Reynolds number and

$$L = \frac{d^2}{dr^2} + \frac{1}{r}\frac{d}{dr} - \frac{1}{r^2} = \frac{d}{dr}\left(\frac{d}{dr} + \frac{1}{r}\right) = \frac{d}{dr}\left[\frac{1}{r}\frac{d}{dr}(r\ )\right].$$

The boundary conditions are (if primes denote d/dr)

$$\phi(1) = 0 = \phi'(1), \quad \phi(r) \quad \text{regular at} \quad r = 0. \tag{32}$$

If (31) is multiplied by $r\phi^* \, dr$ and integrated from zero to one, the result is, after (32) has been applied,

$$I_2 + 2\alpha^2 I_1 + \alpha^4 I_0 = -i\alpha R \int_0^1 (1 - r^2 - c) Q \, dr + i2\alpha R \int_0^1 (r\phi)'(r\phi^*) \, dr, \tag{33}$$

in which

$$Q = r^{-1}|(r\phi)'|^2 + \alpha^2 r|\phi|^2,$$

$$I_0 \int_0^1 r|\phi|^2 \, dr, \quad I_1 = \int_0^1 \frac{1}{r}|(r\phi)'|^2 \, dr, \quad I_2 = \int_0^1 r|L\phi|^2 \, dr.$$

Since

$$J \equiv \int_0^1 (r\phi)'(r\phi^*) \, dr = -\int_0^1 (r\phi^*)'(r\phi) \, dr,$$

the real part of J is zero. Taking the imaginary part of (33), we have

$$\int_0^1 (1 - r^2 - c_r) Q \, dr = 0,$$

---

† If h is zero or negative for some R, the flow is stable (at most neutrally stable) for that value of R, and we do not need theorem 2.

‡ Apart from slight changes in notation, this is equation (1.3.34) in Lin (1955, p. 10), in which σ should read σR.

708   *C.-S. Yih*

which demands that $0 < c_r < 1,$ (34)

which states that c_r is within the range of W/W_0, or that the dimensional wave velocity $c_r W_0$ is within the range of W.

We shall now establish an upper bound for c_i. First we note that the regularity of $\phi(r)$ at $r = 0$ implies that $\phi(0) = 0$, as indeed it must, for otherwise the radial part (u) of the perturbation velocity would be infinite there. Since

$$\phi(1) = 0 = \phi(0) \quad \text{and} \quad 0 \leqslant r \leqslant 1,$$

we have $I_1 \equiv \int (1/r) \, |(r\phi)'_{\,|}|^2 > \int |(r\phi)'|^2 \geqslant \pi^2 \int |r\phi|^2,$ (35)

as is well known. Furthermore, Schwarz's inequality gives

$$i2 \int (r\phi)' \, (r\phi^*) \leqslant 2 \int |(r\phi)'| \, |r\phi^*| \leqslant \int |(r\phi)'|^2 + \int |r\phi|^2.$$ (36)

Hence $i2J \leqslant \dfrac{\pi^2 + 1}{\pi^2} \int |(r\phi)'|^2 < \dfrac{\pi^2 + 1}{\pi^2} I_4, \quad \text{with} \quad I_4 = \int Q \, dr.$ (37)

Taking the real part of (33), we have

$$-\alpha R c_i I_4 + i2\alpha R J = I_2 + 2\alpha^2 I_1 + \alpha^4 I_0,$$

from which we deduce, using (37), the result

$$c_i < h \equiv < \frac{\pi^2 + 1}{\pi^2} - \frac{\lambda^2}{\alpha R},$$ (38)

where $\lambda^2 = \min \dfrac{I_2 + 2\alpha^2 I_1 + \alpha^4 I_0}{I_4}.$ (39)

The value of λ^2 can be calculated from (39) and the boundary conditions on ϕ. We shall state the results obtained in this section in the following two theorems.

THEOREM 3. For Poiseuille flow, the velocity c_r of all shear waves, whether they be stable, neutral or unstable, must be within the range of the velocity of the flow, the maximum or minimum of which is never attained by c_r.

THEOREM 4. For Poiseuille flow, the eigenvalues c for neutral or unstable waves lie inside or on the lower horizontal boundary of a rectangle in the complex-c plane, which has the range of the flow velocity as its base and h defined in (38) as its height, provided h is positive.

This work has been jointly supported by the National Science Foundation and the Office of Naval Research.

REFERENCES

HOWARD, L. N. 1961 Note on a paper by John W. Miles. *J. Fluid Mech.* **10**, 509–512.

JOSEPH, D. D. 1968 Eigenvalue bounds for the Orr–Sommerfeld equation. *J. Fluid Mech.* **33**, 617–621.

LIN, C. C. 1955 *The Theory of Hydrodynamic Stability*. Cambridge University Press.

PAI, S. I. 1954 On a generalization of Synge's criterion for sufficient stability of plane parallel flows. *Quart. Appl. Math.* **12**, 203–206.

SYNGE, J. L. 1938 Hydrodynamical stability. *Semicentenn. Publ. Am. Math. Soc.* **2**, 227–269.

YIH, C.-S. 1969 Note on eigenvalue bounds for the Orr–Sommerfeld equation. *J. Fluid Mech.* **38**, 273–278.

Instability of stratified flows as a result of resonance

Chia-Shun Yih

Department of Applied Mechanics and Engineering Science, The University of Michigan, Ann Arbor, Michigan 48104

(Received 26 October 1973; final manuscript received 20 March 1974)

The stability of stratified flows consisting of a middle layer of homogeneous fluid in linear shear flow and contiguous upper and lower stratified layers of constant velocities is considered. The density and velocity are continuous throughout. It is shown that there are infinitely many pairs of neutral modes with the phase velocity c_r in the range of the velocity which, in general, are not represented by the stability boundary, but which merge as the parameter N (the inverse of the Froude number squared) increases. As N increases further the coalesced neutral modes become modes with complex c, one of which is unstable. The instability may be considered to be caused by the resonance of the original pair of separate modes. In addition, instability of stratified flows is considered for general density and velocity distributions without a layer of constant density and linear velocity, and it is concluded that in that case the modes with complex c on the unstable side of a stability boundary do not continue into any neutral normal modes on the stable side.

I. INTRODUCTION

Miles[1] and Howard[2] showed that if the Richardson number for parallel flows of an inviscid stratified fluid is everywhere greater than 0.25, the flow must be stable. Later, Yih[3] showed that if the density $\bar{\rho}$ decreases monotonically and the velocity U increases monotonically upward, and if (i) $(\bar{\rho}U')'$ and $(ln\bar{\rho})''$ are positive throughout, the primes indicating differentiation with respect to the vertical distance y, or (ii) U'' and $(ln\bar{\rho})''$ are negative throughout, the flow is stable, even if the Richardson number is not everywhere (or even nowhere) greater than 0.25.

The study of stability of stratified flows is then reduced to the study of cases where the sufficient conditions for stability found by Miles, Howard, and Yih do not lead to the conclusion of stability. Calculations by Miles[4] for cases in which U varies monotonically and has a point of inflection fall into this category, and give neutral curves (stability boundaries) which are multivalued. This multivaluedness was explained by Yih[3] in connection with flows in which there is a point where $\bar{\rho}' = U'' = 0$. The calculations of Miles[4] were carried out with a good deal of virtuosity and understanding them requires some knowledge of the theory of hypergeometric functions. And yet neither Miles nor Yih explained exactly what happens to the wave velocity c as the neutral curves cross from the unstable to the stable side.

In this paper we consider a class of flows characterized by (i) a middle layer with constant density and linear velocity, (ii) a stably stratified upper layer with a constant velocity, (iii) a stably stratified lower layer with a constant velocity, and (iv) the density and the velocity are continuous throughout. We discuss the stability of this flow in a general way, and reach the important conclusions that instability is the result of a kind of resonance, that there are infinitely many modes which, in the neutral cases at least, are characterized by the number of internal zeros, and that for the flows considered here gravity is always destabilizing.

It seems that the conclusions to be drawn for the class of flows being considered will lead to a better understanding of the stability of stratified flows, for which the neutral curves, such as those given by Miles,[4] seem to defy any

intuitive interpretation. Numerical results are given for exponential stratifications in the upper and lower layers, with the simplification afforded by the Boussinesq approximation.

Stability of stratified flows, in general, not subject to condition (i) is then considered, and it is shown that neutral normal modes which are continuations of complex-conjugate unstable and damped modes across the stability boundary do not exist.

II. THE MEAN FLOW

We shall consider a two-dimensional flow consisting of three layers. The indices 1, 2, and 3 are assigned to the lower, middle, and upper layers, respectively, and the depths of the layers will be denoted by d_1 d_2 and d_3. Cartesian coordinates x and y will be used, with y measured in the direction of the vertical, and with the origin at the midpoint of the middle layer. For convenience let

$$d_2 = 2d.$$

Then, the velocity in the middle layer is Vy/d, the velocity in the upper layer is V, and that in the lower layer is $-V$. The density in the middle layer is constant and is denoted by ρ_0. The mean density $\bar{\rho}$ in the upper or the lower layer is such that $\bar{\rho}' < 0$, but is otherwise unspecified until the numerical example is discussed.

III. THE DIFFERENTIAL SYSTEM

The differential equation governing stability is well known. However, in formulating the interfacial boundary conditions we need to use some of the equations leading to it; therefore, we give a very brief derivation of it. Let u and v be the components of the velocity perturbation, and let the perturbations in pressure and in density be denoted by p and ρ, respectively. Then, the linearized Euler's equations of motion are, with subscripts indicating partial differentiation,

$$\bar{\rho}(u_t + Uu_x + vU') = -p_x, \tag{1}$$

$$\bar{\rho}(v_t + Uv_x) = -p_y - g\rho. \tag{2}$$

The equation of continuity is, since the fluid is assumed incompressible,

$$u_x + v_y = 0, \tag{3}$$

which allows the use of a stream function ψ, in terms of which

$$u = \psi_y, \qquad v = -\psi_x. \tag{4}$$

The linearized equation of incompressibility is

$$\rho_t + U\rho_x + v\bar{\rho}' = 0. \tag{5}$$

Let

$$\psi = f(y)\, \exp[ik(x - ct)].$$

Then, from (4) and (5) we have

$$(u, v, \rho) = \left(f', -ikf, \frac{1}{U - c}\bar{\rho}' \right) \exp[ik(x - ct)], \tag{6}$$

and (1) gives

$$p = \bar{\rho}(cf' - Uf' + U'f)\, \exp[ik(x - ct)]. \tag{7}$$

Substitution of (6) and (7) into (2) gives

$$(\bar{\rho}f')' - \left(\frac{(\bar{\rho}U')'}{U - c} + k^2\bar{\rho} + \frac{g\bar{\rho}'}{(U - c)^2} \right) f = 0. \tag{8}$$

Let U and c be measured in units of a velocity scale V, $\bar{\rho}$ in units of a constant density ρ_0, y in units of a length scale d, and let

$$\alpha = kd.$$

Then f is measured in units of Vd, and (8) can be written as

$$(\bar{\rho}f')' - \left(\frac{(\bar{\rho}U')'}{U - c} + \alpha^2\bar{\rho} + \frac{N\bar{\rho}'}{(U - c)^2} \right) f = 0, \tag{9}$$

with (note that N is not the Brunt–Väisälä frequency)

$$N = gd/V^2. \tag{10}$$

For the mean velocity distribution specified in Sec. II, the interfacial conditions are, since U and $\bar{\rho}$ are continuous, (i) the continuity of f, (ii) the continuity of p. In dimensionless terms, the mean velocity is given by

$$U = 1 \text{ for } y \geq 1, \qquad U = y \text{ for } |y| \leq 1,$$
$$U = -1 \text{ for } y \leq -1. \tag{11}$$

The interfacial conditions are

$$f_1(-1) = f_2(-1),$$
$$(c + 1)f_1'(-1) = (c + 1)f_2'(-1) + f_2(-1), \tag{12}$$
$$f_2(1) = f_3(1),$$
$$(c - 1)f_3'(1) = (c - 1)f_2'(1 + f_2)(1). \tag{13}$$

The boundary conditions at the rigid boundaries are

$$f_1(-1 - a) = 0, \qquad f_3(1 + b) = 0, \tag{14}$$

where

$$a = d_1/d, \qquad b = d_3/d. \tag{15}$$

IV. THE RESONANCE THEORY OF INSTABILITY

Although Kelvin's[5] solution for the stability (Helmholtz instability) of a vortex sheet between two fluids of different densities already indicated the importance of resonance, it was Taylor[6] who first explicitly recognized the resonance of two wave trains in the shear flow of a stratified fluid to be the cause of instability. However, as far as resonant forcing is concerned, Taylor was discussing the flow of three homogeneous layers only. We shall, for the U specified in Sec. II, develop this resonance theory generally, for all modes, for the U and $\bar{\rho}$ specified in Sec. II. (Note that $\bar{\rho}$ is not specified in the bottom and top layers, except that $\bar{\rho}' < 0$.) When a wave train propagating against the part of the fluid moving with the greater velocity and another propagating with the part of the fluid moving with the smaller velocity have the same velocity in space, they can force each other and cause instability. Thus, the coalescence of two distinct neutral modes signifies the beginning of instability. We consider this mutual forcing to be a kind of resonance. We shall use the constant density ρ_0 in the middle layer to be the density scale, so that the dimensionless density in the middle layer is 1, or

$$\bar{\rho} = 1 \qquad \text{for } |y| \leq 1. \tag{16}$$

First, we note that at the interfaces $\bar{\rho}$ and U are continuous but U' is discontinuous. Integration of (9) in the Stieltjes sense across the interfaces produces the second conditions in (12) and (13), so that these are *natural* conditions, and the Sturm–Liouville theory can be applied to (9) and (14), without concern about (12) and (13), so long as $|c| \neq 1$, so that (9) is not singular. We now apply that theory.

We consider real values of c with $|c| < 1$, for Howard's[2] semicircle theorem tells us that the neutral modes contiguous with the unstable ones must have their c satisfying $|c| \leq 1$, and Miles[1] has ruled out the extreme values of U as possible values for c.

First, we note that for $N = 0$ (zero gravity) there may be one or two positive values of α^2 which enable a solution of (9) to satisfy the boundary conditions and interfacial conditions, since the term in (9) containing $(\rho U')'(U - c)^{-1}$, considered as a generalized function at the interfaces, has, for the U specified in Sec. II, the effect of making the coefficient of f in (9) positive. There can be no more than two modes for $N = 0$, the first having no internal node and the second only one. For if there were a third mode it would, according to the Sturm–Liouville theory, have two internal nodes, and either one of them would be in the bottom and top layers, or both would be in the middle layer. In either case the eigenfunction f in (9) would have two nodes in *one* of the three layers (remembering that f is zero on the solid boundaries), and this is quite impossible, since $N = 0$, and the coefficient of f in (9) is now always negative between these nodes, because no interface is crossed. We are mainly interested in the neutral curves in the N-α plane. All that we have said above means that, for the $\bar{\rho}$ and U specified in Sec. II, there may be one or two values of α (positive by choice) at which the neutral curves intersect the axis $N = 0$.

For higher modes we can always increase N. With the understanding that n may have to be greater than 2 for small α^2, for any given α and for a specified number $(n - 1)$ of internal zeros of the eigenfunction, we can always choose an N and two corresponding c's so that the boundary conditions (14) are satisfied by f, the solution of (9), for we can make $-N\bar{\rho}'/(U - c)^2$ for the bottom or the top layers as large as we please by choosing $|c|$ very near 1. Let the N so chosen be denoted by N_n, and the two corresponding c's be denoted by c_{n1} and c_{n2}, the n always indicating the mode. Then, c_{n1} and c_{n2} are functions of N_n.

Still fixing n and α at any given value, we now increase N_n continuously. The Sturm–Liouville theory applied to (9) then leads to the conclusion that at a sufficiently large N_n no real c_n with $|c_n| < 1$ can exist. At some N_n the two eigenvalues c_{n1} and c_{n2} must coalesce and for greater values of N_n the eigenvalues of c must become complex. When c_{n1} coalesces with c_{n2}, the pair of values (α, N_n) must be on the stability boundary in the α-N plane, or the neutral curve. The coalescence of c_{n1} with c_{n1} (to make c_n a double eigenvalue) is a sort of resonance, for it occurs when two wave trains have the same wave velocity in a shear flow.

Note that for any given α, $n > 2$, and an N_n however small, we can always choose c_n such that

$$1 \gg 1 - |c_n|^2 > 0,$$

in order to satisfy (9) and (14). There are two values, c_{n1} and c_{n2}, for c_n. As n increases, c_{n1} is nearer and nearer 1 and c_{n2} nearer and nearer -1. As N_n is allowed to increase, c_{n1} will coalesce with c_{n2} for a value of N_n, as already explained. Thus, for any α and any integral value of n, at least from 3 onward, there is a positive N_n for which the flow is neutrally stable. That is to say, for any α there are infinitely many eigenvalues for N for neutral stability, and, correspondingly, infinitely many neutral modes.

The fact that for any n the value of N_n must increase to attain complex values of c_n shows that gravity is always destabilizing for the specified U and $\bar{\rho}$.

For more general distributions of U and $\bar{\rho}$ the situation is complicated by the following facts:

(a) If $\bar{\rho}'$ and U'' are not zero at the place where $U = c$, (9) is singular.

(b) Then, if the Richardson number at $U = c$ is less than 0.25, the eigenfunction, if one exists, must be one or the other of the two independent solutions of (9).

(c) As N is allowed to increase, there will be a limit for N beyond which the Richardson number is everywhere greater than 0.25, if $\bar{\rho}' < 0$ everywhere.

Item (c) indicates that if $\bar{\rho}' < 0$ everywhere there cannot be infinitely many neutral modes. There may be a few, or only one such mode, or none. The role of gravity will no longer always be stabilizing, as indicated by the solutions of Miles.[4]

V. AN EXAMPLE

For an example, we shall let

$$a = 2 = b,$$

and

$$\bar{\rho} = \begin{cases} \rho_0 \exp[-\beta(y - 1)] & \text{for the top layer,} \\ \rho_0 & \text{for the middle layer,} \\ \rho_0 \exp[-\beta(y + 1)] & \text{for the bottom layer,} \end{cases}$$

where y is in units of d, the half depth of the middle layer. Then, with U still specified by (11), and with f_1, f_2, and f_3 for f in the bottom, middle, and top layers, respectively, (9) has the forms

$$f_1'' - \beta f_1' - \left(\alpha^2 - \frac{\beta N}{(1 + c)^2}\right)f_1 = 0, \tag{17a}$$

$$f_2'' - \alpha^2 f_2 = 0, \tag{18}$$

$$f_3'' - \beta f_3' - \left(\alpha^2 - \frac{\beta N}{(1 - c)^2}\right)f_3 = 0. \tag{19a}$$

The interfacial conditions are still (12) and (13), and (14) now becomes

$$f_1(-3) = 0, \qquad f_3(3) = 0. \tag{20}$$

The differential system consisting of (12), (13), and (17a), (18), (19a), and (20) define an eigenvalue problem. For given α, β, and N, one can determine c from this system.

For simplicity we shall adopt the Boussinesq approximation and write (17a) and (19a) as

$$f_1'' - \left(\alpha^2 - \frac{\beta N}{(1 + c)^2}\right)f_1 = 0, \tag{17b}$$

$$f_3'' - \left(\alpha^2 - \frac{\beta N}{(1 - c)^2}\right)f_3 = 0. \tag{19b}$$

With the Boussinesq approximation, we can show that if c is an eigenvalue, so is $-c$. This is shown by making the transformation

$$\hat{y} = -y, \qquad \hat{f}_1(\hat{y}) = f_3(y), \qquad \hat{f}_3(\hat{y}) = f_1(y),$$

$$\hat{f}_2(\hat{y}) = f_2(y). \tag{21}$$

Substituting (21) into the system consisting of (12), (13), (17b), (18), (19b), and (20), and then dropping the circumflexes, we regain that system, except that c is replaced by $-c$. Thus, if c is an eigenvalue, so is $-c$.

This fact makes it clear that for any neutral mode (not necessarily corresponding to a stability boundary) and in the notation of the last section,

$$c_{n1} = -c_{n2}. \tag{22}$$

Thus, for any mode, to obtain the relationship between α

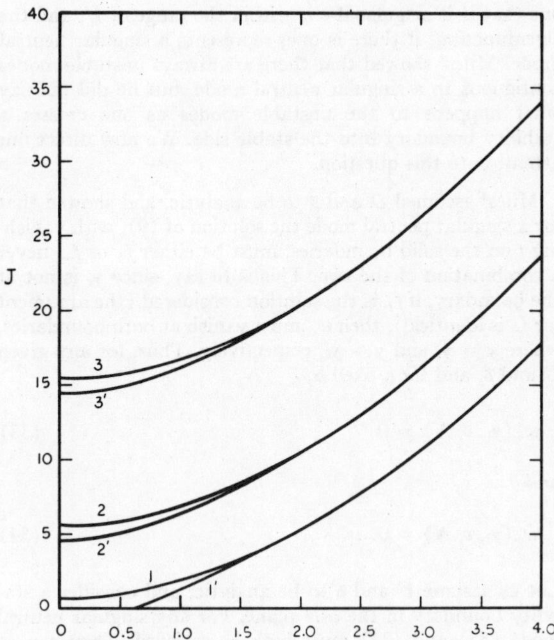

FIG. 1. Stability boundaries in the α-J plane for various modes. The nth mode for an odd eigenfunction is indicated by the number n, and the nth mode for an even eigenfunction is indicated by n'.

and βN (which are the only two parameters left aside from c) at the stability boundary, which corresponds to a double root in c, we can simply put c equal to zero, which is the value that an eigenvalue for c of multiplicity 2 must take. This simplifies matters a great deal. Putting c equal to zero and solving (17b), (18), and (19b) with interfacial conditions (12) and (13) and boundary conditions (20), we obtain the results,

$$(\alpha^2 - J)^{1/2} \coth 2(\alpha^2 - J)^{1/2} = 1 - a \tanh\alpha, \qquad (23)$$

and

$$(\alpha^2 - J)^{1/2} \coth 2(\alpha^2 - J)^{1/2} = 1 - \alpha \coth\alpha, \qquad (24)$$

representing two families of the stability boundary, with

$$J = \beta N. \qquad (25)$$

Equation (23) corresponds to $f_2(y)$ being an even function of y and (24) corresponds to $f_2(y)$ being odd. Figure 1 shows the variation of J with α on the stability boundary. The curve for the nth mode for (24) is indicated by the number n. Only three odd modes are shown. The curves for the nth mode for (23) are indicated by n'. Again, only three modes are shown.

All the conclusions of the last section are borne out. There are infinitely many modes, gravity is always destabilizing for the assumed U and $\bar{\rho}$, and resonance is the cause of instability. At a point in the α-J plane above the curves 1 and 1' but below 2', there are two unstable modes, two damped modes, and infinitely many neutral modes. The enumeration of modes at other points is similar.

Note that although for $N = 0$, Eqs. (17b) and (19b) have the same form as (18), and all these have $\exp(\pm\alpha y)$ for solutions, the boundary conditions (20) can be satisfied because there are two interfaces at which U' is discontinuous, and (12) and (13) must be applied.

For each mode J increases with α. For any given α there are infinitely many values for J, but for any J there are only a finite number of values for α. As expected, increasing α stabilizes the flow.

In addition to the modes separated by the stability boundaries (23) and (24), there are two other infinite sets of real c values outside of the range of U. These are the neutral modes not contiguous to unstable modes, discussed by Yih.[3]

VI. GENERAL DISCUSSION

So far we have discussed only the density and velocity distributions specified in Sec. II, and given an example in Sec. V, for a further specified density distribution. The arguments in Sec. IV clearly remain valid even if there are no regions of constant velocities, provided there is a region of linear velocity and constant density, and provided there are neutral modes, with their c or c_r in this region, which coalesce in the manner described in Sec. IV. Of course, if there are no regions of constant velocity, there cannot be infinitely many unstable modes because there cannot be infinitely many cases of coalescence.

We now turn to the general case, in which there is no region of linear velocity and constant density. First, we shall now use the usual definition of the Richardson number

$$J = -g\bar{\rho}'/\bar{\rho}U'^2, \qquad (26)$$

where all quantities on the right-hand side are dimensional. This definition is consistent with (25) for the density and velocity distributions considered in Secs. IV and V, and is the general definition of the Richardson number for any density and velocity distributions. Miles[4] has shown that a singular neutral mode cannot exist if the local value of J at $y = y_c$ where $U = c$, denoted by J_c, is greater than 0.25. We shall first dispose of the case in which the local J is equal to 0.25. By the method of Frobenius we obtain, in that case, the following two independent solutions of (9):

$$f_1 = (y - y_c)^{1/2} w_1, \qquad (27)$$

where

$$w_1 = 1 + A(y - y_c) + \cdots,$$

$$A = \left[(1 + J) \frac{(\bar{\rho}U')'}{\bar{\rho}U'} - \frac{J\bar{\rho}''}{\bar{\rho}'} + \gamma(\ln\bar{\rho})' \right]_c, \qquad \gamma = \tfrac{1}{2},$$

$$(28)$$

and

$$f_2 = f_1 \ln(y - y_c) - [2A + (\ln\bar{\rho})_c'](y - y_c)^{3/2}$$

$$\times [1 + B(y - y_c) + \cdots]. \qquad (29)$$

In (27) to (29), y is now supposed to be dimensionless, the prime indicates differentiation with respect to the dimensionless y, the subscripts c indicate that the quantity involved is evaluated at $y = y_c$, and B is a constant.

The Reynolds stress is defined by

$$\tau = -\bar{\rho}\overline{uv},$$

where the bar over uv means space average over x. In terms of f,

$$\tau = \frac{\rho_0 V^2}{2}\, \alpha (f'f^*)_i \exp(2\alpha c_i t), \tag{30}$$

in which the asterisk denotes the complex conjugate and the subscript i means the "imaginary part of." Suppose now that a singular neutral mode exists for $J_c = 0.25$, then the solution for f is

$$f = C_1 f_1 + C_2 f_2,$$

in which C_1 and C_2 are constants. If $C_2 \neq 0$, then one can easily show that τ suffers a jump when y crosses y_c. Now, f and f^* are also two independent solutions of (9) if c is real and C_1 and C_2 are not both real. If C_1 and C_2 are both real, then f and f^* are equal for $y > y_c$ and complex conjugate for $y < y_c$. In case C_1 and C_2 are not both real, f and f^* are independent solutions of (9), and the quantity

$$(f'f^*)_i = \frac{1}{2i}\,(f'f^* - ff'^*), \tag{31}$$

being proportional to the Wronskian of independent solutions of (9), is constant so long as the critical point is not crossed. Since it is zero at both solid boundaries (because $f = 0$ there), it cannot afford a jump at y_c if the velocity is monotonic. In case C_1 and C_2 are both real, the quantity (31) is zero for $y > y_c$ since f is real for $y > y_c$, whereas f and f^* are still two independent solutions for $y < y_c$, and the same argument applies. Thus, for $J_c = 0.25$ we can only have solution f_1, since a nonzero C_2 would give rise to a jump in the Reynolds stress. As we shall see presently, the form of f_1 in (27) is the limiting form of the solutions of (9) for $J_c < 0.25$, as J_c approaches 0.25. Thus, we need discuss only the case $J_c < 0.25$, and can treat the case $J_c = 0.25$ as a limiting case for $J_c < 0.25$.

Concentrating on the case $J_c < 0.25$, we recall that the solutions of (9) for real c in the range of U, given by Miles[4] by use of the Frobenius method, are

$$f_{\pm} = (y - y_c)^{(1 \pm \nu)/2} w_{\pm},$$

in which

$$w_{\pm} = 1 + A(y - y_c)/(1 \pm \nu) + \cdots, \tag{32}$$

with A given by (28), but with $\gamma = (1 \pm \nu)/2$ therein, and with

$$\nu = (1 - 4J_c)^{1/2}, \qquad J_c = J(y_c).$$

If $\bar{\rho}'$ and U'' are not both zero, then a look at (9) convinces

one that it is singular if c is within the range of U, and the eigenfunction, if there is one, represents a singular neutral mode. Miles[4] showed that there are always unstable modes contiguous to a singular neutral mode, but he did not say what happens to the unstable modes as one crosses a stability boundary into the stable side. We now direct our attention to this question.

Miles[4] assumed U and $\bar{\rho}$ to be analytic, and showed that for a singular neutral mode the solution of (9), with vanishing f on the solid boundaries, must be either f_+ or f_-, never a combination of the two. This is to say, since y_c is not at the boundary, if f_+ is the solution considered (the argument for f_- is identical), then w_+ must vanish at both boundaries, where $y = y_1$ and $y = y_2$, respectively. Thus, for any given U and $\bar{\rho}$, and for a fixed α,

$$w_+(y_1, c, N) = 0 \tag{33}$$

and

$$w_+(y_2, c, N) = 0. \tag{34}$$

Let us assume U and $\bar{\rho}$ to be analytic, and consider a stability boundary in the α-N plane. For any singular neutral mode (33) and (34) must both be satisfied. They can at most be satisfied by discrete pairs of values of c (real) and N, for (33) and (34) are independent, and not the same relationship between c and N. Hence, when there is a genuine singular neutral mode, it is contiguous to unstable modes (or more precisely, to modes with complex c), but not contiguous to any other singular neutral modes. In other words, the modes with complex c cannot be continued into any neutral modes on the stable side of the stability boundary, where no contiguous normal modes exist. Thus, the significance of all normal-mode analysis of the stability of stratified flows depends on the implicit assumption that when no normal modes exist the flow is stable provided the density is statically stable. These points have not been recognized before by previous investigators.

It is appropriate to mention here that, in general, a given pair (α, N) which lies in the unstable region of the α-N plane can correspond to real values of c outside of the range of U, the existence of which has been discussed by Yih.[3]

The simultaneous solution of (33) and (34) gives discrete pairs of values for c and N. The number of such pairs may be infinite if there are regions of constant velocity, in which case there must, of course, be a limit point for c within the range of U.

Summarizing the results in this and foregoing sections, we state the following results in general terms:

(i) If there is a region of constant density and linear velocity between two stratified regions of constant but different velocities, such that U and $\bar{\rho}$ are continuous, there are infinitely many unstable modes each of which are contiguous to a neutral mode with c within the range of U. As the stability boundary is crossed, the modes with complex values of c (one of which corresponds to instability) are continued into two neutral modes with c real and equal to c_1 and c_2, with

$$c_1 < c_0 < c_2,$$

where c_0 is the c on the stability boundary. In this case instability is entirely due to resonance, and there are neutral modes with their c's within the range of U which are not contiguous to unstable modes. Of course, such modes are not really singular. Therefore, this result does not contradict Miles' statement[4] that singular neutral modes are contiguous to unstable modes.

Note also that if there is a region of constant density and linear velocity, but no regions of constant velocity, there may be a finite number of neutral modes on the stability boundary, with c in this region, resulting from coalescence of pairs of neutral modes with their c's in that region.

(ii) If there are no regions of constant density and linear velocity, there exist no neutral modes contiguous with the modes with complex c as the stability boundary is crossed and the region of stability entered, except the one right on the stability boundary.

(iii) In the α-N plane, aside from the eigenvalues of c divided by the stability boundaries when the resonance theory applies, or those whose existence is bounded by stability boundaries when it does not apply, any pair of values (α, N) may correspond to one or more nonsingular modes with real values of c outside of the range of U.

ACKNOWLEDGMENTS

This work has been supported by the Office of Naval Research and the National Science Foundation.

[1] J. W. Miles, J. Fluid Mech. **10**, 496 (1961).
[2] L. N. Howard, J. Fluid Mech. **10**, 509 (1961).
[3] C.-S. Yih, in *Proceedings of Eighth Symposium of Naval Hydrodynamics* (Office of Naval Research, Washington, D. C., 1972), p. 219.
[4] J. W. Miles, J. Fluid Mech. **16**, 209 (1963).
[5] W. Thomson (Lord Kelvin), Phil. Mag. **42**, 368 (1871).
[6] G I. Taylor, Proc. R. Soc. **A132**, 499 (1931). See p. 500.

Reprinted from:
ADVANCES IN APPLIED MECHANICS, VOL. 16
© 1976
ACADEMIC PRESS, INC.
New York   San Francisco   London

Instability of Surface and Internal Waves

CHIA-SHUN YIH

Department of Applied Mechanics and Engineering Science
University of Michigan, Ann Arbor, Michigan

I. General Introduction

The instability of waves arising from the interaction of wave trains of different wave numbers and frequencies has been a subject of much recent study. The instability of surface waves propagating in water of uniform depth, finite or infinite, has been investigated by Whitham (1966) by a variational method and by Benjamin (1967) by considering two side-band wave numbers and frequencies in addition to the wave number and frequency of the primary wave train. Hasselmann (1967) demonstrated that, for dispersive waves, if the wave numbers k_1, k_2, and k_3 and their corresponding frequencies σ_1, σ_2, and σ_3 satisfy the conditions

$$k_3 = k_1 + k_2 \qquad \text{and} \qquad \sigma_3 = \sigma_1 + \sigma_2,$$

then there is interaction between the three wave trains, and if the wave train with k_1 is of finite amplitude and the other two wave trains are of infinitesimal amplitudes, then the finite wave train is unstable in that its energy will be transferred to the other two wave trains. But Hasselmann assumed the dispersion relation between σ and k to be given by the linear theory, although of course the interaction between wave trains is a result of nonlinearity. Thus it is not possible (Phillips, 1966) for surface waves to satisfy Hasselmann's conditions. Although Davis and Acrivos (1967) did find internal-wave triads satisfying Hasselmann's conditions, they did so only by resorting to different modes of the internal waves. When these conditions are satisfied, instability does result, as Hasselmann predicted.

This article is divided into two parts. The first part treats the instability of surface waves and the second part the instability of internal waves. In each part the instability of stationary waves due to a flow over a wavy boundary is treated first, and then the theory is applied to progressive waves propagating in water (stratified or not) of constant depth. Whether the waves are stationary or progressive, instability is found whenever Hasselmann's conditions are met. Yet the results presented herein are, we think, outside the pale of Hasselmann's theorem, because (a) we consider a flow over a wavy boundary whereas Hasselmann treated free waves, or (b) for freely propagating waves we consider the variation with amplitude of the wave velocity, whereas Hasselmann did not. It is hard to see how all the complicated details in this article that are necessary for reaching our results could be obviated in the proof of Hasselmann's theorem, and yet these results could be directly obtained by an application of that theorem.

When the present theory is applied to progressive surface or internal waves, instability is found only if the wave velocity increases with the amplitude of the basic wave train. The mechanism of instability is different from that of Whitham (1966) and Benjamin (1967) in that the disturbances considered in this article interact only once with the basic waves to achieve resonance, whereas in Benjamin's mechanism of instability they interact twice. (Whitham's results agree with Benjamin's, so that their mechanisms must be identical or equivalent.) A further difference, not unrelated to the one just mentioned, is that the wave numbers of the disturbances are not necessarily near the wave number of the basic wave train. We shall compare our results with Benjamin's later and give explanations for the differences.

II. Instability of Surface Waves

A. INTRODUCTION

This part is primarily a study of the stability of stationary waves that form on the surface of a liquid layer flowing over a wavy bottom, followed by an application to free waves.

At first sight the mechanism of instability seemed to have much to do with that of water in a vertically oscillating container (Benjamin and Ursell, 1954), since the liquid stream may be thought of as rising and sinking as it moves over the wavy bed. This conjecture turned out not to be fruitful. The reason is twofold: the conjecture has force only if the wavelength is long, but if the wavelength is long the vertical acceleration is very small, and its slight spatial variation is able to destroy any tendency toward the kind of instability studied by Benjamin and Ursell.

The primary cause of instability turns out to be a kind of resonance. In the running stream it is possible for two perturbation wave motions to exist, which have the same frequency but different wave numbers m and m' ($> m$), whose difference is the wave number k of the primary wave motion. These two wave motions interact with the primary wave motion and can thus grow in amplitude as a result of resonance.

The major part of this paper is devoted to finding the condition of instability of stationary gravity waves in a liquid flowing over a wavy bottom, and the rate of growth. The effects of surface tension are then investigated. In all cases, when the flow is unstable, the rate of growth of the disturbances is proportional to the amplitude of the primary waves.

When the analysis is applied to progressive gravity waves by adopting a moving frame to render them stationary, the Froude number is the ratio of the wave velocity to long-wave velocity, and therefore depends on the wave number. It turns out that progressive gravity waves are unstable for all nonzero wave numbers. This result differs from the result of Benjamin (1967) and Whitham (1966) that progressive gravity waves are stable if the dimensionless wave number is less than 1.363. The theories of Benjamin and Whitham agree, and Benjamin's, in particular, has been abundantly verified by experiments conducted by Feir (see Benjamin, 1967), so that these theories can be considered well established. The present linear theory does not contradict them; rather it presents a new mechanism of resonance,

372   *Chia-Shun Yih*

which renders all progressive gravity waves unstable, although for deep-water waves the instabilities found by Benjamin and Whitham are often stronger and always more detectable. Detailed comparison with Benjamin's results will be given, with explanations for the differences. However, it should be noted here that since the Froude number is no longer arbitrary, the growth rate of disturbances in a progressive wave train can be of the order of β^2 (β being the amplitude of the primary waves), as shown by (2.59) in Section I,H. It can also be of the order of β. Whether it is of the order of β or β^2 or of some other order of β depends on the wavelength of the waves under study and on the value of β itself.

As will be seen in Section II,D, the method of approach used here is similar to that used by Davis and Acrivos (1967) to study the stability of progressive internal waves. Their method, like the present one, also gives a growth rate proportional to the amplitude of the waves when they are unstable, in contrast with the results of Benjamin, as a result of the difference in the mechanism of resonance.

The difference between the present work and the work of Davis and Acrivos is twofold. First, stationary waves over a wavy boundary are considered, with the Froude number arbitrary. This is unlike the progressive waves, which when made stationary correspond to a definite Froude number. Second, when the stability of progressive waves is considered, instability is found in this paper by considering the increase of the velocity of progressive waves with amplitude, whereas Davis and Acrivos did not consider this increase [or decrease, since they considered internal waves, for which the wave velocity may increase or decrease with amplitude, as shown by Yih (1974)], and found instability only by considering the interaction of various internal modes.

B. The Primary Flow

The primary flow is a steady irrotational flow over a wavy bottom and with a free surface where the pressure is constant. Since it is the flow at the free surface that is the most important, the shape of the bottom being of only secondary importance, we shall use, for the primary flow, a flow that satisfies the nonlinear free-surface condition exactly, with a wavy streamline at the bottom. For this purpose we use one of the two formulas given by Richardson (1920). [These two formulas are reducible to each other, as shown by Yih (1957).]

The formula we use is

$$\frac{dz}{dw} = \left[\frac{1}{H(w)} - \alpha^2 H'^2(w)\right]^{1/2} - i\alpha H'(w) \tag{2.1}$$

in which $H(w)$ and the radical are real for real w,

$$z = x + iy \quad \text{and} \quad w = \phi + i\psi,$$

where x and y are Cartesian coordinates measured in units of depth d, and ϕ and ψ are, respectively, the velocity potential and the stream function of the primary flow, measured in units of Ud, with U denoting a mean velocity of the flow. The quantity α in (2.1) is defined by

$$\alpha = \tfrac{1}{2}F^2, \qquad F^2 = U^2/gd, \tag{2.2}$$

where g is the gravitational acceleration, acting in the direction of decreasing y. Thus (2.1) is in dimensionless terms. The Bernoulli equation for the free surface is, if all quantities are made dimensionless and η denotes y on the free surface,

$$q^2 + \alpha^{-1}\eta = \text{const}, \tag{2.3}$$

where

$$q^2 = u^2 + v^2 = |dw/dz|^2,$$

with velocity components u and v in the directions of increasing x and y, respectively. If we take $\psi = 0$ on the free surface, and make sure that both H and the radical in (2.1) are real on the free surface (on which w is real), then for the free surface, (2.1) gives

$$|dw/dz|^2 = H(w), \tag{2.4}$$

and, by integrating the imaginary part of (2.1),

$$\eta = -\alpha H(w) + \text{const}. \tag{2.5}$$

It is evident then that (2.3) is exactly satisfied.

For our purpose, we shall take

$$H(w) = 1 - \beta \cos kw, \tag{2.6}$$

where

$$\beta < 1.$$

The free surface and the wavy bed are shown schematically in Fig. 1, and the disturbed free surface is shown in Fig. 2. It is immediately clear that if $\beta = 0$, Eqs. (2.1) and (2.6) give a uniform flow in the x direction, with dimensionless velocity 1 or dimensional velocity U, which has been used as the velocity scale. For small β, (2.1) and (2.5) give a flow with a wavy free surface at $\psi = 0$ and a wavy bottom at $\psi = -1$. From (2.5) one sees that the amplitude of the free surface is $\alpha\beta$ and its wave number is k, which is also the wave number of the wavy bed. Were β zero, d would be the depth of the flow

Chia-Shun Yih

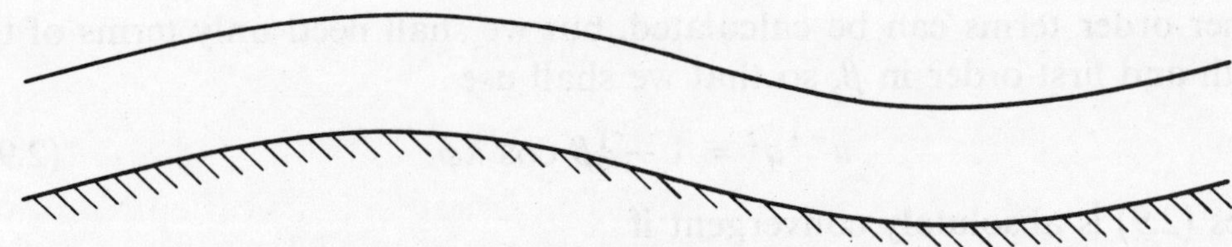

Fig. 1. Free-surface flow over a wavy bed.

everywhere. Since β is not zero, we can, for instance, identify d as the depth at a particular section (such as a section at a crest of the wavy bed), and U as the mean velocity at that section.

It is important that the region of flow between

$$\psi = 0 \quad \text{and} \quad \psi = -1$$

be free from singularities. If β is sufficiently small this can always be achieved, as one can see from (2.1) and (2.4), which never give

$$dz/dw = 0$$

in the region of flow, for sufficiently small β.

From (2.1) we obtain

$$dw/dz = u - iv = H[(H^{-1} - \alpha^2 H'^2)^{1/2} + i\alpha H'], \qquad (2.7)$$

in which H is written for $H(w)$ for brevity.

For the H given by (2.5), (2.4) becomes

$$q^2 = 1 - \beta \cos kw = 1 - \beta \cos k\phi \qquad (2.8)$$

on the free surface. Another quantity needed later is $u^{-1}q^2$ on the free surface. This can be evaluated from (2.7) and (2.8), and after some straightforward calculation and much simplification, is given by

$$u^{-1}q^2 = (H^{-1} - \alpha^2 H'^2)^{1/2} = 1 - \tfrac{1}{16}(1 - 4\alpha^2 k^2)\beta^2 - \tfrac{1}{2}\beta \cos k\phi$$
$$+ \tfrac{1}{16}(7 - 4\alpha^2 k^2)\beta^2 \cos 2k\phi + O(\beta^3). \quad (2.9)$$

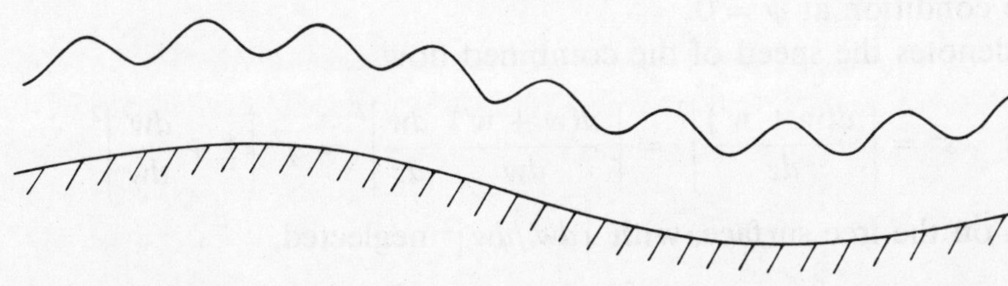

Fig. 2. Disturbed free surface of a liquid flowing over a wavy bed. The undisturbed free surface is not shown.

Higher-order terms can be calculated, but we shall need only terms of the zeroth and first order in β, so that we shall use

$$u^{-1}q^2 = 1 - \tfrac{1}{2}\beta \cos k\phi. \tag{2.9a}$$

Series (2.9) is absolutely convergent if

$$\frac{1}{1-\beta} - 1 + \alpha^2 k^2 \beta^2 < 1, \tag{2.10}$$

as can be seen from the square-root term in (2.9). Condition (2.10) can always be satisfied with a sufficiently small β.

Finally we note that, with subscripts indicating differentiations, the kinematic condition at the free surface is

$$u\eta_x = v = \phi_y. \tag{2.11}$$

The flow is shown schematically in Fig. 1. We emphasize that (2.1) has been used only for the convenience of constructing an exact solution for stationary waves. For any other wavy bed and any other solution, there will be a term containing $\cos k\phi$ in q^2 and $u^{-1}q^2$—quantities appearing as coefficients in the crucial free-surface condition (2.21) to be presented later— and the analysis will follow exactly the same line to reach exactly the same results.

C. Formulation of the Stability Problem

For the disturbance we assume a complex potential

$$w' = \phi' + i\psi',$$

where ϕ' is the velocity potential and ψ' the stream function of the irrotational flow caused by the disturbance, both regarded as functions of ϕ and ψ. It is well known that since w and w' are analytic functions of z, w' is an analytic function of w, except at the singularities, which are excluded from the fluid domain. Using ϕ and ψ as independent variables then, we enjoy the advantage of applying the boundary condition at $\psi = -1$ and the free-surface condition at $\psi = 0$.

If s denotes the speed of the combined flow,

$$s^2 = \left| \frac{d(w+w')}{dz} \right|^2 = \left| \frac{d(w+w')}{dw} \frac{dw}{dz} \right|^2 = q^2 \left| 1 + \frac{dw'}{dw} \right|^2,$$

so that on the free surface, with $|dw'/dw|^2$ neglected,

$$s^2 - q^2 = q^2 \left[\frac{dw'}{dw} + \left(\frac{dw'}{dw} \right)^* \right] = 2q^2 \frac{d\phi'}{d\phi}. \tag{2.12}$$

                    Chia-Shun Yih

The Bernoulli equation at the free surface, where the pressure is zero, is

$$\phi'_t + \tfrac{1}{2}s^2 + F^{-2}(\eta + \eta') = \text{const}, \tag{2.13}$$

where η' is the free-surface displacement in the vertical direction, due to the disturbance. Taking the difference between (2.13) and (2.3), and using (2.12), we have

$$\left(\frac{\partial}{\partial t} + q^2 \frac{\partial}{\partial \phi}\right)\phi' + F^{-2}\eta' = 0, \tag{2.14}$$

where we have assigned the constant in (2.13) the value zero because we expect ϕ' and η' to be sinusoidal in ϕ.

If u' and v' are the perturbations to u and v, corresponding to the potential ϕ', the kinematic condition on the free surface is,

$$\left(\frac{\partial}{\partial t} + (u + u')\frac{\partial}{\partial x}\right)(\eta + \eta') = v + v', \tag{2.15}$$

where the time t is measured in units of $U^{-1}d$. The difference between this equation and (2.11) is

$$\left(\frac{\partial}{\partial t} + u\frac{\partial}{\partial x}\right)\eta' = v' - u'\frac{d\eta}{dx}. \tag{2.16}$$

However,

$$\left(\frac{\partial}{\partial t} + u\frac{\partial}{\partial x}\right)\eta' = \left[\frac{\partial}{\partial t} + u\left(u\frac{\partial}{\partial \phi} - v\frac{\partial}{\partial \psi}\right)\right]\eta' = \left(\frac{\partial}{\partial t} + q^2\frac{\partial}{\partial \phi}\right)\eta', \tag{2.17}$$

since

$$0 = \frac{\partial \eta'}{\partial y} = \left(v\frac{\partial}{\partial \phi} + u\frac{\partial}{\partial \psi}\right)\eta',$$

$$u = \phi_x = \psi_y, \qquad v = \phi_y = -\psi_x.$$

As in (2.17)

$$u\eta_x = q^2\eta_\phi, \tag{2.18}$$

so that the right-hand side of (2.16) is

$$\phi'_y - \phi'_x u^{-1} q^2 \eta_\phi = v\phi'_\phi + u\phi'_\psi - u^{-1}q^2\eta_\phi(u\phi'_\phi - v\phi'_\psi)$$

$$= u^{-1}(u^2 + vq^2\eta_\phi)\phi'_\psi = u^{-1}q^2\phi'_\psi, \tag{2.19}$$

since, by (2.18),

$$q^2\eta_\phi = u\eta_x = v.$$

Thus (2.16) can be written

$$\left(\frac{\partial}{\partial t} + q^2 \frac{\partial}{\partial \phi}\right)\eta' = u^{-1}q^2\phi'_\psi .$$

(2.20)

Combining (2.14) and (2.20), we have

$$\boxed{\left(\frac{\partial}{\partial t} + q^2 \frac{\partial}{\partial \phi}\right)^2 \phi' + F^{-2}u^{-1}q^2\phi'_\psi = 0 \qquad \text{at} \quad \psi = 0.}$$

(2.21)

This is the free-surface condition. As to the condition at the solid boundary constituting the wavy bed, it is simply

$$\phi'_\psi = 0 \qquad \text{at} \quad \psi = -1.$$

(2.22)

The velocity potential satisfies the Laplace equation

$$\phi'_{\phi\phi} + \phi'_{\psi\psi} = 0.$$

(2.23)

Equations (2.21)–(2.23) are the differential system governing the stability of the disturbance or of the flow.

D. Demonstration of Instability

Before presenting the formal demonstration of instability, we shall explain in intuitive terms the motivation for concentrating on disturbances of certain wave numbers. If β were zero and a wavy disturbance of wave number γ were imposed on the uniformly flowing stream, the solution of (2.23) satisfying (2.22) would simply be

$$\phi' = C \exp i(\gamma\phi - \sigma_0 t) \cosh \gamma(\psi + 1),$$

and (2.21) would give the secular equation

$$(\sigma_0 - \gamma)^2 = F^{-2}\gamma \tanh \gamma.$$

(2.24)

We shall denote by R and L the right- and left-hand sides of (2.24), respectively. In Fig. 3, R and L are plotted against γ, and where the two curves intersect the wave numbers are denoted by m and m'. We claim that if

$$m' - m = k,$$

(2.25)

the waviness of the bed may cause instability by a sort of resonance. That this is indeed the case will be shown in this section.

Since the L-curve is a parabola touching the γ-axis at $\gamma = \sigma_0$, and the R-curve rises monotonically as γ increases, it is evident that both m and

Chia-Shun Yih

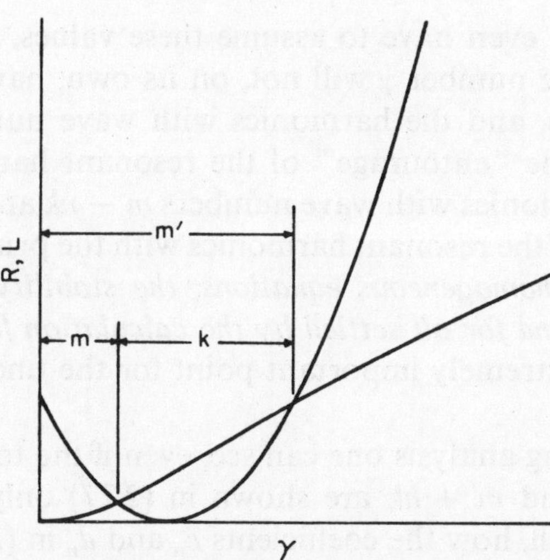

FIG. 3. The existence of wave numbers of resonating modes.

$m' - m$ increases with σ_0, from zero onwards. The variations of m and σ_0 with k for various values of F^2 will be given in the next section.

Knowing that m and m' are the crucial wave numbers, and anticipating the repeated interactions of the m-waves and m'-waves with the primary waves with wave number k, we assume a perturbation velocity potential ϕ' to have the form

$$\phi' = e^{-i\sigma t}[a \cosh m(\psi + 1)e^{im\phi} + b \cosh m'(\psi + 1)e^{im'\phi}$$

$$+ \sum_{n=1}^{\infty} c_n \beta^n \cosh\{(m - nk)(\psi + 1)\} \exp i(m - nk)\phi$$

$$+ \sum_{n=1}^{\infty} d_n \beta^n \cosh\{(m' + nk)(\psi + 1)\} \exp i(m' + nk)\phi], \qquad (2.26)$$

in which m and m' satisfy (2.25). Note that the expansion (2.26) implies that the harmonics with wave numbers $m - nk$ and $m' + nk$ are results of interactions of the harmonics with wave numbers m and m' (which we shall, in anticipation, call the resonant harmonics) with the primary waves with wave number k. Thus the terms under the summation signs in (2.26) are, so to speak, the "entourage" of the resonant harmonics.

The question may immediately be raised: Why must harmonics of wave numbers $m - nk$ and $m' + nk$ be merely the results of interactions of the resonant harmonics with the primary waves? Why can they not exist on their own? The answer to this question is simply that of course they can exist on their own, but when they do their circular frequency σ will not be the same as that for the resonant harmonics, since their σ would be determined from (2.24) with γ equal to $m - nk$ or $m' + nk$, whatever positive integer n is.

(Indeed, γ does not even have to assume these values, but in that case the harmonic with wave number γ will not, on its own, have the same σ as the resonant harmonics, and the harmonics with wave numbers γ and $\gamma \pm nk$ cannot belong to the "entourage" of the resonant harmonics either.) For this reason the harmonics with wave numbers $m - nk$ and $m' + nk$ arise only from interactions of the resonant harmonics with the primary waves, and *are calculated from nonhomogeneous equations, the stability question being exclusively and once and for all settled by the calculation for the resonant pair alone.*† This is an extremely important point for the understanding of what follows.

From the following analysis one can see, even if the terms involving wave numbers $m - nk$ and $m' + nk$ are shown in (2.27) only for $n = 1$ and not shown in (2.28) at all, how the coefficients c_n and d_n in (2.26) are determined by (2.21), step by step. Indeed, it can be shown not only for the flow being considered here but also for any flow with stationary waves that expansion (2.26), with c_n and d_n determined by (2.21), is convergent up to the value of β for which the primary flow exists. There is then nothing arbitrary in the form of ϕ' given by (2.26) and nothing indefinite or obscure in using (2.21) and (2.26) to determine σ and to make conclusions on the stability or instability of the primary flow. As we have said, in this determination the calculation need be done for the resonant pair only.

[We note here also that in the application of the theory for stationary waves to progressive waves made stationary, F^2 will depend on β and have a term of $O(\beta^2)$. Inclusion of this amplitude-dependent term in F^2, using (2.24) to determine, *once and for all*, m and m' for a given k, and then using (2.26) for the analysis, as in the following analysis for stationary waves, does not involve any unallowable truncation and should not lead to any confusion concerning the collection of terms of various orders in β.]

The first term in (2.21), after a straightforward calculation is then

$$\left(\frac{\partial}{\partial t} + q^2 \frac{\partial}{\partial \phi} \right)^2 \phi' = - e^{-i\sigma t} \left\{ \left[(\sigma - m)A + \frac{\beta}{2} m'B \right] e^{im\phi} \right.$$

$$+ \left[(\sigma - m')B + \frac{\beta}{2} mA \right] e^{im'\phi} + \frac{\beta}{2} (\sigma a_1 + mA) e^{i(m-k)\phi}$$

$$\left. + \frac{\beta}{2} (\sigma b_1 + m'B) e^{i(m+2k)\phi} + O(\beta^2) \right\}$$

$$+ \text{ terms containing } c_n \text{ and } d_n, \tag{2.27}$$

† Even if for higher-order terms in σ feedbacks from overtones are needed.

380   *Chia-Shun Yih*

in which

$$A = a(\sigma - m)\cosh m + \tfrac{1}{2}\beta bm' \cosh m',$$

$$B = b(\sigma - m')\cosh m' + \tfrac{1}{2}\beta am \cosh m,$$

$$a_1 = am \cosh m, \qquad b_1 = bm' \cosh m'.$$

By virtue of (2.9a), the second term in (2.21) is

$$F^{-2}u^{-1}q^2\phi'_\psi = e^{-i\sigma t}F^{-2}\{(am \sinh m - \tfrac{1}{4}\beta bm' \sinh m')e^{im\phi}$$

$$+ (bm' \sinh m' - \tfrac{1}{4}\beta am \sinh m)e^{im'\phi}\}$$

$$+ \text{ terms of } O(\beta^2) \text{ or involving } c_n \text{ and } d_n. \qquad (2.28)$$

Equating terms of the same wave number $(m, m', \text{etc.})$ in (2.21), and retaining terms of $O(1)$ and $O(\beta)$ only for the first approximation, we obtain then

$$a(\sigma - m)^2 \cosh m + \tfrac{1}{2}\beta bm'(2\sigma - m - m') \cosh m'$$

$$= F^{-2}(am \sinh m - \tfrac{1}{4}\beta bm' \sinh m'), \qquad (2.29)$$

and

$$b(\sigma - m')^2 \cosh m' + \tfrac{1}{2}\beta am(2\sigma - m - m') \cosh m$$

$$= F^{-2}(bm' \sinh m' - \tfrac{1}{4}\beta am \sinh m). \qquad (2.30)$$

Let

$$(\sigma - m)^2 = (\sigma_0 - m)^2 + \lambda_1 + O(\beta^2), \qquad (2.31)$$

so that

$$\sigma - m = (\sigma_0 - m)[1 + \tfrac{1}{2}\lambda_1(\sigma_0 - m)^{-2} + O(\beta^2)], \qquad (2.32)$$

in which λ_1 is of order $O(\beta)$. Then (2.29) and (2.30) become, upon neglect of terms of $O(\beta^2)$,

$$a\lambda_1 \cosh m + \frac{\beta b}{4}[2m'(2\sigma_0 - m - m') \cosh m' + F^{-2}m' \sinh m'] = 0, \qquad (2.33)$$

$$b\lambda_1 \cosh m' \frac{\sigma_0 - m'}{\sigma_0 - m} + \frac{\beta a}{4}[2m(2\sigma_0 - m - m') \cosh m + F^{-2}m \sinh m] = 0. \qquad (2.34)$$

It is evident from Fig. 3 that $\sigma_0 - m'$ is negative and $\sigma_0 - m$ is positive, so that their ratio in the first term of (2.34) is always negative. The bracketed terms in (2.33) and (2.34) are both negative. This can be shown in the following way. We know that

$$(\sigma_0 - m)^2 = F^{-2}m \tanh m \qquad (2.35)$$

$$(\sigma_0 - m')^2 = F^{-2}m' \tanh m'. \qquad (2.36)$$

Writing (2.35) as

$$(\sigma_0 - m)^2 + F^{-2}(\sigma_0 - m)\tanh m - F^{-2}\sigma_0 \tanh m = 0$$

we have

$$\sigma_0 - m = \tfrac{1}{2}[-F^{-2}\tanh m + (F^{-4}\tanh^2 m + 4F^{-2}\sigma_0 \tanh m)^{1/2}],$$
$$\tag{2.37}$$

the positive sign before the radical being taken because $\sigma_0 - m$ is positive. Similarly, from (2.36) we obtain

$$\sigma_0 - m' = \tfrac{1}{2}[-F^{-2}\tanh m' - (F^{-4}\tanh^2 m' + 4F^{-2}\sigma_0 \tanh m')^{1/2}],$$
$$\tag{2.38}$$

the negative sign before the radical being taken because $\sigma_0 - m'$ is negative. Thus

$$2\sigma_0 - m - m' = \tfrac{1}{2}[-F^{-2}(\tanh m + \tanh m') - M], \tag{2.39}$$

where

$$M = f(m') - f(m), \qquad f(m) = [F^{-2}\tanh m(F^{-2}\tanh m + 4\sigma_0)]^{1/2}.$$
$$\tag{2.40}$$

Thus

$$M > 0.$$

Substituting (2.40) into (2.33) and (2.34), we have

$$a\lambda_1 \cosh m = \frac{b\beta}{4}(F^{-2}\tanh m + M)m' \cosh m' \tag{2.33a}$$

$$b\lambda_1 \cosh m' \frac{\sigma_0 - m'}{\sigma_0 - m} = \frac{a\beta}{4}(F^{-2}\tanh m' + M)m \cosh m. \tag{2.34a}$$

Multiplying (2.33a) by (2.34a), we have

$$\lambda_1^2 = \frac{\sigma_0 - m}{\sigma_0 - m'}\frac{\beta^2 mm'}{16}(F^{-2}\tanh m + M)(F^{-2}\tanh m' + M). \tag{2.41}$$

Thus λ_1^2 is negative and λ_1 purely imaginary. Returning to (2.32), we see that

$$\sigma = \sigma_0 + \tfrac{1}{2}\lambda_1(\sigma_0 - m)^{-1} + O(\beta^2), \tag{2.42}$$

$$\lambda_1/2(\sigma_0 - m) = \pm i|\beta|\lambda, \qquad \lambda > 0.$$

The choice of the positive sign then gives

$$e^{-i\sigma t} = \exp(-i\sigma_0 + |\beta|\lambda)t,$$

and the disturbance (2.26) is unstable, for whatever F^2, whatever k, and whatever β, provided that m is not zero. (See Section II,E.)

382   *Chia-Shun Yih*

It is important to bear in mind that, given β, F^2, and k, m and λ are determined uniquely. The m and m' for the unstable disturbance may be quite different from k, and thus not in the neighborhood of k. Furthermore, the present theory is linear, and the growth rate $|\beta|\lambda$ is proportional to $|\beta|$ rather than β^2. These facts distinguish the present theory from the theories of Benjamin (1967) and Whitham (1966) for progressive gravity waves. We shall treat the stability of progressive gravity waves in Section II,H, to make a direct comparison.

We note that the instability of stationary waves is caused by the resonant interaction of the primary waves with the m-waves and the m'-waves. The m-waves propagate with the flowing stream, but the m'-waves propagate against it.

E. Wavelengths and Growth Rates of Unstable Modes

Given m, we can determine σ_0 from (2.24) upon substituting m for γ. The other root m' of (2.24) is found by numerical computation and then k is found from (2.25). In this way we obtain corresponding values of σ_0, m, and k. In Fig. 4 m is plotted against k for various values of F^2, and in Fig. 5 σ_0 is plotted against k for the same set of values of F^2. We see immediately from Figs. 4 and 5 that the curves go through the origin if $F^2 \geq 1$, but intersect the k axis at positive values (k_c) of k if $F^2 < 1$. We have worked with positive k. For negative k, m and m' are negative, but the conclusions remain.

By virtue of (2.39), or directly from (2.33) and (2.34), Eq. (2.41) giving λ_1^2 can be written

$$\lambda_1^2 = -G\beta^2, \tag{2.43}$$

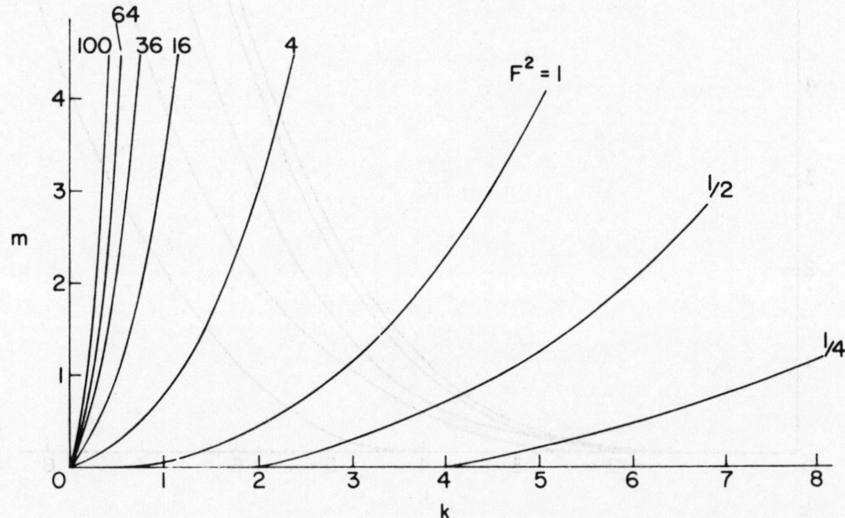

FIG. 4.   Variation of m with k.

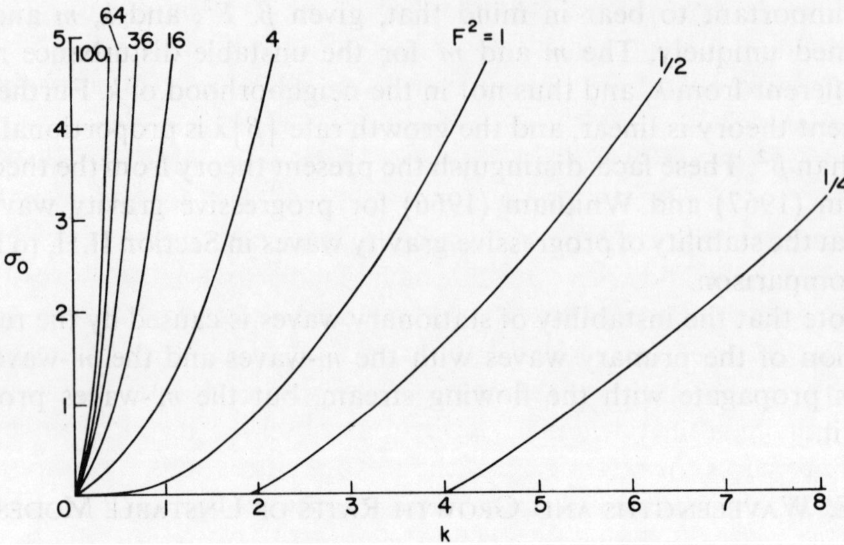

FIG. 5. Variation of σ_0 with k.

where

$$G = -\frac{mm'}{4}\frac{\sigma_0 - m}{\sigma_0 - m'}\left(2\sigma_0 - m - m' + \frac{1}{2}F^{-2}\tanh m\right)$$

$$\left(2\sigma_0 - m - m' + \frac{1}{2}F^{-2}\tanh m'\right). \qquad (2.43a)$$

The quantity G is plotted against k in Fig. 6 for various values of F^2. It is seen that G is positive for $F^2 \geq 1$ and for any positive k, whereas, for $F^2 < 1$,

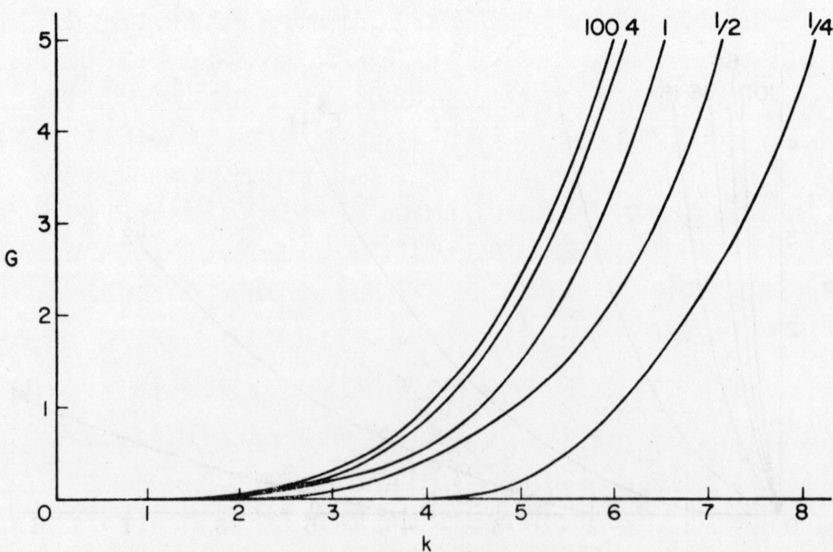

FIG. 6. Variation of G with k.

 Chia-Shun Yih

k has to be greater than a cut-off value k_c for G to be positive. Thus for $F^2 \geq 1$ the flow is always unstable for any nonzero k, whereas for $F^2 < 1$ the flow is unstable only if k is greater than a cut-off value k_c (or, if k is negative, smaller than $-k_c$).

From Fig. 4 we see that m (and hence m') increases with F^2 for any given k. From Fig. 6 we see that G (hence λ_1) increases with F^2 for any given k. Thus for any given k, the unstable modes have shorter and shorter wavelengths and become more and more unstable as F^2 increases. Furthermore, it is seen from Fig. 6 that G changes but little between $F^2 = 4$ and $F^2 = 100$—a fact of some practical usefulness when estimating G at high Froude numbers.

Thus the rather short wavelengths of the surface disturbances and their very strong instability when F^2 is high, as observed in pulp conveyed on Fourdrinier wires (or screens), find their explanation here. It is important to note that if F^2 is sufficiently greater than 1, the growth rate $|\lambda_1|$ is of the order $O(\beta)$, whereas the growth rate of progressive waves for the instability mechanism of Benjamin (1967) is of the order† $O(\beta^2)$ only, in the present notation, and is therefore weaker than that for the present mechanism. However, when progressive waves are made stationary by using a moving frame of coordinates, the F^2 is not arbitrary, and the investigation of instability due to the present mechanism will be presented in Section II,H.

F. Extension to Other Wavy Flows

So far we have only considered the primary flow given by (2.1) and (2.6), but Eq. (2.21) governing the stability of the disturbances is quite general. It is both important and useful to see whether the instability that has just been found will exist for other wavy flows. To reach a decision on this question, we need only to see what forms q^2 and $u^{-1}q^2$ assume for other flows, and what effect these forms will have, through (2.21), on the stability.

For the flow defined by (2.1) and (2.6), q^2 is given by (2.8) exactly and $u^{-1}q^2$ by (2.9a) if terms of order $O(\beta^2)$ or higher are neglected, and the stability analysis shows that only terms of orders $O(1)$ and $O(\beta)$, with the terms of order $O(\beta)$ being multiples of $\beta \cos k\phi$, are needed for q^2 and $u^{-1}q^2$. Now there are infinitely many flows over a wavy bottom for which, in dimensionless terms,

$$u = 1 - \tfrac{1}{2}\beta \cos k\phi + O(\beta^2), \qquad v = O(\beta), \tag{2.44}$$

on the free surface, so that the q^2 and $u^{-1}q^2$ on the free surface are given by (2.8) and (2.9a), if terms of order $O(\beta^2)$ and higher are neglected. In (2.44), β is an amplitude of wave motion, and the form for u can always be achieved

---

† β is proportional to Benjamin's ka. See the two lines after (2.51).

since the origin of ϕ is arbitrary. Any potential flow for which (2.44) holds on the free surface has wavy streamlines, any one of which below the free surface can be taken as the solid, wavy bed. For such flows, the stability analysis given in Section II,D holds exactly. Hence the conclusions reached in that section are not restricted to the flow given by (2.1) and (2.6), but are much more general.

For instance, for gravity waves in a liquid of uniform depth d, the x component of the velocity at the free surface is, when the flow is made steady by a set of moving coordinates and velocity components are measured in terms of the wave velocity,

$$u = 1 - \tfrac{1}{2}\beta \cos k\phi + b_2 \cos 2k\phi + b_3 \cos 3k\phi + \cdots;$$

in which

$$b_2 = O(\beta^2), \qquad b_3 = O(\beta^3),$$

etc. If terms of order higher than $O(\beta)$ are neglected, u has the form given in (2.44), and the stability analysis in Section II,D applies. If, in this flow, we take a (wavy) streamline between the flat bottom and the wavy free surface as a solid lower boundary, the value of F^2 can be made as large as we please by making the mean depth as small as we please. For F^2 greater than 1 then, that flow is unstable for all positive values of the wave number k. We note, incidentally, that the position of the wavy bed determines F^2, and is therefore very important in deciding whether or not the flow is stable. One might say that making any internal wavy streamline rigid destabilizes the flow.

G. Effects of Surface Tension

Surface tension affects the solution for the primary flow as well as the perturbation flow. Crapper (1957) gave an elegant, exact solution for water waves of arbitrary amplitude and for infinite depth of the liquid, with surface tension fully taken into account. But gravity is entirely neglected in his solution. Fortunately, as the analysis in Section II,C shows, only terms of the first order in the amplitude of the waves are important in the determination of stability, and these terms are easily obtainable by the linear theory, even when surface tension is taken into account.

Thus, if the wavy bottom is given in dimensionless terms by

$$y = -1 + a' \cos kx,$$

and the mean depth (dimensionless) is 1, the solution for stationary waves is, again in dimensionless terms,

$$\phi = x - (a \cosh ky + b \sinh ky) \sin kx, \tag{2.45}$$

386   *Chia-Shun Yih*

in which

$$ka - (F^{-2} + Sk^2)b = 0, \qquad (2.46)$$

$$b = a'[\cosh k - (F^{-2}k^{-1} + Sk)\sinh k]^{-1}, \qquad (2.47)$$

$$S = T/\rho U^2 d^2, \qquad (2.48)$$

where T is the surface tension, d the (dimensional) mean depth, and U the (dimensional) mean velocity. The free-surface displacement is

$$\eta = b \cos kx$$

and

$$u = 1 - ak \cos kx + O(a^2k^2) = 1 - \tfrac{1}{2}\beta \cos k\phi + O(\beta^2),$$

in which $2ak = \beta$. If terms of order $O(\beta^2)$ and higher are neglected, again

$$q^2 = 1 - \beta \cos k\phi.$$

We need, however, to modify (2.14) to

$$\boxed{\left(\frac{\partial}{\partial t} + q^2 \frac{\partial}{\partial \phi}\right)\phi' + F^{-2}\eta + S[q(q\eta'_\phi)_\phi] = 0 \qquad \text{at} \quad \psi = 0,} \qquad (2.49)$$

in which certain terms definitely of order $O(\beta^2)$ have been omitted. Then the demonstration of instability can be given as in Section II,D, with m' and m being now the roots of

$$(\sigma_0 - \gamma)^2 = (F^{-2} + S\gamma^2)\gamma \tanh \gamma, \qquad (2.50)$$

and with σ_0 determined by the condition $m' - m = k$. We shall not pursue the details at this time.

H. Instability of Progressive Gravity Waves in a Liquid of Constant Depth

Benjamin (1967) and Whitham (1966) have studied the stability of gravity waves using two different approaches. They agree that when k (kh or K in their notation) is less than 1.363 the waves are stable. Benjamin uses as the disturbance a side-band of wave numbers and frequencies centered around, and therefore in the neighborhood of, the wave number and frequency of the basic waves. When $k > 1.363$ the rate of growth of the unstable disturbances is of the order $O(\beta^2)$ in the present notation, $O(k^2a^2)$ in Benjamin's notation. We shall show that by the present mechanism progressive gravity waves are always unstable, but that the instability is significant only when Benjamin's theory predicts stability.

If we use a frame of reference moving with the waves, and use our dimensionless notation (the velocity scale U now being the wave velocity c), then for Stokes waves[†]

$$\phi = x - \frac{\beta}{2k}\frac{\cosh k(y+1)}{\cosh k}\sin kx + O(\beta^2), \tag{2.51}$$

where our β corresponds to Benjamin's (1967, p. 65)

$$-2k_B a \coth K, \qquad K = k_B d = k, \quad d = \text{depth}, \quad a = \text{wave amplitude},$$

where k_B is used for the dimensional wave number, to distinguish it from the dimensionless k. We use the β in this way in order to have agreement with (2.8) and (2.44). The dimensional wave velocity c, which is used as the velocity scale, is given in the present notation by (Benjamin, 1967, p. 66),

$$F^2 = \frac{c^2}{gd} = \frac{\tanh k}{k}\{1 + \beta^2 f(k)\}, \tag{2.52}$$

where

$$f(k) = \frac{1}{4}\tanh^2 k\left(1 + \csc^2 k + \frac{9 - 2\tanh^2 k}{8\sinh^4 k}\right).$$

Equation (2.52) is valid only if $\beta^2 \ll k^3$ if k is small (see Benjamin, 1967, p. 66).

Equation (2.21) still governs stability, and we can repeat the analysis of Section II,D. Thus we have again (2.41) or its equivalent, (2.43), but we need to investigate the values of m and m'. For this purpose we return to (2.35) and (2.36). If we ignore the term of order $O(\beta^2)$ in (2.52), upon taking the proper root as before, these become

$$\sigma_0 - m = (km \tanh m/\tanh k)^{1/2}, \tag{2.53}$$

$$m' - \sigma_0 = (km' \tanh m'/\tanh k)^{1/2}. \tag{2.54}$$

Taking the sum of (2.53) and (2.54) and using (2.25), we have

$$k = \left(\frac{km \tanh m}{\tanh k}\right)^{1/2} + \left(\frac{k(k+m)\tanh(k+m)}{\tanh k}\right)^{1/2}. \tag{2.55}$$

It is then obvious that

$$m = 0, \qquad m' = k,$$

[†] It is important to note that the ϕ given by (2.51) and the corresponding stream function ψ now serve as the independent variables in (2.21).

         Chia-Shun Yih

and according to (2.41), $\lambda_1 = 0$ and there is no instability.† Any instability then must be due to the term $\beta^2 f(k)$ in (2.52). With (2.52) substituted into (2.35) and (2.36), we obtain the equation

$$[1 + \tfrac{1}{2}\beta^2 f(k)]k = \text{right-hand side of (2.55).} \tag{2.56}$$

From (2.55) and (2.56) it follows that

$$m = \beta^2 k f(k)\left[1 + 2\left(\frac{k}{\tanh k}\right)^{1/2} + \frac{2k}{\sinh 2k}\right]^{-1} + O(\beta^4).$$

Thus, for small k,

$$m = \tfrac{1}{5}\beta^2 k f(k), \qquad m' = k + m.$$

If terms of order $O(\beta^2)$ are not neglected, the left-hand sides of (2.53) and (2.54) should be multiplied by

$$1 + \tfrac{1}{2}\beta^2 f(k),$$

and from the resulting equations one finds that

$$\sigma_0 - m = \left(\frac{k}{\tanh k}\right)m + O(\beta^4),$$

$$m' - \sigma_0 = k + \frac{m}{2} - \frac{k\beta^2}{8} + O(\beta^4).$$

For small k, we have, with higher-order terms (in β) neglected,

$$F^{-2} \tanh m' = k, \qquad M = k, \qquad \sigma_0 - m = m + O(\beta^4),$$

so that

$$\lambda_1^2 = -\tfrac{1}{8}m^2 k^2 \beta^2.$$

and the growth rate is

$$|\lambda_1 / 2(\sigma_0 - m)| = \tfrac{1}{2}k|\beta|. \tag{2.57}$$

Recalling that our β is Benjamin's $-2ka \coth K$ and our k Benjamin's K, we see that the right-hand side of (2.57) is Benjamin's ka, where k is the dimensional wave number and a the dimensional wave amplitude.

---

† Professor O. M. Phillips kindly showed the author the manuscript of the revised edition of his book (1966). In it he mentions the nonexistence of resonant wave triads, in agreement with our statement here.

For large k (deep-water waves), if we assume k fixed and let β be as small as we please, m will be small. In that case from (2.56) we have

$$m = \tfrac{1}{8}k^{1/2}\beta^2, \qquad m' = k + m,$$

$$\sigma_0 - m = k^{1/2}m = \tfrac{1}{8}k\beta^2, \qquad m' - \sigma_0 = k + O(\beta^2), \qquad F^{-2} = k, \qquad M = k,$$

so that (2.41) becomes

$$\lambda_1^2 = -\tfrac{1}{8}k^{2.5}m^2\beta^2,$$

and the growth rate is

$$|\lambda_1/2(\sigma_0 - m)| = k^{0.75}\beta/4\sqrt{2}.$$

We have used c/d as the scale for σ_0 and hence the growth rate also. When d is large this scale is inadequate. If we change the scale for the growth rate to c/L, where L is the wavelength, for large k we have

$$\text{growth rate} = \frac{L}{d}\frac{k^{0.75}|\beta|}{4\sqrt{2}} = \frac{\pi|\beta|}{4\sqrt{2}\,k^{0.25}}. \tag{2.58}$$

Since m is supposed small, $\beta \ll k^{-0.25}$, hence the growth rate based on c/L is then very weak for very large k, being of the order $k^{-1/2}$.

If, for large k we assume $1 \ll m \ll k$, from (2.56) we have

$$m = \tfrac{1}{64}k\beta^4, \qquad m' = k + m,$$

$$\sigma_0 - m = (km)^{1/2} = \tfrac{1}{8}k\beta^2, \qquad m' - \sigma_0 = k + O(\beta^2), \qquad F^{-2} = k = M,$$

so that (2.41) becomes

$$\lambda_1^2 = -(\tfrac{1}{64}k^2\beta^4)^2,$$

and

$$|\lambda_1/2(\sigma_0 - m)| = \tfrac{1}{16}k\beta^2.$$

If again c/L is used as the scale of the growth rate rather than c/d, we have

$$\text{growth rate} = \tfrac{1}{8}\pi\beta^2. \tag{2.59}$$

Equations (2.57)–(2.59) give the rate of growth of unstable disturbances (the m-waves and the m'-waves) for long or short waves. But since, whatever the wavelength of the primary waves, m is positive and G is positive in (2.43a), progressive gravity waves of all wavelengths are unstable. The result that long waves are unstable, so long as the wavelength is finite, can be compared with the result of Benjamin (1967) and Whitham (1966) that progressive gravity waves are stable for $k < 1.363$. The explanation for the difference in results lies in the difference in the mechanism of resonance, theirs being the resonance of disturbances with side-band frequencies with the second harmonic of the primary waves, ours being the resonance of two wave trains with the basic harmonic of the primary waves.

Benjamin's theory as applied to deep-water waves has been abundantly confirmed by Feir's experiments and by observations at the National Physical Laboratory (NPL), reported in Benjamin's paper (1967). It is therefore necessary to compare the present results for deep water with Benjamin's and with available experimental data.

We shall first compare the exponential growth rates given by (2.58) and (2.59) with the exponential growth rate of the side-band disturbances given by Benjamin, which is, for deep water,

$$\tfrac{1}{2}k_B^2 a^2 \omega = \tfrac{1}{8}\beta^2 \omega, \tag{2.60}$$

where ω is the (dimensional) circular frequency of the primary waves.

Since

$$c/d = \omega/k_B d = \omega/k,$$

the dimensional growth rate corresponding to (2.58) is

$$\pi|\beta|\omega/4\sqrt{2}\,k^{1.25}, \tag{2.61}$$

and that according to (2.59) is

$$\pi\beta^2\omega/8k. \tag{2.62}$$

In the NPL observations $k = 50\pi/7.2$, $|\beta| = 0.34$, so that both (2.61) and (2.62) are less than (2.60), but (2.61) is relevant because m is small compared with 1. Hence Benjamin's mechanism dominates the mechanism treated here, under the experimental conditions at NPL. For the Cambridge experiments

$$\omega = 5\pi/s,$$

so that

$$k_B = \tfrac{25}{32}\pi^2 = 7/\text{ft}.$$

The depth of water was not given. Assuming that it is 3 ft, we have $k = 21$, and in the range of β covered by the experiments, m is small and (2.61) should be used. In this case (2.61) is greater than (2.60) for the smaller values of β and less than (2.60) for the larger values β, but the orders of the magnitudes are quite the same. One must nevertheless pose the question of why the growth rate (2.61) was not observed, especially for very small β. The answer is that the dimensionless number δ representing the fractional deviation from ω in the side-band frequencies $(1 \pm \delta)\omega$ was fixed at 0.1 in the Cambridge experiments, but is far from that for the m-waves and m'-waves treated here. Thus naturally they cannot be observed.

Now the m-waves travel with the stream if the primary waves are stationary, and hence against the primary progressive waves in the fixed frame of reference. The opposite is true for the m'-waves. Since m is small or at least much smaller than k, the δ in $(1 - \delta)\omega$ is slightly greater than 1, in any case very near 1. Since m' is very near k, the δ in $(1 + \delta)\omega$ is very near zero. Thus the Cambridge experiments, with δ fixed at 0.1, could not have revealed the m-waves or m'-waves.

Since the frequency of the m-waves is small and the deviation of the frequency of the m'-waves from ω of the primary waves is small, to detect these small quantities time records such as shown on p. 63 of Benjamin's paper must be very long. Analysis with records covering a short period of time can only reveal Benjamin's instability and would necessarily fail to reveal the instability treated here, even when it happens to be stronger than Benjamin's (which it is not if the amplitude is not too small).

The main conclusion of this section is that all progressive gravity waves are unstable. (See note added in proof on p. 419.)

I. Conclusions

(i) Stationary gravity waves in water (or any liquid) flowing over a wavy bottom are unstable for any nonzero wave number of these waves if $F^2 \geq 1$, and for any wave number greater than a critical value k_c (depending on F^2) if $F^2 < 1$.

(ii) Gravity waves of all nonzero wavelengths are unstable.

J. Discussion

As mentioned in the introduction, Hasselmann (1967) gave the theorem that for dispersive waves propagating in one dimension, for which the frequency σ is a function of the wave number k, if there are three wave numbers satisfying the relation

$$k_3 = k_1 + k_2 ,$$

with their corresponding frequencies satisfying

$$\sigma_3 = \sigma_1 + \sigma_2 ,$$

then, on the understanding that the k_1-waves are finite and the other two wave trains infinitesimal, one has $\dot{a}_1 = 0$ and

$$\dot{a}_2 = ih\sigma_2 a_1 a_3^* , \tag{2.63}$$

$$\dot{a}_3 = -ih\sigma_3 a_1^* a_2 , \tag{2.64}$$

                    Chia-Shun Yih

where a_1, a_2, and a_3 are the amplitudes, however defined, of the three wave trains, the dot indicates the time derivative, the asterisk denotes the complex conjugate, i is, as usual, the square root of -1, and h is real. From (2.63) and (2.64) it is easy to show that

$$\ddot{a}_2 = h^2 |a_1|^2 \sigma_2 \sigma_3 a_2 ,$$

so that the k_2-waves are unstable. The same is true of the k_3-waves.

In this paper the k, m, and m' correspond to k_1, k_2, and k_3, respectively, and since the frame of reference is stationary with respect to the k-waves, the quantities corresponding to σ_1, σ_2, and σ_3 are, respectively,

$$k, \quad \sigma_0 - m, \quad \text{and} \quad \sigma_0 - m'.$$

With this in mind, and remembering that a and b in (2.26), (2.33a), and (2.34a) correspond to a_2 and a_3 in (2.63) and (2.64), we can identify [see (2.42)]

$$\frac{\lambda_1}{2(\sigma_0 - m)}(a, b)$$

with the $\dot{a}_2$ and $\dot{a}_3$ in (2.63) and (2.64). Upon multiplying (2.33a) by $\sigma_0 - m$ and (2.34a) by $\sigma_0 - m'$, using (2.35) and (2.36), and multiplying b by an appropriate factor, (2.33a) and (2.34a) can be reduced to (2.63) and (2.64). Thus there seems to be a similarity between the present results and the result of Hasselmann embodied in (2.63) and (2.64).

Yet the similarity is only superficial. First of all the fact that the bracketed terms in (2.33) and (2.34) are both negative, a fact crucial for the proof of instability and ensuring the existence of a real h in (2.63) and (2.64), has been established in such a special and unobvious way that one can justifiably doubt that a general formula established without regard to the particularity of the problems can apply to the problems considered here *a priori*.

It may be useful to point out further the differences of the present results and the result of Hasselmann. As far as we can see, Hasselmann treated the stability of waves freely propagating in water of uniform depth (i.e., where his theory touches upon the present results). If these are made stationary, the general velocity of flow is not arbitrary but equal to the speed of propagation in quiet water. In this paper, where stationary waves are treated, the general velocity of flow embodied in the Froude number is entirely arbitrary. Thus the conditions on which Hasselmann's theory stands do not seem to be met here, and consequently the instability described here cannot be included in that theorem.

Furthermore, whether the waves are due to the wavy bottom or are free waves, the finiteness of their amplitude demands application of the free-surface condition on the free surface and not at a constant elevation. This is taken care of in this article by using ϕ and ψ as independent variables instead of x and y. There is nothing in Hasselmann's paper that indicates how this situation is dealt with.

III. Instability of Internal Waves

A. Introduction

Davis and Acrivos (1967) found that Hasselmann's conditions (mentioned in our Section I) can be satisfied for internal waves in a stratified fluid by resorting to interaction between trains of internal waves not only of different wavelengths but also of different modes. At least one of the wave trains must be of a different mode from the other two. The discovery of Davis and Acrivos is a very interesting one, for the instability they found is truly characteristic of internal waves. It has no counterpart for surface waves in a homogeneous fluid.

Our investigations in the instability of internal waves supplement the work of Davis and Acrivos. In the following sections we will show that Hasselmann's conditions can be met if (i) the primary wave train is due to a flow of a stratified fluid over a boundary, or if (ii) it is a wave train freely progressing over a flat bottom, provided the wave velocity increases with the amplitude. When Hasselmann's conditions are met, the primary wave train is indeed unstable.

In category (i) conditions of stability or instability are found for two cases: (1) waves in two superposed fluid layers, with the upper fluid infinite in extent, and (2) waves in a continuously stratified fluid. The growth rate of the disturbances is given whenever they are unstable. In Case 2 Boussinesq's approximation is used. We emphasize that the mechanism of instability is, as for surface waves, the resonance of a pair of disturbances with the basic waves produced by flows over wavy surfaces.

For interfacial waves the results are nearly the same as for surface waves, but for internal waves in a continuously stratified fluid the results are somewhat different, the main difference being that these waves are *stable* for sufficiently high wave numbers and unstable for sufficiently low wave numbers, whatever the internal Froude number may be.

The stability of progressive internal waves in an otherwise quiet fluid is briefly discussed after stationary waves over a wavy boundary have been treated.

 Chia-Shun Yih

B. STATIONARY INTERFACIAL WAVES

The primary flow, the stability of which will be studied in the next section, is the flow of two superposed incompressible fluids with a "general" velocity U over a wavy bed, which is described by

$$y = -d + \gamma_1 \cos kx, \tag{3.1}$$

where x and y are Cartesian coordinates, with y measured in the direction opposite to that of the gravitational acceleration, d and γ_1 are constants, and k is the wave number of the corrugation of the bed. The general velocity U would be the actual velocity of the fluids if γ_1 were zero.

The lower fluid has density ρ_2, and extends from the bed to the interface

$$y = \eta,$$

η being the (sinusoidal) elevation of the interface above its mean position $y = 0$. That is to say, if γ_1 were zero the lower fluid would extend from $y = -d$ to $y = 0$. The upper fluid has density ρ_1 and extends from the interface to positive infinity.

Neglecting viscous effects, we assume the flow in each layer to be irrotational. Velocity potentials ϕ_1 and ϕ_2 then exist for the upper and lower layers, respectively, both of which satisfy the Laplace equation. Since wave motion must die out as y approaches infinity, we have

$$\phi_1 = Ux + A_1 e^{-ky} \sin kx, \tag{3.2}$$

$$\phi_2 = Ux + (A_2 \cosh ky + B_2 \sinh ky) \sin kx. \tag{3.3}$$

The corresponding stream functions ψ_1 and ψ_2, which are harmonic conjugates of ϕ_1 and ϕ_2, are

$$\psi_1 = Uy - A_1 e^{-ky} \cos kx, \tag{3.4}$$

$$\psi_2 = Uy + (A_2 \sinh ky + B_2 \cosh ky) \cos kx. \tag{3.5}$$

We shall give a linear theory for the primary flow, because we need only the first harmonic of the wave motion for our stability study, and a linear theory gives that.

At the wavy bed, $\psi_2 = -Ud$, so that

$$y = -d + U^{-1}(A_2 \sinh kd - B_2 \cosh kd) \cos kx.$$

Hence

$$U\gamma_1 = A_2 \sinh kd - B_2 \cosh kd. \tag{3.6}$$

On the interface,

$$\psi_1 = 0 = \psi_2,$$

so that

$$B_2 = -A_1. \tag{3.7}$$

Furthermore, at the interface the Bernoulli equation gives, after the mean quantities have been filtered out,

$$\rho_1 U(\phi_1 - Ux)_x = -p - \rho_1 g\eta, \tag{3.8}$$

$$\rho_2 U(\phi_2 - Ux)_x = -p - \rho_2 g\eta, \tag{3.9}$$

where the subscript x denotes partial differentiation and p denotes the pressure due to waves. The interface displacement η is obtained by setting ψ_1 equal to zero in (3.4), and is

$$\eta = A_1 U^{-1} \cos kx. \tag{3.10}$$

When (3.2), (3.3), and (3.10) are used in (3.8) and (3.9), and p is eliminated, we have

$$A_2 = jA_1, \tag{3.11}$$

where

$$F_i^2 = \frac{\rho_2 U^2}{\Delta \rho g d}, \qquad j = \frac{\rho_1}{\rho_2} - \frac{F_i^{-2}}{kd}, \tag{3.12}$$

F_i being an internal Froude number. From (3.6) and (3.7),

$$A_2 = \frac{U\gamma_1}{\sinh kd} - A_1 \coth kd, \tag{3.13}$$

which, together with (3.11), gives

$$A_1 = U\gamma_1 \left(\rho_2 \cosh kd + \rho_1 \sinh kd - \frac{g\,\Delta\rho}{kU^2} \sinh kd \right)^{-1}. \tag{3.14}$$

For the convenience of the subsequent development, we shall make the results given above in dimensionless terms. If ϕ and ψ are measured in units of Ud and linear dimensions are measured in units of d, after using (3.7), we have

$$\phi_1 = x + a_1 e^{-ky} \sin kx, \qquad \phi_2 = x + (a_2 \cosh ky - a_1 \sinh ky) \sin kx,$$

$$\psi_1 = y - a_1 e^{-ky} \cos kx, \qquad \psi_2 = y + (a_2 \sinh ky - a_1 \cosh ky) \cos ky,$$

$$\tag{3.15}$$

where

$$(a_1, a_2) = (Ud)^{-1}(A_1, A_2).$$

                        Chia-Shun Yih

and k is now and henceforth dimensionless (equal to the original kd). We have

$$a_2 = ja_1, \qquad a_1 = \gamma(\cosh k + j \sinh k)^{-1}, \tag{3.16}$$

where

$$\gamma = \frac{\gamma_1}{d}, \qquad j = \frac{\rho_1}{\rho_2} - \frac{F_i^{-2}}{k}. \tag{3.17}$$

If we write, in accordance with the usage in Section II,

$$\beta = -2a_2 k,$$

the horizontal dimensionless velocity components u_1 and u_2 at the interface, to the first order in β, are

$$u_1 = 1 - \frac{\beta}{2j} \cos kx = 1 - \frac{\beta}{2j} \cos k\phi_1 = 1 - \frac{\beta}{2j} \cos k\phi_2,$$

$$u_2 = 1 - \frac{\beta}{2} \cos kx = 1 - \frac{\beta}{2} \cos k\phi_2,$$

so that, to the first order,

$$q_1^2 = 1 - \frac{\beta}{j} \cos k\phi_2, \qquad q_2^2 = 1 - \beta \cos k\phi_2,$$

$$u_2^{-1} q_2^2 = 1 - \frac{\beta}{2} \cos k\phi_2. \tag{3.18}$$

These formulas will be useful in the next section.

C. Instability of Stationary Interfacial Waves

It can be readily verified that for waves with the exponential factor $\exp i(\alpha x - \sigma t)$, where α is the dimensionless wave number and σ the dimensionless circular frequency (i.e., with σ measured in units of U/d), σ is equal to σ_0 (positive), with σ_0 given by

$$(\sigma_0 - \alpha)^2 = F_i^{-2}(\alpha \tanh \alpha)(1 + r \tanh \alpha)^{-1}, \qquad \text{with} \quad r = \rho_1/\rho_2, \tag{3.19}$$

provided that γ is zero, that is, provided the bottom is flat. Since γ is not zero σ will differ from σ_0, and the purpose of this section is to show that the difference may be a positive imaginary number, signifying instability, if the disturbance consists of two wave trains of wave numbers m and m' satisfying (3.19) and the condition

$$m' - m = k, \tag{3.20}$$

where k is the dimensionless wave number of the primary waves treated in the preceding section. We shall first discuss (3.19) and (3.20) before going on to the study of stability.

For a given r and a given F_i^2, Eq. (3.19) has two roots, one greater than σ_0, which we shall denote by m', and one less than σ_0, which we shall denote by m. That there are two such real roots can be seen in the following way. We shall denote the right-hand side of (3.19) by R and its left-hand side by L. If we plot L against α the curve is a parabola touching the α axis at $\alpha = \sigma_0$. If we plot R against α the curve touches the α axis at the origin, rises monotonically (the monotonicity can be easily established) as α increases, but is asymptotically linear for large α. Hence the two curves must intersect at two points, one (m) on the descending branch of the L-α curve and one (m') on its ascending branch.

For given k, r, and F_i^2, we wish to find m and m' satisfying (3.19) and (3.20). To find m (and therefore m') and σ_0 we adopt the following procedure. Given r and F_i^2, we assign various values to m. Substituting m for α in (3.19), we find σ_0 (greater than m). Then with this value of σ_0 we solve (3.19) for the other root m'. The value k is then given by (3.20). In this way we obtain values of m and σ_0 corresponding to k, and m-k and σ_0-k curves can be so constructed. In Figs. 7 and 8 are such curves for various values of F_i^2 and for $r = 1$. The value 1 is of course never reached by r, and assigning the value 1 to r amounts to adopting the Boussinesq approximation, valid when $1 - r \ll 1$.

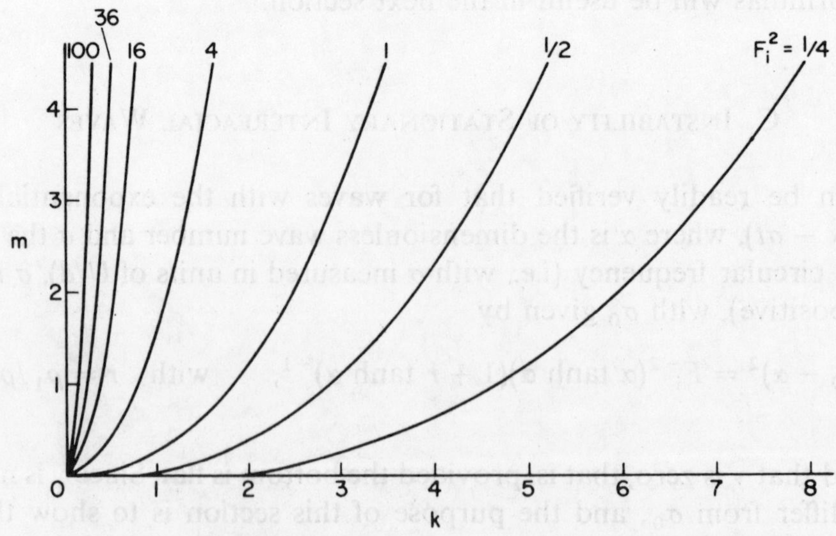

FIG. 7. Variation of m with k for $r = 1$ and various values of F_i^2.

Chia-Shun Yih

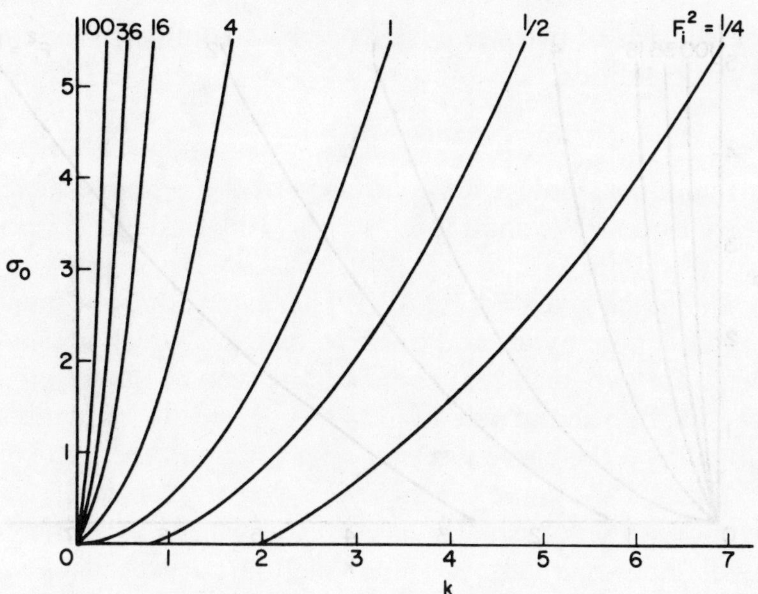

FIG. 8.   Variation of σ_0 with k for $r = 1$ and various values of F_i^2.

From Fig. 7 it is seen that for $F_i^2 \geq 1$ we have a nonzero m for a nonzero k, whereas for $F_i^2 < 1$ m is not zero only if $k > k_c$, k_c depending on F_i^2. Figures 9 and 10 give m-k and σ_0-k curves for $r = 0.5$, and Figs. 11 and 12 give these curves for $r = 0.25$.

It is easy to determine k_c. From (3.19) we have

$$F_i(\sigma_0 - m) = J(m), \tag{3.21}$$

$$F_i(\sigma_0 - m') = -J(m'), \tag{3.22}$$

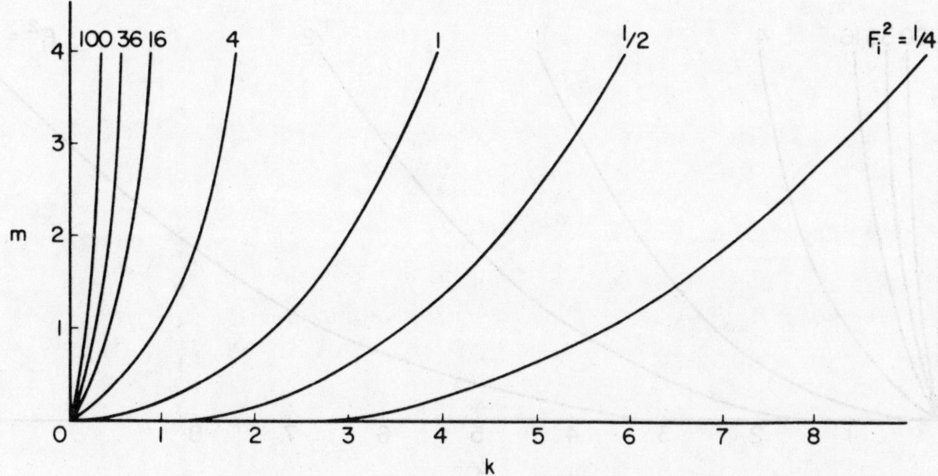

FIG. 9.   Variation of m with k for $r = 0.5$ and various values of F_i^2.

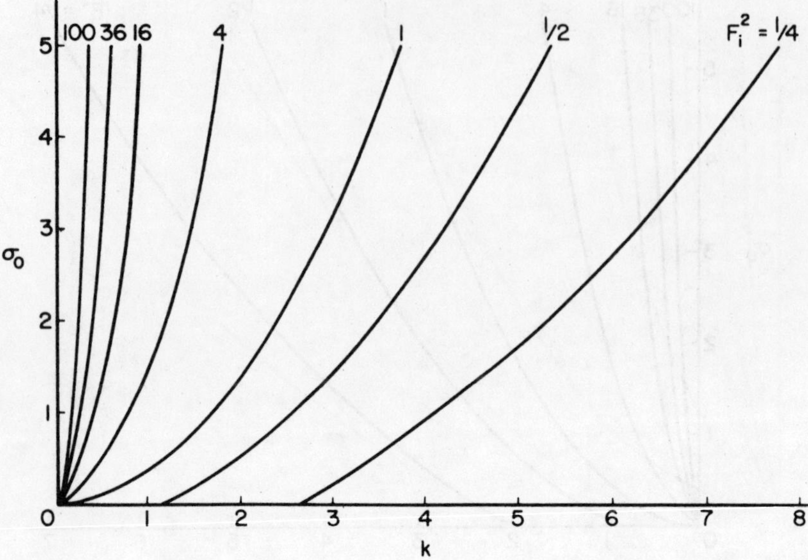

FIG. 10. Variation of σ_0 with k for $r = 0.5$ and various values of F_i^2.

in which

$$J(m) = \left(\frac{m \tanh m}{1 + r \tanh m} \right)^{1/2} \tag{3.23}$$

By virtue of (3.20), the difference between (3.21) and (3.22) is

$$F_i k = J(m) + J(m'). \tag{3.24}$$

Upon equating m to zero in this equation, we have

$$F_i = k^{-1} J(k), \tag{3.25}$$

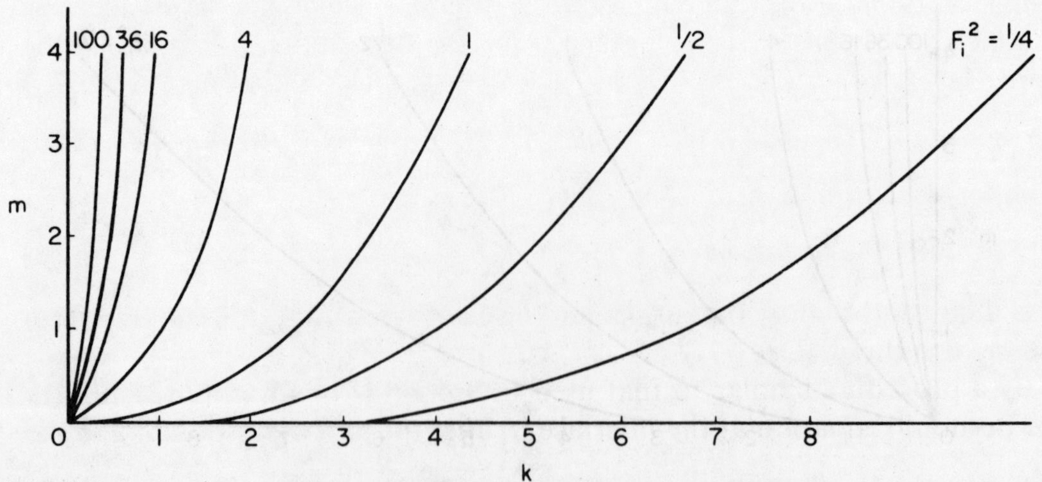

FIG. 11. Variation of m with k for $r = 0.25$ and various values of F_i^2.

                           Chia-Shun Yih

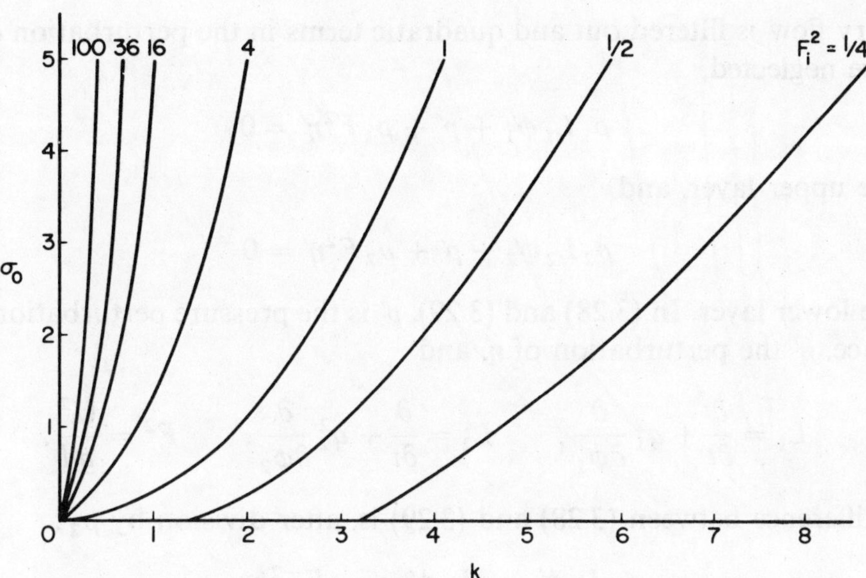

FIG. 12.   Variation of σ_0 with k for $r = 0.25$ and various values of F_i^2.

which states that the general velocity U, on which F_i is based, is the velocity of internal waves of wave number k in the fluid layers under consideration, if they were at rest and $\beta = 0$. This fact can be readily demonstrated independently in the same way as (3.19). The solution of (3.25) for k is k_c. But (3.25) has a real solution only if $F_i < 1$, for $F_i = 1$ for $k = 0$ (very long waves), and the wave velocity decreases with k. We note, however, that the case $k = k_c$ must be excluded,† for if (3.25) is satisfied A_1 is infinite according to (3.14) (where k is still dimensional). This discussion is intended to show that if $F_i < 1$ but $k_c < k$, Eq. (3.24), in which $m' = m + k$, has a nonzero solution for m.

We now give the primary waves a perturbation. The perturbation flow is still irrotational except, of course, at the interface, which is a vortex sheet, as is well known. The velocity potential for the perturbation flow is, for the upper layer,

$$\phi_1' = e^{-i\sigma t}[\alpha_1 \exp(-m\psi_1 + im\phi_1) + \beta_1 \exp(-m'\psi_1 + im'\phi_1)], \quad (3.26)$$

and, for the lower layer,

$$\phi_2' = e^{-i\sigma t}[\alpha_2 \cosh m(\psi_2 + 1)e^{im\phi_2} + \beta_2 \cosh m'(\psi_2 + 1)e^{im'\phi_2}]. \quad (3.27)$$

It is important to note that at the interface both ψ_1 and ψ_2 are equal to zero, but ϕ_1 is not equal to ϕ_2.

By a procedure similar to that used in Section II [see Eqs. (2.12)–(2.14)], the Bernoulli equation at the interface is, after the part corresponding to the

---

† This exclusion is not necessary if nonlinearity is taken into account.

primary flow is filtered out and quadratic terms in the perturbation quantities are neglected,

$$\rho_1 L_1 \phi_1' + p' + \rho_1 F^2 \eta' = 0 \tag{3.28}$$

for the upper layer, and

$$\rho_2 L_2 \phi_2' + p' + \rho_2 F^2 \eta' = 0 \tag{3.29}$$

for the lower layer. In (3.28) and (3.29), p' is the pressure perturbation at the interface, η' the perturbation of η, and

$$L_1 = \frac{\partial}{\partial t} + q_1^2 \frac{\partial}{\partial \phi_1}, \qquad L_2 = \frac{\partial}{\partial t} + q_2^2 \frac{\partial}{\partial \phi_2}, \qquad F^2 = \frac{U^2}{gd}. \tag{3.30}$$

The difference between (3.28) and (3.29) is, after division by ρ_2,

$$L_2 \phi_2' - r L_1 \phi_1' = -F_i^{-2} \eta. \tag{3.31}$$

As in Section II [see Eqs. (2.15)–(2.20)], the kinematic condition at the interface is

$$L_1 \eta' = u_1^{-1} q_1^2 \, \partial \phi_1' / \partial \psi_1 \tag{3.32}$$

for the upper fluid, and

$$L_2 \eta' = u_2^{-1} q_2^2 \, \partial \phi_2' / \partial \psi_2 \tag{3.33}$$

for the lower fluid. We recall that, to the first order in β,

$$u_1 = q_1 \quad \text{and} \quad u_2 = q_2 .$$

Applying the operator L_2 to (3.31) and using (3.33), we have

$$\boxed{L_2^2(\phi_2' - r\phi_1') - r L_2 \left[(q_1 - q_2) q_2 \frac{\partial}{\partial \phi_2} \right] \phi_1' + F_i^{-2} u_2^{-1} q_2^2 \frac{\partial \phi_2'}{\partial \psi_2} = 0,}$$

$$\tag{3.34}$$

since

$$q_2 \, \partial / \partial \phi_2 = q_1 \, \partial / \partial \phi_1 = \partial / \partial s,$$

s being the distance measured along the interface. The next step is to express ϕ_1' in terms of ϕ_2 at the interface. For this purpose we use (3.32) and (3.33), and express η' in the form

$$\eta' = \exp(-i\sigma t)[\xi \exp(im\phi_2) + \xi' \exp(im'\phi_2)]. \tag{3.35}$$

402   *Chia-Shun Yih*

From (3.32) and (3.33) we have, if terms of $O(\beta^2)$ are neglected,

$$\frac{\partial \phi_1'}{\partial \psi_1} - \frac{q_2}{q_1} \frac{\partial \phi_2'}{\partial \psi_2} = (q_1 - q_2) \frac{q_2}{q_1} \frac{\partial \eta'}{\partial \phi_2}, \tag{3.36}$$

which shows that we need not evaluate η' to the order β, since

$$q_1 - q_2 = -2h\beta \cos k\phi_2, \qquad q_2/q_1 = 1 + 2h\beta \cos k\phi_2,$$

where

$$h = (1 - j)/4j. \tag{3.37}$$

Using (3.33), we obtain, upon separating the terms containing $\exp(im\phi_2)$ from those containing $\exp(im'\phi_2)$,

$$\xi = \frac{i\alpha_2 m \sinh m}{\sigma_0 - m} + O(\beta), \qquad \xi' = \frac{i\beta_2 m' \sinh m'}{\sigma_0 - m'} + O(\beta). \tag{3.38}$$

Substituting (3.35) and (3.38) into (3.36), we can evaluate α_1 and β_1 in ϕ_1' in terms of α_2 and β_2, but to do this we have to convert the exponentials $\exp(im\phi_1)$ and $\exp(im'\phi_1)$ into sums of exponentials $\exp(im\phi_2)$ and $\exp(im'\phi_2)$. With higher-order terms omitted, we have

$$\phi_1 - \phi_2 = (a_1 - a_2) \sin k\phi_2 = -\frac{2h\beta}{k} \sin k\phi_2 .$$

Hence

$$\cos m\phi_1 = \cos m(\phi_2 + \phi_1 - \phi_2) = \cos m\phi_2 - \sin m\phi_2 \sin m(\phi_1 - \phi_2)$$

$$= \cos m\phi_2 + \frac{2h\beta m}{k} \sin m\phi_2 \sin k\phi_2 + O(\beta^2)$$

$$= \cos m\phi_2 + \frac{h\beta m}{k} [\cos(k - m)\phi_2 - \cos m'\phi_2] + O(\beta^2). \tag{3.39}$$

The term containing $\cos(k - m)\phi_2$ can be omitted, for the components with wave numbers $m - nk$ ($n = 1, 2, 3, \ldots$) and $m' + nk$ are governed by nonhomogeneous equations with the nonhomogeneous parts produced by the basic components with wave numbers m and m', which are being considered here. Thus the other components are expressible in terms of the basic components, which determine the stability of the flow. Returning to (3.39), then, we see that, as far as the basic components are concerned,

$$\exp(im\phi_1) = \exp(im\phi_2) - \frac{hm\beta}{k} \exp(im'\phi_2). \tag{3.40}$$

Similarly,

$$\exp(im'\phi_1) = \exp(im'\phi_2) + \frac{hm'\beta}{k}\exp(im\phi_2). \qquad (3.41)$$

We now substitute (3.35) and (3.38) into (3.36), use (3.40) and (3.41), and equate the coefficients of the two basic components $\exp(im\phi_2)$ and $\exp(im'\phi_2)$. The results are, after a good deal of straightforward calculations,

$$\alpha_1 = -\alpha_2 \sinh m + h\beta\beta_2 m' \sinh m'\left(\frac{1}{k} - \frac{m'}{m(\sigma - m')}\right), \qquad (3.42)$$

$$\beta_1 = -\beta_2 \sinh m' - h\beta\alpha_2 m \sinh m\left(\frac{1}{k} + \frac{m}{m'(\sigma - m)}\right). \qquad (3.43)$$

Using (3.40) and 3.41), we have, for ϕ'_1 at the interface,

$$\phi'_1 = \alpha_1 \exp(im\phi_1) + \beta_1 \exp(im'\phi_1)$$

$$= -\left(\alpha_2 \sinh m + h\beta\beta_2 \frac{m'^2 \sinh m'}{m(\sigma - m')}\right) \exp(im\phi_2)$$

$$-\left(\beta_2 \sinh m' + h\beta\alpha_2 \frac{m^2 \sinh m}{m'(\sigma - m)}\right) \exp(im'\phi_2). \qquad (3.44)$$

This will be used in the first term of (3.34).

The next step is to calculate the second term in (3.34). Since it contains the factor $q_1 - q_2$, which is of $O(\beta)$, we need only to use the terms of zeroth order in β in (3.44) for ϕ'_1 at the interface. A straightforward calculation then gives

$$rL_2\left[(q_1 - q_2)q_2 \frac{\partial}{\partial\phi_2}\right]\phi'_1 = -h\beta e^{-i\sigma t}[\beta_2 m'(m - \sigma_0) \sinh m' \exp(im\phi_2)$$

$$+ \alpha_2 m(m' - \sigma_0) \sinh m \exp(im'\phi_2)], \qquad (3.45)$$

with all components but the basic ones neglected.

The third term in (3.34) is

$$e^{-i\sigma t}F_i^{-2}\left\{\left(\alpha_2 m \sinh m - \frac{\beta}{4}\beta_2 m' \sinh m'\right) \exp(im\phi_2)\right.$$

$$\left. + \left(\beta_2 m' \sinh m' - \frac{\beta}{4}\alpha_2 m \sinh m\right) \exp(im'\phi_2)\right\}. \qquad (3.46)$$

Chia-Shun Yih

Putting (3.44)–(3.46) into (3.34), and equating terms of the same wave number, we have [see Eqs. (2.27), (3.29), and (2.30) for comparison]

$$\alpha_2(1 + r \tanh m)(\sigma - m)^2 \cosh m$$

$$+ \tfrac{1}{2}\beta_2\beta(1 + r \tanh m')m'(2\sigma - m - m') \cosh m'$$

$$+ \beta_2 rh\beta m' \sinh m'\left(\frac{m'(\sigma_0 - m)}{m(\sigma_0 - m')} + 1\right)(\sigma_0 - m)$$

$$= F_{\mathrm{i}}^{-2}\left(\alpha_2 m \sinh m - \frac{\beta}{4}\beta_2 m' \sinh m'\right) \tag{3.47}$$

and

$$\beta_2(1 + r \tanh m')(\sigma - m')^2 \cosh m'$$

$$+ \tfrac{1}{2}\alpha_2\beta(1 + r \tanh m)m(2\sigma - m - m') \cosh m$$

$$+ \alpha_2 rh\beta m \sinh m\left(\frac{m(m' - \sigma_0)}{m'(\sigma_0 - m)} - 1\right)(m' - \sigma_0)$$

$$= F_{\mathrm{i}}^{-2}\left(\beta_2 m' \sinh m' - \frac{\beta}{4}\alpha_2 m \sinh m\right). \tag{3.48}$$

Let

$$(\sigma - m)^2 = (\sigma_0 - m)^2 + \lambda_1 \beta + O(\beta^2),$$

Then

$$\sigma = \sigma_0 + \frac{\lambda_1 \beta}{2(\sigma_0 - m)} + O(\beta^2), \tag{3.49}$$

and, upon neglect of terms of $O(\beta^2)$, we can write (3.47) as

$$\alpha_2\lambda_1 \cosh m + \frac{m'\beta_2}{4(1 + r \tanh m)}[2(1 + r \tanh m')$$

$$\times (2\sigma_0 - m - m') \cosh m' + F_{\mathrm{i}}^{-2} \sinh m']$$

$$+ H_1\beta_2 \cosh m' = 0, \tag{3.50}$$

where

$$H_1 = \frac{rhm' \tanh m'}{1 + r \tanh m}\left(\frac{m'(\sigma_0 - m)}{m(\sigma_0 - m')} + 1\right)(\sigma_0 - m).$$

Similarly, (3.48) can be written as

$$\beta_2 \lambda_1 \cosh m' \frac{\sigma_0 - m'}{\sigma_0 - m}$$

$$+ \frac{m\alpha_2}{4(1 + r \tanh m')}[2(1 + r \tanh m)(2\sigma_0 - m - m') \cosh m$$

$$+ F_i^{-2} \sinh m] + H_2 \alpha_2 \cosh m = 0, \tag{3.51}$$

where

$$H_2 = \frac{rhm \tanh m}{1 + r \tanh m'} \left(\frac{m(m' - \sigma_0)}{m'(\sigma_0 - m)} - 1 \right)(m' - \sigma_0).$$

The sign of H_1 is determined by the sign of

$$\frac{m'(\sigma_0 - m)}{m(\sigma_0 - m')} + 1,$$

which is equal to

$$-\frac{m'J(m)}{mJ(m')} + 1$$

by virtue of (3.21) and (3.22). It is a simple matter to show that

$$\frac{d}{dm} \left(\frac{J(m)}{m} \right) < 0,$$

so that

$$m'J(m)/mJ(m') > 1,$$

since $m' > m$. Thus the sign of H_1 is negative. Similarly, the sign of H_2 is also negative.

We now evaluate $2\sigma_0 - m - m'$ by the method described in Section II [Eqs. (2.35)–(2.39)]. Equation (3.21) can now be written as

$$(\sigma_0 - m)^2 + F_i^{-2}(\sigma_0 - m)K(m) - F_i^{-2}\sigma_0 K(m) = 0. \tag{3.52}$$

where

$$K(m) = \frac{\tanh m}{1 + r \tanh m}. \tag{3.53}$$

Solving (3.52), we have

$$\sigma_0 - m = \tfrac{1}{2}[-F_i^{-2}K(m) + f(m)], \tag{3.54}$$

                                    Chia-Shun Yih

in which

$$f(m) = [F_i^{-4}K^2(m) + 4F_i^{-2}\sigma_0 K(m)]^{1/2}.$$ (3.55)

The positive sign is taken in (3.54) because $\sigma_0 - m$ is positive. Similarly, $\sigma_0 - m'$ satisfies (3.52), with m replaced by m'. Hence

$$\sigma_0 - m' = \tfrac{1}{2}[-F_i^{-2}K(m') - f(m')],$$ (3.56)

the negative sign before $f(m')$ being taken because $\sigma_0 - m'$ is negative. The sum of (3.54) and (3.56) is, after multiplication by 2,

$$2(2\sigma_0 - m - m') = -F_i^{-2}[K(m) + K(m')] - M,$$ (3.57)

where

$$M = f(m') - f(m) > 0.$$ (3.58)

Returning to (3.50), we see that the term in brackets becomes $-D \cosh m'$, with

$$D = F_i^{-2}\frac{1 + r \tanh m'}{1 + r \tanh m}[K(m) + M]m'.$$ (3.59)

Similarly, the term in brackets in (3.51) becomes $-E \cosh m$, with

$$E = F_i^{-2}\frac{1 + r \tanh m}{1 + r \tanh m'}[K(m') + M]m.$$ (3.60)

Therefore we can write (3.50) and (3.51) as

$$\alpha_2 \lambda_1 = \left(\frac{D}{4} - H_1\right)\frac{\beta_2 \cosh m'}{\cosh m},$$

$$\beta_2 \lambda_1 = \frac{\sigma_0 - m}{\sigma_0 - m'}\left(\frac{E}{4} - H_2\right)\frac{\alpha_2 \cosh m}{\cosh m'},$$

in which D and E are positive and H_1 and H_2 negative. From these two equations we obtain

$$\lambda_1^2 = \frac{\sigma_0 - m}{\sigma_0 - m'}\left(\frac{D}{4} - H_1\right)\left(\frac{E}{4} - H_2\right).$$ (3.61)

Since $\sigma_0 - m$ is positive and $\sigma_0 - m'$ is negative, $\lambda_1^2 < 0$, and the flow is unstable for the disturbances under consideration. Letting

$$\lambda = |\lambda_1|/2(\sigma_0 - m),$$

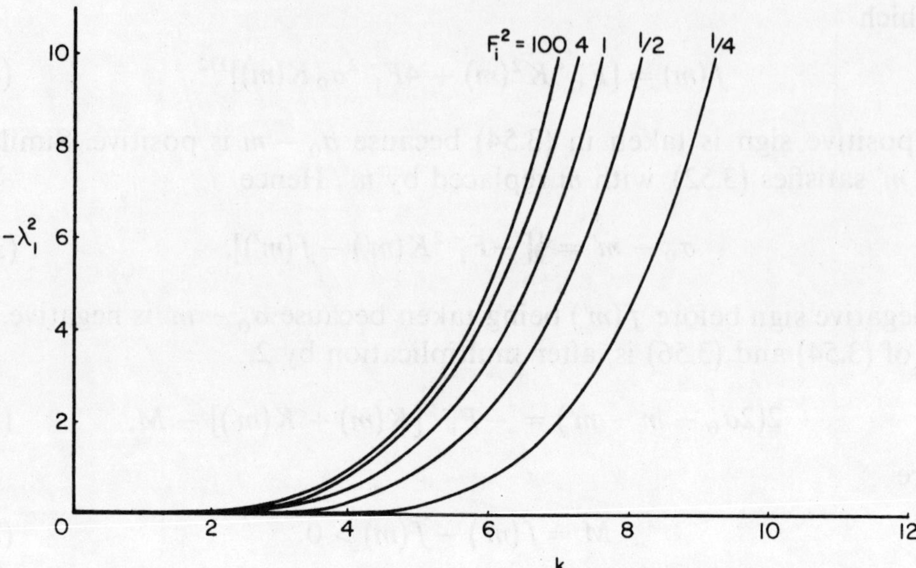

FIG. 13.   Variation of $-\lambda_1^2$ with k for $r = 1$ and various values of F_i^2.

the growth rate is then $\lambda\beta$. In Figs. 13–15, $-\lambda_1^2$ is plotted against k for $r = 1$, 0.5, and 0.25, and for various values of F_i^2.

We note that both E and H_2 contain the factor m. Therefore so long as m is not zero the primary flow is unstable. As mentioned before, if F_i^2 is not less than unity m is always positive. If F_i^2 is less than unity m is positive only if $k > k_c$, k_c being the root of (3.25).

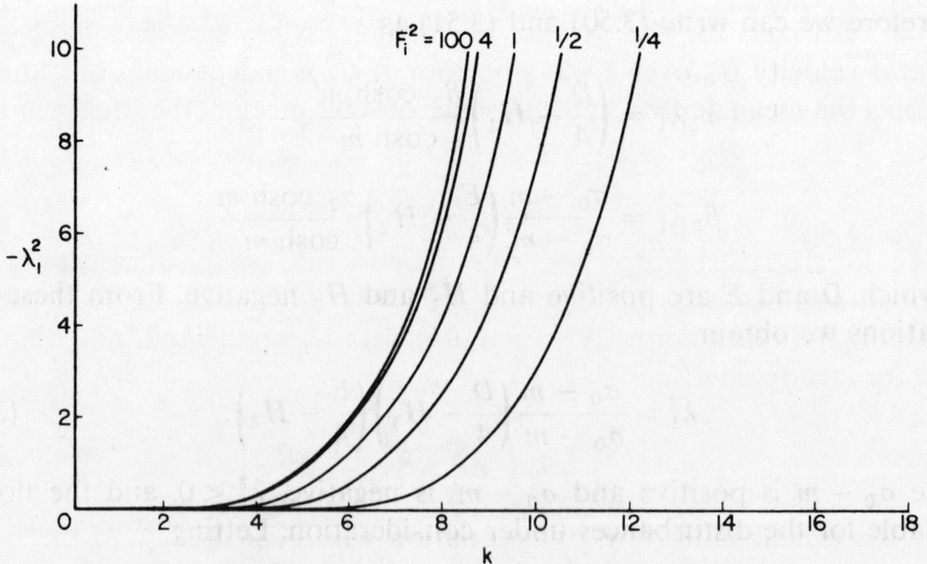

FIG. 14.   Variation of $-\lambda_1^2$ with k for $r = 0.5$ and various values of F_i^2.

Chia-Shun Yih

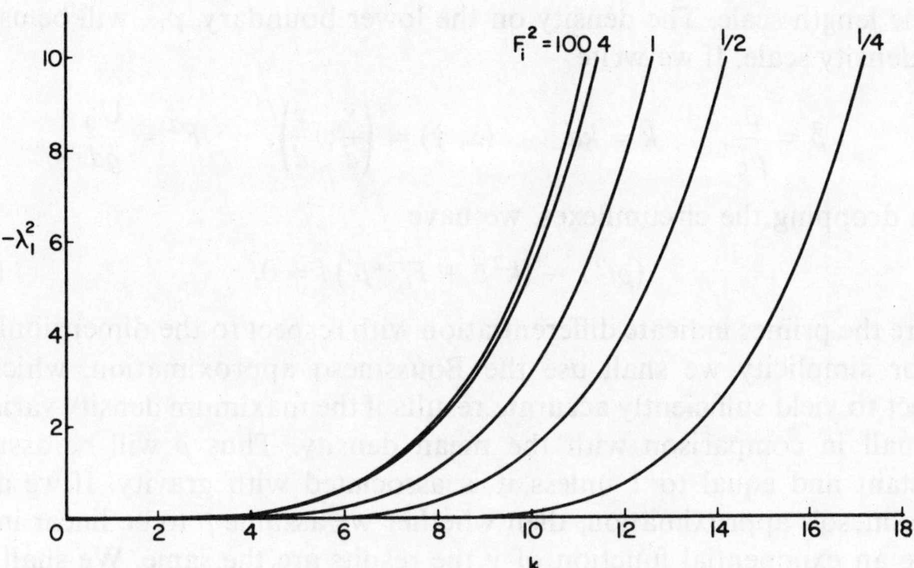

FIG. 15.   Variation of $-\lambda_1^2$ with k for $r = 0.25$ and various values of F_i^2.

In conclusion, stationary internal waves in the fluid system under consideration are unstable for all nonzero wave numbers if $F_i^2 \geq 1$, and for all wave numbers greater than k_c if $F_i^2 < 1$. We note also that (3.21) and (3.22) show that the m-waves travel with the stream and the m'-waves travel against it.

D. STATIONARY WAVES IN A CONTINUOUSLY STRATIFIED FLUID

We shall consider the flow of an incompressible stratified fluid with a general velocity U_0 over a wavy bottom. If U_0 is independent of y and $\bar{\rho}(y)$ denotes the mean density in the absence of wave motion, the stream function is

$$U_0 y + Af(y) \cos kx,$$

where, for the time being, x and y are dimensional, k is the dimensional wave number, and f satisfies the equation [see Yih, 1965, p. 20, Eq. (31), with U_0 replacing the c there, or p. 175, Eq. (104), with U_0 replacing U and c equal to zero for steady flow]

$$(\bar{\rho}f')' - \left(k^2\bar{\rho} + \frac{g\bar{\rho}'}{U_0^2}\right)f = 0, \tag{3.62}$$

with the accent indicating differentiation with respect to y. If the flow is supposed to be confined between two rigid boundaries at distance d apart, the upper one being flat and horizontal and the lower one wavy, we can use d

as the length scale. The density on the lower boundary, ρ_0, will be used as the density scale. If we write

$$\hat{\rho} = \frac{\bar{\rho}}{\rho_0}, \qquad \hat{k} = kd, \qquad (\hat{x}, \hat{y}) = \left(\frac{x}{d}, \frac{y}{d}\right), \qquad F^2 = \frac{U_0^2}{gd},$$

then dropping the circumflexes, we have

$$(\bar{\rho}f')' - (k^2\bar{\rho} + F^{-2}\bar{\rho}')f = 0, \tag{3.63}$$

where the primes indicate differentiation with respect to the dimensionless y.

For simplicity we shall use the Boussinesq approximation, which we expect to yield sufficiently accurate results if the maximum density variation is small in comparison with the mean density. Thus $\bar{\rho}$ will be assumed constant and equal to 1 unless it is associated with gravity. If we adopt Boussinesq's approximation, then whether we assume $\bar{\rho}$ to be linear in y or to be an exponential function of y the results are the same. We shall then assume $\bar{\rho}$ to be a linear function of y, and [note that the present β, chosen to conform to established usage, differs from that in (3.19)]

$$\bar{\rho}' = -\beta. \tag{3.64}$$

Then (3.63) becomes

$$f'' - (k^2 - F_i^{-2})f = 0, \tag{3.65}$$

where

$$F_i^2 = F^2\beta. \tag{3.66}$$

The condition for f at the upper boundary, where $y = 1$, is $f(1) = 0$. The solution of (3.65) satisfying this condition is

$$f(y) = \sin \kappa(1 - y), \qquad \kappa^2 = F_i^2 - k^2. \tag{3.67}$$

If the lower boundary is given in dimensionless terms by

$$y = \gamma \cos kx,$$

then since the dimensionless stream function is

$$\psi = y + h(x, y), \qquad h = Af(y) \cos kx, \tag{3.68}$$

and ψ can be taken to be zero at the lower boundary, A is related to γ by

$$-A \sin \kappa = \gamma.$$

Thus, for the primary flow to exist, κ is not equal to $n\pi$, where n is any integer.†

---

† This condition can be removed by considering nonlinearity.

Chia-Shun Yih

We have given the solution for the stationary waves only by a linear theory. As we have stated before, only the first harmonic is of importance, and a nonlinear theory would give substantially the same results. The amplitude A, being arbitrary (so long as the primary flow exists), can be regarded as the A for the nonlinear theory. The only difference that a nonlinear theory will bring about is the function $f(y)$. But this difference will be of the order $O(A)$, and a glance at (3.68) convinces us that if only terms of the orders $O(1)$ and $O(A)$ are retained, it is sufficient to use (3.67) and (3.68).

E. Instability of Stationary Waves in a Continuously Stratified Fluid

Since the flow is rotational because the fluid is stratified, we must use the Euler equations for the determination of the perturbation flow. If we denote the velocity components of the primary flow by u and v and those of the perturbation by u' and v', and write

$$U = u + u', \qquad V = v + v',$$

the Euler equations are, under the Boussinesq approximation and in dimensionless terms,

$$\frac{\partial u'}{\partial t} + U\frac{\partial U}{\partial x} + V\frac{\partial V}{\partial y} = -p_x, \tag{3.69}$$

$$\frac{\partial v'}{\partial t} + U\frac{\partial V}{\partial x} + V\frac{\partial V}{\partial y} = -p_y - F^{-2}(\bar{\rho} + \rho'), \tag{3.70}$$

where p is the (total) pressure and ρ' the perturbation in density. The equation of incompressibility is

$$\frac{\partial \rho'}{\partial t} + U\frac{\partial}{\partial x}(\bar{\rho} + \rho') + V\frac{\partial}{\partial y}(\bar{\rho} + \rho') = 0, \tag{3.71}$$

and the equation of continuity for the perturbation flow is

$$\frac{\partial u'}{\partial x} + \frac{\partial v'}{\partial y} = 0,$$

which permits us to use a stream function ψ', in terms of which

$$u' = \psi'_y, \qquad v' = -\psi'_x, \tag{3.72}$$

with the subscripts indicating partial differentiation. The velocity components u and v of the primary flow are given by

$$u = \psi_y = 1 + Af'(y)\cos kx, \qquad v = -\psi_x = Akf(y)\sin kx. \tag{3.73}$$

Elimination of p between (3.69) and (3.70) gives

$$\left(\frac{\partial}{\partial t} + U\frac{\partial}{\partial x} + V\frac{\partial}{\partial y}\right)(\bar{\zeta} + \zeta) = -F^{-2}(\bar{\rho}_x + \rho'_x), \tag{3.74}$$

where $\bar{\zeta}$ is the vorticity of the primary flow and ζ that of the perturbation flow, so that

$$\bar{\zeta} = -\nabla^2\bar{\psi}, \qquad \zeta = -\nabla^2\psi'.$$

The vorticity equation for the primary flow is

$$\left(u\frac{\partial}{\partial x} + v\frac{\partial}{\partial y}\right)\bar{\zeta} = -F^{-2}\bar{\rho}_x. \tag{3.75}$$

Taking the difference between (3.74) and (3.75) and neglecting quadratic terms in perturbation quantities, we have

$$L\,\nabla^2\psi' + E = F^{-2}\rho'_x, \tag{3.76}$$

where

$$L = \frac{\partial}{\partial t} + \frac{\partial}{\partial x},$$

$$E = h_y\,\nabla^2\psi'_x - h_x\,\nabla^2\psi'_y + \psi'_y\,\nabla^2 h_x - \psi'_x\,\nabla^2 h_y. \tag{3.77}$$

We now evaluate the right-hand side of (3.76). Using (3.71), we obtain

$$L\rho' = H, \tag{3.78}$$

where

$$H = -u'\bar{\rho}_x - v'\bar{\rho}_y - h_y\rho'_x + h_x\rho'_y. \tag{3.79}$$

In (3.79), the $\bar{\rho}$ differs from the $\bar{\rho}$ in (3.63) by a term of order $O(A)$, for *after* the wave motion represented by (3.63), $\bar{\rho}$ for the primary flow is a function of both x and y. Indeed,

$$u\bar{\rho}_x + v\bar{\rho}_y = 0 \qquad \text{or} \qquad \bar{\rho}_x/\bar{\rho}_y = \psi_x/\psi_y,$$

so that $\bar{\rho}$ is a function of ψ only. If terms of orders higher than A are neglected, we must have, as the linear theory demands,

$$\bar{\rho} = 1 - \beta\psi,$$

for otherwise, in the absence of wave motion (i.e., $A = 0$ and $\psi = y$), we should not have (3.64). Thus,

$$\bar{\rho}_x = -\beta\psi_x, \qquad \bar{\rho}_y = -\beta\psi_y = -\beta(1 + h_y). \tag{3.80}$$

Let

$$\psi' = \psi'_0 + A\psi'_1 + \cdots, \qquad \rho' = \rho'_0 + A\rho'_1 + \cdots. \tag{3.81}$$

                          Chia-Shun Yih

Then from (3.72), (3.76), and (3.78), we have

$$L_0^2 \, \nabla^2 \psi_0' + F_i^2 (\psi_0')_{xx} = 0, \tag{3.82}$$

where L_0 is L when only terms of order $O(1)$ are retained. Let us try the following form for ψ_0':

$$g_0(y) \, \exp[i(\alpha x - \sigma_0 t)].$$

Then

$$g_0'' - \alpha^2 \left(1 - \frac{F_i^{-2}}{(\sigma_0 - \alpha)^2} \right) g_0 = 0.$$

To the order $O(1)$, the boundary conditions are

$$g_0(0) = 0 = g_0(1).$$

The solution of the eigenvalue problem for g_0 is then

$$(\sigma_0 - \alpha)^2 = F_i^{-2} \alpha^2 / (\alpha^2 + n^2 \pi^2), \tag{3.83}$$

where n indicates the mode. Given k, we choose a σ_0 such that the two roots of α in (3.83), m and m', satisfy

$$m' - m = k. \tag{3.84}$$

As in Section III,C, m is less than σ_0 and m' greater than σ_0. This can be seen by plotting the two sides of (3.82) against α for any σ_0 and F_i. Thus

$$\sigma_0 - m = F_i^{-1} m (m^2 + n^2 \pi^2)^{-1/2}, \tag{3.85}$$

$$\sigma_0 - m' = -F_i^{-1} m' (m'^2 + n^2 \pi^2)^{-1/2}. \tag{3.86}$$

The difference of the left-hand sides of (3.85) and (3.86) is k. From the right-hand sides we see then that it is impossible to satisfy (3.84) unless

$$k < 2F_i^{-1}. \tag{3.87}$$

If (3.87) is satisfied, however, it is possible to find m and m' satisfying (3.83) and (3.84), and the quantities m and σ_0 are plotted against k in Figs. 16 and 17 for $n = 1$, Figs. 18 and 19 for $n = 2$, and Figs. 20 and 21 for $n = 3$. These curves are constructed by first assuming m, finding σ_0 by (3.85), and solving (3.83) for m' with the σ_0 just found. Then k is known, and we have for this k the value for m and the value for σ_0. All the curves in Figs. 16–21 have vertical asymptotes at $k = 2F_i^{-1}$.

We shall then take

$$\psi_0' = (ae_1 + be_2) \sin n\pi y, \tag{3.88}$$

with

$$e_1 = \exp[i(mx - \sigma t)], \qquad e_2 = \exp[i(m'x - \sigma t)]. \tag{3.89}$$

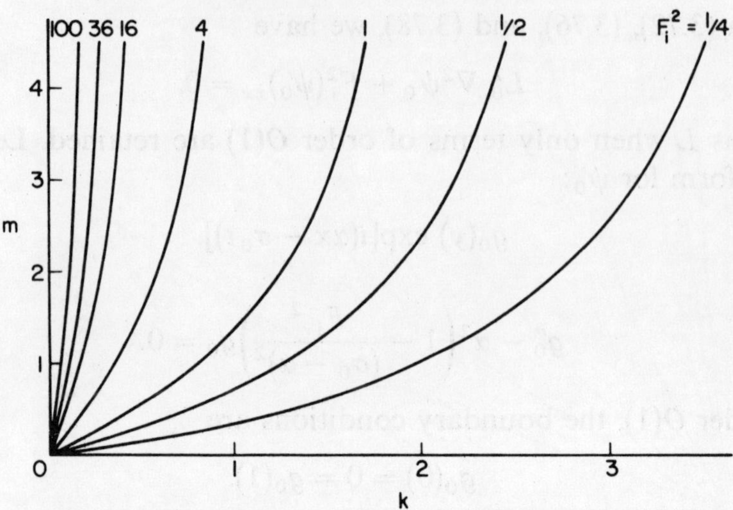

FIG. 16.   Variation of m with k for $n = 1$ and various values of F_i^2.

Note that we use σ in (3.89) rather than σ_0, for we anticipate that the terms of order $O(A)$ in (3.76) and (3.78) will change σ_0 by an amount of order $O(A)$. The use of an exponential time factor is certainly justified by the forms of (3.76) and (3.78).

Let

$$\rho'_0 = (a_1 e_1 + b_1 e_2) \sin n\pi y. \tag{3.90}$$

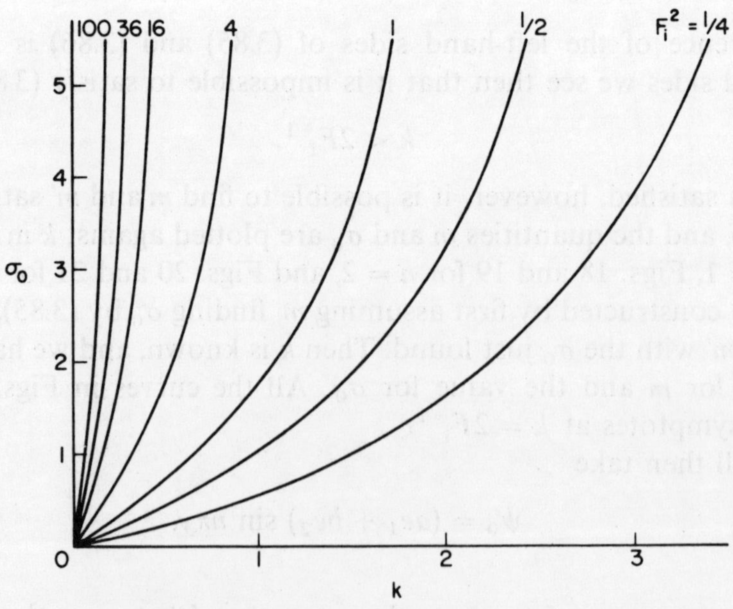

FIG. 17.   Variation of σ_0 with k for $n = 1$ and various values of F_i^2.

Chia-Shun Yih

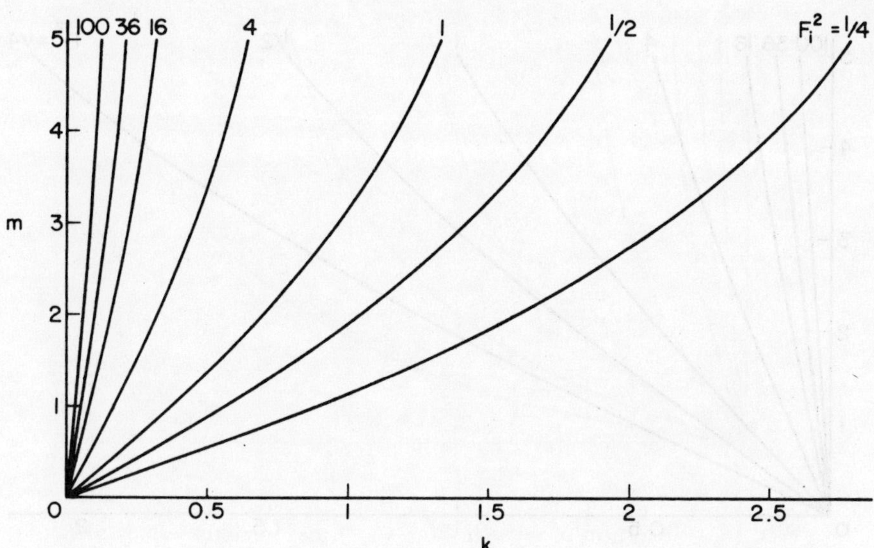

FIG. 18.   Variation of m with k for $n = 2$ and various values of F_i^2.

Then the terms of order $O(1)$ in (3.78) give

$$a_1 = \beta ma/(\sigma_0 - m), \qquad b_1 = \beta m'b/(\sigma_0 - m'). \tag{3.91}$$

Now, from (3.76) and (3.78), we obtain

$$L^2 \nabla^2 \psi' = -LE + F^{-2}H_x. \tag{3.92}$$

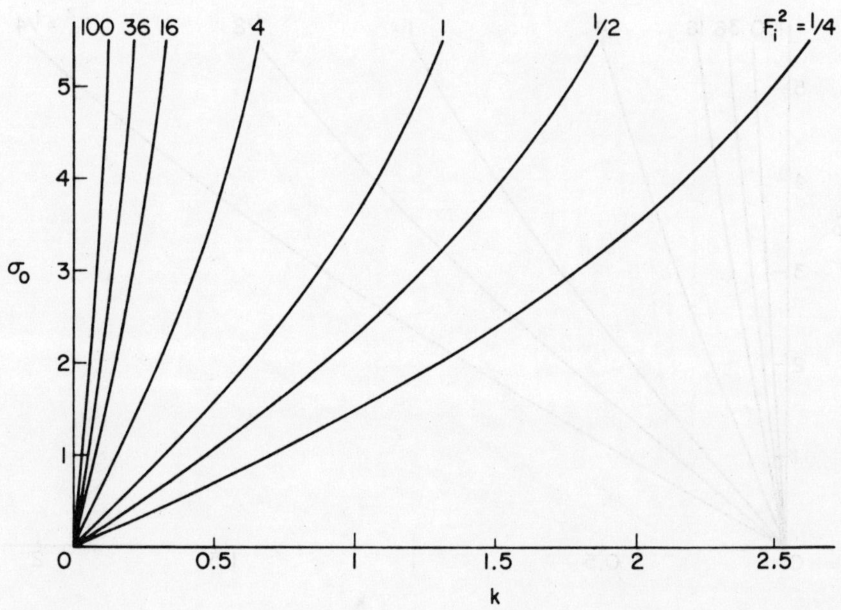

FIG. 19.   Variation of σ_0 with k for $n = 2$ and various values of F_i^2.

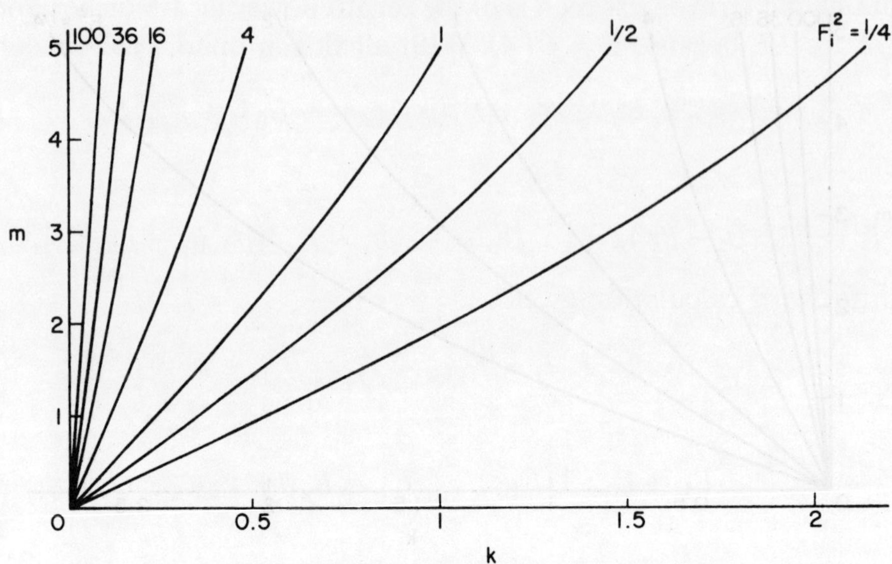

FIG. 20. Variation of m with k for $n = 3$ and various values of F_i^2.

Let

$$(\sigma - m)^2 = (\sigma_0 - m)^2 + \lambda_1 A + O(A^2). \tag{3.93}$$

When terms of the zeroth order in A are collected in (3.92), we have (3.82), which is satisfied by (3.88). When collecting terms of order $O(A)$ in (3.92), we use ψ_0' for ψ' and ρ_0' for ρ' in E and H except in the term $-v'\bar{\rho}_y$ in H, because

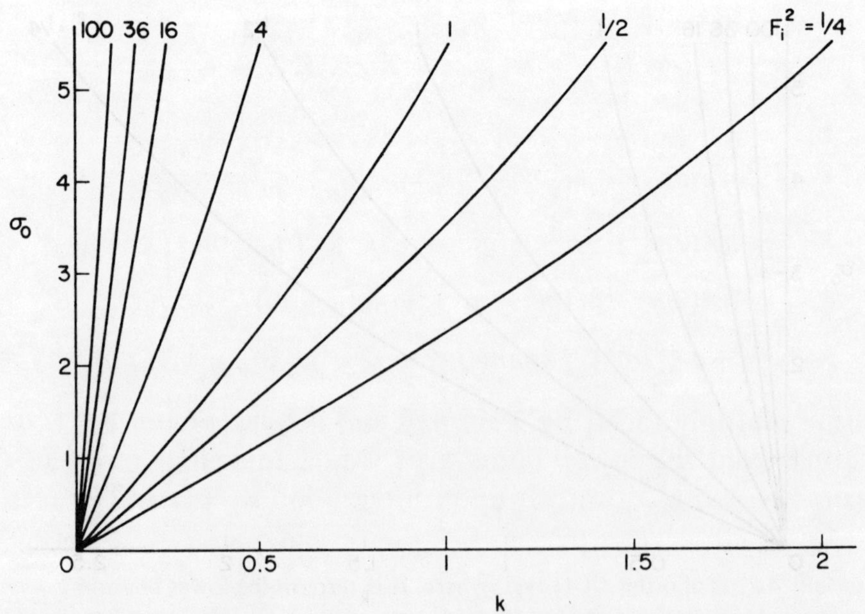

FIG. 21. Variation of σ_0 with k for $n = 3$ and various values of F_i^2.

416   *Chia-Shun Yih*

$\bar{\rho}_y$ contains the term $-\beta$, which is of the zeroth power in A. Furthermore, we use $L_0 E$ for LE because $E = O(A)$. With all this in mind, (3.92) becomes

$$\lambda \nabla^2 \psi'_0 + L_0^2 \nabla^2 \psi'_1 + F_i^2 (\psi'_1)_{xx} = -L_0 E + F_i^{-2} K, \qquad (3.94)$$

where

$$K = \beta^{-1}(H - \beta v')_x = [\psi'_{0y} h_x - \psi'_{0x} h_y - \beta^{-1}(\rho'_{0x} h_y - \rho'_{0y} h_x)]_x .$$

Straightforward calculation gives

$$L_0 E = E_1 e_1 + E_2 e_2 ,$$

where

$$E_1 = E_{11} + E_{12} , \qquad E_2 = E_{21} + E_{22} ,$$

with

$$E_{11} = bA(2m')^{-1}(m'^2 + n^2\pi^2)\sigma_0(\sigma_0 - m)(\sigma_0 - 2m')f' \sin n\pi y,$$

$$E_{12} = bAkn\pi(2m'^2)^{-1}(m'^2 + n^2\pi^2)\sigma_0(\sigma_0 - m)(\sigma_0 - 2m')f \cos n\pi y,$$

$$E_{21} = aA(2m)^{-1}(m^2 + n^2\pi^2)\sigma_0(\sigma_0 - m')(\sigma_0 - 2m)f' \sin n\pi y,$$

$$E_{22} = -aAkn\pi(2m^2)^{-1}(m^2 + n^2\pi^2)\sigma_0(\sigma_0 - m')(\sigma_0 - 2m)f \cos n\pi y.$$

As for K, we have

$$F_i^{-2} K = K_1 e_1 + K_2 e_2 ,$$

where

$$K_1 = K_{11} + K_{12} , \qquad K_2 = K_{21} + K_{22} ,$$

with

$$K_{11} = bA(2m')^{-1}m(m'^2 + n^2\pi^2)\sigma_0(\sigma_0 - m')f' \sin n\pi y,$$

$$K_{12} = bA(2m'^2)^{-1}kn\pi m(m'^2 + n^2\pi^2)\sigma_0(\sigma_0 - m')f \cos n\pi y,$$

$$K_{21} = aA(2m)^{-1}m'(m^2 + n^2\pi^2)\sigma_0(\sigma_0 - m)f' \sin n\pi y,$$

$$K_{22} = -aA(2m^2)^{-1}kn\pi m'(m^2 + n^2\pi^2)\sigma_0(\sigma_0 - m)f \cos n\pi y.$$

We now multiply (3.94) by $2 \sin n\pi y$ and integrate from $y = 0$ to $y = 1$. [Integrating from the lower boundary† would introduce terms of $O(A^2)$.] The terms involving ψ'_1 vanish upon integration by parts. The rest of the

---

† Note that $A\psi'_1$ is of order $O(A)$ everywhere. It is zero on the lower boundary, at which y is also of order $O(A)$. Hence $A\psi'_1$ is of order $O(A^2)$ and $A\psi'_{1y} = O(A)$ between $y = 0$ and the lower boundary. Integration in this interval gives terms of $O(A^2)$.

terms, upon separating terms containing e_1 from those containing e_2, integrating by parts, and neglecting terms of $O(A^2)$, gives

$$-aA(m^2 + n^2\pi^2)\lambda_1 = bA(2m')^{-1}(m'^2 + n^2\pi^2)\sigma_0 M_1\left(1 - \frac{k}{2m'}\right)I,$$

(3.95)

$$-bA\frac{\sigma_0 - m'}{\sigma_0 - m}(m'^2 + n^2\pi^2)\lambda_1 = aA(2m)^{-1}(m^2 + n^2\pi^2)\sigma_0 M_2\left(1 + \frac{k}{2m}\right)I,$$

(3.96)

where

$$I = \int_0^1 f' \sin^2 n\pi y \, dy,$$

$$M_1 = -(\sigma_0 - m)(\sigma_0 - 2m') + m(\sigma_0 - m'),$$

$$M_2 = -(\sigma_0 - m')(\sigma_0 - 2m) + m'(\sigma_0 - m).$$

Now since κ is not equal to any integral multiple of π, I is not zero. Furthermore, M_1 and M_2 are equal, as we can see by a glance at their definitions. Hence

$$\lambda_1^2 = \frac{\sigma_0 - m}{\sigma_0 - m'}\sigma_0^2(4mm')^{-1}M_1^2\left(1 - \frac{k}{2m'}\right)\left(1 + \frac{k}{2m}\right)I^2.$$ (3.97)

Since σ_0 is greater than m but less than m', and since k is less than m', we see that $\lambda_1^2 < 0$, and the primary flow is unstable. The growth rate is $|\lambda_1|A/2(\sigma_0 - m)$, as we can deduce from (3.93).

Thus whenever (3.87) is satisfied, the primary waves are unstable. As k approaches $2F_i^{-1}$, m and m' as well as σ_0 become increasingly large, although $\sigma_0 - m$ and $m' - \sigma_0$ remain less then k, and M_1 remains bounded (by $3k^2/4$). Thus λ_1^2 approaches $-\frac{9}{64}k^4I^2$ or $-\frac{9}{16}F_i^{-4}I^2$ as k approaches $2F_i^{-1}$.

F. Resonance across Modes

As can be seen from (3.83), (3.85), (3.86), (3.88), and (3.89), Section III,E treats the resonance of the m- and m'-waves of the *same mode* with the basic stationary waves. The restriction that the m- and the m'-waves be of the same mode can be removed. All we need to do is to replace n by n_1 (an integer) in (3.85) and by n_2 (an integer not equal to n_1) in (3.86). Then (3.89) and (3.90) become

$$\psi_0' = ae_1 \sin n_1\pi y + be_2 \sin n_2\pi y,$$

$$\rho' = a_1 e_1 \sin n_1\pi y + b_1 e_2 \sin n_2\pi y.$$

Chia-Shun Yih

Subsequent development follows closely the development in Section III,E after (3.90), and again we find the primary waves are unstable whenever nonzero m and m' can be found that satisfy (3.84) and the *modified* (3.85) and (3.86). Thus resonance across modes is possible and the primary waves can be unstable in many ways.

G. Conclusions for Stationary Waves

From the foregoing we conclude that the interfacial waves described in Section III,B are unstable if the internal Froude number F_i is greater than 1, or if $F_i < 1$ but the wave number is greater than the k_c defined in Section III,C. Internal waves in a linearly stratified fluid are also unstable, provided the wave number is less than $2/F_i$ and the Boussinesq approximation can be used. This conclusion must hold also if the fluid is nearly linearly stratified.

H. Progressive Waves

Progressive waves can be made stationary. The present theory can then be applied to them. When this is done, one finds that the above conclusions hold if the speed of the primary waves increases with the amplitude, and that the waves are stable† otherwise. The speed of progressive internal waves for discontinuous stratifications may increase or decrease with the amplitude (Hunt, 1961). The speed of waves in a continuously stratified fluid decreases with the amplitude if the fluid is weakly and exponentially (or linearly or nearly linearly) stratified, according to Yih (1974).

However, without considering amplitude effects on wave speed, Davis and Acrivos (1967) were able to show that instability can result from intermodal interaction.

I. Remarks

As has been noted, the instability of internal waves presented herein, as well as that given by Davis and Acrivos (1967), is a result of resonance when Hasselman's conditions are satisfied. Again, it is hard to see how Hasselman's theorem (1967) could be directly applied to reach the conclusion of instability when the demonstration of that theorem is entirely independent of the details of the flow, the boundary conditions, and the exact manner of interaction of the three wave trains. Both the derivation leading to the final results given in this article and that leading to the results of Davis and

---

† Provided that the disturbances are of the same mode.

Acrivos are rather involved. It is far from clear that the details could be obviated in the establishment of Hasselman's theorem and that theorem could still be generally applied, without further ado, to reach the conclusion of instability once the existence of the wave triad satisfying Hasselman's conditions is assured.

ACKNOWLEDGMENTS

This work has been jointly supported by the Office of Naval Research and the National Science Foundation. I am grateful to my friends Donald Hall, A. E. Day, and Ting Ying for their interest in my work. I also appreciate the help of Beverly Pyle in typing the manuscript and of Andrew Tung and T. C. Ma in producing the graphs.

REFERENCES

BENJAMIN, T. B., and URSELL, F. (1954). The stability of the plane free surface of a liquid in vertical periodic motion. *Proc. Roy. Soc. London, Sec. A* **225**, 505–515.

BENJAMIN, T. B. (1967). Instability of periodic wave trains in nonlinear dispersive systems. *Proc. Roy. Soc. London, Sec. A* **299**, 59–75.

CRAPPER, G. D. (1957). An exact solution for progressive capillary waves of arbitrary amplitude. *J. Fluid Mech.* **2**, 532–540.

DAVIS, R. E., and ACRIVOS, A. (1967). The stability of oscillatory internal waves. *J. Fluid Mech.* **30**, 723–736.

HASSELMANN, K. (1967). A criterion for second-order nonlinear wave stability. *J. Fluid Mech.* **30**, 737–741.

HUNT, J. N. (1961). *Houille Blanche* **4**, 515.

PHILLIPS, O. M. (1966). "The Dynamics of the Upper Ocean." Cambridge Univ. Press, London and New York.

RICHARDSON, A. R. (1920). Stationary waves in water. *Philos. Mag.* (6), **40**, 97–110.

WHITHAM, G. B. (1966). Nonlinear dispersion of water waves. *J. Fluid Mech.* **27**, 399.

YIH, C.-S. (1957). On stratified flows in a gravitational field. *Tellus* **9**, 220–227.

YIH, C.-S. (1965). "Dynamics of Nonhomogeneous Fluids." MacMillan, New York.

YIH, C.-S. (1974). Progressive waves of permanent form in continuously stratified fluids. *Phys. Fluids* **17**, 1489–1495.

NOTE ADDED IN PROOF

We note also (see p. 391) that for a primary wave train with basic wave number k, the higher harmonics (in the velocity potential, the velocity, the surface form, etc.) are unstable even without considering the increase of the wave velocity with amplitude. When the primary waves are made stationary the Froude number based on the wave velocity of the linear theory is such that $m = 0$ and $m' = k$, as mentioned after (2.55), and hence the wave train is stable for the basic harmonic, with wave number k, of the waves. But for the higher harmonics, with wave numbers $2k$, $3k$, etc., a nonzero m exists and those harmonics therefore cause instability. Indeed, the growth rate for the second harmonic (with wave number $2k$) is proportional to the square of the amplitude of the basic harmonic.

J. Fluid Mech. (1977), *vol.* 82, *part* 3, *pp.* 497–505

Stability of time-periodic flows in a circular pipe

By W. H. YANG AND CHIA-SHUN YIH

Department of Applied Mechanics and Engineering Science,
University of Michigan, Ann Arbor

(Received 7 June 1976 and in revised form 29 April 1977)

The stability of time-periodic flows in a circular pipe is investigated. The disturbance is assumed to be axially symmetric and to have a small amplitude, so that the governing differential equation is linear. Calculations are carried out for the first ten modes for a range of values of the frequency of the primary motion, of the wavenumber of the disturbance, and of the Reynolds number of the primary flow. In the ranges of the parameters for which the calculations have been carried out, the flows are found to be stable and, as for Stokes flows (von Kerczek & Davis 1974), it is conjectured that the flows under study here are stable for all frequencies and all Reynolds numbers.

1. Introduction

We consider the flow of a Newtonian fluid with constant density and viscosity through a rigid pipe of circular cross-section, and study its stability against axisymmetric disturbances. Furthermore, the flow is assumed to be time-periodic and without a steady (Poiseuille) component.

In recent years a good deal of studies of the stability of time-dependent flows have been carried out. A review of them has been given by Davis (1976). Of particular relevance to this paper are two excellent papers: one by Grosch & Salwen (1968) on the stability of steady and time-dependent flows between two parallel plates and one by von Kerczeck & Davis (1974) on the stability of Stokes flows, i.e. flows induced by an oscillating plate with a viscous fluid above it. Our results, which lead to the conclusion of stability of the flows considered here, agree, in a broad sense, with both these papers. A detailed discussion of our results and their relation to these papers will be given in the last section of this paper.

2. The primary flow

We shall consider an axisymmetric flow of a fluid of constant density ρ and viscosity μ in a circular pipe of radius a. The flow is due to a time-periodic pressure gradient and has no steady part at all. The pressure gradient is $K \exp(i\omega'\tau)$, in which ω' is the circular frequency, τ is the time and K is the amplitude of the pressure gradient. The longitudinal velocity w produced by this pressure gradient is then governed by the equation

$$\frac{\partial w}{\partial \tau} = \frac{K}{\rho} e^{i\omega'\tau} + \nu\left(\frac{\partial^2 w}{\partial r^2} + \frac{1}{r}\frac{\partial w}{\partial r}\right), \tag{1}$$

in which ν is the kinematic viscosity and r is the first of the cylindrical co-ordinates (r, θ, z), the z axis being the axis of the pipe.

We shall use as the velocity scale the quantity V defined by

$$V^2 = Ka/\rho, \tag{2}$$

and the dimensionless quantities defined by

$$t = V\tau/a, \quad \xi = r/a, \quad W = w/V, \quad \omega t = \omega\tau'. \tag{3}$$

The Reynolds number is given by $\quad R = Va/\nu.$ (4)

The solution of (1) is $\qquad W = e^{i\omega t}W_1(\xi),$ (5)

where

$$W_1 = \frac{1}{i\omega}\left[1 - \frac{J_0(\beta\xi)}{J_0(\beta)}\right], \tag{6}$$

in which $\qquad \beta = (-i\omega R)^{\frac{1}{2}}.$ (7)

It is evident that the solution given by (6) satisfies the boundary conditions

$$W_1'(0) = 0, \quad W_1(1) = 0. \tag{8}$$

After (6) has been substituted into (5), the real part is taken to be the solution for W.

For high values of ωR $(= \omega'a^2/\nu)$, the solution for W given by (5) and (6) is nearly constant except near the pipe boundary, where $\xi = 1$, and the behaviour is very much the same as for the two-dimensional case, for which the solution is, for large β and near the wall,

$$W = \frac{e^{i\omega t}}{i\omega}\{1 - \exp[-(\tfrac{1}{2}\omega R)^{\frac{1}{2}}(1-i)(1-\eta)]\}, \tag{9}$$

where $\eta = y/a$, y corresponding to r and a being the half-width of the two-dimensional channel. One can see from (9) that for one 'wave' in W the change in η is approximately $2^{\frac{3}{2}}\pi\beta^{-1}$, but in that distance W has attenuated by the factor $\exp(-2\pi)$, or less than 0·002. Thus for large β only one 'wave' in W is discernible, owing to the intense attenuation. Even for small values of β, for which (9) needs to be replaced by

$$W = \frac{e^{i\omega t}}{i\omega}\left[1 - \frac{\cosh\beta\eta}{\cosh\beta}\right], \tag{10}$$

only one or two waves in W are discernible.

3. Formulation of the stability problem

To ensure the satisfaction of the equation of continuity, we shall adopt the stream function ψ used by Synge (1938), in terms of which

$$u = -\psi_z, \quad w = r^{-1}(r\psi)_r, \tag{11}$$

where u and w are the components of velocity in the directions of increasing r and z, respectively, and subscripts indicate partial differentiation. The sign convention in (11) is opposite to Synge's, but that is insignificant.

The equation in ψ is obtained by eliminating the pressure p between the Navier–

Stability of time-periodic flows in a circular pipe **499**

Stokes equations for axisymmetric swirl-free flows:

$$\frac{Du}{Dt} = -\frac{1}{\rho}\frac{\partial p}{\partial r} + \nu\left(\nabla^2 u - \frac{u}{r^2}\right), \tag{12}$$

$$\frac{Dw}{Dt} = -\frac{1}{\rho}\frac{\partial p}{\partial z} + \nu\nabla^2 w, \tag{13}$$

where

$$\left.\begin{aligned}
\frac{D}{Dt} &= \frac{\partial}{\partial t} + u\frac{\partial}{\partial r} + w\frac{\partial}{\partial z}, \\
\nabla^2 &= \frac{\partial^2}{\partial r^2} + \frac{1}{r}\frac{\partial}{\partial r} + \frac{\partial^2}{\partial z^2}
\end{aligned}\right\} \tag{14}$$

and the body force is not explicitly present since there is no free surface and the density is constant, so that we can consider p to be the difference between the total pressure and the hydrostatic pressure. The result (Synge 1938, p. 234) of the elimination of p is, upon the use of (11),

$$\left(\frac{D}{Dt} - \frac{u}{r} - \nu L_1\right) L_1\psi = 0, \tag{15}$$

where

$$L_1 = \nabla^2 - 1/r^2. \tag{16}$$

We now express ψ as the sum of its primary part $\overline{\psi}$ and its perturbation part ψ':

$$\psi = \overline{\psi} + \psi', \tag{17}$$

so that, VW being the dimensional velocity for the primary flow,

$$VW = \frac{1}{r}\frac{\partial}{\partial r}(r\overline{\psi}), \quad w' = \frac{1}{r}\frac{\partial}{\partial r}(r\psi'), \quad u = u' = -\psi'_z, \tag{18}$$

in which u' and w' are the perturbation velocity components. Next we substitute (17) and (18) into (15), filter out the primary flow and retain only the first-order terms in ψ'. Finally, after putting

$$\psi' = \phi(\xi)\exp(i\alpha z), \tag{19}$$

where z is now dimensionless (in units of a), and writing the equation in dimensionless form, we obtain

$$R\left[\left(\frac{\partial}{\partial t} + i\alpha W\right)L\phi - i\alpha\left(W'' - \frac{W'}{\xi}\right)\phi\right] = L^2\phi, \tag{20}$$

where the primes on W mean $\partial/\partial\xi$ and

$$L = \frac{\partial^2}{\partial\xi^2} + \frac{1}{\xi}\frac{\partial}{\partial\xi} - \frac{1}{\xi^2} - \alpha^2.$$

The boundary conditions are

$$\phi(1) = 0 = \phi'(1), \quad \phi(0) = 0 = \phi''(0). \tag{21}, \tag{22}$$

Conditions (21) are the no-slip conditions at the pipe wall. The condition that w' be finite at the centre of the pipe gives rise to $\phi(0) = 0$. The condition that

$$\partial w'/\partial r = 0 \quad \text{at} \quad r = 0$$

gives rise to

$$\frac{\partial}{\partial\xi}\left[\frac{1}{\xi}\frac{\partial}{\partial\xi}(\xi\phi)\right] = 0 \quad \text{at} \quad \xi = 0,$$

and this, upon requiring that ϕ be regular near $\xi = 0$, gives rise to $\phi''(0) = 0$.

 W. H. Yang and C.-S. Yih

Equations (20)–(22) constitute the differential system governing stability. Since W is periodic in t, obviously Floquet theory is needed. This has been much used in the theory of stability of time-periodic flows (see, for instance, Yih & Li 1972). Here, however, we shall replace (20) by a system of algebraic equations with constant or time-periodic coefficients, and proceed to find the characteristic values λ, which are the magnification factors of ϕ for 'pure' modes after one period of the primary flow. Numerical analysis is used here, not the Galerkin method.

4. Algebraic formulation

The fourth-order differential equation (20) can be rewritten in terms of two second-order equations:

$$\left.\begin{aligned} \frac{\partial \zeta}{\partial t} &= \frac{1}{R}L\zeta - i\alpha W\zeta + i\alpha\left(W'' - \frac{W'}{\xi}\right)\phi, \\ \zeta &= L\phi. \end{aligned}\right\} \tag{23}$$

With the discrete representations $\phi_i(t) = \phi(\xi_i, t)$ and $\zeta_i(t) = \zeta(\xi_i, t)$, a finite-difference approximation of (23) in matrix notation has the following form, with $[0I0]$ denoting a bordered matrix with a column of n zeros on the left and on the right of I:

$$[0I0]\dot{\zeta} = \frac{1}{Rh^2}[c_0 \, A c_{n+1}]\zeta - i\alpha[0D_1 0]\zeta + i\alpha D_2 \phi \tag{24}$$

$$\zeta = \frac{1}{h^2}\begin{bmatrix} r_0 \\ A \\ r_{n+1} \end{bmatrix}\phi, \tag{25}$$

where $h = 1/(n+1)$ is the mesh size in ξ, I is the $n \times n$ identity matrix, A is an $n \times n$ tridiagonal matrix and D_1 and D_2 are $n \times n$ diagonal matrices. A is too bulky to be given here, but it can be obtained in a straightforward way by writing (23) in finite-difference form. The m, n elements of the matrices D_1 and D_2 are

$$D_{1mn} = W_m \delta_{nm}, \quad D_{2mn} = v_m \delta_{nm},$$

where δ_{nm} is the Kronecker delta and

$$v_m = W''(\xi_m, t) - W'(\xi_m, t)/\xi_m$$

(no summation over m implied). The vectors in (24) and (25) have the following descriptions:

$$\left.\begin{aligned} 0 &= (0, \dots, 0)^T, \quad \text{a zero } n\text{-column,} \\ c_0 &= (\tfrac{1}{2}, 0, \dots, 0)^T, \quad \text{an } n\text{-column,} \\ c_{n+1} &= (0, \dots, 0, 2+1/n)^T, \quad \text{an } n\text{-column,} \\ r_0 &= (0, 0, \dots, 0), \quad \text{an } n\text{-row,} \\ r_{n+1} &= (0, \dots, 0, 1), \quad \text{an } n\text{-row,} \\ \zeta &= (\zeta_0, \zeta_1, \dots, \zeta_{n+1})^T, \quad \text{an } (n+2)\text{-column,} \\ \phi &= (\phi_1, \phi_2, \dots, \phi_n)^T, \quad \text{an } n\text{-column.} \end{aligned}\right\} \tag{26}$$

The system (24) has two more unknowns than the numbers of equations because no boundary conditions are applied to the variables ξ_i. The system (25) has two more equations than the number of unknowns because the four boundary conditions in (21) and (22) have been applied.

Substituting (25) into (24), we obtain

$$A\dot{\phi} = (\mathbf{B} - i\mathbf{D})\,\phi, \tag{27}$$

where
$$\mathbf{B} = (Rh^2)^{-1}(\mathbf{AA} + c_{n+1}\,\mathbf{r}_{n+1})$$

is a five-diagonal matrix and
$$\mathbf{D} = \alpha(\mathbf{D}_1\,\mathbf{A} - h^2\mathbf{D}_2)$$

is a tridiagonal matrix. Since $\mathbf{A}$ is a negative-definite matrix, we may invert $\mathbf{A}$ to obtain a standard form of a system of first-order ordinary differential equations at the expense of a dense coefficient matrix. Instead, we shall preserve the sparsity of the matrices and deal directly with the system (27).

$\mathbf{A}$ and $\mathbf{B}$ are real constant matrices containing parameters R and α, while $\mathbf{D}$ is a real variable matrix which is periodic in time with period $2\pi/\omega$, i.e.

$$\mathbf{D}(t + 2\pi/\omega) = \mathbf{D}(t). \tag{28}$$

From the Floquet theory, the solution of (27) is quasi-periodic such that

$$\phi(t + 2\pi/\omega) = \lambda\phi(t), \tag{29}$$

where λ is a characteristic value of the system (27) called the Floquet parameter. Even if λ is a multiple characteristic value, (29) is still true for one of the characteristic functions belonging to it, although other characteristic functions belonging to it contain polynomial factors. But these factors are always overshadowed by the exponential time factor $\exp(\mu t)$, with $\exp(2\pi\mu/\omega) = \lambda$, provided $|\lambda| < 1$. Hence $|\lambda| = 1$ will always give the stability boundary.

The system (27) has n linearly independent fundamental solutions $z_i(t)$, $i = 1, 2, \ldots, n$, each of which satisfies the differential equation

$$\mathbf{A}\dot{z}_i = (\mathbf{B} - i\mathbf{D})\,z_i \tag{30}$$

and the initial condition
$$z_i(0) = \mathbf{e}_i, \tag{31}$$

where $\mathbf{e}_i$ is the unit vector along the ith co-ordinate of the Euclidean n-space. In matrix notation, the fundamental solutions satisfy

$$\mathbf{A}\dot{\mathbf{Z}} = (\mathbf{B} - i\mathbf{D})\,\mathbf{Z}, \quad \mathbf{Z}(0) = \mathbf{I}, \tag{32}$$

where $\mathbf{Z}$ is a $n \times n$ matrix whose columns are $z_1, z_2, \ldots, z_n$.

Let the solution of (32) be $\mathbf{Z}(t)$. Any particular solution of (27) can be expressed as a linear combination of the fundamental solutions:

$$\phi(t) = \mathbf{Z}(t)\,\mathbf{a}, \tag{33}$$

where $\mathbf{a}$ is a constant vector.

Using (29) and (33), we can obtain

$$\mathbf{Z}(t + 2\pi/\omega)\,\mathbf{a} = \lambda\mathbf{Z}(t)\,\mathbf{a}. \tag{34}$$

502   *W. H. Yang and C.-S. Yih*

Equation (34) must be satisfied for all t. Selecting $t = 0$, since the cycle may be started at any time, we have an algebraic eigenvalue problem

$$[\mathbf{Z}(2\pi/\omega) - \lambda \mathbf{I}]\,\mathbf{a} = 0, \tag{35}$$

for which the Floquet parameters are the eigenvalues of the matrix $\mathbf{Z}(2\pi/\omega)$, which determine the stability of the solution $\boldsymbol{\phi}(t)$ of (27). The solution is stable if $|\lambda| < 1$ and grows with time if $|\lambda| > 1$. For the eigenvalues of (35) it is necessary to have first the matrix $\mathbf{Z}(2\pi/\omega)$, which can be obtained by numerically integrating (32) over one period. Such a procedure can be quite costly since we need to explore the three-dimensional parameter space of R, α and ω. The cost can be greatly reduced if the sparsity of the matrices in (32) is taken into consideration in the construction of a numerical algorithm. Further economy may be realized by use of the half-period property of $\mathbf{D}(t)$ that

$$\mathbf{D}(t + \pi/\omega) = -\mathbf{D}(t). \tag{36}$$

This cuts the time domain of integration by half. Both improvements will no doubt reduce round-off errors owing to the smaller number of operations needed for a given mesh size and time-increment size.

5. Numerical method

A simple integration scheme is used for (32) to preserve the sparsity of the matrices $\mathbf{A}$, $\mathbf{B}$ and $\mathbf{D}$. Let $\mathbf{Z}^{(k)} = \mathbf{Z}(k\Delta t)$, where k is an integer and Δt is the time increment chosen. Equation (32) may be approximated by central differences, so that

$$(\Delta t)^{-1}\mathbf{A}(\mathbf{Z}^{(n+1)} - \mathbf{Z}^{(n)}) = (\mathbf{B} - i\mathbf{D}^{(n+\frac{1}{2})})\tfrac{1}{2}(\mathbf{Z}^{(n+1)} + \mathbf{Z}^{(n)}), \tag{37}$$

where $\mathbf{D}^{(n+\frac{1}{2})}$ is evaluated at $(n + \frac{1}{2})\Delta t$ and $\mathbf{Z}((n + \frac{1}{2})\Delta t)$ is taken as the average of $\mathbf{Z}^{(n+1)}$ and $\mathbf{Z}^{(n)}$. Rearranging (36), we have

$$(\mathbf{A} - \Delta t\mathbf{B} + i\Delta t\mathbf{D}^{(n+\frac{1}{2})})\,\mathbf{Z}^{(n+1)} = (\mathbf{A} + \Delta t\mathbf{B} - i\Delta t\mathbf{D}^{(n+\frac{1}{2})})\,\mathbf{Z}^{(n)}. \tag{38}$$

Since the matrices involved in (38) are at most five-diagonal, the equations can be easily solved for $n = 0, 1, 2, \ldots$, with $\mathbf{Z}^{(0)} = \mathbf{I}$. Let $N\Delta t = \pi/\omega$. We can solve (38) N times to obtain $\mathbf{Z}^{(N)} = \mathbf{Z}(\pi/\omega)$. From (36), we can establish that

$$\mathbf{Z}(2\pi/\omega) = \mathbf{Z}(\pi/\omega)\,\mathbf{Z}^*(\pi/\omega),$$

where the asterisk denotes the conjugate of the complex matrix.

Since we are most interested in the first few eigenvalues of $\mathbf{Z}(2\pi/\omega)$ starting from that of smallest modulus, the Lanczos algorithm (Golub 1973) may best suit the purpose. If the dimension of $\mathbf{Z}$ is modest, the QZ algorithm (Moler & Stewart 1973) can be used, although the QZ algorithm gives the entire set of eigenvalues of $\mathbf{Z}(2\pi/\omega)$. The QZ program is more readily available than the Lanczos program in most computing-centre libraries. For the computations in this paper the QZ algorithm was used.

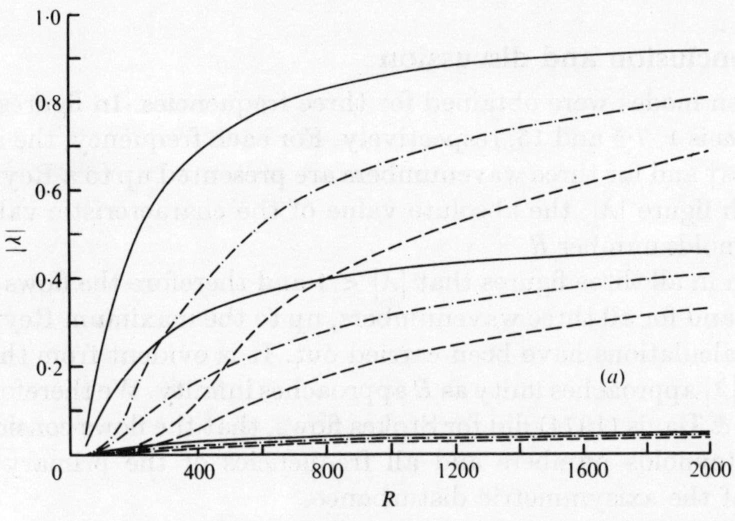

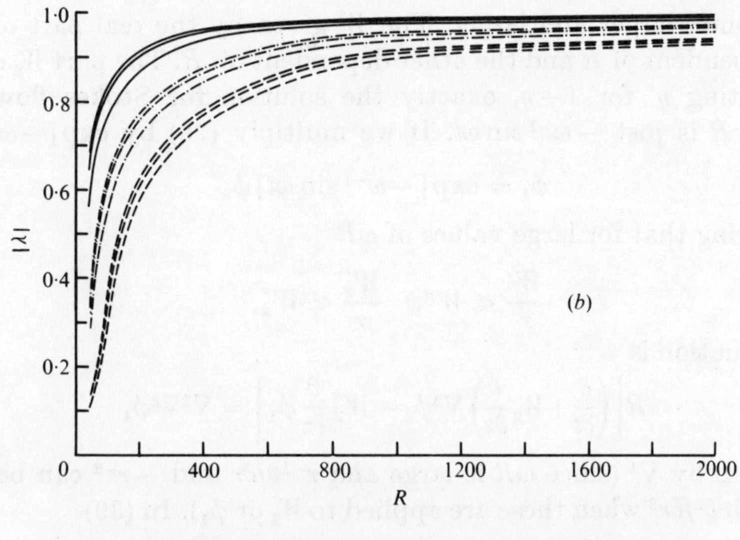

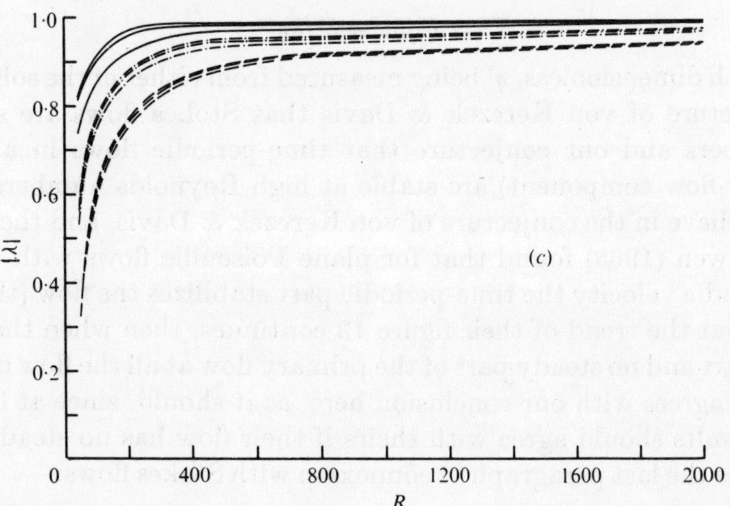

FIGURE 1. Variation of $|\lambda|$ with R for (a) $\omega = 1$, (b) $\omega = 7\cdot5$ and (c) $\omega = 15$ for three values of α. ——, first mode; —·—, second mode; –––, third mode. For each mode, $\alpha = 0, 2, 4$ from the top curve down.

W. H. Yang and C.-S. Yih

6. Results, conclusion and discussion

Results for ten modes were obtained for three frequencies. In figures 1 (*a*), (*b*) and (*c*) the value of ω is 1, 7·5 and 15, respectively. For each frequency, the results for the first three modes† and for three wavenumbers are presented up to a Reynolds number of 2000. In each figure $|\lambda|$, the absolute value of the characteristic value, is plotted against the Reynolds number R.

It can be seen in all three figures that $|\lambda| < 1$ and therefore the flows are stable for all three modes and for all three wavenumbers, up to the maximum Reynolds number for which the calculations have been carried out. It is evident from the tendency of the curves that $|\lambda|$ approaches unity as R approaches infinity. We therefore conjecture, as von Kerczek & Davis (1974) did for Stokes flows, that the flows considered here are stable for all Reynolds numbers and all frequencies of the primary flow and all wavenumbers of the axisymmetric disturbance.

Indeed, as mentioned in §2, the flow becomes increasingly like two-dimensional flows as R becomes larger and larger. The W given by the real part of (9) has two parts: one independent of R and the other dependent on R. The part W_2 dependent on R is, upon writing η' for $1-\eta$, exactly the solution for Stokes flows. The part independent of R is just $-\omega^{-1}\sin\omega t$. If we multiply (20) by $\exp[-\omega^{-1}\sin\omega t]$ and write

$$\phi_1 = \exp[-\omega^{-1}\sin\omega t]\,\phi,$$

then, remembering that for large values of ωR

$$\frac{W'}{r} \ll W'', \quad \frac{W_2'}{r} \ll W''_2,$$

the resulting equation is

$$R\left[\left(\frac{\partial}{\partial t}+W_2\frac{\partial}{\partial z}\right)\nabla^2\phi_1 - W''_2\frac{\partial}{\partial z}\phi_1\right] = \nabla^2\nabla^2\phi_1 \tag{39}$$

upon replacing L by ∇^2 (since ωR is large and $r^{-1}\partial/\partial r$ and $-r^{-2}$ can be neglected in comparison with $\partial^2/\partial r^2$ when these are applied to W_2 or ϕ_1). In (39)

$$\nabla^2 = \partial^2/\partial z^2 + \partial^2/\partial\eta'^2,$$

with z and η' both dimensionless, η' being measured from either of the solid boundaries. Thus the conjecture of von Kerczek & Davis that Stokes flows are stable at high Reynolds numbers and our conjecture that time-periodic flows in a circular pipe (with no steady-flow component) are stable at high Reynolds numbers stand or fall together. We believe in the conjecture of von Kerczek & Davis, and therefore in ours.

Grosch & Salwen (1968) found that for plane Poiseuille flows with both a steady and a time-periodic velocity the time-periodic part stabilizes the flow (their figure 13). If we assume that the trend of their figure 13 continues, then when there is only the time-periodic part and no steady part of the primary flow at all the flow must be stable. This conjecture agrees with our conclusion here, as it should, since at high Reynolds numbers our results should agree with theirs if their flow has no steady part, as has been discussed in the last paragraph in connexion with Stokes flows.

This work has been supported by the National Science Foundation and the Office of Naval Research.

† The higher modes are increasingly stable.

REFERENCES

DAVIS, S. H. 1976 The stability of time-dependent flows. *Ann. Rev. Fluid Mech.* **8**, 57–74.

GOLUB, G. 1973 *Topics in Numerical Analysis* (ed. J. Miller). Academic Press.

GROSCH, C. E. & SALWEN, H. 1968 The stability of steady and time-dependent plane Poiseuille flow. *J. Fluid Mech.* **34**, 177–205.

KERCZEK, C. VON & DAVIS, S. H. 1974 *J. Fluid Mech.* **62**, 753–773.

MOLER, C. B. & STEWART, G. W. 1973 An algorithm for the generalized eigenproblem. *SIAM J. Numer. Anal.* **10**, 241–256.

SYNGE, J. L. 1938 Hydrodynamic stability. *Semi-Centennial Publ., Am. Math. Soc.* **2**, 227–269.

YIH, C.-S. & LI, C.-H. 1972 Instability of unsteady flows or configurations. Part 2. Convective instability. *J. Fluid Mech.* **54**, 143–152.

ARTICLES

Instability resulting from stratification in thermal conductivity

Chia-Shun Yih
University of Michigan, Ann Arbor, Michigan 48109

(Received 16 December 1985; accepted 10 March 1986)

There are many instances of hydrodynamic instability induced by a variation, or stratification, in either a fluid property or a flow property. In this article a new instability is presented. It is shown that when there is a variation in thermal conductivity in the fluid, instability can occur in the presence of a longitudinal gravitational field.

I. INTRODUCTION

In the majority of cases of hydrodynamic instability, there is a stratification of either a fluid property or some quantity of flow. The most obvious case of instability is that of two superposed fluids, with the upper fluid heavier than the lower one. A statically stratified fluid can be unstable if the fluid is accelerated downward with an acceleration greater than the gravitational acceleration g, as noted by Taylor and as is well known now. The stratification in density of an incompressible fluid has its counterpart in the stratification of entropy of a compressible fluid, as meteorologists who invented the concept of potential density to account for the effect of compressibility have long recognized. Stratification in density in the presence of longitudinal gravity can be unstable, as is now well known. Less well known is the instability resulting from a stratification in electric conductivity, as shown by Taylor and McEwan[1] for a steady vertical electric field and by Yih[2] for a vertical time-periodic electric field. Instability resulting from viscosity variation in shear flows (Yih[3]) is a subject that, after many years, is now enjoying a period of revival of interest. In porous media, a less viscous fluid pushing a more viscous one can induce instability and produce fingers of penetration, as Saffman and Taylor[4] showed.

But it does not necessarily need to be a fluid property that, when stratified, can induce instability. If some quantity of the *flow* of a fluid is stratified, it can be unstable too. A prominent example is the Couette flow, which can be unstable if the square of the circulation decreases outwards, resulting in the formation of Taylor vortices. The electromagnetic counterpart (Yih[5]) of Taylor vortices is the result of a radial stratification of a circular magnetic field. In two-dimensional flows the stratification of vorticity can induce instability when there is a point of inflection in the velocity profile, a famous and extreme case of which is the Helmholtz instability, where the density stratification is stabilizing and the instability results from the vortex sheet. Even when there is no point of inflection in the velocity profile of a two-dimensional flow of a viscous fluid, stratification of vorticity is still important for instability, as indicated by the stability of plane Couette flows, which has uniform vorticity. (For axisymmetric flows it is the stratification of the azimuthal vorticity divided by the radial distance that is important. When this quantity is constant, as in Poiseuille flow, the flow is stable against axisymmetric small disturbances.)

In this article, I shall show a new instability: the instability resulting from thermal-conductivity stratification. With the other instances of how a fluid or a flow can be unstable when a stratification is present, one could perhaps make the point that hydrodynamic stability is a subject within the field of stratified flows.

II. PRIMARY TEMPERATURE AND VELOCITY FIELDS

Consider two superposed fluids (Fig. 1), each of thickness d, between two plane boundaries inclined at an angle β to the horizontal. To show that the instability to be revealed results from conductivity variation alone, we shall assume the two fluids to have the same viscosity and the same dependence of density on temperature, but different thermal conductivities: k_2 for the upper fluid and k_1 for the lower fluid. That two such fluids are not easy to find is not necessarily an objection to this study, since instabilities resulting from density and viscosity variations are known, as mentioned already in the Introduction, and the new cause of instability is *in addition* to those other known causes of instability.

Let the origin of Cartesian coordinates be situated on the interface of the fluids, and let x be measured along the interface down the incline, and y be measured upward in a direction normal to the interface. The temperatures at the lower and upper boundaries will be denoted by $T_0 - \Delta T$ and $T_0 + \Delta T$, respectively.

We shall measure x and y in units of d, so that they are dimensionless. The temperature in the lower and upper fluids will be denoted by $T_1(y)$ and $T_2(y)$, respectively. Defining $\bar{h}_1$ and $\bar{h}_2$ by

$$\bar{h}_1 = \frac{T_1(y) - T_0}{\Delta T}, \quad \bar{h}_2 = \frac{T_2(y) - T_0}{\Delta T}, \qquad (1)$$

one can readily solve the Laplace equation governing heat conduction, with regards to the boundary and interfacial conditions, and obtain

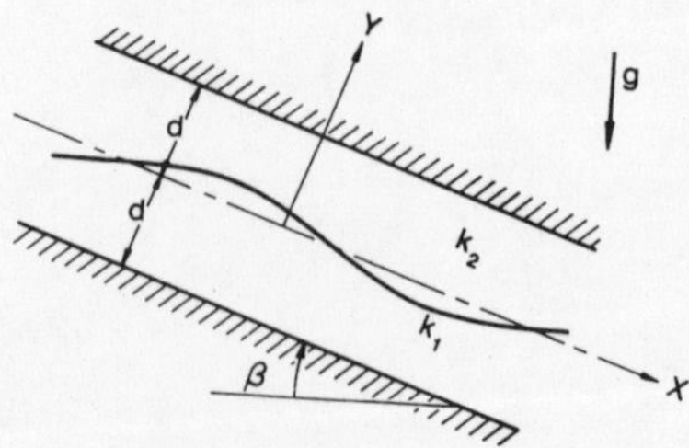

FIG. 1. Definition sketch.

© 1986 American Institute of Physics

$$\bar{h}_1 = (\lambda - 1)/(\lambda + 1) + [2\lambda/(1+\lambda)]\,y, \qquad (2)$$

$$\bar{h}_2 = (\lambda - 1)/(\lambda + 1) + [2/(1+\lambda)]\,y, \qquad (3)$$

where

$$\lambda = k_2/k_1. \qquad (4)$$

The interfacial conditions for the temperature field are the continuity of temperature and the continuity of heat flux across the interface.

The variation of density with temperature is assumed the same for both fluids only for the sake of simplicity. This assumption is not at all necessary. We make it here only to isolate the variation of thermal conductivity as the cause of instability. The dependence of the density ρ on temperature is

$$\rho = \rho_0 [1 - \alpha (T - T_0)], \qquad (5)$$

where ρ_0 is the density at temperature T_0, and α is the coefficient of thermal expansivity. With $\bar{u}$ denoting the velocity (in the x direction) of the primary flow and μ denoting the viscosity (assumed constant), we have

$$\mu \frac{d^2\bar{u}}{dy^2} + gp\sin\beta - K = 0, \qquad (6)$$

where g is the gravitational acceleration, and

$$K = \frac{d\bar{p}}{dx_1}. \qquad (7)$$

In (7), $\bar{p}$ is the pressure in the primary flow, and $x_1 = xd$, x being measured in units of d.

The $\bar{u}$ for the lower and upper fluids are, respectively, denoted by $\bar{u}_1(y)$ and $\bar{u}_2(y)$. The boundary conditions are

$$\bar{u}_1(-1) = 0, \quad \bar{u}_1(1) = 0 \qquad (8)$$

and the interfacial conditions are

$$\bar{u}_1(0) = \bar{u}_2(0), \quad \frac{d\bar{u}_1}{dy} = \frac{d\bar{u}_2}{dy} \text{ at } y = 0. \qquad (9)$$

Equation (6) gives two equations, one for $\bar{u}_1$, and one for $\bar{u}_2$. When these are solved with conditions (9) and (10), one obtains

$$\bar{u}_1 = \frac{Kd^2}{2\mu}(1 - y^2) + \frac{1}{6(\lambda+1)}[(\lambda - 1)(3y^2 - 2)$$
$$- (\lambda + 1)y + 2\lambda y^3]V\sin\beta, \qquad (10)$$

$$\bar{u}_2 = \frac{Kd^2}{2\mu}(1 - y^2) + \frac{1}{6(\lambda+1)}[(\lambda - 1)(3y^2 - 2)$$
$$- (\lambda + 1)y + 2y^3]V\sin\beta, \qquad (11)$$

where

$$V = \alpha g d^2 \Delta T/\nu \quad (\nu = \mu/\rho_0) \qquad (12)$$

has the dimension of a velocity, and will be used as the velocity scale.

For our purpose of demonstrating instability resulting from conductivity variation, it is sufficient to take a special K. We shall take

$$Kd^2/\mu = [(\lambda - 1)/(\lambda + 1)]V\sin\beta, \qquad (13)$$

because it will give us the simplest forms of $\bar{u}_1$ and $\bar{u}_2$. Using V as the velocity scale, and adopting (13), we have

$$U_1 = \bar{u}_1/V = [1/6(\lambda + 1)]$$
$$\times [(\lambda - 1) - (\lambda + 1)y + 2\lambda y^3]\sin\beta, \qquad (14)$$

$$U_2 = \bar{u}_2/V = [1/6(\lambda + 1)]$$
$$\times [(\lambda - 1) - (\lambda + 1)y + 2y^3]\sin\beta. \qquad (15)$$

III. FORMULATION OF THE STABILITY PROBLEM

Let the dimensionless temperature perturbations be expressed by

$$\Theta_1 = T_1'/\Delta T, \quad \Theta_2 = T_2'/\Delta T, \qquad (16)$$

and let $\psi_1(x, y)$ be the stream function for the lower fluid and $\psi_2(x, y)$ that for the upper fluid. Then the velocity perturbations for the two fluid layers are given by

$$u_1' = (\psi_1)_y, \quad v_1' = -(\psi_1)_x,$$
$$u_1' = (\psi_2)_y, \quad v_2' = -(\psi_2)_x. \qquad (17)$$

We shall assume

$$(\theta_1,\theta_2,\psi_1,\psi_2)$$
$$= [h_1(y), h_2(y), \theta(y), \chi(y)]\exp[ia(x - ct)], \qquad (18)$$

where the scale for the time t is d/V, the scale for the wave number a is d^{-1}, and c is the dimensionless wave velocity:

$$c = c_r + ic_i. \qquad (19)$$

The flow is stable or unstable according to whether c_i is positive or negative.

The linearized heat equations are then, upon use of (16)–(18),

$$ia(U_1 - c)h_1 - \frac{i2\lambda a}{\lambda + 1}\phi = \frac{1}{\lambda RP}(h_1'' - a^2 h_1), \qquad (20)$$

$$ia(U_2 - c)h_2 - \frac{i2a}{\lambda + 1}\chi = \frac{1}{RP}(h_2'' - a^2 h_2), \qquad (21)$$

where, for simplicity, we have assumed the thermal diffusivities of the fluid to have the ratio λ also (in effect ignoring the variation of specific heat, which can be accounted for without difficulty), and

$$R = Vd/\nu, \quad P = \nu/\kappa_2 \qquad (22)$$

are the Reynolds number and the Prandtl number (for the upper fluid), respectively. (The thermal diffusivity of the upper fluid is denoted by κ_2.) The boundary conditions are, assuming that the boundaries are thermally much more conductive than the fluid,

$$h_1(-1) = 0 = h_2(1), \qquad (23)$$

and the interfacial conditions are

$$h_1'(0) = \lambda h_2'(0), \qquad (24)$$

$$h_2(0) - h_1(0) = [2(\lambda - 1)/(\lambda + 1)][\phi(0)/c'], \qquad (25)$$

with

$$c' = c - U_1(0).$$

The term on the right-hand side of (25) arises from the difference in slope of $\bar{h}_1$ and $\bar{h}_2$ at $y = 0$, which contributes the term when the interface is displaced from its mean position. The ratio $\phi(0)/c'$ multiplied by the exponential factor $\exp[ia(x - ct)]$ is indeed equal to the interfacial displacement, as can be deduced from the kinematic condition at the interface. This term is crucial in the calculation for stability.

If p_i' denotes the pressure perturbation ($i = 1,2$), and if we write

$$p_i'/\rho V^2 = f_i(y)\exp[ia(x - ct)], \qquad (26)$$

the linearized Navier–Stokes equations are, for the lower fluid,

$$ia(U_1 - c)\phi - iaU_1\phi$$
$$= -iaf_1 + (1/R)(\phi''' - a^2\phi') - (\sin\beta/R)h_1, \quad (27)$$
$$a^2(c - U_1)\phi = f_1' + (ia/R)(\phi'' - a^2\phi) - (\cos\beta/R)h_1. \qquad (28)$$

The last term in (27) arises form the body force term

$$(d/\rho_0 V^2)(\rho_0 g\alpha \Delta T h_1 \sin\beta),$$

the multiplier $d/\rho_0 V^2$ is to make the entire equation dimensionless [similarly for the last term in (28)]. For the upper fluid, the linearized Navier–Stokes equations are

$$ia(U_2 - c)\chi' - iaU_2\chi$$
$$= -iaf_2 + (1/R)(\chi''' - a^2\chi') - (\sin\beta/R)h_2, \quad (29)$$
$$a^2(c - U_2)\chi = f_2' + (ia/R)(\chi'' - a^2\chi) - (\cos\beta/R)h_2. \qquad (30)$$

Eliminating f_1 in (27) and (28), and f_2 in (29) and (30), we obtain the augmented Orr–Sommerfeld equations

$$\phi^{iv} - 2a^2\phi'' + a^4\phi = iaR\left[(U_1 - c)(\phi'' - a^2\phi) - U_1''\phi\right]$$
$$+ h_1' \sin\beta + iah_1 \cos\beta, \qquad (31)$$
$$\chi^{iv} - 2a^2\phi'' + a^4\chi = iaR\left[(U_2 - c)(\chi'' - a^2\chi) - U_2''\chi\right]$$
$$+ h_2' \sin\beta + iah_2 \cos\beta. \qquad (32)$$

The boundary conditions are

$$\phi(-1) = 0 = \phi'(-1), \quad \chi(1) = 0 = \chi^1(1), \qquad (33)$$

expressing the no-slip condition. The interfacial conditions are

$$\phi(0) = \chi(0), \quad \phi'(0) = \chi'(0), \qquad (34)$$

expressing the continuity of velocity, and

$$\phi''(0) = \chi''(0),$$
$$(\phi''' - 3a^2\phi') - (\chi''' - 3a^2\chi') = ia^3S\phi/c' \quad \text{at } y = 0, \quad (35)$$

expressing the continuity of shear and normal stresses. In formulating the second condition in (35), one needs to evaluate f_1 and f_2 from (27) and (29), because the normal stress involves the pressure (and another term involving the viscosity). The S in (35) is defined by

$$S = \hat{S}/\rho V^2 d, \qquad (36)$$

$\hat{S}$ being the surface tension.

The stability problem is thus governed by four simultaneous differential equations, two of which are of the second order and the other two of the fourth order, and twelve boundary or interfacial conditions. Given the parameters R, P, λ, a, β, and S, one seeks to determine c.

IV. SOLUTION

We consider long waves, and adopt the method of solution given by Yih.[6] First, we expand the unknowns in power series of a:

$$h_1 = H_0 + aH_1 + a^2H_2 + \cdots,$$
$$h_2 = G_0 + aG_1 + a^2G_2 + \cdots,$$
$$\phi = \phi_0 + a\phi_1 + a^2\phi_2 + \cdots,$$
$$\chi = \chi_0 + a\chi_1 + a^2\chi_2 + \cdots,$$
$$c = c_0 + ac_1 + a^2c_2 + \cdots.$$

Substituting these into the governing differential system, and collecting terms of order a only, we obtain

$$H_0'' = 0, \quad G_0'' = 0, \qquad (37)$$

with the boundary conditions

$$H_0(-1) = 0 = G_0(1), \quad H_0'(0) = \lambda G_0'(0), \qquad (38)$$

and

$$G_0(0) - H_0(0) = [2(\lambda - 1)/(\lambda + 1)][\phi_0(0)/c_0']. \qquad (39)$$

Leaving (39) alone for the moment, one solves (37) and (38) and obtains

$$H_0 = 1 + y, \quad G_0 = (1/\lambda)(-1 + y). \qquad (40)$$

The equations (31) and (32) yield, upon use of (40),

$$\phi_0'''' = \sin\beta, \quad \chi_0'''' = \sin\beta/\lambda, \qquad (41)$$

for which the boundary conditions are

$$\phi_0(-1) = 0 = \phi_0'(-1), \quad \chi_0(1) = 0 = \chi_0'(1), \qquad (42)$$
$$(\phi_0,\phi_0',\phi_0'',\phi_0''') = (\chi_0,\chi_0',\chi_0'',\chi_0''') \quad \text{at } y = 0. \qquad (43)$$

Solution of (41)–(43) gives

$$\phi_0 = A + By + Cy^2 + Dy^3 + (\sin\beta/24)y^4, \qquad (44)$$
$$\chi_0 = A + By + Cy^2 + Dy^3 + (\sin\beta/24\lambda)y^4, \qquad (45)$$

in which

$$A = [(\lambda + 1)/48\lambda]\sin\beta,$$
$$B = -[(\lambda - 1)/96\lambda]\sin\beta, \qquad (46)$$
$$C = -[(\lambda + 1)/24\lambda]\sin\beta, \quad D = [(\lambda - 1)/32\lambda]\sin\beta.$$

With ϕ_0 given by (44), one returns to (39) and obtains

$$c_0' = -[(\lambda - 1)/24(\lambda + 1)]\sin\beta,$$

or

$$c_0 = [(\lambda - 1)/8(\lambda + 1)]\sin\beta. \qquad (47)$$

We now proceed to the next approximation. Collecting terms of order a in (20) and (21), we have

$$H_1'' = i\lambda RP\{(U_1 - c_0)H_0 - [2\lambda/(\lambda + 1)]\phi_0\}, \qquad (48)$$
$$G_1'' = i\lambda RP\{(U_2 - c_0)G_0 - [2/(\lambda + 1)]\chi_0\}. \qquad (49)$$

The conditions (23) and (24) give

$$H_1(-1) = 0 = G_1(-1), \quad H_1'(0) = \lambda G_1'(0), \qquad (50)$$

and (25) gives

$$G_1(0) - H_1(0) = \frac{2(\lambda - 1)}{\lambda + 1}\left(\frac{\phi_1(0)}{c_0'} - \frac{\phi_0(0)c_1}{(c_0')^2}\right). \qquad (51)$$

Setting (51) aside for the moment and solving (48)–(50), we have

$$H_1 = \frac{i\lambda RP \sin\beta}{48(\lambda + 1)} \left(\frac{15\lambda - 39}{60} y - 2y^2 - \frac{5\lambda + 11}{6} y^3 \right.$$
$$\left. - \frac{\lambda + 1}{3} y^4 + \frac{13\lambda + 3}{20} y^5 + \frac{2\lambda}{5} y^6 \right). \qquad (52)$$

The term of zeroth power in y is deliberately dropped to keep $h_1(0) = 1$, since the amplitude of the disturbance is immaterial and already $H_0(0) = 1$. The result for G_1 is

$$G_1 = \frac{iRP \sin\beta}{48\lambda(\lambda + 1)} \left(\frac{-5\lambda^2 + 26\lambda - 5}{20} + \frac{15\lambda^2 - 39\lambda}{60} y \right.$$
$$- 2\lambda y^2 + \frac{11\lambda + 5}{6} y^3 - \frac{\lambda + 1}{3} y^4$$
$$\left. - \frac{3\lambda + 13}{20} y^5 + \frac{2}{5} y^6 \right). \qquad (53)$$

Equations (31) and (32) give

$$\phi_1'''' = iR \left[(U_1 - c_0)\phi_0'' - U_1'' \phi_0 \right]$$
$$+ H_1' \sin\beta + iH_0 \cos\beta, \qquad (54)$$
$$\chi_1'''' = iR \left[(U_2 - c_0)\chi_0'' - U_2'' \chi_0 \right]$$
$$+ G_1' \sin\beta + iG_0 \cos\beta. \qquad (55)$$

The boundary conditions are

$$\phi_1(-1) = 0 = \phi_1'(-1), \quad \chi_1(1) = 0 = \chi_1'(1), \qquad (56)$$

and the four interfacial conditions are obtained from the continuity of ϕ_1 and χ_1 and of their first three derivatives, at $y = 0$. A straightforward solution gives

$$\phi_1 = F_1 + A_1 + B_1 y + C_1 y^2 + D_1 y^3, \quad F_1 = \phi_{11} + \phi_{12} + \phi_{13}, \qquad (57)$$
$$\phi_{11} = \frac{iR \sin^2\beta}{6\lambda(\lambda + 1)} \left(-\frac{\lambda^2 - 1}{48} \frac{y^4}{4!} - \frac{23\lambda^2 + 34\lambda - 25}{192} \frac{y^5}{5!} + \frac{\lambda^2 - 4\lambda + 3}{8} \frac{y^6}{6!} - \frac{\lambda(\lambda + 1)y^7}{7!} + \frac{60\lambda^2 y^9}{9!} \right), \qquad (58)$$
$$\phi_{12} = \frac{i\lambda RP \sin^2\beta}{48(\lambda + 1)} \left(\frac{15\lambda - 39}{60} \frac{y^4}{4!} - \frac{4y^5}{5!} - \frac{(5\lambda + 11)y^6}{6!} - \frac{8(\lambda + 1)y^7}{7!} + \frac{6(13\lambda + 3)y^8}{8!} + \frac{288\lambda y^9}{9!} \right), \qquad (59)$$
$$\phi_{13} = i \cos\beta \left(\frac{y^4}{4!} + \frac{y^5}{5!} \right), \qquad (60)$$

and

$$\chi_1 = F_2 + A_1 + B_1 y + C_1 y^2 + D_1 y^3, \quad F_2 = \chi_{11} + \chi_{12} + \chi_{13}, \qquad (61)$$
$$\chi_{11} = \frac{iR \sin^2\beta}{6(\lambda + 1)} \left(-\frac{\lambda^2 - 1}{48\lambda} \frac{y^4}{4!} + \frac{25\lambda^2 - 34\lambda - 23}{192\lambda} \frac{y^5}{5!} - \frac{3\lambda^2 - 4\lambda + 1}{8\lambda} \frac{y^6}{6!} - \frac{\lambda + 1}{\lambda} \frac{y^7}{7!} + \frac{60y^9}{9!\lambda} \right), \qquad (62)$$
$$\chi_{12} = \frac{iRP \sin^2\beta}{48\lambda(\lambda + 1)} \left(\frac{15\lambda^2 - 39\lambda}{60} \frac{y^4}{4!} - \frac{4\lambda y^5}{5!} + \frac{(11\lambda + 5)y^6}{6!} - \frac{8(\lambda + 1)y^7}{7!} - \frac{6(3\lambda + 13)y^8}{8!} + \frac{288y^9}{9!} \right), \qquad (63)$$
$$\chi_{13} = - \frac{i \cos\beta}{\lambda} \left(\frac{y^4}{4!} - \frac{y^5}{5!} \right). \qquad (64)$$

The coefficients A_1, B_1, C_1, and D_1 are determined from the boundary conditions (56), which demand

$$F_1(-1) + A_1 - B_1 + C_1 - D_1 = 0, \quad F_1'(-1) + B_1 - 2C_1 + 3D_1 = 0,$$
$$F_2(-1) + A_1 + B_1 + C_1 + D_1 = 0, \quad F_2'(1) + B_1 + 2C_1 + 3D_1 = 0. \qquad (65)$$

In particular

$$A_1 = -\tfrac{1}{2}[F_1(-1) + F_2(1)] + \tfrac{1}{4}[F_2'(1) - F_1'(-1)]. \qquad (66)$$

The value of $\phi_1(0)$ is A_1. When (66) is substituted into (51) together with the quantities determined in the first approximation, we have

$$c_1 = \frac{i(1 - \lambda)}{12(\lambda + 1)^3} \left[\frac{RP \sin^2\beta}{80640} \left(55\lambda^3 + 1437\lambda^2 - 1239\lambda + 85 + \frac{248\lambda(\lambda^2 - 1)}{P} \right) + \frac{7(\lambda^2 - 1)}{20} \cos\beta \right]. \qquad (67)$$

V. DISCUSSION

One can proceed further with the systematic procedure of approximation. But (67) is sufficient as a criterion for instability against long waves. Examination of (67) shows that the term containing P in the denominator in the bracket and the term containing $\cos\beta$ are always stabilizing. The term containing $\cos\beta$ arises from gravity normal to the boundaries, and its stabilizing effect is well recognized. The

term containing P^{-1} in the bracket of (67) arises from the convective terms in (54) and (55), so that these convective terms are stabilizing. This isolates the longitudinal body-force terms in (54) and (55) as the cause of instability. But this instability would not have a chance to manifest itself without the conductivity discontinuity at the interface, which gives rise to the term on the right-hand side of (25). That term is crucial, for without it the calculation could not be started, and long-wave instability would not exist.

Examination of (67) further reveals:

(a) For vertical boundaries the term containing $\cos\beta$ drops out, and if the Prandtl number P is not extremely small the flow is unstable for λ small. In this case the "lower fluid" is the colder fluid.

(b) For $\lambda < 1$ and $1 - \lambda$ small, the flow is unstable, if P and $\sin\beta$ are not very small.

(c) For $\lambda > 1$, the flow is stable.

(d) There is a range of λ within $1 < \lambda < \infty$, for which the flow is stable.

(e) For given values of P and β, and a given λ less than one, if the multiplier of R in (67) is positive the critical R is obtained by setting the quantity within the brackets in (67) equal to zero.

Observations (b) and (c) show that for small $|\lambda - 1|$ the flow is unstable if the less conductive fluid is on top and stable if it is at the bottom. This rather intriguing point, together with observations (a) and (d), indicates the rather complex effect of conductivity variation on the stability of the flow.

Finally, it may not be entirely irrelevant to mention that convective stability of two superposed horizontal layers of immiscible fluids has been studied by Yuriko Renardy,[7] who discussed the effects of thermal conductivities in her work. But the stratification in thermal conductivities never *causes* any instability in her problem, as it does here. The present work brings to light an entirely new cause of hydrodynamic instability.

ACKNOWLEDGMENT

This work has been partially supported by the Fluid Mechanics Program of the Office of Naval Research. It constitutes part of the invited lecture given on the occasion of the awarding of the 1985 Fluid Dynamics Prize by the American Physical Society in Tucson, Arizona.

[1] G. I. Taylor and A. D. McEwan, J. Fluid Mech. **22**, 1 (1965).
[2] C. S. Yih, Phys. Fluids **11**, 1447 (1968).
[3] C. S. Yih, J. Fluid Mech. **27**, 337 (1967).
[4] P. G. Saffman and G. I. Taylor, Proc. Soc. London Ser. A **245**, 312 (1958).
[5] C. S. Yih, J. Fluid Mech. **5**, 436 (1959).
[6] C. S. Yih, Phys. Fluids **6**, 321 (1963).
[7] Y. Renardy, Phys. Fluids **29**, 356 (1986).

QUARTERLY OF APPLIED MATHEMATICS
VOLUME XLV, NUMBER 1
APRIL 1987, PAGES 39–50

STABILITY OF TIME-PERIODIC TEMPERATURE FIELDS*

By

CHIA - SHUN YIH AND JINSONG SHI

University of Michigan and University of Florida

Summary. The energy method developed by Joseph [4], Davis [2], and Homsy [3] is applied to the time-periodic temperature fields considered by Yih and Li [11] to obtain Rayleigh numbers below which the fluid is stable. This is done to see how far the Rayleigh numbers so determined fall below the critical Rayleigh numbers, above which the flow is unstable, as determined by the linear theory [11]. It is found that, unlike the case of classical Bénard cells, the gray area, or area of ignorance, is quite large, indicating the need for some improvement of the energy method to give sharper lower bounds on the Rayleigh number.

1. Introduction. The energy method as applied to hydrodynamic stability is almost as old as the history of hydrodynamic stability itself, having its origin in the work of Orr [6]. The idea of the growth or decay of the kinetic energy of a disturbance was already very evident in Reynolds' work [8]. The method lay dormant for many years, until the paper of Serrin [9] gave it new life. Since then the method has enjoyed extensive development, as witnessed by Joseph's book [5], in which an authoritative account of the method can be found.

The energy method achieves its greatest triumph when it is applied to classical Bénard cells. In this case the Rayleigh number below which the fluid is stable, as determined by the energy method, is exactly the same as the Rayleigh number above which it is unstable, as determined by the linear theory. There is no gray area or area of ignorance. It is then natural to conjecture that for problems of convective instability the gray area between the lower curve for the Rayleigh number provided by the energy theory and the upper curve provided by the linear theory) would be relatively small. But this is a mere conjecture. It is desirable to find, in some specific instances, just how large the gray area is.

In this paper we shall consider the time-periodic temperature distribution treated by Yih and Li [11], who provided the results of linear theory via the Floquet theory. The nonlinear theory developed for time-dependent temperature fields by Joseph [4], Davis [2],

---

*Received February 5, 1985.

©1987 Brown University

and Homsy [3] is then applied to find the "best" lower bounds of the Rayleigh number, below which the fluid is stable. The numerical results to be presented will show that the gray area is quite large, indicating the need to improve the energy theory in order to give sharper results for the lower bounds.

The present problem has already been considered by Carmi [1]. Were his results correct, there would be little need for the present paper. As we shall see later, Carmi's results not only differ significantly from ours, but also contradict many well-established results, including the well-known one that the critical Rayleigh number of ordinary Bénard cells according to the linear theory agrees completely with that according to the nonlinear theory. Thus, no reliable results on the Rayleigh number (below which the fluid is stable for arbitrary disturbance) according to the nonlinear theory exist; and, as far as time-periodic temperature fields are concerned, the energy theory promoted by so many previous investigators, straightforward and uncomplicated though it is, is as yet an empty construction without reliable numerical substantiation, and its implied usefulness is not demonstrated. It is this state of affairs that justifies our calculation and the presentation of its results here.

2. The primary temperature distribution. The primary temperature distribution is that considered by Yih and Li [11]. The fluid is bounded above by a plate at $x_3 = d/2$ and below by a plate at $x_3 = -d/2$. Cartesian coordinates (x_1, x_2, x_3) are used, with x_3 measured vertically upward. The temperature at the upper plate is kept at $T_1 + T_2 \cos \omega_* t$ and that at the lower plate at $T_0 - T_2 \cos \omega_* t$, t being the time and ω_* equal to 2π times the frequency of the temperature variation. Only cases of $T_0 \geqslant T_1$ will be considered. The following dimensionless parameters are used:

$$\left. \begin{array}{ll} \tau = t\kappa/d^2, & (x, y, z) = (1/d)(x_1, x_2, x_3), \\ \omega = \omega_* d^2/\kappa, & \bar{\theta} = (\bar{T} - T_1)/(T_0 - T_1), \end{array} \right\} \tag{1}$$

where κ is the thermal diffusivity and $\bar{T}$ the primary temperature. The dimensionless heat-diffusion equation is then

$$\partial\bar{\theta}/\partial\tau = \partial^2\bar{\theta}/\partial z^2. \tag{2}$$

The boundary conditions are

$$\bar{\theta} = 1 - b\cos\omega\tau \quad \text{at } z = -\tfrac{1}{2}, \tag{3}$$

$$\bar{\theta} = b\cos\omega\tau \quad \text{at } z = \tfrac{1}{2}, \tag{4}$$

$$b = T_2/(T_0 - T_1). \tag{5}$$

The solution of the differential system (1)–(5) is

$$\bar{\theta} = \tfrac{1}{2} - z + bF(z, \tau), \tag{6}$$

where

$$F(z, \tau) = (B\cos\omega\tau - C\sin\omega\tau)\sinh\beta z\cos\beta z$$
$$- (C\cos\omega\tau + B\sin\omega\tau)\cosh\beta z\sin\beta z, \tag{7}$$

with

$$B = -\sinh\beta'\cos\beta'/(\sinh^2\beta' + \sin^2\beta'), \qquad C = -B\tan\beta'\coth\beta', \tag{8}$$

and

$$\beta = \left(\tfrac{1}{2}\omega\right)^{1/2}, \qquad \beta' = \tfrac{1}{2}\beta. \tag{9}$$

If ρ_0 is the density at temperature T_0 and at the prevailing pressure, the density at temperature T not too far from T_0 is

$$\rho = \rho_0\left[1 - \alpha(T - T_0)\right], \tag{10}$$

where α is the thermal-expansion coefficient of the fluid. The Boussinesq approximation will be made.

If $T_0 = T_1$, we set

$$\bar{\theta} = \left(\bar{T} - T_0\right)/T_0. \tag{11}$$

Then the primary temperature distribution satisfies

$$\bar{\theta} = \pm\cos\omega\tau \quad \text{at } z = \pm\tfrac{1}{2}, \tag{12}$$

and the solution for the primary temperature field is simply

$$\bar{\theta} = F(z, \tau). \tag{13}$$

The Rayleigh number is defined by

$$R = g\alpha(T_0 - T_1)d^3/(\kappa\nu) \tag{14}$$

if T_0 is not equal to T_1, and by

$$R = g\alpha T_2 d^3/(\kappa\nu) \tag{15}$$

if $T_0 = T_1$, ν being the kinematic viscosity and g the gravitational acceleration.

3. The energy method. The Navier–Stokes equation of motion and the heat equation are, in dimensionless forms, with $\theta = (T - T_1)/(T_0 - T_1)$ or $(T - T_0)/T_0$,

$$\sigma^{-1}(\partial\mathbf{v}/\partial t + \mathbf{v}\cdot\nabla\mathbf{v}) = -\nabla p + \nabla^2\mathbf{v} + R\theta\mathbf{k}, \tag{16}$$

$$\partial\theta/\partial t + \mathbf{v}\cdot\nabla\theta = \nabla^2\theta - w(\partial\bar{\theta}/\partial z), \tag{17}$$

where σ is the Prandtl number, $\mathbf{v}$ the velocity vector, p the pressure, and $\mathbf{k}$ the unit vector in the z direction. Then [4, p. 164] we obtain from (16) and (17), by integration in the fluid domain after taking appropriate inner products,

$$\frac{1}{2}\frac{dK(\mathbf{v})}{dt} = \frac{1}{2\sigma}\frac{d}{dt}\langle|\mathbf{v}|^2\rangle = -\langle\nabla\mathbf{v}:\nabla\mathbf{v}\rangle + R\langle\omega\theta\rangle, \tag{18}$$

$$\frac{1}{2}\frac{d\Theta(\theta)}{dt} = \frac{1}{2}\frac{d}{dt}\langle\theta^2\rangle = -\langle|\nabla\theta|^2\rangle - \left\langle\theta w\frac{\partial\bar{\theta}}{\partial z}\right\rangle. \tag{19}$$

The sign $\langle\ \rangle$ means integration over the fluid domain. It is implicitly assumed that the integrals converge. If not, one can consider the limits of the integrals divided by the area in the x-y plane over which the integrals are performed (apart from the integration in the z direction).

Following Joseph [4] and Homsy [3], we use the energy functional

$$E' = K + \lambda R\Theta(\theta) \tag{20}$$

and obtain from (18) and (19)

$$\frac{1}{2}\frac{dE'}{dt} = R\left(\langle w\theta\rangle - \lambda\left\langle w\theta\frac{\partial\bar{\theta}}{\partial z}\right\rangle\right) - \langle\nabla\mathbf{v}:\nabla\mathbf{v} + \lambda R|\nabla\theta|^2\rangle. \tag{21}$$

With the substitutions

$$\phi = (\lambda R)^{1/2}\theta, \qquad E = K(\mathbf{v}) + \Theta(\phi), \tag{22}$$

one obtains [3, p. 132]

$$D^{-1}\tfrac{1}{2}dE/dt \leqslant -1 + R^{1/2}/\rho_\lambda, \tag{23}$$

where

$$D \equiv \left\langle \nabla\mathbf{v}:\nabla\mathbf{v} + |\nabla\phi|^2 \right\rangle$$

and ρ_λ is given by

$$\frac{1}{\rho_\lambda} = \max_h \left\{ \frac{\langle w\phi \rangle}{\lambda^{1/2}} - \lambda^{1/2}\left\langle w\phi\frac{\partial\bar\theta}{\partial z}\right\rangle \right\} D^{-1}. \tag{24}$$

D is positive definite. Homsy [3] assumed it to be equal to unity for convenience. But that is not necessary. The letter h signifies the Hilbert space in which w and ϕ are allowed to roam, provided they satisfy the boundary conditions.

If R is less than ρ_λ^2, the fluid is stable against all disturbances. The task, then, is to determine ρ_λ, with $\mathbf{v}$ subject to the restriction of the continuity equation

$$\nabla \cdot \mathbf{v} = 0. \tag{25}$$

The Euler–Lagrange equations obtained from (24) are

$$\frac{\rho_\lambda}{2}\left(\frac{1}{\lambda^{1/2}} - \lambda^{1/2}\frac{\partial\bar\theta}{\partial z}\right)w + \nabla^2\phi = 0, \tag{26}$$

$$\frac{\rho_\lambda}{2}\left(\frac{1}{\lambda^{1/2}} - \lambda^{1/2}\frac{\partial\bar\theta}{\partial z}\right)\phi\mathbf{k} + \nabla^2\mathbf{v} - \nabla\tilde p = 0, \tag{27}$$

where $\tilde p$ is the Lagrangian multiplier of the left-hand side of (25) in the maximizing procedure. We shall now determine the best or greatest ρ_λ from (25)–(27) and the boundary conditions

$$\mathbf{v} = 0 \quad \text{and} \quad \phi = 0 \quad \text{at } z = \pm\tfrac{1}{2}. \tag{28}$$

The equations to be solved permit a spectral analysis. We shall assume

$$(\tilde p, \phi, \mathbf{v}) = f(x, y)(\hat p(z), \hat\phi(z), \hat{\mathbf{v}}(z)), \tag{29}$$

where, with a denoting a wave number,

$$f_{xx} + f_{yy} + a^2 f = 0. \tag{30}$$

In particular,

$$w = f(x, y)\hat w(z). \tag{31}$$

Substituting (29) and (30) into (26) and (27) and eliminating $\hat p$ as in the linear theory (see, for instance, Pellew and Southwell [7]), one obtains, after a brief calculation,

$$(D^2 - a^2)^2\hat w = \tfrac{1}{4}R_\lambda a^2 H\hat\theta, \tag{32}$$

$$(D^2 - a^2)\hat\theta = -H\hat w, \tag{33}$$

where $D = \partial/\partial z$, R_λ has been written for ρ_λ^2,

$$\hat{\theta} = 2R_\lambda^{-1/2}\hat{\phi}, \tag{34}$$

$$H = \lambda^{-1/2} - \lambda^{1/2}\partial\bar{\theta}/\partial z. \tag{35}$$

The boundary conditions are

$$\hat{w} = D\hat{w} = \hat{\theta} = 0 \quad \text{at } z = \pm\tfrac{1}{2}. \tag{36}$$

The four boundary conditions involving w arise from the no-slip condition at the solid boundaries, the equation of continuity having been used to reach the conditions on $D\hat{w}$. We now endeavor to determine the best R_λ by solving the eigenvalue system defined by (32), (33), and (36).

4. Determination of R_e. The object is to determine, by the best choice of λ, the best or largest R_λ, which, however, must be the minimum for all values of a and the minimum for all values of τ. The parameters are ω, b, τ, λ, and a, and

$$R_\lambda = R_\lambda(\omega, b, \tau, \lambda, a), \tag{37}$$

or, for $T_0 = T_1$,

$$R_\lambda = R_\lambda(\omega, \tau, \lambda, a). \tag{38}$$

The Rayleigh number sought in the energy theory is

$$R_e = \max_\lambda \min_\tau \min_a R_\lambda(\omega, b, \tau, \lambda, a), \tag{39}$$

where b should be dropped if $T_0 = T_1$.

As pointed out by Homsy [3], λ is a priori a function of τ, but if so, $\lambda(\tau)$ must not increase with τ in order that conclusions about the decrease of $K(\mathbf{v})$ and $\Theta(\theta)$ can be reached. The primary temperature field being time-periodic, this restriction on $\lambda(\tau)$ demands in effect that λ be constant for all τ. With this in mind, we seek to solve (32) and (33) by assuming

$$\hat{\theta} = \sum_{n=1}^{\infty} B_n(\tau)\cos(2n-1)\pi z, \tag{40}$$

$$\hat{w} = \sum_{n=1}^{\infty} A_n(\tau)\phi_n(z), \tag{41}$$

where $\phi_n(z)$ must satisfy the boundary conditions on $\hat{w}$. We choose $\phi_n(z)$ by demanding that it satisfy these boundary conditions and

$$(d^2 - a^2)^2\phi_n = \cos(2n-1)\pi z. \tag{42}$$

A brief calculation then gives

$$\phi_n(z) = P_n\cosh az + Q_n z \sinh az + C_n^2\cos(2n-1)\pi z, \tag{43}$$

where

$$(P_n, Q_n) = \frac{(-1)^n(2n-1)\pi C_n^2}{a + \sinh a}\left(\sinh\frac{a}{2}, 2\cosh\frac{a}{2}\right), \tag{44}$$

$$C_n = \frac{1}{a^2 + (2n-1)^2\pi^2}. \tag{45}$$

                                    CHIA-SHUN YIH AND JINSONG SHI

We have chosen the cosine functions in (40) and (42) because the corresponding eigenvalue for R_λ is lower than that for sine functions in (40) and (42).

Substituting (40) and (41) into (32), and using (42), we obtain

$$\sum_{n=1}^{\infty} \left[\frac{R_\lambda a^2}{4} H B_n(\tau) - A_n(\tau) \right] \cos(2n-1)\pi z = 0. \tag{46}$$

Because the cosine functions are orthogonal in the range $(-\frac{1}{2}, \frac{1}{2})$, we have

$$A_m(\tau) = R_\lambda \sum_{n=1}^{\infty} b_{mn} B_n(\tau), \tag{47}$$

where

$$b_{mn} = \frac{a^2}{2} \int H \cos(2m-1)\pi z \cos(2n-1)\pi z \, dz, \tag{48}$$

the integration being over the range $(-\frac{1}{2}, \frac{1}{2})$.

Similarly, from (33) we obtain

$$B_m(\tau) = \sum_{n=1}^{\infty} a_{mn} A_n(\tau), \tag{49}$$

where

$$a_{mn} = 2C_m \int H \phi_n \cos(2m-1)\pi z \, dz, \tag{50}$$

the integration being over the same range. Substituting (49) into (47) and truncating at $n = N$, we have

$$B_m(\tau) = R_\lambda \sum_{n=1}^{N} c_{mn} B_n(\tau), \tag{51}$$

where

$$c_{mn} = \sum_{k=1}^{N} a_{mk} b_{kn} \tag{52}$$

and

$$(m, n) = 1, 2, 3, \ldots, N. \tag{53}$$

Let

$$\mathbf{M} = (c_{mn})_{N \times N}, \qquad \mathbf{b} = (B_1, B_2, \ldots, B_N)^T. \tag{54}$$

Then (51) can be written as

$$\mathbf{M} \cdot \mathbf{b} = \frac{1}{R_\lambda} \mathbf{b}, \tag{55}$$

from which the eigenvalue R_λ is determined, since $\mathbf{b}$ is not a zero vector.

Some of the details for calculating a_{mk} and b_{kn} (and therefore c_{mn}) are given in the appendix.

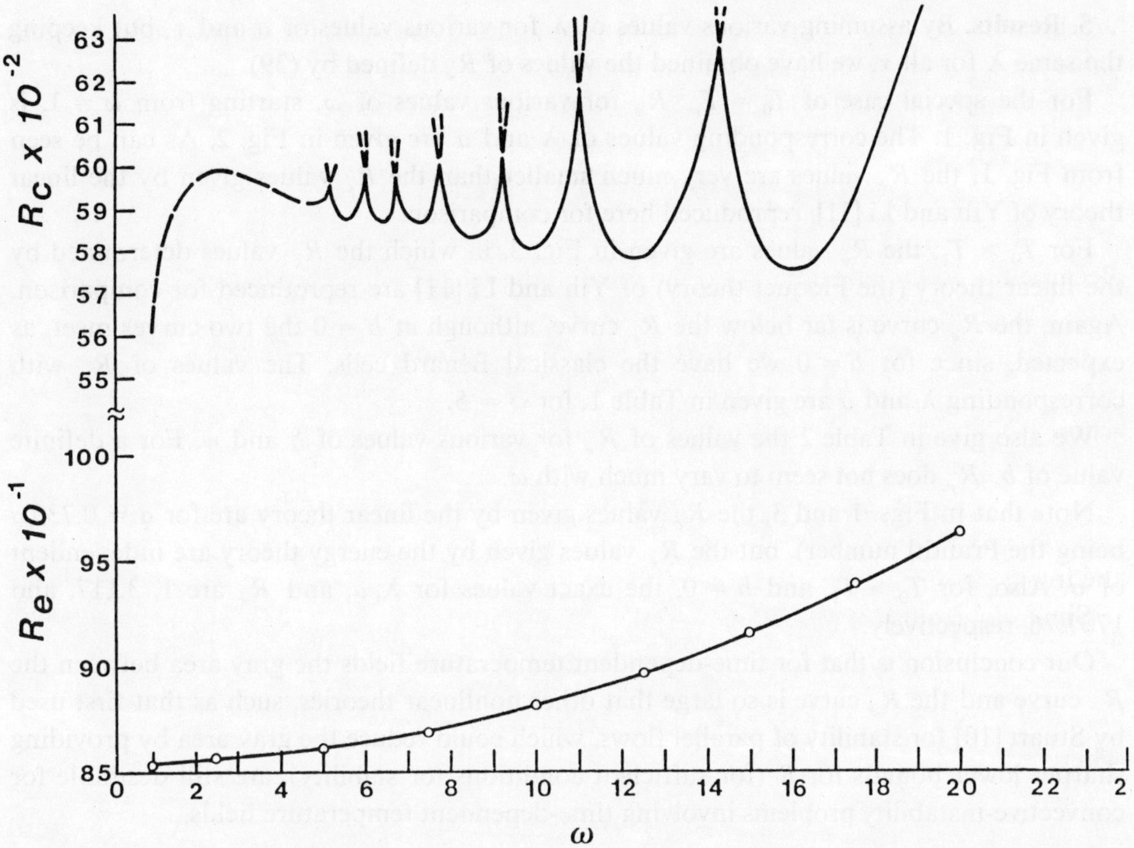

STABILITY OF TIME-PERIODIC TEMPERATURE FIELDS

45

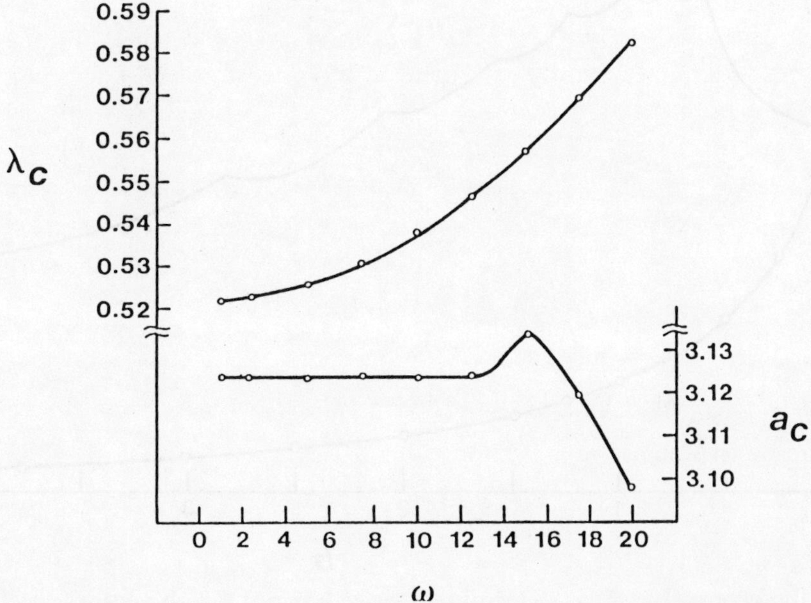

FIG. 1. Comparison of the critical Rayleigh number R_c from the linear theory with the R_e from the energy theory for the special case $T_0 = T_1$ and various values of ω from 1 onward. Note the break of scale of the vertical axis.

FIG. 2. The optimum λ, denoted by λ_c, and the most "dangerous" or "unstable" a, denoted by a_c, for the case $T_0 = T_1$. Note the break of scale of the vertical axis.

5. Results. By assuming various values of λ for various values of a and τ, but keeping the same λ for all τ, we have obtained the values of R_e defined by (39).

For the special case of $T_0 = T_1$, R_e for various values of ω, starting from $\omega = 1$, is given in Fig. 1. The corresponding values of λ and a are given in Fig. 2. As can be seen from Fig. 1, the R_e values are very much smaller than the R_c values given by the linear theory of Yih and Li [11], reproduced here for comparison.

For $T_0 > T_1$, the R_e values are given in Fig. 3, in which the R_c values determined by the linear theory (the Floquet theory) of Yih and Li [11] are reproduced for comparison. Again, the R_e curve is far below the R_c curve, although at $b = 0$ the two curves meet, as expected, since for $b = 0$ we have the classical Bénard cells. The values of R_e with corresponding λ and a are given in Table 1, for $\omega = 5$.

We also give in Table 2 the values of R_e for various values of b and w. For a definite value of b, R_e does not seem to vary much with ω.

Note that in Figs. 1 and 3, the R_c values given by the linear theory are for $\sigma = 0.73$ (σ being the Prandtl number), but the R_e values given by the energy theory are independent of σ. Also, for $T_0 > T_1$, and $b = 0$, the exact values for λ, a, and R_e are 1, 3.117, and 1707.76, respectively.

Our conclusion is that for time-dependent temperature fields the gray area between the R_c curve and the R_e curve is so large that other nonlinear theories, such as that first used by Stuart [10] for stability of parallel flows, which could reduce the gray area by providing sharper lower bounds for R (for sufficient conditions for stability), are still desirable for convective-instability problems involving time-dependent temperature fields.

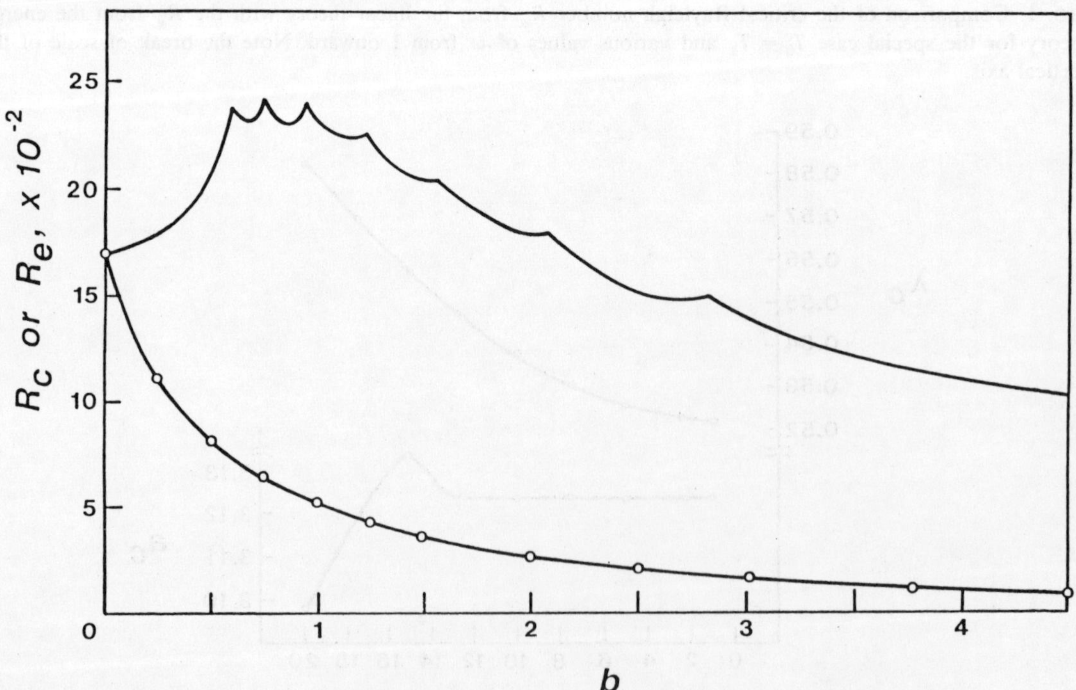

FIG. 3. Comparison of the critical Rayleigh number R_c from the linear theory with the R_e from the energy theory for $\omega = 5$ and various values of b, for $T_0 > T_1$.

TABLE 1. R_e with corresponding λ and a, for $\omega = 5$ and $T_0 > T_1$.

b	λ	a	R_e
0.0	1.0121	3.1240	1707.73
0.25	0.6862	3.1240	1141.47
0.50	0.5239	3.1240	857.04
0.75	0.5072	3.1240	677.31
1.00	0.3698	3.1240	571.03
1.25	0.2030	3.1240	476.27
1.50	0.1729	3.1240	414.87
2.00	0.1410	3.1240	333.16
2.50	0.1169	3.1240	277.44
3.00	0.0758	3.1240	222.13
3.75	0.0712	3.1240	189.78
4.50	0.0488	3.1240	151.34

TABLE 2. R_e for various values of b and ω, for $T_0 > T_1$.

b \ ω	1.0	2.5	5.0	10.0	20.0
0.0	1707.73	1707.73	1707.73	1707.73	1707.73
0.50	853.64	854.39	857.04	867.33	904.41
0.75	674.02	674.44	677.31	687.34	730.94
1.00	567.99	568.66	571.03	580.30	614.40
1.25	472.55	473.34	476.27	486.39	512.92
1.50	412.35	412.94	414.87	422.20	464.36
2.50	275.76	276.21	277.44	283.18	304.46
4.50	157.59	157.79	151.34	155.91	175.26

6. Discussion. Finally, because Carmi [1] has already carried out a calculation for the problem investigated by us, we feel obliged to examine his numerical results and compare them with ours. Carmi's definition of the Rayleigh number, denoted by R_a, is the same as that used by everybody else, and his R is the square root of his R_a. His σ is our ω, and his ε is our b. Examination of his results reveals the following:

1. For the linear theory, the upper curve in his Fig. 3 gives a value for R (of R_L, the subscript indicating "linear") greater than 183, as far as one can read from the vertical axis, on which R_L is 183 and $\varepsilon = 0$. That makes his

$$R_a = R^2 = 33{,}490 \quad \text{for } \varepsilon = 0,$$

which greatly contradicts the well-known fact that R_a for $\varepsilon = 0$ is 1,708. We do not know where Carmi got his curve for R_L. It is not the curve given by Yih and Li [11] in their linear theory, which shows alternating loops for synchronicity and half-frequency and shows a critical Rayleigh number of 1,708 at $b = 0$, b being Carmi's ε.

2. From Carmi's Fig. 3, one gets

$$R_E = 63 \quad \text{at } \varepsilon = 0,$$

which makes his R_a by the energy theory, which we denote here $(R_a)_E$ for clarity, equal to

$$63^2 = 3969,$$

which is much greater than 1,708, the value it should agree with.

3. In any case for $\varepsilon = 0$ his R_E and R_L are not equal, as they should be, but differ by a factor of 183/63, or nearly 3. The corresponding Rayleigh numbers differ by nearly a factor of 9. Equality of these Rayleigh numbers is strictly required, since he used $\lambda = 1$, which is the *correct* λ to use for $\varepsilon = 0$, as is well known. In our Fig. 3, the Rayleigh number for the linear theory is equal to that for the nonlinear theory, for the case b (Carmi's ε) equal to zero, and our curve for R_c is taken from the paper of Yih and Li [11]. Our Fig. 3 (for $\omega = 5$) and Carmi's Fig. 3 (for $\sigma = 1$, σ being our ω) are very different.

We emphasize that the main difficulty in determining our R_e (which corresponds to Carmi's R_E^2) lies in determining the optimum λ, which should give the maximum of the minimum (for various values of τ and a) of R_e. This is laborious work, which Carmi, taking $\lambda = 1$, did not do. But in view of the items stated above, this is not the source of the errors in Carmi's results. After taking $\lambda = 1$, his calculation should have produced a Rayleigh number equal to 1,708 for $\varepsilon = 0$.

7. Appendix. The details for calculating a_{mk} and b_{kn}, given by (50) and (48), are given below.

From (6), we have

$$\frac{\partial \bar{\theta}}{\partial z} = a_0 + b_0 \frac{\partial F(z, \tau)}{\partial z},$$

where

$$a_0 = -1, \quad b_0 = b \quad \text{if } T_0 > T_1,$$
$$a_0 = 0, \quad b_0 = 1 \quad \text{if } T_0 = T_1.$$

Hence

$$H = \lambda^{-1/2} - \lambda^{1/2} \frac{\partial \bar{\theta}}{\partial z} = a_0 + c_0 \cosh \beta z \cos \beta z + s_0 \sinh \beta z \sin \beta z,$$

where λ, for $T_0 > T_1$, satisfies

$$a_0 = \lambda^{-1/2} + \lambda^{1/2},$$

$$c_0 = -b_0 \beta [(B - C) \cos \omega\tau - (B + C) \sin \omega\tau] \lambda^{1/2},$$

$$s_0 = -b_0 \beta [(B + C) \cos \omega\tau + (B - C) \sin \omega\tau] \lambda^{1/2},$$

with b, B, C, and β given by (5), (8), and (9).

Then

$$a_{mk} = 2C_m \left\{ a_0 \left[P_k I_1(a, m) + Q_k I_4(a, m) + \frac{C_k^2}{2} \delta_{mk} \right] \right.$$

$$+ c_0 \left[P_k I_5(a, \omega, m) + Q_k I_7(a, \omega, m) + C_k^2 I_2(m, k) \right]$$

$$\left. + s_0 \left[P_k I_6(a, \omega, m) + Q_k I_8(a, \omega, m) + C_k^2 I_3(m, k) \right] \right\},$$

$$b_{kn} = \frac{a^2}{2} \left\{ \frac{a_0}{2} \delta_{kn} + c_0 I_2(n, k) + s_0 I_3(m, k) \right\},$$

where P_k, Q_k, and C_k are defined by (44) and (45), and the integrals I are defined as follows (in complex form for brevity):

$$h(m, z) \equiv \cos(2m - 1)\pi z,$$

$$I_1(a, m) + iI_4(a, m) = \int (\cosh az + iz \sin az) h(m, z) \, dz,$$

$$I_2(n, k) + iI_3(n, k) = \int \cosh(1 + i)\beta z h(n, z) h(k, z) \, dx,$$

$$I_5(a, \omega, m) + iI_6(a, \omega, m) = \int \cosh(1 + i)\beta z \cdot \cosh az \cdot h(m, z) \, dz,$$

$$I_7(a, \omega, m) + iI_8(a, \omega, m) = \int \cosh(1 + i)\beta z \cdot z \sinh az \cdot h(m, z) \, dz.$$

The limits of integration are from $-\frac{1}{2}$ to $\frac{1}{2}$.

To evaluate the I's, let

$$R_0(\alpha, \gamma) + iR_1(\alpha, \gamma) = \int \cosh(\alpha + i\gamma) z \, dz,$$

$$R_3(\alpha, \gamma) + iR_2(\alpha, \gamma) = \int z \sinh(\alpha + i\gamma) z \, dz,$$

$$\hat{A}(\alpha, \gamma) = \sinh\frac{\alpha}{2} \sin\frac{\gamma}{2}, \qquad \hat{B}(\alpha, \gamma) = \sinh\frac{\alpha}{2} \cos\frac{\gamma}{2},$$

$$\hat{C}(\alpha, \gamma) = \cosh\frac{\alpha}{2} \sin\frac{\gamma}{2}, \qquad \hat{D}(\alpha, \gamma) = \cosh\frac{\alpha}{2} \cosh\frac{\gamma}{2},$$

$$E(\alpha, \gamma) = \alpha^2 + \gamma^2.$$

Then

$$R_0(\alpha, \gamma) = \frac{2\alpha}{E} \left(\hat{B} + \frac{\gamma}{\alpha} \hat{C} \right),$$

$$R_1(\alpha, \gamma) = \frac{2}{\alpha} \hat{C} - \frac{\gamma}{\alpha} R_0(\alpha, \gamma),$$

$$R_2(\alpha, \gamma) = \frac{\alpha}{E} \left[\hat{A} - \frac{2}{\alpha} \hat{C} - \frac{\gamma}{\alpha} \hat{D} + \frac{2\gamma}{\alpha} R_0(\alpha, \gamma) \right],$$

$$R_3(\alpha, \gamma) = \frac{\gamma}{E} \left[A - \frac{2}{\alpha} \hat{C} + \frac{\alpha}{\gamma} \hat{D} + \frac{\gamma^2 - \alpha^2}{\alpha\gamma} R_0(\alpha, \gamma) \right].$$

Finally,

$$I_1(a,m) = R_0(a,(2m-1)\pi],$$

$$I_2(n,k) = \tfrac{1}{4}\{R_0[\beta,\beta + 2(n+k-1)\pi] + R_0[\beta,\beta - 2(n+k-1)\pi]$$
$$+ R_0[\beta,\beta + 2(n-k)\pi] + R_0[\beta,\beta - 2(n-k)\pi]\},$$

$$I_3(n,k) = \tfrac{1}{4}\{R_1[\beta,\beta + 2(n+k-1)\pi] + R_1[\beta,\beta - 2(n+k-1)\pi]$$
$$+ R_1[\beta,\beta + 2(n-k)\pi] + R_1[\beta,\beta - 2(n-k)\pi]\},$$

$$I_4(a,m) = R_3[a,(2m-1)\pi],$$

$$I_5(a,\omega,m) = \tfrac{1}{4}\{R_0[\beta + a,\beta + (2m-1)\pi] + R_0[\beta + a,\beta - (2m-1)\pi]$$
$$+ R_0[\beta - a,\beta + (2m-1)\pi] + R_0[\beta - a,\beta - (2m-1)\pi]\},$$

$$I_6(a,\omega,m) = \tfrac{1}{4}\{R_1[\beta + a,\beta + (2m-1)\pi] + R_1[\beta + a,\beta - (2m-1)\pi]$$
$$+ R_1[\beta - a,\beta + (2m-1)\pi] + R_1[\beta - a,\beta - (2m-1)\pi],$$

$$I_7(a,\omega,m) = \tfrac{1}{4}\{R_3[\beta + a,\beta + (2m-1)\pi] + R_3[\beta + a,\beta - (2m-1)\pi]$$
$$- R_3[\beta - a,\beta + (2m-1)\pi] - R_3[\beta - a,\beta - (2m-1)\pi]\},$$

$$I_8(a,\omega,m) = \tfrac{1}{4}\{R_2[\beta + a,\beta + (2m-1)\pi] + R_2[\beta + a,\beta - (2m-1)\pi]$$
$$- R_2[\beta - a,\beta + (2m-1)\pi] - R_2[\beta - a,\beta - (2m-1)\pi]\}.$$

Acknowledgment. This work has been supported by the Office of Naval Research.

REFERENCES

[1] S. Carmi, *Energy stability of modulated flows*, Phys. Fluids **17**, 1951–1955 (1974)

[2] S. H. Davis, *Buoyancy-surface tension instability by the method of energy*, J. Fluid Mech. **39**, 347–359 (1969)

[3] G. M. Homsy, *Global stability of time-dependent flows: impulsively heated or cooled fluid layers*, J. Fluid Mech. **60**, 129–139 (1973)

[4] D. D. Joseph, *Nonlinear stability of the Boussinesq equations by the method of energy*, Arch. Rat. Mech. Anal. **22**, 163–184 (1966)

[5] D. D. Joseph, *Stability of fluid motions*, vols. I and II, Springer Verlag, 1976

[6] W. McF. Orr, *The stability or instability of the steady motions of a perfect liquid and of a viscous liquid, Part I. A perfect liquid, and Part II, A viscous liquid*, Proc. Roy. Irish Acad. Sect. A **27**, 9–68 and 69–138 (1907)

[7] A. Pellew and R. V. Southwell, *On maintained convective motion in a fluid heated from below*, Proc. Roy. Soc. London Ser. A. **176**, 312–343 (1940)

[8] O. Reynolds, *On the dynamic theory of incompressible viscous fluid and the determination of the criterion*, Philos. Trans .Roy. Soc. London Ser. A **186**, 123–164 (1895)

[9] J. Serrin, *On the stability of viscous fluid motions*, Arch. Rat. Mech. Anal. **3**, 1–13 (1959)

[10] J. T. Stuart, *On the nonlinear mechanics of hydrodynamic stability*, J. Fluid Mech. **4**, 1–21 (1958)

[11] C.-S. Yih and C.-H. Li, *Instability of unsteady flows or configurations, Part ·2. Convective instability*, J. Fluid Mech. **54**, 143–152 (1972)

Convective instability of a spherical fluid inclusion

Chia-Shun Yih

Department of Mechanical Engineering and Applied Mechanics, The University of Michigan, Ann Arbor, Michigan 48109

(Received 23 June 1986; accepted 22 September 1986)

When a vertical temperature gradient is applied to a large solid containing a spherical fluid inclusion, the temperature in the fluid is a function only of height. The stability of this fluid against convection is investigated and it is found that the principle of exchange of stabilities applies. The linear differential system governing stability is then solved; the results show that the thermal conductivity of the surrounding solid is always stabilizing and that the most unstable mode is the first asymmetric mode, for which the critical Rayleigh number is given. The energy method can be applied, with due modifications to account for heat conduction in the surrounding solid. The same mathematical governing differential system would then be obtained, giving the same number for the upper bound of the Rayleigh numbers below which the fluid is stable. This number is then truly critical: The fluid is stable or unstable according to whether the Rayleigh number is below or above it, whatever the magnitude of the disturbance. The results are discussed in the context of the movement of the spherical inclusion in a soluble solid. The greater instability of the asymmetric mode indicates that when instability occurs, the fluid inclusion will have a sidewise component, which is greater for a greater supercritical Rayleigh number. The effect of double diffusion is also discussed.

I. INTRODUCTION

Fluid inclusions in a soluble solid and their movement when a temperature gradient is present constitute an interesting subject of geological studies. Take, for simplicity, the case of a spherical inclusion of a liquid of thermal conductivity k and radius a imbedded in a soluble solid of density ρ_s and thermal conductivity k_s. Let there be a vertical temperature gradient β_s in the solid, disturbed only by the presence of the liquid inclusion. If we assume that there is no flow in the liquid, the temperature $\overline{T}_s$ in the solid and the temperature $\overline{T}$ in the fluid must satisfy the Laplace equation, so that

$$\nabla^2 \overline{T}_s = 0 \quad \text{and} \quad \Delta^2 \overline{T} = 0, \tag{1}$$

in which ∇^2 is the Laplacian operator, which in spherical coordinates (r,θ,Φ) is

$$\nabla^2 = \frac{1}{r^2} \frac{\partial}{\partial r}\left(r^2 \frac{\partial}{\partial r}\right) + \frac{1}{r^2 \sin\theta} \frac{\partial}{\partial \theta}\left(\sin\theta \frac{\partial}{\partial \theta}\right)$$
$$+ \frac{1}{r^2 \sin^2\theta} \frac{\partial^2}{\partial \Phi^2}. \tag{2}$$

The polar axis of the spherical coordinates is directed vertically upward. The boundary conditions at the spherical surface are

$$k_s \frac{\partial \overline{T}_s}{\partial r} = k \frac{\partial \overline{T}}{\partial r} \quad \text{and} \quad \overline{T}_s = \overline{T} \quad \text{at} \quad r = a. \tag{3}$$

In addition, $\overline{T}$ must be regular at $r = 0$ and $\overline{T}_s$ must approach $\beta_s x_3$ far away from the sphere, x_3 being the vertical one of the Cartesian coordinates (x_1, x_2, x_3), with origin at the center of the sphere, which is also the origin of the spherical coordinates.

It can be immediately verified that (with T_0 denoting a constant)

$$\overline{T}_s = \beta_s x_3 + \frac{\beta_1 a^3}{2} \frac{x_3}{r^3} + T_0 \quad \text{and} \quad \overline{T} = \beta x_3 + T_0 \tag{4}$$

satisfy (1), the regularity condition at the origin for $\overline{T}$, and the condition on $\overline{T}_s$ at infinity. Since

$$x_3 = r \cos\theta,$$

the conditions (3) demand

$$k_s(\beta_s - \beta_1) = k\beta \quad \text{and} \quad \beta_s + \beta_1/2 = \beta, \tag{5}$$

FIG. 1. Isotherms showing linear temperature distribution in the spherical fluid inclusion.

    © 1987 American Institute of Physics

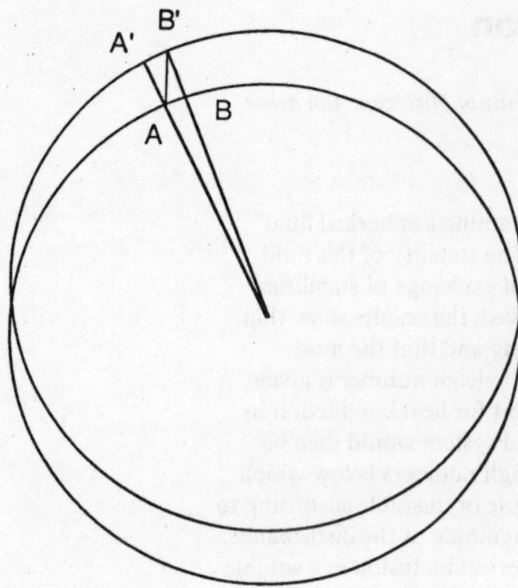

FIG. 2. Sketch showing that erosion causes point A to move to A and B to B, resulting in the apparent vertical movement of A to B′.

which give

$$\beta_1 = [(2\lambda - 2)/(2\lambda + 1)]\beta_s, \quad \beta = [3\lambda/(2\lambda + 1)]\beta_s, \tag{6}$$

where

$$\lambda = k_s/k. \tag{7}$$

The interesting part of the solutions (4) is that (Fig. 1) the temperature $\overline{T}$ in the fluid is a linear function of x_3, so that ordinary thermal convection need not arise. But if the solid is soluble in the liquid, there must be mass transfer from the hotter hemisphere to the colder one and that will push the fluid up (if β_s is positive). We can calculate the velocity of the liquid by assuming the solution is saturated everywhere and that the saturation concentration (in mass per unit volume) c is related to $\overline{T}$, in the temperature range experienced by the fluid, by

$$c = \gamma(\overline{T} - T_0) + c_0. \tag{8}$$

If the mass diffusivity of the substance of the solute is κ_c, its mass is transported downward at a rate of $\kappa_c (\partial c/\partial x_3)$ (mass per unit area per unit time). The speed with which the spherical boundary moves upward is then (ρ_s = density of the solid)

$$u_3 = \frac{\kappa_c}{\rho_s} \frac{\partial c}{\partial x_3} = \frac{\kappa_c \beta \gamma}{\rho_s}. \tag{9}$$

The reader may verify that this conclusion is reached whether the simple argument of vertical transport is used, as here, or whether the *radial* erosion of deposition of mass at the spherical boundary is calculated from $\kappa_c (\partial c/\partial r)$. See Fig. 2.

The fluid, then, is constrained to move upward with the same velocity u_3 everywhere. The heat equations will then have to include the effects of this velocity and a second approximation for both the temperature and the velocity (for the fluid) fields has to be made. However, u_3 is very small, or

the relevant Reynolds and Péclet numbers are very small, so that (9) gives the velocity of the fluid in the same way that the Stokes law gives the fall velocity of a small sphere in a viscous fluid at small Reynolds numbers. Indeed, (9) is a kind of an inverse Stokes law, since it gives the velocity of a liquid sphere moving through a solid.

The erosion and deposition of solute give rise to heat sinks and sources, respectively, because of the absorption or release of latent heat. The effect of these heat sinks and sources can be taken into account quite simply. From the second equation in (4) one obtains that the normal gradient of $\overline{T}$ is $\beta \cos \theta$. The solute dissolved (or deposited) per unit time and per unit area is $\kappa_c \beta \gamma \cos \theta$. The strength of the heat sink per unit area of the boundary is then $m\beta \cos \theta$, where

$$m = L\kappa_c \gamma,$$

with L the latent heat per unit mass. Still using (4), one replaces conditions (3) by

$$k_s \frac{\partial \overline{T}_s}{\partial r} = k \frac{\partial T}{\partial r} + m\beta \cos \theta, \quad \overline{T}_s = \overline{T} \text{ at } r = a.$$

This gives, instead of (5),

$$k_s (\beta_s - \beta_1) = k\beta + m\beta \text{ and } \beta_s + \beta_1/2 = \beta,$$

and instead of (6),

$$\beta_1 = \frac{2(\lambda - 1 - mk^{-1})}{2\lambda + 1 + mk^{-1}} \beta_s, \quad \beta = \frac{3\lambda}{2\lambda + 1 + mk^{-1}} \beta_s.$$

With the β so determined, (9) continues to give the speed of movement of the liquid sphere. It can be seen from (9) and the above equation giving β that the temperature gradient inside the sphere and its speed of movement decreases as the latent heat (and therefore m) increases, as is to be expected.

The question of the stability of the temperature stratification in the fluid then naturally arises, either when β is negative, or if the effect of double diffusion is considered, even if β is positive. As is well known, the problem of nonoscillatory instability when double diffusion is considered can be reduced to that of the simpler case of ordinary thermal-convective instability. When the fluid is unstable, the movement of the fluid inclusion in the solid may be much faster, depending on the Rayleigh number, and may not even be vertical. This rather intriguing situation motivates this study. We shall neglect the effect of the u_3 given by (9) on the stability calculations, since that effect is very small, and we shall concentrate on thermal instability (i.e., without considering double diffusion) first.

II. EQUATIONS GOVERNING THE STABILITY PROBLEM

The mean temperature fields in the solid and the fluid are given by (4), and the mean density ρ_m of the fluid is given by

$$\rho_m = \rho_0 [1 - \alpha(\overline{T} - T_0)], \tag{10}$$

where α is the coefficient of thermal expansion and ρ_0 the density of the fluid at $x_3 = 0$. The mean pressure gradient is in the vertical direction and is given by

$$\frac{\partial p_m}{\partial x_3} = -\rho_0 g [1 - \alpha(\overline{T} - T_0)], \tag{11}$$

where p_m is the mean pressure and g the gravitational acceleration. If T_s denotes the temperature in the solid and T that in the fluid, and if ρ and p denote, respectively, the density and pressure of the fluid, we have

$$T_s = \overline{T}_s + T'_s, \quad T = \overline{T} + T',$$
$$\rho = \rho_m + \rho', \quad p = p_m + p',$$

where the primes indicate perturbation quantities. Since

$$\rho = \rho_0 [1 - \alpha(T - T_0)], \tag{12}$$

we have

$$\rho' = -\alpha T' \rho_0. \tag{13}$$

We shall consider the temperature differences $T_s - T_0$, $T - T_0$, $\overline{T}_s - T_0$, and $\overline{T} - T_0$, and we shall express these as well as T'_s and T' in units of βa. Furthermore, we shall measure time t in units of a^2/κ, and use a as the length scale for x_1, x_2, and x_3. Velocities will be measured in units of κ/a, and pressure in units of $\rho_0 \kappa \nu/a^2$, where ν is the kinematic viscosity. Then all the questions will be in dimensionless terms. For instance, the mean temperature distributions in the solid is now given in dimensionless terms by

$$\overline{T}_s - T_0 = \frac{3\lambda}{2\lambda + 1} x_3 + \frac{\lambda - 1}{3\lambda} \frac{x_3}{r^3}, \tag{14}$$

and that in the fluid by

$$\overline{T} - T_0 = x_3. \tag{15}$$

The velocity perturbation is denoted by u_i $(i = 1,2,3)$ measured in units of κ/a. The usual linearization procedure then filters out the mean quantities in the governing equations except where they are multiplied by a perturbation quantity. If the Boussinesq approximation is adopted, the dimensionless linearized equations of motion are

$$\frac{1}{\Pr} \frac{\partial u_i}{\partial t} = -\frac{\partial p'}{\partial x_i} - R T' \delta_{i3} + \nabla^2 u_i \quad (i = 1,2,3), \tag{16}$$

where δ_{i3} is a Kronecker delta, ∇^2 is the Laplacian operator in Cartesian coordinates, and

$$R = -g\alpha\beta a^4/\kappa\nu \quad \text{and} \quad \Pr = \nu/\kappa \tag{17}$$

are, respectively, the Rayleigh number and the Prandtl number. (For unstable modes β is negative.) The equation of continuity is

$$\frac{\partial u_i}{\partial x_i} = 0. \tag{18}$$

The heat equation is, for the liquid,

$$\frac{\partial T'}{\partial t} + u_3 = \nabla^2 T' \tag{19}$$

and, for the solid, with $\hat{\lambda} = \kappa_s/\kappa$ (κ_s = thermal diffusivity of the solid),

$$\frac{\partial T'_s}{\partial t} = \hat{\lambda} \nabla^2 T'_s. \tag{20}$$

From (16) and (18) one obtains

$$\nabla^2 p' = -R \frac{\partial T'}{\partial x_3}. \tag{21}$$

III. BOUNDARY CONDITIONS

The boundary conditions at the spherical surface are

$$u_i = 0 \quad \text{at} \quad r = 1, \tag{22}$$

$$T' = T'_s \quad \text{at} \quad r = 1, \tag{23}$$

$$\frac{\partial T'}{\partial r} = \lambda \frac{\partial T'_s}{\partial r} \quad \text{at} \quad r = 1. \tag{24}$$

These demand, respectively, no slip at the boundary, continuity of temperature, and continuity of heat flux. (Replace λ by $\lambda/(1 + mk^{-1})$ to include the effect of L.) Further,

$$T'_s = 0 \quad \text{at} \quad r = \infty \tag{25}$$

and

$$T', u'_i, \text{ and } p' \text{ must be regular at } r = 0. \tag{26}$$

IV. NONOSCILLATION OF CONVECTION

Since there are no time-dependent coefficients in all the linear equations involved, one can assume that all perturbation quantities contain the exponential factor $\exp(\sigma t)$, where

$$\sigma = \sigma_r + i\sigma_i.$$

The fluid is therefore stable, neutrally stable, or unstable if σ_r is negative, zero, or positive, respectively.

Multiplying (16) by u_i^*, where the asterisk indicates the complex conjugate, and integrating over the fluid domain V, we have

$$\sigma K = -\Pr Q - \Pr R \int T' u_3^* \, dV, \tag{27}$$

where

$$K = \int u_i u_i^* \, dV, \quad Q = \int \frac{\partial u_i}{\partial x_j} \frac{\partial u_i^*}{\partial x_j} \, dV. \tag{28}$$

Multiplying (19) by T'^* and (20) by $(\lambda/\hat{\lambda}) T'_s{}^*$, integrating over V and the solid domain V_s, respectively, and adding the results, using (23) and (24) when necessary, one has

$$\sigma(H + H_s) = -S - S_s - \int T'^* u_3 \, dV, \tag{29}$$

where

$$H = \int |T'|^2 \, dV, \quad H_s = \frac{\lambda}{\hat{\lambda}} \int |T'_s|^2 \, dV_s, \tag{30}$$

$$S = \int |\text{grad } T'|^2 \, dV, \tag{31}$$

$$S_s = \lambda \int |\text{grad } T'_s|^2 \, dV_s.$$

Multiplying (29) by $-R \Pr$, taking the complex conjugate of the result, and adding (27) to it, one has

$$\sigma K = -\Pr R \sigma^*(H + H_s) = -\Pr Q + \Pr R(S + S_s). \tag{32}$$

The real and imaginary parts of (32) are

$$\sigma_r [K - \Pr R(H + H_s)] = -\Pr Q + \Pr R(S + S_s), \tag{33}$$

$$\sigma_i [K + \Pr R(H + H_s)] = 0, \tag{34}$$

in which, one recalls that all the quantities or numbers represented by capital letters are real and positive. If $\sigma_i \neq 0$, (34) shows that R is negative and then (33) shows that σ_r is negative. Hence for instability or neutral stability, σ_i must be zero.

V. ANALYSIS OF THE PROBLEM OF LINEAR STABILITY

For neutral stability, then, we shall take σ to be zero. This greatly simplifies the calculations. First, the thermal boundary condition for the fluid alone at the spherical surface can now be formulated.

Equation (20) is now

$$\nabla^2 T'_s = 0, \tag{35}$$

where ∇^2 is given by (2). The elemental solution of (35), nonsingular at infinity, is

$$T'_s = r^{-n-1} P^m_n(\cos \theta)\cos m\phi, \tag{36}$$

where P^m_n is Legendre's associated functions of the first kind. (If $m = 0$, they are just the Legendre polynomials.) For this solution,

$$\frac{\partial T'_s}{\partial r} = -(n+1)T'_s \quad \text{at } r = 1. \tag{37}$$

Then (23) and (24) give

$$\frac{\partial T'}{\partial r} = -(n+1)\lambda T' \quad \text{at } r = 1, \tag{38}$$

which allows the separation of the problem for the fluid from the heat equation for the solid.

We shall, for simplicity, write

$$h = RT' \quad \text{and} \quad h_s = RT'_s. \tag{39}$$

Then, for neutral stability, (16) becomes

$$\nabla^2 u_i = \frac{\partial p'}{\partial x_i} + h\delta_{i3} \tag{40}$$

and (19), (21), and (20) assume the forms, respectively,

$$\nabla^2 h = Ru_3, \tag{41}$$

$$\nabla^2 p' = -\frac{\partial h}{\partial x_3}, \tag{42}$$

$$\nabla^2 h_s = 0. \tag{43}$$

The thermal boundary condition (38) now has the form

$$\frac{\partial h}{\partial r} = -(n+1)\lambda h \quad \text{at } r = 1. \tag{44}$$

Since the boundary is spherical, it is natural to use spherical coordinates (r,θ,Φ) and the corresponding velocity components (u,v,w). Then, for neutral stability, the nonoscillation of the disturbance shown in Sec. IV allows us to write the Navier–Stokes equations

$$0 = -\frac{\partial p'}{\partial r} - h\cos\theta + \left(\nabla^2 u - \frac{2u}{r^2} - \frac{2}{r^2}\frac{\partial v}{\partial \theta}\right.$$
$$\left. - \frac{2v\cot\theta}{r^2} - \frac{2}{r^2\sin\theta}\frac{\partial w}{\partial \phi}\right), \tag{45a}$$

$$0 = -\frac{1}{r}\frac{\partial p'}{\partial \theta} + h\sin\theta + \left(\nabla^2 v + \frac{2}{r^2}\frac{\partial u}{\partial \theta}\right.$$
$$\left. - \frac{v}{r^2\sin^2\theta} - \frac{2\cot\theta}{r^2\sin\theta}\frac{\partial w}{\partial \phi}\right), \tag{45b}$$

$$0 = -\frac{1}{r\sin\theta}\frac{\partial p'}{\partial \phi} + \left(\nabla^2 w - \frac{w}{r^2\sin^2\theta}\right.$$
$$\left. + \frac{2}{r^2\sin\theta}\frac{\partial u}{\partial \phi} + \frac{2\cot\theta}{r^2\sin\theta}\frac{\partial v}{\partial \phi}\right), \tag{45c}$$

where ∇^2 is given by (2). The equation of continuity is

$$\frac{1}{r^2}\frac{\partial}{\partial r}(r^2 u) + \frac{1}{r\sin\theta}\frac{\partial}{\partial \theta}(v\sin\theta) + \frac{1}{r\sin\theta}\frac{\partial w}{\partial \phi} = 0. \tag{46}$$

In view of (46), the last three terms of (45a) can be replaced by

$$\frac{2}{r^3}\frac{\partial}{\partial r}(r^2 u) = \frac{4u}{r^2} + \frac{2}{r}\frac{\partial u}{\partial r}, \tag{47}$$

and a simple calculation shows that (45a) reduces to the form

$$\frac{\partial p'}{\partial r} + h\cos\theta = \frac{1}{r}\nabla^2(ru). \tag{48}$$

The velocity components u and v are related to u_3 by

$$u_3 = u\cos\theta - v\sin\theta \tag{49}$$

and in (42) one has

$$\frac{\partial}{\partial x_3} = \cos\theta\frac{\partial}{\partial r} - \frac{\sin\theta}{r}\frac{\partial}{\partial \theta}. \tag{50}$$

One has to solve (41), (42), (48), (45b), and (45c), with (49) and (50) used in (41) and (42). Apart from regularity for all quantities at $r = 0$, the boundary conditions are (44) and

$$u = \frac{\partial u}{\partial r} = 0 \quad \text{at } r = 1, \tag{51}$$

$$v = 0 = w \quad \text{at } r = 1. \tag{52}$$

The condition on $\partial u/\partial r$ in (51) arises from (46). Once (46) is satisfied on $r = 1$, and (51) and (52) guarantee that satisfaction, it is satisfied everywhere in the fluid, since (42) has been derived on the basis of (18). Indeed, (40) gives

$$\nabla^2\frac{\partial u_i}{\partial x_i} = \nabla^2 p' + \frac{\partial h}{\partial x_3}, \tag{53}$$

so that if (42) is satisfied one has

$$\nabla^2\frac{\partial u_i}{\partial x_i} = 0. \tag{54}$$

If $\partial u_i/\partial x_i$ is nonsingular within $r = 1$, and is zero on $r = 1$, it is zero everywhere inside the spherical surface, as is well known in potential theory. Alternatively, one can use (46) to replace (45b) or (45c) in the differential system to be solved.

It has been necessary to present the governing equations in both Cartesian and spherical coordinates because the simplest approach involves the use of both coordinate systems. This approach is as follows.

(a) Expand h in some suitable basis functions satisfying (44).

(b) Solve (42) for p', retaining the undetermined complementary solution.

(c) Solve (48) for u, using the complementary solution available from step (b) to help satisfy (51).

(d) Solve the third equation of (40) for u_3.

(e) Go to (41) to get the determinant whose vanishing gives R.

(f) Solve (49) for v and (46) for w, if v and w are desired.

We shall now use this procedure to solve the problem.

First, we set forth a few well-known formulas regarding associated Legendre functions of the first kind (including Legendre polynomials), and some functions involving Bessel functions of half-orders. The solution of the Laplace equation in spherical coordinates by separation of variables is of the form

$$f(r)P_n^m(\mu)\cos m(\phi + \epsilon),\tag{55}$$

where

$$f(r) = r^n \text{ or } r^{-n-1}, \quad \mu = \cos\theta,\tag{56}$$

ϵ is a phase angle which can be set to zero, $P_n^m(\mu)$ is an associated Legendre function of the first kind, and m and n are integers with $m \leqslant n$. (When $n < m$ the function P_n^m is zero.) The following formulas will be useful:

$$(2n+1)\mu P_n^m = (n-m+1)P_{n+1}^m + (n+m)P_{n-1}^m,\tag{57}$$

$$(\mu^2 - 1)\frac{dP_n^m}{d\mu} = \frac{1}{2n+1}\big(n(n-m+1)P_{n+1}^m$$
$$- (n+1)(n+m)P_{n-1}^m\big).\tag{58}$$

We shall use the basis functions $F_n(\alpha_n r)$ defined by

$$\left(\frac{d^2}{dr^2} + \frac{2}{r}\frac{r}{dr} + \alpha_n^2 - \frac{n(n+1)}{r^2}\right)F_n(\alpha_n r) = 0,\tag{59}$$

the regularity condition at $r = 0$, and, on account of (44),

$$\frac{dF_n(\alpha_n r)}{dr} = -(n+1)\lambda F_n(\alpha_n r) \text{ at } r = 1.\tag{60}$$

For each n, there are infinitely many eigenvalues for α_n, which we denote by α_{nj} ($j = 1,2,3,...$). It is well known that the solutions of (56) are of the form

$$F_n(\alpha_{nj} r) = J_{n+0.5}(\alpha_{nj} r)/\sqrt{\alpha_{nj} r},\tag{61}$$

where the J stands for the Bessel function. Near $r = 0$, then, $F_n(\alpha_{nj} r)$ behaves as r^n. The first several functions F_n are given explicitly in the Appendix. An F_n has a finite number of terms for a finite n. It has been used before by Chandrasekhar.[1]

From corresponding formulas for Bessel functions, one has

$$\frac{dF_n}{dr} = \frac{\alpha_{nj}}{2n+1}\big[-(n+1)F_{n+1} + nF_{n-1}\big],\tag{62}$$

$$\frac{dF_n}{dr} = \frac{n}{r}F_n - \alpha_{nj}F_{n+1} = -\frac{n+1}{r}F_n + \alpha_{nj}F_{n-1},\tag{63}$$

$$\frac{2n+1}{r}F_n = \alpha_{nj}(F_{n+1} + F_{n-1}).\tag{64}$$

The argument of the functions in (62)–(64) is $\alpha_{nj} r$.

Two other useful formulas, upon the use of (57), (58), (63), and (64) are

$$\frac{\partial}{\partial x_3}P_n^m(\mu)F_n(\alpha_{nj} r)$$
$$= \mu P_n^m \frac{dF_n}{dr} + (1-\mu^2)\frac{dP_n^m}{d\mu}\frac{F_n}{r}$$
$$= \frac{\alpha_{nj}}{2n+1}\big[-(n-m+1)P_{n+1}^m F_{n+1}$$
$$+ (n+m)P_{n-1}^m F_{n-1}\big],\tag{65}$$

$$\frac{\partial}{\partial x_3}r^n P_n^m(\mu) = (n+m)r^{n-1}P_{n-1}^m.\tag{66}$$

Equation (65) is gratifying because each term on the right-hand side has the same indices below. That is, P_{n+1}^m is multiplied by F_{n+1} and P_{n-1}^m is multiplied by F_{n-1}. This is a most fortunate situation, as we shall see.

We now expand h as follows:

$$h + \sum_n^\infty \sum_{j=1}^\infty A_{nj}P_n^m(\mu)F_n(\alpha_{nj} r)\cos m\phi,\tag{67}$$

where for each m, n runs through either odd or even integers not less than m. (For instance, if $m = 0$, n can either be 0, 2, 4, ... or 1, 3, 5, ... If $m = 1$, n runs through 1, 3, 5, ..., or through 2, 4, 6, ... That the increment of n is 2 in either series will be clear from the subsequent development.) Then we solve (42) and obtain

$$p = \sum_n \sum_j \frac{A_{nj}}{\alpha_{nj}^2}\left(\frac{\partial}{\partial x_3}P_n^m F_n + B_{nj}' r^{n+1}P_{n+1}^m\right.$$
$$\left. + C_{nj}' r^{n-1}P_{n-1}^m\right)\cos m\phi$$
$$= \sum_n \sum_j \frac{A_{nj}}{(2n+1)\alpha_{nj}}\big[-(n-m+1)P_{n+1}^m F_{n+1}$$
$$+ (n+m)P_{n-1}^m F_{n-1} + B_{nj}r^{n+1}P_{n+1}^m$$
$$+ C_{nj}r^{n-1}P_{n-1}^m\big]\cos m\phi,\tag{68}$$

where

$$(B_{nj}, C_{nj}) = \big[(2n+1)/\alpha_{nj}\big](B_{nj}', C_{nj}').\tag{69}$$

The argument for the P functions is μ and that for the F functions is $\alpha_{nj} r$. From (68) we obtain, after some cancellations,

$$\frac{\partial p'}{\partial r} + \mu h = \sum_n \sum_j \frac{A_{nj}}{(2n+1)\alpha_{nj}}$$
$$\times\left(\frac{(n-m+1)(n+2)}{r}P_{n+1}^m F_{n+1}\right.$$
$$+ \frac{(n+m)(n-1)}{r}P_{n-1}^m F_{n-1}$$
$$+ (n+1)B_{nj}r^n P_{n+1}^m$$
$$\left. + (n-1)C_{nj}r^{n-2}P_{n-1}^m\right)\cos m\phi,\tag{70}$$

where, as in (68), P_{n-1}^m is zero if $n - 1 < m$. We now solve (48) and obtain

$$u = \sum_n \sum_j \frac{A_{nj}}{(2n+1)\alpha_{nj}} \left[-\frac{1}{\alpha_{nj}^2} \left(\frac{(n-m+1)(n+2)}{r} \right. \right.$$

$$\left. \times P_{n+1}^m F_{n+1} + \frac{(n-1)(n+m)}{r} P_{n-1}^m F_{n-1} \right)$$

$$+ \frac{n+1}{4n+10} B_{nj} r^{n+2} P_{n+1}^m + \frac{n-1}{4n+2} C_{nj} r^n P_{n-1}^m$$

$$\left. + D_{nj} r^n P_{n+1}^m + E_{nj} r^{n-2} P_{n-1}^m \right] \cos m\phi. \tag{71}$$

The boundary conditions on u in (51) then determine the coefficients:

$$B_{nj} = \frac{(n-m+1)(n+2)(2n+5)}{(n+1)\alpha_{nj}^2}$$

$$\times \left[\alpha_{nj} F_n(\alpha_{nj}) - (2n+3) F_{n+1}(\alpha_{nj}) \right], \tag{72}$$

$$D_{nj} = \frac{(n-m+1)(n+2)}{2\alpha_{nj}^2}$$

$$\times \left[(2n+5) F_{n+1}(\alpha_{nj}) - \alpha_{nj} F_n(\alpha_{nj}) \right], \tag{73}$$

$$C_{nj} = -\frac{(2n+1)(n+m)}{\alpha_{nj}} F_n(\alpha_{nj}), \tag{74}$$

$$E_{nj} = \frac{(n-1)(n+m)}{2\alpha_{nj}^2} \left[2F_{n-1}(\alpha_{nj}) + \alpha_{nj} F_n(\alpha_{nj}) \right]. \tag{75}$$

For $n < m+1$ C_{nj} and E_{nj} will not be needed. From (71), it is clear that C_{1j} is not needed even for $m = 0$.

We now turn to the third equation in (40), or

$$\nabla^2 u_3 = \frac{\partial p'}{\partial x_3} + h. \tag{76}$$

First,

$$\frac{\partial p'}{\partial x_3} = \sum_n \sum_j \frac{A_{nj}}{(2n+1)\alpha_{nj}} \left(-\frac{n-m+1}{2n+3} \alpha_{nj} \left[-(n-m+2) P_{n+2}^m F_{n+2} + (n+m+1) P_n^m F_n \right] + \frac{n+m}{2n-1} \alpha_{nj} \right.$$

$$\times \left[-(n-m) P_n^m F_n + (n+m-1) P_{n-2}^m F_{n-2} \right] + (n+m+1) B_{nj} r^n P_n^m$$

$$\left. + (n+m-1) C_{nj} r^{n-2} P_{n-2}^m \right) \cos m\phi, \tag{77}$$

in which, as elsewhere, a P function is zero if its subscript is less than its superscript. The argument of the F functions is $\alpha_{nj} r$. Substituting (67) and (77) into (76), and solving it, we obtain

$$u_3 = -\sum_n \sum_j \frac{A_{nj}}{(2n+1)\alpha_{nj}^2} \left(\frac{(n-m+1)(n-m+2)}{2n+3} P_{n+2}^m F_{n+2} + \frac{2(2n+1)(n^2+n-1+m^2)}{(2n-1)(2n+3)} P_n^m F_n \right.$$

$$+ \frac{(n+m)(n+m-1)}{2n-1} P_{n-2}^m F_{n-2} - \frac{(n+m+1)}{4n+6} \alpha_{nj} B_{nj} r^{n+2} P_n^m - \frac{n+m-1}{4n-2} \alpha_{nj} C_{nj} r^n P_{n-2}^m$$

$$\left. + G_{nj} r^{n+2} P_{n+2}^m + H_{nj} r^n P_n^m + K_{nj} r^{n-2} P_{n-2}^m \right) \cos m\phi. \tag{78}$$

TABLE I. Values of eigenvalues of α_{nj}.

n, j	λ = 0.5	1	5	10.72	∞
0,1	1.165 561 19	1.570 796 33	2.570 431 56	2.855 825 15	π
0,2	4.604 216 78	4.712 388 98	5.354 031 84	5.749 063 38	2π
0,3	7.789 883 75	7.853 981 63	8.302 929 18	8.694 984 46	9.424 76
1,1	2.743 707 27	π	4.066 202 10	4.286 387 37	4.493 40
1,2	6.116 764 26	2π	7.056 819 40	7.378 345 88	7.725 24
1,3	9.316 615 63	9.424 777 96	10.059 893 23	10.431 622 41	10.904 11
2,1	4.067 315 91	4.493 409 46	5.392 525 84	5.585 732 25	5.763 45
2,2	7.517 465 12	7.725 251 84	8.542 952 84	8.818 685 90	9.095 00
2,3	10.761 984 24	10.904 121 66	11.625 651 18	11.955 908 18	12.322 93
3,1	5.311 410 66	5.763 459 20	6.648 002 74	6.826 005 71	6.987 93
3,2	8.854 793 54	9.095 011 33	9.931 192 69	10.178 195 06	10.417 11
3,3	12.152 991 68	12.322 940 97	13.090 033 82	13.387 971 99	13.698 01
4,1	6.513 445 84	6.987 932 00	7.862 622 03	8.030 700 50	8.182 55
4,2	10.150 100 30	10.417 118 55	11.261 903 15	11.489 360 84	11.704 90
4,3	13.504 450 97	13.698 023 15	14.491 662 20	14.765 382 91	15.039 66
5,1	7.688 605 78	8.182 561 45	9.049 992 85	9.211 005 21	9.355 81
5,2	11.414 998 45	11.704 907 15	12.553 804 24	12.767 091 90	12.966 52
5,3	14.825 518 09	15.039 664 71	15.849 782 40	16.105 060 48	16.354 70
6,1	8.844 763 42	9.355 812 11	10.217 604 84	10.373 288 84	10.512 83
6,2	12.656 620 94	12.966 530 17	13.817 276 09	14.019 791 29	14.207 39
6,3	16.122 315 18	16.354 709 64	17.175 538 74	17.416 383 74	17.647 97

TABLE II. The critical Rayleigh number R_{cr} for various modes.

Mode	N,J	λ = 0.5	1	5	10.72	∞
(i)	0,3	1161	1160	1158	1158	1156
	2,2	967	1111	907	1181	978
	2,3	938.738	959.579	994.294	1000.92	1008.25
	4,3	938.366	959.206	993.937	1000.57	1008.25
(ii)	3,1	7855	5642	3530	2618	2056
	5,1	7706	7281	5450	4984	4584
	3,2	3077	3063	5957	3277	2867
	3,3	3026.92	3112.36	3264.98	3299.17	3337.55
	5,3	3017.64	3102.63	3254.72	3288.85	3327.11
(iii)	1,1	407	490	660	703	752
	3,1	407	489	653	685	714
	5,1	407	491	659	702	749
	1,2	385	464	648	697	749
	3,2	384	463	645	697	748
	3,3	383.394	462.653	645.021	694.611	744.903
	5,3	383.344	462.276	645.146	693.014	747.015

The coefficients G, H, and K are determined by the condition

$$u_3 = 0 \quad \text{at} \quad r = 1$$

and are

$$G_{nj} = -\frac{(n-m+1)(n-m+2)}{2n+3} F_{n+2}(\alpha_{nj}),$$

$$H_{nj} = -\frac{2(2n+1)(n^2+n-1+m^2)}{(2n-1)(2n+3)} F_n(\alpha_{nj})$$
$$+ \frac{n+m+1}{4n+6} \alpha_{nj} B_{nj}, \tag{79}$$

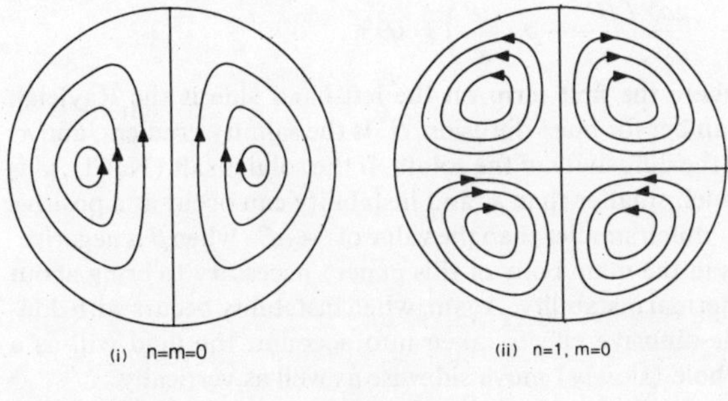

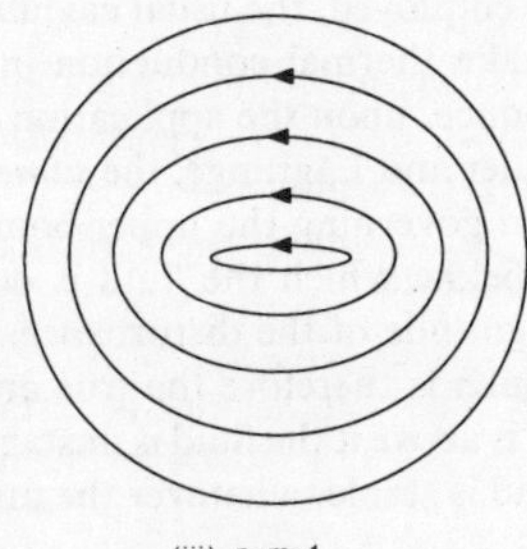

FIG. 3. Flow patterns for the three modes. (i) $m = 0$ even, starting from $n = 0$; (ii) $m = 0$, n odd, starting from $n = 1$; and (iii) $m = 1$, n odd, starting from $n = 1$.

$$K_{nj} = -\frac{(n+m)(n+m-1)}{2n-1} F_{n-2}(\alpha_{nj})$$
$$+ \frac{n+m-1}{4n-2} \alpha_{nj} C_{nj}.$$

Now (67) and (78) are substituted into (41) and one seeks to equate the coefficients of $P_n^m(\mu)F_n(\alpha_{nj}r)$ on the two sides of (41). To do this, one needs only to multiply (41) by $r^2 F_n(\alpha_{nl}r)$ and integrate from $r = 0$ to $r = 1$. The associated Legendre functions, appearing as they do in (67) and (78), need only to be sorted out, and no integration with respect to μ is necessary. In this way one obtains a doubly infinite number of linear homogeneous equations in the coefficients A_{nj}. Taking a finite number of them, and requiring that the A's are not all zero, one obtains a determinant the vanishing of which determines R.

The integration procedure requires the evaluation of certain definite integrals; these are shown in the Appendix.

VI. RESULTS

First, the eigenvalues α_{nj} are determined from (60) and (61). The first two eigenvalues for each n are given in Table I, where $\lambda = 10.72$ is for NaCl and water.

Calculations for the Rayleigh number R were carried out for three modes:

(i) $m = 0$, $n = 0, 2, 4, \ldots$;
(ii) $m = 0$, $n = 1, 3, 5, \ldots$;
(iii) $m = 1$, $n = 1, 3, 5, \ldots$.

The results for the critical R are given in Table II, in which N is the maximum of the values of n taken and J is the maximum of j in a_{nj}. The number of terms with coefficients A_{nj} in (67) taken for calculation is $J(N+2)/2$ if N is even and $J(N+1)/2$ if N is odd. Thus for each mode, the last two lines in Table II give the critical R calculated from a 6×6 and a 9×9 determinant, respectively. The convergence seems quite satisfactory in general, with a discrepancy of less than one part in 300 between the results given by the last successive approximations, even in the worst cases. The flow patterns for the three modes are sketched in Fig. 3.

From Table II it is clear that mode (iii) is the most unstable. This is in agreement with the findings of Hale[2] and Yih,[3] who treated the stability of a thermally stratified fluid in a vertical circular tube, that overturning from one half of the tube to the other half is the most unstable mode. It is also evident from Table II that the effect of the conductivity ratio on the critical R is much greater for mode (iii) than for modes (i) and (ii) on the percentage basis. In general, J has a greater influence on the accuracy of the results than N. The value 5957 for mode (ii) and $(N,J) = 3,2$ indicates a large truncation error for $\lambda = 5$. Otherwise the R_{cr} values seem systematic. It is fortunate that for mode (iii), which is the most unstable mode, the R_{cr} values are very consistent and rapidly convergent from $J = 2$ onward for all values of λ. Even for $J = 1$ the values of R_{cr} are not very different from their values for greater J, except for $N = 3$ and $\lambda = \infty$ [for which the value of 714 given for R_{cr} seems to have a rather high error because of truncation (in N or J)].

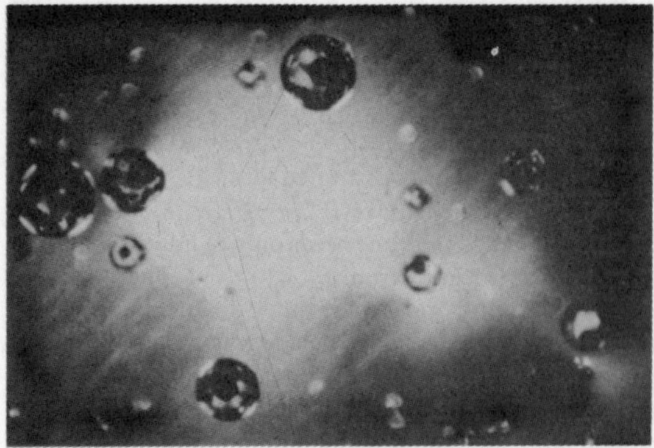

FIG. 4. Oil inclusions in fluorite (CaF_2). (Courtesy of Professor W. Kelly.)

VII. DISCUSSION

It is clear from the results that the critical R increases with λ. To reach this conclusion for modes (i) and (ii) it was necessary to take N and J sufficiently large. (Taking $N = 0$ and $J = 1$ gives the wrong trend.) For mode (iii) even taking $N = 1 = J$ gives the right trend and nearly the correct critical R. The increase of R with λ can also be demonstrated by a rather involved parameter differentiation, and agrees with Hurl *et al.*,[4] who treated the Bénard problem.

When the Rayleigh number is above 693 in the case of salt and water, including the third-order terms in the governing equations will, in the usual way (although the calculation is now necessarily more complicated), show that the magnitude of the perturbation quantities is of the order of $(R - 693)^{1/2}$. Since the asymmetric mode is most unstable, and since it contains the factor $\sin \phi$ or $\cos \phi$, the deposition or erosion of the solid by the fluid, when the solid is soluble, will have a sidewise component. The greater $R - 693$ is, the more the movement will be sidewise. When instability occurs, then, larger fluid inclusions will move in a cone of a larger vertex angle, if the surrounding solid is soluble. In that case, keeping in mind that the flux is saturated with the solute, and thus the mass concentration of the solute is propor-

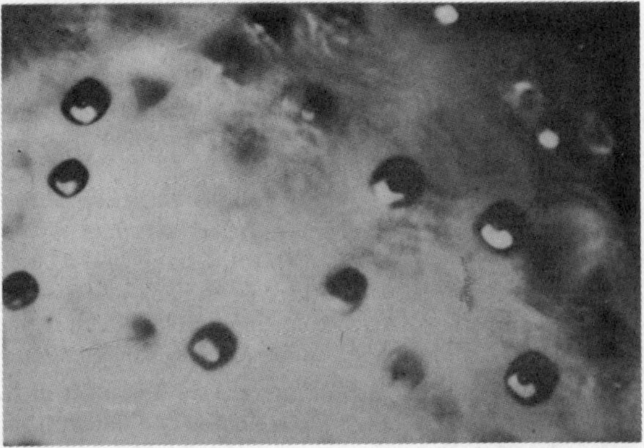

FIG. 5. Aqueous inclusions in synthetic KNO_3. (Courtesy of Professor W. Kelly.)

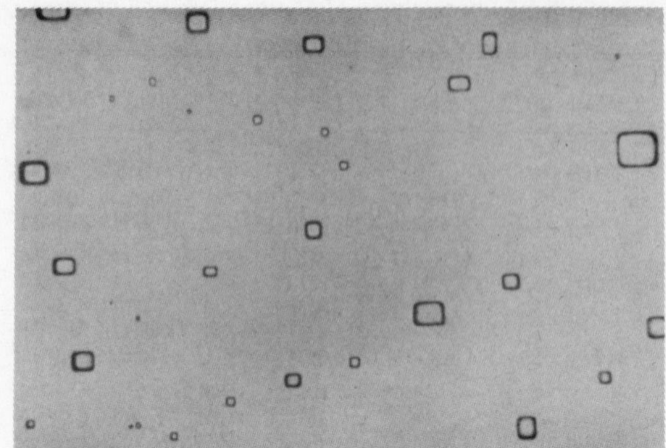

FIG. 6. Aqueous inclusions in NaCl, Windsor, Ontario, Canada. The inclusions imitate salt crystals and are called negative crystals. (Courtesy of Professor W. Kelly.)

tional to h, one obtains the erosion and deposition rates at the boundary from the solution (67). The dominant term in (67) contains the factor (for the most unstable case $m = 1$)

$$P_1^1 (\mu)\cos m\phi \quad \text{or} \quad \sin \theta \cos m\phi.$$

If only this dominant term were present, the spherical inclusion would move in a slanted direction without change of shape. However, the other (less important) terms would cause it slowly to vary its shape.

We have ignored the effect of double diffusion. When that effect is taken into account, the fluid can be unstable even when the temperature gradient β is positive. For neutral stability,

$$\frac{ga^4}{\rho_0 \nu}\left(\frac{\beta'}{\kappa'} - \rho_0 \frac{\alpha\beta}{\kappa}\right) = 693,$$

where the first term on the left-hand side is the Rayleigh number for mass diffusion, β' is the salinity gradient, and κ' is the diffusivity of the solute. If the solid is salt (NaCl), κ' is much smaller than κ, and instability can occur at a positive β' much smaller than the value of $-\alpha\beta$ (when β is negative as in the main body of this paper) necessary to bring about thermal instability. Again, when instability occurs with double-diffusive effects taken into account, the fluid will as a whole (slowly) move sidewise as well as vertically.

It may be noted that if the energy method for hydrodynamic stability is employed, the usual calculation, with due modification to take thermal conduction in the solid into account, will produce, upon the application of the calculus of variation of Euler and Lagrange, the *same mathematical* differential system governing the upper bound of the Rayleigh number R below which the fluid is definitely stable, whatever the magnitude of the disturbance. That bound is therefore 693, which is therefore the true critical Rayleigh number: When R is above it the fluid is unstable, and when R is below it the fluid is stable, whatever the magnitude of the disturbance.

Finally, we wish to show a few photographs of fluid inclusions in minerals. Figure 4 shows perfectly spherical inclusions. Unfortunately, they are oil inclusions, in which the mineral is not soluble. Figure 5 shows nearly spherical shapes, but the crystal planes of the mineral already have an influence on them, while Fig. 6 shows negative crystals, or aqueous inclusions imitating the shape of salt crystals. All these shapes occur in isothermal conditions. We have not been able to find shapes of fluid inclusions in minerals when a thermal gradient had been present for a long time.

In a previous paper, Yih[5] showed that general ellipsoidal liquid inclusions can move with a constant velocity in a soluble solid provided gravity acts in a direction parallel to any one axis of the ellipsoid. Thus infinitely many permanent shapes are possible if surface energy associated with crystals is ignored. The photographs shown here seem to indicate, for isothermal conditions at any rate, a preferred asymptotic (with time) shape. For isothermal conditions Cline and Anthony[6] showed a rounded-cubic shape of an aqueous inclusion in KCL after seven years in equilibrium. Thus there seems to be a preferred shape. Cline and Anthony[6] also calculated the shapes (each of which is presumably unique under the specified conditions) of liquid inclusions, which depend, among other things, on the volume of the liquid. But Cline and Anthony[6] ignored the temperature distribution in both the solid and the liquid, and this distribution is, as shown by Yih,[5] important for determining the speed of migration of liquid inclusions and relevant to the permanence of their shapes. Yih,[5] on the other hand, ignored the effect of surface energy in crystals and did not touch the question of the uniqueness and determination of the permanent shape of a liquid inclusion in a soluble solid with a temperature gradient. This question remains open.

ACKNOWLEDGMENTS

The content of this paper constitutes part of the lecture given at the Fluid-Dynamics Divisional Meeting of the American Physical Society at Tucson, AZ, November 1985, on the occasion of the awarding of the 1985 Fluid Dynamics Prize of that Society to the author. It is a pleasure to express here my thanks to my colleague William Kelly, Professor of Geology at The University of Michigan, for providing the photographs of fluid inclusions in minerals and for two interesting and instructive discussions, and to Songping Zhu for assistance in numerical computation.

This work has been supported by the Fluid Dynamics Program of the Office of Naval Research.

APPENDIX: $F_n(x)$ AND DEFINITE INTEGRALS

The first several functions $F_n(x)$ are

$$F_0(x) = (2/\pi)^{1/2}(\sin x/x),$$

$$F_1(x) = \left(\frac{2}{\pi}\right)^{1/2}\frac{1}{x}\left(\frac{\sin x}{x} - \cos x\right),$$

$$F_2(x) = -\left(\frac{2}{\pi}\right)^{1/2}\frac{1}{x}\left[\frac{3\cos x}{x} + \left(1 - \frac{3}{x^2}\right)\sin x\right],$$

$$F_3(x) = \left(\frac{2}{\pi}\right)^{1/2}\frac{1}{x}\left[\left(1 - \frac{15}{x^2}\right)\cos x - \left(\frac{6}{x} - \frac{15}{x^3}\right)\sin x\right],$$

$$F_n(x) = \frac{n-1}{x}F_{n-1}(x) - \frac{dF_{n-1}(x)}{dx}.$$

The following definite integrals have been needed in the calculations:

$$I_0(\alpha) = \int_0^1 r^4 F_0(\alpha r)dr = \frac{1}{\alpha^2}\left[2F_0(\alpha) - \left(\frac{6}{\alpha} - \alpha\right)F_1(\alpha)\right],$$

$$I_n(\alpha) = \int_0^1 r^5 F_n(\alpha r)dr$$

$$= (1/\alpha)[(2n+3)I_{n-1}(\alpha) - F_{n-1}(\alpha)];$$

$$L_0(\alpha) = \int_0^1 r^2 F_0(\alpha r)dr = \frac{1}{\alpha}F_1(\alpha),$$

$$L_n(\alpha) = \int_0^1 r^{n+2}F_n(\alpha r)dr$$

$$= (1/2)[(2n+1)L_{n-1}(\alpha) - F_{n-1}(\alpha)];$$

$$I_0(\alpha,\beta)$$

$$= \int_0^1 r^2 F_0(\alpha r)F_0(\beta r)dr$$

$$= [1/\alpha\beta(2\pi)^{1/2}][F_0(\alpha - \beta) - F_0(\alpha + \beta)],$$

$$I_n(\alpha,\beta)$$

$$= \int_0^1 r^2 F_n(\alpha r)F_n(\beta r)dr$$

$$= \alpha^{-1}[\beta I_{n-1}(\alpha,\beta) - F_{n-1}(\alpha)F_n(\beta)];$$

$$\int_0^1 r^2 F_n^2(\alpha r)dr = I_n(\alpha,\alpha);$$

$$\int_0^1 r^2 F_0^2(\alpha r)dr = \frac{1}{2\alpha^3\pi}(2\alpha - \sin 2\alpha);$$

$$\int_0^1 r^2 F_1^2(\alpha r)dr = \frac{1}{2\alpha\pi^3}\left(\sin^2\alpha + 2\alpha - \frac{4\sin^2\alpha}{\alpha}\right);$$

$$\int_0^1 r^2 F_2^2(\alpha r)dr$$

$$= (1/2\pi\alpha^3)[2\alpha - \sin 2\alpha - 6\alpha^{-3}(\alpha^2 - 2\alpha\sin 2\alpha$$

$$+ \alpha^2\cos 2\alpha + 1 - \cos 2\alpha)];$$

$$\int_0^1 r^2 F_3^2(\alpha r)dr$$

$$= (1/2\pi\alpha^3)(2\alpha + \sin 2\alpha - 6\alpha^{-5}(2\alpha^4 + 5\alpha^2 + 15)$$

$$+ 6\alpha^{-5}[(2\alpha^4 - 25\alpha^2 + 15)\cos 2\alpha$$

$$- (10\alpha^3 - 30\alpha)\sin 2\alpha]).$$

[1]S. Chandrasekhar, *Hydrodynamic and Hydromagnetic Stability* (Oxford U. P., Oxford, 1961), pp. 232–234.
[2]A. L. Hale, Month. Not. R. Astron. Soc. Geophys. Suppl. **4**, 122 (1937).
[3]C.-S. Yih, Q. Appl. Math. XVII, 25 (1959).
[4]D. T. J. Hurle, E. Jakeman, and E. R. Pike, Proc. R. Soc. London Ser. A **296**, 469 (1967).
[5]C.-S. Yih, Phys. Fluids **29**, 2785 (1986).
[6]H. E. Cline and T. R. Anthony, J. Appl. Phys. **48**, 5096 (1977).

J. Fluid Mech. (1990), *vol.* 212, *pp.* 41–53

Wave formation on a liquid layer for de-icing airplane wings

By CHIA-SHUN YIH

University of Florida, Gainesville, Florida 32611, USA

(Received 1 February 1989)

Wave formation on a thin liquid layer used for de-icing air-plane wings is investigated by studying the stability of air flow over a liquid-coated flat plate at zero angle of incidence. The ratio of the viscosity of the liquid to that of air is very high (over half a million), and the Reynolds number based on liquid depth and air viscosity is of the order of a few thousand in actual practice. Under these circumstances the analysis gives two formulas, in closed form, for the growth rate and phase velocity of the waves in terms of the wavenumber and other relevant parameters, including the Froude number F representing the gravity effect and a parameter S representing the surface-tension effect. In the calculation, the wavenumber is not restricted in any way.

The wavenumber of the waves that one expects to observe is that for which the growth rate is the maximum. The instability is one in which the viscosity difference between the two fluids (air and liquid) plays the dominant role, and is of the kind found by Yih (1967).

1. Introduction

In wintertime in northern countries, ice formation or snow accumulation on airplane wings while the airplanes are on the ground poses a threat to safety of flight. The practice of de-icing consists in spraying on the wings a layer of non-Newtonian liquid which has a very high viscosity at low shear rates but lower viscosity at higher shear rates, so that it can stay on the wings for a long time while the airplane is at rest, but is blown off after the airplane is in flight. But during a period after take-off and before the liquid is finally blown off, waves are formed on the liquid, which may affect the aerodynamic behaviour of the wings. The instability of the flow of the fluids (air and liquid) responsible for this formation is therefore a problem of practical interest, and is the subject of this study. For simplicity we shall consider the wing as a flat plate at zero angle of incidence.

The analysis in this paper will show that the instability is one in which the difference in viscosity of the two fluids plays the dominant role, because it induces a jump in the velocity gradient. Thus it is of the kind found by Yih (1967) and further investigated by Li (1969) and Hickox (1970), among other later workers, for long waves, and by Hooper & Boyd (1983), for waves not necessarily long. This study differs from the long-wave treatments in that no restriction is placed on the wavenumber, and that the Reynolds number is assumed large compared with unity. It differs from the work of Hooper & Boyd in that the problem chosen not only does not require infinite velocity at boundaries infinitely far away, but also is of some practical interest, and in that the viscosity ratio is very high, allowing results for the growth rate and the phase velocity of the disturbance to be obtained in closed

42   *C.-S. Yih*

formulas in terms of the wavenumber and the other relevant parameters, including those representing gravity and surface-tension effects.

Since the liquid is non-Newtonian, it was thought at first that the nonlinear constitution equations of the liquid should be constructed and used. The construction was done by using the table of viscosity variation with shear rate provided by the manufacturer of the de-icing liquid (Hoechst 1704), and by assuming the simplest tensorially consistent forms of the constitutive equations – actually by allowing the viscosity to contain invariants of the rate-of-deformation tensor. When the result was used in the equations of motion we found on elimination of the pressure terms a fourth-order differential equation like the Orr–Sommerfeld equation, but with additional terms. However, these terms turned out to be very small, as a result of the smallness of the rates of deformation in the primary flow of the liquid. We were therefore spared the pain of dealing with the non-Newtonian nature of the liquid, and could simply treat as constant the viscosity at the prevailing shear rate of the primary flow. This simplifies matters considerably.

2. The primary flow

We consider Blasius flow over a horizontal flat plate at zero angle of incidence, shown in figure 1. The free-stream velocity is denoted by $\hat{U}_0$, X is measured along the plate form its leading edge, and Y measured vertically upward from the undisturbed interface. We shall ignore the variation of the liquid depth d with X in the determination of the primary flow.

The viscosity of the air flow will be denoted by μ, and that of the liquid by μ_2. The ratio

$$m = \mu_2/\mu \tag{1}$$

is very large, and consequently (as will be shown later) the interfacial velocity $\hat{U}_s$ is very low. Then the flow of the air is just Blasius flow. The velocity of air in the direction of increasing X, measured in units of $\hat{U}_0$, is

$$U_1 = f'(\eta), \tag{2}$$

where f satisfies

$$2f''' + ff'' = 0,$$

and

$$\eta = (\hat{U}_0/\nu X)^{\frac{1}{2}} Y, \tag{3}$$

with $\nu = \mu/\rho$ denoting the kinematic viscosity of air and ρ its density.

Since, as is well known,

$$f''(0) = 0.332,$$

the shear stress at the interface is

$$\tau_0 = 0.332 \mu \hat{U}_0 (\hat{U}_0/\nu X)^{\frac{1}{2}}. \tag{4}$$

Since the depth d of the liquid is assumed constant, the velocity distribution in the liquid is linear, and if $\hat{U}_s$ denotes the velocity of the interface, continuity of shear stress demands

$$\mu_2 \hat{U}_s/d = \tau_0, \tag{5}$$

which determines $\hat{U}_s$. The dimensionless velocity gradient in the liquid is

$$a_2 = (\hat{U}_s/\hat{U}_0) \times 1 = \hat{U}_s/\hat{U}_0 = U_s, \tag{6}$$

which can be shown to be very small for practical cases of interest. In (6), U_s is the velocity at the interface in units of $\hat{U}_0$.

For the kind of instability we have in mind, the variation of U_1 near the interface

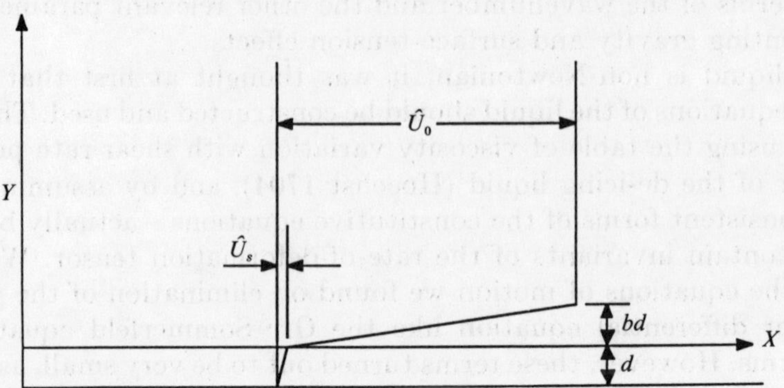

FIGURE 1. Definition sketch.

is the most important, and the curvature of U_1 given by (2) is zero at $Y = 0$, so that we can profitably replace (2) by

$$U_1 = Y/bd \quad \text{for} \quad 0 \leqslant Y \leqslant bd, \\ U_1 = 1 \quad \text{for} \quad Y \geqslant bd. \tag{7}$$

The boundary-layer thickness is thereby replaced by bd, where b is a dimensionless number defined by

$$\frac{\partial U_1}{\partial Y}\bigg|_{Y=0}(bd) = 1, \tag{8}$$

in which (recall that U_1 is in units of U_0)

$$\frac{\partial U_1}{\partial Y} = 0.332\, R_X^{\frac{1}{2}}/X \tag{9}$$

by virtue of (4), with $\qquad R_X = \hat{U}_0 X/\nu.$

As to the liquid, its velocity in units of U_0 is

$$U_2 = a_2\, Y/d. \tag{10}$$

Introducing the dimensionless coordinates

$$x = X/d, \quad y = Y/d, \tag{11}$$

we can write (7) and (10) as

$$U_1 = a_1 y \quad \text{for} \quad 0 \leqslant y \leqslant b, \quad \text{with} \quad a_1 = b^{-1}, \\ U_1 = 1 \quad \text{for} \quad y \geqslant b, \tag{12}$$

and $\qquad\qquad U_2 = a_2 y. \tag{13}$

3. Formulation of the stability problem

The flow is nearly parallel. For any value of x, we shall assume the flow to be a parallel one, with the velocity distribution given by (12) and (13), in which a_1 and a_2 are henceforth treated as constant, and not varying with x. This is the standard procedure for treating nearly parallel flows. In it, the origin of x need not be at the leading edge of the flat plate, but may be taken at the section where the stability of the flow is being studied.

44   *C.-S. Yih*

The velocity components u and v (both in units of U_0) in the directions of increasing x and y satisfy the continuity equation

$$u_x + v_y = 0,$$

in which subscripts indicate partial differentiation. If the pressure p is measured in units of ρU_0^2 and the time t in units of d/U_0, the Navier–Stokes equations are, for air,

$$\frac{Du}{Dt} = -p_x + R^{-1}\nabla^2 u, \tag{14}$$

$$\frac{Dv}{Dt} = -p_y - F_0^{-2} + R^{-1}\nabla^2 v, \tag{15}$$

in which

$$R = \hat{U}_0 d/\nu, \quad F_0 = \hat{U}_0/(gd)^{\frac{1}{2}} \tag{16}$$

are the Reynolds number and Froude number, respectively, and

$$\frac{D}{Dt} = \frac{\partial}{\partial t} + u\frac{\partial}{\partial x} + v\frac{\partial}{\partial y}, \quad \nabla^2 = \frac{\partial^2}{\partial y^2} + \frac{\partial^2}{\partial y^2}.$$

We shall, as usual, resolve the flow into its primary and perturbation parts. For air,

$$u = U_1 + u', \quad v = v', \quad p = P + p',$$

in which P is the dimensionless pressure for the primary flow, assumed independent of x. Then, since

$$u'_x + v'_y = 0,$$

we can introduce the stream function ψ, and write

$$u' = \psi_y, \quad v' = -\psi_x. \tag{17}$$

Assume $(\psi, p') = \{\phi(y), f(y)\}\exp i\alpha(x - ct),$ (18)

where $c = c_r + ic_i$ (19)

is the eigenvalue. For given R, F_0, and other relevant parameters, we seek to determine the α which makes the growth rate

$$\sigma_i = \alpha c_i \tag{20}$$

the maximum. With (17) and (18), (14) and (15) become, upon linearization,

$$i\alpha\{(U_1 - c)\phi' - U_1'\phi\} = -i\alpha f + R^{-1}(\phi'' - \alpha^2\phi'), \tag{21}$$

$$\alpha^2(c - U_1)\phi = f' + (i\alpha/R)(\phi'' - \alpha^2\phi), \tag{22}$$

in which primes indicate differentiation with respect to y. Note that for the primary flow

$$-P_y - F_0^{-2} = 0,$$

which allows us to obtain (22) from (15). Since U_1' is the constant a_1, (21) and (22) give the Orr–Sommerfeld equation

$$\phi^{iv} - 2\alpha^2\phi'' + \alpha^4\phi = i\alpha R(U_1 - c)(\phi'' - \alpha^2\phi). \tag{23}$$

For the liquid, we choose to retain the meanings of R and f, and to write χ for ϕ. Then (21) and (22) become

$$i\alpha r\{(U_2 - c)\chi' - U_2'\chi\} = -i\alpha f + (m/R)(\chi''' - \alpha^2\chi'), \tag{24}$$

$$\alpha^2 r(c - U_2)\chi = f' + (i\alpha m/R)(\chi'' - \alpha^2\chi), \tag{25}$$

Wave formation on a liquid layer for de-icing airplane wings **45**

and the equation corresponding to (23) is

$$\chi^{\mathrm{iv}} - 2\alpha^2\chi + \alpha^4\chi = i\alpha R m^{-1} r (U_2 - c)(\chi'' - \alpha^2\chi), \tag{26}$$

in which

$$r = \rho_2/\rho \tag{27}$$

is the density ratio, with ρ_2 denoting the density of the liquid.

We now turn to the boundary conditions. For clarity let ϕ be denoted by ϕ_0 in the free stream ($b \leqslant y$), and by ϕ_1 for the boundary layer ($0 \leqslant y \leqslant b$). For the upper fluid, then,

$$\phi_0 \to 0 \quad \text{as} \quad y \to \infty. \tag{28}$$

At $y = b$, U_1 given by (12) is not analytic, and four conditions should be imposed there. For this purpose let η_1 be the displacement of the (artificial) lower boundary of the free stream, when disturbed, from $y = b$. Then the kinematic condition at $y = b$ is

$$(\eta_1)_t + (\eta_1)_x = -i\alpha\phi(b)\exp i\alpha(x - ct),$$

since $U_1(b) = 1$. Thus

$$\eta_1 = \frac{\phi(b)}{c - 1}\exp i\alpha(x - ct). \tag{29}$$

The continuity of velocity then demands

$$\phi_0(b) = \phi_1(b), \tag{30}$$

$$\phi_0'(b) - \phi_1'(b) = \frac{\phi_0(b)}{b(c - 1)}, \tag{31}$$

since $U_1' = b^{-1}$ for the boundary layer. Continuity of shear stress at $y = b$ demands

$$\phi_0''(b) + \alpha^2\phi_0(b) = \phi_1''(b) + \alpha^2\phi_1(b), \tag{32}$$

and continuity of normal stress (see Yih 1967, equations (28)–(30), for derivation) demands

$$\{-i\alpha R(c - 1)\phi_0' - \phi_0''' + \alpha^2\phi_0'\} + 2\alpha^2\phi_0'$$
$$= \{-i\alpha R[(c - 1)\phi_1' + a_1\phi_1] - \phi_1''' + \alpha^2\phi_1'\} + 2\alpha^2\phi_1' \tag{33}$$

at $y = b$, since there is no density difference across $y = b$, and no surface tension there. For (32), recall that in fact the mean shear stress has no jump at $y = b$.

For the liquid layer the no-slip conditions at the solid boundary are

$$\chi(-1) = 0, \quad \chi'(-1) = 0. \tag{34}$$

At the interface of air and liquid, where $y = 0$, the conditions are as derived in Yih (1967, p. 341), and are, upon writing ϕ for ϕ_1 for brevity,

$$\phi(0) = \chi(0), \tag{35}$$

$$\phi'(0) - \chi'(0) = \frac{\phi(0)}{c'}(a_2 - a_1), \tag{36}$$

$$\phi''(0) + \alpha^2\phi(0) = m\{\chi''(0) + \alpha^2\chi(0)\}, \tag{37}$$

$$-i\alpha R(c'\phi' + a_1\phi) - (\phi''' - \alpha^2\phi') + 2\alpha^2\phi' + ir\alpha R(c'\chi' + a_2\chi)$$
$$+ m(\chi''' - \alpha^2\chi') - 2\alpha^2 m\chi' = i\alpha R(F^{-2} + \alpha^2 S)\phi/c', \tag{38}$$

in which

$$F^{-2} = (r - 1)F_0^{-2}, \quad S = T/\rho\hat{U}_0^2 d, \quad c' = c - a_2. \tag{39}$$

Since, as will be shown, a_2 is very small, we may put a_2 to zero, and write c for c' in (35)–(38). In (38), all variables are for $y = 0$. The T in (39) is surface tension.

46   *C.-S. Yih*

The differential system governing stability of the flow then consists of differential equations (23) and (26), and boundary conditions (28), and (30)–(38). It seems at first sight daunting, since R is large and α is unrestricted. It is surprising and fortunate that an explicit analytical solution is possible, principally because m is extremely large. This will be shown in what follows.

4. A simplification

We shall first simplify boundary conditions (31)–(33), while keeping (30) intact, and show that the four boundary conditions at $y = b$ can be reduced to two, in which only the inviscid solutions of (23) appear.

The solution of (23) satisfying (28) is, for the free stream,

$$\phi_0 = A_{01} \exp(-\alpha y) + A_{02} \exp\{-\beta(y-b)\}, \tag{40}$$

where

$$\beta^2 = i\alpha R(1-c) + \alpha^2, \tag{41}$$

since $U_1 = 1$ for the free stream. We have taken that root of β which has a positive real part. The c in (41) is very small and therefore negligible, as will be verified *a posteriori*. The solution for (23) for ϕ_1 is

$$\phi_1 = A_{11} \exp(-\alpha y) + A_{12} \exp(\alpha y) + A_{13} \exp\{\beta(y-b)\}. \tag{42}$$

This is only approximate, for (23) has one variable coefficient when applied to the boundary layer. But (42) is sufficiently accurate, for $\exp\{\beta(y-b)\}$ decreases toward zero as y decreases from b only a small distance, since β is large (because R is large). Thus the variability of U_1 will not have an appreciable effect on the development here. Using (40) and (42) in (30)–(32), we readily find that if A_{01}, A_{11}, and A_{12} are of $O(1)$ in magnitude, A_{02} and A_{13} are both of order $O(R^{-\frac{1}{2}})$ and their difference of order $O(R^{-1})$. Furthermore, substituting (40) and (42) into (33), we find that the brace on the right-hand side does not contain A_{02}, and in the brace on the other side the term containing A_{13} is of $O(R^{-\frac{1}{2}})$. The ϕ' and ϕ'_1 are all of $O(1)$. Thus (33) becomes, upon division by $i\alpha R$ and ignoring terms of $O(R^{-\frac{1}{2}})$, at $y = b$,

$$(c-1)\phi'_0 = (c-1)\phi'_1 + a_1\phi_1, \tag{43}$$

in which all viscous solutions (i.e. those with coefficient A_{02} or A_{13}) are dropped. Correspondingly, in

$$\phi_0(b) = \phi_1(b), \tag{44}$$

which is (30), one now need only use the inviscid solutions, as in (43). Note that (43) incidentally agrees with (31). That is because there is no jump either in density or in velocity of the primary flow.

5. Construction of the eigenfunction ϕ

The simplification of the boundary conditions at $y = b$ to (43) and (44), which consist now entirely of inviscid solutions, allows us to construct ϕ by forming its inviscid part first, and then adding to that the viscous part to take care of the interfacial conditions at $y = 0$.

To obtain the inviscid part, let

$$\phi_0 = A_0 e^{-\alpha y}, \tag{45}$$

$$\phi_1 = A_1 e^{\alpha y} + A_2 e^{-\alpha y}. \tag{46}$$

These are just simplified versions of (40) and (42), with the viscous parts therein omitted. Application of (43) and (44) give two equations relating the A, the solution of which gives

$$A_1 = \frac{1}{2\alpha b(1-c)}\, e^{-2\alpha b} A_0, \quad A_2 = \left(1 - \frac{1}{2\alpha b(1-c)}\right) A_0,$$
(47)

so that

$$\phi_1(0) = A_1 + A_2 = \frac{1}{1-c}(1-\lambda-c)A_0,$$
(48)

$$\phi_1'(0) = \alpha(A_1 - A_2) = \left\{\frac{1}{b(1-c)} - \alpha\left(\frac{1}{1-c} + \lambda\right)\right\} A_0,$$
(49)

in which

$$\lambda = \frac{1}{2\alpha b}(1 - e^{-2\alpha b}).$$

Note that

$$0 \leqslant \lambda \leqslant 1.$$

Assuming c to the very small compared with 1, we can write (48) and (49) as

$$\phi_1(0) = (1-\lambda)A_0,$$
(50)

$$\phi_1'(0) = \{b^{-1} - \alpha(1+\lambda)\} A_0.$$
(51)

These will be used in place of (48) and (49).

Equation (45) already satisfies condition (28), and (45) and (46) satisfy (43) and (44) if A_1 and A_2 are given by (47). We shall now add to ϕ_1 the viscous solution $A_3 \phi_3$ to from the eigenfunction ϕ for the boundary layer $(0 \leqslant y \leqslant b)$. Thus,

$$\phi = \phi_1 + A_3 \phi_3,$$
(52)

in which (see Lin 1955, p. 40)

$$\phi_3 = \int_\infty^\eta d\eta \int_\infty^\eta H_{\frac{1}{3}}^{(1)}\{\tfrac{2}{3}(i\eta)^{\frac{3}{2}}\}\eta^{\frac{1}{2}}\, d\eta,$$
(53)

where

$$\eta = \frac{y - y_c}{\epsilon}, \quad \epsilon = (\alpha R U_1')^{-\frac{1}{3}} = \left(\frac{b}{\alpha R}\right)^{\frac{1}{3}},$$
(54)

where y_c is the value of y at which $U_1 = c$. Since c is expected to be very small, we can henceforth take $y_c = 0$. The subscript 3 in ϕ_3 is used to honour tradition. There is no ϕ_2. In (52), A_3 is not yet related to A_0. That relation awaits the application of the interfacial conditions.

We note in passing that neither ϕ_1 nor ϕ_3 is singular, nor indeed is ϕ_0. Since $U_1'' = 0$, the well-known Rayleigh equation loses its singular term, and the solutions ϕ_0 and ϕ_1, consisting of exponential functions, are exact. This is the great advantage of adopting (12) to replace (2). That ϕ_3 is not singular is of course well known. In computing ϕ_3, Holstein (1950) took advantage of the fact that R is large, and thereby ignored terms of smaller orders of magnitude to obtain the asymptotic form of the Orr–Sommerfeld equation, which he proceeded to solve to obtain ϕ_3. But that asymptotic form is not singular. Hence ϕ_3 is not singular.

6. Construction of the eigenfunction χ

We shall show that in cases of practical interest a_2 in (13) and therefore U_2 in (26) are very small compared with 1 since m is large. Furthermore it will be assumed (since we do not know c yet) that $\alpha R r m^{-1} c$ in (26) is very small since m is very large.

48   *C.-S. Yih*

This assumption will be verified *a posteriori*. Under this assumption, then, the right-hand side can be neglected and the solution of (26) is

$$\chi = A\cosh\alpha y + B\sinh\alpha y + Cy\cosh\alpha y + Dy\sinh\alpha y. \tag{55}$$

Since m is very large, we shall simplify (37) to

$$\chi''(0) + \alpha^2\chi(0) = 0, \tag{56}$$

which gives

$$-\alpha A = D. \tag{57}$$

Applying (34), and eliminating B, we have

$$\alpha A = (\alpha - \sinh\alpha\cosh\alpha)\,C + (\sinh^2\alpha)\,D, \tag{58}$$

which combines with (57) to give

$$(\alpha\cosh^2\alpha)\,A = (\alpha - \sinh\alpha\cosh\alpha)\,C. \tag{59}$$

Finally $\chi(-1) = 0$ gives

$$(\cosh^2\alpha + \alpha^2)\,A = (\sinh\alpha\cosh\alpha - \alpha)\,B. \tag{60}$$

Thus all the coefficients B, C, and D have been expressed in terms of A.

The following equalities will be useful later:

$$\chi(0) = A, \tag{61}$$

$$\chi'(0) = \alpha B + C = \frac{\alpha^3}{\sinh\alpha\cosh\alpha - \alpha}A, \tag{62}$$

$$\chi'''(0) - 3\alpha^2\chi'(0) = -\frac{2\alpha^3(\cosh^2\alpha + \alpha^2)}{\sinh\alpha\cosh\alpha - \alpha}A. \tag{63}$$

We are now in a position to apply the interfacial conditions.

7. Calculation of the growth rate

Upon neglecting a_2 in the parentheses on the right-hand side of (36), elimination of $\phi(0)$ between (35) and (36) gives

$$-bc'\phi'(0)f = \chi(0) - bc'\chi'(0). \tag{64}$$

Let

$$\phi_3(0) = \beta, \tag{65}$$

$$(\mathrm{d}\phi_3/\mathrm{d}\eta)_{\eta=0} = \gamma, \tag{66}$$

where the β is not the same as that in (41), which is no longer needed. Holstein (1950, p. 36) gave

$$\beta = -0.8660 + 0.2320\mathrm{i}, \quad \gamma = 1.1154 + 0.2989\mathrm{i}.$$

Equation (64) then takes the form

$$-bc'[\{b^{-1} - \alpha(1+\lambda)\}A_0 + \epsilon^{-1}\gamma A_3] = A - \frac{bc'\alpha^3}{\sinh\alpha\cosh\alpha - \alpha}A. \tag{67}$$

On the assumption that c' is very small for large m (to be verified *a posteriori*), a glance at (60) reassures us that the last term in (67) is small compared with A, so that (67) can be written as

$$-c'[\{1 - \alpha b(1+\lambda)\}A_0 + b\epsilon^{-1}\gamma A_3] = A. \tag{68}$$

Equations (50), (52), and (61) enable us to write (35) as

$$(1-\lambda)A_0 + \beta A_3 = A. \tag{69}$$

Elimination of A_3 between (68) and (69) gives

$$c'\{-1+\alpha b(1+\lambda)+b\epsilon^{-1}\gamma\beta^{-1}(1-\lambda)\}A_0 = (1+b\epsilon^{-1}\beta^{-1}c')A.$$

Since $\epsilon^{-1}c'$ is still very small, and

$$\gamma\beta^{-1} = -(1.1155+0.6440\mathrm{i}),$$

this can be written as $\qquad -bc'(P_\mathrm{r}+\mathrm{i}P_\mathrm{i})A_0 = A, \qquad\qquad (70)$

where (P is now not the pressure in the primary flow)

$$\begin{aligned}
P = P_\mathrm{r}+\mathrm{i}P_\mathrm{i} \\
= b^{-1}-\alpha(1+\lambda)+-\gamma\beta^{-1}\epsilon^{-1}(1-\lambda). \qquad (71)
\end{aligned}$$

Equation (70) shows that the A in (69) can be neglected, since c' is small. Thus

$$(1-\lambda)A_0+\beta A_3 = 0,$$

or $\qquad\qquad A_3 = -\beta^{-1}(1-\lambda)A_0$

$$= \frac{1}{bc'(P_\mathrm{r}+\mathrm{i}P_\mathrm{i})}\beta^{-1}(1-\lambda)A. \qquad\qquad (72)$$

We now turn to (38) to evaluate c' and $\sigma_\mathrm{i} = \alpha c_\mathrm{i}$.

Because a_2 is very small, (36) enables us to write (38) as

$$\mathrm{i}(r-1)\alpha Rc'\chi' + m(\chi'''-3\alpha^2\chi') - (\phi'''-3\alpha^2\phi') - \mathrm{i}\alpha R(F^{-2}+\alpha^2 S)\chi/c' = 0, \qquad (73)$$

all functions being evaluated at $y = 0$. All the terms involving χ have been given by (61), (62), and (63). It remains to evaluate the term containing ϕ, which is

$$\begin{aligned}
\phi'''-3\alpha^2\phi' &= -2\alpha^3\phi_1'+A_3\{\epsilon^{-3}(\mathrm{d}^3\phi_3/\mathrm{d}\eta^3)-3\alpha^3\epsilon^{-1}\,\mathrm{d}\phi_3/\mathrm{d}\eta\} \\
&= -2\alpha^2\{b^{-1}-\alpha(1+\lambda)\}A_0+\epsilon^{-3}(-\mathrm{i}\beta-3\alpha^2\epsilon^2\gamma)A_3,
\end{aligned}$$

where $\mathrm{d}^3\phi_3/\mathrm{d}\eta^3$ at $\eta = 0$ is found by integration by parts of the differential equation for ϕ_3, with $\phi_3(0)$ given by (65).

Using (70) and (72), we have

$$\phi'''-3\alpha^2\phi' = -\frac{\alpha RA}{c'b^2}\frac{Q_\mathrm{r}+\mathrm{i}Q_\mathrm{i}}{P_\mathrm{r}+\mathrm{i}P_\mathrm{i}}, \qquad\qquad (74)$$

where $\qquad Q = Q_\mathrm{r}+\mathrm{i}Q_\mathrm{i} = (1-\lambda)(\mathrm{i}+3\gamma\beta^{-1}\alpha^2\epsilon^2)-\dfrac{2\alpha}{R}\{1-\alpha b(1+\lambda)\}. \qquad (75)$

In the above calculation, recall that $\epsilon^3 = b/\alpha R$.

Examination of (61), (62), (63), and (74) shows that (73) is a quadratic equation in c'. But even the solution of a quadratic equation is not necessary. Because m is very large, the two roots of the quadratic equation are obtained for the first root by ignoring the last term, and for the second root by ignoring the first term. In the first case a large negative c_i is obtained, corresponding to strong damping. Any instability would have to come from the second case, which gives

$$\frac{2\alpha^2(\cosh^2 a+\alpha^2)}{\sinh\alpha\cosh\alpha-\alpha}\frac{b^2mc'}{R} = \left\{\frac{Q_\mathrm{r}+\mathrm{i}Q_\mathrm{i}}{P_\mathrm{r}+\mathrm{i}P_\mathrm{i}}-\mathrm{i}b^2(F^{-2}+\alpha^2 S)\right\}, \qquad (76)$$

50   *C.-S. Yih*

or, with $c_{\rm r}' = c_{\rm r} - a_2$, $\sigma_{\rm i} = \alpha c_{\rm i}$,

$$\frac{b^2 m}{R}\, c_{\rm r}' = \frac{P_{\rm r} Q_{\rm r} + P_{\rm i} Q_{\rm i}}{|P|^2}\, \frac{\sinh\alpha\cosh\alpha - \alpha}{2\alpha^2(\cosh^2\alpha + \alpha^2)}, \tag{77}$$

$$\frac{b^2 m}{R}\, \sigma_{\rm i} = \left[\frac{P_{\rm r} Q_{\rm i} - P_{\rm i} Q_{\rm r}}{|P|^2} - b^2(F^{-2} + \alpha^2 S)\right] \frac{\sinh\alpha\cosh\alpha - \alpha}{2\alpha(\cosh^2\alpha + \alpha^2)}. \tag{78}$$

Equation (77) gives the phase velocity and (78) gives the growth rate. They are the main results of this study.

From (76), it is clear that the instability under study arises from the term Q/P. Examination of (71) shows that the dominant term in P is

$$-\gamma\beta^{-1}\epsilon^{-1}(1-\lambda),$$

since ϵ is small, and examination of (75) shows that the dominant term in Q is

$$i(1-\lambda).$$

Thus the dominant term in Q/P is $\quad i\beta\gamma^{-1}\epsilon$.

Since $\qquad\qquad\qquad\qquad \beta = \phi_3(0), \quad \gamma = \phi_3'(0),$

and ϕ_3 is the solution of $\qquad \phi_3^{\rm iv} = i\alpha R U_1'(0)\,(y - y_c)\,\phi_3'',$

in which only the velocity gradient $U'(0)$ appears (and no other representatives of U_1), it is clear that the instability under study arises only from the velocity gradients of the fluids at their interface, and that the exact form of the velocity profile of the air and, in particular, its curvature (to which fluid dynamicists have historically attached an enormous importance), have little consequence here. The difference in the velocity gradients of the two fluids come from the difference in their viscosity, and therefore the instability under examination here is of the kind found by Yih (1967).

Note also that, since the m under consideration is roughly 250 times R, (76) presents no difficulty in determining c' when both m and R are large, because we do not regard them as tending toward infinity, but, rather, simply use their actual values.

In the next section we shall take a case for which some experimental data are available, and calculate the α for which $\sigma_{\rm i}$ is the maximum, for given values of the relevant parameters b, R, F, and S. This will be compared with the observed α. To make sure that this calculation will not be futile, however, it is timely to look at (78) more closely here. Examination of P defined by (71) and Q defined by (75) reveals that, since $\lambda \to 1$ as $\alpha \to 0$,

$$P \to b^{-1} \quad \text{and} \quad Q \to 0 \quad \text{as} \quad \alpha \to 0.$$

Thus the bracket in (78) becomes negative for small α, and the flow is stable. Furthermore, for fixed R and b

$$P \sim \alpha \quad \text{and} \quad Q \sim 2bR^{-1}\alpha^2 \quad \text{for large } \alpha,$$

so that again the bracket becomes negative. For small enough F^{-2} and S and intermediate α, instability is possible, and whenever there is instability a maximum $\sigma_{\rm i}$ is guaranteed. Note from the definitions of F^{-2} and S that they are small if $\hat{U}_0$ is large. Thus instability is likely at high velocities.

8. Application of the theory to a special case

Some experimental data on wave formation in a de-icing fluid on an experimental wing are available in a report by Hendrickson & Hill (1987, henceforth referred to as HH). The experiments were not elaborate, but the data give indications of the wavelengths of the waves, and the order of magnitude of their phase velocity. It seems desirable that (78) be applied to one of the experiments.

In these experiments, the de-icing fluid was the Hoechst 1704 liquid. In the experiment chosen for comparison, it was not diluted, and its viscosity (μ_2) near 0 °C or below and at the prevailing (very small) shear rate to which it was subjected, was near 10 Pa s. We shall use this figure for its viscosity. Since μ for air at -10 °C is 1.67×10^{-5} Pa s, the viscosity ratio m is 598 802, which is very large indeed. Its surface tension at -10 °C is 31.3 mN/m, which will be used for T. The liquid–air density ratio r is 972. The free-stream speed was 53 knots, or 27.28 m/s. The chord length was 0.279 m.

We shall take for investigation the flow at the $\frac{3}{4}$-chord section, where $X = 0.2092$ m, because the uncertainty of depth seems less there and the waves seem more developed. The initial average depth of the liquid was 0.91 mm, but the data show considerable variation even in the initial depth. After 5.6 s, the depth differed from its initial value everywhere, and near the $\frac{3}{4}$-chord point figure 19 of HH gives (roughly) a mean depth of 1.1 mm. This will be the value taken for d.

The kinematic viscosity ν for air is 1.24×10^{-5} m²/s. At $\frac{3}{4}$-chord, the Reynolds number R_X based on $X = 0.2092$ m and the free-stream speed is 460 248. The shear stress at the interface, upon neglect of the interfacial velocity which will be shown to be small, is $\tau_0 = 29\,364.09\mu$. Thus, if $\hat{U}_1$ denotes the dimensional velocity in air,

$$\mathrm{d}\hat{U}_1/\mathrm{d}Y = 29364.09/\mathrm{s} \quad \text{at} \quad Y = 0,$$

or, in dimensionless terms, $\quad U_1' = 1.1841 \quad \text{at} \quad y = 0.$

Since $U_1' = b^{-1}$, we have $\qquad\qquad b = 0.8446.$

The Reynolds number R based on d, ν, and the free-stream velocity is

$$R = 2419.$$

For the liquid, $\qquad\qquad \mu_2 \mathrm{d}\hat{U}_2/\mathrm{d}Y = 29364.09\mu/\mathrm{s},$

or $\qquad\qquad\qquad\qquad \mathrm{d}\hat{U}_2/\mathrm{d}Y = 0.0490/\mathrm{s},$

This gives $\qquad\qquad a_2 = U_2' = \mathrm{d}U_2/\mathrm{d}y = 1.976 \times 10^{-6},$

which is very small indeed, as assumed. The dimensional interfacial velocity corresponding to this value of a_2 is

$$\hat{U}_s = a_2 \hat{U}_0 = 0.0539\,\mathrm{mm/s},$$

which is negligible, as assumed, for the purpose of calculating τ_0 (shear stress at the interface, for the primary flow). The values of F^{-2} and S can be readily computed.

Summarizing, we have, for free-stream speed 27.28 m/s, $d = 1.1$ mm, and $r = 972$,

$$R = 2419, \quad b = 0.8446, \quad m = 598802,$$
$$F^{-2} = 0.014101, \quad S = 0.27621.$$

With these parameters given, a brief calculation shows that the flow is stable for

$$\alpha \leqslant 0.01 \quad \text{or} \quad \alpha \geqslant 0.5 \tag{79}$$

52   *C.-S. Yih*

and is neutrally stable, or very nearly so, when the equality signs hold. The maximum σ_i occurs at

$$\alpha = 0.33, \tag{80}$$

at which (with $\sigma_i = \alpha c_i$)

$$\frac{b^2 m}{R}\sigma_i = 8.86 \times 10^{-4}, \quad \frac{b^2 m}{R}c'_r = 2.58 \times 10^{-3}. \tag{81}$$

Thus the assumption that $c'\ (= c'_r + ic_i)$ is small is amply verified. The value of α of the waves observed by HH (pp. 29–30) is, by the best estimate from their figure 19 on p. 30,

$$\alpha = 0.5. \tag{82}$$

Thus the theoretical prediction of α is 34 % too low, but seems to be of the right order of magnitude.

Although HH did not measure c_r, their photographs taken at various times suggest that it is small, certainly far less than the c_r predicted for the classical Tollmien–Schlichting waves for Blasius flow, which is of the order of 0.2 (Shen 1954, see Schlichting 1960, p. 396), or at least 0.05 according to the earlier prediction of Tollmien (1929, see Schlichting 1960, p. 397). The α^* for the most unstable mode in the Tollmien– Schlichting theory for Blasius flow is approximately 0.26 (Shen 1954, or Schlichting 1960, p. 396), where α^* is the wavenumber based on the momentum thickness δ^*, which is 0.534 mm for the case at hand. This α^* corresponds to an α (based on d) of only 0.126, far less than the experimental value of 0.5. (Note that $\alpha^* = 0.26$ corresponds to a Reynolds number based on δ^* of 1174.) Thus the waves photographed by HH do not seem to be classical Tollmien–Schlichting waves.

9. Conclusion

With the assumptions that a_2 and c' are very small verified *a posteriori*, (77) gives the phase velocity and (78) the growth rate. The reasonable agreement between the theoretical and experimental values of the wavenumber of the most unstable mode suggests that the wave formation arises from the instability treated here, which is of the kind found earlier by Yih (1967), and is a result principally of the viscosity differences between air and the de-icing liquid.

This work has been supported by a grant awarded by the Lewis Research Center of the National Aeronautics and Space Administration to the University of Florida. This support is much appreciated.

REFERENCES

HENDRICKSON, G. S. & HILL, E. G. 1987 Effects of de-/anti-icing fluids on airfoil characteristics. *Boeing Rep.*

HICKOX, C. E. 1971 Stability of two fluids in a pipe. *Phys. Fluids* **14**, 251.

HOLSTEIN, H. 1950 Über die äussere und innere Reibungschicht by Störungen laminarer Strömungen. *Z. Angew. Math. Mech.* **30**, 25–49.

HOOPER, A. P. & BOYD, W. G. C. 1983 Shear-flow instability at the interface between two viscous fluids. *J. Fluid Mech.* **128**, 507–528.

LI, C. H. 1969 Instability of 3-layer viscous stratified fluids. *Phys. Fluids* **12**, 2473.

LIN, C. C. 1955 *The Theory of Hydrodynamic Stability*. Cambridge University Press.

SCHLICHTING, H. 1960 *Boundary Layer Theory*. McGraw-Hill.

SHEN, S. F. 1954 Calculated amplified oscillations in plane Poiseuille and Blasius flows. *J. Aero. Sci.* **21**, 62–64.

TOLLMIEN, W. 1929 ÜBER DIE ENTSTEHUNG DER TURBULENZ. 1. Mitteilung. *Nachr. Ges. Wiss. Göttingen, Math. Phys. Klasse*, 21–44.

YIH, C.-S. 1967 Instability due to viscosity stratification. *J. Fluid Mech.* **27**, 337–352.